AIRLINER PRODUCTION LIST 1987

Completely New Edition

By Nigel M. Tomkins
and Ricky-Dene Halliday

London • England

This edition© 1986 Aviation Data Centre

Published by:
The Aviation Data Centre Ltd.
Browcom House,
Browells Lane, Feltham,
Middlesex TW13 7EQ
England
Telephone: 01-890-8933

ACKNOWLEDGEMENTS

We would like to extend our sincere appreciation once again to everyone who has contributed to year's Airliner Production List Directory, friends, Acquaintances, correspondents and manufacturers.

In particular, thanks must go to John Blatherwick, Kevin Cobb, Frank Ellemaers, A. J. M. Hofstra, Frank Jager, William Lloyd, Kazuhiro Murai, S. Ouzounian, Ian Smith and Peter Van Driel plus the following aircraft manufacturers Aerospatiale, Aeritalia, Airbus Industrie, Beech, Boeing, British Aerospace, CASA, De Havilland Canada, Dornier, Embraer, Fairchild Industries, Fokker, McDonnell Douglas and SAAB.

plus the hundreds of Aviation Data Centre correspondents who have contributed over the year to the main data base, unfortunately too numerous to mention individually.

Finally we must acknowledge the tireless efforts of Jonathan Cousens of the Aviation Data Centre editorial department.

ISBN: 0 946141 25 8

Printed in England by Intergraphic Print (UK) Ltd., Browcom House, Browells Lane, Feltham, Middlesex, TW13 7EQ, England.

Printed in England by:
Intergraphic Print (UK) Ltd., Browcom House, Browells Lane, Feltham, Middlesex, TW13 7EQ, England.

INTRODUCTION

Welcome to the all-new 1987 edition of the AIRLINER PRODUCTION LIST the airliner enthusiast's essential handbook and sister publication of the popular WORLD AIRLINE FLEETS handbook. This year, A.P.L appears in an exciting new format especially created for aviation hobbyists, enthusiasts, 'spotter' and those with any sort of interest in the fascinating world of commercial airliners

Within the pages of this handbook you will find the individual histories of almost every major western-built airliner type in service throughout the world today.

Airliner types are listed in categories such as High Capacity, Supersonic Transport, Regional Commuter, Short-Medium Haul Turbojet etc. to enable similar aircraft to be compared. Each listing includes full history of every aircraft built and a registration/Construction number cross reference index. For some older airliner types, where only a small proportion of the total production remains airworthy, we have included only those that still exist, whether they are flying, stored, derelict or preserved.

AIRLINER PRODUCTION LIST is internationally acknowledged as the leading handbook of its type, and no effort is spared to make it the most accurate and up to date listing possible. The information is compiled with the assistance of the world's airliner manufacturers and the Aviation Data Centre's unique network of dedicated correspondents.

AIRCRAFT/PAGE NUMBER INDEX

HOW TO USE THIS DIRECTORY

Construction number →

Registration/ tail number →

Owner/ operator →

LOCKHEED L.1011 TRISTAR → **Aircraft type**

→ **Aircraft model/series**

→ **First flight date**

→ **Delivery/sale date**

→ **Lease details**

C/N	Registration	Owner/Operator	Series	First Flight	Delivery	Remarks
1001	N1011	Lockheed	1	16/NOV/70		
1002	N31001	Lockheed	1	15/FEB/71		
	N1031L	Lockheed				
	N301EA	Eastern Air Lines			24/MAR/73	
1003	N301EA	Lockheed	1		17/MAY/71	
	N302EA	Eastern Air Lines			22/MAY/73	
1004	N302EA	Lockheed	1	24/OCT/71		
	N303EA	Lockheed			15/DEC/72	
1005	N6752	Lockheed	1	23/JUN/72		
	N304EA	Eastern Air Lines			11/JUL/72	
	N304EA	Aviation Sales Co.			16/JAN/84	WFU 16/JAN/84, stored Marana
1006	N303EA	Lockheed	1	10/NOV/72		
	N305EA	Eastern Air Lines			23/NOV/72	
1007	N306EA	Eastern Air Lines	1	12/MAR/72	05/APR/72	
	N306EA	Aviation Sales Co.			7/JAN/84	WFU 30/JAN/84, stored Marana
1008	N307EA	Eastern Air Lines	1	24/MAY/72	7/JUN/72	
	D-AFRO	Lockheed			1/APR/77	
	D-ALC	LTU			1/APR/77	
	D-AL-C	LTU			28/FEB/79	
	N	American Overseas			JAN/81	Not taken-up
	N371EA	Eastern Air Lines			17/MAR/81	
	N371EA	Aviation Sales Co.			18/JAN/84	WFU 18/JAN/84, stored Marana
	D-AERY	LTU			19/MAR/86	
1009	N308EA	Eastern Air Lines	1	12/JUN/72	11/JUL/72	
1010	N309EA	Eastern Air Lines	1	10/JUL/72	25/JUL/72	
	N309EA	Trans World Airlines			30/APR/73	Leased
	N309EA	Eastern Air Lines			28/OCT/73	
	N309EA	Trans World Airlines			30/APR/74	Leased
	N309EA	Eastern Airlines			30/OCT/74	
1011	N310EA	Eastern Air Lines	1	30/JUL/72	18/AUG/72	W/O 29/DEC/72, nr. Miami
1012	N311EA	Eastern Air Lines	1	22/OCT/72	02/NOV/72	
	N311EA	Aviation Sales Co.			JAN/84	WFU JAN/84, stored Marana
	N31EA	Aircraft Sales Co.			22/MAY/85	WFU 22/MAY/85, stored Miami
1013	N31001	Trans World Airlines	1	01/APR/74	09/MAY/72	
	N381EA	Eastern Air Lines			24/NOV/73	Leased
	N31001	Trans World Airlines			29/APR/74	Leased
	N31001	Interface Group Inc.			29/OCT/84	
	N31001	Five Star			01/MAR/85	Leased, Op. by IASCO
1014	N11002	Trans World Airlines	1	03/JUN/72	04/JUL/72	
	N382EA	Eastern Air Lines			12/NOV/73	Leased
	N11002	Trans World Airlines			21/MAY/74	
	N11002	Interface Group Inc.			19/NOV/84	
	N11002	Five Star			30/APR/85	Leased, Op. by IASCO
1015	N11003	Trans World Airlines	1	13/JUL/72	11/AUG/72	
1016	N11004	Trans World Airlines	1	14/JUL/72	30/AUG/72	
1017	N11005	Trans World Airlines	1	09/SEP/72	27/SEP/72	
1018	N11006	Trans World Airlines	1	08/SEP/72	26/SEP/72	
	N380EA	Eastern Air Lines			22/NOV/72	Leased
	N11006	Trans World Airlines			23/MAY/74	
1019	N312EA	Haas Turner	1	18/NOV/72	13/DEC/72	
	N312EA	Eastern Air Lines			29/OCT/73	Leased
	C-FTNA	Air Canada			06/MAY/73	Leased
	N312EA	Eastern Air Lines			27/OCT/74	Leased
	C-FTNA	Air Canada			07/MAY/75	Leased
	N312EA	Eastern Air Lines			26/OCT/75	Leased
	C-FTNA	Air Canada			07/MAY/76	Leased
	N312EA	Eastern Air Lines			01/NOV/76	Leased
	C-FTNA	Air Canada			09/MAY/77	Leased
	N312EA	Eastern Air Lines			30/OCT/77	Leased
	C-FTNA	Air Canada			06/MAY/78	Leased
	N312EA	Eastern Air Lines			29/OCT/78	Leased
	C-FTNA	Air Canada			07/MAY/79	Leased
	N312EA	Eastern Air Lines			28/OCT/79	Leased
	C-FTNA	Air Canada			05/MAY/80	Leased
	N312EA	Eastern Air Lines			09/OCT/80	Leased
	C-FTNA	Air Canada			04/MAY/81	Leased
1020	N313EA	Eastern Air Lines	1	09/DEC/72	15/DEC/72	
1021	C-FTNB	Air Canada	1	24/DEC/72	14/JAN/73	
1022	N314EA	Eastern Air Lines	1	25/DEC/72	02/JAN/73	
	N314EA	Cathay Pacific			06/OCT/79	Leased
1023	N315EA	Haas-Turner	1	06/JAN/73	11/APR/73	
	N315EA	Eastern Air Lines			15/MAY/74	Leased
	C-FTNC	Air Canada			03/MAY/74	Leased
	N315EA	Eastern Air Lines			16/MAY/75	Leased
	C-FTNC	Air Canada			01/NOV/75	Leased
	N315EA	Eastern Air Lines			13/MAY/76	Leased
	C-FTNC	Air Canada			07/MAY/76	Leased
	N315EA	Eastern Air Lines			03/JUN/77	Leased
	C-FTNC	Air Canada			06/MAY/77	Leased
	N315EA	Eastern Air Lines			18/MAY/78	Leased
	C-FTNC	Air Canada			05/NOV/78	Leased
	N315EA	Eastern Air Lines			14/MAY/79	Leased
	C-FTNC	Air Canada			01/NOV/79	Leased
	N315EA	Eastern Air Lines			11/MAY/80	Leased
	C-FTNC	Air Canada			02/NOV/80	Leased
	N315EA	Eastern Air Lines			18/MAY/81	Leased
	C-FTNC	Air Canada				
1024	G-BAAA	Aerolease	1	28/FEB/73	28/FEB/73	
	G-BAAA	Courtline			28/FEB/73	Leased,
	G-BAAA	Lockheed			16/AUG/74	WFU 16/AUG/74
	VR-HHV	Cathay Pacific			24/MAR/77	Leased
	VR-HHV	Cathay Pacific			24/NOV/77	Purchased
1025	C-FTND	Air Canada	1	09/FEB/73	09/MAY/73	
	4R-ALG	Air Lanka			21/MAY/81	Leased
	C-FTND	Air Canada			29/DEC/81	
	A40-TP	Guinness Peat Aviation			06/MAY/84	Leased
	A40-TP	Gulf Air			06/MAY/84	Sub-leased
1026	N31007	Trans World Airlines	1	25/FEB/73	07/APR/73	W/O 20/APR/74, Boston
1027	C-FTNE	Air Canada	1	18/MAR/73	12/APR/73	
1028	N31008	Trans World Airlines	1	27/MAR/73	21/APR/73	
1029	N31009	Trans World Airlines	1	28/APR/73	16/MAY/73	
1030	N31010	Trans World Airlines	1	05/MAY/73	29/MAY/73	
1031	N31011	Trans World Airlines	1	13/MAY/73	30/MAY/73	
1032	G-BAAB	Aerolease	1	23/APR/73	30/APR/73	
	G-BAAB	Courtline			30/APR/73	Leased,
	G-BAAB	Lockheed			16/AUG/74	WFU 16/AUG/74

ABBREVIATIONS	
W/O -	written off
WFU -	withdrawn from use
Op. by -	operated by

AIRBUS INDUSTRIE A300

Short/medium range wide-body transport with twin wing-mounted turbofan engines. A joint-venture between Aerospatiale, British Aerospace, MBB and CASA, the A300 made its first flight on 28 October 1972 and entered service with Air France on the Paris-London route on 30 May 1974. The basic model is the A300 B2-100, and the B2-200, B2-300, A300B4-100 and 200 are similar with various refinements, increased gross weights and higher thrust. The A300-600 is the latest development, incorporating technology from the A310. To date, 266 aircraft have been delivered and a further 15 are on order with the production rate currently two aircraft per month.

Dimensions : Wing span: 147ft 1in (44.84m) Length: 175ft 9in (53.75m) Height: 54ft 3in (16.53m) (B2/B4)
Wing span: 147ft 1in (44.84m) Length: 177ft 5in (54.08m) Height: 54ft 3in (16.53m) (600)

Powerplants : Two General Electric CF6-50C2 or Pratt & Whitney JT9D-59A1 turbofans, (B2/B4)
two Pratt & Whitney JT9D-7R4, General Electric CF6-80C or Pratt & Whitney PW4000 turbofans (600)

Performance : Max cruising speed 497 knots (920km/h) (B2-200) Range: with max payload 1,350nm (2,500km) (B2-200)
Max cruising speed 480 knots (891km/h) (B2-300/B4/600) Range: with max payload 1,190nm (2,200km)
(B2-300)   Range: with max payload 2,470nm (4,570km) (B4)
Range: with max payload 2,310nm (5,390km) (600)

Accommodation: 345 passengers in a 9 abreast layout (B2/B4), 375 passengers in a 9 abreast layout (600)

Manufacturer : Airbus Industrie - Avenue Lucien Servanty, BP No. 33, 31700 Blagnac, France
Telephone: 033-61 93 33 33 Telex: 530526 F AITO

 Airbus

C/N	Registration	Owner/Operator	Series	First Flight	Delivery	Remarks
1	F-WUAB	Airbus Industrie	B1	28/OCT/72		First prototype
	F-OCAZ	Airbus Industrie			13/SEP/73	Scrapped 27/AUG/74,
2	F-WUAC	Airbus Industrie	B1	05/FEB/73		
	OO-TEF	Trans European Airways			25/NOV/74	
	OO-TEF	Air Algerie			27/NOV/74	Leased
	OO-TEF	Trans European Airways			19/JAN/75	
	OO-TEF	Air Inter			08/JAN/80	Leased
	OO-TEF	Trans European Airways			20/MAR/80	
	OO-TEF	Air Algerie			23/SEP/80	Leased
	OO-TEF	Trans European Airways			DEC/80	
3	F-ODCX	Airbus Industrie	B2-1C	28/JUN/73		
	F-WUAD	Airbus Industrie				
	F-BUAD	Airbus Industrie	B2-103			Demonstrator
4	F-WUAA	Airbus Industrie	B2-1C	20/NOV/73		
	F-BUAE	Air Inter			22/JAN/77	
5	F-BVGA	Air France	B2-1A	15/APR/74	10/MAY/74	
	F-BVGA	Air France	B2-1C			Converted
	F-BVGA	Air France	B2-101		82	Converted
6	F-BVGB	Air France	B2-1A	23/JUN/74	28/JUN/74	
	F-BVGB	Air France	B2-1C			Converted
	F-BVGB	Air France	B2-101		82	Converted
7	F-BVGC	Air France	B2-1A	06/AUG/74	10/AUG/74	
	F-BVGC	Air France	B2-1C			Converted
	F-BVGC	Air France	B2-101		82	Converted
8	F-WNDB	Airbus Industrie	B2-1C	02/OCT/74		
	HS-VGD	Air Siam			17/OCT/74	Leased
	F-ODHC	Airbus Industrie			13/OCT/75	
	PH-TVL	Transavia			06/MAY/76	Leased
	PH-TVL	Airbus Industrie			18/JAN/77	
	F-BUAF	Air Inter			11/MAR/78	
9	F-WLGA	Airbus Industrie	B4-2C	26/DEC/74		
	HS-VGF	Air Siam				Cancelled order
	F-ODCY	Air France			16/JUL/76	Leased
	F-ODCY	Airbus Industrie			27/JUL/76	
	D-AMAP	Bavaria-Germanair			20/FEB/78	
	D-AMAP	Hapag Lloyd			05/APR/79	
	D-AMAP	Hapag Lloyd	B4-203		APR/80	Converted
	G-BMNB	Dan Air			NOV/86	Sched.delivery
10	F-BVGD	Air France	B2-1A	07/MAR/75	21/MAR/75	
	F-BVGD	Air France	B2-1C			Converted
	F-BVGD	Air France	B2-101		82	Converted
	F-BVGD	Air Inter			FEB/84	
11	F-BVGE	Air France	B2-1A	23/APR/75	01/MAY/75	
	F-BVGE	Air France	B2-1C			Converted
	F-BVGE	Air France	B2-101		82	Converted
	F-BVGE	Air Inter			07/OCT/82	
12	F-WLGC	Airbus Industrie	B4-2C	20/MAY/75		
	D-AMAX	Germanair			23/MAY/75	
	D-AMAX	Bavaria-Germanair			01/JAN/77	
	D-AMAX	Hapag Lloyd			05/APR/79	
	D-AMAX	Hapag Lloyd	B4-203		APR/80	Converted
13	F-BVGF	Air France	B2-1A	31/MAY/75	11/JUN/75	
	F-BVGF	Air France	B2-1C			Converted
	F-BVGF	Air France	B2-101		82	Converted
	F-BVGF	Air Inter			25/FEB/83	
14	F-WLGB	Airbus Industrie	B4-2C	23/JUL/75		
	HL7218	Korean Airlines			01/AUG/75	
	HL7218	Korean Airlines	B4-103			Converted
15	F-WLGC	Airbus Industrie	B2-1C	18/JUN/65		
	F-BUAG	Air Inter			15/OCT/76	
16	F-WLGB	Airbus Industrie	B4-2C	22/AUG/75		
	HL7219	Korean Airlines			01/SEP/75	
	HL7219	Korean Airlines	B4-103			Converted
17	OO-TEG	Trans European Airways	B4-2C	07/OCT/75	15/OCT/75	
	OO-TEG	Zaire Aero Services				Leased
	OO-TEG	Trans European Airways				
	OO-TEG	Egyptair			07/APR/77	Leased
	OO-TEG	Hapag Lloyd			02/JUL/79	

AIRBUS INDUSTRIE A300

C/N	Registration	Owner/Operator	Series	First Flight	Delivery	Remarks
	SU-BBS	Egyptair			02/JUL/79	Leased
	D-AHLC	Hapag Lloyd	B4-203		01/FEB/82	
18	HL7220	Korean Airlines	B4-2C	23/OCT/75	31/OCT/75	
	HL7220	Korean Airlines	B4-103			Converted
19	F-BVGG	Air France	B4-2C	11/NOV/75	16/NOV/75	
	F-BVGG	Air France	B4-203		80	Converted
20	D-AMAY	Germanair	B4-2C	10/DEC/75	01/APR/76	
	D-AMAY	Bavaria Germanair			01/JUL/77	
	D-AMAY	Hapag Lloyd			05/APR/79	
	D-AMAY	Hapag Lloyd	B4-203		APR/80	Converted
21	F-WNDA	Airbus Industrie	B2-1C	29/NOV/75		
	D-AIAA	Lufthansa			02/FEB/76	
	F-BUAM	Air Inter			16/DEC/83	
22	F-WNDC	Airbus Industrie	B2-1C	23/JAN/76		
	D-AIAB	Lufthansa			19/MAR/76	
	F-WZMB	Airbus Industrie			14/DEC/83	
	F-ODRD	Northeastern International			29/MAY/84	
	F-ODRD	Airbus Industrie			16/OCT/84	Stored 16/OCT/84 to MAY/86
	7T-	Air Algerie			DEC/85	Not taken-up
	F-ODRD	Indian Airlines			MAY/86	Leased
23	F-BVGH	Air France	B4-203	12/FEB/76	14/APR/76	
24	F-WNDD	Airbus Industrie	B4-2C	03/MAR/76		
	HL7221	Korean Airlines			23/APR/76	
	HL7221	Korean Airlines	B4-103			Converted
25	F-WNDA	Airbus Industrie	B4-103	23/MAR/76		
	D-AMAZ	Bavaria Germanair			02/MAY/77	
	D-AMAZ	Egyptair			12/MAY/77	Leased
	SU-AZY	Egyptair			19/JAN/78	Leased
	SU-AZY	Egyptair	B4-201			Converted
	D-AHLZ	Hapag Lloyd			01/NOV/82	
	D-AHLZ	Kuwait Airways			01/JUL/83	Leased
	D-AHLZ	Hapag Lloyd			04/OCT/83	
	D-AHLZ	Capitol Air			AUG/84	Leased
	D-AHLZ	Hapag Lloyd			85	
	D-AHLZ	Air Jamaica			85	Leased
	D-AHLZ	Hapag Lloyd			24/APR/85	
	D-AHLZ	Condor			24/APR/85	Leased
	D-AHLZ	Hapag Lloyd			85	
	AP-BCP	Pakistan International			21/APR/86	
26	F-WNDB	Airbus Industrie	B2-1C	11/MAR/76		
	D-AIAC	Lufthansa			25/APR/76	
	F-WZMJ	Airbus Industrie			16/DEC/83	
	F-ODRE	Northeastern International			29/MAY/84	
	F-ODRE	Airbus Industrie			15/OCT/84	Stored 15/OCT/84 to MAY/86
	7T-	Air Algerie			DEC/85	Not taken-up
	F-ODRE	Indian Airlines			MAY/86	Leased
27	F-WLGC	Airbus Industrie	B2-1C	03/MAY/76		
	F-BUAH	Air Inter			28/SEP/78	
28	F-WNDC	Airbus Industrie	B4-2C	16/APR/76		
	HL7223	Korean Airlines			08/JUL/76	
	HL7223	Saudia			01/NOV/80	Leased
	HL7223	Korean Airlines			31/OCT/81	
	HL7223	Korean Airlines	B4-103			Converted
29	F-WNDD	Airbus Industrie	B4-102	08/MAY/76		
	HK-2057	Aerocondor			10/DEC/77	
	F-ODJU	Airbus Industrie			18/APR/79	
	F-BUAL	Air Inter			31/MAR/81	Leased
30	F-WNDB	Airbus Industrie	B4-2C	04/JUN/76		
	HL7224	Korean Airlines			28/FEB/77	
	HL7224	Saudia			10/AUG/80	Leased
	HL7224	Korean Airlines			31/OCT/81	
	HL7224	Korean Airlines	B4-103			Converted
31	F-WLGG	Airbus Industrie	B4-2C	08/JUN/76		
	F-WZEQ	Airbus Industrie				
	HL7238	Korean Airlines			09/AUG/78	
	HL7238	Korean Airlines	B4-103			Converted
32	F-WLGA	Airbus Industrie	B2-K3C	30/JUL/76		
	ZS-SDA	South African Airways			15/NOV/76	
33	F-WNDC	Airbus Industrie	B4-2C	21/SEP/76		
	HS-TGH	Thai International			25/OCT/77	
	HS-TGH	Thai International	B4-103			Converted
34	F-WLGB	Airbus Industrie	B2-1C	30/AUG/76		
	VT-EDV	Indian Airlines			31/OCT/76	
	VT-EDV	Indian Airlines	B2-101			Converted
35	F-WLGA	Airbus Industrie	B4-2C	02/FEB/77		
	HS-TGK	Thai International			14/DEC/77	
	HS-TGK	Thai International	B4-103			Converted
36	F-WUAT	Airbus Industrie	B2-1C	05/OCT/76		
	VT-EDW	Indian Airlines			29/NOV/76	
	VT-EDW	Indian Airlines	B2-101			Converted
37	F-WUAU	Airbus Industrie	B2-K3C	02/NOV/76		
	ZS-SDB	South African Airways			22/DEC/76	
38	F-WUAV	Airbus Industrie	B2-1C	16/NOV/76		
	VT-EDX	Indian Airlines			29/DEC/76	
	VT-EDX	Indian Airlines	B2-101			
39	F-WLGB	Airbus Industrie	B2-K3C	01/DEC/76		
	ZS-SDC	South African Airways			21/JAN/77	
40	F-WUAX	Airbus Industrie	B2-K3C	13/DEC/76		
	ZS-SDD	South African Airways			15/FEB/77	
41	F-WUAZ	Airbus Industrie	B4-2C	11/JAN/77		
	N201EA	Eastern Air Lines			03/DEC/77	
	N201EA	Eastern Air Lines	B4-103			Converted
42	F-WUAU	Airbus Industrie	B4-2C	24/FEB/77		
	N202EA	Eastern Air Lines			19/NOV/77	
	N202EA	Eastern Air Lines	B4-103			Converted
43	F-WUAT	Airbus Industrie	B4-2C	13/MAY/77		
	N203EA	Eastern Air Lines			29/OCT/77	
	N203EA	Eastern Air Lines	B4-103			Converted
44	F-WUAX	Airbus Industrie	B4-2C	13/JUL/77		
	N204EA	Eastern Air Lines			24/AUG/77	
	N204EA	Eastern Air Lines	B4-103			Converted
45	F-BVGI	Air France	B4-2C	18/FEB/77	24/MAR/77	
	F-BVGI	Air France	B4-201		80	Converted
46	F-WLGB	Airbus Industrie	B4-102	28/MAR/77		
	F-WZER	Airbus Industrie				

C/N	Registration	Owner/Operator	Series	First Flight	Delivery	Remarks
	SX-BEB	Olympic Airways			05/FEB/79	
47	F-WUAX	Airbus Industrie	B4-2C	22/APR/77		
	F-BVGJ	Air France			20/OCT/77	
	F-BVGJ	Air France	B4-201		80	Converted
48	F-WNDB	Airbus Industrie	B2-1C	14/MAR/77		
	D-AIAD	Lufthansa			16/APR/77	
	D-AIAD	Airbus Industrie			10/JAN/84	
	F-ODRF	Northeastern International			04/FEB/84	Leased
	F-ODRF	Airbus Industrie			19/OCT/84	Stored 19/OCT/84 to 14/JUN/85
	F-ODRF	Olympic Airways			14/JUN/85	Leased
	F-BUAO	Olympic Airways			86	Leased
	F-BUAO	Airbus Industrie			OCT/86	Sched.return
	F-BUAO	Air Inter			Spring/87	Sched.delivery
49	F-WUAV	Airbus Industrie	B2-202	10/MAY/77		
	F-WZES	Airbus Industrie				
	F-ODHY	Iran Air			07/MAR/78	Leased
	F-ODHY	Airbus Industrie			01/JAN/79	
	F-GBNI	Airbus Industrie			79	
	N291EA	Eastern Air Lines	B2-203		16/JAN/80	Converted
50	F-WNDB	Airbus Industrie	B2-1C	16/JUN/77		
	F-GBEA	Aerospatiale			77	
	F-GBEA	Air France			21/JUN/78	
	F-GBEA	Air Inter			26/MAR/84	
51	F-WNDA	Airbus Industrie	B2-202	03/FEB/78		
	F-WZEA	Airbus Industrie				
	F-ODHZ	Iran Air			16/MAR/78	Leased
	F-ODHZ	Airbus Industrie			01/JAN/79	
	F-GBNJ	Airbus Industrie				
	N292EA	Eastern Air Lines	B2-203		07/JAN/80	
52	F-WNDC	Airbus Industrie	B2-1C	17/NOV/77		
	F-WZEB	Airbus Industrie				
	D-AIAE	Lufthansa			07/JAN/78	
	D-AIAE	Airbus Industrie			18/JAN/84	
	F-ODRG	Northeastern International			04/FEB/84	Leased
	F-ODRG	Airbus Industrie			11/OCT/84	Stored 11/OCT/84 to 15/MAY/85
	F-ODRG	Olympic Airways			15/MAY/85	Leased
	F-BUAP	Olympic Airways			86	Leased
	F-BUAP	Airbus Industrie			OCT/86	Sched.return
	F-BUAP	Air Inter			Spring/87	Sched.delivery
53	F-WUAT	Airbus Industrie	B4-2C	16/AUG/77		
	F-WZEE	Airbus Industrie				
	D-AIBA	Lufthansa			29/SEP/77	
	D-AIBA	Air Algerie			MAR/81	Leased
	D-AIBA	Lufthansa			01/JAN/85	
54	F-WZED	Airbus Industrie	B4-2C	05/JAN/78		
	HS-TGL	Thai International			16/FEB/78	
	HS-TGL	Thai International	B4-103			Converted
55	F-WZEC	Airbus Industrie	B4-2C	01/MAR/78		
	HS-TGM	Thai International			14/APR/78	
	HS-TGM	Thai International	B4-103			Converted
56	F-WZEF	Airbus Industrie	B4-102	19/DEC/78		
	SX-BEC	Olympic Airways			15/FEB/79	
57	F-WZEG	Airbus Industrie	B4-2C	23/JAN/78		
	D-AIBB	Lufthansa			23/MAR/78	
	D-AIBB	Air Algerie			MAR/81	Leased
	D-AIBB	Lufthansa			05/JAN/85	
58	F-WZEH	Airbus Industrie	B4-102	19/FEB/80		
	SX-BED	Olympic Airways			28/MAR/80	
59	F-WZEI	Airbus Industrie	B2-1C	29/MAR/78		
	VT-EDY	Indian Airlines			11/MAY/78	
	VT-EDY	Indian Airlines	B2-101			Converted
60	F-WZEJ	Airbus Industrie	B2-1C	19/APR/78		
	VT-EDZ	Indian Airlines			08/JUN/78	
	VT-EDZ	Indian Airlines	B2-101			Converted
61	F-WZEK	Airbus Industrie	B2-203	21/DEC/79		
	EP-IBR	Iran Air			17/MAR/80	
62	F-WZEL	Airbus Industrie	B2-1C	18/AUG/78		
	F-BUAI	Air Inter			13/OCT/78	
63	F-WZEL	Airbus Industrie	B4-103	10/OCT/79		
	RP-C3001	Philippine Airlines			25/NOV/79	
64	F-WZEM	Airbus Industrie	B4-203	27/FEB/79		
	D-AHLA	Hapag Lloyd			03/APR/79	
	AP-BBM	Pakistan International			03/AUG/83	
	AP-BBM	Emirates Airlines			25/NOV/85	Leased
65	F-GBNA	Airbus Industrie	B4-2C	13/SEP/78		
	N205EA	Eastern Air Lines			15/NOV/78	
	N205EA	Eastern Air Lines	B4-103			Converted
66	F-GBNB	Airbus Industrie	B4-2C	06/OCT/78		
	N206EA	Eastern Air Lines			01/DEC/78	
	N206EA	Eastern Air Lines	B4-103			Converted
67	F-GBNC	Airbus Industrie	B4-2C	20/OCT/78		
	N207EA	Eastern Air Lines			11/DEC/78	
	N207EA	Eastern Air Lines	B4-103			Converted
68	F-GBND	Airbus Industrie	B4-103	06/AUG/79		
	N208EA	Eastern Air Lines			12/OCT/79	
69	F-WZEB	Airbus Industrie	B4-103	23/OCT/79		
	RP-C3002	Philippine Airlines			20/DEC/79	
70	F-BVGK	Air France	B4-203	22/FEB/79	27/APR/79	W/O 17/MAR/82, El Rahaba Airport, Sanaa
71	F-WZEC	Airbus Industrie	B4-2C	17/DEC/78		
	HS-TGN	Thai International			06/MAR/79	
	HS-TGN	Thai International	B4-103			Converted
72	F-WZED	Airbus Industrie	B4-2C	22/JAN/79		
	HS-TGO	Thai International			16/MAR/79	
	HS-TGO	Thai International	B4-103			Converted
73	F-WZEE	Airbus Industrie	B4-203	12/JUL/79		
	9M-MHA	Malaysian Airline System			30/OCT/79	
74	F-BVGL	Air France	B4-203	27/MAR/79	15/MAY/79	
75	F-WZEG	Airbus Industrie	B4-2C	31/JAN/79		
	D-AIBC	Lufthansa			23/MAR/79	
	D-AIBC	Condor			01/APR/83	Leased
	D-AIBC	Lufthansa			04/NOV/83	
	D-AIBC	Lufthansa	B4-203		JAN/84	Converted
76	F-WZEI	Airbus Industrie	B4-2C	19/FEB/79		
	D-AIBD	Lufthansa			30/MAR/79	

Airliner Production List 1987

AIRBUS INDUSTRIE A300

C/N	Registration	Owner/Operator	Series	First Flight	Delivery	Remarks
	D-AIBD	Condor			01/APR/83	Leased
	D-AIBD	Lufthansa			04/NOV/83	Converted
77	F-WZEJ	Airbus Industrie	B4-2C	08/MAR/79		
	D-AIBF	Lufthansa			19/APR/79	
	D-AIBF	Condor			06/MAY/79	Leased
	D-AIBF	Lufthansa			20/JAN/80	
	D-AIBF	Lufthansa	B4-203		83	Converted
78	F-BVGM	Air France	B4-203	06/APR/79	31/MAY/79	
	F-BVGM	Air Seychelles			01/NOV/85	Leased
79	F-WZEN	Airbus Industrie	B2-320	28/APR/79		
	LN-RCA	SAS			15/JAN/80	
	LN-RCA	Scanair	B4-120		25/MAR/83	
	OY-	Conair			86	Sched.delivery
80	F-WZEO	Airbus Industrie	B2-203	13/FEB/80		
	EP-IBS	Iran Air			16/APR/80	Impounded at Baghdad 28/AUG/84 following hijack, WFU
81	F-WZEP	Airbus Industrie	B4-2C	09/MAY/79		
	HL7246	Korean Airlines			29/JUN/79	
	HL7246	Korean Airlines	B4-103			Converted
82	F-WZEQ	Airbus Industrie	B2-K3C	18/AUG/80		
	JA8464	Toa Domestic Airlines			02/OCT/80	
83	F-WZES	Airbus Industrie	C4-203	16/MAY/79		
	D-AHLB	Hapag Lloyd			31/JAN/80	
84	F-WZET	Airbus Industrie	B4-2C	08/JUN/79		
	HS-TGP	Thai International			09/AUG/79	
	HS-TGP	Thai International	B4-103			Converted
85	F-WZEC	Airbus Industrie	B4-2C	03/JUL/79		
	HS-TGR	Thai International			06/SEP/79	
	HS-TGR	Thai International	B4-103			Converted
86	F-GBNE	Airbus Industrie	B4-103	26/JUL/79		
	N209EA	Eastern Air Lines			14/NOV/79	
87	F-GBNF	Airbus Industrie	B4-103	22/AUG/79		
	N210EA	Eastern Air Lines			15/NOV/79	
88	F-WZED	Airbus Industrie	B2-1C	03/SEP/79		
	VT-EFV	Indian Airlines			25/OCT/79	
89	F-WZEF	Airbus Industrie	B2-K3C	28/OCT/80		
	JA8465	Toa Domestic Airlines			15/DEC/80	
90	F-WZEG	Airbus Industrie	B2-K3C	05/NOV/80		
	JA8466	Toa Domestic Airlines			18/DEC/80	
91	F-GBNG	Airbus Industrie	B4-103	26/SEP/79		
	N212EA	Eastern Air Lines			30/NOV/79	
92	F-GBNH	Airbus Industrie	B4-103	17/OCT/79		
	N213EA	Eastern Air Lines			10/DEC/79	
93	F-WZEI	Airbus Industrie	B4-203	18/OCT/79		
	9M-MHB	Malaysian Airline System			28/DEC/79	
94	F-WZEJ	Airbus Industrie	B2-320	06/DEC/79		
	SE-DFK	SAS			10/MAR/80	
	SE-DFK	Scanair	B4-120		30/MAR/83	
	OY-	Conair			86	Sched.delivery
95	F-WZEM	Airbus Industrie	B4-203	20/NOV/79		
	9M-MHC	Malaysian Airline System			18/JAN/80	
96	F-WZEP	Airbus Industrie	B4-203	30/NOV/79		
	AP-BAX	Pakistan International			03/MAR/80	
97	F-BUAJ	Air Inter	B2-1C	17/JAN/80	28/FEB/80	
98	F-WZER	Airbus Industrie	B4-203	25/JAN/80		
	AP-BAY	Pakistan International			12/MAR/80	
99	F-WZET	Airbus Industrie	B4-203	22/FEB/80		
	AP-BAZ	Pakistan International			03/APR/80	
100	F-BVGN	Air France	B4-203	21/JAN/80	06/MAR/80	
101	F-WZEA	Airbus Industrie	B4-203	30/JAN/80		
	I-BUSB	Alitalia			28/APR/80	
102	F-GBEB	Air France	B2-1C	08/FEB/80	20/MAR/80	
	F-GBEB	Air Inter			28/MAR/86	
103	F-WZEC	Airbus Industrie	B4-102	06/MAR/80		
	SX-BEE	Olympic Airways			21/APR/80	
104	F-GBEC	Air France	B2-1C	28/FEB/80	08/APR/80	
	F-GBEC	Air Inter			87	Sched.delivery
105	F-WZED	Airbus Industrie	B4-102	14/MAR/80		
	SX-BEF	Olympic Airways			30/APR/80	
106	F-WZEE	Airbus Industrie	B4-203	21/MAR/80		
	I-BUSC	Alitalia			29/MAY/80	
107	F-WZEL	Airbus Industrie	B4-203	31/MAR/80		
	I-BUSD	Alitalia			20/JUN/80	
108	F-GBNK	Airbus Industrie	B4-103	11/APR/80		
	N215EA	Eastern Air Lines			10/JUN/80	
109	F-WZEM	Airbus Industrie	B4-203	23/APR/80		
	PP-CLA	Cruzeiro			20/JUN/80	
110	F-WZEB	Airbus Industrie	B4-203	06/MAY/80		
	PP-CLB	Cruzeiro			26/JUN/80	
111	F-WZEI	Airbus Industrie	B2-1C	19/MAY/80		
	VT-EFW	Indian Airlines			18/JUL/80	
112	F-BUAK	Air Inter	B2-K3C	24/SEP/80	25/NOV/80	
113	F-WZEJ	Airbus Industrie	B2-1C	10/JUN/80		
	VT-EFX	Indian Airlines			07/AUG/80	
114	F-WZEN	Airbus Industrie	B4-203	16/JUN/80		
	AP-BBA	Pakistan International			27/AUG/80	
115	F-WZEP	Airbus Industrie	B4-203	03/JUL/80		
	SU-BCA	Egyptair			19/SEP/80	
116	F-WZES	Airbus Industrie	B4-203	10/JUL/80		
	SU-BCB	Egyptair			30/SEP/80	
117	F-WZER	Airbus Industrie	B4-203	19/AUG/80		
	9V-STA	Singapore Airlines			20/DEC/80	
	F-OGTB	Airbus Industrie			12/APR/85	Stored 12/APR/85 to 06/JUN/86
	N966C	Continental Airlines			06/JUN/86	
118	F-GBNL	Airbus Industrie	B4-103	26/AUG/80		
	N216EA	Eastern Air Lines			13/OCT/80	
119	F-WZEM	Airbus Industrie	B4-103	04/SEP/80		
	N217EA	Eastern Air Lines			22/OCT/80	
120	F-WZEN	Airbus Industrie	B4-103	15/SEP/80		
	N219EA	Eastern Air Lines			01/DEC/80	
121	F-WZEK	Airbus Industrie	B4-203	24/NOV/80		
	9V-STB	Singapore Airlines			24/FEB/81	
	F-OGTC	Airbus Industrie			18/APR/85	Stored 18/APR/85 to 19/JUN/86
	N967C	Continental Airlines			19/JUN/86	
122	F-WZEH	Airbus Industrie	B4-120	07/OCT/80		

C/N	Registration	Owner/Operator	Series	First Flight	Delivery	Remarks
	OY-KAA	SAS			12/DEC/80	
	OY-KAA	SAS			83	Converted
	OY-KAA	Malaysian Airline System			11/OCT/83	Leased,
						W/O 18/DEC/83, Kuala Lumpur
123	F-WZET	Airbus Industrie	B4-203	10/OCT/80		
	I-BUSF	Alitalia			02/DEC/80	
124	F-GBNO	Airbus Industrie	B4-103	22/OCT/80		
	N220EA	Eastern Air Lines			10/DEC/80	
125	F-WZEO	Airbus Industrie	B4-203	31/OCT/80		
	RP-C3003	Philippine Airlines			10/APR/81	
126	F-WZEC	Airbus Industrie	B4-203	29/JAN/81		
	9V-STC	Singapore Airlines			20/MAR/81	
	F-OGTA	Airbus Industrie			12/MAR/85	Stored 12/MAR/85 to MAY/86
	N968C	Continental Airlines			MAY/86	
127	F-WZED	Airbus Industrie	B4-203	14/NOV/80		
	G-BIMA	Laker			07/JAN/81	Stored 05/FEB/82 to 18/FEB/83
	6Y-JMJ	Air Jamaica			18/FEB/83	
128	F-WZEE	Airbus Industrie	B4-120	11/DEC/80		
	SE-DFL	SAS			12/MAR/81	
	SE-DFL	Scanair			17/JAN/84	
	OY-	Conair			86	Sched.delivery
129	F-BVGO	Air France	B4-203	05/DEC/80	05/FEB/81	
130	F-WZEI	Airbus Industrie	B4-120	13/JAN/81		
	EC-DLE	Iberia			27/FEB/81	
131	F-WZEL	Airbus Industrie	B4-203	30/DEC/80		
	G-BIMB	Laker Airways			17/FEB/81	Stored 05/FEB/82 to 18/FEB/83
	6Y-JMK	Air Jamaica			18/FEB/83	
132	F-WZEM	Airbus Industrie	B2-1C	08/JAN/81		
	D-AIAF	Lufthansa			19/FEB/81	
	D-AIAF	Airbus Industrie			09/NOV/84	
	F-BUAN	Air Inter			14/MAR/85	
133	F-WZEB	Airbus Industrie	B4-120	10/FEB/81		
	EC-DLF	Iberia			20/MAR/81	
134	F-WZEJ	Airbus Industrie	B4-103	06/MAY/81		
	VH-TAA	Trans Australia Airlines			29/JUN/81	
	D-AITA	Condor			19/MAR/84	Leased
	VH-TAA	Trans Australia Airlines			31/OCT/84	
	P2-ANG	Air Niugini			27/NOV/84	Leased
135	F-WZEA	Airbus Industrie	B4-120	25/FEB/81		
	EC-DLG	Iberia			03/APR/81	
136	F-WZEN	Airbus Industrie	B4-120	07/MAR/81		
	EC-DLH	Iberia			14/APR/81	
137	F-WZEP	Airbus Industrie	B4-203	20/FEB/81		
	TU-TAO	Air Afrique			07/MAY/81	
138	F-WZEQ	Airbus Industrie	B4-103	03/MAR/81		
	ZS-SDE	South African Airways			23/APR/81	
	C-GIZJ	Wardair			AUG/86	
139	F-WZES	Airbus Industrie	B4-203	11/MAR/81		
	I-BUSG	Alitalia			28/APR/81	
140	F-WZEF	Airbus Industrie	B4-203	24/MAR/81		
	I-BUSH	Alitalia			13/MAY/81	
141	F-WZEH	Airbus Industrie	B4-203	31/MAR/81		
	HS-TGT	Thai International			15/MAY/81	
142	F-WZET	Airbus Industrie	B4-203	03/APR/81		
	I-BUSJ	Alitalia			27/MAY/81	
143	PP-CLC	Cruzeiro	B4-203			Not taken-up
	F-WZED	Airbus Industrie		08/APR/81		
	PP-VND	Varig			03/JUN/81	
144	F-WZEG	Airbus Industrie	B4-203	16/APR/81		
	G-BIMC	Laker Airways			11/JUN/81	
	G-BIMC	Airbus Industrie			10/FEB/82	Stored 10/FEB/82 to 26/JUN/84
	AP-BBV	Pakistan International			26/JUN/84	
145	F-BVGP	Air France	B4-203	23/APR/81	15/JUN/81	
146	F-BVGQ	Air France	B4-203	04/MAY/81	26/JUN/81	
147	F-WZMA	Airbus Industrie	B4-203	11/MAY/81		
	9M-MHD	Malaysian Airline System			24/JUL/81	
148	F-WZMB	Airbus Industrie	B4-102	19/MAY/81		
	SX-BEG	Olympic Airways			29/JUL/81	
149	F-WZAC	Airbus Industrie	B4-203	27/MAY/81		
	HS-TGW	Thai International			30/SEP/81	
150	F-WZMD	Airbus Industrie	B4-203	10/JUN/81		
	SU-BCC	Egyptair			11/AUG/81	
151	F-WZME	Airbus Industrie	B4-103	09/JUN/81		
	VH-TAB	Trans Australia Airlines			18/AUG/81	
	D-AITB	Condor			28/MAR/84	Leased
	VH-TAB	Trans Australia Airlines			01/NOV/84	
	VH-TAB	Australian Airlines			04/AUG/86	
152	F-GBNP	Airbus Industrie	B4-203	22/JUN/81		
	N221EA	Eastern Air Lines			07/OCT/81	
153	F-GBNQ	Airbus Industrie	B4-203	30/JUN/81		
	N222EA	Eastern Air Lines			15/OCT/81	
154	F-GBNR	Airbus Industrie	B4-203	07/JUL/81		
	N223EA	Eastern Air Lines			09/NOV/81	
155	F-GBNS	Airbus Industrie	B4-203	12/AUG/81		
	N224EA	Eastern Air Lines			09/OCT/81	
156	F-WZMH	Airbus Industrie	B4-120	28/OCT/81		
	EC-DNQ	Iberia			02/FEB/82	
157	F-WZMG	Airbus Industrie	B4-103	24/AUG/81		
	VH-TAC	Trans Australia Airlines			09/OCT/81	
	VH-TAC	Australian Airlines			04/AUG/86	
158	F-GBNT	Airbus Industrie	B4-203	03/SEP/81		
	N225EA	Eastern Air Lines			24/NOV/81	
159	F-WZMH	Airbus Industrie	B4-220	06/OCT/81		Stored 06/OCT/81 to 04/MAR/82
	PK-GAA	Garuda			04/MAR/82	
160	F-WZMI	Airbus Industrie	B2K-3C	17/SEP/81		
	JA8471	Toa Domestic Airlines			13/NOV/81	
161	F-GBNU	Airbus Industrie	B4-203	24/SEP/81		
	N226EA	Eastern Air Lines			04/DEC/81	
163	F-WZMJ	Airbus Industrie	B2K-3C	06/OCT/81		
	JA8472	Toa Domestic Airlines			08/DEC/81	
164	F-WZMK	Airbus Industrie	B4-220	03/NOV/81		
	PK-GAC	Garuda			25/FEB/82	
165	F-WZML	Airbus Industrie	B4-220	12/NOV/81		
	PK-GAD	Garuda			11/JAN/82	
166	F-WZMM	Airbus Industrie	B4-220	25/NOV/81		

C/N	Registration	Owner/Operator	Series	First Flight	Delivery	Remarks
	PK-GAE	Garuda			19/JAN/82	
167	F-WZMN	Airbus Industrie	B4-220	10/DEC/81		
	PK-GAF	Garuda			03/FEB/82	
168	F-WZMO	Airbus Industrie	B4-220	30/DEC/81		
	PK-GAG	Garuda			10/FEB/82	
169	F-WZMP	Airbus Industrie	B4-203	18/NOV/81		
	9V-STD	Singapore Airlines			12/FEB/82	
	9V-STD	Boeing			01/APR/85	
	D-AHLJ	Hapag Lloyd			03/APR/85	
	G-BMNA	Dan Air			07/MAY/86	Leased
	D-AHLJ	Hapag Lloyd			OCT/86	Sched.return
170	F-WZMQ	Airbus Industrie	B4-120	13/JAN/82		
	EC-DNR	Iberia			26/FEB/82	
171	F-WZMR	Airbus Industrie	B4-120	23/APR/82		
	EC-	Iberia				Cancelled Order
	F-WZMR	Airbus Industrie	B4-220		JUL/82	Converted
	PK-GAG	Garuda				Cancelled Order
	F-WZMR	Airbus Industrie			08/OCT/82	Stored since 23/APR/82
	B-	China Airlines			JUL/86	Sched.delivery
173	F-WZMS	Airbus Industrie	B4-203	14/DEC/81		
	I-BUSL	Alitalia			23/FEB/82	
174	F-WZMT	Airbus Industrie	B4-203	15/DEC/81		
	9V-STE	Singapore Airlines			22/FEB/82	
	9V-STE	Boeing			20/APR/85	
	D-AHLK	Hapag Lloyd			21/APR/85	
	D-AHLK	Condor			29/JAN/86	Leased
175	F-BVGR	Air France	B4-203	02/FEB/82	07/APR/82	
176	F-WZMU	Airbus Industrie	B2K-3C	06/JAN/81		
	JA8473	Toa Domestic Airlines			17/FEB/82	
177	G-BIMD	Laker Airways	B4-203			Cancelled Order
	F-WZMV	Airbus Industrie		15/JAN/82		
	VT-EHN	Air India			28/JUL/82	
178	F-BVGS	Air France	B4-203	21/JAN/82	10/MAR/82	
179	F-WZMW	Airbus Industrie	B4-120	29/APR/82		
	EC-	Iberia				Cancelled Order
	F-WZMW	Airbus Industrie	B4-220		JUL/82	Converted
	PK-GAH	Garuda			JUL/82	Cancelled Order
	F-WZMW	Airbus Industrie			JUL/82	Stored JUL/82 to 85
	B-1810	China Airlines			05/JUL/85	
180	G-BIME	Laker Airways	B4-203			Cancelled Order
	F-WZMX	Airbus Industrie		17/JUN/82		
	VT-EHO	Air India			10/AUG/82	
181	F-WZMY	Airbus Industrie	B4-203	18/MAR/82		
	VT-EHC	Indian Airlines			24/MAY/82	
	VT-EHC	Air India			01/JUL/82	Leased
	VT-EHC	Indian Airlines			AUG/82	
182	F-WZMZ	Airbus Industrie	B4-203	26/MAR/82		
	VT-EHD	Indian Airlines			27/MAY/82	
183	F-BVGT	Air France	B4-203	25/FEB/82	15/APR/82	
184	F-WZMA	Airbus Industrie	B4-102	06/MAR/82		
	SX-BEH	Olympic Airways			08/APR/82	
185	F-WZMB	Airbus Industrie	B2-203	09/MAR/82		
	EP-IBT	Iran Air			30/APR/82	
186	F-WZMC	Airbus Industrie	B2-203	16/MAR/82		
	EP-IBU	Iran Air			30/APR/82	
187	F-WZMD	Airbus Industrie	B2-203	23/MAR/82		
	EP-IBV	Iran Air			12/MAY/82	
188	F-WZME	Airbus Industrie	B4-203	13/APR/82		
	TS-IMA	Tunis Air			28/MAY/82	
189	F-WZMF	Airbus Industrie	B4-102	02/APR/82		
	SX-BEI	Olympic Airways			17/MAY/82	
190	F-WZMI	Airbus Industrie	B4-203	02/AUG/82		
	G-BIMF	Laker Airways				Cancelled order
	VT-EHQ	Air India			05/NOV/82	
192	F-WZML	Airbus Industrie	B4-203	20/APR/82		
	ZS-SDF	South African Airways			09/JUN/82	
	C-GIZL	Wardair			AUG/86	
193	F-WZMM	Airbus Industrie	B4-220	28/APR/82		
	B-190	China Airlines			22/JUN/82	
194	F-WZMR	Airbus Industrie	B4-203	04/MAY/82		
	PP-CLD	Cruzeiro				
	PP-VNE	Varig			23/JUN/82	
195	F-WZES	Airbus Industrie	B4-203	16/SEP/82		
	5A-	Libyan Arab Airlines				Cancelled order
	F-WZES	Airbus Industrie				Stored 21/OCT/82 to 21/DEC/82
	N202PA	Pan American			21/DEC/84	
196	F-WZET	Airbus Industrie	B4-103	13/MAY/82		
	VH-TAD	Trans Australia Airlines			30/JUN/82	
	VH-TAD	Australian Airlines			04/AUG/86	
197	F-WZEP	Airbus Industrie	B4-220	01/JUN/82		
	B-192	China Airlines			23/JUL/82	
198	F-WZEQ	Airbus Industrie	B4-203	08/OCT/82		
	5A-	Libyan Arab Airlines				Cancelled order
	F-WZEQ	Airbus Industrie				Stored 13/OCT/82 to 21/DEC/84
	N204PA	Pan American			21/DEC/84	
199	F-WZMF	Airbus Industrie	B4-203	09/JUN/82		
	SU-BCD	Egyptair				Reg. not taken-up
	SU-BDF	Egyptair			16/AUG/82	
200	F-WZMN	Airbus Industrie	B4-203	17/JUN/82		
	SU-BCE	Egyptair				Reg. not taken-up
	SU-BDG	Egyptair			25/AUG/82	
202	F-WZMJ	Airbus Industrie	B2-203	28/JUN/82	82	
	PP-SNL	VASP			05/NOV/82	
203	F-WZMO	Airbus Industrie	B4-203	01/JUL/82		
	RP-C3004	Philippine Airlines			29/MAR/83	Stored 29/MAR/83 to JUL/84,
204	F-GBNI	Airbus Industrie	B4-203	29/JUL/82		
	N227EA	Eastern Air Lines			14/OCT/82	
205	F-WZMP	Airbus Industrie	B2-203	13/JUL/82		
	PP-SNM	Vasp			08/NOV/82	
207	F-GBNJ	Airbus Industrie	B4-203	20/AUG/82		
	N228EA	Eastern Air Lines			21/DEC/82	
208	F-WZMQ	Airbus Industrie	B4-203	23/AUG/82		
	6Y-	Air Jamaica				Cancelled order
	F-WZMQ	Airbus Industrie				Stored 03/SEP/82 to 17/MAY/85
	N212PA	Pan American			10/MAY/85	

C/N	Registration	Owner/Operator	Series	First Flight	Delivery	Remarks
209	F-WZMH	Airbus Industrie	B2K-3C	10/NOV/82		
	JA8476	Toa Domestic Airlines			28/FEB/83	
210	F-WZMK	Airbus Industrie	B4-203	10/SEP/82		
	6Y-	Air Jamaica				Cancelled order
	F-WZMK	Airbus Industrie				Stored 06/MAY/83 to 10/MAY/85
	N213PA	Pan American			17/MAY/85	
211	F-GBNV	Airbus Industrie	B4-203	15/SEP/82		
	N229EA	Eastern Air Lines			22/DEC/82	
212	F-WZMS	Airbus Industrie	C4-203	17/SEP/82		
	ZS-SDG	South African Airways			29/OCT/82	
	C-GIZN	Wardair			AUG/86	
213	F-WZMT	Airbus Industrie	B4-220	29/SEP/82		
	PK-GAH	Garuda			10/NOV/82	
214	F-WZMU	Airbus Industrie	B4-220	06/OCT/82		
	PK-GAI	Garuda			16/NOV/82	
215	F-WZMY	Airbus industrie	B4-220	13/OCT/82		
	PK-GAJ	Garuda			23/NOV/82	
216	F-GBNX	Airbus Industrie	B4-203	18/OCT/82		
	N230EA	Eastern Air Lines			22/DEC/82	
218	F-WZMZ	Airbus Industrie	B4-103	29/OCT/82		
	VH-TAE	Trans Australia Airlines			01/DEC/83	
	VH-TAE	Australian Airlines			04/AUG/86	
219	F-WZMV	Airbus Industrie	B4-203	04/NOV/82		
	RP-C3005	Philippine Airlines			29/MAR/83	Stored 29/MAR/83 to JUL/84
220	F-GBNY	Airbus Industrie	B4-203	05/NOV/82		
	N231EA	Eastern Air Lines			29/DEC/82	
221	F-WZMX	Airbus Industrie	B4-220	18/NOV/82		
	B-194	China Airlines			21/DEC/82	
222	F-WZMA	Airbus Industrie	B4-203	22/NOV/82		
	9V-STF	Singapore Airlines			23/DEC/82	
	9V-STF	Boeing			84	Stored
	ZS-SDH	South African Airways			24/APR/85	
225	F-WZMB	Airbus Industrie	B2-203	16/DEC/82		
	PP-SNN	VASP			31/JAN/83	
226	F-WZME	Airbus Industrie	B2-203	13/DEC/82		
	EP-IBZ	Iran Air			31/JAN/83	
227	F-WZMC	Airbus Industrie	B4-203	01/MAR/83		
	5A-	Libyan Arab Airlines				Cancelled order
	F-WZMC	Airbus Industrie				Stored 01/MAR/83 to 21/DEC/84
	N203PA	Pan American			21/DEC/84	
232	F-WZMD	Airbus Industrie	B4-220	03/JAN/83		
	B-196	China Airlines			27/JUL/83	
234	F-WZMF	Airbus Industrie	B4-203	18/JUL/83		Stored 18/JUL/83 to 29/MAR/85
	N206PA	Pan American			18/MAR/85	
235	F-WZMG	Airbus Industrie	B4-203	18/JAN/83		Stored 18/JAN/83 to 25/APR/85
	N211PA	Pan American			24/APR/85	
236	F-WZMI	Airbus Industrie	B4-203	18/OCT/83		Stored 18/OCT/83 to 18/MAR/85
	N207PA	Pan American			28/MAR/85	
238	G-BIMG	Laker Airways	B4-203	24/FEB/83		Cancelled order
	F-WZMN	Airbus Industrie				Stored 24/FEB/83 to 25/APR/85
	N210PA	Pan American			24/APR/85	
239	F-WZML	Airbus Industrie	B4-203	14/FEB/83		
	SU-GAA	Egyptair			11/APR/83	
240	F-WZMM	Airbus Industrie	B4-203	18/FEB/83		
	SU-GAB	Egyptair			03/MAY/83	
243	F-WZMJ	Airbus Industrie	B4-203	04/MAR/83		
	TU-TAS	Air Afrique			12/JUL/83	
244	F-WZMS	Airbus Industrie	B2K-3C	09/MAR/83		
	JA8477	Toa Domestic Airlines			22/APR/83	
247	F-WZMP	Airbus Industrie	B4-203	09/SEP/83		
	5A-	Libyan Arab Airlines				Cancelled order
	F-WZMP	Airbus Industrie				Stored 09/SEP/83 to 21/DEC/84
	N205PA	Pan American			21/DEC/84	
249	F-WZMT	Airbus Industrie	B4-203	23/JUN/83		Stored 23/JUN/83 to 08/MAR/85
	HS-TGX	Thai International			07/MAR/85	
250	F-WZMU	Airbus Industrie	B4-203	31/MAY/82		Stored 31/MAY/82 to 25/APR/86
	N970C	Continental Airlines			25/APR/86	
252	F-WZLR	Airbus Industrie	B4-620	08/JUL/83		A300-600 prototype
	F-WZLR	Airbus Industrie	B4-602		FEB/85	Converted
253	F-WZMX	Airbus Industrie	B2K-3C	04/MAY/83		
	JA8478	Toa Domestic Airlines			16/JUN/83	
255	F-WZMY	Airbus Industrie	B4-203	11/MAY/83		
	SU-GAC	Egyptair			04/JUL/83	
256	F-WZMA	Airbus Industrie	C4-203	18/MAY/83		
	5A-	Libyan Arab Airlines				Cancelled order
	F-WZMA	Airbus Industrie			02/AUG/83	Stored 02/AUG/83 to 25/MAR/86
	JA8237	Toa Domestic Airlines			25/MAR/86	
259	F-GBNZ	Airbus Industrie	B4-203	17/AUG/83		
	N232EA	Eastern Air Lines			16/DEC/83	
261	F-GDVA	Airbus Industrie	B4-203	25/AUG/83		
	N233EA	Eastern Air Lines			16/DEC/83	
262	F-WZMH	Airbus Industrie	B4-203	17/NOV/83		Stored 07/NOV/83 to 07/MAY/86
	N971C	Continental Airlines			07/MAY/86	
265	F-WZMO	Airbus Industrie	B4-203	10/AUG/83		Stored 10/AUG/83 to 28/MAR/85
	HS-TGY	Thai International			28/MAR/85	
268	F-WZMV	Airbus Industrie	B4-203	29/JUL/83		
	9V-STG	Singapore Airlines			09/SEP/83	
	9V-STG	Boeing			84	Stored
	AP-BCJ	Pakistan International			15/MAY/85	
269	F-WZMB	Airbus Industrie	B4-203	12/AUG/83		
	9V-STH	Singapore Airlines			22/SEP/83	
	9V-STH	Boeing			19/DEC/84	
	LX-LGP	Luxair			19/DEC/84	
271	F-GDVB	Airbus Industrie	B4-203	01/SEP/83		
	N234EA	Eastern Air Lines			19/DEC/83	
274	F-GDVC	Airbus Industrie	B4-203	20/SEP/83		
	N235EA	Eastern Air Lines			19/DEC/83	
275	PK-	Garuda	B4-220			Cancelled order, Not built
277	F-WZME	Airbus Industrie	C4-203			
	5A-	Libyan Arab Airlines				Cancelled order
	F-WZME	Airbus Industrie				Stored
	3X-	Air Guinea				Cancelled order
	F-WZME	Airbus Industrie				Stored since 02/JAN/84
	HL	Korean Air	F4-203		MAY/86	Sched.delivery
280	PK-	Garuda	B4-220			Cancelled order, Not built

AIRBUS INDUSTRIE A300

C/N	Registration	Owner/Operator	Series	First Flight	Delivery	Remarks
282	F-WZML	Airbus Industrie	B4-203	13/OCT/83		
	TU-TAT	Air Afrique			18/OCT/83	Delivery delayed
	F-WZXP	Airbus Industrie				Stored 18/OCT/83 to 13/SEP/84
	TU-TAT	Air Afrique			13/SEP/84	
284	F-WZLS	Airbus Industrie	B4-621	15/NOV/83		
	HZ-AJA	Saudia			01/JUN/84	
286	PK-	Garuda	B4-220			Cancelled order, Not built
287	VT-	Indian Airlines	B4-203			Cancelled order, Not built
289	F-WZMM	Airbus Industrie	B4-203	22/NOV/83		Stored 22/NOV/83 to 25/APR/86
	N972C	Continental Airlines			25/APR/86	
292	ZS-	South African Airways	C4-203			Cancelled order
	F-WZMS	Airbus Industrie				Stored
	HL	Korean Air	F4-203		86	Sched.delivery
294	F-WZYA	Airbus Industrie	B4-621	20/DEC/83		
	HZ-AJB	Saudia			09/APR/84	
296	TS-IMB	Tunis Air	B4-203			Cancelled order, Not built
299	F-WZMX	Airbus Industrie	B4-203		84	Stored
	LX-LGP	Luxair			31/OCT/84	Not taken-up
	F-WZMX	Airbus Industrie				Stored since 31/OCT/84
	TS-	Tunis Air			MAY/86	Not taken-up
	OH-LAA	Finnair			DEC/86	Sched.delivery
301	F-WZYB	Airbus Industrie	B4-621	03/JAN/84		
	HZ-AJC	Saudia			25/MAR/84	
302	F-WZMY	Airbus Industrie	B4-203			
	TS-	Tunis Air			JUN/86	Not taken-up
	OH-LAB	Finnair			MAR/87	Sched.delivery
304	F-WZMD	Airbus Industrie	B4-203	02/JAN/84		
	N208PA	Pan American			28/MAR/85	
305	F-WZMV	Airbus Industrie	B4-203	30/DEC/84		
	N209PA	Pan American			24/MAR/84	
307	F-WZYC	Airbus Industrie	B4-621	02/FEB/84		
	HZ-AJD	Saudia			03/APR/84	
308	9V-STI	Singapore Airlines	B4-203			Cancelled order, Not built
310	9V-STJ	Singapore Airlines	B4-203			Cancelled order, Not built
312	F-WZYD	Airbus Industrie	B4-621	20/FEB/84		
	HZ-AJE	Saudia			20/APR/84	
314	AP-	Pakistan International	B4-203		JUL/83	Cancelled order, Not built
315	AP-	Pakistan International	B4-203		82	Cancelled order, Not built
317	F-WZYE	Airbus Industrie	B4-621	07/MAR/84		
	HZ-AJF	Saudia			28/APR/84	
319			B4-203			Not built
321	F-WZYF	Airbus Industrie	B4-621	29/MAR/84		
	HZ-AJG	Saudia			14/MAY/84	
324			B4-203			Not built
325			B4-204			Not built
327	F-WZYG	Airbus Industrie	C4-620	12/APR/84		
	9K-AHF	Kuwait Airways			30/MAY/84	
328			B4-203			Not built
332	F-WZYH	Airbus Industrie	C4-620	26/APR/84		
	9K-AHG	Kuwait Airways			08/JUN/84	
336	F-WZYI	Airbus Industrie	B4-621	29/MAY/84		
	HZ-AJH	Saudia			04/JUL/84	
337			B4-203			Not built
341	F-WZYJ	Airbus Industrie	B4-621	28/JUN/84		
	HZ-AJI	Saudia			18/AUG/84	
	9K-AHI	Kuwait Airways	C4-620	16/JUN/84	31/AUG/84	
344	F-WZYK	Airbus Industrie	C4-620	16/JUN/84	31/AUG/84	
348	F-WZYL	Airbus Industrie	B4-621	10/JUL/84		
	HZ-AJJ	Saudia			27/AUG/84	
351	F-WZYB	Airbus Industrie	B4-621	23/JUL/84		
	HZ-AJK	Saudia			08/OCT/84	
354	F-WZYA	Airbus Industrie	B4-620	10/DEC/84		
	A6-SHZ	United Arab Emirates Govt.			JUL/85	Reg. Not taken-up
	F-ODRM	United Arab Emirates Govt.			JUL/85	
	A6-SHZ	United Arab Emirates Govt.			30/SEP/85	
357	9V-	Singapore Airlines	B4-600			Cancelled order
358	F-WZYC	Airbus Industrie	B4-620			
	HL	Korean Air			APR/87	Sched.delivery
360	9V-	Singapore Airlines	B4-600			Cancelled order
361	F-WWAE	Airbus Industrie	B4-620			
	HL	Korean Air			86	Sched.delivery
365	F-WWAF	Airbus Industrie	B4-620		86	
	HL	Korean Air			86	Sched.delivery
366	HZ-AJL	Saudia	B4-620			
368	F-WWAG	Airbus Industrie	B4-602	01/JUL/85		
	HS-TAA	Thai International			26/SEP/85	
371	F-WWAH	Airbus Industrie	B4-602	12/JUL/85		
	HS-TAB	Thai International			30/SEP/85	
372	F-	Airbus Industrie	B4-620			
374	F-WWAJ	Airbus Industrie	B4-620	02/OCT/85		
	A6-PFD	United Arab Emirates Govt.			05/DEC/85	
375	F-	Airbus Industrie	B4-620			
377	F-WWAI	Airbus Industrie	B4-602	16/SEP/85		
	HS-TAC	Thai International			06/DEC/85	
380	D-AIAH	Lufthansa	B4-602		FEB/87	Sched.delivery
384	F-WWAK	Airbus Industrie	B4-602	27/NOV/85		
	HS-TAD	Thai International			03/FEB/86	
388	F-	Airbus Industrie	B4-620			
391	D-AIAI	Lufthansa	B4-602		FEB/87	Sched.delivery
395	HS-TAE	Thai International	B4-602		OCT/86	Sched.delivery
398	HS-TAF	Thai International	B4-602		DEC/86	Sched.delivery
401	D-AIAK	Lufthansa	B4-602		MAR/87	Sched.delivery
405	D-AIAL	Lufthansa	B4-602		APR/87	Sched.delivery
408	D-AIAM	Lufthansa	B4-602		MAY/87	Sched.delivery
411	D-AIAN	Lufthansa	B4-602		JUN/87	Sched.delivery
414	D-AIAP	Lufthansa	B4-602		JUL/87	Sched.delivery
417	HS-TAG	Thai International	B4-602			
420	HS-TAH	Thai International	B4-602		JUN/89	
464	HS-	Thai International	B4-602			

6Y- Jamaica

127	6Y-JMJ
131	6Y-JMK

9K- Kuwait

327	9K-AHF
332	9K-AHG
344	9K-AHI

9M- Malaysia

73	9M-MHA
93	9M-MHB
95	9M-MHC
147	9M-MHD

9V- Singapore

117	9V-STA
121	9V-STB
126	9V-STC
169	9V-STD
174	9V-STE
222	9V-STF
268	9V-STG
269	9V-STH
308	9V-STI
310	9V-STJ

A6- United Arab Emirates

374	A6-PFD
354	A6-SHZ

AP- Pakistan

96	AP-BAX
98	AP-BAY
99	AP-BAZ
114	AP-BBA
64	AP-BBM
144	AP-BBV
268	AP-BCJ
25	AP-BCP

B- Taiwan

179	B-1810
193	B-190
197	B-192
221	B-194
232	B-196

C- Canada

138	C-GIZJ
192	C-GIZL
212	C-GIZN

D- West Germany

64	D-AHLA
83	D-AHLB
17	D-AHLC
169	D-AHLJ
169	D-AHLJ
174	D-AHLK
25	D-AHLZ
21	D-AIAA
22	D-AIAB
26	D-AIAC
48	D-AIAD
52	D-AIAE
132	D-AIAF
380	D-AIAH
391	D-AIAI
401	D-AIAK
405	D-AIAL
408	D-AIAM
411	D-AIAN
414	D-AIAP
53	D-AIBA
57	D-AIBB
75	D-AIBC
76	D-AIBD
77	D-AIBF
134	D-AITA
151	D-AITB
9	D-AMAP
12	D-AMAX
20	D-AMAY
25	D-AMAZ

EC- Spain

130	EC-DLE
133	EC-DLF
135	EC-DLG
136	EC-DLH
156	EC-DNQ
170	EC-DNR

EP- Iran

61	EP-IBR
80	EP-IBS
185	EP-IBT
186	EP-IBU
187	EP-IBV
226	EP-IBZ

F- France

3	F-BUAD
8	F-BUAE
8	F-BUAF
15	F-BUAG
27	F-BUAH
62	F-BUAI
97	F-BUAJ
112	F-BUAK
29	F-BUAL
21	F-BUAM
132	F-BUAN
48	F-BUAO
52	F-BUAP
5	F-BVGA
6	F-BVGB
7	F-BVGC
10	F-BVGD
11	F-BVGE
13	F-BVGF
19	F-BVGG
23	F-BVGH
45	F-BVGI
47	F-BVGJ
70	F-BVGK
74	F-BVGL
78	F-BVGM
78	F-BVGM
100	F-BVGN
129	F-BVGO
145	F-BVGP
146	F-BVGQ
175	F-BVGR
178	F-BVGS
183	F-BVGT
50	F-GBEA
102	F-GBEB
104	F-GBEC
65	F-GBNA
66	F-GBNB
67	F-GBNC
68	F-GBND
86	F-GBNE
87	F-GBNF
91	F-GBNG
92	F-GBNH
49	F-GBNI
204	
51	F-GBNJ
207	
108	F-GBNK
118	F-GBNL
124	F-GBNO
152	F-GBNP
153	F-GBNP
154	F-GBNR
155	F-GBNS
158	F-GBNT
161	F-GBNU
211	F-GBNV
216	F-GBNX
220	F-GBNY
259	F-GBNZ
261	F-GDVA
271	F-GDVB
274	F-GDVC
2	F-OCAZ
1	F-ODCX
3	F-ODCY
9	F-ODHC
8	F-ODHY
49	F-ODHZ
51	F-ODJU
29	F-ODRD
22	F-ODRE
26	F-ODRF
48	F-ODRG
52	F-ODRM
354	F-OGTA
126	F-OGTB
117	F-OGTC
121	F-WLGA
9	F-WLGA
32	F-WLGA
35	F-WLGB
14	F-WLGB
16	F-WLGB
34	F-WLGB
39	F-WLGC
46	F-WLGC
12	F-WLGC
15	F-WLGC
27	F-WLGG
31	F-WNDA
21	F-WNDA
25	F-WNDA
51	F-WNDA
8	F-WNDB
26	F-WNDB
30	F-WNDB
48	F-WNDB
50	F-WNDB
22	F-WNDC
28	F-WNDC
33	F-WNDC
52	F-WNDC
24	F-WNDD
29	F-WNDD
4	F-WUAA
1	F-WUAB
2	F-WUAC
3	F-WUAD
36	F-WUAT
43	F-WUAT
53	F-WUAT
37	F-WUAU
42	F-WUAU
38	F-WUAV
49	F-WUAV
40	F-WUAX
44	F-WUAX
47	F-WUAX
41	F-WUAZ
361	F-WWAE
365	F-WWAF
368	F-WWAG
371	F-WWAH
377	F-WWAI
374	F-WWAJ
384	F-WWAK
51	F-WZEA
101	F-WZEA
135	F-WZEA
52	F-WZEB
69	F-WZEB
110	F-WZEB
133	F-WZEB
55	F-WZEC
71	F-WZEC
85	F-WZEC
103	F-WZEC
126	F-WZEC
54	F-WZED
72	F-WZED
88	F-WZED
105	F-WZED
127	F-WZED
143	F-WZED
53	F-WZEE
73	F-WZEE
106	F-WZEE
128	F-WZEE
56	F-WZEF
89	F-WZEF
140	F-WZEF
57	F-WZEG
75	F-WZEG
90	F-WZEG
144	F-WZEG
58	F-WZEH
122	F-WZEH
141	F-WZEH
59	F-WZEI
76	F-WZEI
93	F-WZEI
111	F-WZEI
130	F-WZEI
60	F-WZEJ
77	F-WZEJ
94	F-WZEJ
113	F-WZEJ
134	F-WZEJ
61	F-WZEK
121	F-WZEK
62	F-WZEL
63	F-WZEL
107	F-WZEL
131	F-WZEL
64	F-WZEM
95	F-WZEM
109	F-WZEM
119	F-WZEM
132	F-WZEM
79	F-WZEN
114	F-WZEN
120	F-WZEN
136	F-WZEN
80	F-WZEO
125	F-WZEO
81	F-WZEP
96	F-WZEP
115	F-WZEP
137	F-WZEP
197	F-WZEP
31	F-WZEQ
82	F-WZEQ
138	F-WZEQ
198	F-WZEQ
46	F-WZER
98	F-WZER
117	F-WZER
49	F-WZES
83	F-WZES
116	F-WZES
139	F-WZES
195	F-WZES
84	F-WZET
99	F-WZET
123	F-WZET
142	F-WZET
196	F-WZET
252	F-WZLR
284	F-WZLS
147	F-WZMA
184	F-WZMA
222	F-WZMA
256	F-WZMA
22	F-WZMB
148	F-WZMB
185	F-WZMB
225	F-WZMB
269	F-WZMB
149	F-WZMC
186	F-WZMC
227	F-WZMC
150	F-WZMD
187	F-WZMD
232	F-WZMD
304	F-WZMD
151	F-WZME
188	F-WZME
226	F-WZME
277	F-WZME
189	F-WZMF
199	F-WZMF
234	F-WZMF
157	F-WZMG
235	F-WZMG
156	F-WZMH
159	F-WZMH
209	F-WZMH
262	F-WZMH
160	F-WZMI
190	F-WZMI
236	F-WZMI
26	F-WZMJ
163	F-WZMJ
202	F-WZMJ
243	F-WZMJ
164	F-WZMK
210	F-WZMK
165	F-WZML
192	F-WZML
239	F-WZML
282	F-WZML
166	F-WZMM
193	F-WZMM
240	F-WZMM
289	F-WZMM
167	F-WZMN
200	F-WZMN
238	F-WZMN
168	F-WZMO
203	F-WZMO
265	F-WZMO
169	F-WZMP
205	F-WZMP
247	F-WZMP
170	F-WZMQ
208	F-WZMQ
171	F-WZMR
194	F-WZMR
173	F-WZMS
212	F-WZMS
244	F-WZMS
292	F-WZMS
174	F-WZMT
213	F-WZMT
249	F-WZMT
176	F-WZMU
214	F-WZMU
250	F-WZMU
177	F-WZMV
219	F-WZMV
268	F-WZMV
305	F-WZMV
179	F-WZMW
180	F-WZMX
221	F-WZMX
253	F-WZMX
299	F-WZMX
181	F-WZMY
215	F-WZMY
255	F-WZMY
302	F-WZMY
182	F-WZMZ
218	F-WZMZ
282	F-WZXP
294	F-WZYA
354	F-WZYA
301	F-WZYB
351	F-WZYB
307	F-WZYC
358	F-WZYC
312	F-WZYD
317	F-WZYE
321	F-WZYF
327	F-WZYG
332	F-WZYH
336	F-WZYI
341	F-WZYJ
344	F-WZYK
348	F-WZYL

G- United Kingdom

127	G-BIMA
131	G-BIMB
144	G-BIMC
177	G-BIMD
180	G-BIME
190	G-BIMF
238	G-BIMG
169	G-BMNA
9	G-BMNB

HK- Colombia

29	HK-2057

HL South Korea

14	HL7218
16	HL7219
18	HL7220
24	HL7221
28	HL7223
30	HL7224
31	HL7238
81	HL7246

HS- Thailand

368	HS-TAA
371	HS-TAB
377	HS-TAC
384	HS-TAD
395	HS-TAE
398	HS-TAF
417	HS-TAG
420	HS-TAH
33	HS-TGH
35	HS-TGK
54	HS-TGL
55	HS-TGM
71	HS-TGN
72	HS-TGO
84	HS-TGP
85	HS-TGR
141	HS-TGT
149	HS-TGW
249	HS-TGX
265	HS-TGY
8	HS-VGD
9	HS-VGF

HZ- Saudi Arabia

284	HZ-AJA
294	HZ-AJB
301	HZ-AJC
307	HZ-AJD
312	HZ-AJE
317	HZ-AJF
321	HZ-AJG
336	HZ-AJH
341	HZ-AJI
348	HZ-AJJ
351	HZ-AJK
366	HZ-AJL

I- Italy

101	I-BUSB
106	I-BUSC
107	I-BUSD
123	I-BUSF
139	I-BUSG
140	I-BUSH
142	I-BUSJ
173	I-BUSL

JA Japan

256	JA8237
82	JA8464
89	JA8465
90	JA8466
160	JA8471
163	JA8472
176	JA8473
209	JA8476
244	JA8477
253	JA8478

LN- Norway

79	LN-RCA

LX- Luxembourg

269	LX-LGP
299	LX-LGP

N United States

41	N201EA
42	N202EA
195	N202PA
43	N203EA
227	N203PA

Airbus Industrie A300 cross-reference index

44	N204EA	271	N234EA	165	PK-GAD		
198	N204PA	274	N235EA	166	PK-GAE		
65	N205EA	49	N291EA	167	PK-GAF		
247	N205PA	51	N292EA	168	PK-GAG		
66	N206EA	117	N966C	171	PK-GAG		
234	N206PA	121	N967C	179	PK-GAH		
67	N207EA	126	N968C	213	PK-GAH		
236	N207PA	250	N970C	214	PK-GAI		
68	N208EA	262	N971C	215	PK-GAJ		
304	N208PA	289	N972C				

SU- Egypt

25	SU-AZY
17	SU-BBS
115	SU-BCA
116	SU-BCB
150	SU-BCC
199	SU-BCD
200	SU-BCE
199	SU-BDF
200	SU-BDG
239	SU-GAA
240	SU-GAB
255	SU-GAC

VH- Australia

134	VH-TAA
151	VH-TAB
157	VH-TAC
196	VH-TAD
218	VH-TAE

86	N209EA
305	N209PA
87	N210EA
238	N210PA
235	N211PA
91	N212EA
208	N212PA
92	N213EA
210	N213PA
108	N215EA
118	N216EA
119	N217EA
120	N219EA
124	N220EA
152	N221EA
153	N222EA
154	N223EA
155	N224EA
158	N225EA
161	N226EA
204	N227EA
207	N228EA
211	N229EA
216	N230EA
220	N231EA
259	N232EA
261	N233EA

OH- Finland

299	OH-LAA
302	OH-LAB

OO- Belgium

2	OO-TEF
17	OO-TEG

OY- Denmark

122	OY-KAA

P2- Papua New Guinea

134	P2-ANG

PH- Netherlands

8	PH-TVL

PK- Indonesia

159	PK-GAA
164	PK-GAC

PP- Brasil

109	PP-CLA
110	PP-CLB
143	PP-CLC
194	PP-CLD
202	PP-SNL
205	PP-SNM
225	PP-SNN
143	PP-VND
194	PP-VNE

RP-C Philippines

63	RP-C3001
69	RP-C3002
125	RP-C3003
203	RP-C3004
219	RP-C3005

SE- Sweden

94	SE-DFK
128	SE-DFL

SX- Greece

46	SX-BEB
56	SX-BEC
58	SX-BED
103	SX-BEE
105	SX-BEF
148	SX-BEG
184	SX-BEH
189	SX-BEI

TS- Tunisia

188	TS-IMA
296	TS-IMB

TU- Ivory Coast

137	TU-TAO
243	TU-TAS
282	TU-TAT

VT- India

34	VT-EDV
36	VT-EDW
38	VT-EDX
59	VT-EDY
60	VT-EDZ
88	VT-EFV
111	VT-EFW
113	VT-EFX
181	VT-EHC
182	VT-EHD
177	VT-EHN
180	VT-EHO
190	VT-EHQ

ZS- South Africa

32	ZS-SDA
37	ZS-SDB
39	ZS-SDC
40	ZS-SDD
138	ZS-SDE
192	ZS-SDF
212	ZS-SDG
222	ZS-SDH

AIRBUS INDUSTRIE A310

Short/medium-range wide-body transport with twin wing-mounted turbofans engines. A smaller development of the A300B, the A310-200 made its maiden flight on 3 April 1982, and entered service with Lufthansa and Swissair in April 1983. The A310-300 is an extended range version which first flew on 8 July 1985. To date, 90 aircraft have been delivered and a further 37 are on order with the production rate currently two aircraft per month.

Dimensions :	Wing span: 143 ft 11 in (43.90m) Length: 153 ft 1 in (46.66m) Height: 51 ft 10 in (15.81m)
	Powerplant : Two General Electric CF6-80A3 turbofans or Pratt & Whitney JT9D-7R4D1 turbofans (200)
	Two General Electric CF6-80C2-A2 turbofans, Pratt & Whitney JT9D-7R4E1 turbofans or PW 4150 turbofans (200/300)
Performance :	Max cruising speed 484 knots (897km/h) Range: with max payload 2,790nm (5,170km) (200)
Range:	with max payload 3,750nm (6,950km) (300)
Accommodation:	280 passengers in a 9 abreast layout
Manufacturer :	Airbus Industrie - Avenue Lucien Servanty, BP No. 33, 31700 Blagnac, France Telephone: 033-61 93 33 33 Telex: 530526 F AITO

 Airbus

C/N	Registration	Owner/Operator	Series	First Flight	Delivery	Remarks
162	F-WZLH	Airbus Industrie	221	03/APR/82		
	HB-IPE	Swissair			21/MAR/84	
172	F-WZLI	Airbus Industrie	221	13/MAY/82		Development aircraft
	F-GEMF	Air France	203		14/MAR/86	
191	F-WZLJ	Airbus Industrie	203	05/AUG/82		
	D-AICA	Lufthansa			09/MAR/84	
201	F-WZLK	Airbus Industrie	203	20/OCT/82		
	D-AICB	Lufthansa			29/JUN/83	
217	F-WZLL	Airbus Industrie	221	01/DEC/82		
	HB-IPC	Swissair			28/JUN/83	
224	F-WZEA	Airbus Industrie	221	05/JAN/83		
	HB-IPA	Swissair			25/MAR/83	
230	F-WZEB	Airbus Industrie	203	27/JAN/83		
	D-AICC	Lufthansa			07/MAR/83	
233	F-WZEC	Airbus Industrie	203	07/FEB/83		
	D-AICD	Lufthansa			30/MAR/83	
237	F-WZED	Airbus Industrie	203	22/FEB/83		
	D-AICF	Lufthansa			31/MAR/83	
241	F-WZEE	Airbus Industrie	203	08/MAR/83		
	PH-AGA	KLM			26/APR/83	
	F-WZEE	Airbus Industrie			28/APR/83	Leased, demonstrator
	PH-AGA	KLM			15/OCT/83	
245	F-WZEG	Airbus Industrie	203	04/MAY/83		
	PH-AGB	KLM			17/JUN/83	
248	F-WZEF	Airbus Industrie	203	12/APR/83		
	PH-AGC	KLM			27/MAY/83	
251	F-WZEH	Airbus Industrie	221	20/APR/83		
	HB-IPB	Swissair			30/MAY/83	
254	F-WZLJ	Airbus Industrie	203	27/APR/83		
	D-AICH	Lufthansa			01/JUN/83	
257	F-WZEJ	Airbus Industrie	203	25/MAY/83		
	D-AICK	Lufthansa			07/JUL/83	
260	F-WZEK	Airbus Industrie	221	27/JUN/83		
	HB-IPD	Swissair			14/OCT/83	
264	F-WZEL	Airbus Industrie	203	04/AUG/83		
	PH-AGD	KLM			12/DEC/83	
267	F-WZEM	Airbus Industrie	222	29/JUL/83		
	9K-AHA	Kuwait Airways			28/SEP/83	
270	F-WZEN	Airbus Industrie	221	24/AUG/83		
	5N-AUE	Nigeria Airways			19/DEC/84	
273	F-WZEO	Airbus Industrie	203	13/OCT/83		
	D-AICL	Lufthansa			20/JAN/84	
276	F-WZEP	Airbus Industrie	222	19/SEP/83		
	9K-AHB	Kuwait Airways			26/OCT/83	
278	F-WZER	Airbus Industrie	222	30/SEP/83		
	9K-AHC	Kuwait Airways			09/DEC/83	WFU 04/DEC/84 to 07/MAY/86, Tehran, following hijack
281	F-WZET	Airbus Industrie	203	13/OCT/83		
	PH-MCA	Martinair			15/MAR/84	
283	F-WZEA	Airbus Industrie	203	24/OCT/83		
	PH-AGE	KLM			13/JAN/84	
285	F-WZEB	Airbus Industrie	221	09/NOV/83		
	5N-AUF	Nigeria Airways			14/DEC/84	
288	PP-	Vasp	221			Cancelled order
	F-WZEC	Airbus Industrie		21/NOV/83		Stored 21/NOV/83 to 24/MAY/85
	N801PA	Pan American			24/MAY/85	
291	F-WZED	Airbus Industrie	203	20/JUN/84		
	7T-VJC	Air Algerie			31/AUG/84	
293	F-WZEE	Airbus Industrie	203	02/AUG/84		
	7T-VJD	Air Algerie			20/DEC/84	
295	F-WZEF	Airbus Industrie	203	15/DEC/83		
	G-BKWT	British Caledonian			20/FEB/84	
	G-BKWT	Service Airlines			MAY/86	
297	F-WZEH	Airbus Industrie	203	21/DEC/83		
	PH-AGF	KLM			07/FEB/84	
300	F-WZEG	Airbus Industrie	203	27/DEC/83		
	5B-DAQ	Cyprus Airways			16/FEB/84	
303	F-WZEI	Airbus Industrie	221	10/JAN/84		

AIRBUS INDUSTRIE A310

C/N	Registration	Owner/Operator	Series	First Flight	Delivery	Remarks
	OO-SCA	Sabena			23/FEB/84	
306	F-WZEK	Airbus Industrie	203	20/JAN/84		
	G-BKWU	British Caledonian			20/MAR/84	
	G-BKWU	Service Airlines			MAY/86	
309	F-WZEM	Airbus Industrie	203	03/FEB/84		
	5B-DAR	Cyprus Airways			23/MAR/84	
311	OD-	MEA	222			Cancelled order
	F-WZEJ	Airbus Industrie		29/FEB/84		Stored 29/FEB/84 to 25/JUN/85
	N	Royal Coach Airlines				Cancelled order
	B-2301	CAAC			25/JUN/85	
313	F-WZEP	Airbus Industrie	221	23/FEB/84		
	OO-SCB	Sabena			30/MAR/84	
316	F-GEMA	Air France	203	10/MAR/84	27/APR/84	
318	F-WZEL	Airbus Industrie	222	16/MAR/84		
	9K-AHD	Kuwait Airways			26/APR/84	
320	OD-	MEA	222			Cancelled order
	F-WZER	Airbus Industrie		11/AUG/84		Stored 11/AUG/84 to 28/JUN/85
	N	Royal Coach Airlines				Cancelled order
	B-2302	CAAC			28/JUN/85	
326	F-GEMB	Air France	203	30/MAR/84	04/JUN/84	
329	F-WZEA	Airbus Industrie	221	02/MAY/84		
	5N-AUG	Nigeria Airways			14/DEC/84	
331	F-WZEO	Airbus Industrie	222	11/APR/84		
	9K-AHE	Kuwait Airways			30/MAY/84	
333	PP-	Vasp	221			Cancelled order
	F-WZEG	Airbus Industrie		15/FEB/85		
	N802PA	Pan American			24/MAY/85	
335	F-GEMC	Air France	203	15/MAY/84	21/JUN/84	
338	F-WZET	Airbus Industrie	203	05/APR/85		
	TC-JCL	Turk Hava Yollari			24/MAY/85	
339	F-WZEF	Airbus Industrie	222	11/JUL/84		
	9K-AHH	Kuwait Airways			27/SEP/84	
	9K-AHH	Boeing			28/SEP/84	Stored 28/SEP/84 to 27/FEB/86
	N805PA	Pan American			27/FEB/86	
340	F-WZEH	Airbus Industrie	221	15/JUN/84		
	5N-AUH	Nigeria Airways			14/DEC/84	
342	F-WZEI	Airbus Industrie	222	20/AUG/84		
	9K-AHJ	Kuwait Airways			28/SEP/84	
	9K-AHJ	Boeing			29/SEP/84	Stored 29/SEP/84 to 08/FEB/86
	N806PA	Pan American			08/FEB/86	
343	PP-	Vasp	221			Cancelled order
	F-WZEK	Airbus Industrie		27/FEB/85		
	N803PA	Pan American			31/MAY/85	
345	PP-	Vasp	221			Cancelled order
	F-WZEL	Airbus Industrie		21/MAR/85		
	N804PA	Pan American			12/JUN/85	
346	F-WZEM	Airbus Industrie	222	20/SEP/84		
	9K-AHK	Kuwait Airways			29/OCT/84	
	9K-AHK	Boeing			30/OCT/84	Stored 30/OCT/84 to 12/FEB/86
	N807PA	Pan American			12/FEB/86	
347	F-WZEO	Airbus Industrie	222	26/SEP/84		
	9V-STI	Singapore Airlines			19/NOV/84	
349	F-WZEP	Airbus Industrie	203	03/OCT/84		
	PH-MCB	Martinair			29/NOV/84	
350	F-WZLH	Airbus Industrie	222	15/OCT/84		
	9V-STJ	Singapore Airlines			28/NOV/84	
352	F-WZEO	Airbus Industrie	203	31/JAN/85		
	5B-DAS	Cyprus Airways			28/MAR/85	
353	F-WZLJ	Airbus Industrie	203	26/OCT/84		
	PH-AGG	KLM			11/JAN/85	
355	F-GEMD	Air France	203	13/NOV/84	04/JAN/85	
356	F-WZLK	Airbus Industrie	203	21/NOV/84		
	D-AICM	Condor			10/JAN/85	
	D-AICM	Kenya Airways			85	Leased
	D-AICM	Condor			22/MAY/86	
357	F-WZLL	Airbus Industrie	222	27/NOV/84		
	9V-STK	Singapore Airlines			28/JAN/85	
359	F-WZLS	Airbus Industrie	203	14/DEC/85		
	D-AICN	Condor			07/FEB/85	
360	F-WZED	Airbus Industrie	203	26/DEC/84		
	D-AICP	Condor			14/FEB/85	
362	F-WZEF	Airbus Industrie	203	04/JAN/85		
	PH-AGH	KLM			19/JAN/85	
363	F-WZEI	Airbus Industrie	222	17/JAN/85		
	9V-STL	Singapore Airlines			07/MAR/85	
364	F-WZEM	Airbus Industrie	203	07/FEB/85		
	PH-AGI	KLM			21/MAR/85	
367	F-WZEP	Airbus Industrie	222	21/FEB/85		
	9V-STM	Singapore Airlines			02/APR/85	
369	F-GEME	Air France	203	01/MAR/85	12/APR/85	
370	G-BLPS	British Caledonian	203			Cancelled order
	F-WZLH	Airbus Industrie				
	TC-JCR	Turk Hava Yollari			86	
372	F-WZEN	Airbus Industrie	222	19/MAR/85		
	9V-STN	Singapore Airlines			30/APR/85	
375	F-WWBA	Airbus Industrie	203	16/APR/85		
	TC-JCM	Turk Hava Yollari			30/MAY/85	
378	F-WWCA	Airbus Industrie	322	08/JUL/85		
	F-WWCA	Airbus Industrie	321		03/AUG/85	Converted
	OE-LAA	Austrian Airlines			DEC/88	Sched.delivery
379	F-WWBB	Airbus Industrie	203	24/APR/85		
	TC-JCN	Turk Hava Yollari			21/JUN/85	
	OE-LAI	Austrian Airlines	321		JAN/89	Sched.delivery
386	F-WWBC	Airbus Industrie	203	29/APR/85		
	TC-JCO	Turk Hava Yollari			26/JUN/85	
388	OE-LAA	Austrian Airlines	221			
389	F-WWBG	Airbus Industrie	203	20/JAN/86		
	TC-JCS	Turk Hava Yollari			12/MAR/86	
390	F-WWBH	Airbus Industrie	203	19/FEB/86		
	TC-JCU	Turk Hava Yollari			14/APR/86	
392	F-WWCB	Airbus Industrie	304	06/SEP/85		
	VT-EJJ	Air India			APR/86	
394	F-WWBD	Airbus Industrie	203	10/JUL/85		
	PH-AGK	KLM			25/SEP/85	
397	F-WWBE	Airbus Industrie	203	14/AUG/85		

C/N	Registration	Owner/Operator	Series	First Flight	Delivery	Remarks
	D-AICR	Lufthansa			10/JAN/86	
399	HB-IPF	Swissair	321	16/OCT/85	17/DEC/85	
400	D-AICS	Lufthansa	203	05/NOV/85	27/FEB/86	
404	HB-IPG	Swissair	321	29/OCT/85	21/DEC/85	
406	F-WWCG	Airbus Industrie	304	10/FEB/86		
	VT-EJG	Air India			20/APR/86	
407	F-WWCH	Airbus Industrie	304	07/MAR/86		
	VT-EJH	Air India			18/MAY/86	
409	HB-IPH	Swissair	321	21/NOV/85	15/JAN/86	
410	HB-IPI	Swissair	321	29/NOV/85	31/JAN/86	
412	F-WWCI	Airbus Industrie	322	03/FEB/86		
	HB-IPK	Balair			21/MAR/86	
413	F-WWCJ	Airbus Industrie	304	07/MAR/86		
	VT-EJI	Air India			01/JUN/86	
415	F-WWBI	Airbus Industrie	204	03/MAR/86		
	HS-TIA	Thai Airways			29/APR/86	
416	F-WWCK	Airbus Industrie	304	21/MAR/86		
	5Y-BEL	Kenya Airways			15/MAY/86	
418	9V-	Singapore Airlines	322		JUN/87	Sched.delivery
419	F-WWBJ	Airbus Industrie	222	07/APR/86		
	B-2303	CAAC			30/MAY/86	
421	JY-	Alia	304		APR/87	Sched.delivery
422	JY-	Alia	304		APR/87	Sched.delivery
424	HS-TIB	Thai Airways	204		JUN/87	Sched.delivery
425	B-	CAAC	304		DEC/86	Sched.delivery
426	5Y-	Kenya Airways	304		SEP/86	Sched.delivery
428	VT-EJK	Air India	304		OCT/86	Sched.delivery
429	VT-EJL	Air India	304		OCT/86	Sched.delivery
433	PH-MCC	Martinair	203C			Cancelled order
434	D-	Condor	304			
437	OO-SCC	Sabena	322		MAR/87	Sched.delivery
449	D-AICT	Lufthansa	203		DEC/86	Sched.delivery
450	D-AICU	Lufthansa	203		DEC/86	Sched.delivery
454	F-GEMG	Air France	304			

ADDITIONAL ORDERS

C/N	Registration	Owner/Operator	Series	First Flight	Delivery	Remarks
	HS-TIC	Thai Airways			86	Sched.delivery
	D-AICW	Lufthansa	203		87	Sched.delivery
	D-AICX	Lufthansa	203		87	Sched.delivery
	D-AICY	Lufthansa	203		87	Sched.delivery
	D-AICZ	Lufthansa	203		88	Sched.delivery
	D-AIDA	Lufthansa	203		88	Sched.delivery
	D-AIDB	Lufthansa	203		89	Sched.delivery
	D-AIDC	Luftahnsa	203		89	Sched.delivery
	D-AIDD	Lufthansa	203		89	Sched.delivery
	D-AIDE	Lufthansa	303		87	Sched.delivery
	D-AIDF	Lufthansa	303		87	Sched.delivery
	D-	Lufthansa	303		87	Sched.delivery
	D-	Lufthansa	303		87	Sched.delivery
	D-	Lufthansa	303		87	Sched.delivery
	9V-	Singapore Airlines	322		MAR/88	Sched.delivery
	JY-	Alia	304		88	Sched.delivery
	JY-	Alia	304			Sched.delivery
	JY-	Alia	304			Sched.delivery
	JY-	Alia	304		90	Sched.delivery
	TC-	Turk Hava Yollari	304			
	TC-	Turk Hava Yollari	304			
	TC-	Turk Hava Yollari	304			

Airbus Industrie A310 cross-reference index

5B- Cyprus

300	5B-DAQ
309	5B-DAR
352	5B-DAS

5N- Nigeria

270	5N-AUE
285	5N-AUF
329	5N-AUG
340	5N-AUH

5Y- Kenya

416	5Y-BEL

7T- Algerie

291	7T-VJC
293	7T-VJD

9K- Kuwait

267	9K-AHA
276	9K-AHB
278	9K-AHC
318	9K-AHD
331	9K-AHE
339	9K-AHH
342	9K-AHJ
346	9K-AHK

9V- Singapore

347	9V-STI
350	9V-STJ
357	9V-STK
363	9V-STL
367	9V-STM
372	9V-STN

B- Taiwan

311	B-2301
320	B-2302
419	B-2303

D- West Germany

191	D-AICA
201	D-AICB
230	D-AICC
233	D-AICD
237	D-AICF
254	D-AICH
257	D-AICK
273	D-AICL
356	D-AICM
359	D-AICN
360	D-AICP
397	D-AICR
400	D-AICS
449	D-AICT
450	D-AICU

F- France

316	F-GEMA
326	F-GEMB
335	F-GEMC
355	F-GEMD
369	F-GEME
172	F-GEMF
454	F-GEMG
375	F-WWBA
379	F-WWBB
386	F-WWBC
394	F-WWBD
397	F-WWBE
389	F-WWBG
390	F-WWBH
415	F-WWBI
419	F-WWBJ
378	F-WWCA
392	F-WWCB
406	F-WWCG
407	F-WWCH
412	F-WWCI
413	F-WWCJ
416	F-WWCK
224	F-WZEA
283	F-WZEA
329	F-WZEA
230	F-WZEB
285	F-WZEB
233	F-WZEC
288	F-WZEC
237	F-WZED
291	F-WZED
360	F-WZED
241	F-WZEE
293	F-WZEE
248	F-WZEF
295	F-WZEF
339	F-WZEF
362	F-WZEF
245	F-WZEG
300	F-WZEG
333	F-WZEG
251	F-WZEH
297	F-WZEH
340	F-WZEH
303	F-WZEI
342	F-WZEI
363	F-WZEI
257	F-WZEJ
311	F-WZEJ
260	F-WZEK
306	F-WZEK
343	F-WZEK
264	F-WZEL
318	F-WZEL
345	F-WZEL
267	F-WZEM
309	F-WZEM
346	F-WZEM
364	F-WZEM
270	F-WZEN
372	F-WZEN
273	F-WZEO
331	F-WZEO
347	F-WZEO
352	F-WZEO
276	F-WZEP
313	F-WZEP
349	F-WZEP
367	F-WZEP
278	F-WZER
320	F-WZER
281	F-WZET
338	F-WZET
162	F-WZLH
350	F-WZLH
370	F-WZLH
172	F-WZLI
191	F-WZLJ
254	F-WZLJ
353	F-WZLJ
201	F-WZLK
356	F-WZLK
217	F-WZLL
357	F-WZLL
359	F-WZLS

G- United Kingdom

295	G-BKWT
306	G-BKWU
370	G-BLPS

HB- Switzerland

224	HB-IPA
251	HB-IPB
217	HB-IPC
260	HB-IPD
162	HB-IPE
399	HB-IPF
404	HB-IPG
409	HB-IPH
410	HB-IPI
412	HB-IPK

HS- Thailand

415	HS-TIA
424	HS-TIB

N United States

288	N801PA
333	N802PA
343	N803PA
345	N804PA
339	N805PA
342	N806PA
346	N807PA

OE- Austria

378	OE-LAA
388	OE-LAA
379	OE-LAI

OO- Belgium

303	OO-SCA
313	OO-SCB
437	OO-SCC

PH- Netherlands

241	PH-AGA
245	PH-AGB
248	PH-AGC
264	PH-AGD
283	PH-AGE
297	PH-AGF
353	PH-AGG
362	PH-AGH
364	PH-AGI
394	PH-AGK
281	PH-MCA
349	PH-MCB
433	PH-MCC

TC- Turkey

338	TC-JCL
375	TC-JCM
379	TC-JCN
386	TC-JCO
370	TC-JCR
389	TC-JCS
390	TC-JCU

VT- India

406	VT-EJG
407	VT-EJH
413	VT-EJI
392	VT-EJJ
428	VT-EJK
429	VT-EJL

BOEING 747

Large commercial transport for up to 550 passengers. powered by four wing-mounted Pratt & Whitney JT9D turbofans. The 747, more popularly referred to as the 'Jumbo Jet' made its first flight appearance on 9 February 1969, and entered service with Pan American on the New York-London route on 22 January 1970. Production models include the 747-100, 100B and 200B, all of similar capacity and performance, the 747SR short-range version of the 100B, and the 747-200 Combi dual passenger/freighter, the 747-200C Convertible passenger/freighter, the 747-200F pure freighters, the 747-300 Extended Upper Deck version with a maximum high-density seating for 660 passengers, and the new 747-400 which is basically a series -300 with extended and vertical winglets. Deliveries of the series -400 are due to commence at the end of 1988. Optional engines for all models are the General Electric CF6-50 and Rolls Royce RB.211 turbofans. All versions are currently available with 635 aircraft of all models delivered to date and 112 on order. Current production rate is three aircraft per month.

Dimensions :	Wing span: 195ft 8in (59.6m) Length: 231ft 4in (70.5m) Height 63ft 5in (19.3m) (100B) Wing span: 195ft 8in (59.6m) Length: 231ft 10in (70.7m) Height: 63ft 5in (19.3m) (200B/300)
Powerplants :	Four Pratt & Whitney JT9D-7R4G2 turbofans, four General Electric CF6-50E2 turbofans of four Rolls Royce RB.211-524D4 turbofans
Performance :	Max cruising speed 507knots (939km/h) Range: with max payload 4,430nm (8,200km) (100B) Range: with max payload 5,090nm (9,430km) (200B) Range: with max payload 5,660nm (10,300km) (300)
Accommodation:	500 passenger in an eleven abreast layout (100B), 550 passengers in an eleven abreast layout (200B), 660 passengers in an eleven abreast layout (300)
Manufacturer :	Boeing - PO Box 3707, Seattle, Washington 98124, USA Telephone: (206) 237-2121 Telex: 32 94 30

BOEING

C/N	Registration	Owner/Operator	Series	First Flight	Delivery	Remarks
19637	N731PA	Pan American	121	10/MAY/68	11/JUL/70	
	N731PA	Eastern Airlines			03/JAN/71	Leased
	N731PA	Pan American			29/APR/71	
	9Q-ARW	Zaire Aero Services			20/APR/80	
	N731PA	Pan American			80	
19638	N732PA	Pan American	121	10/JUL/69	13/JUL/70	
19639	N747PA	Pan American	121	11/APR/69	03/OCT/70	
	N747QC	Air Zaire			21/NOV/73	Leased
	N747PA	Pan American			31/MAR/75	
19640	N733PA	Pan American	121	24/OCT/69	13/DEC/69	
	N733PA	G.E. Credit Corp.			JUN/81	
	N733PA	Pan American			JUN/81	Leased
19641	N734PA	Pan American	121	31/OCT/69	19/DEC/69	
19642	N735PA	Pan American	121	22/DEC/69	09/JAN/70	
	N735PA	Eastern Airlines			26/JAN/70	Leased
	N735PA	Pan American			30/APR/72	
	N735PA	G.E. Credit Corp.			JUN/81	
	N735PA	Pan American			JUN/81	Leased
19643	N736PA	Pan American	121	24/DEC/69	20/JAN/70	
						W/O 27/MAR/77, Los Rodeos, Tenerife
19644	N737PA	Pan American	121	09/JAN/70	21/JAN/70	
	N737PA	Eastern Airlines			01/FEB/70	Leased
	N737PA	Pan American			05/MAY/72	
	N737PA	G.E. Credit Corp.			JUN/81	
	N737PA	Pan American			JUN/81	Leased
19645	N738PA	Pan American	121	19/JAN/70	05/FEB/70	
	N738PA	G.E. Credit Corp.			JUN/81	
	N738PA	Pan American			JUN/81	Leased
						W/O 18/OCT/83, Karachi
19646	N739PA	Pan American	121	25/JAN/70	15/FEB/70	
19647	N740PA	Pan American	121	31/JAN/70	24/FEB/70	
	N740PA	American Airlines			25/FEB/70	Leased
	N740PA	Pan American			14/MAY/71	
	N740PA	G.E. Credit Corp.			JUN/81	
	N740PA	Pan American			JUN/81	Leased
19648	N741PA	Pan American	121	13/FEB/70	28/FEB/70	
	N741PA	G.E. Credit Corp.			JUN/81	
	N741PA	Pan American			JUN/81	Leased
19649	N742PA	Pan American	121	18/FEB/70	02/MAR/70	
	N742PA	G.E. Credit Corp.			JUN/81	
	N742PA	Pan American			JUN/81	Leased
19650	N743PA	Pan American	121		28/MAR/70	
	N743PA	American Airlines			29/FEB/70	Leased
	N743PA	Pan American			01/OCT/70	
19651	N744PA	Pan American	121		21/MAR/70	
	N744PA	G.E. Credit Corp.			JUN/81	
	N744PA	Pan American			JUN/81	Leased
19652	N748PA	Pan American	121		31/MAR/70	
19653	N749PA	Pan American	121		10/APR/70	
19654	N750PA	Pan American	121		26/APR/70	
19655	N751PA	Pan American	121		24/APR/70	
19656	N752PA	Pan American	121		02/MAY/70	W/O 06/SEP/70, Cairo
19657	N753PA	Pan American	121		29/APR/70	
19658	N754PA	Pan American	121		26/MAY/70	
19659	N755PA	Pan American	121		31/MAY/70	
19660	N770PA	Pan American	121		31/MAY/70	
19661	N771PA	Pan American	121		04/OCT/70	
	N771PA	Pan American	121F/SC		30/MAR/75	Converted
	N819FT	Flying Tigers			FEB/83	
19667	N93101	Trans World Airlines	131	13/JUL/69	18/AUG/70	
	5-280	Imperial Iranian Air Force			14/MAR/75	
	5-8101	Imperial Iranian Air Force	131F		07/JUL/75	Converted
	5-8101	Iranian Air Force			FEB/78	
	EP-NHJ	Iran Air			84	
19668	N93102	Trans World Airlines	131	07/DEC/69	31/DEC/69	
	5-282	Imperial Iranian Air Force			14/NOV/75	
	5-8106	Imperial Iranian Air Force	131F		14/NOV/75	Converted

BOEING 747

C/N	Registration	Owner/Operator	Series	First Flight	Delivery	Remarks
	5-8106	Iranian Air Force			FEB/78	
	EP-NHD	Iran Air			APR/83	
19669	N93103	Trans World Airlines	131	05/DEC/69	31/DEC/69	
	5-287	Imperial Iranian Air Force			12/DEC/75	
	5-8108	Imperial Iranian Air Force	131F		12/DEC/75	Converted
	5-8108	Iranian Air Force			FEB/78	
	EP-NHK	Iran Air			APR/83	
19670	N93104	Trans World Airlines	131	09/FEB/70	20/FEB/70	
19671	N93105	Trans World Airlines	131	23/FEB/70	09/MAR/70	
19672	N93106	Trans World Airlines	131		03/APR/70	
19673	N93107	Trans World Airlines	131		29/APR/70	
19674	N93108	Trans World Airlines	131		07/MAY/70	
19675	N93109	Trans World Airlines	131		23/MAY/70	
19676	N53110	Trans World Airlines	131		10/AUG/70	
19677	N53111	Trans World Airlines	131		26/SEP/70	
	5-283	Imperial Iranian Air Force			15/OCT/75	
	5-8104	Imperial Iranian Air Force	131F		15/OCT/75	Converted
						W/O 09/MAY/76, nr. Madrid
19678	N53112	Trans World Airlines	131		04/OCT/70	
	5-281	Imperial Iranian Air Force			15/MAR/75	
	5-8102	Imperial Iranian Air Force	131F		AUG/75	Converted
	5-8102	Iranian Air Force			FEB/78	
	EP-NHT	Iran Air			JUN/84	
19725	JA8101	Japan Air Lines	146		22/APR/70	
19726	JA8102	Japan Air Lines	146		28/MAY/70	
	JA8102	Japan Asia			DEC/82	
19727	JA8103	Japan Air Lines	146		27/JUN/70	
	JA8103	Japan Asia			NOV/82	
19729	I-DEMA	Alitalia	143		13/MAY/70	
	N355AS	Boeing			03/NOV/81	
	N355AS	Hawaii Express			12/AUG/82	Leased
	N355AS	Boeing			13/MAY/83	
	N355AS	Metro International			08/JUN/83	Leased
	N355AS	Boeing			18/OCT/83	
	N603PE	People Express			27/JUN/84	Leased
19730	I-DEME	Alitalia	143		01/JUL/70	
	I-DEME	Aer Lingus			26/SEP/76	Leased
	I-DEME	Alitalia			17/OCT/76	
	N356AS	Boeing			17/SEP/81	
	N356AS	SAS			26/JUL/82	Leased
	N356AS	Scanair			26/JUL/82	Sub-Leased
	N356AS	Icelandair			09/SEP/82	Sub-Leased
	N356AS	Air Algerie			09/SEP/82	Sub-Leased
	N356AS	Icelandair			25/OCT/82	
	N356AS	Scanair			25/OCT/82	
	N356AS	SAS			82	
	N356AS	Boeing			09/DEC/82	
	N356AS	Overseas National			29/JUL/83	Leased
	N356AS	Boeing			24/OCT/83	
	N356AS	PIA			84	Leased
	N356AS	Boeing			03/OCT/84	WFU 03/OCT/84 to 17/JUN/85
	N606PE	People Express			17/JUN/85	
19731	I-DEMO	Alitalia	243B		09/MAR/71	
	N357AS	Boeing			10/DEC/81	
	N357AS	Cargolux			17/AUG/83	Leased
	N357AS	Boeing			28/OCT/83	
	N604PE	People Express			06/JUN/84	Leased
	N604PE	Boeing			MAR/86	
	N604PE	Intergrated Aircraft Inc.			MAR/86	
	N604PE	People Express			MAR/86	Leased
19732	I-DEMU	Alitalia	243B		27/MAY/71	
	N358AS	Boeing			19/NOV/81	
	N358AS	Overseas National			01/AUG/83	
	N358AS	Boeing			OCT/83	
	N358AS	National Airlines			84	Leased
	N358AS	Boeing			25/FEB/85	
	N611PE	People Express				Not taken-up
	N358AS	Boeing				
	B-2440	CAAC			20/MAY/85	Leased
	N747BL	Boeing			18/DEC/85	
	G-VGIN	Virgin Atlantic			31/MAY/86	
19733	N26861	Continental Airlines	124		18/MAY/70	
	5-289	Imperial Iranian Air Force			22/SEP/75	
	5-8110	Imperial Iranian Air Force	124F		SEP/75	Converted
	N26861	Boeing			06/JAN/78	
	N750WA	World Airways			09/FEB/78	
	N809FT	Flying Tiger Line			01/JUL/78	Leased
	N809FT	Cargo Airlines				Sub-leased
	N809FT	Flying Tiger Line				Leased
	N750WA	World Airways			15/JUL/80	
	N750WA	Flying Tiger Line			25/NOV/81	Leased
	N750WA	World Airways			22/DEC/81	
	HK-2900	Avianca			02/JUL/82	Leased
	HK-2900	Avianca			86	Purchased
19734	N26862	Continental Airlines	124		13/JUL/70	
	5-290	Imperial Iranian Air Force			15/OCT/75	
	5-8111	Imperial Iranian Air Force			76	
	N747AV	Boeing			SEP/76	
	N747AV	Avianca			SEP/76	Leased
	HK-2000	Avianca			NOV/76	Leased
	N747BA	Boeing			31/JAN/83	
	N747BA	SAS			14/AUG/83	Leased
	N747BA	Air Algerie			14/AUG/83	Sub-leased
	N747BA	SAS			20/OCT/83	Leased
	N747BA	Boeing			20/OCT/83	
	N747BA	Avianca			15/DEC/83	Leased
	N747BA	Boeing			14/JAN/84	
	N747BA	Tower Air			31/MAY/84	Leased
	N602FF	Tower Air			JAN/86	Purchased
19735	N26863	Continental Airlines	124		12/AUG/70	
	5-291	Imperial Iranian Air Force			30/OCT/75	
	5-8112	Imperial Iranian Air Force	124F		OCT/75	Converted
	N8289V	Boeing			11/APR/77	
	4X-AXZ	El Al			21/JUN/77	
	HK-2400	Avianca			21/JUL/81	Leased

C/N	Registration	Owner/Operator	Series	First Flight	Delivery	Remarks
	4X-AXZ	El Al			JUL/82	
	4X-AXZ	Cargo Air Lines				Leased
19744	EI-ASI	Aer Lingus	148		15/DEC/70	
	HS-VGB	Air Siam			SEP/73	Leased
	EI-ASI	Aer Lingus			17/APR/76	
	EI-ASI	Air Algerie			04/OCT/79	Leased
	EI-ASI	Aer Lingus			13/OCT/79	
19745	EI-ASJ	Aer Lingus	148	04/MAR/71	18/MAR/71	
	HS-VGF	Air Siam			19/APR/75	Leased
	EI-ASJ	Aer Lingus			15/MAY/75	
	G-BDPZ	British Airways			31/MAR/78	Leased
	G-BDPZ	Aer Lingus			OCT/78	
	G-BDPZ	British Caledonian			28/OCT/78	Leased
	G-BDPZ	Aer Lingus			02/FEB/79	
	G-BDPZ	British Airways			01/APR/79	Leased
	EI-ASJ	Aer Lingus			12/MAY/81	
19746	N1800B	Boeing	130	18/FEB/70		
	D-ABYA	Lufthansa			10/MAR/70	
	N610BN	ITEL			NOV/78	
	N610BN	Braniff			NOV/78	Leased
	N610BN	ITEL			DEC/80	
	N610BN	GATX Leasing			DEC/80	
	N610BN	Guinness Peat Aviation			DEC/80	
	N610BN	Braniff			DEC/80	Leased
	N610BN	GATX Leasing			23/OCT/81	
	N480GX	Viasa			82	Leased
	N480GX	GATX Leasing			30/SEP/82	
	N480GX	Overseas National			08/MAY/83	Leased
	N480GX	Egyptair			08/MAY/83	Sub-leased
	N480GX	Overseas National			DEC/83	Leased
	N480GX	GATX Leasing			21/MAY/84	
	N480GX	Transamerica			01/JUN/84	Leased
	N780T	Transamerica			01/JUN/84	Leased
	N780T	GATX Leasing			08/NOV/85	
	N603FF	Tower Air			22/NOV/85	Leased
	N603FF	GATX Leasing			NOV/95	Sched.return
19747	D-ABYB	Lufthansa	130		13/APR/70	
						W/O 20/NOV/74, Nairobi
19748	D-ABYC	Lufthansa	130		23/MAY/70	
	D-ABYC	ITEL			JAN/79	
	EI-BED	Aer Lingus			03/JAN/79	Leased
	EI-BED	Air Algerie			15/OCT/79	Sub-leased
	EI-BED	Aer Lingus			31/MAR/80	
	EI-BED	ITEL			DEC/80	
	EI-BED	GATX Leasing			DEC/80	
	EI-BED	Air Jamaica			82	Leased
	EI-BED	Aer Lingus			83	
19749	F-BPVA	Air France	128		20/MAR/70	
	F-BPVA	Air Italia			FEB/76	For the film "La Bonne Annee"
	F-BPVA	Air France			FEB/76	
19750	F-BPVB	Air France	128		25/MAR/70	
19751	F-BPVC	Air France	128		12/MAY/70	
19752	F-BPVD	Air France	128		14/JUL/70	
19753	N4703U	United Airlines	122		30/JUN/70	
	N4703U	General Electric Credit Corp			26/JUN/85	
	N4703U	Pan American			DEC/85	
19754	N4704U	United Airlines	122		04/AUG/70	
	N4704U	General Electric Credit Corp			03/AUG/85	
	N4704U	Pan American			DEC/85	
19755	N4710U	United Airlines	122		28/AUG/70	
	N4710U	General Electric Credit Corp			07/AUG/85	
	N4710U	Pan American			DEC/85	
19756	N4711U	United Airlines	122	18/AUG/70	31/AUG/70	
	N4711U	General Electric Credit Corp			27/AUG/85	
	N4711U	Pan American			DEC/85	
19757	N4712U	United Airlines	122		AUG/70	
	N4712U	General Electric Credit Corp			30/AUG/85	
	N4712U	Pan American			DEC/85	
19761	N1799B	Boeing	136	15/MAR/70		
	G-AWNA	BOAC			23/MAY/70	
	G-AWNA	British Airways			01/APR/72	
19762	G-AWNB	BOAC	136		22/MAY/70	
	G-AWNB	British Airways			01/APR/72	
19763	G-AWNC	BOAC	136		29/JUN/70	
	G-AWNC	British Airways			01/APR/72	
19764	G-AWND	BOAC	136	20/JAN/71	28/FEB/71	
	G-AWND	British Airways			01/APR/72	
19765	G-AWNE	BOAC	136	10/FEB/71	05/MAR/71	
	G-AWNE	British Airways			01/APR/72	
19766	G-AWNF	BOAC	136	13/FEB/71	14/MAR/71	
	G-AWNF	British Airways			01/APR/72	
19778	N601US	Northwest Orient	151		30/APR/70	
19779	N602US	Northwest Orient	151		12/MAY/70	
19780	N603US	Northwest Orient	151		22/MAY/70	
19781	N604US	Northwest Orient	151		24/JUN/70	
19782	N605US	Northwest Orient	151		24/JUN/70	
19783	N606US	Northwest Orient	151	22/AUG/70	30/AUG/70	
19784	N607US	Northwest Orient	151		09/SEP/70	
19785	N608US	Northwest Orient	151		12/SEP/70	
19786	N609US	Northwest Orient	151		28/OCT/70	
19787	N610US	Northwest Orient	151	06/JAN/70	11/NOV/70	
	N610US	Boeing			11/NOV/70	Leased
	N610US	Northwest Orient			71	
19790	N	World Airways	273C			Cancelled order
19791	N	World Airways	273C			Cancelled order
19792	N	World Airways	273C			Cancelled order
19823	JA8104	Japan Air Lines	246B		11/FEB/71	
19824	JA8105	Japan Air Lines	246B	12/FEB/71	01/MAR/71	
19825	JA8106	Japan Air Lines	246B	29/APR/71	14/MAY/71	
19875	N4713U	United Airlines	122		03/NOV/70	
19876	N4714U	United Airlines	122		28/NOV/70	
19877	N4716U	United Airlines	122		12/DEC/70	
19878	N4717U	United Airlines	122		28/DEC/70	
19879	N4718U	United Airlines	122	16/MAY/71	27/MAY/71	

BOEING 747

C/N	Registration	Owner/Operator	Series	First Flight	Delivery	Remarks
19880	N4719U	United Airlines	122	15/JUN/71	26/JUN/71	
19881	N4720U	United Airlines	122	13/JUL/71	23/JUL/71	
19882	N4723U	United Airlines	122	17/DEC/71	06/JAN/72	
19883	N4727U	United Airlines	122	16/JUN/72	27/JUN/72	
19896	N9896	Delta Air Lines	132		16/SEP/70	
	N9896	Boeing			16/SEP/74	
	LV-LRG	Aerolineas Argentinas				Not taken-up
	N40108	Boeing			76	
	B-1868	China Airlines			15/JUN/76	Leased
	N902PA	Boeing			28/APR/78	
	N902PA	Pan American			09/MAY/78	
19897	N9897	Delta Air Lines	132		22/OCT/70	
	N9897	Boeing			01/FEB/77	
	N803FT	Flying Tigers	132F		01/JUL/77	Converted
	N803FT	Pan American				Leased
	N803FT	Flying Tigers			79	
	N803FT	Cargo Airlines			79	Leased
	N803FT	Flying Tigers			79	
	N803FT	Cargo Airlines			17/DEC/79	Leased
	N803FT	Flying Tigers			25/JAN/80	
19898	N9898	Delta Air Lines	132		18/NOV/70	
	N9898	Boeing			11/MAY/75	
	B-1860	China Airlines			16/MAY/75	Leased
	B-1860	China Airlines			15/APR/76	Purchased
	N9898	Braniff			79	Leased
	B-1860	China Airlines			79	
	EI-BOS	Guinness Peat			01/MAY/84	
	N725PA	Pan Am			01/MAY/84	
19918	N77772	National Airlines	135		08/SEP/70	
	N620US	Northwest Orient			MAY/76	
19919	N77773	National Airlines	135		20/OCT/70	
	N621US	Northwest Orient			MAY/76	
19922	PH-BUA	KLM	206B		16/JAN/71	
19923	PH-BUB	KLM	206B	15/FEB/71	04/MAR/71	
19924	PH-BUC	KLM	206B	09/MAY/71	21/MAY/71	
19925	N4728U	United Airlines	122	22/JAN/73	27/APR/73	
19926	N4729U	United Airlines	122	30/JAN/73	24/APR/73	
19927	N4732U	United Airlines	122	14/FEB/73	19/MAR/73	
19928	N4735U	United Airlines	122	16/MAY/73	20/MAY/73	
19957	EC-BRO	Iberia	156		02/OCT/70	
	N133TW	Trans World Airlines			01/MAY/80	
19958	EC-BRP	Iberia	156		10/NOV/70	
	N134TW	Trans World Airlines			17/MAR/81	
19959	VT-EBD	Air India	237B	08/MAR/71	22/MAR/71	W/O 01/JAN/78, Bombay
19960	VT-EBE	Air India	237B	02/APR/71	20/APR/71	
20007	N	Alaska Airlines	90			Cancelled order
20009	VH-EBA	Qantas	238B	08/JUL/71	30/JUL/71	
	N	Eastern Airlines				Not taken-up
	VH-EBA	Air New Zealand			FEB/84	Leased
	VH-EBA	Qantas			MAR/84	
	4R-ULF	Guinness Peat Aviation			08/JUN/84	
	4R-ULF	Air Lanka			08/JUN/84	
20010	VH-EBB	Qantas	238B	23/JUL/71	14/AUG/71	
	VH-EBB	Guinness Peat Aviation			10/JUL/84	
	VH-EBB	Qantas			10/JUL/84	Leased
	VH-EBB	Guinness Peat Aviation			23/OCT/85	
	4R-ULG	Air Lanka			30/OCT/85	
20011	VH-EBC	Qantas	238B	07/OCT/71	21/OCT/71	
	N747BM	Boeing			03/DEC/84	
	N607PE	People Express			15/APR/85	
20012	VH-EBD	Qantas	238B	23/NOV/71	08/DEC/71	
	N371EA	Eastern Air Lines				Not taken-up
	N747BN	Boeing			MAR/85	
	N608PE	People Express			27/SEP/85	
20013	CF-TOA	Air Canada	133		11/FEB/71	WFU 27/NOV/82
	C-FTOA	Global International			01/JUN/83	Leased
	C-FTOA	Air Canada			SEP/83	
	C-FTOA	Guinness Peat Aviation			28/JUL/84	
	N749R	National Airlines			28/JUL/84	Leased
	N749R	Malaysian Airline System			DEC/84	Sub-leased
	N749R	National Airlines			08/OCT/84	Leased
	EI-BPH	Guinness Peat Aviation			08/OCT/84	
	EI-BPH	People Express			12/FEB/85	Leased
	EI-BPH	Guinness Peat Aviation			01/MAY/85	
	EI-BPH	MEA			26/JUN/85	Leased
	EI-BPH	Guinness Peat Aviation			22/SEP/85	
	EI-BPH	Flying Tigers			22/SEP/85	Leased
20014	CF-TOB	Air Canada	133	01/MAR/71	18/MAR/71	WFU 30/NOV/82
	CF-TOB	Guinness Peat Aviation			02/MAY/85	
	EC-DXE	Iberia			03/MAY/85	Leased
	EC-DXE	Aviaco			03/MAY/85	Sub-leased
	EI-BRR	Guinness Peat Aviation			01/NOV/85	
	EI-BRR	MEA			30/MAY/86	Leased
	EI-BRR	Olympic Airways			JUN/86	Sub-leased
	EI-BRR	MEA			JUN/86	Leased
	EI-BRR	Egyptair			27/JUN/86	Sub-leased
	EI-BRR	MEA			30/JUN/86	Leased
20015	CF-TOC	Air Canada	133	11/JUN/71	24/JUN/71	
	CF-TOC	Royal Air Maroc			01/SEP/82	Leased
	CF-TOC	Air Canada			22/SEP/82	
	CF-TOC	Royal Air Maroc			01/OCT/82	Leased
	CF-TOC	Air Canada			23/OCT/82	
	C-FTOC	Royal Air Maroc			01/SEP/83	Leased
	C-FTOC	Air Canada			OCT/83	
20080	N7410Q	Eastern Airlines	125			Not taken-up
	N93113	Trans World Airlines			22/OCT/70	
	5-282	Imperial Iranian Air Force			31/MAR/75	
	5-8103	Imperial Iranian Air Force	125F		03/OCT/75	Converted
	5-8103	Iranian Air Force			FEB/78	
	EP-NHS	Iran Air			84	
20081	N7402Q	Eastern Airlines	125			Not taken-up
	N93114	Trans World Airlines			02/NOV/70	
	5-284	Imperial Iranian Air Force			03/NOV/75	
	5-8105	Imperial Iranian Air Force	125F		13/FEB/76	Converted
	5-8105	Iranian Air Force			FEB/78	

C/N	Registration	Owner/Operator	Series	First Flight	Delivery	Remarks
	EP-NHR	Iran Air			JUN/84	
20082	N7403Q	Eastern Airlines	125	04/AUG/71		Not taken-up
	N93118	Trans World Airlines			29/SEP/71	
	5-286	Imperial Iranian Air Force			13/NOV/75	
	5-8107	Imperial Iranian Air Force	125F		14/JAN/76	Converted
	5-8107	Iranian Air Force			FEB/78	
	EP-NHP	Iran Air			JUN/84	
20083	N7404Q	Eastern Airlines	125			Not taken-up
	N93119	Trans World Airlines		18/AUG/71	27/OCT/71	
	5-8109	Imperial Iranian Air Force			15/DEC/75	Never entered service
	N93119	Trans World Airlines			15/DEC/76	
20100	N9661	American Airlines	123		18/JUN/70	
	N9661	Boeing			FEB/74	
	N800FT	Flying Tiger Line	123F		AUG/74	Converted
	N903PA	Pan American			JAN/78	Leased
	N800FT	Flying Tiger Line			02/AUG/79	
	N9661	American Airlines			05/FEB/81	
	N9661	United Parcel Service			20/DEC/84	Op. by Orion Air
	N674UP	United Parcel Service			JAN/85	Op. by Orion Air
20101	N9662	American Airlines	123		16/JUL/70	
	N9662	Boeing			14/FEB/74	
	N801FT	Flying Tiger Line	123F		24/SEP/74	Converted
	N801FT	Lufthansa			24/JAN/75	Leased
	N801FT	Flying Tiger Line			01/MAR/75	
	N801FT	El Al			21/SEP/77	Leased
	N801FT	Flying Tiger Line			29/JUN/78	
	N662AA	American Airlines			25/FEB/80	Leased
	N801FT	Flying Tiger Line			19/APR/80	
	N9676	American Airlines			JUN/81	
	N9676	United Parcel Service			18/DEC/84	Op. by Orion Air
	N676UP	United Parcel Service			JAN/85	Op. by Orion Air
20102	N9663	American Airlines	123		30/JUL/70	
	N9663	Citicorp			06/JUN/84	
	N9663	National Airlines			06/JUN/84	Leased
	N9663	Dominicana			MAY/85	Sub-leased
	N9663	National Airlines			85	Leased
	N9663	Citicorp			21/NOV/85	WFU 21/NOV/85
	N14943	Jet 24 International Airways			14/MAR/86	Leased
	N14943	Cargolux			19/JUN/86	Leased
20103	N9664	American Airlines	123		27/AUG/70	
	N9664	Citicorp			20/MAY/84	
	N9664	Avianca			20/MAY/84	Leased
20104	N9665	American Airlines	123		18/SEP/70	
	N9665	Citicorp			02/MAY/84	
	N9665	American Airlines			02/MAY/84	
	N9665	Citicorp			84	
	N9665	Dominicana			20/APR/85	Leased
	HI-472	Dominicana			JAN/86	Leased
20105	N9666	American Airlines	123		02/OCT/70	
	N9666	Braniff			01/MAR/78	Leased
	N9666	American Airlines			31/MAY/80	
	N9666	Citicorp			15/JUN/84	
	N9666	National Airlines			15/JUN/84	Leased
	N9666	Citicorp			SEP/85	
	N14936	Citicorp			JUN/86	
	N14936	Cargolux			19/JUN/86	Leased
20106	N9667	American Airlines	123		08/OCT/70	
	N9667	Steven's Corp.				For the movie "Airport 77"
	N9667	American Airlines				
	N9667	Citicorp			30/MAY/84	
	N9667	National Airlines			23/JUL/84	Leased
	N9667	Citicorp			20/MAY/85	
	N14937	Citicorp			JUN/86	
	LX-MCV	Cargolux			19/JUN/86	Leased
20107	N9668	American Airlines	123		29/OCT/70	
	N905NA	NASA			18/JUL/74	
20108	N9669	American Airlines	123		27/NOV/70	
	N9669	Citicorp			11/MAY/84	
	N9669	National Airlines			27/JUL/84	Leased
	N9669	Citicorp			SEP/85	
	N14939	Citicorp			JUN/86	
	N14939	Cargolux			19/JUN/86	Leased
20109	N9670	American Airlines	123		29/DEC/70	
	N9670	Citicorp			25/MAY/84	
	N9670	Pan American			29/MAY/84	
20116	HB-IGA	Swissair	257B		30/JAN/71	
	HB-IGA	Salenia			27/OCT/82	
	HB-IGA	Swissair			27/OCT/82	Leased
	LX-SAL	Salenia			30/DEC/83	
	LX-SAL	Air National			02/MAR/84	Leased
	LX-SAL	Salenia			84	
	LX-SAL	National Airlines			27/MAR/85	Leased
	LX-SAL	Egyptair			05/MAR/85	Sub-leased
	LX-SAL	National Airlines			MAY/85	Leased
	LX-SAL	Salenia			MAY/85	
	N303TW	Trans World Airlines			MAY/85	
20117	HB-IGB	Swissair	257B	13/MAR/71	26/MAR/71	
	HB-IGB	Wilhemsens			DEC/82	
	HB-IGB	Swissair			DEC/82	Leased
	HB-IGB	KANSA			FEB/84	WFU FEB/84, stored Marana
	SU-GAK	National Airlines			15/MAY/84	Leased
	SU-GAK	Egyptair			15/MAY/84	Sub-leased
	SU-GAK	National Airlines			25/FEB/85	Leased
	SU-GAK	KANSA			25/FEB/85	
	N304TW	Trans World Airlines			26/MAR/85	
20118	HB-	Swissair	257B			Cancelled order
20119	HB-	Swissair	257B			Cancelled order
20120	SE-DDL	SAS	283B	06/FEB/71	11/MAR/71	
	SE-DDL	Scanair			SEP/82	
	SE-DDL	SAS			MAR/83	
	SE-DDL	Air Invest			10/OCT/83	
	LN-AET	SAS			10/OCT/83	Leased
	LN-AET	Air Invest			27/JUL/85	
	LN-AET	Gulf Air			27/JUL/85	Leased

BOEING 747

C/N	Registration	Owner/Operator	Series	First Flight	Delivery	Remarks
	LN-AET	Air Invest			SEP/87	Sched.return
20121	OY-KFA	SAS	283B	28/OCT/71		Not taken-up
	OY-KHA	SAS			20/NOV/71	
	LN-AEO	Air Invest			29/JAN/82	
	LN-AEO	SAS			29/JAN/82	Leased
	LN-AEO	Nigeria Airways			01/APR/82	Sub-leased
	LN-AEO	SAS			03/JUN/83	Leased
	LN-AEO	Air Invest			03/MAR/86	
	G-BMGS	British Airtours			03/MAR/86	Leased
20135	4X-AXA	El Al	258B	15/MAY/71	26/MAY/71	WFU NOV/79
20137	EC-BRQ	Iberia	256B	09/DEC/71	04/JAN/72	
20207	N601BN	Braniff	127		05/JAN/71	WFU 12/MAY/82
	N601BN	Polaris Leasing			DEC/82	
	N601BN	Metro International			02/MAR/83	Leased
	N601BN	Polaris Leasing			NOV/83	
	N601BN	Tower Air			NOV/83	Leased
20208	N602BN	Braniff	127	25/MAR/71		Not taken-up
	N800U	Universal Airlines				Not taken-up
	C-FDJC	Wardair	1D1		23/APR/73	
20235	N7470	Boeing	121	09/FEB/69		Prototype
	N1352B	Boeing			01/JUL/70	Demonstrator
20237	N1795M	Boeing	244B	25/AUG/71		
	ZS-SAL	South African Airways			26/JAN/72	
20238	ZS-SAM	South African Airways	244B	05/DEC/71	13/DEC/71	
20239	ZS-SAN	South African Airways	244B	30/SEP/71	22/OCT/71	
20246	N9899	Delta Air Lines	132		30/SEP/71	
	N9899	Boeing			MAR/77	
	N804FT	Flying Tigers			24/MAR/77	
	N804FT	Flying Tigers	132F		24/MAR/77	Converted
	N804FT	Cargo Airlines			16/DEC/79	Leased
	N804FT	Flying Tigers			27/MAR/80	
20247	N9900	Delta Airlines	132		11/NOV/71	
	N9900	Boeing			APR/77	
	N805FT	Flying Tigers			06/MAY/77	
	N805FT	Flying Tigers	132F		06/MAY/77	Converted
20269	G-AWNG	BOAC	136	30/JUL/71	08/SEP/71	
	G-AWNG	British Airways			01/APR/72	
20270	G-AWNH	BOAC	136	09/NOV/71	23/NOV/71	
	G-AWNH	British Airways			01/APR/72	
20271	G-AWNI	BOAC	136	03/DEC/71	07/JAN/72	
	G-AWNI	British Airways			01/APR/72	
	N17125	Trans World Airlines			25/MAR/81	
20272	G-AWNJ	BOAC	136	06/MAR/72	21/MAR/72	
	G-AWNJ	British Airways			01/APR/72	
20273	G-AWNK	BOAC	136	10/MAR/72	24/MAR/72	
	G-AWNK	British Airways			01/APR/72	
	N17126	Trans World Airlines			30/MAR/81	
20274	4X-AXB	El Al	258B	29/OCT/71	22/NOV/71	
20284	G-AWNL	British Airways	136	04/APR/72	19/APR/72	
20305	N26864	Continental Airlines	124	18/JUN/71	25/JUN/71	
	C-FFUN	Wardair	1D1		15/DEC/74	
20320	N93115	Trans World Airlines	131	22/DEC/70	20/MAY/71	
	N93115	GATX Leasing			JUN/86	
20321	N53116	Trans World Airlines	131	07/MAY/71	22/MAY/71	
	N53116	GATX Leasing			JUN/86	
20322	N93117	Trans World Airlines	131	16/MAY/71	24/MAY/71	
	N93117	GATX Leasing			JUN/86	
20323	N9671	American Airlines	123	10/FEB/71	26/FEB/71	
	N9671	Boeing			MAR/75	
	N802FT	Flying Tigers	123F/SC		22/JUL/75	Converted
	N802FT	American Airlines			FEB/81	Leased
	N9671	American Airlines			MAY/81	Purchased
	N9671	United Parcel Service			13/NOV/84	Op. by Orion Air
	N671UP	United Parcel Service			JAN/85	Op. by Orion Air
20324	N9672	American Airlines	123	17/MAR/71	16/APR/71	
	N9672	American Airlines	123F		12/APR/76	Converted
	N9672	United Parcel Service			02/OCT/84	Op. by Orion Air
	N672UP	United Parcel Service			JAN/85	Op. by Orion Air
20325	N9673	American Airlines	123	31/MAR/71	20/APR/71	
	N9673	American Airlines	123F		JUL/76	Converted
	N9673	El Al			OCT/78	Leased
	N9673	American Airlines			NOV/78	
	N9673	United Parcel Service			28/AUG/84	Op. by Orion Air
	N673UP	United Parcel Service			JAN/85	Op. by Orion Air
20326	N9674	American Airlines	123	23/APR/71	12/MAY/71	
	N9674	Pan American			01/DEC/83	
20332	JA8107	Japan Air Lines	246B	04/OCT/71	28/OCT/71	
	JA8107	Japan Air Lines	246SCD		SEP/77	Converted
20333	JA8108	Japan Air Lines	246B	25/OCT/71	30/NOV/71	
20337	N	Western Airlines	147			Cancelled order
20338	N	Western Airlines	147			Cancelled order
20339	N	Western Airlines	147			Cancelled order
20347	N652PA	Pan American	121	17/DEC/70	25/APR/71	
20348	N653PA	Pan American	121	31/DEC/70	08/APR/71	
	N653PA	Pan American	121/SCD			Converted
20349	N654PA	Pan American	121	14/APR/71	27/APR/71	
	N654PA	Pan American	121/SCD		MAR/77	Converted
	N817FT	Flying Tigers			24/FEB/83	
20350	N655PA	Pan American	121	03/MAY/71	28/MAY/71	
	N655PA	Pan American	121/SCD		75	Converted
20351	N656PA	Pan American	121	21/MAY/71	18/JUN/71	
20352	N657PA	Pan American	121	27/MAY/71	19/JUN/71	
20353	N658PA	Boeing	121	02/JUN/71		WFU JUN/71, stored
	N658PA	Pan American	121/SCD		02/JUL/76	Converted
	N818FT	Flying Tigers			24/FEB/83	
20354	N659PA	Boeing	121	09/JUL/71		WFU JUL/71, stored
	N659PA	Pan American			19/DEC/73	Leased
	N659PA	Iran Air			20/NOV/74	Leased
	N659PA	Pan American			18/JAN/75	
20355	F-BPVE	Air France	128	02/FEB/71	16/MAR/71	
20356	N611US	Northwest Orient	251B	11/OCT/70	26/MAR/71	
20357	N612US	Northwest Orient	251B	05/MAY/71	16/MAY/71	
20358	N613US	Northwest Orient	251B	04/JUN/71	22/JUN/71	
20359	N614US	Northwest Orient	251B	22/OCT/71	13/NOV/71	
20360	N615US	Northwest Orient	251B	13/NOV/71	23/NOV/71	

C/N	Registration	Owner/Operator	Series	First Flight	Delivery	Remarks
20372	D-ABYD	Lufthansa	230B	16/APR/71	05/MAY/71	
	D-ABYD	ITEL			26/NOV/78	
	HL7440	Korean Airlines			09/DEC/78	Leased
	HL7440	ITEL			DEC/80	
	HL7440	GATX Boothe			DEC/80	
	HL7440	Korean Airlines			DEC/80	Leased
20373	N1794B	Boeing	230F	30/NOV/71		
	D-ABYE	Lufthansa			31/MAR/72	
	D-ABYE	ITEL			15/DEC/78	
	HL7441	Korean Airlines			15/DEC/78	Leased
	HL7441	ITEL			DEC/80	
	HL7441	GATX Boothe			DEC/80	
	HL7441	Korean Airlines			DEC/80	Leased
20376	F-BPVF	Air France	128		04/FEB/72	
20377	F-BPVG	Air France	128		02/FEB/72	
20378	F-BPVH	Air France	128		01/MAR/72	
20390	N9675	American Airlines	123	07/MAY/71	25/MAY/71	
	N9675	Columbia Airways			74	For film "Airport 75"
	N9675	American Airlines	123F		DEC/74	Converted
	OD-AGM	TMA			01/JUN/76	Leased
	N9675	American Airlines			08/JAN/77	
	N9675	United Parcel Service			12/SEP/84	Op. by Orion Air
	N675UP	United Parcel Service			JAN/85	Op. by Orion Air
20391	N9676	American Airlines	123	11/JUN/71	25/JUN/71	
	N9676	American Airlines	123F		31/OCT/74	Converted
	N9676	TMA			15/MAY/75	Leased
	OD-AGC	TMA			12/SEP/75	Purchased
	N901PA	Pan American			28/JUN/77	
	N820FT	Flying Tigers			24/FEB/83	
20398	PH-BUD	KLM	206B	06/AUG/71	31/AUG/71	
	PH-BUD	Kenya Airways			07/NOV/80	Leased
	PH-BUD	KLM			20/APR/81	
20399	PH-BUE	KLM	206B	03/SEP/71	30/SEP/71	
	HS-VGG	Air Siam			16/APR/76	Leased
	PH-BUE	KLM			19/JAN/77	
20400	PH-BUF	KLM	206B	14/SEP/71	19/OCT/71	W/O 27/MAR/77, Los Rodeos Ap., Tenerife
20401	OO-SGA	Sabena	129		19/NOV/70	
	OO-SGA	Sabena	129/COM		15/FEB/74	Converted
20402	OO-SGB	Sabena	129		04/DEC/70	
	OO-SGB	Sabena	129/COM		01/APR/74	Converted
20427	PH-BUG	KLM	206B	22/NOV/71	15/DEC/71	
	PH-BUG	Viasa/KLM				
	PH-BUG	KLM				
20459	VT-EBN	Air India	237B		MAR/72	
20493	D-ABYF	Condor	230B	17/MAR/71	20/APR/71	
	HL7447	ITEL			18/JUN/79	
	HL7447	Korean Airlines			22/JUN/79	Leased
	HL7447	Saudia			22/JUN/79	Sub-leased
	HL7447	Korean Airlines			DEC/79	Leased
	HL7447	Saudia			01/NOV/80	Sub-leased
	HL7447	Korean Airlines			30/NOV/80	Leased
	HL7447	ITEL			DEC/80	
	HL7447	Gatx/Boothe			DEC/80	
	HL7447	Korean Airlines			DEC/80	Leased
20501	CS-TJA	TAP Air Portugal	282B		16/FEB/72	
	N301TW	Trans World Airlines			04/JUN/84	
20502	CS-TJB	TAP Air Portugal	282B	04/MAY/72	16/MAY/72	
	N302TW	Trans World Airlines			30/OCT/84	
20503	JA8109	Japan Air Lines	246B		02/MAR/72	W/O 23/JUL/73, Benghazi
20504	JA8110	Japan Air Lines	246B		13/MAR/72	
20505	JA8111	Japan Air Lines	246B	03/MAR/72	21/MAR/72	
20520	I-DEMB	Alitalia	243B		26/MAY/72	
	N45224	Boeing			10/DEC/80	
	N359AS	Boeing			DEC/80	
	N359AS	Cargolux			24/AUG/82	Leased
	N359AS	Kabo Air			24/AUG/82	Sub-leased
	N359AS	Cargolux			82	Leased
	N359AS	Boeing			22/NOV/82	
	N359AS	Overseas National			14/JUN/83	Leased
	N359AS	Boeing			08/NOV/83	
	N605PE	People Express			15/JUN/84	Leased
	N605PE	People Express			20/DEC/84	Purchased
20527	D-ABYG	Lufthansa	230B	09/FEB/72	25/FEB/72	
	D-ABYG	ITEL			03/MAY/79	
	N611BN	Braniff			03/MAY/79	Leased, WFU 26/OCT/80 Dallas
	N611BN	GATX Leasing			14/APR/82	
	N611BN	Chemco Leasing			14/APR/82	
	G-BJXN	British Caledonian			14/APR/82	Leased
20528	JA8112	Japan Airlines	246B	26/MAY/72	14/JUN/72	
20529	JA8113	Japan Airlines	246B	09/JUN/72	29/JUN/72	
20530	N1800B	Boeing	246B	23/AUG/72		
	JA8114	Japan Airlines			03/NOV/72	
20531	JA8115	Japan Airlines	246B	18/AUG/72	04/OCT/72	
20532	JA8116	Japan Airlines	246B	06/OCT/72	08/DEC/72	
20534	VH-EBE	Qantas	238B	27/JUL/72	10/AUG/73	
	VH-EBE	Boeing			JUN/85	
	VH-EBE	Qantas			JUN/85	Leased
	VH-EBE	Boeing			31/JAN/86	
	N609PE	People Express			01/MAY/86	
20535	VH-EBF	Qantas	238B	13/JUL/72	01/AUG/72	
	VH-EBF	Boeing			NOV/85	
	VH-EBF	Qantas			NOV/85	Leased
	VH-EBF	Boeing			28/FEB/86	
	N610PE	People Express			JUL/86	Sched.delivery
20541	N28903	Wilmington Trust Co.	128	26/OCT/72		
	N28903	Air France			21/FEB/73	
	F-BPVJ	Air France			29/DEC/81	
20542	N28888	Wilmington Trust Co.	128	30/OCT/72		
	N28888	Air France			21/MAR/73	W/O 12/JUN/75, Bombay
20543	N28899	Wilmington Trust Co.	128	15/DEC/72		
	N28899	Air France			31/MAR/73	
	F-BPVK	Air France			29/DEC/81	
20556	ZS-SAO	South African Airways	244B	14/JUL/72	07/AUG/72	
20557	ZS-SAP	South African Airways	244B	15/SEP/72	29/SEP/72	

BOEING 747

C/N	Registration	Owner/Operator	Series	First Flight	Delivery	Remarks
20558	VT-EBO	Air India	237B	14/APR/72	01/JUN/72	
20559	D-ABYH	Condor	230B	17/MAR/72	07/APR/72	
	D-ABYH	ITEL			07/FEB/79	
	HL7442	Korean Airlines			07/FEB/79	Leased
						W/O 01/SEP/83, nr. Hokkaido
20651	N747WA	Greyhound Leasing	273C	23/MAR/73	27/APR/73	
	N747WA	World Airways			27/APR/73	Leased
	N535PA	Pan Am			20/OCT/74	Sub-leased
	N747WR	World Airways			21/DEC/79	Leased
	N747WR	Air Algerie			02/APR/80	Sub-leased
	N747WR	World Airways			31/MAR/81	Leased
	N747WR	World Airways			81	Leased
	N747WR	Malaysian Airline System			82	Sub-leased
	N747WR	World Airways			82	Leased
	N747WR	Viasa			06/DEC/82	Sub-leased
	N747WR	World Airways			31/JAN/83	Leased
	N747WR	Greyhound Leasing			OCT/83	
	N747WR	National Airlines			17/NOV/83	
	N747WR	National Airlines				
	N747WR	Evergreen International			16/MAR/85	
	N747WR	Flying Tigers			16/MAR/85	Leased
	N747WR	Evergreen International			01/MAR/86	
	N747WR	Air India			MAR/86	Leased
20652	N748WA	Greyhound Leasing	273C	25/APR/72	25/MAY/73	
	N748WA	World Airways			25/MAY/73	Leased
	N748WA	Air Algerie			12/NOV/75	Sub-leased
	N748WA	World Airways			11/JAN/76	Leased
	N748WA	El Al			JAN/77	Sub-leased
	N748WA	World Airways			13/MAR/77	Leased
	N748WA	Air Algerie/Air Niger			01/NOV/78	Sub-leased
	N748WA	World Airways			06/DEC/78	Leased
	N748WA	Seaboard World			01/OCT/78	Sub-leased
	N748WA	Flying Tigers			01/OCT/80	Sub-leased
	N748WA	World Airways			05/OCT/80	Leased
	N748WA	Malaysian Airlines System			82	Sub-leased
	N748WA	World Airways			82	Leased
	N748WA	Metro International			24/FEB/83	Sub-leased
	N748WA	World Airways			83	Leased
	N748WA	Greyhound Leasing			05/NOV/83	
	N748WA	National Airlines			05/NOV/83	
	N748WA	Flying Tigers			05/NOV/83	Leased
	N748WA	National Airlines			84	
	N748WA	American Airlines			84	Leased
	N748WA	National Airlines			84	
	N748WA	Flying Tigers			84	Leased
	N748WA	National Airlines			15/APR/85	
	HL7471	Korean Air			15/APR/85	Leased
	HL7471	Saudia			08/MAY/85	Sub-leased
	HL7471	Korean Air			12/AUG/85	Purchased
	HL7471	Saudia			12/AUG/85	Leased
	HL7471	Korean Air			27/MAY/86	
20653	N749WA	World Airways	273C	02/MAY/74	10/JUN/74	
	N749WA	Korean Airlines			11/JUN/74	Leased
	N749WA	World Airways			20/MAR/79	
	N749WA	Braniff			10/APR/79	Leased
	N749WA	World Airways			09/JUN/81	
	N749WA	Viasa			JUN/81	Leased
	N749WA	World Airways			NOV/83	
	N749WA	Lufthansa			27/OCT/83	Leased
	N749WA	World Airways			04/APR/84	
	N749WA	American Airlines			15/APR/84	Leased
	N749WA	World Airways			84	
	N749WA	Flying Tigers			10/OCT/84	Leased
20682	73-01676	United States Air Force	E4A	13/JUN/73	16/JUL/73	
20683	73-01677	United States Air Force	E4A	11/SEP/73	03/OCT/73	
20684	74-00787	United States Air Force	E4A	06/JUN/74	15/OCT/74	
20704	N1799B	Boeing	258B	05/APR/73		
	4X-AXC	El Al			18/APR/73	
20708	G-AWNM	British Airways	136	06/APR/73	03/MAY/73	
20712	9V-SIA	Singapore Airlines	212B	13/JUL/73	31/JUL/73	
	N747TA	Tigerair			08/DEC/79	
	N747TA	Flying Tiger Line			DEC/79	
	N747TA	Metro International			FEB/81	Leased
	N747FT	Metro International			16/APR/82	Leased
	N747FT	Flying Tiger Line			24/FEB/83	
	N747FT	Pan American			24/FEB/83	
	N747FT	Metro International			24/FEB/83	Leased
	N728PA	Pan American			25/MAR/83	
20713	9V-SIB	Singapore Airlines	212B	01/AUG/73	29/AUG/73	
	N748TA	Tigerair			31/JUL/80	
	N748TA	Flying Tiger Line			AUG/80	
	N748TA	Metro International			FEB/81	Leased
	N748FT	Metro International			09/APR/82	Leased
	N748FT	Flying Tiger Line			24/FEB/83	
	N729PA	Pan American			24/FEB/83	
20742	SX-OAA	Olympic Airways	284B	02/JUN/73	21/JUN/73	
	N305TW	Trans World Airlines			11/APR/85	
20767	C-FTOD	Air Canada	133	03/MAY/73	14/MAY/73	
20770	N1798B	Boeing	2B5B	16/APR/73		
	HL7410	Korean Air Lines			01/MAY/73	
	N747BA	Boeing			15/APR/81	
	HL7463	Orient Leasing			27/JUL/82	
	HL7463	Korean Air Lines			27/JUL/82	Leased
20771	N1796B	Boeing	2B5B			
	HL7411	Korean Air Lines			12/JUL/73	
	N747BC	Boeing			25/NOV/81	
	HL7464	Orient Leasing			30/JUL/82	
	HL7464	Korean Airlines			30/JUL/82	Leased
20781	N1795B	Boeing	SR46	31/AUG/73		
	JA8117	Japan Air Lines			26/SEP/73	
20782	JA8118	Japan Air Lines	SR46	10/DEC/73	21/DEC/73	
20783	JA8119	Japan Air Lines	SR46	28/JAN/74	19/FEB/74	W/O 12/AUG/85, nr. Tokyo
20784	JA8120	Japan Air Lines	SR46	08/FEB/74	20/FEB/74	
20798	N88931	Wilmington Trust Co.	128	25/OCT/73		
	N88931	Air France			21/MAR/74	

C/N	Registration	Owner/Operator	Series	First Flight	Delivery	Remarks
	F-BPVL	Air France				
20799	N63305	Wilmington Trust Co.	128	30/NOV/73		
	N63305	Air France			21/DEC/73	
	F-BPVM	Air France			APR/82	
20800	N28366	Wilmington Trust Co.	128	10/JAN/74		
	N28366	Air France			08/FEB/74	
	F-BPVN	Air France			01/APR/82	
20801	N1794B	Boeing	217B	02/NOV/73		
	C-FCRA	CP Air			15/NOV/73	
	AP-BCN	Pakistan International			SEP/86	Sched.delivery
20802	C-FCRB	CP Air	217B	15/NOV/73	03/DEC/73	
	AP-BCM	Pakistan International			08/MAY/86	
20809	G-AWNN	British Airways	136	20/SEP/73	07/NOV/73	
20810	G-AWNO	British Airways	136	08/OCT/73	07/DEC/73	
20825	SX-OAB	Olympic Airways	284B	12/OCT/73	07/DEC/73	
20826	N701SW	Seaboard World	245F	12/JUL/74	31/JUL/74	
	N701SW	Viasa				Leased
	N701SW	Seaboard World			80	
	N811FT	Flying Tiger Line			01/OCT/80	
20827	N702SW	Seaboard World	245F		30/APR/76	
	N812FT	Flying Tiger Line			01/OCT/80	
20828	N703SW	Seaboard World	245F			Cancelled order
20829	9Q-CKF	Air Zaire	198			Cancelled order
20841	VH-EBG	Qantas	238B	28/FEB/74	22/MAR/74	
20842	VH-EBH	Qantas	238B	13/MAY/74	24/MAY/74	
20881	C-FTOE	Air Canada	133B	19/APR/74	13/MAY/74	
20887	N18815	Wilmington Trust Co.	128F	11/SEP/74		
	N18815	Air France			04/OCT/74	
	F-BPVO	Air France			01/APR/82	
20888	9V-SQC	Singapore Airlines	212B	21/JUN/74	29/JUL/74	
	N749TA	Tigerair			16/SEP/80	
	N749TA	Flying Tiger Line			SEP/80	
	N749TA	Metro International			FEB/81	Leased
	N749FT	Metro International			01/APR/82	Sub-leased
	N749FT	Pan American			24/FEB/83	
	N749FT	Metro International			24/FEB/83	
	N730PA	Pan American			06/MAR/83	
20921	VH-EBI	Qantas	238B	28/JUL/74	10/OCT/74	
20923	JA8121	Japan Air Lines	SR46	14/MAR/74	28/MAR/74	
20924	JA8122	Japan Air Lines	246B	21/MAR/74	29/MAR/74	
20927	C-FCRD	CP Air	217B	04/OCT/74	05/NOV/74	
	N620BN	Braniff			15/NOV/78	Leased
	C-FCRD	CP Air			06/DEC/78	
	AP-BCO	Pakistan International			OCT/86	Sched.delivery
20928	CS-TJC	TAP	282B	30/MAY/74	07/JUN/74	
	AP-AYV	Pakistan International			23/APR/76	Leased
	AP-AYV	Pakistan International			APR/80	Purchased
20929	C-FCRE	CP Air	217B	15/NOV/74	02/DEC/74	
	AP-BCL	Pakistan International			18/DEC/85	
20949	75-00125	USAF	E4B	29/APR/75	04/AUG/75	
20952	G-AWNP	British Airways	136	20/SEP/74	06/NOV/74	
20953	G-BBPU	British Airways	136	22/OCT/74	15/MAR/75	
20954	F-BPVP	Air France	128	18/DEC/74	13/MAR/75	
	F-BPVP	Sabena			SEP/78	Leased
	F-BPVP	Air France				
20977	C-FTOF	Air Canada	233B/CO			Not taken-up
	N8297V	Boeing				
	C-GAGA	Air Canada			07/MAR/75	
	C-GAGA	Air National			15/JUN/83	Leased
	C-GAGA	Air Canada			NOV/83	
21029	JA8128	Japan Air Lines	146		20/JUN/75	
21030	JA8125	Japan Air Lines	246B	05/DEC/74	17/DEC/74	
21031	JA8127	Japan Air Lines	246B	10/FEB/75	12/MAY/75	
21032	JA8124	Japan Air Lines	SR46	04/NOV/74	22/NOV/74	
21033	JA8126	Japan Air Lines	SR46	24/JAN/75	02/APR/75	
21034	JA8123	Japan Air Lines	246F	02/AUG/74	17/SEP/74	
21035	CS-TJD	TAP	282B	27/FEB/75	27/OCT/75	
	AP-AYW	Pakistan International			13/APR/76	Leased
	AP-AYW	Pakistan International			APR/80	Purchased
21048	9V-SQD	Singapore Airlines	212B	20/JAN/75	06/FEB/75	
	N747BC	Boeing			28/JUN/83	
	N747BC	Cargolux			83	Leased
	N747BC	Boeing			25/OCT/83	
	N726PA	Pan American			08/JUN/84	Reg. not taken-up
	N747BC	Pan American			08/JUN/84	
	N726PA	Pan American			18/AUG/83	Leased
21054	VH-EBJ	Qantas	238B	21/APR/75	30/MAY/75	
21097	OD-AGH	Middle East Airlines	2B46/CO	30/MAY/75	05/JUN/75	
	OD-AGH	Saudia			01/JUN/77	Leased
	OD-AGH	Middle East Airlines			JUN/81	
	OD-AGH	Saudia			APR/84	Leased
	OD-AGH	Middle East Airlines			APR/85	
	N202AE	CPC Leasing/American Express			DEC/84	
	N202AE	Middle East Airlines			DEC/84	Leased
	G-BLVE	British Airways			01/JUN/85	Sub-leased
21098	OD-AGI	Middle East Airlines	2B46/CO	05/JUN/75	20/JUN/75	
	OD-AGI	Saudia			01/JUN/77	Leased
	OD-AGI	Middle East Airlines			JUN/81	
	OD-AGI	Gulf Air			27/MAR/84	Leased
	N203AE	CPC Leasing/American Express			15/DEC/84	
	N203AE	Middle East Airlines			15/DEC/84	Leased
	N203AE	Gulf Air			15/DEC/84	Sub-leased
	N203AE	Middle East Airlines			AUG/85	Leased
	G-BLVF	British Airways			NOV/85	Sub-leased
21099	OD-AGJ	Middle East Airlines	2B46/CO	07/AUG/75	20/AUG/75	
	OD-AGJ	Royal Air Maroc/Tunis Air			JAN/77	Leased
	OD-AGJ	Middle East Airlines			77	
	OD-AGJ	Air France			01/JUN/77	Leased
	OD-AGJ	Air Gabon			01/JUN/77	Sub-leased
	OD-AGJ	Middle East Airlines			11/MAY/78	
	OD-AGJ	Saudia			SEP/78	Leased
	OD-AGJ	Middle East Airlines			01/DEC/80	
	OD-AGJ	Saudia			FEB/81	Leased
	N204AE	CPC Leasing/American Express			MAY/85	

BOEING 747

C/N	Registration	Owner/Operator	Series	First Flight	Delivery	Remarks
	N204AE	Middle East Airlines			MAY/85	Leased
	N204AE	Egyptair			MAY/85	Sub-leased
	N204AE	Middle East Airlines			06/JUL/86	Leased
21110	PH-BUH	KLM	206B/CO	26/SEP/75	19/OCT/75	
	PH-BUH	KLM	206B/SU		12/AUG/85	Converted
21111	N8297V	Boeing	206B/CO	26/NOV/75		
	PH-BUI	KLM			16/DEC/75	
	PH-BUI	KLM	206B/SU		09/OCT/85	Converted
21120	N616US	Northwest Orient	251F/SC	27/MAY/75	03/JUL/75	
21121	N617US	Northwest Orient	251F/SC	23/JUN/75	09/JUL/75	
21122	N618US	Northwest Orient	251F/SC	15/AUG/75	29/AUG/75	
21140	VH-EBK	Qantas	238B	15/AUG/75	07/NOV/75	
	VH-EBK	Air Pacific			85	
21141	N40116	Wilmington Trust Co.	128	27/JAN/76		
	N40116	Air France			25/FEB/76	
	F-BPVQ	Air France			31/OCT/83	
21162	9V-SQE	Singapore Airlines	212B	19/MAR/76	30/MAR/76	
	N747BH	Boeing			11/JUL/83	
	N727PA	Pan American			26/JUN/84	
21180	YI-AGN	Iraqi Airways	270C	27/MAY/76	24/JUN/76	
21181	YI-AGO	Iraqi Airways	270C	21/JUN/76	15/AUG/76	
21182	VT-EDU	Air India	237B	15/DEC/75	23/DEC/75	
21189	N1791B	Boeing	287B	11/NOV/75		
	LV-LZD	Aerolineas Argentinas			16/DEC/76	Leased
	N354AS	Boeing			14/JAN/82	
	G-VIRG	Virgin Atlantic			14/JUN/84	Leased
21190	4X-AXD	El Al	258C	22/OCT/75	31/DEC/75	
	4X-AXD	Cargo Air Lines				Leased
21213	G-BDPV	British Airways	136	25/FEB/76	08/APR/76	
21217	EP-IAG	Iran Air	286B/CO	21/JUL/76	05/OCT/76	
21218	EP-IAH	Iran Air	286B/CO	22/DEC/76	14/MAR/77	
21220	N1786B	Boeing	230B/SC	24/SEP/76		
	D-ABYJ	Lufthansa			24/NOV/76	
21221	D-ABYK	Lufthansa	230B/SC	04/DEC/76	15/DEC/76	
21237	VH-EBL	Qantas	238B	14/JUN/76	01/JUL/76	
21238	N1790B	Boeing	236B	03/SEP/76		
	G-BDXA	British Airways			27/JUL/77	
21239	G-BDXB	British Airways	236B	22/FEB/77	17/JUN/77	
21240	G-BDXC	British Airways	236B	08/APR/77	23/JUN/77	
21241	N8285V	Boeing	236B			
	G-BDXD	British Airways			APR/78	
21251	N1239E	Boeing	2D3B/CO	12/OCT/76		
	JY-AFA	Alia			13/APR/77	
21252	JY-AFB	Alia	2D3B/CO	26/OCT/76	11/MAY/77	
	G-HUGE	BCAL			18/MAR/85	
21255	N1783B	Boeing	228F	28/SEP/76		
	F-BPVR	Air France			13/OCT/76	
21316	9V-SQF	Singapore Airlines	212B	19/JUN/77	27/JUN/77	
	N747BJ	Boeing			05/JUL/84	
	N724PA	Pan American			31/AUG/84	
21321	N619US	Northwest Orient	251F/SC	03/JUN/77	27/JUN/77	
21326	F-BPVS	Air France	228B/SC	04/MAR/77	04/APR/77	
21350	G-BDXE	British Airways	236B		MAR/78	
21351	G-BDXF	British Airways	236B		APR/78	
21352	N8295V	Boeing	238B	11/JUL/77		
	VH-EBM	Qantas			15/AUG/77	
21353	VH-EBN	Qantas	238B	06/DEC/77	20/DEC/77	
21354	VH-ECA	Qantas	238B/CO	04/OCT/77	27/OCT/77	
21380	D-ABYL	Lufthansa	230B/SC		MAR/78	
21381	LN-RNA	SAS	283B/CO	24/AUG/77	27/OCT/77	
	LN-RNA	Scanair			APR/82	Leased
	LN-RNA	SAS			03/AUG/82	
	HK-2910	Avianca			03/AUG/82	Leased
						W/O 27/NOV/83 nr. Majorada del Campo, Spain
21429	F-BPVT	Air France	228B/SC	21/SEP/77	30/SEP/77	
21439	9V-SQG	Singapore Airlines	212B	31/AUG/77	14/SEP/77	
	N747BK	Boeing			12/DEC/84	
	N723PA	Pan American			16/JAN/85	
21446	VT-EFJ	Air India	237B		FEB/78	
21454	B-1864	China Airlines	209B/CO		APR/78	
21468	N1248E	Air Gabon	2Q2B/SC	23/APR/78	05/OCT/78	
	F-ODJG	Air Gabon			78	
21473	VT-EFO	Air India	237B	19/JUN/78	30/JUN/78	W/O 23/JUN/85, Atlantic Ocean
21486	5-8113	Imperial Iranian Air Force	2J9F	28/NOV/77	22/DEC/77	
	5-8113	Iranian Air Force			FEB/78	
	EP-NHN	Iran Air			84	
21487	5-8114	Iranian Air Force	2J9F	16/FEB/78	27/FEB/78	
	EP-ICA	Iran Air			NOV/80	
	5-8114	Iranian Air Force			JAN/83	
	EP-NHQ	Iran Air			JUN/84	
21507	N8277V	Boeing	2J9F	18/SEP/78		
	5-8115	Iranian Air Force			28/SEP/78	
	EP-ICB	Iran Air			SEP/80	
21514	N8293V	Boeing	2J9F	11/OCT/78		
	5-8116	Iranian Air Force			23/OCT/78	
	EP-ICC	Iran Air			80	Presumed W/O.
21515	N1780B	Boeing	2B3F	21/AUG/78		
	F-GPAN	UTA			26/SEP/78	
	F-GPAN	National Airlines			01/MAR/84	Leased
	F-GPAN	Saudia			01/MAR/84	Sub-leased
	F-GPAN	National Airlines			30/APR/85	Leased
	F-GPAN	UTA			30/APR/85	
	F-GPAN	Air France			28/MAR/86	
21516	N1785B	Boeing	211B	15/SEP/78		
	C-GXRA	Wardair			09/JUN/78	
	G-	British Caledonian			OCT/86	Sched.delivery
21517	C-GXRD	Wardair	211B	02/APR/79	25/APR/79	
	G-	British Caledonian			MAR/87	Sched.delivery
21536	G-BDXG	British Airways	236B	02/JUN/78	16/JUN/78	
21537	N1252E	Boeing	228B/SC	21/JUL/78		
	N1252E	Air France			07/AUG/78	
	F-BPVU	Air France				
21541	9K-ADA	Kuwait Airways	269B/CO	17/JUL/78	28/JUL/78	
21542	9K-ADB	Kuwait Airways	269B/CO	03/AUG/78	17/AUG/78	

C/N	Registration	Owner/Operator	Series	First Flight	Delivery	Remarks
21543	9K-ADC	Kuwait Airways	269B/CO	14/FEB/79	28/FEB/79	
21549	PH-BUK	KLM	206B/CO	17/AUG/78	01/SEP/78	
	PH-BUK	KLM	206B/SU		15/APR/85	Converted
21550	PH-BUL	KLM	206B/CO	17/OCT/78	03/NOV/78	
	PH-BUL	KLM	206B/SU		18/JUN/85	Converted
21575	SE-DFZ	SAS	283B/CO	17/FEB/79	02/MAR/79	
	SE-DFZ	Nigeria Airways			03/JUN/83	Leased
	SE-DFZ	Nigeria Airways			24/JUL/86	Leased
	SE-DFZ	SAS			OCT/86	Sched.return
21576	F-BPVV	Air France	228F	27/JUL/78	09/AUG/78	
21588	D-ABYM	Lufthansa	230B/SC	03/OCT/78	20/OCT/78	
21589	D-ABYN	Lufthansa	230B	25/OCT/78	10/NOV/78	
21590	N8291V	Boeing	230B	22/NOV/78		
	D-ABYP	Lufthansa			07/MAR/79	
21591	D-ABYQ	Lufthansa	230B	01/DEC/78	31/DEC/78	
21592	D-ABYO	Lufthansa	230B	10/NOV/78	22/NOV/78	
21594	4X-AXF	El Al	258C	07/JUN/78	16/JUN/78	
	4X-AXF	CAL Cargo Airline				Leased
21604	N8286V	Boeing	SR81	03/NOV/78		
	JA8133	All Nippon Airways			21/DEC/78	
21605	JA8134	All Nippon Airways	SRB1	09/DEC/78	20/DEC/78	
21606	JA8135	All Nippon Airways	SRB1	21/FEB/79	28/FEB/79	
21614	5R-MFT	Air Madagascar	2B2B/CO	12/JAN/79	26/JAN/79	
21615	CN-RME	Royal Air Maroc	2B6B/CO	06/SEP/79	29/SEP/78	
21627	C-GAGB	Air Canada	233B/CO	16/JAN/79	31/JAN/79	WFU 83, stored Toronto
21635	G-BDXH	British Airways	236B	14/MAR/79	27/MAR/79	
21643	D-ABYR	Lufthansa	230B/SC	16/DEC/78	11/JAN/79	
	D-ABYR	Condor			11/JAN/79	Leased
	D-ABYR	Lufthansa			02/MAY/80	
21644	D-ABYS	Lufthansa	230B/SC	23/JAN/79	08/FEB/79	
21650	LX-DCV	Cargolux	2R7F	23/JAN/79	31/JAN/79	
21657	VH-EBO	Qantas	238B	08/SEP/78	18/SEP/78	
21658	VH-EBP	Qantas	238B	20/SEP/78	16/OCT/78	
21659	PH-BUM	KLM	206B/CO	09/APR/79	15/MAY/79	
	PH-BUM	KLM	206B/SU		01/DEC/85	Converted
21660	PH-BUN	KLM	206B/CO	03/AUG/79	17/AUG/79	
	PH-BUN	KLM	206B/SU		27/MAR/86	Converted
21668	N1288E	Boeing	2J9F	17/SEP/79		Not delivered
	5-	Iranian Air Force				WFU 17/SEP/79 to 15/SEP/83
	N1288E	Boeing				at Everett, Wa.
	N630US	Northwest Orient			15/SEP/83	
21678	JA8129	Japan Air Lines	246B	24/FEB/79	06/MAR/79	
21679	JA8130	Japan Air Lines	246B	31/MAY/79	14/JUN/79	
21680	JA8131	Japan Air Lines	246B	20/JUN/79	28/JUN/79	
21681	JA8132	Japan Air Lines	246B	27/JUN/79	27/JUL/79	
21682	N602BN	Braniff	227B	17/MAY/79	31/MAY/79	WFU MAY/82
	N602PE	People Express			MAY/83	Leased
	N602PE	People Express				Purchased
	N635US	Northwest Orient			28/FEB/85	
21683	9V-SQH	Singapore Airlines	212B	19/JUL/79	02/AUG/79	
	SX-OAC	Olympic Airways			01/SEP/84	
21684	9V-SQI	Singapore Airlines	212B	09/AUG/79	16/AUG/79	
	SX-OAD	Olympic Airways			01/APR/85	
21704	N622US	Northwest Orient	251B	15/FEB/79	24/SEP/79	
21705	N623US	Northwest Orient	251B	11/MAY/79	25/MAY/79	
21706	N624US	Northwest Orient	251B	26/MAY/79	06/JUN/79	
21707	N625US	Northwest Orient	251B	08/JUN/79	17/JUN/79	
21708	N626US	Northwest Orient	251B	21/JUN/79	28/JUN/79	
21709	N627US	Northwest Orient	251B	21/DEC/79	02/JAN/80	
21725	N1789B	Boeing	287B	08/DEC/79		
	LV-MLO	Aerolineas Argentinas			13/JAN/79	
	LV-MLO	Flying Tigers			04/JUL/83	Leased
21726	LV-MLP	Aerolineas Argentinas	287B	01/OCT/79	11/OCT/79	
21727	LV-MLR	Aerolineas Argentinas	287B	05/OCT/79	26/OCT/79	
21730	HK-2300	Avianca	259B/CO	11/MAY/79	08/JUN/79	
	HK-2300	Chemco Leasing			30/MAY/83	
	HK-2980	Avianca			30/MAY/83	Leased
21731	N1252E	Air France	228B/SC		29/MAY/79	
	F-BPVX	Air France				
21737	4X-AXG	El Al	258F	07/MAR/79	19/MAR/79	
	4X-AXG	Cargo Air Lines				Leased
21743	N904PA	Pan American	221F	05/JUL/79	25/JUL/79	
	JA8165	Japan Air Lines			20/DEC/83	
21744	N905PA	Pan American	221F	11/AUG/79	28/AUG/79	WFU 82
	JA8160	Japan Air Lines			OCT/82	
21745	F-BPVY	Air France	228B	13/APR/79	28/APR/79	
21746	VR-HKG	Cathay Pacific	267B	04/JUL/79	20/JUL/79	
21759	EP-IAM	Iran Air	186B	20/JUN/79	02/JUL/79	
21760	EP-IAN	Iran Air	186B			Cancelled order
21761	EP-IAP	Iran Air	186B			Cancelled order
21762	EP-IAR	Iran Air	186B			Cancelled order
21764	N703SW	Seaboard World	245F	25/AUG/79	06/SEP/79	
	N813FT	Flying Tigers			01/OCT/80	
21772	HL7443	Korean Air Lines	2B5B	08/MAR/79	23/MAR/79	
21773	HL7445	Korean Air Lines	2B5B	23/MAR/79	11/APR/79	W/O 18/NOV/80, Kimpo Ap. Seoul
21782	HS-TGA	Thai International	207B	01/OCT/79	02/NOV/79	
21783	HS-TGB	Thai International	207B	03/DEC/79	15/DEC/79	
21784	HS-TGC	Thai International	207B	04/FEB/80	23/FEB/80	
21787	F-BPVZ	Air France	228F	07/SEP/79	18/SEP/79	
21825	AP-BAK	PIA	240B/CO	02/JUL/79	26/JUL/79	
21827	N806FT	Flying Tiger Line	249F	15/OCT/79	31/OCT/79	
21828	N807FT	Flying Tiger Line	249F	01/NOV/79	11/DEC/79	
21829	VT-EFU	Air India	237B	03/AUG/79	14/AUG/79	
21830	G-BDXI	British Airways	236B	16/FEB/80	05/MAR/80	
21831	G-BDXJ	British Airways	236B	26/MAR/80	02/MAY/80	
21832	N1288E	Boeing	2F6B	14/DEC/79		
	N741PR	Philippine Airlines			21/DEC/79	
21833	N1289E	Boeing	2F6B			
	N742PR	Philippine Airlines		07/JAN/80	22/FEB/80	
21834	N1290E	Boeing	2F6B	17/JAN/80		
	N743PR	Philippine Airlines			21/MAR/80	
21835	F-GBOX	UTA	2B3F	25/JUL/79	06/AUG/79	
	F-GBOX	Saudia			85	Leased
	F-GBOX	UTA			85	

BOEING 747

C/N	Registration	Owner/Operator	Series	First Flight	Delivery	Remarks
21841	N704SW	Seaboard World	245F	16/SEP/79	26/SEP/79	
	N814FT	Flying Tiger Line			01/OCT/80	
21843	B-1866	China Airlines	209B	16/JUL/79	31/JUL/79	
21848	PH-BUO	KLM	206B	06/SEP/79	22/SEP/79	
	PH-BUO	KLM	206B/SU		29/JAN/85	Converted
21922	JA8136	All Nippon Airways	SR81	21/AUG/79	10/SEP/79	
21923	JA8137	All Nippon Airways	SR81	25/AUG/79	10/SEP/79	
21924	JA8138	All Nippon Airways	SRB1	18/DEC/79	16/JAN/80	
21925	JA8139	All Nippon Airways	SRB1	15/JAN/80	15/FEB/80	
21935	9V-SQJ	Singapore Airlines	212B	17/SEP/79	25/SEP/79	
	SX-OAE	Olympic Airways			23/DEC/85	
21936	9V-SQK	Singapore Airlines	212B	25/SEP/79	01/OCT/79	
21937	9V-SQL	Singapore Airlines	212B	14/JAN/80	01/FEB/80	
21938	9V-SQM	Singapore Airlines	212B	10/MAR/80	10/APR/80	
21939	9V-SQN	Singapore Airlines	212B		MAY/80	
21940	9V-SQO	Singapore Airlines	212B	12/JUN/80	27/JUN/80	
21941	9V-SQP	Singapore Airlines	212B	15/AUG/80	12/SEP/80	
21942	9V-SQQ	Singapore Airlines	212B	11/SEP/80	25/SEP/80	
21943	9V-SQR	Singapore Airlines	212B	16/OCT/80	30/OCT/80	
21944	9V-SQS	Singapore Airlines	212B	18/FEB/81	19/MAR/81	
21964	N741TV	Transamerica Airlines	271C	30/NOV/79	21/DEC/79	
	N741TV	UTA			03/MAY/85	Leased
	N741TV	Transamerica Airlines			16/MAR/86	
21965	N742TV	Transamerica Airlines	271C	08/MAR/80	26/MAR/80	
21966	VR-HIA	Cathay Pacific	267B	07/APR/80	24/APR/80	
21977	VH-ECB	Qantas	238B/CO	25/OCT/79	14/NOV/79	
21982	F-GCBA	Air France	228B	30/JAN/80	29/FEB/80	
21991	N605BN	Braniff	227B	25/MAR/80		Cancelled order
	N8284V	Boeing				WFU 25/MAR/80 to 19/APR/84, at Everett, Wa.
	7T-	Air Algerie				Not taken-up
	N633US	Northwest Orient			19/APR/84	
21993	VT-EGA	Air India	237B	11/DEC/79	21/DEC/79	
21994	VT-EGB	Air India	237B	07/FEB/80	20/FEB/80	
21995	VT-EGC	Air India	237B	28/FEB/80	04/APR/80	
22063	JA8144	Japan Air Lines	246F	24/FEB/80	17/MAR/80	
22064	JA8140	Japan Air Lines	246B		NOV/79	
22065	JA8141	Japan Air Lines	246B	12/NOV/79	03/DEC/79	
22066	JA8142	Japan Air Lines	246B	21/JAN/80	31/JAN/80	
22067	JA8143	Japan Air Lines	246B	25/JAN/80	14/FEB/80	
22077	AP-BAT	PIA	240B/CO	02/FEB/80	07/MAR/80	
22105	5A-DIJ	Libyan Arab Airlines	2L5B	28/FEB/80		Cancelled order
	PP-VNA	Boeing			30/JAN/81	
	PP-VNA	Orient Leasing			30/JAN/81	
	PP-VNA	Varig			30/JAN/81	Leased
22106	5A-DIK	Libyan Arab Airlines	2L5B	26/MAR/80		Cancelled order
	PP-VNB	Boeing			09/FEB/81	
	PP-VNB	Orient Leasing			09/FEB/81	
	PP-VNB	Varig			09/FEB/81	Leased
22107	5A-DIL	Libyan Arab Airlines	2L5B			Cancelled order
	N1290E	Boeing			05/MAR/81	
	PP-VNC	Orient Leasing			05/MAR/81	
	PP-VNC	Varig		05/DEC/80	05/MAR/81	Leased
22145	VH-EBQ	Qantas	238B	28/NOV/79	11/DEC/79	
22149	VR-HIB	Cathay Pacific	267B	30/JUN/80	16/JUL/80	
22150	N705SW	Seaboard World	245F			Not taken-up
	N815FT	Flying Tigers		22/SEP/80	03/OCT/80	
22151	N706SW	Seaboard World	245F			Not taken-up
	N816FT	Flying Tigers		03/OCT/80	14/OCT/80	
22169	TU-TAP	Air Afrique	254F	12/SEP/80	03/OCT/80	
	TU-TAP	National Airlines			01/MAR/84	Leased
	TU-TAP	Saudia			01/MAR/84	Sub-leased
	TU-TAP	National Airlines			01/APR/85	Leased
	TU-TAP	Air Afrique			01/APR/85	
	TU-TAP	Cargolux			MAY/85	Leased
	TU-TAP	Air Afrique			24/SEP/85	
	TU-TAP	Japan Leasing Corp.			24/SEP/85	
	TU-TAP	Korean Air			24/SEP/85	Leased
	LX-TAP	Cargolux			24/SEP/85	Sub-leased
	HL7474	Korean Air			11/APR/86	Leased
22170	ZS-SAA	South African Airways	244B/CO			Reg.not taken-up
	ZS-SAR	South African Airways		24/OCT/80	06/NOV/80	
22171	ZS-SAB	South African Airways	244B/CO			Reg.not taken-up
	ZS-SAS	South African Airways		12/NOV/80	24/NOV/80	
22234	N607BN	Braniff	227B	14/JAN/81		Cancelled order
	N1607B	Braniff				
	N8285V	Boeing				WFU 14/JAN/81 to 29/MAY/84, Everett, Wa.
	7T-	Air Algerie				Not taken-up
	N634US	Northwest Orient			29/MAY/84	
22235	N609BN	Braniff	227B			Cancelled order
22236	N612BN	Braniff	227B			Cancelled order
22237	N809FT	Flying Tiger Line	249F			Not taken-up
	N810FT	Flying Tiger Line		31/JUL/80	12/SEP/80	
	N810FT	Cargo Air Lines			80	Leased
	N810FT	Flying Tiger Line			80	
22238	EC-DIA	Iberia	256B	23/APR/80	01/MAY/80	
22239	EC-DIB	Iberia	256B	02/MAY/80	22/MAY/80	
22245	N808FT	Flying Tiger Line	249F	20/JUN/80	03/JUL/80	
22246	PK-GSA	Garuda	2U3B	12/JUN/80	02/JUL/80	
22247	PK-GSB	Garuda	2U3B	03/JUL/80	30/JUL/80	
22248	PK-GSC	Garuda	2U3B	22/JUL/80	11/AUG/80	
22249	PK-GSD	Garuda	2U3B	08/AUG/80	26/AUG/80	
22254	4X-AXH	El Al	258B	06/DEC/79	21/DEC/79	
22272	N1289E	Air France	228B/SC	18/JUN/80	03/JUL/80	
22291	JA8145	All Nippon Airways	SR81	03/MAY/80	16/MAY/80	
22292	JA8146	All Nippon Airways	SR81	23/MAY/80	16/JUN/80	
22293	JA8147	All Nippon Airways	SR81	15/AUG/80	25/NOV/80	
22294	JA8148	All Nippon Airways	SR81	30/SEP/80	25/NOV/80	
22297	LV-OEP	Aerolineas Argentinas	287B	04/NOV/80	18/NOV/80	
22299	B-1885	China Airlines	209F	11/JUL/80		Not taken-up
	B-1894	China Airlines			24/JUL/80	
22303	G-BDXK	British Airways	236B	30/MAR/83	MAR/83	
22304	G-BDXM	British Airways	236B	24/JAN/81		Reg. Not taken-up

C/N	Registration	Owner/Operator	Series	First Flight	Delivery	Remarks
	9M-MHI	Malaysian Airline System			14/MAR/82	
22305	N8280V	Boeing	236B	12/FEB/81		
	G-BDXL	British Airways			14/MAR/82	Not taken-up
	G-BDXL	British Airtours			10/FEB/84	
	G-BDXL	British Airways			31/OCT/84	
22306	G-BDXK	British Airways	236F			Not taken-up
	G-KILO	British Airways		19/SEP/80	30/SEP/80	
	VR-HVY	Cathay Pacific			15/MAY/82	
22337	HS-TGF	Thai International	2D7B	11/SEP/80	24/SEP/80	
22363	D-ABYT	Lufthansa	230B/SC	04/NOV/80	19/NOV/80	
22366	YI-AGP	Iraqi Airways	270C	25/JUN/82	15/JUL/82	
22376	N1295E	KLM	206B	06/AUG/80	11/SEP/80	
	N1295E	KLM	206B/SU		13/DEC/84	Converted
22378	TJ-CAB	Cameroon Airlines	2H7B/CO	06/FEB/81	26/FEB/81	
22379	N1298E	KLM	206B	06/NOV/80	15/DEC/80	
	N1298E	KLM	206B/SU		11/MAR/85	Converted
22380	N1301E	KLM	206B/CO			Not taken-up
	N1309E	KLM		21/AUG/81	29/SEP/81	
	N1309E	KLM	206B/SU		JAN/86	Converted
22381	OY-KHB	SAS	283B/CO	20/DEC/80		
	N4501Q	SAS			17/FEB/81	
22382	N744PR	Philippine Airlines	2F6B	02/DEC/80	12/DEC/80	
22388	N629US	Northwest Orient	251F	01/APR/80	18/APR/80	
22389	N628US	Northwest Orient	251B	21/MAR/80	08/APR/80	
22390	LX-ECV	Cargolux	2R7F	30/SEP/80	10/OCT/80	
	B-198	China Airlines			26/FEB/85	
	B-198	Cargolux			26/FEB/85	Leased
	B-198	China Airlines			02/JUN/85	
22403	N743TV	Transamerica Airlines	271C	01/MAY/81	01/JUN/81	
	N743TV	Saudia			14/APR/85	Leased
	N743TV	Transamerica Airlines			01/APR/86	
	N743TV	Cargolux			01/APR/86	Leased
22404	N744TV	Transamerica Airlines	271C		APR/82	Cancelled order
22405	N745TV	Transamerica Airlines	271C		MAY/82	Cancelled order
22427	F-GCBC	Air France	228B/SC	07/OCT/80	21/OCT/80	W/O 02/DEC/85, Rio de Janeiro Intl. Ap., Brasil.
22428	F-GCBD	Air France	228B/SC	23/DEC/80		Reg. Not taken-up
	N1305E	Air France			02/MAR/81	
22429	VR-HIC	Cathay Pacific	267B	05/DEC/80	19/DEC/80	
22442	G-BDXN	British Airways	236B		08/APR/82	
	9M-MHJ	Malaysian Airline System			08/APR/82	
22446	B-1886	China Airlines	209B	07/APR/81	17/APR/81	
22447	B-1888	China Airlines	209B	17/FEB/82	04/MAR/82	
22454	EC-DLC	Iberia	256B	06/FEB/81	18/FEB/81	
	EC-DLC	Iberia	256B/CO		04/OCT/84	
22455	EC-DLD	Iberia	256B	12/MAR/81	24/MAR/81	
	EC-DLD	Iberia	256B/CO		29/NOV/84	
22471	HS-TGG	Thai International	2D7B	16/JAN/81	16/MAR/81	
22472	HS-TGD	Thai International	2D7B			Reg. not taken-up
	N6066U	Boeing		16/MAY/84		
	HS-TGS	Thai International			01/JUN/84	
22477	JA8151	Japan Air Lines	246F	26/NOV/80	15/DEC/80	
22478	JA8149	Japan Air Lines	246B	26/NOV/80	13/MAR/81	
22479	N1783B	Boeing	246B	13/DEC/80		
	JA8150	Japan Air Lines			19/MAR/81	
22480	HL7451	Korean Air Lines	2B5F	30/APR/80	25/JUN/80	
	HL7451	Saudia			27/MAY/86	Leased
22481	N5573F	Boeing	2B5F	04/JUN/80		
	HL7452	Korean Air Lines			25/JUN/80	
	HL7452	Saudia			27/FEB/81	Leased
	HL7452	Korean Air Lines			11/MAY/81	
	HL7452	Saudia			17/FEB/83	Leased
	HL7452	Korean Air Lines			13/FEB/84	
22482	HL7454	Korean Air Lines	2B5B	17/OCT/80	13/NOV/80	
22485	HL7458	Korean Air Lines	2B5B	06/MAR/81	13/APR/81	
22486	N8281V	Boeing	2B5F	10/APR/81		
	HL7459	Korean Air Lines			08/MAY/81	
	HL7459	Saudia			08/MAY/81	Leased
	HL7459	Korean Air Lines			28/FEB/84	
22487	N6069D	Boeing	3B5			
	HL7468	Korean Air Lines			12/DEC/84	
22488	HL	Korean Air Lines	2B5F			Cancelled order
22489	N6009F	Boeing	3B5	30/MAR/85		
	HL7469	Korean Air Lines			15/APR/85	
22496	LN-RNB	SAS	283B/CO			Reg. Not taken-up
	N4502R	SAS		26/AUG/81	22/OCT/81	
	N4502R	Nigeria Airways			03/JUN/83	Leased
	N4502R	SAS			83	
22498	N8281V	Boeing	168B	02/MAR/81		
	HZ-AIA	Saudia			24/MAR/81	
22499	HZ-AIB	Saudia	168B	23/MAR/81	02/APR/81	
22500	HZ-AIC	Saudia	168B	23/APR/81	30/MAY/81	
22501	HZ-AID	Saudia	168B	08/MAY/81	21/MAY/81	
22502	HZ-AIE	Saudia	168B		JUL/81	
22506	I-DEMC	Alitalia	243B/CO	14/NOV/80	26/NOV/80	
22507	I-DEMD	Alitalia	243B/CO	26/NOV/80	12/DEC/80	
22508	I-DEMF	Alitalia	243B/CO	11/DEC/80	22/DEC/80	
22509	I-	Alitalia	243B/CO			Cancelled Order
22510	I-DEMG	Alitalia	243B		AUG/81	
22511	I-DEML	Alitalia	243B		SEP/81	
22512	I-DEMN	Alitalia	243B	21/SEP/81	05/NOV/81	
22513	I-DEMP	Alitalia	243B	02/NOV/81	03/DEC/81	
22514	F-BTDG	UTA	2B3B/CO	01/APR/81	23/APR/81	
	F-BTDG	UTA	2B3B/SU		MAR/86	Converted
22515	F-BTDH	UTA	2B3B/CO	17/APR/81	05/MAY/81	
	F-BTDH	UTA	2B3B/SU		15/MAY/86	Converted
22530	VR-HID	Cathay Pacific	267B		JUN/81	
22545	I-DEMR	Alitalia	243F	15/OCT/81	18/DEC/81	
22546	B-	China Airlines	209B			Cancelled order
22579	JY-AFS	Alia	2D3B	09/MAR/81	26/MAR/81	
22592	LV-OOZ	Aerolineas Argentinas	287B		AUG/81	
22593	LV-OPA	Aerolineas Argentinas	287B	16/DEC/81	23/JAN/82	
22594	JA8152	All Nippon Airways	SR81	18/FEB/81	27/FEB/81	
22595	JA8153	All Nippon Airways	SR81	29/MAY/81	28/MAY/81	
22614	VH-EBR	Qantas	238B	24/JUN/80	30/SEP/80	

BOEING 747

C/N	Registration	Owner/Operator	Series	First Flight	Delivery	Remarks
22615	VH-ECC	Qantas	238B/CO	29/SEP/80	15/OCT/80	
22616	VH-EBS	Qantas	238B	25/SEP/81	30/NOV/81	
22617	VH-EBT	Qantas	238B			Cancelled order
22668	D-ABYU	Lufthansa	230F		SEP/81	Damaged 18/OCT/83, Kai Tak Ap., Hong Kong. Later repaired
22669	D-ABYW	Lufthansa	230B/SC	19/NOV/81	23/DEC/81	
22670	D-ABYX	Lufthansa	230B	01/DEC/81	25/FEB/82	
22671	D-ABYY	Lufthansa	230B	04/DEC/82	20/DEC/82	
22678	N4508E	Air France	228F		11/SEP/81	
22704	N6005C	Boeing	357	05/OCT/82		
	N8277V	Boeing				
	HB-IGC	Swissair			19/MAR/83	
22705	N1784B	Boeing	357/SCD	14/FEB/83		
	HB-IGD	Swissair			05/MAR/83	
22709	JA8156	All Nippon Airways	SR81	21/SEP/81	17/DEC/81	
22710	JA8157	All Nippon Airways	SR81	15/OCT/81	17/DEC/81	
22711	JA8158	All Nippon Airways	SR81	01/APR/82	17/JUN/82	
22712	JA8159	All Nippon Airways	SR81	23/OCT/82	12/NOV/82	
22722	ZK-NZV	Air New Zealand	243B	06/MAY/81	22/MAY/81	
22723	ZK-NZW	Air New Zealand	243B	22/MAY/81	09/JUN/81	
22724	ZK-NZX	Air New Zealand	243B		JUN/81	
22725	ZK-NZY	Air New Zealand	243B	27/MAY/82	22/JUN/82	
22740	9K-ADD	Kuwait Airways	269B/CO	14/JAN/82	20/JAN/82	
22745	JA8154	Japan Air Lines	246B	04/NOV/81	17/NOV/81	
22746	JA8155	Japan Air Lines	246B	17/NOV/81	15/DEC/81	
22747	HZ-AIG	Saudia	168B	11/DEC/81	JAN/82	
22748	HZ-AIH	Saudia	168B	03/FEB/82	17/MAR/82	
22749	HZ-AII	Saudia	168B	19/MAR/82	02/APR/82	
22764	N8296V	Boeing	256B	25/JAN/82		
	EC-DNP	Iberia			26/FEB/82	
22768	PK-GSE	Garuda	2U3B	24/APR/82	05/MAY/82	
22769	PK-GSF	Garuda	2U3B	08/MAY/82	18/MAY/82	
22791	ZK-NZZ	Air New Zealand	219B	05/AUG/82	25/AUG/82	
22794	N4506H	Air France	228B/SC	17/MAR/82	26/MAR/82	
22870	F-GDUT	UTA	3B3			Reg. Not taken-up
	N6067B	Boeing		10/DEC/82		
	N8278V	Boeing				
	F-GDUA	UTA			01/MAR/83	W/O 16/MAR/85, Paris CDG Ap.
22871	F-GDUB	UTA	3B3			Cancelled Order
22872	VR-HIE	Cathay Pacific	267B	09/JUL/82	23/JUL/82	
22939	F-GCBG	Air France	228F			Reg. not taken-up
	N4544F	Air France		25/AUG/82	01/OCT/82	
22969	N8289V	Boeing	243B	11/FEB/83		
	I-DEMS	Alitalia			28/FEB/83	
22970	N8279V	Boeing	344	16/FEB/83		
	ZS-SAT	South African Airways			02/MAY/83	
22971	N8296V	Boeing	344	27/MAR/83		
	ZS-SAU	South African Airways			14/APR/83	
22989	JA8160	Japan Air Lines	246F			Reg. not taken-up
	N211JL	Japan Air Lines		07/OCT/82	14/DEC/82	
22990	N6046B	Boeing	246B	25/APR/83		
	JA8161	Japan Air Lines			16/JUN/83	
22991	N5573K	Boeing	246B	17/MAY/83		
	JA8162	Japan Air Lines			06/JUN/83	
22995	HB-IGE	Swissair	357	22/SEP/83		Reg. Not taken-up
	N221GE	Swissair			16/DEC/83	
22996	HB-IGF	Swissair	357			Reg. Not taken-up
	N221GF	Swissair		12/SEP/83	30/NOV/83	
22997	HB-IGG	Swissair	357		DEC/87	Cancelled order
23025	PH-	KLM	206B			Cancelled order
23026	N6006C	Boeing	312	15/APR/83		
	N8279V	Boeing			APR/83	
	9V-SQT	Singapore Airlines				Reg. Not taken-up
	9V-SKA	Singapore Airlines			29/APR/83	
23027	9V-SQU	Singapore Airlines	312			Reg. Not taken-up
	9V-SKB	Singapore Airlines				Reg. not taken-up
	N116KB	Singapore Airlines		12/JUN/83	21/JUN/83	
23028	9V-SQV	Singapore Airlines	312			Reg. Not taken-up
	9V-SKC	Singapore Airlines				Reg. not taken-up
	N117KC	Singapore Airlines		23/JUN/83	30/JUN/83	
23029	9V-SQW	Singapore Airlines	312/COM			Reg. Not taken-up
	9V-SKD	Singapore Airlines				Reg. not taken-up
	N118KD	Singapore Airlines		11/NOV/83	22/NOV/83	
23030	9V-SQX	Singapore Airlines	312			Reg. Not taken-up
	9V-SKE	Singapore Airlines				Reg. not taken-up
	N119KE	Singapore Airlines		01/FEB/84	24/FEB/84	
23031	9V-SQY	Singapore Airlines	312			Reg. Not taken-up
	9V-SKF	Singapore Airlines				Reg. not taken-up
	N120KF	Singapore Airlines		18/JUN/84	28/JUN/84	
23032	9V-SQZ	Singapore Airlines	312			Reg. Not taken-up
	9V-SKG	Singapore Airlines				Reg. not taken-up
	N121KG	Singapore Airlines		17/OCT/84	30/OCT/84	
23033	9V-SQA	Singapore Airlines	312			Reg. Not taken-up
	9V-SKH	Singapore Airlines				Reg. Not taken-up
	N122KH	Singapore Airlines		01/MAR/85	20/MAR/85	
23048	N6066U	Boeing	267B	13/MAY/83		
	VR-HIF	Cathay Pacific			23/MAY/83	
23056	N4548M	KLM	306/COM	15/SEP/83	30/SEP/83	
23067	JA8163	Japan Air Lines	346			Reg. not taken-up
	N212JL	Japan Air Lines		10/OCT/83	29/NOV/83	
23068	JA8164	Japan Air Lines	346			Reg. not taken-up
	N213JL	Japan Air Lines		26/OCT/83	08/DEC/83	
23070	N1784B	Boeing	3G1	15/DEC/83		
	HZ-HM1A	Saudi Royal Flight			22/DEC/83	
23071	N1781B	Boeing	2J6B/CO	06/DEC/83		
	B-2446	CAAC			20/DEC/83	
23111	N631US	Northwest Orient	251B	28/FEB/84	02/APR/84	
23112	N632US	Northwest Orient	251B	27/MAR/84	01/MAY/84	
23120	N5573B	Boeing	267B	17/APR/84		
	VR-HIH	Cathay Pacific			27/APR/84	
23137	N4551N	KLM	306/CO	09/AUG/84	13/SEP/84	
23138	N6066Z	Boeing	281F			
	JA8167	All Nippon Airways			13/DEC/84	
	JA8167	Nippon Air Cargo			13/DEC/84	Leased
23139	N6046P	Boeing	281F	20/FEB/85		

C/N	Registration	Owner/Operator	Series	First Flight	Delivery	Remarks
	JA8168	All Nippon Airways			28/FEB/85	
	JA8168	Nippon Air Cargo			28/FEB/85	Leased
23149	N5573B	Boeing	346			
	JA8163	Japan Air Lines			06/DEC/84	
23150	N1781B	Boeing	146B			
	JA8164	Japan Air Lines			04/DEC/84	
23151	N1786B	Boeing	346	17/JAN/85		
	JA8166	Japan Air Lines			04/FEB/85	
23221	N6018N	Boeing	367	31/MAY/85		
	VR-HII	Cathay Pacific			13/JUN/85	
23222	N1784B	Boeing	338	06/OCT/84		
	VH-EBT	Qantas			13/NOV/84	
23223	N5573P	Boeing	338	21/DEC/84		
	VH-EBU	Qantas			24/JAN/85	
23224	N6005C	Boeing	338	21/MAR/85		
	VH-EBV	Qantas			15/APR/85	
23243	N123KJ	Singapore Airlines	312	19/APR/85	30/APR/85	
23244	N124KK	Singapore Airlines	312	23/AUG/85	24/SEP/85	
23245	N125KL	Singapore Airlines	312	05/NOV/85	11/DEC/85	
23246	9V-SKP	Singapore Airlines	312		AUG/86	Cancelled order
23262	N6005C	Boeing	368	13/JUN/85		
	HZ-AIK	Saudia			12/JUL/85	
23263	N6009F	Boeing	368	26/JUL/85		
	HZ-AIL	Saudia			02/AUG/85	
23264	N6046P	Boeing	368	09/AUG/85		
	HZ-AIM	Saudia			21/AUG/85	
23265	N6046P	Boeing	368	11/OCT/85		
	HZ-AIN	Saudia			20/DEC/85	
23266	N6005C	Boeing	368	09/OCT/85		
	HZ-AIO	Saudia			24/OCT/85	
23267	N6055X	Boeing	368	03/JAN/86		
	HZ-AIP	Saudia			17/JAN/86	
23268	N6005C	Boeing	368	14/JAN/86		
	HZ-AIQ	Saudia			14/MAR/86	
23269	N6038E	Boeing	368	01/MAY/86		
	HZ-AIR	Saudia			24/JUL/86	
23270	HZ-AIS	Saudia	368		86	Sched.delivery
23271	HZ-AIT	Saudia	368		86	Sched.delivery
23286	N6055X	Boeing	230B	16/MAY/85		
	D-ABYZ	Lufthansa			24/MAY/85	
23287	N6038E	Boeing	230B	21/JUN/85		
	D-ABZA	Lufthansa			28/JUN/85	
23300	N6009F	Boeing	243B	08/MAY/85		
	I-DEMT	Alitalia			29/MAY/85	
23301	N6018N	Boeing	243B/SC	12/JUL/85		
	I-DEMV	Alitalia			24/JUL/85	
	I-DEMV	Egyptair			03/JUL/86	Leased
23348	N6005F	Boeing	230F	15/OCT/85		
	D-ABZB	Lufthansa			25/OCT/85	
23350	N6018N	Boeing	281F	01/OCT/85		
	JA8172	Nippon Cargo			15/OCT/85	
23389	N6018N	Boeing	246B	01/MAR/86		
	JA8169	Japan Air Lines			19/MAR/86	
23390	N6009F	Boeing	SR46/SU	26/FEB/86		
	JA8170	Japan Air Lines			24/MAR/86	
23391	JA8171	Japan Air Lines	246F		AUG/86	Sched.delivery
23392	N6005C	Boeing	367	08/FEB/86		
	VR-HIJ	Cathay Pacific			14/FEB/86	
23393	N6046P	Boeing	230B	24/JAN/86		
	D-ABZC	Lufthansa			14/FEB/86	
23394	N6005C	Boeing	341	22/NOV/85		
	PP-VNH	Varig			10/DEC/85	
23395	N6009F	Boeing	341	13/DEC/85		
	PP-VNI	Varig			19/DEC/85	
23407	N6005C	Boeing	230B	31/MAR/86		
	D-ABZD	Lufthansa			10/APR/86	
23408	N6055X	Boeing	338	19/MAR/86		
	VH-EBW	Qantas			31/MAR/86	
23409	N6065Y	Boeing	312/CO	10/MAR/86		
	9V-SKM	Singapore Airlines			25/MAR/86	
23410	9V-	Singapore Airlines	312/CO		MAR/87	Sched.delivery
23413	F-GDUE	UTA	3B3/SC			Reg. not taken-up
	F-GETA	UTA		23/JAN/86	31/JAN/86	
23439	N6005C	Boeing	329/CO	29/MAY/86		
	OO-SGC	Sabena			10/JUN/86	
23461	N60668	Boeing	2J6B	30/NOV/85		
	B-2448	CAAC			10/DEC/85	
23476	I-DEMW	Alitalia	243B	06/JUN/86	13/JUN/86	
23480	N6018N	Boeing	3B3	14/APR/86		
	F-GETB	UTA			24/APR/86	
23482	N6009F	Boeing	346	06/APR/86		
	JA8173	Japan Air Lines			15/APR/86	
23501	N6055X	Boeing	281B	16/JUN/86		
	JA8174	All Nippon Airways			25/JUN/86	
23502	N60659	Boeing	281B	23/JUN/86		
	JA8175	All Nippon Airways			02/JUL/86	
23508	PH-BUW	KLM	306/CO		SEP/86	Sched.delivery
23509	D-ABZE	Lufthansa	230B		86	Sched.delivery
23534	VR-HIK	Cathay Pacific	367		OCT/86	Sched.delivery
23547	N636US	Northwest Orient	251B	22/APR/86	06/MAY/86	
23548	N637US	Northwest Orient	251B	10/MAY/86	19/MAY/86	
23549	N638US	Northwest Orient	251B	11/JUL/86	18/JUL/86	
23600	9M-MHK	Malaysian Airline System	3H6/CO	02/JUL/86	17/JUL/86	
23611	F-GCBH	Air France	228B/CO		OCT/86	Sched.delivery
23621	D-ABZF	Lufthansa	230F		DEC/86	Sched.delivery
23622	D-ABZH	Lufthansa	230B		FEB/87	Sched.delivery
23637	JA8176	Japan Air Lines	SR46/SU		OCT/86	Sched.delivery
23638	JA8177	Japan Air Lines	346		SEP/86	Sched.delivery
23639	JA8178	Japan Air Lines	346		APR/87	Sched.delivery
23640	JA8179	Japan Air Lines	346		AUG/87	Sched.delivery
23641	JA8180	Japan Air Lines	246F		JUN/87	Sched.delivery
23652	PH-MCE	Martinair	2A1C/CO		MAR/87	Sched.delivery
23688	VH-EBX	Qantas	338		DEC/86	Sched.delivery
23709	VR-HIL	Cathay Pacific	367		FEB/87	Sched.delivery
23711	G-BDXM	British Airways	236B/CO		MAR/87	Sched.delivery

BOEING 747

C/N	Registration	Owner/Operator	Series	First Flight	Delivery	Remarks
23719	N	Northwest Orient	451		DEC/88	Sched.delivery
23720	N	Northwest Orient	451		DEC/88	Sched.delivery
23721	HS-TGJ	Thai International	3D7		DEC/87	Sched.delivery
23722	HS-TGV	Thai International	3D7		MAR/88	Sched.delivery
23735	G-BDXN	British Airways	236B/CO		MAR/87	Sched.delivery
23736	N151UA	United Airlines	222B		MAR/87	Sched.delivery
23737	N152UA	United Airlines	222B		APR/87	Sched.delivery
23746	B-2450	CAAC	216B		MAR/87	Sched.delivery
23751	HB-IGG	Swissair	357/CO			
23769	9V-SQP	Singapore Airlines	312/CO			
23799	G-BDXO	British Airways	236B		MAY/87	Sched.delivery

ADDITIONAL ORDERS

C/N	Registration	Owner/Operator	Series	First Flight	Delivery	Remarks
	N	Northwest Orient	451		89	Sched.delivery
	N	Northwest Orient	451			
	N	Northwest Orient	451			
	N	Northwest Orient	451			
	N	Northwest Orient	451			
	N	Northwest Orient	451			
	N	Northwest Orient	451			
	N	Northwest Orient	451		DEC/90	Sched.delivery
	9V-	Singapore Airlines	412		89	Sched.delivery
	9V-	Singapore Airlines	412		89	Sched.delivery
	9V-	Singapore Airlines	412		89	Sched.delivery
	9V-	Singapore Airlines	412			
	9V-	Singapore Airlines	412			
	9V-	Singapore Airlines	412			
	9V-	Singapore Airlines	412			
	9V-	Singapore Airlines	412			
	9V-	Singapore Airlines	412			
	9V-	Singapore Airlines	412			
	9V-	Singapore Airlines	412			
	9V-	Singapore Airlines	412			
	9V-	Singapore Airlines	412		93	Sched.delivery
	N	United Airlines	222		88	Sched.delivery
	N	United Airlines	222		88	Sched.delivery
	N	United Airlines	222		89	Sched.delivery
	N	United Airlines	222		89	Sched.delivery
	PH-	Martinair	2A1		MAR/89	Sched.delivery
	VR-	Cathay Pacific	467		APR/89	Sched.delivery
	VR-	Cathay Pacific	467		MAY/89	Sched.delivery
	D-	Lufthansa	430		89	Sched.delivery
	D-	Lufthansa	430		89	Sched.delivery
	D-	Lufthansa	430		90	Sched.delivery
	D-	Lufthansa	430		90	Sched.delivery
	D-	Lufthansa	430		91	Sched.delivery
	D-	Lufthansa	430		91	Sched.delivery
	B-	CAAC	2J6		MAR/88	Sched.delivery
	B-	CAAC	2J6		MAR/89	Sched.delivery
	B-	CAAC	2J6		MAR/90	Sched.delivery
	PH-	KLM	406		89	Sched.delivery
	PH-	KLM	406		89	Sched.delivery
	PH-	KLM	406		89	Sched.delivery
	PH-	KLM	406		90	Sched.delivery
	PH-	KLM	406		90	Sched.delivery
	PH-	KLM	406		90	Sched.delivery
	F-	UTA	4B3		APR/89	Sched.delivery
	F-	UTA	4B3		APR/91	Sched.delivery
	G-	British Airways	436		FEB/89	Sched.delivery
	G-	British Airways	436			Sched.delivery
	G-	British Airways	436			Sched.delivery
	G-	British Airways	436			Sched.delivery
	G-	British Airways	436			Sched.delivery
	G-	British Airways	436			Sched.delivery
	G-	British Airways	436			Sched.delivery
	G-	British Airways	436			Sched.delivery
	G-	British Airways	436			Sched.delivery
	G-	British Airways	436			Sched.delivery
	G-	British Airways	436			Sched.delivery
	G-	British Airways	436			Sched.delivery
	G-	British Airways	436			Sched.delivery
	G-	British Airways	436			Sched.delivery
	G-	British Airways	436		DEC/90	Sched.delivery

Boeing 747 cross-reference index

4R- Sri Lanka

20009	4R-ULF
20010	4R-ULG

4X- Israel

20135	4X-AXA
20274	4X-AXB
20704	4X-AXC
21190	4X-AXD
21594	4X-AXF
21737	4X-AXG
22254	4X-AXH
19735	4X-AXZ

5A- Libya

22105	5A-DIJ
22106	5A-DIK
22107	5A-DIL

5R- Madagasgar

21614	5R-MFT

9K- Kuwait

21541	9K-ADA
21542	9K-ADB
21543	9K-ADC
22740	9K-ADD

9M- Malaysia

22304	9M-MHI
22442	9M-MHJ
23600	9M-MHK

9Q- Zaire

19637	9Q-ARW
20829	9Q-CKF

9V- Singapore

20712	9V-SIA
20713	9V-SIB
23026	9V-SKA
23027	9V-SKB
23028	9V-SKC
23029	9V-SKD
23030	9V-SKE
23031	9V-SKF
23032	9V-SKG
23033	9V-SKH
23409	9V-SKM
23246	9V-SKP
23033	9V-SQA
20888	9V-SQC
21048	9V-SQD
21162	9V-SQE
21316	9V-SQF
21439	9V-SQG
21683	9V-SQH
21684	9V-SQI
21935	9V-SQJ
21936	9V-SQK
21937	9V-SQL
21938	9V-SQM
21939	9V-SQN
21940	9V-SQO
21941	9V-SQP
23769	9V-SQP
21942	9V-SQQ
21943	9V-SQR
21944	9V-SQS
23026	9V-SQT
23027	9V-SQU
23028	9V-SQV
23029	9V-SQW
23030	9V-SQX
23031	9V-SQY
23032	9V-SQZ

AP- Pakistan

20928	AP-AYV
21035	AP-AYW
21825	AP-BAK
22077	AP-BAT
20929	AP-BCL
20802	AP-BCM
20801	AP-BCN
20927	AP-BCO

B- Taiwan

19898	B-1860
19454	B-1864
21843	B-1866
19896	B-1868
22299	B-1885
22446	B-1886
22447	B-1888
22299	B-1894
22390	B-198

B- China

19732	B-2440
23071	B-2446
23461	B-2448
23746	B-2450

C/CF- Canada

20801	C-FCRA
20802	C-FCRB
20927	C-FCRD
20929	C-FCRE
20208	C-FDJC
20305	C-FFUN
20013	C-FTOA
20015	C-FTOC
20767	C-FTOD
20881	C-FTOE
20977	C-FTOF
20977	C-GAGA
21627	C-GAGB
21516	C-GXRA
21517	C-GXRD
20013	CF-TOA
20014	CF-TOB
20015	CF-TOC

CN- Morocco

21615	CN-RME

CS- Portugal

20501	CS-TJA
20502	CS-TJB
20928	CS-TJC
21035	CS-TJD

D- West Germany

19746	D-ABYA
19747	D-ABYB
19748	D-ABYC
20372	D-ABYD
20373	D-ABYE
20493	D-ABYF
20527	D-ABYG
20559	D-ABYH
21220	D-ABYJ
21221	D-ABYK
21380	D-ABYL
21588	D-ABYM
21589	D-ABYN
21592	D-ABYO
21590	D-ABYP
21591	D-ABYQ
21643	D-ABYR
21644	D-ABYS
22363	D-ABYT
22668	D-ABYU
22669	D-ABYW
22670	D-ABYX
22671	D-ABYY
23286	D-ABYZ
23287	D-ABZA
23348	D-ABZB
23393	D-ABZC
23407	D-ABZD
23509	D-ABZE
23621	D-ABZF
23622	D-ABZH

EC- Spain

19957	EC-BRO
19958	EC-BRP
20137	EC-BRQ
22238	EC-DIA
22239	EC-DIB
22454	EC-DLC
22455	EC-DLD
22764	EC-DNP
20014	EC-DXE

EI- Eire

19744	EI-ASI
19745	EI-ASJ
19748	EI-BED
19898	EI-BOS
20013	EI-BPH
20014	EI-BRR

EP- Iran

21217	EP-IAG
21218	EP-IAH
21759	EP-IAM
21760	EP-IAN
21761	EP-IAP
21762	EP-IAR
21487	EP-ICA
21507	EP-ICB
21514	EP-ICC
19668	EP-NHD
19667	EP-NHJ
19669	EP-NHK
21486	EP-NHN
20082	EP-NHP
21487	EP-NHQ
20081	EP-NHR
20080	EP-NHS
19678	EP-NHT

F- France

19749	F-BPVA
19750	F-BPVB
19751	F-BPVC
19752	F-BPVD
20355	F-BPVE
20376	F-BPVF
20377	F-BPVG
20378	F-BPVH
20541	F-BPVJ
20543	F-BPVK
20798	F-BPVL
20799	F-BPVM
20800	F-BPVN
20887	F-BPVO
20954	F-BPVP
21141	F-BPVQ
21255	F-BPVR
21326	F-BPVS
21429	F-BPVT
21537	F-BPVU
21576	F-BPVV
21731	F-BPVX
21745	F-BPVY
21787	F-BPVZ
22514	F-BTDG
22515	F-BTDH
21835	F-GBOX
21982	F-GCBA
22427	F-GCBC
22428	F-GCBD
22939	F-GCBG
23611	F-GCBH
22870	F-GDUA
22871	F-GDUB
23413	F-GDUE
22870	F-GDUT
23413	F-GETA
23480	F-GETB
21515	F-GPAN
21468	F-ODJG

G- United Kingdom

19761	G-AWNA
19762	G-AWNB
19763	G-AWNC
19764	G-AWND
19765	G-AWNE
19766	G-AWNF
20269	G-AWNG
20270	G-AWNH
20271	G-AWNI
20272	G-AWNJ
20273	G-AWNK
20284	G-AWNL
20708	G-AWNM
20809	G-AWNN
20810	G-AWNO
20952	G-AWNP
20953	G-BBPU
21213	G-BDPV
21745	G-BDPZ
21238	G-BDXA
21239	G-BDXB
21240	G-BDXC
21241	G-BDXD
21350	G-BDXE
21351	G-BDXF
21536	G-BDXG
21635	G-BDXH
21830	G-BDXI
21831	G-BDXJ
22303	G-BDXK
22306	G-BDXK
22305	G-BDXL
22304	G-BDXM
23711	G-BDXM
22442	G-BDXN
23735	G-BDXN
23799	G-BDXO
20527	G-BJXN
21097	G-BLVE
21098	G-BLVF
20121	G-BMGS
21252	G-HUGE
22306	G-KILO
19732	G-VGIN
21189	G-VIRG

HB- Switzerland

20116	HB-IGA
20117	HB-IGB
22704	HB-IGC
22705	HB-IGD
22995	HB-IGE
22996	HB-IGF
22997	HB-IGG
23751	HB-IGG

HI- Dominican Republic

20104	HI-472

HK- Colombia

19734	HK-2000
21730	HK-2300
21735	HK-2400
19733	HK-2900
21381	HK-2910
21730	HK-2980

HL South Korea

20770	HL7410
20771	HL7411
20372	HL7440
20373	HL7441
20559	HL7442
21772	HL7443
21773	HL7447
20493	HL7447
22480	HL7451
22481	HL7452
22482	HL7454
22485	HL7458
22486	HL7459
20770	HL7463
20771	HL7464
22487	HL7468
22489	HL7469
20652	HL7471
22169	HL7474

HS- Thailand

21782	HS-TGA
21783	HS-TGB
21784	HS-TGC
22472	HS-TGD
22337	HS-TGF
22471	HS-TGG
23721	HS-TGJ
22472	HS-TGS
23722	HS-TGV
19744	HS-VGB
19745	HS-VGF
20399	HS-VGG

HZ- Saudi Arabia

22498	HZ-AIA
22499	HZ-AIB
22500	HZ-AIC
22501	HZ-AID
22502	HZ-AIE
22747	HZ-AIG
22748	HZ-AIH
22749	HZ-AII
23262	HZ-AIK
23263	HZ-AIL
23264	HZ-AIM
23265	HZ-AIN
23266	HZ-AIO
23267	HZ-AIP
23268	HZ-AIQ
23269	HZ-AIR
23270	HZ-AIS
23271	HZ-AIT
23070	HZ-HM1A

I- Italy

19729	I-DEMA
20520	I-DEMB
22506	I-DEMC
22507	I-DEMD
19730	I-DEME
22508	I-DEMF
22510	I-DEMG
22511	I-DEML
22512	I-DEMN
19731	I-DEMO
22513	I-DEMP
22545	I-DEMR
22969	I-DEMS
23300	I-DEMT
19732	I-DEMU
23301	I-DEMV
23476	I-DEMW

JA Japan

19725	JA8101
19726	JA8102
19727	JA8103
19823	JA8104
19824	JA8105
19825	JA8106
20332	JA8107
20333	JA8108
20503	JA8109
20504	JA8110
20505	JA8111
20528	JA8112
20529	JA8113
20530	JA8114
20531	JA8115
20532	JA8116
20781	JA8117
20782	JA8118
20783	JA8119
20784	JA8120
20923	JA8121
20924	JA8122
21034	JA8123
21032	JA8124
21030	JA8125
21033	JA8126
21031	JA8127
21029	JA8128
21678	JA8129
21679	JA8130
21680	JA8131
21681	JA8132
21604	JA8133
21605	JA8134
21606	JA8135
21922	JA8136
21923	JA8137
21924	JA8138
21925	JA8139
22064	JA8140
22065	JA8141
22066	JA8142
22067	JA8143
22063	JA8144
22291	JA8145
22292	JA8146
22293	JA8147
22294	JA8148
22478	JA8149
22479	JA8150
22477	JA8151
22594	JA8152
22595	JA8153
22745	JA8154
22746	JA8155
22709	JA8156
22710	JA8157
22711	JA8158
22712	JA8159
22989	JA8160
21744	JA8161
22990	JA8161
22991	JA8162
23067	JA8163
23149	JA8163
23068	JA8164
23150	JA8164
21743	JA8165
23151	JA8166
23138	JA8167
23139	JA8168
23389	JA8169
23390	JA8170
23391	JA8171
23350	JA8172
23482	JA8173
23501	JA8174
23502	JA8175
23632	JA8176
23638	JA8177
23639	JA8178
23640	JA8179
23641	JA8180

JY- Jordan

21251	JY-AFA
21252	JY-AFB
22579	JY-AFS

LN- Norway

20121	LN-AEO
20120	LN-AET
21381	LN-RNA
22496	LN-RNB

LV- Argentina

19896	LV-LRG
21189	LV-LZD
21725	LV-MLO
21726	LV-MLP
21727	LV-MLR
22297	LV-OEP
22592	LV-OOZ
22593	LV-OPA

LX- Luxembourg

21650	LX-DCV
22390	LX-ECV
20106	LX-MCV
20116	LX-SAL
22169	LX-TAP

N United States

23027	N116KB	19754	N4704U	20360	N615US	19652	N748PA	20101	N9676
23028	N117KC	19755	N4710U	21120	N616US	20713	N748TA	19896	N9896
23029	N118KD	19756	N4711U	21121	N617US	20652	N748WA	19897	N9897
23030	N119KE	19757	N4712U	21122	N618US	20888	N749FT	19898	N9898
23031	N120KF	19875	N4713U	21321	N619US	19653	N749PA	20246	N9899
23032	N121KG	19876	N4714U	20927	N620BN	20013	N749R	20247	N9900
23033	N122KH	19877	N4716U	21918	N620US	20888	N749TA		
21251	N1239E	19878	N4717U	19919	N621US	20653	N749WA		
23243	N123KJ	19879	N4718U	21704	N622US	19654	N750PA		
21468	N1248E	19880	N4719U	21705	N623US	19733	N750WA		
23244	N124KK	19881	N4720U	21706	N624US	19733	N750WA		
21537	N1252E	19882	N4723U	21707	N625US	19655	N751PA		
21731	N1252E	19883	N4727U	21708	N626US	19656	N752PA		
23245	N125KL	19925	N4728U	21709	N627US	19657	N753PA		
21668	N1288E	19926	N4729U	22389	N628US	19658	N754PA		
21832	N1288E	19927	N4732U	22388	N629US	19659	N755PA		
21833	N1289E	19928	N4735U	21668	N630US	19660	N770PA		
22272	N1289E	19746	N480GX	23111	N631US	19661	N771PA		
21834	N1290E	19676	N53110	23112	N632US	19918	N77772		
22107	N1290E	19677	N53111	20799	N63305	19919	N77773		
22376	N1295E	19678	N53112	21991	N633US	19746	N780T		
22379	N1298E	20321	N53116	22234	N634US	20100	N800FT		
22380	N1301E	20651	N535PA	21682	N635US	20208	N800U		
22428	N1305E	23120	N5573B	23547	N636US	20101	N801FT		
22380	N1309E	23149	N5573B	23548	N637US	20323	N802FT		
19957	N133TW	22481	N5573F	23549	N638US	19897	N803FT		
19958	N134TW	22991	N5573K	20347	N652PA	20246	N804FT		
20235	N1352B	23223	N5573P	20348	N653PA	20247	N805FT		
20105	N14936	22704	N6005C	20349	N654PA	21827	N806FT		
20106	N14937	23224	N6005C	20350	N655PA	21828	N807FT		
20108	N14939	23262	N6005C	20351	N656PA	22245	N808FT		
20102	N14943	23266	N6005C	20352	N657PA	22237	N809FT		
23736	N151UA	23268	N6005C	20353	N658PA	19733	N809FT		
23737	N152UA	23392	N6005C	20354	N659PA	22237	N810FT		
22234	N1607B	23394	N6005C	20101	N662AA	20826	N811FT		
20271	N17125	23407	N6005C	20323	N671UP	20827	N812FT		
20273	N17126	23439	N6005C	20374	N672UP	21764	N813FT		
21515	N1780B	23348	N6005F	20325	N673UP	21841	N814FT		
23071	N1781B	23026	N6006C	20100	N674UP	22150	N815FT		
23150	N1781B	22489	N6009F	20390	N675UP	22151	N816FT		
21255	N1783B	23263	N6009F	20101	N676UP	20349	N817FT		
22479	N1783B	23300	N6009F	20826	N701SW	20353	N818FT		
22705	N1784B	23390	N6009F	20827	N702SW	19661	N819FT		
23070	N1784B	23395	N6009F	20828	N703SW	20391	N820FT		
23222	N1784B	23482	N6009F	21764	N703SW	21507	N8277V		
21516	N1785B	23221	N6018N	21841	N704SW	22704	N8277V		
21220	N1786B	23301	N6018N	22150	N705SW	22870	N8278V		
23151	N1786B	23350	N6018N	22151	N706SW	22970	N8279V		
21725	N1789B	23389	N6018N	21439	N723PA	23026	N8279V		
21238	N1790B	23480	N6018N	21316	N724PA	22305	N8280V		
2 189	N1791B	20207	N601BN	19898	N725PA	22486	N8281V		
20801	N1794B	19778	N601US	21048	N726PA	22498	N8281V		
20373	N1794B	21682	N602BN	21048	N726PA	21991	N8284V		
20781	N1795B	20208	N602D	21162	N727PA	21241	N8285V		
20237	N1795B	19734	N602FF	20712	N728PA	22234	N8285V		
20771	N1796B	21682	N602PE	20713	N729PA	21604	N8286V		
20770	N1796B	19779	N602US	20888	N730PA	22969	N8289V		
20704	N1799B	23269	N6038E	19637	N731PA	11735	N8290V		
19761	N1799B	23287	N6038E	19638	N732PA	21590	N8291V		
19746	N1800B	19746	N603FF	19640	N733PA	21514	N8293V		
20530	N1800B	19729	N603PE	19641	N734PA	21352	N8295V		
20887	N18815	19780	N603US	19642	N735PA	22764	N8296V		
21097	N202AE	22990	N6046B	19643	N736PA	22971	N8296V		
21098	N203AE	23139	N6046P	19644	N737PA	20977	N8297V		
21099	N204AE	23264	N6046P	19645	N738PA	21111	N8297V		
22989	N211JL	23265	N6046P	19646	N739PA	20798	N88931		
23067	N212JL	23393	N6046P	20081	N7402Q	20391	N901PA		
23068	N213JL	19731	N604PE	20082	N7403Q	19896	N902PA		
22995	N221GE	19781	N604US	20083	N7404Q	20100	N903PA		
22996	N221GF	23267	N6055X	19647	N740PA	21743	N904PA		
19733	N26861	23286	N6055X	20080	N7410Q	20107	N905NA		
19734	N26862	23408	N6055X	19648	N741PA	21744	N905PA		
19735	N26863	23501	N6055X	21832	N741PR	19667	N93101		
20305	N26864	21991	N605BN	21964	N741TV	19668	N93102		
20800	N28366	20520	N605PE	19649	N742PA	19669	N93103		
20542	N28888	19782	N605US	21833	N742PR	19670	N93104		
20543	N28899	23502	N6065O	21965	N742TV	19671	N93105		
20541	N28903	23409	N6065Y	19650	N743PA	19672	N93106		
20501	N301TW	23461	N6066B	21834	N743PR	19673	N93107		
20502	N302TW	22472	N6066U	22403	N743TV	19674	N93108		
20116	N303TW	23048	N6066U	19651	N744PA	19675	N93109		
20117	N304TW	23138	N6066Z	22382	N744PR	20080	N93113		
20742	N305TW	22870	N6067B	22404	N744TV	20081	N93114		
21189	N354AS	22487	N6069D	22405	N745TV	20320	N93115		
19729	N355AS	19730	N606PE	20235	N7470	20322	N93117		
19730	N356AS	19783	N606US	19734	N747AV	20082	N93118		
19731	N357AS	22234	N607BN	20770	N747BA	20083	N93119		
19732	N358AS	20011	N607PE	19734	N747BA	20100	N9661		
20520	N359AS	19784	N607US	20771	N747BC	20100	N9661		
20012	N371EA	20012	N608PE	21048	N747BC	20101	N9662		
19896	N401DB	19785	N608US	21048	N747BC	20102	N9663		
21141	N40116	22235	N609BN	21162	N747BH	20103	N9664		
22381	N4501Q	20534	N609PE	21316	N747BJ	20104	N9665		
22496	N4502R	19786	N609US	21439	N747BK	20105	N9666		
22794	N4506H	19746	N610BN	19732	N747BL	20106	N9667		
22678	N450BE	20535	N610PE	20011	N747BM	20107	N9668		
20520	N45225	19787	N610US	20012	N747BN	20108	N9669		
22939	N4544F	20527	N611BN	20712	N747FT	20109	N9670		
23056	N4548M	19732	N611PE	19639	N747PA	20323	N9671		
23137	N4551N	20356	N611US	19639	N747QC	20324	N9672		
19753	N4703U	22236	N612BN	20712	N747TA	20325	N9673		
		20357	N612US	20651	N747WA	20326	N9674		
		20358	N613US	20651	N747WR	20390	N9675		
		20359	N614US	20713	N748FT	20391	N9676		

OD- Lebanon

20391	OD-AGC
21097	OD-AGH
21098	OD-AGI
21099	OD-AGJ
20390	OD-AGM

OO- Belgium

20401	OO-SGA
20402	OO-SGB
23439	OO-SGC

OY- Denmark

20121	OY-KFA
20121	OY-KHA
22381	OY-KHB

PH- Netherlands

19922	PH-BUA
19923	PH-BUB
19924	PH-BUC
20398	PH-BUD
20399	PH-BUE
20400	PH-BUF
20427	PH-BUG
21110	PH-BUH
21111	PH-BUI
21549	PH-BUK
21550	PH-BUL
21659	PH-BUM
21660	PH-BUN
21848	PH-BUO
23508	PH-BUW
23652	PH-MCE

PK- Indonesia

22246	PK-GSA
22247	PK-GSB
22248	PK-GSC
22249	PK-GSD
22768	PK-GSE
22769	PK-GSF

PP- Brasil

22105	PP-VNA
22106	PP-VNB
22107	PP-VNC
23394	PP-VNH
23395	PP-VNI

SE- Sweden

20120	SE-DDL
21575	SE-DFZ

SU- Egypt

20117	SU-GAK

SX- Greece

20742	SX-OAA
20825	SX-OAB
21683	SX-OAC
21684	SX-OAD
21935	SX-OAE

TJ- Cameroon

22378	TJ-CAB

TU- Ivory Coast

22169	TU-TAP

VH- Australia

20009	VH-EBA
20010	VH-EBB
20011	VH-EBC
20012	VH-EBD
20534	VH-EBE
20535	VH-EBF
20841	VH-EBG
20842	VH-EBH
20921	VH-EBI
21054	VH-EBJ
21140	VH-EBK
21237	VH-EBL
21352	VH-EBM
21353	VH-EBN

21657	VH-EBO	23120	VR-HIH	21180	YI-AGN	22970	ZS-SAT	19668	5-8106
21658	VH-EBP	23221	VR-HII	21181	YI-AGO	22971	ZS-SAU	20082	5-8107
22145	VH-EBQ	23392	VR-HIJ	22366	YI-AGP			19669	5-8108
22614	VH-EBR	23534	VR-HIK			**Military operated**		20083	5-8109
22616	VH-EBS	23709	VR-HIL	**ZK- New Zealand**				19733	5-8110
22617	VH-EBT	21746	VR-HKG			**Iran**		19734	5-8111
23222	VH-EBT	22306	VR-HVY	22722	ZK-NZV			19735	5-8112
23223	VH-EBU			22723	ZK-NZW	19667	5-280	21486	5-8113
23224	VH-EBV	**VT- India**		22724	ZK-NZX	19678	5-281	21487	5-8114
23408	VH-EBW			22725	ZK-NZY	19668	5-282	21507	5-8115
23688	VH-EBX	19959	VT-EBD	22791	ZK-NZZ	20080	5-282	21514	5-8116
21354	VH-ECA	19960	VT-EBE			19677	5-283		
21977	VH-ECB	20459	VT-EBN	**ZS- South Africa**		20081	5-284	**United States**	
22615	VH-ECC	20558	VT-EBO			20082	5-286		
		21182	VT-EDU	22170	ZS-SAA	19669	5-287	20682	73-01676
VR- Hong Kong		21446	VT-EFJ	22171	ZS-SAB	19733	5-289	20683	73-01677
		21473	VT-EFO	20237	ZS-SAL	19734	5-290	20684	74-00787
21966	VR-HIA	21829	VT-EFU	20238	ZS-SAM	19735	5-291	20949	75-00125
22149	VR-HIB	21993	VT-EGA	20239	ZS-SAN	19667	5-8101		
22429	VR-HIC	21994	VT-EGB	20556	ZS-SAO	19678	5-8102		
22530	VR-HID	21995	VT-EGC	20557	ZS-SAP	20080	5-8103		
22872	VR-HIE			22170	ZS-SAR	19677	5-8104		
23048	VR-HIF	**YI- Iraqi**		22171	ZS-SAS	20081	5-8105		

BOEING 747SP

Large, long-range commercial transport, powered by four Pratt & Whitney JT9D turbofans. The 747SP ('Special Performance') is a shorter version of the 747-100B, providing a maximum high density seating of 440, as well as greatly improved range as a result of increased fuel tankage. The 747SP first flew on 4 July 1975. A total of 46 aircraft were built and production ceased in July 1982.

Dimensions :	Wing span: 195ft 8in (59.64m) Length: 184ft 9in (53.61m) Height: 65ft 5in (19.94m)
	Powerplant : Four Pratt & Whitney JT9D-7A turbofans or four Rolls Royce RB.211-524D4 turbofans
Performance :	Max cruising speed 505 knots (935km/h) Range: with max payload 7,150nm (13,240km)
Accommodation:	440 passengers in an eleven abreast layout
Manufacturer :	Boeing - PO Box 3707, Seattle, Washington 98124, USA
	Telephone: (206) 237-2121 Telex: 32 94 30

C/N	Registration	Owner/Operator	Series	First Flight	Delivery	Remarks
20998	EP-IAA	Iran Air	SP86	20/FEB/76	12/MAR/76	
20999	EP-IAB	Iran Air	SP86	22/APR/76	10/MAY/76	
21022	N747SP	Boeing	SP21	04/JUL/75		
	N530PA	Pan American			26/APR/76	
	N140UA	United Airlines			11/FEB/86	
21023	N247SP	Boeing	SP21	14/AUG/75		
	N531PA	Pan American			17/MAY/76	
	N141UA	United Airlines			12/FEB/86	
21024	N342SP	Boeing	SP21	10/OCT/75		
	N532PA	Pan American			29/MAR/76	
	N142UA	United Airlines			11/FEB/86	
21025	N41035	Boeing	SP21	03/NOV/75		
	N533PA	Pan American			05/MAR/76	
	N143UA	United Airlines			11/FEB/86	
21026	N534PA	Pan American	SP21	07/MAY/76	28/MAY/78	
	N144UA	United Airlines			12/FEB/86	
21027	N535PA	Pan American	SP21			Cancelled order
21028	N536PA	Pan American	SP21			Cancelled order
21093	EP-IAC	Iran Air	SP86	16/MAY/77	25/JUL/77	
21132	ZS-SPA	South African Airways	SP44	17/FEB/76	19/MAR/76	
	LX-LTM	Luxair			80	Not taken-up
	ZS-SPA	South African Airways			80	
21133	ZS-SPB	South African Airways	SP44	10/MAR/76	22/APR/76	
	7Q-YKL	Air Malawi			12/APR/85	Leased
	ZS-SPB	South African Airways			15/MAY/85	
21134	ZS-SPC	South African Airways	SP44	04/JUN/76	16/JUN/76	
	3B-NAG	Air Mauritius			28/OCT/84	Leased
	ZS-SPC	South African Airways			01/NOV/86	Sched.return
21174	YK-AHA	Syrianair	SP94	15/APR/76	21/MAY/76	
21175	YK-AHB	Syrianair	SP94	01/JUL/76	16/JUL/76	
21253	ZS-SPD	South African Airways	SP44	27/AUG/76	10/SEP/76	
	CN-RMS	Royal Air Maroc			14/MAR/85	
21254	ZS-SPE	South African Airways	SP44	05/NOV/76	22/NOV/76	
21263	ZS-SPF	South African Airways	SP44	14/JAN/77	31/JAN/77	
	ZS-SPF	Luxair			80	Not taken-up
	ZS-SPF	South African Airways			80	
21300	B-1862	China Airlines	SP09	18/MAR/77	06/APR/77	
21441	N536PA	Pan American	SP21	77	06/MAY/77	
	N145UA	United Airlines			13/FEB/86	
21547	N537PA	Pan American	SP21	05/MAY/78	09/JUN/78	
	N146UA	United Airlines			13/FEB/86	
21548	N538PA	Pan American	SP21	30/JUN/78	12/JUL/78	
	N147UA	United Airlines			12/FEB/86	
21648	N539PA	Pan American	SP21	30/MAR/79	30/APR/79	
	N148UA	United Airlines			12/FEB/86	
21649	N540PA	Pan American	SP21	01/MAY/79	11/MAY/79	
	N149UA	United Airlines			12/FEB/86	
21652	HZ-HM1	Saudi Royal Flight	SP86	28/AUG/78	11/JUL/79	
	HZ-HM1B	Saudi Royal Flight			84	
21758	EP-IAD	Iran Air	SP86	26/APR/79	12/JUL/79	
21785	N603BN	Braniff	SP27	07/OCT/79	30/OCT/79	
	N351AS	Boeing			23/JAN/81	Stored Boeing Field
	A40-SO	Oman Government			07/FEB/85	
21786	N604BN	Braniff	SP27	29/NOV/79	23/APR/80	
	LV-OHV	Aerolineas Argentinas			12/SEP/80	
21932	B-2442	CAAC	SPJ6	14/FEB/80	29/FEB/80	
21933	B-2444	CAAC	SPJ6	06/JUN/80	26/JUN/80	
21934	B-2446	CAAC	SPJ6			Reg. not taken-up
	N1304E	CAAC		11/JUL/80	23/SEP/80	
21961	N58201	Trans World Airlines	SP31	02/DEC/79	14/APR/80	
	A6-SMR	United Arab Emirates Govt.			01/MAR/85	
21962	N57202	Trans World Airlines	SP31	12/MAR/80	21/MAR/80	
	N57202	Jet Aviation			04/JUL/84	
	VB-	Brunei Royal Flight				Not taken-up
	N57202	Jet Associates			DEC/85	
	N57202	American Airlines			01/OCT/86	Sched.delivery
21963	N57203	Trans World Airlines	SP31	11/APR/80	08/MAY/80	
	N57203	American Airlines			01/OCT/86	Sched.delivery

C/N	Registration	Owner/Operator	Series	First Flight	Delivery	Remarks
21992	N606BN	Braniff	SP27	19/MAY/80	30/MAY/80	WFU MAY/82, stored Dallas
	N529PA	Pan American			23/SEP/83	
	N150UA	United Airlines			09/FEB/86	
22298	B-1861	China Airlines	SP09			Not taken-up
	B-1880	China Airlines		18/APR/80	30/APR/80	
22302	N608BN	Braniff	SP27	02/DEC/80		Not taken-up
	N1608B	Braniff				Stored Seattle
	N1301E	CAAC			11/JUN/83	
22483	HL7456	Korean Air Lines	SPB5	23/DEC/80	22/JAN/81	
22484	HL7457	Korean Air Lines	SPB5	30/JAN/81	18/MAR/81	
22495	VH-EAA	Qantas	SP38	11/JAN/81	19/JAN/81	
22503	HZ-AIF	Saudia	SP68		JUN/81	
22547	B-1882	China Airlines	SP09			Not taken-up
	N4508H	Wilmington Trust		20/JUL/81	30/SEP/81	
	N4508H	China Airlines			30/SEP/81	Leased
22672	VH-EAB	Qantas	SP38		AUG/81	
22750	N6046P	Boeing	SP68			
	HZ-AIJ	Saudia			MAY/82	
22805	N4522V	Wilmington Trust	SP09	10/JUN/82	10/JUN/82	
	N4522V	China Airlines			10/JUN/82	Leased
22858	YI-ALM	Iraqi Government	SP70	02/AUG/82	30/AUG/82	

Boeing 747SP cross-reference index

BOEING 767

Medium-range commercial transport, powered by two Pratt & Whitney JT9D-7R4D or General Electric CF6-804 advanced turbofans. Developed simultaneously with the 757, the Boeing 767-200 differs primarily in having a wider cross-section cabin providing accommodation for up to 289 passengers in twin-aisle configuration, and higher-thrust engines. A 767-200ER is available, and the 767-300 with lengthened fuselage and seating for a maximum 330 passengers, is due to fly in early 1986. The 767 first flew on September 26th 1981 and entered service with United Airlines on September 8th 1982. To date 146 aircraft have been delivered and a further 61 are on order with production rate currently 2.5 aircraft per month.

Dimensions :	Wing span: 156ft 1in (47.57m) Length: 159ft 2in (48.51m) Height: 52ft 0in (15.85m) (200/200ER) Wing span: 156ft 1in (47.57m) Length: 180ft 3in (54.9m) Height: 52ft 0in (15.85m) (300)
Powerplant :	Two Pratt & Whitney JT9D-7R4D turbofans, two General Electric CF6-80A turbofans (200), two Pratt & Whitney JT9D-7R4E turbofans or General Electric CF6-80A2 turbofans (200ER), two Pratt & Whitney JT9D-7RE4 turbofans or two General Electric CF6-80A2 turbofans (300)
Performance :	Max cruising speed 484 knots (897km/h) Range: with max payload 2,460nm (4,555km) (200) Range: with max payload 4,340nm (8,040km) (200ER) Range: with max payload 2,780nm (5,150km) (300)
Accommodation:	220 passengers in a seven abreast layout (200), 216 passengers in a seven abreast layout (200ER), 269 passengers in seven abreast layout (300)
Manufacturer :	Boeing - PO Box 3707, Seattle, Washington 98124, USA Telephone: (206) 237-2121 Telex: 32 94 30

BOEING

C/N	Registration	Owner/Operator	Series	First Flight	Delivery	Remarks
21862	N601UA	United Airlines	222	04/NOV/81	29/APR/83	
21863	N602UA	United Airlines	222	24/NOV/81	24/JAN/83	
21864	N603UA	United Airlines	222	19/DEC/81	13/APR/83	
21865	N604UA	United Airlines	222	18/JAN/82	12/JAN/83	
21866	N605UA	United Airlines	222	25/MAR/82	03/NOV/82	
21867	N606UA	United Airlines	222	20/JUL/82	19/AUG/82	
21868	N607UA	United Airlines	222	13/AUG/82	01/SEP/82	
21869	N608UA	United Airlines	222	31/AUG/82	16/SEP/82	
21870	N609UA	United Airlines	222	17/SEP/82	29/SEP/82	
21871	N610UA	United Airlines	222	17/SEP/82	27/SEP/82	
21872	N611UA	United Airlines	222	30/OCT/82	29/NOV/82	
21873	N612UA	United Airlines	222	27/JAN/83	23/FEB/83	
21874	N613UA	United Airlines	222	04/FEB/83	25/FEB/83	
21875	N614UA	United Airlines	222	09/FEB/83	02/MAR/83	
21876	N615UA	United Airlines	222	24/FEB/83	14/MAR/83	
21877	N617UA	United Airlines	222	04/MAR/83	24/MAR/83	
21878	N618UA	United Airlines	222	18/MAR/83	18/APR/83	
21879	N619UA	United Airlines	222	24/MAR/83	20/APR/83	
21880	N620UA	United Airlines	222	04/APR/83	25/APR/83	
21881	N621UA	United Airlines	222		87	Cancelled order
21882	N622UA	United Airlines	222		87	Cancelled order
21883	N623UA	United Airlines	222		87	Cancelled order
21884	N624UA	United Airlines	222		87	Cancelled order
21885	N625UA	United Airlines	222		88	Cancelled order
21886	N626UA	United Airlines	222		88	Cancelled order
21887	N627UA	United Airlines	222		88	Cancelled order
21888	N628UA	United Airlines	222		88	Cancelled order
21899	N629UA	United Airlines	222		89	Cancelled order
21890	N630UA	United Airlines	222		89	Cancelled order
21891	N631UA	United Airlines	222		89	Cancelled order
22213	N101DA	Delta Air Lines	232	19/FEB/82	25/MAR/83	
22214	N102DA	Delta Air Lines	232	27/AUG/82	25/OCT/82	
22215	N103DA	Delta Air Lines	232	25/SEP/82	29/OCT/82	
22216	N104DA	Delta Air Lines	232	24/NOV/82	20/DEC/82	
22217	N105DA	Delta Air Lines	232	07/DEC/82	19/JAN/83	
22218	N106DA	Delta Air Lines	232	10/NOV/82	08/DEC/82	
22219	N107DL	Delta Air Lines	232	17/DEC/82	22/JAN/83	
22220	N108DL	Delta Air Lines	232	09/JAN/83	28/JAN/83	
22221	N109DL	Delta Air Lines	232	23/APR/83	10/MAY/83	
22222	N110DL	Delta Air Lines	232	12/MAY/83	04/JUN/83	
22223	N111DA	Delta Air Lines	232		83	NOV/83
22224	N112DL	Delta Air Lines	232	17/NOV/83	08/DEC/83	
22225	N113DA	Delta Air Lines	232	29/NOV/83	14/DEC/83	
22226	N114DL	Delta Air Lines	232	11/DEC/83	25/JAN/84	
22227	N115DA	Delta Air Lines	232	08/FEB/84	28/FEB/84	
22228	N116DL	Delta Air Lines	232			Cancelled order
22229	N117DL	Delta Air Lines	232			Cancelled order
22230	N118DL	Delta Air Lines	232			Cancelled order
22231	N119DL	Delta Air Lines	232			Cancelled order
22232	N120DL	Delta Air Lines	232			Cancelled order
22233	N767BA	Boeing	200	26/SEP/81		Prototype
22307	N301AA	American Airlines	223	06/OCT/82	04/NOV/82	
22308	N302AA	American Airlines	223	01/NOV/82	18/NOV/82	
22309	N303AA	American Airlines	223	16/NOV/82	09/DEC/82	
22310	N304AA	American Airlines	223	18/JAN/83	30/MAR/83	
22311	N305AA	American Airlines	223	05/APR/83	27/MAY/83	
22312	N306AA	American Airlines	223	01/MAR/83	14/APR/83	
22313	N307AA	American Airlines	223	11/OCT/83	07/NOV/83	
22314	N308AA	American Airlines	223	20/OCT/83	10/NOV/83	
22315	N312AA	American Airlines	223	22/MAY/84	11/JUN/84	
22316	N313AA	American Airlines	223	04/JUN/84	21/JUN/84	
22317	N315AA	American Airlines	223	29/JAN/85	15/FEB/85	
22318	N316AA	American Airlines	223	18/MAR/85	01/APR/85	
22319	N317AA	American Airlines	223	12/APR/85	29/APR/85	
22320	N319AA	American Airlines	223ER	22/OCT/85	18/NOV/85	
22321	N320AA	American Airlines	223ER	18/NOV/85	18/DEC/85	
22322	N321AA	American Airlines	223ER	10/APR/86	22/APR/86	
22323	N322AA	American Airlines	223ER	22/APR/86	06/MAY/86	

C/N	Registration	Owner/Operator	Series	First Flight	Delivery	Remarks
22324	N323AA	American Airlines	223ER	10/JUL/86	25/JUL/86	
22325	N324AA	American Airlines	223ER		86	Sched.delivery
22326	N325AA	American Airlines	223ER		86	Sched.delivery
22327	N327AA	American Airlines	223ER		86	Sched.delivery
22328	N328AA	American Airlines	223ER		86	Sched.delivery
22329	N329AA	American Airlines	223ER		86	Sched.delivery
22330	N330AA	American Airlines	223ER		FEB/87	Sched.delivery
22331	N332AA	American Airlines	223ER		MAR/87	Sched.delivery
22332	N334AA	American Airlin.s	223ER		APR/87	Sched.delivery
22333	N335AA	American Airlines	223ER		MAY/87	Sched.delivery
22334	N336AA	American Airlines	223ER		JAN/88	Sched.delivery
22335	N338AA	American Airlines	223ER		FEB/88	Sched.delivery
22336	N339AA	American Airlines	223ER		89	Sched.delivery
22517	C-GAUB	Air Canada	233	09/OCT/82	30/OCT/82	
22518	C-GAUE	Air Canada	233	09/NOV/82	14/DEC/82	
22519	C-GAUH	Air Canada	233	21/JAN/83	11/FEB/83	
22520	C-GAUN	Air Canada	233	10/MAR/83	30/MAR/83	
22521	N1791B	Boeing	233	28/JUL/83		
	C-GAUP	Air Canada			01/SEP/83	
22522	N60659	Boeing	233	09/NOV/83		
	C-GAUS	Air Canada			01/DEC/83	
22523	N1784B	Boeing	233	15/MAR/84		
	C-GAUU	Air Canada			12/APR/84	
22524	N6038E	Boeing	233	28/MAR/84		
	C-GAUW	Air Canada			19/APR/84	
22525	N6055X	Boeing	233	26/APR/84		
	C-GAUY	Air Canada			31/MAY/84	
22526	C-GAVA	Air Canada	233	15/MAY/84	13/JUN/84	
22527	N1783B	Boeing	233ER	26/SEP/84		
	C-GAVC	Air Canada			18/OCT/84	
22528	N6006U	Boeing	233ER	06/NOV/84		
	C-GAVF	Air Canada			21/NOV/84	
22564	N601TW	Trans World Airlines	231	15/OCT/82	22/NOV/82	
22565	N602TW	Trans World Airlines	231	13/NOV/82	08/DEC/82	
22566	N603TW	Trans World Airlines	231	14/DEC/82	13/JAN/83	
22567	N604TW	Trans World Airlines	231	28/JAN/83	23/FEB/83	
22568	N605TW	Trans World Airlines	231	24/NOV/82	17/DEC/82	
22569	N606TW	Trans World Airlines	231	11/JAN/83	13/APR/83	
22570	N607TW	Trans World Airlines	231	01/JUL/83	26/JUL/83	
22571	N608TW	Trans World Airlines	231	11/JUL/83	28/SEP/83	
22572	N609TW	Trans World Airlines	231	20/JUL/83	07/SEP/83	
22573	N610TW	Trans World Airlines	231	22/SEP/83	03/DEC/83	
22681	B-1836	China Airlines	209	23/NOV/82	20/DEC/82	
22682	N1781B	Boeing	209	10/JUN/83		
	B-1838	China Airlines			27/JUN/83	
22683	C-GPWA	Pacific Western	275	17/DEC/83	04/MAR/83	
	C-GPWA	City Bank Leasing Canada Ltd			22/JAN/85	
	C-GPWA	Pacific Western			22/JAN/85	Leased
22684	N1791B	Boeing	275	14/APR/84		
	C-GPWB	Pacific Western			23/APR/83	
	C-GPWB	City Bank Leasing Canada Ltd			22/JAN/85	
	C-GPWB	Pacific Western			22/JAN/85	Leased
22685	C-GPWC	Pacific Western	275		NOV/83	Cancelled order
22686	C-GPWD	Pacific Western	275		APR/84	Cancelled order
22692	N8278V	Boeing	277	04/MAY/83		
	VH-RMD	Ansett			06/JUN/83	
22693	N8292V	Boeing	277	20/MAY/83		
	VH-RME	Ansett			13/JUN/83	
22694	N8287V	Boeing	277	08/JUN/83		
	VH-RMF	Ansett			22/JUN/83	
22695	N8289V	Boeing	277	01/JUL/83		
	VH-RMG	Ansett			23/AUG/83	
22696	N1791B	Boeing	277	28/AUG/84		
	VH-RMH	Ansett			20/SEP/84	
22713	N632UA	United Airlines	222		89	Cancelled order
22714	N633UA	United Airlines	222		90	Cancelled order
22715	N634UA	United Airlines	222		90	Cancelled order
22716	N635UA	United Airlines	222		90	Cancelled order
22717	N636UA	United Airlines	222		90	Cancelled order
22718	N637UA	United Airlines	222		91	Cancelled order
22719	N638UA	United Airlines	222		91	Cancelled order
22720	N639UA	United Airlines	222		91	Cancelled order
22721	N640UA	United Airlines	222		91	Cancelled order
22785	N1784B	Boeing	281	07/APR/83		
	JA8479	All Nippon Airways			25/APR/83	
22786	N6018N	Boeing	281	29/APR/83		
	JA8480	All Nippon Airways			17/MAY/83	
22787	N60668	Boeing	281	83		
	JA8481	All Nippon Airways			14/JUN/83	
22788	N1784B	Boeing	281	17/JUN/83		
	JA8482	All Nippon Airways			07/JUL/83	
22789	N1792B	Boeing	281	23/AUG/83		
	JA8483	All Nippon Airways			12/SEP/83	
22790	N5573B	Boeing	281	13/SEP/83		
	JA8484	All Nippon Airways			11/OCT/83	
22921	N6038E	Boeing	2Q4	04/MAY/83		
	N8277V	Boeing				
	N4574M	Boeing			23/JUN/83	
	PT-TAA	TransBrasil			23/JUN/83	
22922	N6067B	Boeing	2Q4	19/MAY/83		
	N45742	Boeing			11/JUL/83	
	PT-TAB	TransBrasil			11/JUL/83	
22923	N6018N	Boeing	2Q4	07/JUN/83		
	N8286V	Boeing				
	N4575L	Boeing			11/JUL/83	
	PT-TAC	TransBrasil			11/JUL/83	
22972	N6066Z	Boeing	258	23/JUN/83		
	4X-EAA	El Al			12/JUL/83	
22973	N6018N	Boeing	258	30/AUG/83		
	4X-EAB	El Al			13/SEP/83	
22974	N6018N	Boeing	258ER	06/MAR/84		
	4X-EAC	El Al			26/MAR/84	
22975	N6046P	Boeing	258ER	10/APR/84		
	4X-EAD	El Al			01/JUN/84	
22980	N5573K	Boeing	204	30/SEP/83		

C/N	Registration	Owner/Operator	Series	First Flight	Delivery	Remarks
	N8289V	Boeing				
	G-BKPW	Britannia Airways			27/FEB/84	
22981	N1785B	Boeing	204	13/JAN/84		
	G-BKVZ	Britannia Airways			06/FEB/84	
23016	N1788B	Boeing	281	11/JAN/84		
	JA8485	All Nippon Airways			31/JAN/84	
23017	N1789B	Boeing	281	27/JAN/84		
	N56807	Boeing				
	JA8486	All Nippon Airways			01/MAR/84	
23018	N1781B	Boeing	281	17/FEB/84		
	JA8487	All Nippon Airways			09/APR/84	
23019	N1719B	Boeing	281	20/MAR/84		
	JA8488	All Nippon Airways			01/MAY/84	
23020	N1784B	Boeing	281	14/JUN/84		
	JA8489	All Nippon Airways			03/JUL/84	
23021	N1785B	Boeing	281	08/OCT/84		
	JA8490	All Nippon Airways			22/OCT/84	
23022	N1792B	Boeing	281	23/OCT/84		
	JA8491	All Nippon Airways			15/NOV/84	
23034	N	Alaska International Air	200		DEC/83	Cancelled order
23035	N	Alaska International Air	200		DEC/83	Cancelled order
23057	N57008	Boeing	205	27/FEB/84		
	LN-SUV	Braathens SAFE			23/MAR/84	
	N767BE	Boeing			30/SEP/85	
	N767BE	TACA			01/OCT/85	Leased
	N767BE	Boeing			29/MAY/86	
	PP-VNL	Varig			26/JUN/86	Leased
23058	N6018N	Boeing	205	12/SEP/84		
	LN-SUW	Braathens SAFE			28/SEP/84	
	PP-	Varig			01/SEP/86	Sched.lease
	LN-SUW	Braathens SAFE			01/JUL/87	Sched.return
23072	N6067E	Boeing	204	11/JAN/85		
	G-BLKV	Britannia Airways			11/FEB/85	
23106	N1792B	Boeing	260ER	18/APR/84		
	ET-AIE	Ethiopian Airlines			23/MAY/84	
23107	N6065Y	Boeing	260ER	14/MAY/84		
	ET-AIF	Ethiopian Airlines			06/JUN/84	
23140	N6067B	Boeing	281	27/NOV/84		
	JA8238	All Nippon Airways			07/FEB/85	
23141	N5573K	Boeing	281	12/FEB/85		
	JA8239	All Nippon Airways			05/MAR/85	
23142	N6038E	Boeing	281	21/MAR/85		
	JA8240	All Nippon Airways			04/APR/85	
23143	N6018N	Boeing	281	25/APR/85		
	JA8241	All Nippon Airways			10/MAY/85	
23144	N6038E	Boeing	281	22/MAY/85		
	JA8242	All Nippon Airways			10/JUN/85	
23145	N6005C	Boeing	281	02/AUG/85		
	JA8243	All Nippon Airways			03/SEP/85	
23146	N6055X	Boeing	281	22/JUL/85		
	JA8244	All Nippon Airways			10/OCT/85	
23147	N6005C	Boeing	281	30/OCT/85		
	JA8245	All Nippon Airways			19/NOV/85	
23178	N1785B	Boeing	266ER	28/JUN/84		
	SU-GAH	Egyptair			20/JUL/84	
23179	N1788B	Boeing	266ER	13/JUL/84		
	SU-GAI	Egyptair			13/AUG/84	
23180	N1789B	Boeing	266ER	15/AUG/84		
	SU-GAJ	Egyptair			31/AUG/84	
23212	N6046P	Boeing	246	31/MAY/85		
	JA8231	Japan Air Lines			22/JUL/85	
23213	N6038E	Boeing	246	15/JUL/85		
	JA8232	Japan Air Lines			15/AUG/85	
23214	N6038E	Boeing	246	05/SEP/85		
	JA8233	Japan Air Lines			12/NOV/85	
23215	N767S	Boeing	346			Prototype series -300
	JA8236	Japan Air Lines			86	Sched.delivery
23216	JA8234	Japan Air Lines	346			
23217	JA8235	Japan Air Lines	346			
23250	N6066U	Boeing	204	08/MAR/85		
	G-BLKW	Britannia Airways			25/MAR/85	
23275	N116DL	Delta Air Lines	332		86	Sched.delivery
23276	N117DL	Delta Air Lines	332		86	Sched.delivery
23277	N118DL	Delta Air Lines	332		86	Sched.delivery
23278	N119DL	Delta Air Lines	332		86	Sched.delivery
23279	N120DL	Delta Air Lines	332		86	Sched.delivery
23280	N6038E	Boeing	269ER	30/JAN/86		
	9K-AIA	Kuwait Airways			30/MAR/86	
23281	N60659	Boeing	269ER	24/FEB/86		
	9K-AIB	Kuwait Airways			02/APR/86	
23282	N60668	Boeing	269ER	20/MAR/86		
	9K-AIC	Kuwait Airways			15/APR/86	
23304	N6055X	Boeing	238ER	12/JUN/85		
	VH-EAJ	Qantas			03/JUL/85	
23305	N6009F	Boeing	238ER	28/JUN/85		
	VH-EAK	Qantas			11/JUL/85	
23306	N6009F	Boeing	238ER	16/SEP/85		
	VH-EAL	Qantas			30/SEP/85	
23307	N6065Y	Boeing	2J6ER	16/SEP/85		
	B-2551	CAAC			08/OCT/85	
23308	N60659	Boeing	2J6ER	20/SEP/85		
	B-2552	CAAC			29/OCT/85	
23309	N6018N	Boeing	238ER	06/NOV/85		
	VH-EAM	Qantas			12/DEC/85	
23326	N6018N	Boeing	219ER	14/AUG/85		
	ZK-NBA	Air New Zealand			03/SEP/85	
23327	N6055X	Boeing	219ER	11/FEB/86		
	ZK-NBB	Air New Zealand			04/MAR/86	
23328	ZK-NBC	Air New Zealand	219ER		SEP/86	
23402	N6018N	Boeing	238ER	16/JAN/86		
	VH-EAN	Qantas			05/FEB/86	
23403	N6046P	Boeing	238ER	07/MAR/86		
	VH-EAO	Qantas			19/MAR/86	
23431	N6009F	Boeing	281	04/JUN/86		
	JA8251	All Nippon Airways			18/JUN/86	

C/N	Registration	Owner/Operator	Series	First Flight	Delivery	Remarks
23432	N6005C	Boeing	281	26/JUN/86		
	JA8252	All Nippon Airways			08/JUL/86	
23433	JA8254	All Nippon Airways	281		86	Sched.delivery
23434	JA8255	All Nippon Airways	281		86	Sched.delivery
23435	N121DE	Delta Air Lines	332		MAR/87	Sched.delivery
23436	N122DL	Delta Air Lines	332		MAR/87	Sched.delivery
23437	N123DN	Delta Air Lines	332		NOV/87	Sched.delivery
23438	N124DE	Delta Air Lines	332		NOV/87	Sched.delivery
23494	N767TA	TACA	2S1	06/MAY/86	22/MAY/86	
23623	N45297	Interlease	216ER	16/MAY/86	29/MAY/86	
	CC-CJU	Lan Chile			29/MAY/86	Leased
23624	N4528Y	Interlease	216ER	17/JUN/86	30/JUN/86	
	CC-CJV	Lan Chile			30/JUN/86	Leased
23645	JA8253	Japan Air Lines	346			
23744	B-2553	CAAC	2J6		FEB/87	Sched.delivery
23745	B-2554	CAAC	2J6		FEB/87	Sched.delivery
23756	JA	All Nippon Airways	381		OCT/87	Sched.delivery
23757	JA	All Nippon Airways	381		NOV/87	Sched.delivery
23758	JA	All Nippon Airways	381		DEC/87	Sched.delivery
23759	JA	All Nippon Airways	381		88	Sched.delivery
23801	PP-	Varig	241ER		MAY/87	Sched.delivery
23802	PP-	Varig	241ER		87	Sched.delivery
23803	PP-	Varig	241ER		87	Sched.delivery
23804	PP-	Varig	241ER		87	Sched.delivery
23805	PP-	Varig	241ER		87	Sched.delivery
23806	PP-	Varig	241ER		DEC/87	Sched.delivery

ADDITIONAL ORDERS

C/N	Registration	Owner/Operator	Series	First Flight	Delivery	Remarks
	JA	Japan Air Lines	246		DEC/87	Sched.delivery
	JA	Japan Air Lines	346			
	JA	Japan Air Lines	346			
	HK-	Avianca	259		MAY/88	Sched.delivery
	HK-	Avianca	259			
	HK-	Avianca	259			
	B-	CAAC	2J6		88	Sched.delivery
	B-	CAAC	2J6		89	Sched.delivery
	VH-	Qantas	238ER			
	VH-	Qantas	238ER			
	VH-	Qantas	238ER			
	VH-	Qantas	238ER			
	VH-	Qantas	238ER			
	VH-	Qantas	238ER			
	JA	All Nippon Airways	381		88	Sched.delivery
	JA	All Nippon Airways	381		88	Sched.delivery
	JA	All Nippon Airways	381		88	Sched.delivery
	JA	All Nippon Airways	381		88	Sched.delivery
	JA	All Nippon Airways	381		89	Sched.delivery
	JA	All Nippon Airways	381		89	Sched.delivery
	JA	All Nippon Airways	381		89	Sched.delivery
	JA	All Nippon Airways	381		89	Sched.delivery
	JA	All Nippon Airways	381		89	Sched.delivery
	JA	All Nippon Airways	381		90	Sched.delivery
	JA	All Nippon Airways	381		90	Sched.delivery
	N	Piedmont Airlines	201ER		MAY/87	Sched.delivery
	N	Piedmont Airlines	201ER		87	Sched.delivery
	N	Piedmont Airlines	201ER		87	Sched.delivery
	N	Piedmont Airlines	201ER		87	Sched.delivery
	N	Piedmont Airlines	201ER		87	Sched.delivery
	N	Piedmont Airlines	201ER		87	Sched.delivery

4X- Israel

22972	4X-EAA
22973	4X-EAB
22974	4X-EAC
22975	4X-EAD

9K- Kuwait

| 223282 | 9K-AIC |

B- Taiwan

| 22681 | B-1836 |
| 22682 | B-1838 |

B- China

23307	B-2551
23308	B-2552
23744	B-2553
23745	B-2554

C- Canada

22517	C-GAUB
22518	C-GAUE
22519	C-GAUH
22520	C-GAUN
22521	C-GAUP
22522	C-GAUS
22523	C-GAUU
22524	C-GAUW
22525	C-GAUY
22526	C-GAVA
22527	C-GAVC
22528	C-GAVF
22683	C-GPWA
22684	C-GPWB
22685	C-GPWC
22686	C-GPWD

CC- Chile

| 23623 | CC-CJU |
| 23624 | CC-CJV |

ET- Ethiopia

| 23106 | ET-AIE |
| 23107 | ET-AIF |

G- United Kingdom

22980	G-BKPW
22981	G-BKVZ
23072	G-BLKV
23250	G-BLKW

JA Japan

23212	JA8231
23213	JA8232
23214	JA8233
23216	JA8234
23217	JA8235
23215	JA8236
23140	JA8238
23141	JA8239
23142	JA8240
23143	JA8241
23144	JA8242
23145	JA8243
23146	JA8244
23147	JA8245
23431	JA8251
23432	JA8252
23645	JA8253
23433	JA8254
23434	JA8255
22785	JA8479
22786	JA8480
22787	JA8481
22788	JA8482
22789	JA8483
22790	JA8484
23016	JA8485
23017	JA8486
23018	JA8487
23019	JA8488
23020	JA8489
23021	JA8490
23022	JA8491

LN- Norway

| 23057 | LN-SUV |
| 23058 | LN-SUW |

N United States

22213	N101DA
22214	N102DA
22215	N103DA
22216	N104DA
22217	N105DA
22218	N106DA
22219	N107DL
22220	N108DL
22221	N109DL
22222	N110DL
22223	N111DA
22224	N112DL
22225	N113DA
22226	N114DL
22227	N115DA
23275	N116DL
22228	N116DL
23276	N117DL
22229	N117DL
23277	N118DL
22230	N118DL
23278	N119DL
22231	N119DL
23279	N120DL
22232	N120DL
23435	N121DE
23436	N122DL
23437	N123DN
23438	N124DE
23019	N1719B
23018	N1781B
22682	N1781B
22527	N1783B
22523	N1784B
22788	N1784B
23020	N1784B
22785	N1784B
22981	N1785B
23021	N1785B
23178	N1785B
23016	N1788B
23179	N1788B
23017	N1789B
23180	N1789B
22696	N1791B
22521	N1791B
22684	N1791B
22789	N1792B
23022	N1792B
23106	N1792B
22307	N301AA
22308	N302AA
22309	N303AA
22310	N304AA
22311	N305AA
22312	N306AA
22313	N307AA
22314	N308AA
22315	N312AA
22316	N313AA
22317	N315AA
22318	N316AA
22319	N317AA
22320	N319AA
22321	N320AA
22322	N321AA
22323	N322AA
22324	N323AA
22325	N324AA
22326	N325AA
22327	N327AA
22328	N328AA
22329	N329AA
22330	N330AA
22331	N332AA
22332	N334AA
22333	N335AA
22334	N336AA
22335	N338AA
22336	N339AA
23624	N4528Y
23623	N4529T
22922	N45742
22921	N4574M
22923	N4575L
22790	N5573B
23141	N5573K
22980	N5573R
23017	N56807
23057	N57008
23145	N6005C
23147	N6005C
23432	N6005C
23305	N6009F
23306	N6009F
23431	N6009F
23058	N6018N
23143	N6018N
23309	N6018N
23326	N6018N
22973	N6018N
22974	N6018N
22786	N6018N
22923	N6018N
23402	N6018N
22564	N601TW
21862	N601UA
22565	N602TW
21863	N602UA
22524	N6038E
23280	N6038E
22921	N6038E
23213	N6038E
23214	N6038E
23144	N6038E
23142	N6038E
22566	N603TW
21864	N603UA
23212	N6046P
22975	N6046P
23403	N6046P
22567	N604TW
21865	N604UA
22525	N6055X
23146	N6055X
23304	N6055X
23327	N6055X
22568	N605TW
21866	N605UA
22522	N6059
23281	N6059
23308	N6059
23107	N6065Y
23307	N6065Y
22787	N6066B
23282	N6066B
23250	N6066U
22528	N6066U
22972	N6066Z
23140	N6067B
22922	N6067B
23072	N6067E
22569	N606TW
21867	N606UA
22570	N607TW
21868	N607UA
22571	N608TW
21869	N608UA
22572	N609TW
21870	N609UA
22573	N610TW
21871	N610UA
21872	N611UA
21873	N612UA
21874	N613UA
21875	N614UA
21876	N615UA
21877	N617UA
21878	N618UA
21879	N619UA
21880	N620UA
21881	N621UA
21882	N622UA
21883	N623UA
21884	N624UA
21885	N625UA
21886	N626UA
21887	N627UA
21888	N628UA
21899	N629UA
21890	N630UA
21891	N631UA
22713	N632UA
22714	N633UA
22715	N634UA
22716	N635UA
22717	N636UA
22718	N637UA
22719	N638UA
22720	N639UA
22721	N640UA
22233	N767BA
23057	N767BE
23215	N767S
23494	N767TA
22921	N8277V
22692	N8278V
22923	N8286V
22694	N8287V
22695	N8289V
22980	N8289V
22693	N8292V

PP/PT- Brasil

23057	PP-VNL
22921	PT-TAA
22922	PT-TAB
22923	PT-TAC

SU- Egypt

23178	SU-GAH
23179	SU-GAI
23180	SU-GAJ

VH- Australia

23304	VH-EAJ
23305	VH-EAK
23306	VH-EAL
23309	VH-EAM
23402	VH-EAN
23403	VH-EAO
22692	VH-RMD
22693	VH-RME
22694	VH-RMF
22695	VH-RMG
22696	VH-RMH

ZK- New Zealand

23326	ZK-NBA
23327	ZK-NBB
23328	ZK-NBC

LOCKHEED TRISTAR

Wide-body commercial transport for up to 400 passengers, powered by three Rolls-Royce RB211 advanced turbofans. The Tristar made its maiden flight on 17 November 1970 and entered service with Eastern Airlines on 26 April 1972. Production versions included the L1011-1 with RB211-22B engines, followed by the extended-range-100 and -200 models, the latter with more powerful engines. A much longer range L1011-500 with increased fuel capacity but reduced seating was added in 1981. A total of 250 production aircraft were built and production ceased in 1984.

Dimensions :	Wing span: 155ft 4in (47.35m) Length: 177ft 8in (54.36m) Height: 55ft 4in (18.88m) (1/100/200)
	Wing span: 164ft 3in (50.09m) Length: 164ft 1in (50.05m) Height: 55ft 4in (16.87m) (500)
Powerplant :	Three Rolls Royce RB.211-22B turbofans (1/100), three Rolls Royce RB.211-524B turbofans (200), three Rolls Royce RB.211-524B4 turbofans (500)
Performance :	Max cruising speed 512 knots (948km/h) (1/100) Range: with max payload 2,950nm (5,465km) (1)
	Max cruising speed 518 knots (959km/h) (200/500) Range: with max payload 4,030nm (7,464km) (100)
	Range: with max payload 4,260nm (7,890km) (200)
	Range: with max payload 4,580nm (8,480km) (500)
Accommodation:	400 passengers in a ten abreast layout (1/100/200), 330 passengers in a ten abreast layout (500)
Manufacturer :	Lockheed - PO Box 551, 2555 N. Hollywood Way, Burbank, California 91520, USA
	Telephone: (213) 87-5730

C/N	Registration	Owner/Operator	Series	First Flight	Delivery	Remarks
1001	N1011	Lockheed	1	16/NOV/70		
1002	N31001	Lockheed	1	15/FEB/71		
	N1031L	Lockheed				
	N301EA	Eastern Air Lines			24/MAR/73	
1003	N301EA	Lockheed	1		17/MAY/71	
	N302EA	Eastern Air Lines			22/MAY/73	
1004	N302EA	Lockheed	1	24/OCT/71		
	N303EA	Eastern Air Lines			15/DEC/72	
1005	N6752	Lockheed	1	23/JUN/72		
	N304EA	Eastern Air Lines			11/JUL/72	
	N304EA	Aviation Sales Co.			16/JAN/84	WFU 16/JAN/84, stored Marana
1006	N303EA	Lockheed	1	10/NOV/72		
	N305EA	Eastern Air Lines			23/NOV/72	
1007	N306EA	Eastern Air Lines	1	12/MAR/72	05/APR/72	
	N306EA	Aviation Sales Co.			30/JAN/84	WFU 30/JAN/84, stored Marana
1008	N307EA	Eastern Air Lines	1	24/MAY/72	26/MAY/72	
	D-AERO	LTU			24/NOV/75	
	N22679	Lockheed			20/APR/77	
	D-AERO	LTU			28/FEB/79	
	N	American Overseas			JAN/81	Not taken-up
	N371EA	Eastern Air Lines			17/MAR/81	
	N371EA	Aviation Sales Co.			18/JAN/84	WFU 18/JAN/84, stored Marana
	D-AERY	LTU			19/MAR/86	
1009	N308EA	Eastern Air Lines	1	12/JUN/72	11/JUL/72	
1010	N309EA	Eastern Air Lines	1	10/JUL/72	25/JUL/72	
	N309EA	Trans World Airlines			30/APR/73	Leased
	N309EA	Eastern Air Lines			28/OCT/73	
	N309EA	Trans World Airlines			30/APR/74	Leased
	N309EA	Eastern Air Lines			30/OCT/74	
1011	N310EA	Eastern Air Lines	1	30/JUL/72	18/AUG/72	W/O 29/DEC/72, nr. Miami
1012	N311EA	Eastern Air Lines	1	22/OCT/72	02/NOV/72	
	N311EA	Aviation Sales Co.			JAN/84	WFU JAN/84, stored Marana
	N311EA	Aircraft Sales Co.			22/MAY/85	WFU 22/MAY/85, stored Miami
1013	N31001	Trans World Airlines	1	01/APR/72	09/MAY/72	
	N381EA	Eastern Air Lines			24/NOV/73	Leased
	N31001	Trans World Airlines			29/APR/74	
	N31001	Interface Group Inc.			29/OCT/84	
	N31001	Five Star			01/MAY/85	Leased, Op. by IASCO
1014	N11002	Trans World Airlines	1	03/JUN/72	04/JUL/72	
	N382EA	Eastern Air Lines			12/NOV/73	Leased
	N11002	Trans World Airlines			21/MAY/74	
	N11002	Interface Group Inc.			19/NOV/84	
	N11002	Five Star			30/APR/85	Leased, Op. by IASCO
1015	N11003	Trans World Airlines	1	13/JUL/72	11/AUG/72	
1016	N11004	Trans World Airlines	1	14/JUL/72	30/AUG/72	
1017	N11005	Trans World Airlines	1	09/SEP/72	27/SEP/72	
1018	N11006	Trans World Airlines	1	08/SEP/72	26/SEP/72	
	N380EA	Eastern Air Lines			22/NOV/72	Leased
	N11006	Trans World Airlines			23/NOV/74	
1019	N312EA	Haas Turner	1	18/NOV/72	13/DEC/72	
	N312EA	Eastern Air Lines			29/OCT/73	Leased
	C-FTNA	Air Canada			06/MAY/73	Leased
	N312EA	Eastern Air Lines			27/OCT/74	Leased
	C-FTNA	Air Canada			07/MAY/75	Leased
	N312EA	Eastern Air Lines			26/OCT/75	Leased
	C-FTNA	Air Canada			07/MAY/76	Leased
	N312EA	Eastern Air Lines			01/NOV/76	Leased
	C-FTNA	Air Canada			09/MAY/77	Leased
	N312EA	Eastern Air Lines			30/OCT/77	Leased
	C-FTNA	Air Canada			06/MAY/78	Leased
	N312EA	Eastern Air Lines			29/OCT/78	Leased
	C-FTNA	Air Canada			07/MAY/79	Leased
	N312EA	Eastern Air Lines			28/OCT/79	Leased
	C-FTNA	Air Canada			05/MAY/80	Leased
	N312EA	Eastern Air Lines			09/OCT/80	Leased
	C-FTNA	Air Canada			04/MAY/81	Leased
1020	N313EA	Eastern Air Lines	1	09/DEC/72	15/DEC/72	
1021	C-FTNB	Air Canada	1	24/DEC/72	14/JAN/73	

LOCKHEED L.1011 TRISTAR

C/N	Registration	Owner/Operator	Series	First Flight	Delivery	Remarks
1022	N314EA	Eastern Air Lines	1	25/DEC/72	02/JAN/73	
	N314EA	Cathay Pacific			06/OCT/79	Leased
1023	N315EA	Haas-Turner	1	25/DEC/72	06/JAN/73	
	N315EA	Eastern Air Lines			11/APR/73	Leased
	C-FTNC	Air Canada			15/MAY/74	Leased
	N315EA	Eastern Air Lines			03/NOV/74	Leased
	C-FTNC	Air Canada			16/MAY/75	Leased
	N315EA	Eastern Air Lines			01/NOV/75	Leased
	C-FTNC	Air Canada			13/MAY/76	Leased
	N315EA	Eastern Air Lines			07/NOV/76	Leased
	C-FTNC	Air Canada			03/JUN/77	Leased
	N315EA	Eastern Air Lines			06/NOV/77	Leased
	C-FTNC	Air Canada			18/MAY/78	Leased
	N315EA	Eastern Air Lines			05/NOV/78	Leased
	C-FTNC	Air Canada			14/MAY/79	Leased
	N315EA	Eastern Air Lines			01/OCT/79	Leased
	C-FTNC	Air Canada			11/MAY/80	Leased
	N315EA	Eastern Air Lines			02/NOV/80	Leased
	C-FTNC	Air Canada			18/MAY/81	Leased
1024	G-BAAA	Aerolease	1		28/FEB/73	
	G-BAAA	Courtline			28/FEB/73	Leased,
	G-BAAA	Lockheed			16/AUG/74	WFU 16/AUG/74
	VR-HHV	Cathay Pacific			24/MAR/77	Leased
	VR-HHV	Cathay Pacific			24/NOV/77	Purchased
1025	C-FTND	Air Canada	1	09/FEB/73	09/MAR/73	
	4R-ALG	Air Lanka			21/MAY/81	Leased
	C-FTND	Air Canada			29/DEC/81	
	A40-TP	Guinness Peat Aviation			06/MAY/84	Leased
	A40-TP	Gulf Air			06/MAY/84	Sub-leased
1026	N31007	Trans World Airlines	1	25/FEB/73	07/APR/73	W/O 20/APR/74, Boston
1027	C-FTNE	Air Canada	1	18/MAR/73	12/APR/73	
1028	N31008	Trans World Airlines	1	27/MAR/73	21/APR/73	
1029	N31009	Trans World Airlines	1	28/APR/73	16/MAY/73	
1030	N31010	Trans World Airlines	1	05/MAY/73	29/MAY/73	
1031	N31011	Trans World Airlines	1	13/MAY/73	30/MAY/73	
1032	G-BAAB	Aerolease	1	23/APR/73	30/APR/73	
	G-BAAB	Courtline			30/APR/73	Leased,
	G-BAAB	Lockheed			16/AUG/74	WFU 16/AUG/74
	VR-HHW	Cathay Pacific			14/OCT/77	
1033	D-AERA	LTU	1	02/JUN/73	29/MAY/73	
	N	American Overseas			JAN/81	Not taken-up
	N372EA	Eastern Air Lines			MAR/81	
1034	N31012	Trans World Airlines	1	03/JUN/73	20/JUN/73	
	N41012	Trans World Airlines				
1035	N31013	Trans World Airlines	1	25/MAY/73	04/JUL/73	
1036	N31014	Trans World Airlines	1	17/JUN/73	04/JUL/73	
1037	N316EA	Eastern Air Lines	1	17/JUN/73	30/JUN/73	
	N316EA	Cathay Pacific			01/MAR/80	Leased
1038	N317EA	Eastern Air Lines	1	24/JUN/73	17/JUL/73	
1039	N318EA	Eastern Air Lines	1	03/JUL/73	13/AUG/73	
1040	N319EA	Eastern Air Lines	1	23/JUL/73	13/AUG/73	
1041	N701DA	Delta Air Lines	1	07/SEP/73	03/OCT/73	
	N701DA	Boeing				Traded-in
	N701TT	Total Air	50		AUG/84	
1042	N320EA	Eastern Air Lines	1	21/AUG/73	01/SEP/73	
1043	N321EA	Eastern Air Lines	1	08/JUL/73	20/SEP/73	
	N321EA	Cathay Pacific			18/OCT/78	Leased
1044	N322EA	Eastern Air Lines	1	15/SEP/73	12/OCT/73	
1045	N323EA	Eastern Air Lines	1	24/SEP/73	16/OCT/73	
	N323EA	British Airways			06/OCT/78	Leased
	N323EA	Eastern Air Lines			15/FEB/80	
1046	N702DA	Delta Air Lines	1	30/SEP/73	25/OCT/73	
	N702DA	Boeing				Traded-in
	N702TT	Total Air	50		AUG/84	
1047	C-FTNF	Air Canada	1	07/OCT/73	11/NOV/73	
	4R-ALE	Air Lanka			29/OCT/80	Leased
	C-FTNF	Air Canada			22/MAY/81	
	4R-ALE	Guinness Peat			82	
	4R-ALE	Air Lanka			82	Leased
	4R-ALE	Guinness Peat				
	C-FTNF	Air Canada				
	A40-TR	Guinness Peat			JUN/84	Leased
	A40-TR	Gulf Air			JUN/84	Sub-leased
1048	C-FTNG	Air Canada	1	21/OCT/73	18/NOV/73	
1049	C-FTNH	Air Canada	1		06/DEC/73	
1050	N324EA	Eastern Air Lines	1	08/NOV/73	13/NOV/73	
1051	N325EA	Eastern Air Lines	1	28/OCT/73	22/NOV/73	
	N325EA	Trans World Airlines			17/MAY/75	Leased
	N325EA	Eastern Air Lines			25/OCT/75	
	VR-HHY	Cathay Pacific			18/JUL/78	
1052	N703DA	Delta Air Lines	1	10/NOV/73	07/DEC/73	
	N703DA	Boeing				Traded-in
	N185AT	American Transair			12/MAR/85	
1053	JA8501	All Nippon Airways	1	10/NOV/73	18/DEC/73	
	4R-ALF	Guinness Peat Aviation			24/MAR/81	
	4R-ALF	Air Lanka			24/MAR/81	Leased
	4R-ULC	Air Lanka	100		MAY/83	Leased, Converted
1054	N326EA	Eastern Air Lines	1	21/NOV/73	22/NOV/73	
	N326EA	Trans World Airlines			24/MAY/74	Leased
	N326EA	Eastern Air Lines			16/OCT/74	
	VR-HHX	Cathay Pacific			26/SEP/76	Leased
	VR-HHX	Cathay Pacific			21/NOV/77	Purchased
1055	N327EA	Eastern Air Lines	1	01/DEC/73	28/DEC/73	
1056	N328EA	Eastern Air Lines	1	05/DEC/73	20/DEC/73	
	VR-HHG	Cathay Pacific			01/DEC/76	
	VR-HHG	Cathay Pacific	100		31/DEC/76	Converted
	A40-TV	Arab Leasing Co.			18/AUG/80	
	A40-TV	Gulf Air			17/SEP/80	Leased
1057	N704DA	Delta Air Lines	1	10/DEC/73	22/DEC/73	
	N704DA	Boeing			27/SEP/83	
	N704DA	Total Air			84	Leased
	N704DA	Boeing			84	
	N192AT	American Transair			NOV/85	
1058	N64854	Lockheed	1	21/DEC/73		
	C-FTNI	Air Canada			22/JAN/74	

C/N	Registration	Owner/Operator	Series	First Flight	Delivery	Remarks
	C-FTNI	Air Canada	100		10/JAN/79	Converted
1059	N31015	Trans World Airlines	1	12/JAN/74	23/JAN/74	
1060	N31016	Trans World Airlines	1	14/JAN/74		
	N41016	Trans World Airlines			01/FEB/74	
1061	JA8502	All Nippon Airways	1	14/JAN/74	28/JAN/74	
	JA8502	Guinness Peat Aviation			19/MAR/82	
	4R-ALH	Air Lanka			19/MAR/82	Leased
	4R-ULD	Air Lanka	100		APR/83	Leased, converted
						W/O 03/MAY/86, Colombo
1062	JA8503	All Nippon Airways	1	24/JAN/74	18/FEB/74	
	4R-ULE	Guinness Peat Aviation			22/MAR/83	
	4R-ULE	Air Lanka	200		22/MAR/83	Leased
1063	N15017	Trans World Airlines	1	06/FEB/74	23/FEB/74	
1064	N10112	Pacific Southwest Airlines	1	31/MAY/74	02/JUL/74	
	N10112	Lockheed			AUG/78	
	N10112	Lockheed	100		01/DEC/78	Converted
	N10112	Aero Peru			14/DEC/78	Leased
	N10112	Lockheed			82	Stored Marana
	N10112	Pacific Southwest Airlines				
	C-GIES	Worldways Canada			20/JUN/85	
1065	N31018	Trans World Airlines	1	10/FEB/74	23/MAR/74	
	N31018	Trans World Airlines	50			Converted
1066	N31019	Trans World Airlines	1	31/MAR/74	18/APR/74	
	N31019	Trans World Airlines	50			Converted
1067	N64854	Lockheed	1	22/FEB/74		
	C-FTNJ	Air Canada			09/MAR/74	
	C-FTNJ	Air Canada	100		FEB/77	Converted
1068	JA8505	All Nippon Airways	1	28/FEB/74	11/MAR/74	
	A40-TS	Guinness Peat Aviation			22/MAR/83	
	A40-TS	Gulf Air			22/MAR/83	Leased
1069	N64854	Lockheed	1	11/MAR/74		
	C-FTNK	Air Canada			23/MAR/74	
	C-FTNK	Air Canada	100		24/MAR/77	Converted
	4R-TNK	Air Lanka			29/DEC/81	Leased
	C-FTNK	Air Canada			24/SEP/82	
1070	JA8506	All Nippon Airways	1	15/MAR/74	06/APR/74	
	N762BE	Boeing			28/FEB/85	Traded-in
	N762BE	Hawaiian Air	50		29/MAR/85	
1071	N705DA	Delta Air Lines	1	23/MAR/74	11/APR/74	
	N705DA	Boeing			28/MAR/84	
	N193AT	American Trans Air			86	
1072	N41020	Trans World Airlines	1	13/APR/74	27/APR/74	
	N384EA	Eastern Air Lines			13/NOV/74	Leased
	N41020	Trans World Airlines			28/APR/75	
	N41020	Gulf Air			15/NOV/77	Leased
	N41020	Trans World Airlines			09/MAR/81	
	N41020	Trans World Airlines	50			Converted
1073	N64854	Lockheed	1	16/APR/74		
	C-FTNL	Air Canada			28/APR/74	
	C-FTNL	Air Canada	100		FEB/77	Converted
	4R-TNL	Air Lanka			DEC/81	Leased
	C-FTNL	Air Canada			DEC/82	
1074	N706DA	Delta Air Lines	1	12/APR/74	02/MAY/74	
	N706DA	Boeing				Traded-in
	N186AT	American Transair			16/JAN/85	
	N186AT	Icelandair			27/JUN/86	Leased
	N186AT	Air Algerie			27/JUN/86	Sub-leased
1075	N31021	Trans World Airlines	1	28/APR/74	29/MAY/74	
	N31021	Trans World Airlines	50			Converted
1076	N31022	Trans World Airlines	1	04/MAY/74	03/JUN/74	
	N31022	Trans World Airlines	50			Converted
1077	N707DA	Delta Air Lines	1	05/MAY/74	24/MAY/74	
	N707DA	Boeing				Traded-in
	N187AT	American Transair			09/JAN/85	
1078	N708DA	Delta Air Lines	1	10/MAY/74	10/JUN/74	
	N708DA	Boeing				Traded-in
	N188AT	American Transair			28/MAR/85	
1079	N10114	Pacific Southwest Airlines	1	13/JUL/74	28/AUG/74	
	N10114	Lockheed			AUG/78	
	N10114	Lockheed	100		APR/79	Converted
	N10114	Aero Peru			07/NOV/79	Leased
	N10114	Lockheed			82	
	N10114	Pacific Southwest Airlines/			83	Stored
		Associated Air Center				
	C-GIFE	Worldways Canada			20/JUN/85	
1080	N31023	Trans World Airlines	1	02/JUN/74	20/JUN/74	
	N31023	Trans World Airlines	50			Converted
1081	N709DA	Delta Air Lines	1	02/JUN/74	28/JUN/74	
	N709DA	Boeing				Traded-in
	N189AT	American Transair			05/MAY/85	
1082	JA8507	All Nippon Airways	1	08/JUN/74	25/JUN/74	
	N763BE	Boeing			27/MAR/85	Traded-in
	N763BE	Hawaiian Air	50		MAY/85	
1083	N64854	Lockheed	1	30/AUG/74		
	G-BBAE	British Airways			19/OCT/74	
	G-BBAE	British Airtours			APR/85	Leased
1084	N710DA	Delta Air Lines	1	27/JUN/74	19/JUL/74	
	N710DA	Boeing				Traded-in
	N191AT	American Transair			12/JUN/85	
1085	N329EA	Eastern Air Lines	1		17/OCT/74	
1086	N711DA	Delta Air Lines	1		06/SEP/74	
	N711DA	Boeing				Traded-in
	N190AT	American Transair			06/MAY/85	
1087	N330EA	Eastern Air Lines	1	05/AUG/74	30/JUN/75	
1088	N712DA	Delta Air Lines	1	20/AUG/74	18/SEP/74	
1089	N713DA	Delta Air Lines	1	30/AUG/74	02/OCT/74	
1090	N714DA	Delta Air Lines	1	12/SEP/74	09/OCT/74	
1091	N31024	Trans World Airlines	1	23/NOV/74	10/DEC/74	
	N31024	Trans World Airlines	50			Converted
1092	N715DA	Delta Air Lines	1	21/SEP/74	15/NOV/74	
1093	G-BBAF	British Airways	1	14/OCT/74	08/NOV/74	
1094	G-BBAG	British Airways	1	31/OCT/74	22/NOV/74	
1095	N716DA	Delta Air Lines	1	12/OCT/74	22/NOV/74	
1096	N717DA	Delta Air Lines	1	25/OCT/74	13/DEC/74	
1097	N718DA	Delta Air Lines	1	31/OCT/74	20/DEC/74	

LOCKHEED L.1011 TRISTAR

C/N	Registration	Owner/Operator	Series	First Flight	Delivery	Remarks
1098	N81025	Trans World Airlines	1	30/NOV/74	13/DEC/74	
	N81025	Trans World Airlines	100		03/FEB/78	Converted
1099	JA8508	All Nippon Airways	1	19/NOV/74	16/DEC/74	
1100	JA8509	All Nippon Airways	1	07/DEC/74	18/JAN/75	
1101	G-BBAH	British Airways	1	11/JAN/75	24/JAN/75	
1102	G-BBAI	British Airways	1	24/JAN/75	04/FEB/75	
	G-BBAI	British Airtours			14/APR/84	
1103	N62535	Lockheed	1	20/JAN/75		
	JA8510	All Nippon Airways			19/FEB/75	
	N764BE	Boeing			24/JUN/85	
	N703TT	Total Air	50		24/JUN/85	Converted
1104	N81026	Lockheed	1	28/JAN/75	17/FEB/75	
	N81026	Trans World Airlines	100		03/MAR/78	Converted
1105	N62537	Lockheed	1	11/FEB/75		
	JA8511	All Nippon Airways			27/FEB/75	
	N765BE	Hawaiian Air	50		03/JUL/85	
1106	G-BBAJ	British Airways	1	18/FEB/75	19/MAR/75	
	G-BBAJ	British Airtours			25/JAN/82	
1107	N81027	Trans World Airlines	1	05/MAR/75	30/MAY/75	
	N81027	Gulf Air			15/OCT/77	Leased
	N81027	Trans World Airlines			01/APR/81	
	N81027	Trans World Airlines	50			Converted
1108	N81028	Trans World Airlines	1	13/MAR/75	09/JUL/75	
	N81028	Trans World Airlines	100		04/OCT/77	Converted
	N798DA	Delta Air Lines			01/JAN/78	Leased, Reg. Not taken-up
	N81028	Delta Air Lines	200		APR/78	Converted
	N81028	Delta Air Lines	100		01/MAR/80	Converted
	N81028	Trans World Airlines			08/APR/80	
1109	N31029	Trans World Airlines	1	24/MAR/75	09/AUG/75	
	N31029	Trans World Airlines	100		19/DEC/77	Converted
	N799DA	Delta Air Lines			01/JAN/78	Leased, Reg. Not taken-up
	N31029	Delta Air Lines	200		15/APR/80	Converted
	N31029	Delta Air Lines	100		17/MAY/80	Converted
	N31029	Trans World Airlines			18/MAY/80	
1110	N64854	Lockheed	100	25/APR/75		
	HZ-AHA	Saudia			25/MAY/75	
	HZ-AHA	Saudia	200		21/AUG/77	Converted
1111	N31030	Trans World Airlines	1	01/APR/75	27/AUG/75	
	N31030	Trans World Airlines	100		06/JUL/78	Converted
1112	JA8512	All Nippon Airways	1	11/APR/75	12/MAY/75	
	N766BE	Hawaiian Air	50		85	
1113	JA8513	All Nippon Airways	1	21/APR/75	19/MAY/75	
	N764BE	Hawaiian Air	50		85	
1114	N10115	Pacific Southwest Airlines	1	20/MAY/75		Not taken-up
	D-AERI	LTU			15/MAR/77	
1115	N31031	Trans World Airlines	1	07/MAY/75	29/AUG/75	
	N31031	Trans World Airlines	100		01/FEB/78	Converted
1116	HZ-AHB	Saudia	100	28/JUN/75	12/JUL/75	
	HZ-AHB	Saudia	200		02/OCT/77	Converted
1117	JA8514	All Nippon Airways	1	03/JUN/75	30/JUN/75	
1118	N64854	Lockheed	100	13/JUL/75		
	VR-HHK	Cathay Pacific			08/AUG/75	
1119	JA8515	All Nippon Airways	1	13/JUN/75	07/JUL/75	
1120	N10116	Pacific Southwest Airlines	1	04/MAY/76		Not taken-up
	D-AERE	LTU			10/MAY/77	
1121	N48354	Lockheed	1	23/JUL/75		
	N331EA	Eastern Air Lines			06/DEC/75	
1122	VR-HHL	Cathay Pacific	100	08/SEP/75	30/SEP/75	
1123	N332EA	Eastern Air Lines	1	23/AUG/75	21/NOV/75	
1124	N31032	Trans World Airlines	1	19/DEC/75		Not taken-up
	HZ-AHE	Saudia			25/FEB/76	
	HZ-AHE	Saudia	100		FEB/76	Converted
	HZ-AHE	Saudia	200		01/FEB/78	Converted
1125	N10117	Pacific Southwest Airlines	1	07/OCT/77		Not taken-up
	D-AERU	LTU			24/OCT/77	
1126	N333EA	Eastern Air Lines	1	24/SEP/75	26/MAR/76	
1127	JA8516	All Nippon Airways	1	16/OCT/75	05/DEC/75	
1128	JA8517	All Nippon Airways	1	04/OCT/75	15/DEC/75	
1129	JA8518	All Nippon Airways	1	12/FEB/76	19/APR/76	
1130	N31033	Trans World Airlines	1	11/DEC/75		Not taken-up
	HZ-AHF	Saudia	200		24/FEB/76	
	HZ-AHF	Saudia	200		27/FEB/78	Converted
1131	G-BDCW	Gulf Air	100	16/DEC/75		
	A40-TW	Gulf Air	200		16/JAN/76	
1132	G-BEAK	British Airways	50	10/JAN/76	23/JAN/76	
1133	G-BDCX	Gulf Air	100	29/JAN/76		
	A40-TX	Gulf Air	200		13/FEB/76	
1134	JA8519	All Nippon Airways	1	27/FEB/76	20/APR/76	
1135	N719DA	Delta Air Lines	1	16/MAR/76	10/APR/76	
1136	N720DA	Delta Air Lines	1	05/MAY/76	07/MAY/76	
1137	HZ-AHC	Saudia	100	13/MAY/76	01/JUN/76	
	HZ-AHC	Saudia	200		11/DEC/77	Converted
1138	G-BDCY	Gulf Air	100	27/MAY/76		
	A40-TY	Gulf Air	200		05/JUN/76	
1139	N721DA	Delta Air Lines	1	16/JUN/76	26/JUN/76	
1140	G-BDCZ	Gulf Air	100	18/JUL/76		
	A40-TZ	Gulf Air	200		27/JUL/76	
1141	N334EA	Eastern Air Lines	1	14/SEP/76	11/NOV/76	
1142	N335EA	Eastern Air Lines	1	21/APR/77	20/MAY/77	
1143	N336EA	Eastern Air Lines	1	17/MAY/77	29/MAY/77	
1144	N48354	Lockheed	200	08/OCT/76		
	HZ-AHD	Saudia			28/MAY/77	
1145	G-BEAL	British Airways	1	15/NOV/76	10/DEC/76	
	G-BEAL	British Airtours			03/APR/83	
	G-BEAL	British Airtours			18/MAR/84	
	G-BEAL	British Airways	50		MAY/85	Converted
1146	G-BEAM	British Airways	1	21/JAN/77	12/FEB/77	
	G-BEAM	British Airtours			84	
	G-BEAM	British Airtours			09/NOV/84	
	G-BEAM	British Airways	50			Converted
	G-BEAM	British Airtours			31/MAR/85	
1147	N722DA	Delta Air Lines	1	21/JUL/77	07/NOV/77	
1148	HZ-AHG	Saudia	200	11/SEP/77	02/OCT/77	
1149	HZ-AHH	Saudia	200	02/NOV/77	18/DEC/77	
1150	N723DA	Delta Air Lines	1	10/NOV/77	02/DEC/77	

C/N	Registration	Owner/Operator	Series	First Flight	Delivery	Remarks
1151	N724DA	Delta Air Lines	200	26/MAY/78	18/JUN/78	
1152	N337EA	Eastern Air Lines	1	11/JUL/78	27/JUL/78	
	D-AERP	LTU			22/DEC/81	
	D-AERP	Eastern Air Lines			22/DEC/81	Leased
	D-AERP	LTU			15/APR/82	
1153	N338EA	Eastern Air Lines	1	25/AUG/78	13/SEP/78	
	D-AERM	LTU			18/DEC/80	
1154	JA8520	All Nippon Airways	1	02/JUN/78	15/JUN/78	
1155	JA8521	All Nippon Airways	1	22/JUN/78	14/JUL/78	
1156	JA8522	All Nippon Airways	1	02/AUG/78	14/AUG/78	
1157	N48354	Lockheed	500	16/OCT/78		
	G-BFCA	British Airways			13/APR/80	
	ZD948	Royal Air Force			29/MAR/83	
1158	N339EA	Eastern Air Lines	1	23/OCT/78	09/NOV/78	
	D-AERN	LTU			06/FEB/81	
	D-AERN	LTU	200		APR/86	Converted
1159	G-BFCB	British Airways	500	10/JAN/79	02/JUL/79	
	G-BFCB	Royal Air Force			29/MAR/83	
	G-BFCB	British Airtours			29/MAR/83	Leased
	ZD949	Royal Air Force			02/NOV/83	
1160	HZ-AHI	Saudia	200	03/DEC/78	31/DEC/78	
1161	HZ-AHJ	Saudia	200	22/JAN/79	25/MAR/79	
1162	N725DA	Delta Air Lines	1	03/FEB/79	21/FEB/79	
1163	N726DA	Delta Air Lines	1	18/FEB/79	28/FEB/79	W/O 02/AUG/85, Dallas Ft. Worth Intl. Airport.
1164	G-BFCC	British Airways	500	08/APR/79	29/APR/79	
	ZD950	Royal Air Force			29/MAR/83	
	ZD950	Royal Air Force	K.1		09/JUL/85	Converted
1165	G-BFCD	British Airways	500	01/MAY/79	15/MAY/79	
	ZD951	Royal Air Force			27/MAR/83	
1166	N751DA	Delta Air Lines	500	20/MAY/79	31/MAY/79	
1167	N727DA	Delta Air Lines	1	03/JUN/79	20/JUN/79	
1168	G-BFCE	British Airways	500	10/JUL/79	22/JUL/79	
	ZD952	Royal Air Force			28/MAR/83	
	G-BFCE	British Airtours			16/JUL/85	Leased
1169	HZ-AHK	Saudia	200	13/JUL/79	22/AUG/79	W/O 14/AUG/80, Riyadh
1170	HZ-AHL	Saudia	200	20/JUL/79	25/SEP/79	
1171	HZ-AHM	Saudia	200	04/AUG/79	06/OCT/79	
1172	N752DA	Delta Air Lines	500	13/SEP/79	03/OCT/79	
1173	N728DA	Delta Air Lines	1	18/FEB/80	09/NOV/79	
1174	G-BFCF	British Airways	500	22/APR/80	02/MAY/80	
	ZD953	Royal Air Force			06/FEB/83	
1175	HZ-AHN	Saudia	200	29/AUG/80	20/OCT/80	
1176	N64911	Lockheed	500	16/NOV/79		
	N501PA	Pan American			02/JUL/81	
	N501PA	United Airlines			FEB/86	
1177	N4003G	Lockheed	500	16/JAN/80		
	N503PA	Pan American			05/AUG/81	
	ZE706	Royal Air Force			27/MAR/85	
1178	G-BGBB	British Airways	200	12/OCT/79	09/MAR/80	
1179	9Y-TGJ	BWIA	500	04/JAN/80	28/JAN/80	
1180	N729DA	Delta Air Lines	1	01/MAR/80	25/MAR/80	
1181	N504PA	Pan American	500	18/MAR/80	11/APR/80	
	N754DA	Delta Air Lines			84	
1182	G-BGBC	British Airways	200	05/APR/80	22/APR/80	
1183	D-AERT	LTU	500	05/APR/80	14/APR/80	
1184	N505PA	Pan American	500	26/APR/80	23/MAY/80	
	N755DL	Delta Air Lines			85	
1185	N507PA	Pan American	500	10/MAY/80	06/JUN/80	
	N756DR	Delta Air Lines			85	
1186	N508PA	Pan American	500	10/JUN/80	27/JUN/80	
	ZE704	Royal Air Force			NOV/84	
1187	HZ-AHO	Saudia	200	02/JUL/80	05/SEP/80	
1188	N509PA	Pan American	500	16/JUN/80	15/JUL/80	
	ZE705	Royal Air Force			DEC/84	
1189	N753DA	Delta Air Lines	500	01/JUL/80	06/AUG/80	
1190	HZ-AHP	Saudia	200	02/AUG/80	23/SEP/80	
1191	9Y-TGN	BWIA	500	30/JUL/80	14/AUG/80	
1192	HZ-AHQ	Saudia	200	07/OCT/80	03/FEB/81	
1193	G-BHBL	British Airways	200	10/SEP/80	29/SEP/80	
1194	N4003G	Lockheed	500	12/SEP/80		
	N510PA	Pan American			15/APR/81	
	N510PA	United Airlines			FEB/86	
1195	N511PA	Pan American	500		13/MAR/81	
	N511PA	United Airlines			FEB/86	
1196	D-AERL	LTU		11/OCT/80	27/OCT/80	
1197	N512PA	Pan American	500		02/DEC/81	
	N512PA	United Airlines			FEB/86	
1198	G-BHBM	British Airways	200		22/NOV/80	
1199	N730DA	Delta Air Lines	1		14/DEC/80	
1200	N1731D	Delta Air Lines	1		23/DEC/80	
1201	N92TA	Lockheed Finance Co.	200		18/DEC/80	
	N92TA	Gulf Air			18/DEC/80	Leased
1202	C-GAGF	Air Canada	500		26/FEB/81	
1203	N92TB	Lockheed Finance Co.	200		28/FEB/81	
	N92TB	Gulf Air			28/FEB/81	Leased
1204	G-BHBN	British Airways	200		01/APR/81	
	G-BHBN	British Airtours				Leased
	G-BHBN	British Airways				
1205	G-BHBO	British Airways	200		13/APR/81	
1206	C-GAGG	Air Canada	500		11/SEP/81	
1207	C-GAGH	Air Canada	500		11/APR/81	
1208	N513PA	Pan American	500		27/MAY/81	
	N513PA	United Airlines			FEB/86	
1209	C-GAGI	Air Canada	500		14/MAY/81	
1210	N514PA	Pan American	500		04/DEC/81	
	N514PA	United Airlines			FEB/86	
1211	G-BHBP	British Airtours	200		15/MAY/81	
	G-BHBP	British Airways			OCT/85	
1212	G-BHBR	British Airtours	200		27/MAY/81	
	G-BHBR	British Airways			15/DEC/81	
	G-BHBR	British Airtours			03/MAY/85	
	G-BHBR	British Airways			SEP/85	
1213	N1732D	Delta Air Lines	1		26/JUN/81	
1214	HZ-AHR	Saudia	200		19/AUG/81	

LOCKHEED L.1011 TRISTAR

C/N	Registration	Owner/Operator	Series	First Flight	Delivery	Remarks
1215	N31032	Trans World Airlines	100		04/NOV/81	
1216	N4009G	Lockheed	500			
	C-GAGJ	Air Canada			24/NOV/81	
1217	JY-AGA	Alia	500		11/SEP/81	
1218	C-GAGK	Air Canada	500		25/NOV/81	
1219	JY-AGB	Alia	500		20/OCT/81	
1220	JY-AGC	Alia	500		18/MAR/82	
1221	N31033	Trans World Airlines	100		21/DEC/81	
1222	9Y-THA	BWIA	500		09/NOV/81	
1223	A40-TT	Gulf Air	200		02/DEC/81	
1224	N733DS	Delta Air Lines	1		11/DEC/81	
1225	N1734D	Delta Air Lines	1		18/DEC/81	
1226	N735D	Delta Air Lines	1		27/JAN/82	
1227	N736DY	Delta Air Lines	1		11/MAR/82	
1228	N737D	Delta Air Lines	1		MAY/82	
1229	JY-AGD	Alia	500		JUL/82	
	JY-AGD	British Caledonian			11/JUN/85	Leased
	JY-AGD	Alia			21/JUN/85	
1230	N8034T	Trans World Airlines	100		08/MAR/82	
1231	N7035T	Trans World Airlines	100		08/MAR/82	
1232	N7036T	Trans World Airlines	100		MAY/82	
1233	9Y-THB	BWIA	500		JUN/82	Reg. not taken-up
	N3140D	BWIA			JUN/82	
1234	N1738D	Delta Air Lines	1		JUL/82	
	N1738D	Delta Air Lines	250		MAR/86	Converted
1235	4R-ULA	Air Lanka	500		27/AUG/82	
	G-BLUS	British Airways			17/APR/85	Leased
	4R-ULA	Air Lanka			MAR/88	Sched.return
1236	4R-ULB	Air Lanka	500		SEP/82	
	G-BLUT	British Airways			02/APR/85	Leased
	4R-ULB	Air Lanka			APR/88	Sched.return
1237	N1739D	Delta Air Lines	1		OCT/82	
	N1739D	Delta Air Lines	250		APR/86	Converted
1238	JY-AGE	Alia	500		NOV/82	
1239	CS-TEA	TAP Air Portugal	500		15/JAN/83	
1240	CS-TEB	TAP Air Portugal	500		MAR/83	
1241	CS-TEC	TAP Air Portugal	500		MAR/83	
1242	CS-TED	TAP Air Portugal	500		JUN/83	
1243	CS-TEE	TAP Air Portugal	500		MAR/84	
1244	N740DA	Delta Air Lines	1		APR/83	
1245	N741DA	Delta Air Lines	1		MAY/83	
1246	N64959	Lockheed	500			
	JY-AGI	Alia			03/JUN/85	
1247	JY-HKJ	Jordanian Royal Flight	500		MAR/86	
1248	JY-AGJ	Alia	500		03/JUN/85	
1249	JY-AGH	Alia	500		84	
1250	7T-VRA	Algerian Government	500		AUG/84	

4R- Sri Lanka

1047	4R-ALE
1053	4R-ALF
1025	4R-ALG
1061	4R-ALH
1069	4R-TNK
1073	4R-TNL
1235	4R-ULA
1236	4R-ULB
1053	4R-ULC
1061	4R-ULD
1062	4R-ULE

7T- Algerie

1250	7T-VRA

9Y- Trinidad & Tobago

1179	9Y-TGJ
1191	9Y-TGN
1222	9Y-THA
1233	9Y-THB

A40- Oman

1025	A40-TP
1047	A40-TR
1068	A40-TS
1223	A40-TT
1056	A40-TV
1131	A40-TW
1133	A40-TX
1138	A40-TY
1140	A40-TZ

C- Canada

1019	C-FTNA
1021	C-FTNB
1023	C-FTNC
1025	C-FTND
1027	C-FTNE
1047	C-FTNF
1048	C-FTNG
1049	C-FTNH
1058	C-FTNI
1067	C-FTNJ
1069	C-FTNK
1073	C-FTNL
1202	C-GAGF
1206	C-GAGG
1207	C-GAGH
1209	C-GAGI
1216	C-GAGJ
1218	C-GAGK
1064	C-GIES
1079	C-GIFE

CS- Portugal

1239	CS-TEA
1240	CS-TEB
1241	CS-TEC
1242	CS-TED
1243	CS-TEE

D- West Germany

1033	D-AERA
1120	D-AERE
1114	D-AERI
1196	D-AERL
1153	D-AERM
1158	D-AERN
1008	D-AERO
1152	D-AERP
1183	D-AERT
1125	D-AERU
1008	D-AERY

G- United Kingdom

1024	G-BAAA
1032	G-BAAB
1083	G-BBAE
1093	G-BBAF
1094	G-BBAG
1101	G-BBAH
1102	G-BBAI
1106	G-BBAJ
1131	G-BDCW
1133	G-BDCX
1138	G-BDCY
1140	G-BDCZ
1132	G-BEAK
1145	G-BEAL
1146	G-BEAM
1157	G-BFCA
1159	G-BFCB
1164	G-BFCC
1165	G-BFCD
1168	G-BFCE
1174	G-BFCF
1178	G-BGBB
1182	G-BGBC
1193	G-BHBL
1198	G-BHBM
1204	G-BHBN
1205	G-BHBO
1211	G-BHBP
1212	G-BHBR
1235	G-BLUS
1236	G-PLUT

HZ- Saudi Arabia

1110	HZ-AHA
1116	HZ-AHB
1137	HZ-AHC
1144	HZ-AHD
1124	HZ-AHE
1130	HZ-AHF
1148	HZ-AHG
1149	HZ-AHH
1160	HZ-AHI
1161	HZ-AHJ
1169	HZ-AHK
1170	HZ-AHL
1171	HZ-AHM
1175	HZ-AHN
1187	HZ-AHO
1190	HZ-AHP
1192	HZ-AHQ
1214	HZ-AHR

JA Japan

1053	JA8501
1061	JA8502
1062	JA8503
1068	JA8505
1070	JA8506
1082	JA8507
1099	JA8508
1100	JA8509
1103	JA8510
1105	JA8511
1112	JA8512
1113	JA8513
1117	JA8514
1119	JA8515
1127	JA8516
1128	JA8517
1129	JA8518
1134	JA8519
1154	JA8520
1155	JA8521
1156	JA8522

JY- Jordan

1217	JY-AGA
1219	JY-AGB
1220	JY-AGC
1229	JY-AGD
1238	JY-AGE
1249	JY-AGH
1246	JY-AGI
1248	JY-AGJ

N United States

1001	N1011
1064	N10112
1079	N10114
1114	N10115
1120	N10116
1125	N10117
1002	N1031L
1014	N11002
1015	N11003
1016	N11004
1017	N11005
1018	N11006
1063	N15017
1200	N1731D
1213	N1732D
1225	N1734D
1234	N1738D
1237	N1739D
1052	N185AT
1074	N186AT
1077	N187AT
1078	N188AT
1081	N189AT
1086	N190AT
1084	N191AT
1057	N192AT
1071	N193AT
1008	N22679
1003	N301EA
1003	N302EA
1004	N302EA
1004	N303EA
1005	N304EA
1006	N305EA
1007	N306EA
1008	N307EA
1009	N308EA
1010	N309EA
1002	N31001
1013	N31001
1026	N31007
1028	N31008
1029	N31009
1030	N31010
1031	N31011
1034	N31012
1035	N31013
1036	N31014
1059	N31015
1060	N31016
1065	N31018
1066	N31019
1075	N31021
1076	N31022
1080	N31023
1091	N31024
1109	N31029
1111	N31030
1115	N31031
1124	N31032
1215	N31032
1130	N31033
1221	N31033
1011	N310EA
1012	N311EA
1019	N312EA
1020	N313EA
1233	N3140D
1022	N314EA
1023	N315EA
1037	N316EA
1038	N317EA
1039	N318EA
1040	N319EA
1042	N320EA
1043	N321EA
1044	N322EA
1045	N323EA
1050	N324EA
1051	N325EA
1054	N326EA
1055	N327EA
1056	N328EA
1085	N329EA
1087	N330EA
1121	N331EA
1123	N332EA
1126	N333EA
1141	N334EA
1142	N335EA
1143	N336EA
1152	N337EA
1153	N338EA
1158	N339EA
1008	N371EA
1033	N372EA
1018	N380EA
1013	N381EA
1014	N382EA
1072	N384EA
1177	N4003G
1194	N4003G
1216	N4009G
1034	N41012
1072	N41020
1060	N41036
1121	N48354
1144	N48354
1157	N48354
1176	N501PA
1177	N503PA
1181	N504PA
1184	N505PA
1185	N507PA
1186	N508PA
1188	N509PA
1194	N510PA
1195	N511PA
1197	N512PA
1208	N513PA
1210	N514PA
1103	N62535
1105	N62537
1058	N64854
1067	N64854
1069	N64854
1073	N64854
1083	N64854
1110	N64854
1118	N64854
1247	N64854
1176	N64911
1246	N64959
1005	N6752
1041	N701DA
1041	N701TT
1046	N702DA
1046	N702TT
1231	N7035T
1232	N7036T
1052	N703DA
1103	N703TT
1057	N704DA
1071	N705DA
1074	N706DA
1077	N707DA
1078	N708DA
1081	N709DA
1084	N710DA
1086	N711DA
1088	N712DA
1089	N713DA
1090	N714DA
1092	N715DA
1095	N716DA
1096	N717DA
1097	N718DA
1135	N719DA
1136	N720DA
1139	N721DA
1147	N722DA
1150	N723DA
1151	N724DA
1162	N725DA
1163	N726DA
1167	N727DA
1173	N728DA
1180	N729DA
1199	N730DA
1224	N733DS
1226	N735D
1227	N736DY
1228	N737D
1244	N740DA
1245	N741DA
1166	N751DA
1172	N752DA
1189	N753DA
1181	N754DA
1184	N755DL
1185	N756DR
1070	N762BE
1082	N763BE
1113	N764BE
1103	N764BE
1105	N765BE
1112	N766BE
1108	N798DA
1109	N799DA
1230	N8034T
1098	N81025
1104	N81026
1107	N81027
1108	N81028
1201	N92TA
1203	N92TB

VR- Hong Hong

1056	VR-HHG
1118	VR-HHK
1122	VR-HHL
1024	VR-HHV
1032	VR-HHW
1054	VR-HHX
1051	VR-HHY

Military operated

United Kingdom

1157	ZD948
1159	ZD949
1164	ZD950
1165	ZD951
1168	ZD952
1174	ZD953
1186	ZE704
1188	ZE705
1177	ZE706

MCDONNELL DOUGLAS DC-8-61/63/71/73

Long range, four-engined jet transport. The series -61 was a considerably stretched versions of the DC-8-50, launched in 1965 with accomodation for up to 259 passengers. The series -63 combined the length of the -61 with the wing of the series -62. All were originally powered by Pratt & Whitney turbofans but many have now been upgraded with the installation of the CMFI CFM 56 advance technology turbofans, and are designated DC-8-71 and 73. A total of 280 production aircraft were built and production ceased in April 1972.

Dimensions :	Wing span: 142ft 5in (53.41m) Length: 187ft 4in (57.12m) Height: 42ft 5in (12.92m) (61/71)
	: Wing span: 148ft 5in (45.23m) Length: 187ft 4in (57.12m) Height: 42ft 5in (12.92m) (63/73)
Powerplant :	Four Pratt & Whitney JT3D-1, JT3D-3, JT3D-3B or JT3D-7 turbojets (61/63), four CFMI CFM56-2-C5 turbofans (71/73)
Performance :	Max cruising speed 503 knots (933km/h) (61) Range: with max payload 3,258nm (6,035km) (61)
	Max cruising speed 506 knots (938km/h) (63) Range: with max payload 3,909nm (7,240km) (63)
	Max cruising speed 477 knots (883km/h) (71) Range: with max payload 3,400nm (6,296km) (71)
	Max cruising speed 479 knots (887km/h) (73) Range: with max payload 4,190nm (7,759km) (73)
Accommodation:	259 passengers
Manufacturer :	McDonnell Douglas - 3855 Lakewood Boulevard, Long Beach, California 90846, USA
	Telephone: (213) 593-5511

C/N	Registration	Owner/Operator	Series	First Flight	Delivery	Remarks
45810	N8070U	United Airlines	61		07/MAY/67	
	N8070U	United Airlines	71		12/JUL/83	Converted
45811	N8071U	United Airlines	61		15/AUG/67	
	N8071U	United Airlines	71		19/DEC/83	Converted
45812	N8072U	United Airlines	61		17/FEB/68	
	N8072U	United Airlines	71		05/OCT/83	Converted
45813	N8073U	United Airlines	61		26/JAN/67	
	N8073U	United Airlines	71		01/SEP/82	Converted.
45848	N8778	Eastern Air Lines	61		23/FEB/67	
	JA8050	Japan Air Lines			11/JUN/71	
	JA8050	Japan Asia Airways			29/MAR/79	
45849	N8074U	United Airlines	61		30/APR/67	
	N8074U	United Airlines	71		08/MAR/83	Converted
45887	N8777	Eastern Air Lines	61		27/MAR/67	
	JA8049	Japan Air Lines			24/MAY/71	
45888	N8776	Eastern Air Lines	61		16/MAY/67	
	N8776	Capitol International			12/JUN/71	Leased
	N8776	Eastern Air Lines			31/OCT/71	
	JA8060	Japan Air Lines			30/JUN/73	
	N755UA	United Aviation			16/JAN/86	
	EC-DYY	Canafrica			MAY/86	Leased
45889	N8775	Eastern Air Lines	61		28/MAY/67	
	JA8061	Japan Air Lines			23/JUL/73	W/O 09/FEB/82
45890	CF-TJT	Air Canada	61		13/SEP/67	WFU 14/OCT/82 to 86, Marana
	N20UA	United Aviation			86	
	N20UA	Icelandair			APR/86	Leased
45891	CF-TJU	Air Canada	61		04/OCT/67	WFU-15/DEC/83 to 86, Marana
	N21UA	United Aviation			MAR/86	
45892	CF-TJV	Air Canada	61		14/OCT/67	WFU 15/DEC/83 to 86, Marana
	N22UA	United Aviation			MAR/86	
45893	CF-TJW	Air Canada	61		04/NOV/67	WFU 15/DEC/83 to 86, Marana
	N23UA	United Aviation			MAR/86	
45894	N8774	Eastern Air Lines	61		06/AUG/67	
	6Y-JGG	Air Jamaica			02/NOV/73	
	N915CL	Capitol International			09/JUN/83	
	N915CL	Red Apple Services			26/NOV/84	
45897	N8786R	Trans Caribbean	61CF		06/DEC/67	
	N8786R	American Airlines			01/MAR/71	
	N8786R	Trans International			30/APR/71	
	EC-CCF	Spantax			28/JAN/73	
	EI-BPF	Guinness Peat Aviation			15/NOV/84	
	N797UP	United Parcel Service	71CF		MAR/85	Op. by Interstate
45898	N8787R	Trans Caribbean	61F		28/DEC/67	
	N8787R	Trans International			29/MAY/71	Leased
	N8787R	Trans Caribbean			04/FEB/73	
	EC-CCG	Spantax			21/FEB/73	
	EI-BPG	United Parcel Service			15/NOV/84	
	N798UP	United Parcel Service	71CF		MAR/85	Op. by Interstate
45900	N8962T	Trans International	61CF		01/DEC/67	
	N803U	Universal Airlines			26/MAY/70	Leased
	N8962T	Trans International			05/MAY/72	
	N8962T	Seaboard World			24/MAY/73	Leased
	N8962T	Loftleidir			30/MAY/73	Sub-leased
	N8962T	Cargolux			08/OCT/73	
	TF-BCV	Cargolux			20/OCT/73	
	N8962T	Seaboard World			06/MAY/74	
	N8962T	Loftleidir			06/MAY/74	Leased
	N8962T	Seaboard World			10/APR/75	
	N8962T	Trans International			31/MAY/76	
	N8962T	Viasa			01/NOV/77	Leased
	N8962T	Trans International				
	N861FT	Flying Tigers			01/JUN/78	Leased
	N861FT	Transamerica Airlines			06/MAY/84	
	N700UP	United Parcel Service	71CF		SEP/85	Op. by Interstate
45901	N1504U	Douglas	63			
	PH-DEB	KLM			15/JUL/67	WFU APR/85
	PH-DEB	Euralair			12/JUN/84	
	N929R	Capitol International			13/JUN/84	

C/N	Registration	Owner/Operator	Series	First Flight	Delivery	Remarks
	N929R	National Airlines			20/OCT/84	
	N929R	Emery Worldwide/Rosenbalm	63F		85	
	N963R	Emery Worldwide/Rosenbalm			MAR/86	
45902	N8961T	Trans International	61CF		16/JUN/67	
	N8961T	Universal Airlines			04/JUN/71	Leased
	N8961T	Trans International			17/SEP/71	
	9V-BEH	Saber Air			12/NOV/71	Leased
	N8961T	Trans International			07/JAN/73	
	C-GNDA	Nordair			21/OCT/74	
	C-GNDA	Evergreen International			01/APR/78	
	C-GNDA	Nordair			01/APR/78	Leased
	C-GNDA	Air Afrique			13/OCT/78	Sub-leased
	C-GNDA	Nordair			31/OCT/78	Leased
	C-GNDA	Air Afrique			13/NOV/78	Sub-leased
	C-GNDA	Nordair			01/DEC/78	Leased
	N810EV	Evergreen International			06/DEC/78	
	N810EV	Overseas National Airways			19/FEB/81	Leased
	N810EV	Evergreen International			31/OCT/82	
	N702UP	United Parcel Service	71CF		MAY/85	Op. by Interstate
45903	N1503U	Douglas	63		10/APR/67	
	PH-DEA	KLM			08/NOV/67	
	N908CL	Capitol Air			23/NOV/83	
	N908CL	Airlift International	63F		25/OCT/84	
	N950R	Emery Worldwide/Rosenbalm			SEP/85	
45907	N822E	Delta Air Lines	61		09/APR/67	
	N822E	Delta Air Lines	71		25/APR/82	Converted
45908	N45090	National Airlines	61		06/AUG/67	
	N912CL	Capitol International			14/MAY/75	
	N912CL	United Aircraft Leasing			01/OCT/79	
	N912CL	Saudia			80	Leased
	N912CL	United Aircraft Leasing			80	
	N912R	Overseas National Airways				
	N912R	Saudia			82	Leased
	N912R	Overseas National Airways			FEB/82	
	N912R	Saudia				Leased
	N912R	National Airlines			30/APR/85	
	N954R	National Airlines				
	N954R	Aviation Transaction Inc.			MAR/86	
45912	N8771	Eastern Air Lines	61		09/DEC/67	
	6Y-JGH	Air Jamaica			11/DEC/73	
	N914CL	Capitol International			28/JUN/83	
45913	N8770	Eastern Air Lines	61		19/JAN/68	
	N869F	Overseas National Airways			27/DEC/73	
	EC-CZE	Spantax			01/APR/77	Leased
45914	N823E	Delta Air Lines	61		11/JUN/67	
	N823E	Delta Air Lines	71		24/MAY/83	Converted
45915	N824E	Delta Air Lines	61		19/JUL/67	
	N824E	Delta Air Lines	71		19/APR/83	Converted
45923	LN-MOU	SAS	63		16/AUG/68	
	HS-TGX	Thai International			21/MAR/74	
	HS-TGX	Boeing			15/DEC/82	
	HS-TGX	Thai International			01/JAN/83	
	OY-SBK	Sterling Airways			18/FEB/84	
	OY-SBK	Scanair			86	Sched.delivery
45924	SE-DBH	SAS	63		18/SEP/68	
	HS-TGZ	Thai International			26/MAR/74	
	HS-TGZ	Icelandair			27/MAR/82	Leased
	HS-TGZ	Thai International			20/NOV/82	
	HS-TGZ	Icelandair			05/MAY/83	Leased
	HS-TGZ	Thai International			31/OCT/83	
	OY-SBM	Sterling Airways			15/JUL/84	
	OY-SBM	Scanair			86	Sched.delivery
45926	CF-CPO	CP Air	63		17/JAN/68	WFU 01/MAR/82 to 01/MAR/83
	C-FCPO	Worldways Canada			01/MAR/83	
45927	N19B	Douglas	63			
	CF-CPP	CP Air			31/JAN/68	
	F-BOLJ	UTA			09/MAR/72	Leased
	CF-CPP	CP Air			13/MAR/73	WFU 01/APR/82 to 01/MAR/83
	C-FCPP	Worldways Canada			01/MAR/83	
45928	CF-CPQ	CP Air	63		24/FEB/68	
	N625FT	Flying Tigers			02/JUL/68	Leased
	CF-CPQ	CP Air			30/DEC/68	
	CF-CPQ	Overseas National Airways			APR/82	Not taken-up, stored Las Vegas
	C-FCPQ	Worldways Canada			01/MAR/83	
45929	N19B	Douglas	63			
	CF-CPS	CP Air			01/JUN/68	
	N624FT	Flying Tigers			19/JUN/68	Leased
	CF-CPS	CP Air			01/JUL/69	WFU 01/APR/82 to 01/MAR/83
	C-FCPS	Worldways Canada			01/MAR/83	
45930	EC-BMX	Iberia	63		06/AUG/68	W/O 03/MAR/78, Santiago de Compostela, Spain
45931	EC-BMY	Iberia	63		18/SEP/68	
	EC-BMY	Aviaco			06/MAR/81	
	N4935C	British American Air			FEB/84	Not taken-up
	N4935C	International Air Leases			19/APR/84	
	N4935C	Arrow Air			19/JUN/84	Leased
	N4935C	International Air Leases				
	N4935C	Surinam Airways			APR/86	Leased
45936	N8631	Seaboard World	63CF		21/JUN/68	
	N8631	Loftleidir			04/MAY/70	Leased
	N8631	Seaboard World			29/MAY/73	
	N8631	Loftleidir			24/JAN/74	
	TF-FLB	Loftleidir			AUG/75	
	TF-FLB	Air Algerie			01/NOV/75	Leased
	TF-FLB	Loftleidir				
	TF-FLB	Air India			JAN/79	Leased
	TF-FLB	Icelandair				
	N836UP	United Parcel Service	73CF		12/OCT/84	Op. by Orion Air
45938	N8960T	Trans International	61CF		02/FEB/68	
	N804U	Universal Airlines			29/JAN/71	Leased
	N8960T	Trans International			05/MAY/72	
	N8960T	Seaboard World			30/APR/73	Leased
	N8960T	Loftleidir			06/MAY/73	Sub-leased
	N8960T	Seaboard World			29/OCT/74	Leased
	N8960T	Air Cargo Egypt			01/APR/77	Sub-leased
	N8960T	Seaboard World			15/JUL/77	Leased

MCDONNELL DOUGLAS DC-8-61/63 (71/73)

C/N	Registration	Owner/Operator	Series	First Flight	Delivery	Remarks
	N8960T	PIA			15/JUL/77	Sub-leased
	N8960T	Seaboard World			26/MAR/78	Leased
	N8960T	Trans International			26/MAR/78	
	N860FT	Flying Tigers			03/APR/78	Leased, WFU Las Vegas 82
	N860FT	Transamerica Airlines			18/JUL/84	
	N701UP	United Parcel Service	71CF		OCT/85	Op. by Interstate
45939	N801U	Universal Airlines	61CF		18/APR/68	
	N801U	Capitol International			18/APR/68	Leasd
	N801U	Universal Airlines			30/SEP/68	
	N867F	Overseas National Airways			01/MAY/72	
	N867F	Capitol International			16/APR/73	Leased
	N867F	Overseas National Airways			13/SEP/73	
	N867F	Seaboard World			20/MAR/73	Leased
	N867F	Korean Airlines			02/APR/74	Sub-leased
	N867F	Seaboard World			25/FEB/75	
	N867F	Overseas National Airways			01/MAR/75	
	N867FT	Flying Tigers			16/DEC/77	
	N867FT	Standard International			MAY/82	Leased
	N867FT	Flying Tigers			82	
	N867FT	Pacific East Air			01/AUG/82	Leased
	N867FT	Flying Tigers			09/JAN/84	WFU 31/DEC/84
	N703UP	United Parcel Service	71CF		JUN/85	Op by Interstate
45940	N8075U	United Airlines	61		08/DEC/67	
	N8075U	Arrow Air			01/JUN/83	
	N8075U	Elk Grove Inc.			DEC/84	Stored Marana
45941	N8076U	United Airlines	61		23/DEC/67	
	N8076U	United Airlines	71		22/MAR/83	Converted
45942	N8773	Eastern Air Lines	61		12/APR/68	
	JA8058	Japan Air Lines			10/MAY/71	Leased
	JA8058	Japan Air Lines			25/SEP/72	Purchased
45943	N8772	Eastern Air Lines	61		18/MAY/68	
	JA8059	Japan Air Lines			22/APR/71	Leased
	JA8059	Japan Air Lines			25/SEP/72	Purchased
	N4578C	Global Aviation Services			14/JAN/84	
	C-GMXB	Nationair			10/DEC/84	
45944	N825E	Delta Air Lines	61		24/JAN/68	
	N825E	Delta Air Lines	71		24/JAN/83	Converted
45945	N8077U	United Airlines	61		06/MAR/68	
	N8077U	United Airlines	71		22/JUN/83	Converted
45946	N8078U	United Airlines	61		14/MAR/68	
	N8078U	United Airlines	71		05/JAN/82	Converted
45947	N8079U	United Airlines	61		20/MAR/68	
	N8079U	United Airlines	71		19/MAY/83	Converted
45948	N8955U	Saturn Airways	61F		28/DEC/67	
	N8955U	Seaboard World			20/JAN/75	Leased
	N8955U	EFS Bahamas			01/SEP/76	Sub-leased
	N8955U	Seaboard World			01/APR/77	
	N8955U	Trans International			25/APR/77	
	N8955U	Capitol International			01/NOV/77	Leased
	N8955U	Trans International			24/JAN/78	
	N862FT	Flying Tigers			01/FEB/78	Leased
	N862FT	Rosenbalm Aviation			20/AUG/82	
	N862FT	Flying Tigers			26/APR/84	
	N862FT	Transamerica Airlines			30/DEC/84	
	N748UP	United Parcel Service	71CF		AUG/85	Op. by Interstate
45949	N8956U	Saturn Airways	61F		30/JAN/68	
	N8956U	Seaboard World			27/NOV/74	Leased
	N8956U	Overseas National Airways			22/APR/76	Sub-leased
	N8956U	Seaboard World			18/OCT/76	Leased
	N8956U	EFS Bahamas			04/NOV/76	Sub-leased
	N8956U	Seaboard World			01/APR/77	Leased
	HS-TGF	Thai International			15/JUN/77	Sub-leased
	HS-TGF	Seaboard World			31/MAR/79	Leased
	HS-TGF	Trans International			31/MAR/79	
	N863FT	Flying Tigers			20/APR/79	Leased
	N863FT	Transamerica Airlines			30/DEC/84	
	N705UP	United Parcel Service	71CF		OCT/85	Op. by Interstate
45950	N802U	Universal Airlines	61F		26/APR/68	
	N802U	Capitol International			26/APR/68	Leased
	N802U	Universal Airlines			30/SEP/68	
	N868F	Overseas National Airways			01/MAY/72	
	N868F	Seaboard World			22/MAR/73	Leased
	N868F	Loftleidir			25/APR/73	Sub-leased
	N868F	Seaboard World			18/SEP/73	Leased
	N868F	Korean Airlines			16/MAR/74	Sub-leased
	N868F	Seaboard World			21/APR/75	Leased
	N868F	Overseas National Airways			26/APR/75	
	N868FT	Flying Tigers			21/DEC/77	
	N868FT	Standard International			JUN/82	Leased
	N868FT	Flying Tigers			82	
	N750UP	United Parcel Service	71F		JUL/85	Op. by Interstate
45951	N4863T	Trans International	63CF		22/NOV/68	W/O 08/SEP/70, J.F.Kennedy Ap.
45952	N8788R	Trans Caribbean	61F		29/FEB/68	
	N8788R	American Airlines			01/MAR/71	
	N8788R	Trans International			26/APR/71	Leased
	N8788R	American Airlines			01/MAY/72	
	N8788R	Saturn Airways			01/MAY/72	Leased
	N8788R	Seaboard World			28/FEB/75	Sub-leased
	N8788R	EFS Bahamas			20/JAN/76	Sub-leased
	N8788R	Seaboard World			01/APR/77	Sub-leased
	HS-TGG	Thai International			15/JUN/77	Sub-leased
	HS-TGG	Seaboard World			31/MAR/79	
	HS-TGG	Trans International			31/MAR/79	
	N864FT	Flying Tigers			20/APR/79	Leased, WFU Las Vegas 82
	N864FT	Transamerica Airlines			30/DEC/84	
	N752UP	United Parcel Service	71F		JAN/86	Op. by Interstate
45963	CF-TJX	Air Canada	61		29/APR/68	
	6Y-JGC	Air Jamaica			25/MAR/69	Leased
	CF-TJX	Air Canada			22/OCT/73	
	C-FTJX	Syrianair			03/SEP/83	Leased
						Impounded Damascus 08/SEP/83
	C-FTJX	Air Canada				Stored
	C-FTJX	United Aviation			MAR/86	
45964	CF-TJY	Air Canada	61		30/MAY/68	
	C-FTJY	United Aviation			85	

C/N	Registration	Owner/Operator	Series	First Flight	Delivery	Remarks
	TF-ISB	Eagle Air			DEC/85	Leased
	TF-ISB	Minerve			20/JUN/86	Leased
45966	N8632	Seaboard World	63F		16/SEP/68	
	N8632	Saudia			01/MAR/77	Leased
	N773FT	Saudia			81	Leased
	N773FT	Flying Tigers			30/APR/81	
	N773FT	Air India			08/AUG/81	Leased
	N773FT	Flying Tigers			05/DEC/82	
	N773FT	Flying Tigers	73CF		04/MAY/84	Converted
	N866UP	United Parcel Service			07/MAY/84	Op. by Orion Air
45967	N4907C	Capitol International	63CF		20/AUG/68	
	N4907C	Overseas National Airways			27/JUN/75	Leased
	N907CL	Capitol International			05/APR/76	
	N907CL	Evergreen International	73CF		30/SEP/84	Converted
	N867UP	United Parcel Service			DEC/84	Op. by Evergreen
45968	N4908C	Capitol International	63CF		29/AUG/68	
	N4908C	Flying Tigers			01/OCT/72	
	N908CL	Capitol International			01/OCT/72	Leased
	N908CL	Flying Tigers			29/SEP/75	
	HB-IDS	SATA			01/OCT/75	
	N871TV	Flying Tigers			16/FEB/78	
	N871TV	Trans International			11/MAY/79	
	N871FT	Flying Tigers			27/MAY/80	Leased
	N871FT	Transamerica			27/SEP/80	
	N871FT	Flying Tigers			01/JUL/84	
	N871FT	Flying Tigers	73CF		14/SEP/84	Converted
	N868UP	United Parcel Service			14/SEP/84	Op. by Interstate
45969	N6161A	Airlift International	61		25/SEP/68	
	N6161A	GATX Leasing			81	
	N6161A	Airlift International			81	Leased
	N6161A	International Air Leases			12/MAY/82	
	N6161A	Arrow Air			JUN/83	Leased
	N6161A	International Air Leases	63CF		FEB/86	
45970	N8080U	United Airlines	61		29/MAR/68	
	N8080U	United Airlines	71		21/JUN/83	Converted
45971	N8081U	United Airlines	61		12/MAR/68	
	N8081U	United Airlines	71		06/MAR/83	Converted
45972	N8082U	United Airlines	61		22/MAY/68	W/O 28/DEC/78, Portland, Or.
45973	N8083U	United Airlines	61		20/MAY/68	
	N8083U	United Airlines	71		19/MAR/82	Converted
45974	N8084U	United Airlines	61		21/JUN/68	
	N8084U	United Airlines	71		22/APR/82	Converted
45975	N8085U	United Airlines	61		25/JUN/68	
	N8085U	United Airlines	71		11/MAY/82	Converted
45976	N8086U	United Airlines	61		10/JUL/68	
	N8086U	United Airlines	71		06/JUL/82	Converted
45977	N8087U	United Airlines	61		16/JUL/68	
	N8087U	United Airlines	71		09/MAY/83	Converted
45978	N8088U	United Airlines	61		31/JUL/68	
	N8088U	United Airlines	71		07/FEB/83	Converted
45979	N8226E	Delta Air Lines	61		30/MAY/68	
	N8226E	Delta Air Lines	71		12/AUG/82	Converted
45980	CF-TJZ	Air Canada	61		13/JUL/68	
	TF-ISA	United Aviation			85	
	TF-ISA	Eagle Air			JUL/85	Leased
45981	N45091	National Airlines	61		23/APR/68	
	N911CL	Capitol International			05/MAY/75	
	N911CL	World Airways			09/NOV/75	Leased
	N911CL	Capitol International			FEB/76	
	N911CL	Overseas National Airways			26/JUL/80	Leased
	N911CL	Saudia			26/JUL/80	Sub-leased
	N911CL	Capitol International			15/NOV/80	
	F-GDPS	Point Air			29/APR/82	
45982	N8769	Eastern Air Lines	61		29/MAR/68	
	JA8057	Japan Air Lines			19/MAR/70	Leased
	JA8057	Japan Air Lines			25/SEP/72	Purchased
	N4582N	Global Aviation Services			14/JAN/84	
	N4582N	Capitol Air			14/JAN/84	
	C-GMXQ	Nationair			04/DEC/84	
	C-GMXQ	Icelandair			20/JUN/86	Leased
	C-GMXQ	Air Algerie			20/JUN/86	Sub-leased
45983	N8768	Eastern Air Lines	61		19/APR/68	
	N8768	Japan Air Lines			06/JUL/70	Leased
	JA8068	Kasumigaseki Kosan			24/OCT/75	
	JA8068	Japan Air Lines			24/OCT/75	Leased
	N8177U	C.Itoh and Co.			05/APR/77	
	N8177U	United Airlines			05/APR/77	Leased
	N8177U	United Airlines	71		21/APR/83	Converted
45988	EC-BMZ	Iberia	63CF		16/DEC/68	
	EC-BMZ	Aviaco			81	Leased
	EC-BMZ	Iberia			83	
	N941JW	International Air Leases			01/DEC/83	
	N941JW	Arrow Air			01/DEC/83	Leased
	N941JW	International Air Leases				
45989	N779FT	Flying Tigers	63F		28/JUN/68	
	LX-ACV	Cargolux			21/MAY/76	
	LX-ACV	Air India			SEP/79	Leased
	LX-ACV	Cargolux			12/OCT/80	
	LX-ACV	Aero Uruguay			NOV/80	Leased
	LX-ACV	Cargolux			81	
	LX-ACV	Aero Uruguay			01/MAY/81	Leased
	CX-BOU	Aero Uruguay			82	Leased
	LX-ACV	Cargolux			12/JUN/82	
	LX-ACV	Aer Turas			01/OCT/82	Leased
	EI-BNA	Aer Turas			15/APR/83	
45990	N780FT	Flying Tigers	63CF		17/JUL/68	
	TF-CCV	Cargolux			30/JUL/77	
	TF-CCV	Martinair			AUG/81	Leased
	TF-CCV	Cargolux			13/NOV/81	
	TF-CCV	Air India			21/APR/83	Leased
	TF-CCV	Cargolux			83	
	N816EV	Evergreen International	73F		01/JUL/84	
	N816EV	Air India			01/JUL/85	Leased
	N816EV	Evergreen International			MAY/86	
45991	N781FT	Flying Tigers	63CF		26/JUL/68	
	D-ADUI	German Cargo Services	73AF		12/JUL/84	

MCDONNELL DOUGLAS DC-8-61/63 (71/73)

C/N	Registration	Owner/Operator	Series	First Flight	Delivery	Remarks
45992	N8767	Eastern Air Lines	61		21/MAY/68	
	N8767	Japan Air Lines			03/MAR/71	Leased
	JA8067	Kasumigaseki Kosan			23/OCT/75	
	JA8067	Japan Air Lines			23/OCT/75	Leased
	JA8067	C. Itoh Aviation			23/MAY/80	
	JA8067	Japan Air Lines			23/MAY/80	Leased
	OB-R-1222	Aeroperu	61F		25/JUN/81	
	OB-R-1222	Aeronaves Del Peru				
45993	N8089U	United Airlines	61		06/AUG/68	
	N8089U	United Airlines	71		18/FEB/83	Converted
45994	N8090U	United Airlines	61		27/AUG/68	
	N8090U	United Airlines	71		11/NOV/82	Converted
45995	N8091U	United Airlines	61		04/SEP/68	
	N8091U	United Airlines	71		22/JAN/83	Converted
45996	N8092U	United Airlines	61		01/OCT/68	
	N8092U	United Airlines	71		04/SEP/81	Converted
45997	N8093U	United Airlines	61		08/OCT/68	
	N8093U	United Airlines	71		30/SEP/80	Converted
45998	N8094U	United Airlines	61		22/OCT/68	
	N8094U	United Airlines	71			Converted
45999	PH-DEC	KLM	63		21/JUL/68	WFU NOV/83 to 13/MAR/84
	TF-FLU	Icelandair			13/MAR/84	
46000	PH-DED	KLM	63		25/AUG/69	
	N964R	Emery Worldwide/Rosenbalm			29/NOV/84	
46001	N863F	Overseas National Airways	63CF		23/SEP/68	
	N863F	Flying Tigers			01/OCT/70	
	N863F	Overseas National Airways			01/OCT/70	Leased
	N863F	Air Siam			28/MAR/71	Sub-Leased
	N863F	Overseas National Airways			31/JAN/72	Leased
	N799FT	Flying Tigers			17/SEP/73	
	HB-IDM	SATA			18/JUN/74	
	HB-IDM	Air Afrique			NOV/75	Leased
	HB-IDM	SATA			JAN/76	
	N872TV	Trans International			02/DEC/78	
	N872TV	Trans International			02/MAR/79	
	N872TV	Transamerica Airlines	73CF		16/MAR/84	Converted
46002	N782FT	Flying Tigers	63CF		17/SEP/68	
	LX-BCV	Cargolux			20/OCT/73	
	TF-BCV	Cargolux			27/NOV/75	
	TF-BCV	Air India			04/FEB/83	Leased
	TF-BCV	Cargolux			83	
	LX-BCV	Cargolux			83	
	LX-BCV	Evergreen International			01/AUG/83	Leased
	N815EV	Evergreen International	73CF		JUL/84	Purchased
46003	N783FT	Flying Tigers	63AF		22/OCT/68	
	N783FT	Air India			25/NOV/82	Leased
	N783FT	Flying Tigers			07/APR/83	
	N783FT	Flying Tigers	73AF		01/AUG/84	Converted
	D-ADUA	German Cargo Services			01/OCT/84	
46004	N784FT	Flying Tigers	63AF		25/OCT/68	
	N804UP	United Parcel Service	73AF		15/JUN/82	Op. by Evergreen
46005	N785FT	Flying Tigers	63AF		25/NOV/68	W/O 27/JUL/70, Naha Intl.Ap., Japan
46006	N786FT	Flying Tigers	63AF		03/DEC/68	
	N786FT	Evergreen International			01/DEC/81	
	N786FT	Evergreen International	73CF		15/DEC/82	Converted
	N806UP	United Parcel Service			07/MAR/83	Op. by Orion Air
46007	N787FT	Flying Tigers	63AF		03/JAN/69	
	N787FT	Evergreen International			15/JAN/82	
	N807UP	United Parcel Service	73AF		24/AUG/82	Op. by Evergreen
46008	N788FT	Flying Tigers	63AF		06/JAN/69	
	N788FT	Flying Tigers	73CF		14/DEC/82	Converted
	N808UP	United Parcel Service			07/MAR/83	Op. by Orion Air
46014	N1300L	Delta Air Lines	61		18/OCT/68	
	N1300L	Delta Air Lines	71		15/AUG/83	Converted
46015	N8766	Eastern Air Lines	61		01/NOV/68	
	N8766	Japan Air Lines			16/OCT/72	Leased
	N8766	Capitol International			06/APR/76	
	N8766	Eastern Air Lines			19/JUN/76	Leased
	N8766	Overseas National			25/DEC/82	
	N8766	Airlift International			01/MAY/83	
	N766RD	Airlift International			14/DEC/83	
	EC-DZC	Aviaco			APR/86	Leased
46016	N8765	Eastern Air Lines	61		15/NOV/68	
	N8765	Japan Air Lines			21/NOV/72	Leased
	N8765	Eastern Air Lines			30/MAR/76	
	N8765	Capitol International			01/AUG/76	Leased
	N8765	Overseas National Airways			14/JUN/80	Sub-Leased
	N8765	Saudia			14/JUN/80	Sub-leased
	N8765	Overseas National Airways			26/JUL/80	Sub-leased
	N8765	Capitol International			26/JUL/80	Leased
	N8765	Eastern Air Lines			25/DEC/82	
	N8765	Airlift International			01/MAY/84	Leased
	N8765	Bankers Trust Co.			07/AUG/84	
	EC-DVC	Spantax			27/OCT/84	
46017	N8764	Eastern Air Lines	61		17/DEC/68	
	N8764	Japan Air Lines			25/OCT/73	Leased
	N8764	Eastern Air Lines			03/MAR/80	
	N8764	Capitol International			03/MAR/80	Leased
	N8764	Eastern Air Lines			25/DEC/82	
	N8764	Airlift International			21/SEP/83	
	N64RD	Airlift International				WFU DEC/85, Miami
46018	N1301L	Delta Air Lines	61		19/DEC/68	
	N1301L	Delta Air Lines	71		01/NOV/81	Converted
46019	PH-DEE	KLM	63		27/NOV/68	
	TF-VLY	Eagle Air			03/MAY/85	
	TF-VLY	Icelandair			85	Leased
	TF-VLY	Air Algerie			85	Sub-leased
	TF-VLY	Eagle Air			OCT/85	
	TF-VLY	Egyptair			85	Leased
	TF-VLY	Eagle Air			85	
	N819UP	United Parcel Service	73CF		23/OCT/85	
46020	N8633	Seaboard World	63CF		27/NOV/68	
	TF-FLA	Cargolux			03/JUL/75	Leased
	N8633	Seaboard World			27/MAR/76	

C/N	Registration	Owner/Operator	Series	First Flight	Delivery	Remarks
	TF-FLA	Loftleidir			28/MAR/76	Leased
	TF-FLA	Cargolux			05/JAN/78	Sub-leased
	TF-FLA	Loftleidir			01/MAR/78	Leased
						W/O 15/NOV/78, Colombo
46021	N8634	Seaboard World	63CF		09/JAN/69	W/O 16/OCT/69, Stockton, Ca.
46029	N1302L	Delta Air Lines	61		16/JAN/69	
	N1302L	Delta Air Lines	71		09/JUL/83	Converted
46030	N1303L	Delta Air Lines	61		22/JAN/69	
	N1303L	Delta Air Lines	71		10/OCT/83	Converted
46031	JA8038	Japan Air Lines	61		20/FEB/69	
	JA8038	Japan Asia Airways			28/DEC/75	
46032	JA8039	Japan Air Lines	61		25/FEB/69	
	JA8039	Japan Asia Airways			23/JUL/76	
	JA8039	United Aviation			APR/86	
46033	C-FTIK	Air Canada	63		15/FEB/69	
	C-FTIK	Air Canada	63F		AUG/80	Converted
	C-FTIK	Air Canada	73CF		03/MAR/84	Converted
46034	C-FTIL	Air Canada	63F		16/FEB/69	WFU 15/DEC/83 to 86, Marana
	N868BX	Burlington/Rosenbalm			DEC/85	
46035	C-FTIM	Air Canada	63F		27/FEB/69	WFU 15/DEC/83 to 86, Marana
	N869BX	Burlington/Rosenbalm			NOV/85	
46036	C-FTIN	Air Canada	63F		27/MAR/69	WFU 15/DEC/83 to 86, Marana
	N870BX	Burlington/Rosenbalm			NOV/85	
46037	N8763	Eastern Air Lines	61		19/DEC/68	
	N8763	Japan Air Lines			26/SEP/72	Leased
	N8763	Eastern Air Lines			28/MAR/76	
	N8763	Capitol International			02/MAY/76	Leased
	N8763	Eastern Air Lines			25/DEC/82	
	N8763	Overseas National			01/MAY/83	
	N8763	Airlift International			01/NOV/83	Leased
	EC-DVB	Spantax			27/OCT/84	
46038	N8762	Eastern Air Lines	61		03/FEB/69	
	N8762	Japan Air Lines			15/OCT/73	Leased
	N8762	Eastern Air Lines			11/JAN/80	
	N8762	Capitol International			11/JAN/80	Leased
	N8762	Eastern Air Lines			83	
	N8762	Manufacturers Hanover			DEC/83	WFU DEC/83, Stored Marana
	F-GETM	Minerve			AUG/86	Sched.delivery
46039	N8095U	United Airlines	61		14/MAY/69	
	N8095U	United Airlines	71		27/AUG/82	Converted
46040	N8096U	United Airlines	61		14/MAY/69	
	N8096U	United Airlines	71		28/JUL/83	Converted
46041	OY-KTF	SAS	63		28/FEB/69	
	OY-KTF	Icelandair			04/NOV/81	Leased
	OY-KTF	Air Algerie			04/NOV/81	Sub-leased
	OY-KTF	SAS			07/NOV/81	
	OY-KTF	Scanair			06/DEC/81	Leased
46042	YV-C-VIA	Viasa	63		22/DEC/68	
	YV-125C	Viasa			75	
46044	N790FT	Flying Tigers	63F		28/FEB/69	
	N790FT	Air India			05/DEC/82	Leased
	N790FT	Flying Tigers			01/FEB/83	
	N790FT	Flying Tigers	73AF		08/AUG/84	Converted
	D-ADUE	German Cargo Services			06/AUG/84	
46045	N791FT	Flying Tigers	63AF		17/MAR/69	
	N791FT	American Flyers Airlines			01/MAY/69	Leased
	N791FT	Flying Tigers			30/APR/70	
	N791FT	El Al			22/MAR/79	Leased
	N791FT	Flying Tigers			30/APR/79	
	N791FT	Flying Tigers	73CF		06/APR/84	Converted
	N791FT	Emery Worldwide/Rosenbalm			06/APR/84	
46046	N792FT	Flying Tigers	63F		21/MAR/69	
	N792FT	American Flyers Airlines			26/MAY/69	Leased
	N792FT	Flying Tigers			21/MAY/70	
	N792FT	Flying Tigers	73AF		15/JAN/84	Converted
	N792FT	Emery Worldwide			27/JAN/84	
	N792FT	Emery Worldwide/Rosenbalm			17/FEB/84	
46047	N793FT	Flying Tigers	63AF		31/MAR/69	
	N793FT	Overseas National Airways			04/APR/69	Leased
	N793FT	Flying Tigers			30/SEP/70	
	N793FT	Trans International			01/JUN/78	Leased
	N793FT	Flying Tigers			23/SEP/78	
	D-ADUO	German Cargo Services	73AF		11/SEP/84	
46048	N1304L	Delta Air Lines			24/APR/69	
	N1304L	Delta Air Lines	71		10/AUG/83	Converted
46049	N8639	Seaboard World	63CF		08/AUG/69	
	N8639	Loftleidir			27/MAY/70	Leased
	N8639	Seaboard World			01/OCT/70	
	N8639	Loftleidir			18/MAY/71	Leased
	N8639	Seaboard World			01/SEP/72	
	N8639	Loftleidir			01/MAY/73	Leased
	N8639	Seaboard World			25/JAN/74	
	N8639	Cargolux			26/OCT/74	Leased
	N8639	Seaboard World			11/DEC/74	
	N8639	Loftleidir			16/DEC/75	Leased
	N8639	Seaboard World			15/JAN/76	
	N8639	Saudia			01/JUN/77	Leased
	N8639	Saudia			79	Leased
	TF-FLC	Loftleidir			01/JUL/79	Leased
	TF-FLC	Saudia			79	Sub-leased
	TF-FLC	Icelandair			80	
	TF-FLC	Air India			01/DEC/80	Sub-leased
	TF-FLC	Icelandair			81	
	TF-FLC	Overseas National Airways			01/MAR/81	Leased
	TF-FLC	Saudia			81	Sub-leased
	N778FT	Flying Tigers			82	Leased
	N778FT	Saudia			82	Sub-leased
	N778FT	Flying Tigers			82	Leased
	TF-FLC	Icelandair				Leased
	TF-FLC	Overseas National Airways				Sub-leased
	TF-FLC	Saudia			JAN/85	Leased
	TF-FLC	National Airlines			JAN/85	Leased
	TF-FLC	Saudia			APR/85	Sub-leased
	TF-FLC	National Airlines			85	Leased
	TF-FLC	Icelandair			85	
46050	N8635	Seaboard World	63CF		30/JAN/69	

C/N	Registration	Owner/Operator	Series	First Flight	Delivery	Remarks
	N8635	Korean Airlines			13/JAN/73	Leased
	N8635	Seaboard World			10/MAR/75	
	N8635	Overseas National Airways			10/MAY/76	Leased
						W/O 04/MAR/77, Niamey, Niger
46051	N8636	Seaboard World	63CF		28/FEB/69	
	N8636	Korean Airlines			13/DEC/71	Leased
	N8636	Seaboard World			01/APR/76	
	N8636	Overseas National Airways			02/APR/76	Leased
	N8636	Seaboard World			05/OCT/76	
	N8636	Saudia			09/MAR/77	Leased
	N8636	Seaboard World				
	N8636EV	Evergreen International			27/DEC/79	
	N863EV	Evergreen International			80	
	N811EV	Evergreen International			80	
	N811EV	Nesher International			80	Leased
	N811EV	Evergreen International			OCT/80	
	N851UP	United Parcel Service	73CF		MAR/85	Op. by Evergreen
46052	N8637	Seaboard World	63CF		11/MAR/69	
	N8637	Korean Airlines			11/MAR/73	Leased
	N8637	Seaboard World			03/MAR/74	
	YV-C-VIN	Transcarga			03/JUN/76	Leased
	YV-130C	Viasa			15/DEC/80	
	YV-130C	Transcarga			76	
	N2919N	Douglas			29/JAN/82	
	N31EK	Connie Kalitta			15/FEB/84	
	N852UP	United Parcel Service	73CF		MAY/85	Op. by Evergreen
46053	N8638	Seaboard World	63CF		28/MAR/69	
	N8638	Korean Airlines			11/APR/73	Leased
	N8638	Seaboard World			18/MAR/74	
	TR-LTZ	Affretair			27/NOV/74	
	TR-LTZ	Gabon Government	73CF		15/JUL/82	Converted
46054	LN-MOY	SAS	63		26/APR/69	
	HS-TGY	Thai International			25/OCT/74	
	HS-TGY	Boeing			15/DEC/82	
	HS-TGY	Thai International			01/JAN/83	
	OY-SBL	Sterling Airways			09/MAY/84	
	OY-SBL	Scanair			86	Sched.delivery
46055	N1306L	Delta Air Lines	61		05/NOV/69	
	N1306L	Delta Air Lines	71		23/JUN/82	Converted
46056	N1307L	Delta Air Lines	61		06/NOV/69	
	N1307L	Delta Air Lines	71		22/APR/83	Converted
46058	N8759	Eastern Air Lines	63CF		24/FEB/69	
	F-BOLM	UTA			05/FEB/74	
	F-BOLM	Air Inter			74	Leased
	F-BOLM	UTA				
	F-BOLM	Air Afrique			NOV/75	Leased
	F-BOLM	UTA			JAN/76	
	N920CL	International Air Leases			09/NOV/81	
	N920CL	Capitol International			09/NOV/81	Leased
	N920CL	International Air Leases			03/OCT/83	
	N920JW	Arista International			11/NOV/83	Leased
	N920JW	National Airlines			01/JUL/84	
	N950JW	Arrow Air			18/OCT/84	W/O 12/DEC/85, Gander
46059	N4864T	Trans International	63CF		25/APR/69	
	N4864T	Air Afrique			12/DEC/74	Leased
	N4864T	Trans International			FEB/75	
	N4864T	Transamerica Airlines				
	N4864T	Overseas National Airways			09/JUN/81	Leased
	N4864T	Transamerica Airlines			19/NOV/81	
	N4864T	Evergreen International			12/DEC/81	Leased
	N4864T	Transamerica Airlines	73CF		31/DEC/84	
46060	N4909C	Capitol International	63CF		02/JUL/69	W/O 27/NOV/70, Anchorage, Ak.
46061	N6162A	Airlift International	63CF		20/AUG/69	
	N6162A	Capitol International			15/JUL/81	
	N6162A	International Air Leases			01/OCT/82	
	N6162A	Arrow Air			01/OCT/82	Leased
	N952R	National Airlines			15/SEP/84	
	N952R	Air India			84	Leased
	N952R	National Airlines			85	
	N952R	Eagle Air				Leased
	N952R	National Airlines				
	N952R	Emery Worldwide/Rosenbalm			MAR/86	
46062	N6163A	Airlift International	63CF		15/SEP/69	
	TF-FLF	Icelandair			81	
	TF-FLF	Overseas National Airways			22/AUG/81	Leased
	TF-FLF	Saudia			81	Sub-leased
	TF-FLF	Icelandair			81	
	N6163A	Capitol International			22/OCT/81	
	N6163A	International Air Leases			01/MAR/82	
	N6163A	Arrow Air			01/MAR/82	
	N6163A	Wien Alaska			09/JUL/82	Leased
	N2674U	Arrow Air			06/MAY/83	
	N2674U	Emery Worldwide/Rosenbalm	73CF		01/DEC/84	
46063	YV-C-VIB	Viasa	63		09/MAY/69	
	YV-126C	Viasa			74	
	N4805J	Charlotte Aircraft	73		29/MAR/84	
	F-GDRM	Minerve			MAY/84	
46064	N8097U	United Airlines	61		23/MAY/69	
	N8097U	United Airlines	71		15/AUG/83	Converted
46065	N8098U	United Airlines	61		04/JUN/69	
	N8098U	United Airlines	71		31/AUG/83	Converted
46066	N8099U	United Airlines	61		16/JUN/69	
	N8099U	United Airlines	71		15/SEP/82	Converted
46072	N1305L	Delta Air Lines	61		08/AUG/69	
	N1305L	Delta Air Lines	71		23/APR/82	Converted
46073	N4865T	Trans International	63CF		22/AUG/69	
	N4865T	Aeromexico			17/MAR/71	Leased
	N4865T	Trans International			30/MAR/74	
	N4865T	Air Afrique			NOV/75	Leased
	N4865T	Trans International			JAN/76	
	N4865T	Transamerica Airlines			79	
	N4865T	Air Afrique			21/SEP/80	Leased
	N4865T	Transamerica Airlines			13/OCT/80	
	N4865T	Transamerica Airlines	73CF		06/JUL/82	
46074	N8760	Eastern Air Lines	63F		21/JUN/69	
	N8760	Overseas National Airways			25/MAY/71	Leased

C/N	Registration	Owner/Operator	Series	First Flight	Delivery	Remarks
	N8760	Eastern Air Lines			22/NOV/71	
	HB-IDZ	Balair			01/MAY/72	
	HB-IDZ	Nigeria Airways			01/NOV/76	Leased
	HB-IDZ	Balair			22/NOV/76	
	N874UP	United Parcel Service	73F		NOV/86	
46075	PH-DEH	KLM	63		29/AUG/69	
	TF-FLT	Icelandair			19/MAR/85	
46076	CF-TIO	Air Canada	63		19/APR/69	
	C-FTIO	Air Canada	63AF		DEC/80	Converted
	C-FTIO	Air Canada	73CF		23/OCT/84	Converted
46079	EC-BQS	Iberia	63		02/AUG/69	
	EC-BQS	Aviaco			07/MAR/81	
	N	British American Air			FEB/84	Not taken-up
	EC-BQS	International Air Leases			18/APR/84	
	N4934Z	CIS Corp.			05/JUN/84	
	N4934Z	Hawaiian Air			05/JUN/84	Leased
46080	PH-DEF	KLM	63		20/JUN/69	
	TF-VLZ	Eagle Air			03/MAY/85	
	TF-VLZ	Icelandair			85	Leased
	TF-VLZ	Air Algerie			85	Sub-leased
	TF-VLZ	Eagle Air			OCT/85	
	TF-VLP	Egyptair			85	Leased
	TF-VLP	Eagle Air			85	
	N880UP	United Parcel Service	73F		23/OCT/85	Op. by Orion Air
46086	N794FT	Flying Tiger Line	63CF		04/AUG/69	
	N794FT	World Airways			06/NOV/75	Leased
	N794FT	Flying Tiger Line			09/MAY/76	
	N794FT	Trans International			01/MAR/78	Leased
	N870TV	Transamerica Airlines				Leased
	N870TV	Cargolux				Sub-leased
	N870TV	Transamerica Airlines			12/JUN/84	
	N870TV	Flying Tigers			19/JUL/84	
	N870TV	Flying Tigers	73CF		19/JUL/84	Converted
	N870TV	Emery Worldwide/Rosenbalm			28/APR/84	
46087	N864F	Overseas National Airways	63CF		28/APR/69	
	N864F	Air Afrique			NOV/77	Leased
	N864F	Overseas National Airways			77	
	N864F	Seaboard World			17/DEC/77	
	N864F	Capitol International			29/MAY/79	Leased
	N864F	Seaboard World			30/NOV/79	
	N864F	Saudia			30/NOV/79	Leased
	N774FT	Saudia			81	Leased
	N906R	Overseas National Airways			10/APR/81	
	N906R	Wien Air Alaska			10/MAY/81	Leased
	N906R	Overseas National Airways			09/JUL/82	
	N906R	Airlift International			05/NOV/82	Leased
	N906R	Overseas National Airways			16/JUL/83	
	N906R	Airlift International			01/SEP/83	Leased
	N906R	Overseas National Airways			24/OCT/83	
	N906R	Air India			84	Leased
	N906R	National Airlines				
	N906R	Emery Worldwide/Rosenbalm			MAR/86	
46088	N865F	Overseas National Airways	63CF		29/MAY/69	
	OE-IBO	Austrian Airlines			24/SEP/73	Leased
	N865F	Overseas National Airways			05/DEC/73	
	N865F	Seaboard World			30/JAN/75	Leased
	N865F	Cargolux			15/MAR/76	Sub-leased
	N865F	Seaboard World			01/JUN/77	Leased
	N865F	Overseas National Airways			01/JUN/77	
	N865F	Seaboard World			20/OCT/77	Leased
	TF-FLC	Loftleidir			28/OCT/77	Leased
	TF-FLC	Air India			JAN/79	Sub-leased
	TF-FLC	Loftleidir			79	Sub-leased
	TF-FLC	Seaboard World			19/FEB/79	Leased
	TF-FLC	Nigeria Airways			19/FEB/79	Sub-leased
	TF-FLC	Loftleidir			01/APR/79	
	N865F	Saudia			14/MAY/79	Leased
	N865F	Overseas National Airways			23/JUN/81	Leased
	N865F	Saudia			81	Leased
	N865F	Overseas National Airways			MAR/84	
	N865F	National Airlines			JUL/84	
	N865F	Emery Worldwide/Rosenbalm				
46089	N4866T	Trans International	63CF		29/DEC/69	
	N4866T	Aeromexico			13/MAR/71	Leased
	N4866T	Trans International			30/MAR/74	
	N4866T	Transamerica Airlines	73CF		28/OCT/82	Converted
	N4866T	Spirit of America Airlines			86	Leased
46090	N4867T	Trans International	63CF		29/DEC/69	
	N4867T	Air Afrique			DEC/74	Leased
	N4867T	Trans International			JAN/75	
	N4867T	Air Afrique			SEP/75	Leased
	N4867T	Trans International			DEC/75	
	N4867T	Transamerica Airlines			79	
	N4867T	Transamerica Airlines	73CF		05/JAN/83	Converted
	N4867T	Spirit of America Airlines			86	Leased
46091	N4868T	Trans International	63CF		04/APR/70	
	N4868T	Transamerica Airlines			79	
	N4868T	Air Afrique			SEP/80	Leased
	N4868T	Transamerica Airlines			13/OCT/80	
46092	PH-DEG	KLM	63		23/DEC/69	
	N926CL	Capitol Air			23/NOV/83	
	N926CL	Airlift International	63F		26/OCT/84	
	N951R	Emery Worldwide/Rosenbalm			SEP/85	
46093	N8758	Eastern Air Lines	63PF		06/NOC/69	
	OY-KTG	SAS			11/MAR/73	
	OY-KTG	Scanair			16/FEB/81	
	OY-KTG	Icelandair			03/SEP/82	Leased
	OY-KTG	Air Algerie			03/SEP/82	Sub-leased
	OY-KTG	Icelandair			19/OCT/82	Leased
	OY-KTG	Scanair			19/OCT/82	
	OY-KTG	SAS				
46094	N4910C	Capitol International	63CF		15/AUG/69	
	N910CL	Capitol International			75	
	N910CL	Seaboard World			01/NOV/76	
	N910CL	Capitol International			30/DEC/76	
	N910CL	United Aircraft Leasing			01/OCT/79	

MCDONNELL DOUGLAS DC-8-61/63 (71/73)

C/N	Registration	Owner/Operator	Series	First Flight	Delivery	Remarks
	N910CL	Capitol International			26/NOV/79	Leased
	N910CL	Evergreen International			29/AUG/84	
	N910CL	Evergreen International	73CF		29/AUG/84	Converted
	N894UP	United Parcel Service			NOV/84	Op. by Evergreen
46095	N8757	Eastern Airlines	63PF		15/AUG/69	
	CF-CPL	C.P.Air			26/SEP/72	
	N29180	Cammacorp.	73F		22/DEC/81	
	VR-CKL	A. Khashoggi/Handlingair			DEC/83	
	VR-CKA	A. Khashoggi/Handlingair				
46096	N8756	Eastern Air Lines	63PF		21/NOV/69	
	F-BOLL	UTA			30/APR/73	
	TU-TXT	Air Afrique			18/JUN/77	Leased
	F-BOLL	UTA			01/MAY/79	W/O 10/MAR/84, N'Djamena Ap., Chad
46097	N8755	Eastern Air Lines	63PF		14/DEC/69	
	OY-KTH	SAS			22/FEB/74	
	LN-MOF	SAS			14/AUG/79	
	LN-MOF	Scanair			29/MAY/80	
	LN-MOF	SAS			80	
	LN-MOF	SAS			80	Leased
	LN-MOF	Scanair			29/NOV/81	
	LN-MOF	SAS			82	Leased
	LN-MOF	Scanair			82	
	LN-MOF	SAS			03/SEP/82	
	LN-MOF	Icelandair			03/SEP/82	
	LN-MOF	Air Algerie			19/OCT/82	
	LN-MOF	Icelandair			19/OCT/82	
	LN-MOF	SAS				
46099	JA8041	Japan Air Lines	61		15/JAN/70	
	N917R	Overseas National Airways			12/JUN/81	
	N917R	Saudia			12/JUN/81	Leased
	N917R	Overseas National Airways	71		30/NOV/81	Converted
	N917R	Icelandair			18/AUG/83	Leased
	N917R	Overseas National Airways			17/OCT/83	
	N917R	Icelandair			01/JAN/85	Leased
	N917R	National Airlines			01/JUL/85	
	F-GMFM	Point Air			DEC/85	
46100	CF-TIP	Air Canada	63		11/DEC/69	
	C-FTIP	Air Canada	63F		MAR/82	Converted
	C-FTIP	Air Canada	73CF		15/AUG/83	Converted
46101	N8630	Seaboard World	63CF		25/SEP/69	
	N8630	International Air Bahama			21/MAY/70	Leased
	TF-FLE	International Air Bahama			NOV/77	
	TF-FLE	Icelandair				
	TF-FLE	Overseas National Airways			01/MAR/81	Leased
	TF-FLE	Saudia			81	Sub-leased
	TF-FLE	Overseas National Airways			81	Leased
	TF-FLE	Icelandair				
	N801UP	United Parcel Service	73CF		27/AUG/84	Op. by Orion Air
46103	N795FT	Flying Tigers	63FT		29/AUG/69	
	N795FT	Flying Tigers	73CF		12/JUN/84	Converted
	N795FT	Emery Worldwide/Rosenbalm			12/JUN/84	
46104	N796FT	Flying Tigers	63CF		03/OCT/69	
	N796FT	Air India			16/AUG/81	Leased
	N796FT	Flying Tigers			25/NOV/82	
	N796FT	Flying Tigers	73CF		28/MAY/84	Converted
	N796FT	Emery Worldwide/Rosenbalm			15/JUN/84	
46106	N8641	Seaboard World	63CF		02/OCT/69	
	N8641	Loftleidir			14/MAY/70	Leased
	N8641	Seaboard World			01/NOV/70	
	N8641	Lofleidir			03/MAY/71	Leased
	N8641	Seaboard World			24/OCT/71	
	N8641	Loftleidir			01/JUL/72	Leased
	N8641	Seaboard World			30/SEP/72	
	N8641	Loftleidir			22/MAY/74	Leased
	N8641	Seaboard World			19/SEP/74	
	N8641	Loftleidir			10/APR/75	Leased
	N8641	Seaboard World			29/MAY/76	
	N8641	Overseas National Airways			30/MAR/76	Leased
	N8641	Seaboard World			10/MAY/76	
	N8641	Loftleidir			13/MAY/76	Leased
	N8641	Seaboard World			09/JAN/77	
	N8641	Loftleidir			08/MAY/77	Leased
	N8641	Seaboard World			29/OCT/77	
	F-GATO	UTA			02/NOV/77	
	N919CL	Capitol International			26/JUL/81	
	N919JW	International Air Leases	73CF		14/DEC/82	Converted
	N919JW	Arrow Air			29/APR/83	
	D-ADUC	Lufthansa			10/OCT/84	Stored 10/OCT/84
	D-ADUC	Condor			26/APR/85	Leased
	D-ADUC	Lufthansa			NOV/85	
	D-ADUC	German Cargo Services			NOV/85	Leased
	D-ADUC	Condor			APR/86	Leased
46108	N123AF	American Flyers Airlines	63CF		23/APR/70	
	N798FT	Flying Tigers			04/JUN/71	
	N123AF	Trans International			04/JUN/71	Leased
	N798FT	Flying Tigers			17/SEP/71	
	N798FT	Trans International			15/DEC/71	Leased
	N798FT	Flying Tigers			NOV/72	
	N798FT	World Airways			12/NOV/75	Leased
	N798FT	Flying Tigers			76	
	N798FT	Overseas National Airways			08/MAY/81	
	N798FT	Flying Tigers			08/MAY/81	Leased
	N798FT	Flying Tigers	73CF		05/JUL/84	Converted
	N818UP	United Parcel Service			05/JUL/84	Op. by Orion Air
46109	N8642	Seaboard World	63CF		23/OCT/69	
	N8642	Loftleidir			04/MAY/75	Leased
	N8642	Seaboard World			20/SEP/75	
	N8642	Loftleidir			02/NOV/76	
	N8642	Seaboard World			04/JAN/77	
	N8642	Overseas National Airways			25/MAR/77	
	N8642	Seaboard World			12/MAY/77	
	N8642	Air India			31/DEC/77	Leased
	N8642	Loftleidir			01/APR/79	
	N8642	Air India			01/DEC/80	Leased
	N772FT	Air India			MAR/81	Leased
	N772FT	Overseas National Airways			08/MAY/81	

C/N	Registration	Owner/Operator	Series	First Flight	Delivery	Remarks
	N772FT	Flying Tigers			08/MAY/81	Leased
	N772FT	Air India			08/MAY/81	Sub-leased
	N772FT	Flying Tigers			06/AUG/81	Leased
	N772FT	Air India			82	Sub-leased
	N772FT	Flying Tigers			82	
	N809UP	United Parcel Service	73CF		22/JAN/84	Op. by Evergreen
46112	N866F	Overseas National Airways	63CF		07/APR/70	
	N866F	Seaboard World			24/OCT/73	Leased
	N866F	Overseas National Airways			21/DEC/73	
	N866F	Seaboard World			14/OCT/74	Leased
	N866F	Cargolux			10/DEC/74	Leased
	N866F	Seaboard World			03/JUL/75	
	N866F	Cargolux			01/AUG/75	Leased
	N866F	Seaboard World			14/MAY/76	
	N866F	Overseas National Airways			15/MAY/76	
	N866F	Seaboard World			29/DEC/77	Leased
	TF-FLF	Loftleidir			09/MAY/78	
	N866F	Seaboard World			09/OCT/78	
	N866F	Loftleidir			01/APR/79	
	N866F	Saudia			21/DEC/79	Leased
	TF-FLF	Icelandair			22/FEB/80	Leased
	N776FT	Flying Tigers			29/JAN/81	
	N776FT	Air India			29/JAN/81	Leased
	N776FT	Flying Tigers			16/AUG/81	
	N812UP	United Parcel Service	73CF		28/SEP/84	Op. by Evergreen
46113	CF-TIT	Air Canada	63			Not taken-up
	CF-TIU	Air Canada			12/MAR/70	WFU 01/JUN/83 to 18/NOV/84
	C-FTIU	Air Canada	73CF		NOV/84	Converted
46114	CF-TIV	Air Canada	63			Not taken-up
	CF-TIW	Air Canada			30/APR/70	
46115	CF-TIW	Air Canada	63			W/O 05/JUL/70, Nr.Toronto Ap. Not taken-up
	CF-TIX	Air Canada			23/MAY/70	
	ZP-CCH	Lineas Aereas Paraguays			20/DEC/84	
46116	EC-BSD	Iberia	63		23/DEC/70	
	EC-BSD	Aviaco			01/MAY/80	
	N4574P	International Air Leases			13/DEC/83	
	N4574P	Arrow Air			13/DEC/83	
	N4574P	International Air Leases			22/NOV/84	
	C-GQBF	Quebecair			22/NOV/84	
46117	N4869T	Trans International	63CF		15/MAY/70	
	N4869T	Transamerica Airlines			79	
	N4869T	Transamerica Airlines	73CF		25/MAY/84	Converted
46118	N8717U	United Airlines				Cancelled order
46119	N8724U	United Airlines				Cancelled order
46120	N8731U	United Airlines				Cancelled order
46121	PI-C827	Philippine Airlines	63			Not taken-up
	PH-DEK	KLM			25/NOV/69	
	PH-DEK	Philippine Airlines			01/MAY/73	Leased
	PH-DEK	KLM			03/MAY/75	
	TF-FLV	Icelandair			04/APR/84	Leased
46122	PI-C829	Philippine Airlines	63			Not taken-up
	PH-DEL	KLM			30/DEC/69	
	PH-DEL	Philippine Airlines			01/APR/73	Leased
	PH-DEL	KLM			05/APR/75	
	PH-DEL	African Safari			24/MAR/82	
	5Y-ZEB	African Safari			02/JUN/82	
46123	CF-TIQ	Air Canada	63		04/FEB/70	
	C-FTIQ	Air Canada	63AF		APR/81	Converted
	C-FTIQ	Air Canada	73CF		22/AUG/84	Converted
46124	CF-TIR	Air Canada	63		05/FEB/70	
	CF-TIR	Nordair				Leased
	CF-TIR	Air Afrique			13/OCT/78	Sub-leased
	CF-TIR	Nordair			31/OCT/78	Leased
	CF-TIR	Air Afrique			13/NOV/78	Sub-leased
	CF-TIR	Nordair			01/DEC/78	Leased
	C-FTIR	Air Canada	63AF		AUG/81	Converted
	C-FTIR	Air Canada	73CF		20/APR/84	Converted
46125	CF-TIS	Air Canada	63		27/FEB/70	
	C-FTIS	Air Canada	63AF		JAN/82	Converted
	C-FTIS	Air Canada	73CF		22/JUN/84	Converted
46126	CF-TIU	Air Canada	63			Not taken-up
	CF-TIV	Air Canada			01/APR/70	
46127	JA8042	Japan Airlines	61		02/FEB/70	
	JA8042	Orient Lease			28/APR/82	
	JA8042	Japan Airlines			28/APR/82	Leased
46128	JA8043	Japan Airlines	61		24/FEB/70	
	N913R	Overseas National Airways			27/MAY/80	
	N913R	Saudia			27/MAY/80	Leased
	N913R	Overseas National Airways			81	W/O 15/JAN/81, Findel Ap. Lux.
46129	SE-DBI	SAS	63CF		05/APR/70	
	SE-DBI	Scanair			26/APR/79	
	SE-DBI	SAS			80	
	SE-DBI	Scanair			80	Leased
	SE-DBI	SAS			82	
	SE-DBI	Arista International			15/FEB/82	Leased
	SE-DBI	SAS			MAY/84	
	SE-DBI	Thai International			14/MAY/84	Leased
	HS-TGZ	Thai International			DEC/84	Purchased
46133	N6165A	Airlift International	63CF			Not taken-up
	N801WA	World Airways			19/MAR/71	
	N801WA	Loftleidir			14/OCT/79	Leased
	N801WA	World Airways			15/MAR/80	
	N801WA	Overseas National Airways			10/JUN/82	Leased
	N801WA	World Airways			31/OCT/82	
	N801WA	Capitol International			23/DEC/82	Leased
	N801WA	World Airways			27/OCT/83	
	N801WA	Viasa			04/NOV/83	Leased
	N801WA	World Airways			20/MAR/84	
	N801WA	National Airlines	73F		27/AUG/84	
	N801WA	Emery Worldwide/Rosenbalm			27/AUG/84	
	N961R	Emery Worldwide/Rosenbalm			NOV/84	
46135	TU-TCF	Air Afrique	63CF		28/MAY/70	
	TU-TCF	UTA			76	
	TU-TCF	Air Afrique			82	Leased
46136	SE-DBK	SAS	63		13/JAN/70	

MCDONNELL DOUGLAS DC-8-61/63 (71/73)

C/N	Registration	Owner/Operator	Series	First Flight	Delivery	Remarks
	SE-DBK	Scanair			03/APR/81	
46137	D-ADIX	Atlantis	63CF		29/APR/70	
	N804WA	World Airways			18/DEC/72	
	N804WA	Air Algerie			NOV/75	Leased
	N804WA	World Airways			JAN/76	
	N804WA	Cargolux			31/JUL/78	Leased
	N804WA	World Airways			01/FEB/79	
	N804WA	Cargolux			04/OCT/79	Leased
	N804WA	Air Algerie				Sub-leased
	N804WA	Cargolux			01/DEC/80	Leased
	N804WA	World Airways			01/DEC/80	
	N804WA	Capitol International			18/JUN/83	Leased
	N804WA	GATX Leasing			18/NOV/83	
	N804WA	Transamerica			18/NOV/83	Leased
	N957R	Emery Worldwide/Rosenbalm			JAN/85	
46138		Flying Tigers	63CF			Cancelled order
46140	N124AF	American Flyers Airlines	63CF		19/MAY/70	
	N797FT	Flying Tigers			04/JUN/71	
	N797FT	Trans International			01/JUN/72	Leased
	N797FT	Flying Tigers			30/SEP/73	
	N797FT	Cargolux			11/MAY/77	Leased
	N797FT	Loftleidir			11/MAY/77	Sub-leased
	N797FT	Cargolux			SEP/77	Leased
	N797FT	Flying Tigers			20/SEP/78	
	N797FT	Overseas National Airways			08/MAY/81	
	N797FT	Flying Tigers			08/MAY/81	Leased
	N797FT	Pacific East Air			07/JUN/82	Leased
	N797FT	Flying Tigers			25/SEP/83	
	N797FT	Flying Tigers	73CF		18/MAY/84	Converted
	N840UP	United Parcel Service			18/MAY/84	Op. by Evergreen
46141	PH-DEM	KLM	63		22/JUN/70	
	PH-DEM	Surinam Airways			03/NOV/75	
	PH-DEM	KLM			15/OCT/83	
	S7-SIS	Seychelles International			22/DEC/83	
46143	D-ADIY	Atlantis	63CF		15/APR/71	
	N65516	Greyhound Leasing			03/JAN/73	
	N805WA	World Airways			01/APR/73	
	N805WA	Garuda			NOV/74	Leased
	N805WA	World Airways			FEB/75	WFU 10/FEB/82 to 23/DEC/82
	N805WA	Capitol Air			23/DEC/82	Leased
	N805WA	GATX Leasing			19/OCT/83	
	N805WA	Transamerica Airlines			02/DEC/83	Leased
	N805WA	GATX Leasing			85	
	N805WA	National Airlines			85	
	N959R	Emery Worldwide/Rosenbalm			JUL/85	
46144	N6164A	Airlift International	63CF		26/JUN/70	W/O 23/MAR/74, Travis AFB, Ca.
46145	D-ADIZ	Atlantis	63CF		26/MAY/71	
	N65517	Greyhound Leasing			01/JAN/73	
	N806WA	World Airways			18/DEC/72	
	N806WA	Air Algerie			10/DEC/74	Leased
	N806WA	World Airways			19/JAN/75	
	N806WA	Cargolux			15/SEP/78	Leased
	N806WA	World Airways			01/FEB/79	
	N806WA	Air Algerie			80	Leased
	N806WA	World Airways			NOV/80	WFU 13/FEB/82 to 16/JUN/82
	N806WA	Overseas National Airways			16/JUN/82	Leased
	N806WA	World Airways			09/NOV/82	
	N806WA	Capitol International			23/DEC/82	
	N806WA	World Airways			19/JAN/83	
	N806WA	Icelandair			24/MAR/83	
	N921R	Overseas National Airways			27/OCT/83	
	N921R	Capitol International			27/OCT/83	Leased
	N921R	National Airlines			22/JUL/84	
	N921R	Emery Worldwide			84	Leased
	N921R	National Airlines				
	N921R	Air India			85	Leased
	N921R	National Airlines				
	N921R	Emery Worldwide/Rosenbalm			AUG/85	
46146	N6166A	Airlift International	63CF			Not taken-up
	N802WA	World Airways			12/MAR/71	W/O 08/SEP/73, Mt. Ditton, Cold Bay, Ak.
46147	9Q-CLH	Air Congo	63C		19/JUL/71	
	9Q-CLH	Air Zaire			25/OCT/71	
	9Q-CLH	SATA			AUG/77	Leased
	9Q-CLH	Air Zaire				
	9Q-CLH	Air Zaire	63F		DEC/79	Converted
46149	N6167A	Airlift International	63CF			Not taken-up
	N803WA	World Airways			29/MAR/71	
	N803WA	Air Algerie			NOV/76	Leased
	N803WA	World Airways			JAN/77	
	N803WA	Jet Aviation Switzerland			31/DEC/79	
	A40-HMQ	Sultan H.M. Qaboos bin Said			28/MAY/81	
	A40-HMQ	Sultan H.M. Qaboos bin Said	73CF		27/JAN/82	Converted
46151	9Q-CLG	Air Congo	63CF		09/NOV/70	
	9Q-CLG	Air Zaire			25/OCT/71	
	9Q-CLG	African Air Charter			76	Leased
	9Q-CLG	Air Zaire			76	
	9Q-CLG	Bursa Hava Yollari			JUL/80	Leased
	9Q-CLG	Air Zaire			80	
46155	EC-BSE	Iberia	63		23/DEC/70	
	EC-BSE	Aviaco			08/APR/81	
	N940JW	International Air Leases			28/DEC/83	
	N940JW	Arrow Air			28/DEC/83	
	N940JW	International Air Leases			03/MAY/84	
	C-GQBA	Quebecair			03/MAY/84	
46156		Indian Airlies				Cancelled order
46157	JA8045	Japan Air Lines	61		04/DEC/70	
46158	JA8046	Japan Air Lines	61		20/JAN/71	
46159	JA8047	Japan Air Lines	61		18/FEB/71	
	JA8047	Orient Lease			28/APR/82	
	JA8047	Japan Air Lines			28/APR/82	Leased
	JA8047	Japan Asia Airways			85	
46160	JA8048	Japan Air Lines	61		12/MAR/71	
	JA8048	Orient Lease			28/JUL/82	
	JA8048	Japan Air Lines			28/JUL/82	Leased, W/O 17/SEP/82, Shanghai
46163	SE-DBL	SAS	63		13/MAY/72	
	SE-DBL	Scanair			01/APR/82	

5Y- Kenya

46122	5Y-ZEB

6Y- Jamaica

45963	6Y-JGC
45894	6Y-JGG
45912	6Y-JGH

9Q- Zaire

46151	9Q-CLG
46147	9Q-CLH

9V- Singapore

45902	9V-BEH

A40- Oman

46149	A40-HMQ

C/CF- Canada

45926	C-FCPO
45927	C-FCPP
45928	C-FCPQ
45929	C-FCPS
46033	C-FTIK
46034	C-FTIL
46035	C-FTIM
46036	C-FTIN
46076	C-FTIO
46100	C-FTIP
46123	C-FTIQ
46124	C-FTIR
46125	C-FTIS
46113	C-FTIU
45963	C-FTJX
45964	C-FTJY
45980	C-FTJZ
45943	C-GMXB
45982	C-GMXQ
45902	C-GQBA
46155	C-GQBA
46116	C-GQBF
46095	CF-CPL
45926	CF-CPO
45927	CF-CPP
45928	CF-CPQ
45929	CF-CPS
46076	CF-TIO
46100	CF-TIP
46123	CF-TIP
46124	CF-TIR
46125	CF-TIS
46113	CF-TIT
46126	CF-TIU
46113	CF-TIU
46114	CF-TIV
46126	CF-TIV
46114	CF-TIW
46115	CF-TIW
46115	CF-TIX
45890	CF-TJU
45891	CF-TJU
45892	CF-TJV
45893	CF-TJW
45963	CF-TJX
45964	CF-TJY
45980	CF-TJZ

CX- Uruguay

45989	CX-BOU

D- West Germany

46137	D-ADIX
46143	D-ADIY
46145	D-ADIZ
46003	D-ADUA
46106	D-ADUC
46044	D-ADUE
45991	D-ADUI
46047	D-ADUO

EC- Spain

45930	EC-BMX
45931	EC-BMY
45988	EC-BMZ
46079	EC-BQS
46116	EC-BSD
46155	EC-BSE
45897	EC-CCF
45898	EC-CCG
45913	EC-CZE
46037	EC-DVB
46016	EC-DVC
45888	EC-DYY
46015	EC-DZC

EI- Eire

45989	EI-BNA
45897	EI-BPF
45898	EI-BPG

F- France

45927	F-BOLJ
46096	F-BOLL
46058	F-BOLM
46106	F-GATO
45981	F-GDPS
46063	F-GDRM
46038	F-GETM
46099	F-GMFM

HB- Switzerland

46001	HB-IDM
45968	HB-IDS
46074	HB-IDZ

HS- Thailand

45949	HS-TGF
45952	HS-TGG
45923	HS-TGX
46054	HS-TGY
45924	HS-TGZ
46129	HS-TGZ

JA Japan

46031	JA8038
46032	JA8039
46099	JA8041
46127	JA8042
46157	JA8045
46158	JA8046
46159	JA8047
46160	JA8048
45887	JA8049
45848	JA8050
45982	JA8057
45942	JA8059
45888	JA8060
45889	JA8061
45992	JA8067
45983	JA8068

LN- Norway

46097	LN-MOF
45923	LN-MOU
46054	LN-MOY

LX- Luxembourg

45989	LX-ACV
46002	LX-BCV

N United States

46108	N123AF
46140	N124AF
46014	N1300L
46018	N1301L
46029	N1302L
46030	N1303L
46048	N1304L
46072	N1305L
46055	N1306L
46056	N1307L
45903	N1503U
45901	N1504U
45927	N19B
45929	N19B
45890	N20UA
45891	N21UA
45892	N22UA
45893	N23UA
46062	N2674U
46095	N29180
46052	N2919N
46052	N31EK
45908	N45090
45981	N45091
46116	N4574P
45943	N4578C
45982	N4582N
46063	N4805J
45951	N4863T
46059	N4864T
46073	N4865T
46089	N4866T
46090	N4867T
46091	N4868T
46117	N4869T
45967	N4907C
45968	N4908C
46060	N4909C
46094	N4910C
46079	N4934Z
45931	N4935C
45969	N6161A
46061	N6162A
46062	N6163A
46144	N6164A
46133	N6165A
46146	N6166A
46149	N6167A
45929	N624FT
45928	N625FT
46017	N64RD
46143	N65516
46145	N65517
45900	N700UP
45938	N701UP
45902	N702UP
45939	N703UP
45949	N705UP
45948	N748UP
49550	N750UP
45952	N752UP
45888	N755UA
46015	N766RD
46109	N772FT
45966	N773FT
46087	N774FT
46112	N776FT
46049	N778FT
45989	N779FT
45990	N780FT
45991	N781FT
46002	N782FT
46003	N783FT
46004	N784FT
46005	N785FT
46006	N786FT
46007	N787FT
46008	N788FT
46044	N790FT
46045	N791FT
46046	N792FT
46047	N793FT
46086	N794FT
46103	N795FT
46104	N796FT
46140	N797FT
45897	N797UP
46108	N798FT
45898	N798UP
46001	N799FT
45939	N801U
46101	N801UP
46133	N801WA
45950	N802U
46146	N802WA
45900	N803U
46149	N803WA
45938	N804UP
46004	N804UP
46137	N804WA
46143	N805WA
46006	N806UP
46145	N806WA
45810	N8070U
45811	N8071U
45812	N8072U
45813	N8073U
45849	N8074U
45940	N8075U
45941	N8076U
45945	N8077U
45946	N8078U
45947	N8079U
46007	N807UP
45970	N8080U
45971	N8081U
45972	N8082U
45973	N8083U
45974	N8084U
45975	N8085U
45976	N8086U
45977	N8087U
45978	N8088U
45993	N8089U
46008	N808UP
45994	N8090U
45995	N8091U
45996	N8092U
45997	N8093U
45998	N8094U
46039	N8095U
46040	N8096U
46064	N8097U
46065	N8098U
46066	N8099U
46109	N810EV
45902	N810EV
46051	N811EV
46112	N812UP
46002	N815EV
45990	N816EV
45983	N8177U
46108	N818UP
46019	N819UP
45907	N822E
45914	N823E
45915	N824E
45944	N825E
45979	N826E
45936	N836UP
46140	N840UP
46051	N851UP
46052	N852UP
45938	N860FT
45900	N861FT
45948	N862FT
46101	N8630
45936	N8631
45966	N8632
46020	N8633
46021	N8634
46050	N8635
46051	N8636
46051	N8636EV
46052	N8637
46053	N8638
46049	N8639
46051	N863EV
46001	N863F
45949	N863FT
46106	N8641
46109	N8642
46087	N864F
45952	N864FT
46088	N865F
46112	N866F
45966	N866UP
45939	N867F
45939	N867FT
45967	N867UP
46034	N868BX
45950	N868F
45950	N868FT
45968	N868UP
46035	N869BX
45913	N869F
46036	N870BX
46086	N870TV
46118	N8717U
45968	N871TV
46119	N8724U
46001	N872TV
46120	N8731U
46074	N874UP
46097	N8755
46096	N8756
46095	N8757
46093	N8758
46058	N8759
46074	N8760
46038	N8762
46037	N8763
46017	N8764
46016	N8765
46015	N8766
45992	N8767
45983	N8768
45982	N8769
45913	N8770
45912	N8771
45943	N8772
45942	N8773
45894	N8774
45889	N8775
45888	N8776
45887	N8777
45848	N8778
45897	N8786R
45898	N8787R
45952	N8788R
46080	N880UP
46094	N894UP
45948	N8955U
45949	N8956U
45938	N8960T
45902	N8961T
45900	N8962T
46087	N906R
45967	N907CL
45903	N908CL
45968	N908CL
46094	N910CL
45981	N911CL
45908	N912CL
45908	N912R
46128	N913R
45912	N914CL
45894	N915CL
46099	N917R
46106	N919CL
46106	N919JW
46058	N920CL
46058	N920JW
46145	N921R
46092	N926CL
45901	N929R
46155	N940JW
45988	N941JW
46058	N950JW
45903	N950R
46092	N951R
46061	N952R
45908	N954R
46137	N957R
46143	N959R
46133	N961R
45901	N963R
46000	N964R

OB- Peru

45992	OB-R-1222

OE- Austria

46088	OE-IBO

OY- Denmark

46041	OY-KTF
46093	OY-KTG
46097	OY-KTH
45923	OY-SBK
46054	OY-SBL
45924	OY-SBM

PH- Netherlands

45903	PH-DEA
45901	PH-DEB
45999	PH-DEC
46000	PH-DED
46019	PH-DEE
46080	PH-DEF
46092	PH-DEG
46075	PH-DEH
46121	PH-DEK
46122	PH-DEL
46141	PH-DEM

PI- Philippines

46121	PI-C827
46122	PI-C829

S7- Seychelles

46141	S7-SIS

SE- Sweden

45924	SE-DBH
46129	SE-DBI
46136	SE-DBK
46163	SE-DBL

TF- Iceland

45900	TF-BCV
46002	TF-BCV
45990	TF-CCV
46020	TF-FLA
45936	TF-FLB
46049	TF-FLC
46088	TF-FLC
46101	TF-FLE
46062	TF-FLF
46112	TF-FLF
46075	TF-FLT
45999	TF-FLU
46121	TF-FLV
45980	TF-ISA
45964	TF-ISB
46080	TF-VLP
46019	TF-VLY
46080	TF-VLZ

TR- Gabon

46053	TR-LTZ

TU- Ivory Coast

46135	TU-TCF
46096	TU-TXT

VR-C Cayman Islands

46095	VR-CKA
46095	VR-CKL

YV- Venezuela

46042	YV-125C
46063	YV-126C
46052	YV-130C
46042	YV-C-VIA
46063	YV-C-VIB
46052	YV-C-VIN

ZP- Paraguay

46115	ZP-CCH

MCDONNELL DOUGLAS DC-10

Medium/long range wide-body commercial transport, powered by three General Electric CF6-50C turbofans. The DC-10 was developed to meet an American Airlines requirement, and the first aircraft DC-10-10 for domestic use, made its maiden flight on 29 August 1971. The Series 15 has more powerful engines, as has the Series 30. Other changes in the DC-10-30 included an increased wing and greater fuel capacity giving it intercontinental capability. Even longer-range was achieved in the Series 30ER (Extended Range), and the DC10-40 differed in having higher-thrust Pratt & Whitney JT9D-59A engines. Convertible passenger/cargo versions are also available, and the USAF use the DC-10 as a tanker and cargo transport under the designation KC-10A. To date, 418 aircraft have been delivered (including KC-10's), and a further 21 are on order.

Dimensions :   Wing span: 155ft 4in (47.34m) Length: 182ft 3in (55.55m) Height: 58ft 1in (17.7m) (-10)
                  Wing span: 165ft 4in (50.41m) Length: 181ft 7in (55.5m) Height: 58ft 1in (17.7m) (-30)
                  Wing span: 165ft 4in (50.41m) Length: 182ft 3in (55.49m) Height: 58ft 1in (17.7m) (-40)

Powerplant :   Three General Electric CF6-6D turbofans (-10), three General Electric CF6-50C2 turbofans (-30), three Pratt & Whitney JT9D-59A turbofans (-40)

Performance :   Max cruising speed 490 knots (908km/h) Range: with max payload 2,950nm (5,643km) (-10)
                  Range: with max payload 5,350nm (9,950km) (-30)
                  Range: with max payload 5,330nm (9,910km) (-40)

Accommodation: 380 passengers in a ten abreast layout

Manufacturer :   McDonnell Douglas - 3855 Lakewood Boulevard, Long Beach, California 90846, USA
                  Telephone: (213) 593-5511

C/N	Registration	Owner/Operator	Series	First Flight	Delivery	Remarks
46500	N10DC	Douglas	10		29/JUL/72	Prototype
	N101AA	American Airlines			08/DEC/72	
46501	N101AA	American Airlines	10			Not taken-up
	N10DC	Douglas			17/DEC/70	Autoland system trials
	G-BELO	Laker Airways			03/JUN/77	WFU 28/FEB/82
	N183AT	American Trans Air			21/FEB/83	
	N183AT	Omni Aircraft			NOV/85	
	N183AT	Air Hawaii			NOV/85	Leased
	N183AT	Omni Aircraft			28/FEB/86	
	G-GCAL	Cal Air International			MAR/86	
46502	N102AA	American Airlines	10		27/JUN/72	
46503	N103AA	American Airlines	10		29/JUL/71	
46504	N104AA	American Airlines	10		17/SEP/71	
46505	N105AA	American Airlines	10		09/NOV/71	
46506	N106AA	American Airlines	10		10/DEC/71	
46507	N107AA	American Airlines	10		15/DEC/71	
46508	N108AA	American Airlines	10		31/JAN/72	
46509	N109AA	American Airlines	10		21/JAN/72	
46510	N110AA	American Airlines	10		28/FEB/72	W/O 25/MAY/79, O'Hare, Ill.
46511	N111AA	American Airlines	10		15/MAR/72	
46512	N112AA	American Airlines	10		30/MAR/72	
46513	N113AA	American Airlines	10		20/APR/72	
46514	N114AA	American Airlines	10		17/MAY/72	
46515	N115AA	American Airlines	10		26/MAY/72	
46516	N116AA	American Airlines	10		14/JUL/72	
46517	N117AA	American Airlines	10		21/JUL/72	
46518	N118AA	American Airlines	10		30/JUL/72	
46519	N119AA	American Airlines	10		12/AUG/72	
46520	N120AA	American Airlines	10		25/AUG/72	
46521	N121AA	American Airlines	10		01/SEP/72	
46522	N122AA	American Airlines	10		18/SEP/72	
46523	N123AA	American Airlines	10		20/OCT/72	
46524	N124AA	American Airlines	10		17/NOV/72	
46525	N125AA	American Airlines	10		19/DEC/72	
46540	N8715Q	Douglas	30			
	C-GCPC	CP Air			27/MAR/79	
	PP-VMO	Varig			05/APR/79	Leased
	C-GCPC	CP Air			03/APR/80	
46541	C-GCPD	CP Air	30		19/JUL/79	
	PP-VMP	Varig			21/JUL/79	Leased
	C-GCPD	CP Air			14/JUN/80	
46542	C-GCPE	CP Air	30		02/NOV/79	
46543	C-GCPF	CP Air	30		26/NOV/80	
	C-GCPF	United Airlines			11/JUL/83	Leased
46550	N1339U	Douglas	30ER	21/JUN/72		
	PH-DTA	KLM			15/MAR/74	
46551	N1342U	Douglas	30			
	PH-DTB	KLM			03/DEC/72	
46552	PH-DTC	KLM	30		06/FEB/73	
	PH-DTC	Garuda			OCT/73	Leased
	PH-DTC	Philippine Airlines			03/MAY/75	Leased
	PH-DTC	KLM			31/OCT/76	
46553	PH-DTD	KLM	30		28/FEB/73	
46554	PH-DTE	KLM	30		09/MAR/73	
						WFU 04/JUN/83 to 21/FEB/84 after accident at Panama City
	N130FA	Trans Union Leasing Corp.			21/FEB/84	WFU 21/FEB/84
	SE-DFG	SAS			OCT/85	
46555	PH-DTF	KLM	30		13/APR/73	
	PH-DTF	Viasa			DEC/76	Leased
	YV-133C	Viasa			01/APR/77	Purchased
	YV-133C	World Airways			28/JUL/83	Leased
	YV-133C	Viasa			01/NOV/83	
	N143AA	American Airlines			22/JUN/84	
46556	PH-DTG	KLM	30		03/APR/74	
	PH-DTG	Viasa			03/APR/74	Leased
	YV-134C	Viasa				Purchased
46557	PH-DTH	KLM	30		15/APR/75	

C/N	Registration	Owner/Operator	Series	First Flight	Delivery	Remarks
	PH-DTH	Viasa			15/APR/75	Leased
	PH-DTH	KLM			01/MAY/79	
	YV-138C	Viasa			26/JUL/80	Leased
46575	N1340U	Douglas	30			
	HB-IHA	Swissair			30/NOV/72	
	HC-BKO	Ecuatoriana			31/AUG/83	Leased
	HC-BKO	Ecuatoriana			MAR/84	Purchased
46576	HB-IHB	Swissair	30		05/FEB/73	
	HC-	Ecuatoriana			JAN/83	Not taken-up
	HB-IHB	Aeronautics & Astronautics			08/MAR/84	Leased
	EC-DUG	Spantax			08/MAR/84	Sub-leased
	HB-IHB	Aeronautics & Astronautics			08/MAR/94	Sched.return, Leased
	HB-IHB	Swissair			08/MAR/94	Sched.return
46577	HB-IHC	Swissair	30		10/SEP/73	
46578	HB-IHD	Swissair	30		06/DEC/73	
46579	HB-IHE	Swissair	30	18/DEC/73	06/FEB/74	
46580	HB-IHF	Swissair	30		11/JAN/75	
46581	HB-IHG	Swissair	30		15/FEB/75	
46582	HB-IHH	Swissair	30		21/FEB/75	
46583	N1002X	Douglas	30ER			
	HB-IHL	Swissair			03/MAR/80	
46584	N1002Y	Douglas	30ER			
	HB-IHM	Swissair			01/FEB/80	
46590	G-BFGI	British Caledonian	30		22/JAN/79	
46591	G-BGAT	British Caledonian	30		08/AUG/79	
46595	D-ADPO	Condor	30		21/NOV/79	
	N	Aero Americana				Leased, Not taken-up
	D-ADPO	Condor			DEC/83	
46596	D-ADQO	Condor	30		15/DEC/79	
46600	N1801U	United Airlines	10	23/DEC/70	25/MAY/72	
46601	N1802U	United Airlines	10	29/JUL/71		
46602	N1803U	United Airlines	10	19/MAY/71	03/JUN/72	
46603	N1804U	United Airlines	10		27/SEP/71	
46604	N1805U	United Airlines	10		29/OCT/71	
46605	N1806U	United Airlines	10		23/DEC/71	
46606	N1807U	United Airlines	10		20/DEC/71	
46607	N1808U	United Airlines	10		27/FEB/72	
46608	N1809U	United Airlines	10		05/MAR/72	
46609	N1810U	United Airlines	10		20/APR/72	
46610	N1811U	United Airlines	10		25/APR/72	
46611	N1812U	United Airlines	10		27/APR/72	
46612	N1813U	United Airlines	10		27/MAY/72	
46613	N1814U	United Airlines	10		24/JUN/72	
46614	N1815U	United Airlines	10		07/JUL/72	
46615	N1816U	United Airlines	10		30/JAN/73	
46616	N1817U	United Airlines	10		22/MAR/73	
46617	N1818U	United Airlines	10		09/APR/73	
46618	N1819U	United Airlines	10		12/APR/72	
46619	N1820U	United Airlines	10		23/FEB/74	
46620	N1821U	United Airlines	10		13/FEB/74	
46621	N1822U	United Airlines	10		25/APR/74	
46622	N1823U	United Airlines	10		02/MAY/74	
46623	N1824U	United Airlines	10		19/JUN/74	
46624	N1825U	United Airlines	10		26/JUN/74	
46625	N1826U	United Airlines	10		27/FEB/75	
	N1826U	World Airways			MAR/86	Leased
46626	N1827U	United Airlines	10		25/APR/75	
	N1827U	World Airways			APR/86	Leased
46627	N1828U	United Airlines	10		23/JUN/75	
	N1828U	World Airways			APR/86	Leased
46628	N1829U	United Airlines	10		25/JUL/75	
	N1829U	World Airways			MAY/86	Leased
46629	N1830U	United Airlines	10		04/AUG/75	
46630	N1831U	United Airlines	10		20/AUG/75	
46631	N1832U	United Airlines	10		23/SEP/75	
46632	N1838U	United Airlines	10		30/NOV/79	
46633	N1839U	United Airlines	10		15/FEB/80	
46634	N1841U	United Airlines	10		31/JAN/80	
46635	N1842U	United Airlines	10		28/FEB/80	
46636	N1843U	United Airlines	10		14/MAR 80	
46640	9M-MAT	Malaysian Airline System	30		21/SEP/77	
46645	N912WA	Western Airlines	10		19/JUL/79	
46646	N913WA	Western Airlines	10		26/JUL/79	
46660	N8705Q	Douglas	40			
	JA8532	Japan Air Lines			16/APR/76	
46661	N19B	Douglas	40			
	JA8533	Japan Air Lines			25/MAY/76	
46662	JA8535	Japan Air Lines	40		13/AUG/76	
	JA8535	Japan Asia Airways			80	Leased
	JA8535	Japan Air Lines			82	
46685	PK-GIE	Garuda	30		28/JUL/79	
46686	PK-GIF	Garuda	30		22/AUG/79	
46700	N60NA	National Airlines	10		01/NOV/71	
	N60NA	Pan American			07/JAN/80	
	N145AA	American Airlines			24/JAN/84	
46701	N61NA	National Airlines	10		19/NOV/71	
	N61NA	Pan American			07/JAN/80	
	N146AA	American Airlines			15/JUN/84	
46702	N62NA	National Airlines	10		21/DEC/71	
	N62NA	Pan American			07/JAN/80	
	N147AA	American Airlines			14/MAY/84	
46703	N63NA	National Airlines	10		12/JAN/72	
	N63NA	Pan American			07/JAN/80	
	N148AA	American Airlines			20/MAY/84	
46704	N1337U	Douglas	10			
	TC-JAV	Turk Hava Yollari			10/DEC/72	04/MAR/74, nr. Paris
46705	N1338U	Douglas	10			
	TC-JAU	Turk Hava Yollari			01/DEC/72	WFU 86, Stored
46706	N64NA	National Airlines	10		10/MAY/72	
	N64NA	Pan American			07/JAN/80	
	N151AA	American Airlines			12/FEB/84	
46707	N65NA	National Airlines	10		13/OCT/72	
	N65NA	Pan American			07/JAN/80	
	N152AA	American Airlines			06/JUN/84	
46708	N66NA	National Airlines	10		18/OCT/72	

MCDONNELL DOUGLAS DC-10

C/N	Registration	Owner/Operator	Series	First Flight	Delivery	Remarks
	N66NA	Pan American			07/JAN/80	
	N153AA	American Airlines			03/JUL/84	
46709	N67NA	National Airlines	10		30/NOV/72	
	N67NA	Pan American			07/JAN/80	
	N154AA	American Airlines			04/NOV/83	
46710	N68NA	National Airlines	10		12/DEC/72	
	N68NA	Pan American			07/JAN/80	
	N160AA	American Airlines			01/NOV/83	
46711	N80NA	National Airlines	30		11/JUN/73	
	N80NA	Pan American			07/JAN/80	
	N139AA	American Airlines			24/FEB/84	
46712	N81NA	National Airlines	30		18/JUN/73	
	N81NA	Pan American			07/JAN/80	
	CC-CJN	Lan-Chile			12/JUN/81	Leased
	N81NA	Pan American			13/JUN/82	
	N140AA	American Airlines			15/MAR/84	
46713	N82NA	National Airlines	30		20/JUN/75	
	N82NA	Pan American			07/JAN/80	
	N	Air Florida				Not taken-up
	N141AA	American Airlines			15/APR/84	
46714	N83NA	National Airlines	30		17/JUN/75	
	N83NA	Pan American			07/JAN/80	
	N142AA	American Airlines			19/APR/84	
46727	N1348U	Douglas	10			
	G-BBSZ	Laker Airways			20/MAY/74	
	G-BBSZ	Caribbean Airways			01/APR/77	Leased
	G-BBSZ	Laker Airways				
	N917CL	Capitol Air			01/APR/82	Leased
	N917CL	International Air Leases			30/JUL/83	WFU 30/JUL/83 to 06/SEP/83
	F-	Point Air			83	Not taken-up
	N917CL	Arrow Air			06/SEP/83	
	N917JW	Arrow Air			MAR/84	
	N917JW	International Air Leases			01/NOV/84	
	N917JW	World Airways			01/NOV/84	Leased
	N917JW	International Air Leases			DEC/86	Sched.return
	N	American Airlines			87	Sched.delivery
46750	N141US	Northwest Orient	40	28/FEB/72	13/JUN/73	
46751	N142US	Northwest Orient	40		19/FEB/73	
	N142US	Boeing			06/JUN/84	
	N184AT	American Transair			07/JUN/84	W/O 10/AUG/86, Chicago-O'Hare
46752	N143US	Northwest Orient	40		10/NOV/72	
	N143US	Boeing			15/MAY/84	
	N143US	Progress Aviation			JUN/84	
	N143US	Jet Charter Service			20/JUN/84	Leased
	N143US	Dominicana			84	Sub-leased
	N133JC	Jet Charter Service			86	Leased
	N133JC	Air Panama			86	Sub-leased
	N133JC	Jet Charter Service			86	Leased
	N133JC	Boeing			APR/86	
	N143US	Progress Aviation			APR/86	
	N143US	Northwest Orient			APR/86	Leased
46753	N144US	Northwest Orient	40		12/DEC/72	
	N144US	Boeing			30/APR/84	
	N144US	Progress Aviation			07/MAY/84	
	N144JC	Jet Charter Service			07/MAY/84	Leased
	N144JC	Progress Aviation				Leased
	N144JC	Northwest Orient				Leased
	N144JC	Sun Country Airlines			APR/86	Sub-leased
46754	N145US	Northwest Orient	40		31/JAN/73	
46755	N146US	Northwest Orient	40		09/MAY/73	
46756	N147US	Northwest Orient	40		02/JUN/73	
46757	N148US	Northwest Orient	40		06/JUL/73	
46758	N149US	Northwest Orient	40		25/JUL/73	
46759	N150US	Northwest Orient	40		31/JUL/73	
46760	N151US	Northwest Orient	40		30/OCT/73	
46761	N152US	Northwest Orient	40		07/NOV/73	
46762	N153US	Northwest Orient	40		14/NOV/73	
46763	N154US	Northwest Orient	40		28/NOV/73	
46764	N155US	Northwest Orient	40		12/DEC/73	
46765	N156US	Northwest Orient	40		08/MAR/74	
46766	N157US	Northwest Orient	40		17/MAY/74	
46767	N158US	Northwest Orient	40		19/JUL/74	
46768	N159US	Northwest Orient	40		09/AUG/74	
46769	N160US	Northwest Orient	40		10/SEP/74	
46770	N161US	Northwest Orient	40		05/NOV/74	
46771	N162US	Northwest Orient	40		06/DEC/74	
46800	N101TV	Trans International	30CF		27/APR/73	
	N101TV	Transamerica Airlines			01/OCT/79	
	N101TV	Air Florida			15/MAR/81	Leased
	N101TV	Transamerica Airlines			05/OCT/82	WFU 05/OCT/82 to 25/NOV/83 at Marana Air Park.
	N301FE	Federal Express			25/NOV/83	
46801	N102TV	Trans International	30CF		10/JUN/73	
	N102TV	Transamerica Airlines			01/OCT/79	
	N102TV	Air Florida			15/APR/81	Leased
	N102TV	Transamerica Airlines			24/FEB/83	WFU 24/FEB/83 to 19/MAR/84 at Marana Air Park.
	N302FE	Federal Express			19/MAR/84	
46802	N103TV	Trans International	30CF		06/JUL/73	
	N103TV	Transamerica Airlines			01/OCT/79	
	N103TV	Air Florida			18/DEC/81	Leased
	N103TV	Transamerica Airlines			12/OCT/82	WFU 12/OCT/82 to 29/FEB/84 at Marana Air Park.
	N303FE	Federal Express			29/FEB/84	
46825	N1031F	Overseas National Airways	30CF	28/FEB/73	01/MAY/73	W/O 02/JAN/76, Istanbul Ap.
46826	N1032F	Overseas National Airways	30CF		30/JUN/73	W/O 12/NOV/75, J.F. Kennedy Ap.
46835	N106WA	World Airways	30		27/APR/79	
46836	N107WA	World Airways	30		21/MAY/79	
46837	N108WA	World Airways	30		29/MAY/79	
	N108WA	Malaysian Airline System			28/MAR/80	Leased
	N108WA	Viasa			01/JUL/81	Leased
	N108WA	World Airways			31/AUG/81	
	N108WA	Air Florida			83	Leased
	N108WA	World Airways			83	
46850	N1341U	Douglas	30			

C/N	Registration	Owner/Operator	Series	First Flight	Delivery	Remarks
	F-BTDA	UTA				Not taken-up
	F-BTDB	UTA			18/FEB/73	
46851	N1350U	Douglas	30			
	F-BTDB	UTA				Not Taken-up
	F-BTDC	UTA			19/MAR/73	
	HS-TGA	Thai International			30/MAR/75	Leased
	F-BTDC	UTA			15/MAY/77	
46852	F-BTDC	UTA	30			Not taken-up
	F-BTDD	UTA				
	N54629	Wilmington Trust Co.				
	N54629	UTA			01/MAY/73	
46853	F-BTDD	UTA	30			Not taken-up
	F-BTDE	UTA				
	N54639	US Trust Co.				
	N54639	UTA			19/JAN/74	
	F-BTDE	UTA				
46854	F-BTDF	UTA	30			
	N54649	US Trust Co.			19/MAR/75	
	N54649	UTA				
46868	LN-RKA	SAS	30	10/SEP/74	05/OCT/74	
46869	SE-DEA	SAS	30			Not taken-up
	SE-DFD	SAS			05/NOV/74	
46870	OY-KDA	SAS	30		19/DEC/75	
46871	LN-RKB	SAS	30		24/JAN/76	
						Damaged FEB/84
	LN-RKB	Douglas			15/OCT/84	WFU 15/OCT/84
	LN-RKB	Federal Express			29/NOV/84	WFU 29/NOV/84 for repair
	N311FE	Federal Express			DEC/85	
46872	SE-DEB	SAS	30			Not taken-up
	SE-DFE	SAS			02/DEC/76	
46890	TU-TCG	Air Afrique	30			Not taken-up
	TU-TAL	Air Afrique			29/FEB/73	
	TU-TAL	JAT			JAN/85	Leased
46891	TU-	Air Afrique	30CF			Not taken-up
	PH-MBG	Martinair			13/NOV/73	
	PH-MBG	Garuda			27/SEP/79	Leased
	PH-MBG	Martinair			26/OCT/79	
	PH-MBG	Red Cross			23/NOV/79	Leased
	PH-MBG	Martinair			30/DEC/79	
	PH-MBG	TAAG Angola			13/JAN/81	Leased
	PH-MBG	Martinair			81	
46892	TU-TBD	Air Afrique	30			Not taken-up
	TU-TAM	Air Afrique			19/JUN/75	
	HS-TGB	Thai International			28/JUN/75	Leased
	TU-TAM	Air Afrique			20/MAY/76	
46900	N68041	Continental Airlines	10		14/APR/72	
46901	N68042	Continental Airlines	10		22/MAY/72	
46902	N68043	Continental Airlines	10		19/MAY/72	
46903	N68044	Continental Airlines	10		09/JUN/72	
46904	N68045	Continental Airlines	10		23/JUN/72	W/O 01/MAR/78, Los Angeles Intl.
46905	G-AZZC	Laker Airways	10		26/OCT/72	
	G-AZZC	Malaysian Airline System			79	Leased
	G-AZZC	Laker Airways				
	N906CL	International Air Leases			07/OCT/82	
	N906CL	Capitol Air			07/OCT/82	Leased
	N906CL	International Air Leases			31/JAN/83	WFU 31/JAN/83 to 11/MAY/83
	N906CL	Arrow Air			11/MAY/83	Leased
	N902JW	Arrow Air			83	Leased
	N902JW	International Air Leases			84	
	N902JW	Dominicana			DEC/84	Leased
	N902JW	International Air Leases			DEC/84	
	N902JW	World Airways			07/DEC/84	Leased
	N902JW	Dominicana			86	Sub-leased
	N902JW	World Airways			86	Leased
	N902JW	International Air Leases			DEC/86	Sched.return
	N	American Airlines			87	Sched.delivery
46906	G-AZZD	Laker Airways	10		16/NOV/72	
	G-AZZD	Air Algerie			OCT/77	Leased
	G-AZZD	Laker Airways			01/APR/82	
	N916CL	Capitol Air				WFU 01/APR/83 to 11/MAY/82
	N916CL	International Air Leases			01/SEP/83	
	N916JW	Arrow Air			16/APR/84	Leased
	N916JW	International Air Leases			18/OCT/84	
	N916JW	World Airways			18/OCT/84	Leased
	N916JW	International Air Leases			DEC/86	Sched.return
	N	American Airlines			87	Sched.delivery
46907	TC-JAY	Turk Hava Yollari	10		26/FEB/73	
	TC-JAY	Nigeria Airways			01/AUG/80	Leased
	TC-JAY	Turk Hava Yollari			01/SEP/80	
	TC-JAY	Nigeria Airways			80	Leased
	TC-JAY	Turk Hava Yollari			10/OCT/80	
	TC-JAY	Nigeria Airways			19/OCT/80	Leased
	TC-JAY	Turk Hava Yollari			SEP/80	WFU 86, Stored
46908	N901WA	Western Airlines	10		27/APR/73	
	N166AA	American Airlines			APR/85	
46910	ZK-NZP	Air New Zealand	30		13/DEC/74	W/O 28/NOV/79, Antarctica
46911	ZK-NZQ	Air New Zealand	30		20/FEB/75	
	ZK-NZQ	International Lease Finance			16/SEP/82	
	N138AA	American Airlines			16/SEP/82	
46912	HL7316	Korean Airlines	30		10/FEB/75	
46913	N54652	Douglas	40			
	JA8534	Japan Air Lines			23/NOV/76	
	JA8534	Japan Asia Airways			DEC/80	Leased
	JA8534	Japan Air Lines			82	
46914	PH-DTK	KLM	30		27/MAR/75	
	PH-DTK	Philippine Airlines			27/MAR/75	Leased
	PH-DTK	KLM			84	
	PH-DTK	British Midland Airways			84	Leased
	PH-DTK	Thai International			16/MAY/84	Sub-Leased
	PH-DTK	British Midland Airways			01/APR/85	Leased
	PH-DTK	KLM			01/APR/85	
	N163AA	American Airlines			01/APR/85	
46915	HL7317	Korean Airlines	30		25/APR/75	
46916	PP-VMD	Varig	30		12/JUN/75	
46917	D-ADLO	Lufthansa	30		02/DEC/75	

C/N	Registration	Owner/Operator	Series	First Flight	Delivery	Remarks
46918	PK-GWA	Garuda	30			Not taken-up
	PK-GIA	Garuda			22/MAR/76	Op. with Continental
46919	PK-GWB	Garuda	30			Not taken-up
	PK-GIB	Garuda			29/MAY/76	Op. with Continental
46920	N8702Q	Douglas	40			
	JA8530	Japan Air Lines			01/APR/76	
46921	G-BEBM	British Caledonian	30		23/FEB/77	
46922	EC-CSJ	Iberia	30		17/FEB/76	
46923	N8703Q	Douglas	40			
	JA8531	Japan Air Lines			12/APR/76	
46924	PH-MBN	Martinair	30CF		22/NOV/75	
	PH-MBN	Merpati Nusantara			OCT/77	Leased
	PH-MBN	Martinair			JAN/78	
	PH-MBN	SIA			10/SEP/79	Leased
	PH-MBN	Martinair			26/SEP/79	
	PH-MBN	Garuda			OCT/79	Leased
	PH-MBN	Martinair			25/OCT/79	
	PH-MBN	Garuda			07/NOV/79	Leased
	PH-MBN	Martinair			08/DEC/79	
46925	N54627	Douglas	30			
	EC-CBN	Iberia			20/MAR/73	
						W/O 17/DEC/73, Boston, Ma.
46926	EC-CBO	Iberia	30		19/MAY/73	
46927	EC-CBP	Iberia	30		29/MAY/73	
46928	N902WA	Western Airlines	10		12/JUN/73	
46929	N903WA	Western Airlines	10		27/JUN/73	W/O 31/OCT/79, Mexico City
46930	N904WA	Western Airlines	10		25/JUL/73	
	N904WA	International Air Leases			01/JUN/81	
	N904WA	Capitol International			01/JUN/81	Leased
	N904WA	Hawaii Express			30/APR/83	Leased
	N904WA	World Airways			23/MAR/84	Leased
	N904WA	Arrow Air			10/NOV/84	Leased
	N904WA	International Air Leases			85	
	N904WA	Air Hawaii			85	Leased
	N904WA	International Air Leases			86	
	N	American Airlines			01/OCT/86	Sched.delivery
46931	N54637	Douglas	30			
	AP-AXC	Pakistan International			01/MAR/74	
	C-	CP Air			86	Sched.delivery
46932	9Q-CLT	Air Zaire	30		26/JUN/74	
	G-NIUK	British Caledonian			01/JUN/85	
46933	PH-DTI	KLM	30		27/JUN/74	
	PH-DTI	Philippine Airlines			11/JUL/74	Leased
	PH-DTI	KLM			84	
	PH-DTI	British Midland Airways			01/MAY/84	
	N801AL	Aloha Airlines			01/MAY/84	Leased
	N801AL	Aloha Airlines			84	Purchased
	OY-KDB	SAS			MAY/85	Leased
46934	PH-DTK	KLM	30			Not taken-up
	N19B	Douglas				
	HL7315	Korean Airlines			09/FEB/75	
46935	AP-AXE	Pakistan International	30		19/OCT/74	W/O 03/FEB/81, Karachi Ap.
46936	XA-DUG	Aeromexico	30		17/APR/74	
46937	XA-DUH	Aeromexico	30		15/JUN/74	
46938	N905WA	Western Airlines	10		20/MAY/74	
	N905WA	International Air Leases			01/JUL/81	
	N905WA	Capitol International			01/JUL/81	Leased
	N905WA	Pacific East Air			83	Leased
	N905WA	Capitol Air			18/FEB/83	Leased
	N905WA	Hawaii Express			05/APR/84	Leased
	N905WA	World Airways			23/MAR/84	Leased
	N905WA	Arrow Air			15/NOV/84	Leased
	N905WA	Air Hawaii			DEC/85	Leased
	N905WA	International Air Leases			86	
	N	American Airlines			01/OCT/86	Sched.delivery
46939	N906WA	Western Airlines	10		06/JUN/74	
46940	AP-AXD	Pakistan International	30		02/APR/74	
	C-FCRB	CP Air			MAY/86	
46941	PP-VMC	Varig	30			Not taken-up
	PP-VMQ	Varig			11/NOV/74	
46942	N69NA	National Airlines	10		25/JUN/75	
	N69NA	Pan American			07/JAN/80	
	N161AA	American Airlines			25/NOV/83	
46943	N70NA	National Airlines	10		23/JUN/75	
	N70NA	Pan American			07/JAN/80	
	N162AA	American Airlines			20/JUL/84	
46944	PP-VMA	Varig	30		29/MAY/74	
46945	PP-VMB	Varig	30		18/JUN/74	
46946	N907WA	Western Airlines	10		22/JUN/76	
46947	N126AA	American Airlines	10		10/FEB/78	
46948	N127AA	American Airlines	10		20/MAR/78	
46949	N54643	Douglas	30			
	G-BEBL	British Caledonian			31/MAR/77	
46950	ZK-NZT	Air New Zealand	30		11/NOV/77	
	ZK-NZT	International Lease Finance			10/JUN/82	
	CC-CJT	Lan Chile			10/JUN/82	
	N164AA	American Airlines			86	
46951	PK-GID	Garuda	30		13/JAN/78	
46952	PH-DTL	KLM	30		26/FEB/75	
	PK-GWA	Garuda				Not taken-up
	PH-DTL	Garuda			26/FEB/75	Leased
	PH-DTL	KLM			02/APR/76	
	HS-TGC	Thai International			18/MAY/76	Leased
	PH-DTL	KLM			26/MAR/77	
46953	EC-CSK	Iberia	30		15/MAY/76	
46954	ZK-NZS	Air New Zealand	30		07/JUN/76	
	ZK-NZS	Pan Am			01/APR/79	Leased
	ZK-NZS	Air New Zealand			27/OCT/79	
	ZK-NZS	International Lease Finance			29/JUN/82	
	CC-CJS	Lan Chile			29/JUN/82	
	SE-DFH	SAS			01/AUG/86	
46955	9M-MAS	Malaysian Airline System	30		12/AUG/76	
46956	PH-MBP	Martinair	30CF		24/DEC/76	
	PH-MBP	Philippine Airlines			20/DEC/78	Leased
	PH-MBP	Martinair			03/JAN/80	

C/N	Registration	Owner/Operator	Series	First Flight	Delivery	Remarks
	PH-MBP	Nigeria Airways			SEP/82	Leased
	PH-MBP	Martinair			OCT/82	
46957	5N-ANN	Nigeria Airways	30		27/SEP/76	
46958	PH-DTM	KLM	30			Not taken-up
	RP-C2000	Philippine Airlines				Not taken-up
	RP-C2003	Philippine Airlines			23/OCT/76	
	RP-C2003	Nigeria Airways			23/JUN/81	Leased
	RP-C2003	Philippine Airlines			25/JAN/82	
46959	HS-TGD	Thai International	30		03/MAR/77	
46960	N1033F	Overseas National	30		09/MAY/77	
	N1033F	Seaboard World			10/AUG/78	
	HL7339	Korean Airlines			11/AUG/78	W/O 23/DEC/83, Anchorage
46961	HS-TGE	Thai International	30		05/MAY/77	
46962	N1034F	Overseas National	30		06/JUN/77	
	N1034F	Seaboard World Airlines			24/OCT/78	
	EC-DEG	Spantax			24/OCT/78	W/O 13/SEP/82, Malaga
46963	F-BTDD	UTA	30		02/NOV/77	
46964	PK-GIC	Garuda	30		03/OCT/77	
46965	D-ADMO	Lufthansa	30		09/DEC/77	
46966	JA8536	Japan Air Lines	40		20/NOV/78	
46967	JA8537	Japan Air Lines	40		18/JAN/79	
46968	5N-ANO	Nigeria Airways	30			Not taken-up
	5N-ANR	Nigeria Airways			18/OCT/77	
46969	HB-IHI	Swissair	30	06/SEP/77	22/OCT/77	
46970	G-GFAL	Laker Airways	10		27/FEB/82	
	G-BJZD	British Caledonian			22/FEB/82	
	G-BJZD	British Caledonian Charter			APR/83	Leased
	G-BJZD	Cal Air International			OCT/85	
46971	YV-135C	Viasa	30		21/SEP/78	
46972	YV-136C	Viasa	30		20/APR/79	
46973	G-GSKY	Laker Airways	10		21/MAR/79	
	G-BJZE	British Caledonian			31/MAR/82	Leased
	G-BJZE	British Caledonian Charter			APR/83	Leased
	G-BJZE	Cal Air International			OCT/85	
46974	JA8538	Japan Air Lines	40		04/APR/79	
46975	N103WA	World Airways	30CF		07/MAR/78	
	N103WA	Garuda			14/SEP/80	Leased
	N103WA	World Airways				
	N1856U	United Airlines			86	Leased
46976	N8712Q	Douglas	30			
	C-GXRB	Wardair			14/DEC/78	
46977	N908WA	Western Airlines	10		13/MAR/78	
46978	C-GXRC	Wardair	30		03/NOV/78	
46981	YU-AMA	JAT	30		08/DEC/78	
46982	YV-137C	Viasa	30		05/OCT/79	
46983	N909WA	Western Airlines	10		18/MAY/78	
46984	N128AA	American Airlines	10		01/MAY/78	
46985	PH-MBT	Martinair	30CF		21/DEC/78	
46986	N104WA	World Airways	30CF		15/JUN/78	
	N1857U	United Airlines			JUN/86	Leased
46987	N105WA	World Airways	30CF		04/AUG/78	
	N105WA	United Airlines			86	Sched.lease
46988	YU-AMB	JAT	30		14/MAY/79	
46989	N130AA	American Airlines	10		15/MAR/79	
46990	9V-SDA	SIA	30		23/OCT/78	
	C-GFHX	Wardair			18/SEP/81	
46991	9V-SDC	SIA	30		16/MAR/79	
	C-GCPJ	CP Air			18/MAR/82	
46992	N1035F	Overseas National Airways	30CF		08/SEP/78	
	N1035F	Seaboard World Airlines			15/OCT/78	
	N1035F	United Air Carriers			15/OCT/78	
	N1035F	Seaboard World			19/DEC/78	
	N1035F	Icelandair			03/JAN/79	Leased
	N1035F	TigerAir			80	
	N1035F	Air Florida			13/MAR/80	Leased
	N1035F	TigerAir			16/SEP/82	
	N1035F	Spantax			16/SEP/82	Leased
	EC-DSF	Spantax			82	
	N304FE	TigerAir			05/MAY/84	
	N304FE	Federal Express			05/MAY/84	
46993	9V-SDB	SIA	30		29/NOV/78	
	S2-ACO	Bangladesh Biman			16/AUG/83	
46994	N131AA	American Airlines	10		03/APR/79	
46995	9V-SDD	SIA	30		06/APR/79	
	S2-ACP	Bangladesh Biman			16/AUG/83	
46996	N129AA	American Airlines	10		27/FEB/79	
46997	TU-TAN	Air Afrique	30		10/AUG/79	
46998	HB-IHK	Balair	30		31/JAN/79	
46999	9V-SDE	SIA	30		29/AUG/79	
	PP-VMZ	Varig			01/DEC/79	
47800	N68046	Continental Airlines	10		12/APR/73	
47801	N68047	Continental Airlines	10		10/MAY/73	
47802	N68048	Continental Airlines	10		23/MAY/73	
47803	N68049	Continental Airlines	10CF		04/FEB/74	
	N68049	Federal Express			21/MAY/81	
47804	N68050	Continental Airlines	10CF		04/MAR/74	
	N68050	Federal Express			15/SEP/80	
47805	N68051	Continental Airlines	10CF		08/APR/74	
	N68051	Federal Express			FEB/86	
47806	N68052	Continental Airlines	10CF		11/APR/74	
	N68052	Federal Express			25/MAY/83	
47807	N68053	Continental Airlines	10CF		18/FEB/75	
	N68053	Federal Express			26/OCT/83	
47808	N68054	Continental Airlines	10CF		10/MAR/75	
	N68054	Federal Express			19/MAR/80	
47809	N68055	Continental Airlines	10CF		17/MAR/75	
	N68055	Federal Express			19/MAY/80	
47810	N68056	Continental Airlines	10CF		24/MAR/75	
	N68056	Federal Express			FEB/86	
47811	G-BGXE	Laker Airways	30		15/DEC/79	
	G-BGXE	Douglas			16/APR/82	WFU 16/APR/82 to 14/SEP/84, at Long Beach
	N1852U	United Airlines			14/SEP/84	
47812	G-BGXF	Laker Airways	30		05/JAN/80	
	G-BGXF	Lan Chile			18/JAN/81	Leased

MCDONNELL DOUGLAS DC-10

C/N	Registration	Owner/Operator	Series	First Flight	Delivery	Remarks
	G-8GXF	Laker Airways			18/MAR/81	WFU 28/FEB/82 to 13/MAY/82
	G-8GXF	Douglas			13/MAY/82	WFU 13/MAY/82 to 31/AUG/84
	N1853U	United Airlines			31/AUG/84	
47813	G-8GXG	Laker Airways	30		24/MAR/80	
	G-8GXG	Douglas			07/APR/82	WFU 07/APR/82 to 29/SEP/84
	N1854U	United Airlines			21/SEP/84	
47814	G-8GXH	Laker Airways	30		30/APR/80	
	N5463Y	Douglas			23/APR/82	WFU 23/APR/82 to JUN/85
	LN-RKC	SAS			JUN/85	
47815	G-8GXI	Laker Airways	30		24/JUN/80	
	G-8GXI	Lan Chile			17/DEC/80	Leased
	G-8GXI	Laker Airways			18/JAN/81	
	N5464M	Douglas			30/APR/82	WFU 30/APR/82 to JUL/85
	SE-DFF	SAS			JUL/85	
47816	G-BHDH	British Caledonian	30		30/APR/80	
47817	9V-SDF	SIA	30		30/NOV/79	
	PP-VMR	Varig			30/NOV/79	Leased
	9V-SDF	SIA			24/NOV/80	
	S2-ACQ	Bangladesh Biman			30/NOV/83	
47818	9V-SDG	SIA	30		24/JAN/80	
	PP-VMS	Varig			26/JAN/80	
47819	N109WA	World Airways	30CF		09/APR/80	
	N109WA	Garuda			OCT/80	Leased
	N109WA	World Airways			26/NOV/80	
	N109WA	Air Florida			25/MAR/83	Leased
	N109WA	World Airways			09/JUL/84	
	N109WA	United Airlines			86	Sched.lease
47820	N112WA	World Airways	30CF		14/MAY/80	
47821	N113WA	World Airways	30CF		27/MAY/80	W/O 23/JAN/82, Boston, Ma.
47822	JA8539	Japan Air Lines	40		03/JAN/80	
47823	JA8540	Japan Air Lines	40		24/DEC/79	
47824	N10020	Douglas	40			
	JA8541	Japan Air Lines			20/MAR/80	
47825	JA8542	Japan Air Lines	40		17/APR/80	
47826	JA8543	Japan Air Lines	40		22/MAY/80	
47827	N132AA	American Airlines	10		29/NOV/79	
47828	N133AA	American Airlines	10		15/MAY/80	
	N133AA	Douglas			15/JAN/81	Leased
	N133AA	American Airlines			15/JUN/81	
47829	N134AA	American Airlines	10		23/JUN/80	
47830	N135AA	American Airlines	10		09/JUN/80	
47831	G-BHDI	British Caledonian	30		21/JUL/80	
47832	N914WA	Western Airlines	10		12/MAY/80	
47833	N915WA	Western Airlines	10		05/JUN/80	
47834	EC-DHZ	Iberia	30		23/JUN/80	
47835	OO-SLD	Sabena	30CF		09/JUL/80	
47836	OO-SLE	Sabena	30CF		15/AUG/80	
47837	N84NA	Pan American	30		06/AUG/80	
	N	Air Florida				Not taken-up
	N84NA	Pan American				WFU 15/AUG/80 to 01/DEC/81, Marana Air Park.
	N1855U	United Airlines				
47838	RP-C2114	Philippine Airlines	30		26/NOV/80	
47840	G-BHDJ	British Caledonian	30		18/OCT/80	
47841	PP-VMT	Varig	30		31/JUL/80	
47842	PP-VMU	Varig	30		06/SEP/80	
47843	PP-VMV	Varig	30		09/OCT/80	
47844	PP-VMW	Varig	30		10/NOV/80	
47845	PP-VMX	Varig	30		09/JUN/81	
47846	ZK-NZL	Air New Zealand	30		11/JAN/73	
	ZK-NZL	International Lease Finance			21/OCT/82	
	N136AA	American Airlines			21/OCT/82	
47847	ZK-NZM	Air New Zealand	30		14/SEP/73	
	ZK-NZM	International Lease Finance			16/JUL/82	
	N137AA	American Airlines			16/JUL/82	
47848	ZK-NZN	Air New Zealand	30		18/JAN/74	
	ZK-NZN	Malaysian Airline System			26/NOV/78	Leased
	ZK-NZN	Air New Zealand			16/DEC/78	
	N821L	International Lease Finance			09/APR/81	
	N821L	Western Airlines			09/APR/81	Leased
	N821L	Air Pacific			83	Sub-leased
	N821L	International Lease Finance				
	N144AA	American Airlines			JAN/85	
47849	ZK-NZR	Air New Zealand	30		02/OCT/75	
	ZK-NZR	International Lease Finance			01/DEC/82	
	F-GDJK	UTA			01/DEC/82	
	F-GDJK	LAM			DEC/82	Leased
47850	N68060	Continental Airlines	30		28/AUG/80	Sub-leased
47851	N12061	Continental Airlines	30		25/SEP/80	
47852	JA8544	Japan Air Lines	40		09/DEC/80	
47853	JA8545	Japan Air Lines	40		19/DEC/80	
47854	D-ADRO	Lufthansa	30			Cancelled order
47855	JA8546	Japan Air Lines	40		26/MAR/81	
47856	JA8547	Japan Air Lines	40		09/DEC/81	
47857	JA8548	Japan Air Lines	40		27/JAN/82	
47861	I-DYNA	Alitalia	30		06/FEB/73	
	N3878P	Douglas			27/DEC/82	WFU 27/DEC/82 to 18/DEC/83
	N3878P	Aeromexico			18/DEC/83	
47862	I-DYNE	Alitalia	30		21/MAR/73	
	N390EA	Eastern Airlines			85	
47863	I-DYNI	Alitalia	30		20/APR/73	
	N3878M	Douglas			28/DEC/82	WFU 28/DEC/82 to 27/APR/84
	N3878M	Continental Airlines			27/APR/84	
	N14062	Continental Airlines			JUN/85	Re-registered
47864	I-DYNO	Alitalia	30		14/NOV/73	
	I-DYNO	Sabena			16/SEP/82	Leased
	I-DYNO	Alitalia			20/OCT/82	
	N3878F	Douglas			29/DEC/82	WFU 29/DEC/82 to 18/JUN/84
	N3878F	Continental Airlines			18/JUN/84	
	N14063	Continental Airlines			JUN/85	Re-registered
47865	I-DYNU	Alitalia	30		25/FEB/74	
	OH-LHD	Finnair			26/OCT/83	
	OH-LHD	Malaysian Airline System			10/SEP/84	Leased
	OH-LHD	Finnair			01/OCT/84	
47866	I-DYNB	Alitalia	30		19/APR/74	

C/N	Registration	Owner/Operator	Series	First Flight	Delivery	Remarks
	N391EA	Eastern Airlines			85	
47867	I-DYNC	Alitalia	30		18/FEB/75	
	I-DYNC	Sabena			10/MAY/82	Leased
	I-DYNC	Alitalia			11/JUN/82	
	N392EA	Eastern Airlines			85	
47868	I-DYND	Alitalia	30		05/MAY/75	
	AP-BBL	Pakistan International			23/MAY/83	
	C-FCRE	CP Air			DEC/85	
47869	D-ADTO	Lufthansa	30			Cancelled order
47870	OE-ILD	Lauda Air	30CF			Cancelled order
	N305FE	Federal Express			11/SEP/84	
47886	D-	Atlantis	30			Not taken-up
	N94633	Douglas			12/JUN/73	
	9Q-CLI	Air Zaire			18/OCT/77	Leased
	9Q-CLI	Sabena			01/DEC/77	
	9Q-CLI	Air Zaire			15/JAN/78	Leased
	9Q-CLI	Sabena			15/JAN/79	
	9Q-CLI	Air Zaire			FEB/86	Leased
	F-OGQC	Air Zaire				Leased
47887	D-	Atlantis	30			Not taken-up
	N54634	Douglas			18/NOV/74	
	HS-VGE	Air Siam			10/NOV/76	
	N54634	Douglas			25/FEB/77	
	HL7328	Korean Airlines			21/SEP/79	
47888	YA-LAS	Ariana	30		MAR/85	
	G-MULL	British Caledonian				
47889	N19B	Douglas	30		25/AUG/76	
	AP-AYM	Pakistan International			86	Sched.delivery
	C-	CP Air			18/SEP/73	
47906	OO-SLA	Sabena	30CF		10/JUN/74	
47907	OO-SLB	Sabena	30CF		28/OCT/75	
47908	OO-SLC	Sabena	30CF		12/NOV/73	
47921	D-ADAO	Lufthansa	30		15/JAN/74	
47922	D-ADBO	Lufthansa	30		11/FEB/74	
47923	D-ADCO	Lufthansa	30		25/FEB/74	
47924	D-ADDO	Lufthansa	30		14/NOV/74	
47925	D-ADFO	Lufthansa	30		30/JAN/75	
47926	D-ADGO	Lufthansa	30		28/FEB/75	
47927	D-ADHO	Lufthansa	30		10/MAR/75	
47928	D-ADJO	Lufthansa	30		31/FEB/75	
47929	D-ADKO	Lufthansa	30		27/JAN/75	
47956	OH-LHA	Finnair	30		20/MAY/75	
47957	OH-LHB	Finnair	30		10/OCT/72	
47965	N601DA	Delta	10		16/APR/75	
	N1833U	United Airlines			10/NOV/72	Leased
47966	N602DA	Delta	10		23/APR/75	
	N1834U	United Airlines			21/MAR/83	Reg. not taken-up
	C-FCPB	CP Air			21/MAR/83	Leased
	N1834U	CP Air			28/NOV/72	Leased
47967	N603DA	Delta	10		30/APR/75	
	N1835U	United Airlines			06/JAN/73	Leased
47968	N604DA	Delta	10		07/MAY/75	
	N1836U	United Airlines			27/JUN/83	Reg. not taken-up
	C-FCPC	CP Air			27/JUN/83	Leased
	N1836U	CP Air			16/FEB/73	Leased
47969	N605DA	Delta	10		14/MAY/75	
	N1837U	United Airlines			31/MAR/83	Reg. not taken-up
	C-FCPD	CP Air			31/MAR/83	Leased
	N1837U	CP Air			19/MAY/74	Leased
47980	EC-CEZ	Iberia	30		25/JAN/75	
47981	EC-CLB	Iberia	30		14/MAY/79	
47982	EC-DEA	Iberia	30		15/MAR/83	
48031	JA8549	Japan Air Lines	40			
48200	N110KC	Douglas	KC-10A		01/OCT/81	
48201	79-0433	United States Air Force	KC-10A		17/MAR/81	
48202	79-0434	United States Air Force	KC-10A		30/JUL/81	
48203	79-1711	United States Air Force	KC-10A		28/AUG/81	
48204	79-1712	United States Air Force	KC-10A		22/SEP/81	
48205	79-1713	United States Air Force	KC-10A		24/OCT/81	
48206	79-1946	United States Air Force	KC-10A		26/MAY/82	
48207	79-1947	United States Air Force	KC-10A		21/JUN/82	
48208	79-1948	United States Air Force	KC-10A		28/JUL/82	
48209	79-1949	United States Air Force	KC-10A		09/AUG/82	
48210	79-1950	United States Air Force	KC-10A		08/SEP/82	
48211	79-1951	United States Air Force	KC-10A		18/NOV/82	
48212	82-0190	United States Air Force	KC-10A		06/APR/83	
48213	82-0191	United States Air Force	KC-10A		16/APR/83	
48214	82-0192	United States Air Force	KC-10A		23/MAY/83	
48215	82-0193	United States Air Force	KC-10A		29/JUL/83	
48216	83-0075	United States Air Force	KC-10A		25/AUG/83	
48217	83-0076	United States Air Force	KC-10A		21/SEP/83	
48218	83-0077	United States Air Force	KC-10A		03/NOV/83	
48219	83-0078	United States Air Force	KC-10A		16/DEC/83	
48220	83-0079	United States Air Force	KC-10A		28/FEB/84	
48221	83-0080	United States Air Force	KC-10A		28/MAR/84	
48222	83-0081	United States Air Force	KC-10A		08/JUN/84	
48223	83-0082	United States Air Force	KC-10A		20/JUL/84	
48224	84-0185	United States Air Force	KC-10A		04/SEP/84	
48225	84-0186	United States Air Force	KC-10A		15/OCT/84	
48226	84-0187	United States Air Force	KC-10A		28/NOV/84	
48227	84-0188	United States Air Force	KC-10A		19/DEC/84	
48228	84-0189	United States Air Force	KC-10A		05/FEB/85	
48229	84-0190	United States Air Force	KC-10A		19/MAR/85	
48230	84-0191	United States Air Force	KC-10A		22/APR/85	
48231	84-0192	United States Air Force	KC-10A		05/JUN/85	
48232	85-0027	United States Air Force	KC-10A		21/AUG/85	
48233	85-0028	United States Air Force	KC-10A		02/AUG/85	
48234	85-0029	United States Air Force	KC-10A		04/SEP/85	
48235	85-0030	United States Air Force	KC-10A		19/SEP/85	
48236	85-0031	United States Air Force	KC-10A		11/OCT/85	
48237	85-0032	United States Air Force	KC-10A		04/NOV/85	
48238	85-0033	United States Air Force	KC-10A		03/DEC/85	
48239	85-0034	United States Air Force	KC-10A		04/FEB/86	
48240	86-0027	United States Air Force	KC-10A		27/FEB/86	

MCDONNELL DOUGLAS DC-10

C/N	Registration	Owner/Operator	Series	First Flight	Delivery	Remarks
48241	86-0028	United States Air Force	KC-10A		MAR/86	
48242	86-0029	United States Air Force	KC-10A		APR/86	
48243	86-0030	United States Air Force	KC-10A		MAY/86	
48244	86-0031	United States Air Force	KC-10A		JUN/86	
48252	D-ADSO	Condor	30		22/JAN/81	
48253	I-	Alitalia	30			
48254	I-	Alitalia	30			Cancelled order
48255	I-	Alitalia	30			Cancelled order
48256	I-	Alitalia	30AF			Cancelled order
48257	I-	Alitalia	30			Cancelled order
48258	N19B	Douglas	15	08/JAN/81		Cancelled order
	N1003L	Greyhound Leasing			15/JUN/81	
	N1003L	Mexicana			15/JUN/81	Leased
48259	N13627	Douglas	15			
	N10045	Bank of New York			15/JUN/81	
	N10045	Mexicana			15/JUN/81	Leased
48260	N1844U	United Airlines	10		24/FEB/81	
48261	N1845U	United Airlines	10		09/MAR/81	
48262	N1846U	United Airlines	10		27/MAR/81	
48263	N1847U	United Airlines .	10		20/APR/81	
48264	N1848U	United Airlines	10		20/SEP/82	
48265	SU-	Egyptair	30			Cancelled order
	N345HC	Finnair			11/AUG/81	
	N345HC	Finnair	30ER		DEC/82	
48266	SU-	Egyptair	30			Cancelled order
	N3016Z	Douglas				
	N3016Z	IACO			20/JUL/84	
	N3016Z	Zambia Airways			31/JUL/84	Leased
	N3016Z	IACO				Sched.return
48267	SU-	Egyptair	30		JUL/99	
	N313FE	Federal Express	30AF			Cancelled order
48269	9V-	Singapore Airlines	30		MAR/88	Sched.delivery
48275	N10038	Wilmington Trust	15		06/JUL/81	Cancelled order
	XA-AMM	Aeromexico				Reg. not taken-up
	N10038	Aeromexico			06/JUL/81	Leased
48276	N1003N	Wilmington Trust	15		11/DEC/81	
	XA-AMN	Aeromexico				Reg. not taken-up
	N1003N	Aeromexico			11/DEC/81	Leased
48277	G-DCIO	British Caledonian	30		15/APR/81	
48282	PP-VMY	Varig	30		30/APR/81	
48283	9M-MAV	Malaysian Airline System	30		28/MAR/81	
48285	C-GCPG	CP Air	30		27/FEB/81	
	C-GCPG	United Airlines			05/APR/83	Leased
48286	9G-ANA	Douglas	30			Stored Long Beach JUL/82-FEB/83
	9G-ANA	Ghana Airways			26/FEB/83	
48287	N306FE	Federal Express	30AF		JAN/86	
48288	C-GCPH	CP Air	30		03/NOV/81	
	C-GCPH	United Airlines			25/MAR/83	Leased
48289	N1003W	Bank of New York	15		03/DEC/81	
	N1003W	Mexicana			03/DEC/81	Leased
48290	SU-	Egyptair	30			Cancelled order
	N314FE	Federal Express	30AF		MAY/88	Sched.delivery
48291	N307FE	Federal Express	30AF		MAR/86	
48292	HB-IHN	Swissair	30ER		28/FEB/82	
48293	HB-IHO	Swissair	30ER		03/APR/82	
48294	N1004A	Douglas	15			
	N1004A	Mexicana			13/JAN/83	
48295	XA-MEX	Mexicana	15		13/JAN/83	
48296	C-GCPI	CP Air	30		19/FEB/82	
48297	N308FE	Federal Express	30AF		MAY/86	
48298	N309FE	Federal Express	30AF			
48299	N310FE	Federal Express	30AF			
48300	N312FE	Federal Express	30AF		FEB/88	Sched.delivery
48301	JA8549	Japan Air Lines	30		15/MAR/83	

ADDITIONAL ORDERS

C/N	Registration	Owner/Operator	Series	First Flight	Delivery	Remarks
		United States Air Force	KC-10A		86	Sched.delivery
		United States Air Force	KC-10A		86	Sched.delivery
		United States Air Force	KC-10A		86	Sched.delivery
		United States Air Force	KC-10A		86	Sched.delivery
		United States Air Force	KC-10A		86	Sched.delivery
		United States Air Force	KC-10A		86	Sched.delivery
		United States Air Force	KC-10A		86	Sched.delivery
		United States Air Force	KC-10A		87	Sched.delivery
		United States Air Force	KC-10A		87	Sched.delivery
		United States Air Force	KC-10A		87	Sched.delivery
		United States Air Force	KC-10A		87	Sched.delivery
		United States Air Force	KC-10A		87	Sched.delivery
		United States Air Force	KC-10A		87	Sched.delivery
		United States Air Force	KC-10A		87	Sched.delivery
		United States Air Force	KC-10A		87	Sched.delivery

5N- Nigeria

46957	5N-ANN
46968	5N-ANO
46968	5N-ANR

9G- Ghana

48286	9G-ANA

9M- Malaysia

46955	9M-MAS
46640	9M-MAT
48283	9M-MAV

9Q- Zaire

47886	9Q-CLI
46932	9Q-CLT

9V- Singapore

46990	9V-SDA
46993	9V-SDB
46991	9V-SDC
46995	9V-SDD
46999	9V-SDE
47817	9V-SDF
47818	9V-SDG

AP- Pakistan

46931	AP-AXC
46940	AP-AXD
46935	AP-AXE
47889	AP-AYM
47868	AP-BBL

C- Canada

47966	C-FCPB
47968	C-FCPC
47969	C-FCPD
46940	C-FCRB
47868	C-FCRE
46540	C-GCPC
46541	C-GCPD
46542	C-GCPE
46543	C-GCPF
48285	C-GCPG
48288	C-GCPH
48296	C-GCPI
46991	C-GCPJ
46990	C-GFHX
46976	C-GXRB
46978	C-GXRC

CC- Chile

46712	CC-CJN
46954	CC-CJS
46950	CC-CJT

D- West Germany

47921	D-ADAO
47922	D-ADBO
47923	D-ADCO
47924	D-ADDO
47925	D-ADFO
47926	D-ADGO
47927	D-ADHO
47928	D-ADJO
47929	D-ADKO
46917	D-ADLO
46965	D-ADMO
46595	D-ADPO
46596	D-ADQO
47854	D-ADRO
48252	D-ADSO
47869	D-ADTO

EC- Spain

46925	EC-CBN
46926	EC-CBO
46927	EC-CBP
47980	EC-CEZ
47981	EC-CLB
46922	EC-CSJ
46953	EC-CSK
47982	EC-DEA
46962	EC-DEG
47834	EC-DHZ
46992	EC-DSF
46576	EC-DUG

F- France

46850	F-BTDA
46850	F-BTDB
46851	F-BTDB
46851	F-BTDC
46852	F-BTDC
46852	F-BTDD
46853	F-BTDD
46963	F-BTDD
46853	F-BTDE
46854	F-BTDF
47849	F-GDJK
47886	F-OGQC

G- United Kingdom

46905	G-AZZC
46906	G-AZZD
46727	G-BBSZ
46949	G-BEBL
46921	G-BEBM
46501	G-BELO
46590	G-BFGI
46591	G-BGAT
47811	G-BGXE
47812	G-BGXF
47813	G-BGXG
47814	G-BGXH
47815	G-BGXI
47816	G-BHDH
47831	G-BHDI
47840	G-BHDJ
46970	G-BJZD
46973	G-BJZE
48277	G-DCIO
46501	G-GCAL
46970	G-GFAL
46973	G-GSKY
47888	G-MULL
46932	G-NIUK

HB- Switzerland

46575	HB-IHA
46576	HB-IHB
46577	HB-IHC
46578	HB-IHD
46579	HB-IHE
46580	HB-IHF
46581	HB-IHG
46582	HB-IHH
46969	HB-IHI
46998	HB-IHK
46583	HB-IHL
46584	HB-IHM
48292	HB-IHN
48293	HB-IHO

HC- Ecuador

46575	HC-BKO

HL South Korea

46934	HL7315
46912	HL7316
46915	HL7317
47887	HL7328
46960	HL7339

HS- Thailand

46851	HS-TGA
46892	HS-TGB
46952	HS-TGC
46959	HS-TGD
46961	HS-TGE
47887	HS-VGE

I- Italy

47861	I-DYNA
47866	I-DYNB
47867	I-DYNC
47868	I-DYND
47862	I-DYNE
47863	I-DYNI
47864	I-DYNO
47865	I-DYNU

JA Japan

46920	JA8530
46923	JA8531
46660	JA8532
46661	JA8533
46913	JA8534
46662	JA8535
46966	JA8536
46967	JA8537
46974	JA8538
47822	JA8539
47823	JA8540
47824	JA8541
47825	JA8542
47826	JA8543
47852	JA8544
47853	JA8545
47855	JA8546
47856	JA8547
47857	JA8548
48031	JA8549
48301	JA8549

LN- Norway

46868	LN-RKA
46871	LN-RKB
46871	LN-RKB
47814	LN-RKC

N- United States

47824	N10020
46583	N1002X
46584	N1002Y
48275	N10038
48258	N1003L
48276	N1003N
48289	N1003W
48259	N1004A
48294	N1004A
46500	N101AA
46501	N101AA
46800	N101TV
46502	N102AA
46801	N102TV
46825	N1031F
46826	N1032F
46960	N1033F
46962	N1034F
46992	N1035F
46503	N103AA
46802	N103TV
46975	N103WA
46504	N104AA
46986	N104WA
46505	N105AA
46987	N105WA
46506	N106AA
46835	N106WA
46507	N107AA
46836	N107WA
46508	N108AA
46837	N108WA
46509	N109AA
47819	N109WA
46500	N10DC
46501	N10DC
46510	N110AA
48200	N110KC
46511	N111AA
46512	N112AA
47820	N112WA
46513	N113AA
47821	N113WA
46514	N114AA
46515	N115AA
46516	N116AA
46517	N117AA
46518	N118AA
46519	N119AA
47851	N12061
46520	N120AA
46521	N121AA
46522	N122AA
46523	N123AA
46524	N124AA
46525	N125AA
46947	N126AA
46948	N127AA
46984	N128AA
46996	N129AA
46989	N130AA
46554	N130FA
46994	N131AA
46827	N132AA
46704	N133TU
46705	N133BU
46550	N133PU
47828	N133AA
46752	N133JC
46575	N1340U
46850	N1341U
46551	N1342U
46727	N1348U
47829	N134AA
46851	N1350U
47830	N135AA
48259	N13627
47846	N136AA
47847	N137AA
46911	N138AA
46711	N139AA
47863	N14062
47864	N14063
46712	N140AA
46713	N141AA
46750	N141US
46714	N142AA
46751	N142US
46555	N143AA
46752	N143US
47848	N144AA
46753	N144JC
46753	N144US
46700	N145AA
46754	N145US
46701	N146AA
46755	N146US
46702	N147AA
46756	N147US
46703	N148AA
46757	N148US
46758	N149US
46759	N150US
46706	N151AA
46760	N151US
46707	N152AA
46761	N152US
46708	N153AA
46762	N153US
46709	N154AA
46763	N154US
46764	N155US
46765	N156US
46766	N157US
46767	N158US
46768	N159US
46710	N160AA
46769	N160US
46942	N161AA
46770	N161US
46943	N162AA
46771	N162US
46914	N163AA
46950	N164AA
46908	N166AA
46600	N1801U
46601	N1802U
46602	N1803U
46603	N1804U
46604	N1805U
46605	N1806U
46606	N1807U
46607	N1808U
46608	N1809U
46609	N1810U
46610	N1811U
46611	N1812U
46612	N1813U
46613	N1814U
46614	N1815U
46615	N1816U
46616	N1817U
46617	N1818U
46618	N1819U
46619	N1820U
46620	N1821U
46621	N1822U
46622	N1823U
46623	N1824U
46624	N1825U
46625	N1826U
46626	N1827U
46627	N1828U
46628	N1829U
46629	N1830U
46630	N1831U
46631	N1832U
47965	N1833U
47966	N1834U
47967	N1835U
47968	N1836U
47969	N1837U
46632	N1838U
46633	N1839U
46501	N183AT
46634	N1841U
46635	N1842U
46636	N1843U
48260	N1844U
48261	N1845U
48262	N1846U
48263	N1847U
48264	N1848U
46751	N184AT
47811	N1852U
47812	N1853U
47813	N1854U
47837	N1855U
46975	N1856U
46986	N1857U
46661	N19B
46934	N19B
47889	N19B
48258	N19B
48266	N3016Z
46800	N301FE
46801	N302FE
46802	N303FE
46992	N304FE
47870	N305FE
48287	N306FE
46291	N307FE
48297	N308FE
48298	N309FE
48299	N310FE
46871	N311FE
48300	N312FE
48267	N313FE
48290	N314FE
48265	N345HC
47864	N3878F
47863	N3878M
47861	N3878P
47862	N390EA
47866	N391EA
47867	N392EA
46925	N54627
46852	N54629
47887	N54634
46931	N54637
46853	N54639
47814	N5463Y
46949	N54643
46854	N54649
47815	N5464M
46913	N54652
47965	N601DA
47966	N602DA
47967	N603DA
47968	N604DA
47969	N605DA
46700	N60NA
46701	N61NA
46702	N62NA
46703	N63NA
46706	N64NA
46707	N65NA
46708	N66NA
46709	N67NA
46900	N68041
46901	N68042
46902	N68043
46903	N68044
46904	N68045
47800	N68046
47801	N68047
47802	N68048
47803	N68049
47804	N68050
47805	N68051
47806	N68052
47807	N68053
47808	N68054
47809	N68055
47810	N68056
47850	N68060
46710	N68NA
46942	N69NA
46943	N70NA
46933	N801AL
46711	N80NA
46712	N81NA
47848	N821L
46713	N82NA
46714	N83NA
47837	N84NA
46920	N8702Q
46923	N8703Q
46660	N8705Q
46976	N8712Q
46540	N8715Q
46908	N901WA
46905	N902JW
46928	N902WA
46929	N903WA
46930	N904WA
46938	N905WA
46905	N906CL
46939	N906WA
46946	N907WA
46977	N908WA
46983	N909WA
46645	N912WA
46646	N913WA
47832	N914WA
47833	N915WA
46906	N916CL
46906	N916WA
46727	N917CL
46727	N917JW
47886	N94633

OE- Austria

47870	OE-ILD

OH- Finland

47956	OH-LHA
47957	OH-LHB
47865	OH-LHD

OO- Belgium

47906	OO-SLA
47907	OO-SLB
47908	OO-SLC
47835	OO-SLD
47836	OO-SLE

OY- Denmark

46870	OY-KDA
46933	OY-KDB

McDonnell Douglas DC-10 cross-reference index

PH- Netherlands

46550	PH-DTA
46551	PH-DTB
46552	PH-DTC
46553	PH-DTD
46554	PH-DTE
46555	PH-DTF
46556	PH-DTG
46557	PH-DTH
46933	PH-DTI
46914	PH-DTK
46934	PH-DTK
46952	PH-DTL
46958	PH-DTM
46891	PH-MBG
46924	PH-MBN
46956	PH-MBP
46985	PH-MBT

PK- Indonesia

46918	PK-GIA
46919	PK-GIB
46964	PK-GIC
46951	PK-GID
46685	PK-GIE
46686	PK-GIF
46918	PK-GWA
46952	PK-GWA
46919	PK-GWB

PP- Brasil

46944	PP-VMA
46945	PP-VMB
46941	PP-VMC
46916	PP-VMD
46540	PP-VMO
46541	PP-VMP
46941	PP-VMQ
47817	PP-VMR
47818	PP-VMS
47841	PP-VMT
47842	PP-VMU
47843	PP-VMV
47844	PP-VMW
47845	PP-VMX
48282	PP-VMY
46999	PP-VMZ

RP-C Philippines

46958	RP-C2000
46958	RP-C2003
47838	RP-C2114

S2- Bangladesh

46993	S2-ACO
46995	S2-ACP
47817	S2-ACQ

SE- Sweden

46869	SE-DEA
46872	SE-DEB
46869	SE-DFD
46872	SE-DFE
47815	SE-DFF
46554	SE-DFG
46954	SE-DFH

TC- Turkey

46705	TC-JAU
46704	TC-JAV
46907	TC-JAY

TU- Ivory Coast

46890	TU-TAL
46892	TU-TAM
46997	TU-TAN
46892	TU-TBD
46890	TU-TCG

XA- Mexico

48275	XA-AMM
48276	XA-AMN
48936	XA-DUG
48937	XA-DUH
48295	XA-MEX

YA- Afghanistan

47888	YA-LAS

YU- Yugoslavia

46981	YU-AMA
46988	YU-AMB

YV- Venezuela

46555	YV-133C
46556	YV-134C
46971	YV-135C
46972	YV-136C
46982	YV-137C
46557	YV-138C

ZK- New Zealand

47846	ZK-NZL
47847	ZK-NZM
47848	ZK-NZN
46910	ZK-NZP
46911	ZK-NZQ
46949	ZK-NZR
46954	ZK-NZS
46950	ZK-NZT

Military operated

United States

48200	79-0433
48201	79-0434
48202	79-1710
48203	79-1711
48204	79-1712
48205	79-1713
48206	79-1946
48207	79-1947
48208	79-1948
48209	79-1949
48210	79-1950
48211	79-1951
48212	82-0190
48213	82-0191
48214	82-0192
48215	82-0193
48216	83-0075
48217	83-0076
48218	83-0077
48219	83-0078
48220	83-0079
48221	83-0080
48222	83-0081
48223	83-0082
48224	84-0185
48225	84-0186
48226	84-0187
48227	84-0188
48228	84-0189
48229	84-0190
48230	84-0191
48231	84-0192
48232	85-0027
48233	85-0028
48234	85-0029
48235	85-0030
48236	85-0031
48237	85-0032
48238	85-0033
48239	85-0034
48240	86-0027
48241	86-0028
48242	86-0029
48243	86-0030
48244	86-0031

BRITISH AEROSPACE/AEROSPATIALE CONCORDE

Medium-range supersonic commercial airliner. The world's only supersonic aircraft in scheduled passenger service, the Anglo/French Concorde made its maiden flight in 2 March 1969, and entered service simultaneously with Air France and British Airways on 21 January 1976. It has a maximum speed of Mach 2.04 more than twice the speed of sound. A total of 16 aircraft were produced and production ceased in March 1979.

Dimensions :   Wing span: 83 ft 10 in (25.56m) Length: 203 ft 6 in (62.10m) Height: 39 ft 11 in (12.19m)
Powerplant :   Four Rolls Royce/SNECMA Olympus 593 Turbojets
Performance :   Max cruising speed 1,176 knots (2,179km/h) Range: with max payload 3,363nm (6,230km)
Accommodation: 100 passengers in a four-abreast layout
Manufacturer :   British Aerospace - Weybridge/Bristol Division, Brooklands Road, Weybridge, Surrey KT12 0RN, England
Telephone: (97) 45522 Telex: 27111
Aerospatiale - 37 Boulevard de Montmorency, F-75781, Paris Cedex 16, France
Telephone: (33) 1 524 438 Telex: 620059 F AISPA

C/N	Registration	Owner/Operator	Series	First Flight	Delivery	Remarks
001	F-WTSS	Aerospatiale	Proto.	02/MAR/69		WFU 19/OCT/73
						Preserved Le Bourget
002	G-BSST	BAC	Proto.	09/APR/69		WFU 04/MAR/76
						Preserved Yeovilton
01	G-AXDN	BAC	100	17/DEC/71		WFU 20/AUG/77
						Preserved Duxford
02	F-WTSA	Aerospatiale	100	10/JAN/73		WFU 20/MAY/74
						Preserved Orly
201	F-WTSB	Aerospatiale	100	06/DEC/73		
202	G-BBDG	BAC	100	13/FEB/74		Stored Filton
203	F-WTSC	Aerospatiale	101	31/JAN/75		
	F-BTSC	Aerospatiale			05/JAN/76	
	F-BTSC	Air France			06/JAN/76	Leased
	F-BTSC	Aerospatiale			08/DEC/76	
	F-BTSC	Air France			11/JUN/79	Leased
	F-BTSC	Air France			23/OCT/80	Purchased
204	G-BOAC	British Airways	102	27/FEB/76	13/FEB/76	
	G-N81AC	British Airways			07/JAN/79	
	N81AC	Braniff				Leased
	G-BOAC	British Airways			JUN/80	
205	F-BVFA	Air France	101	25/OCT/75	19/DEC/75	
	N94FA	Air France			12/JAN/79	
	N94FA	Braniff				Leased
	F-BVFA	Air France			0?/JUN/80	
206	G-BOAA	British Airways	102	05/NOV/75	14/JAN/76	
	G-N94AA	British Airways			07/JAN/79	
	N94AA	Braniff				Leased
	G-BOAA	British Airways			JUN/80	
207	F-BVFB	Air France	101	06/MAR/76	08/APR/76	
	N94FB	Air France			12/JAN/79	
	N94FB	Braniff				Leased
	F-BVFB	Air France			01/JUN/80	
208	G-BOAB	British Airways	102	18/MAY/76	30/SEP/76	
	G-N94AB	British Airways			07/JAN/79	
	N94AB	Braniff				Leased
	G-BOAB	British Airways			JUN/80	
209	F-BVFC	Air France	101	09/JUL/76	03/AUG/76	
	N94FC	Air France			12/JAN/79	
	N94FC	Braniff				Leased
	F-BVFC	Air France			01/JUN/80	WFU, stored Paris
210	G-BOAD	British Airways	102	25/AUG/76	06/DEC/76	
	G-BOAD	British Airways/SIA			09/DEC/77	Jointly operated with SIA livery
						carried on port side
	G-N94AD	British Airways			07/JAN/79	
	N94AD	Braniff				Leased
	G-BOAD	British Airways			JUN/80	
211	F-BVFD	Air France	101	10/FEB/77	26/MAR/77	
	N94FD	Air France			12/JAN/79	
	N94FD	Braniff				Leased
	F-BVFD	Air France			01/JUN/80	WFU, stored Paris
212	G-BOAE	British Airways	102	17/MAR/77	20/JUL/77	
	G-N94AE	British Airways			07/JAN/79	
	N94AE	Braniff				Leased
	G-BOAE	British Airways			JUN/80	
213	F-WJAM	Aerospatiale	101	26//JUN/78		
	F-BTSD	Aerospatiale			04/SEP/78	
	F-BTSD	Air France			18/SEP/78	Leased
	N94SD	Air France			12/JAN/79	
	N94SD	Braniff				Leased
	F-BTSD	Aerospatiale			12/MAR/79	
	F-BTSD	Air France			09/MAY/80	Leased
	F-BTSD	Air France			23/OCT/80	Purchased
214	G-BFKW	British Aerospace	100	21/APR/78		
	G-BFKW	British Airways			06/FEB/80	Leased
	G-BOAG	British Airways			MAR/81	WFU 82 to 1985

BRITISH AEROSPACE/AEROSPATIALE CONCORDE

C/N	Registration	Owner/Operator	Series	First Flight	Delivery	Remarks
215	F-WJAN	Aerospatiale	101	26/DEC/78		
	F-BVFF	Air France			23/OCT/80	Leased
216	G-BFKX	British Aerospace	100	20/APR/79		
	G-BFKX	British Airways			31/MAY/80	Leased
	G-BOAF	British Airways			13/JUN/80	

British Aerospace/Aerospatiale Concorde
cross-reference index

F- France

		215	F-WJAN	214	G-BFKW	204	G-N81AC	208	N94AB
		02	F-WTSA	216	G-BFKX	206	G-N94AA	210	N94AD
203	F-BTSC	201	F-WTSB	206	G-BOAA	208	G-N94AB	212	N94AE
213	F-BTSD	203	F-WTSC	208	G-BOAB	210	G-N94AD	205	N94FA
205	F-BVFA	001	F-WTSS	204	G-BOAC	212	G-N94AE	207	N94FB
207	F-BVFB			210	G-BOAD			209	N94FC
209	F-BVFC	**G- Great Britain**		212	G-BOAE	**N United States**		211	N94FD
211	F-BVFD			216	G-BOAF			213	N94SD
215	F-BVFF	01	G-AXDN	214	G-BOAG	204	N81AC		
213	F-WJAM	202	G-BBDG	002	G-BSST	206	N94AA		

AIRBUS INDUSTRIE A320

Short/medium-range twin-engined airliner. The new 150-seat A320 is due to fly in February 1987 with deliveries to airlines commencing in 1988. It is being considered in two main versions, the A320-100 to fill short/medium haul requirements, and the extended range A320-200. To date orders total 134 aircraft and production rate is expected to be six and a half aircraft per month by the end of 1989.

Dimensions :	Wing span: 111 ft 3 in (33.91m) Length: 123 ft 3 in (37.57m) Height: 38 ft 7 in (11.76m)
Powerplant :	will be the CFMI CFM56-5 or the IAE V2500
Performance :	Max cruising speed 487 knots (903km/h) Range: with max payload 1,860km. (3,450km)
Accommodation:	179 passengers in a six abreast layout
Manufacturer :	Airbus Industrie - Avenue Lucien Servanty, BP No. 33, 31700 Blagnac, France Telephone: 033-61 93 33 33 Telex: 530526 F AITO

C/N	Registration	Owner/Operator	Series	First Flight	Delivery	Remarks
01	F-	Airbus Industrie	110	FEB/87		Prototype
02	F-	Airbus Industrie	110			Prototype
03	F-	Air Inter	110		88	Sched.delivery
04	F-	Air Inter	110			
05	F-	Air France	110		88	Sched.delivery
06	G-	British Caledonian	110		APR/88	Sched.delivery
07	F-	Air France	110		88	Sched.delivery
08	G-	British Caledonian	110		88	Sched.delivery
09	F-	Air France	110		88	Sched.delivery
10	F-	Air Inter	110			
11	G-	British Caledonian	110		88	Sched.delivery
12	F-	Air Inter	110			
13	F-	Air Inter	110			
14	F-	Air France	110		88	Sched.delivery
15	F-	Air Inter	110			
16	F-	Air Inter	110			
17	G-	British Caledonian	110		89	Sched.delivery
18	G-	British Caledonian	110		89	Sched.delivery
19	F-	Air France	110		89	Sched.delivery
20	F-	Air France	110		89	Sched.delivery
21	F-	Air France	110		89	Sched.delivery
22	VH-	Ansett	210		SEP/88	Sched.delivery
23	VH-	Ansett	210		88	Sched.delivery
24	VH-	Ansett	210		88	Sched.delivery
25	VH-	Ansett	210		88	Sched.delivery
26	VH-	Ansett	210		88	Sched.delivery
27	VH-	Ansett	210		88	Sched.delivery
28	5B-	Cyprus Airways	230		FEB/89	Sched.delivery
29	VH-	Ansett	210		88	Sched.delivery
30	VH-	Ansett	210		DEC/88	Sched.delivery
31	VH-	Australian Airlines	230		APR/89	Sched.delivery
32	VH-	Australian Airlines	230		89	Sched.delivery
33	F-	Air Inter	110			
34	5B-	Cyprus Airways	230		MAR/89	Sched.delivery
35	5B-	Cyprus Airways	230		APR/89	Sched.delivery
36	F-	Air Inter	110			
37	5B-	Cyprus Airways	230		MAY/89	Sched.delivery
38	VH-	Australian Airlines	230		89	Sched.delivery
39	G-	British Caledonian	110		89	Sched.delivery
40	VH-	Australian Airlines	230		89	Sched.delivery
41	VH-	Australian Airlines	230		89	Sched.delivery
42	G-	British Caledonian	110		89	Sched.delivery
43	YU-	Adria Airways	230		MAR/89	Sched.delivery
44	F-	Air Inter	110			
45	VT-	Indian Airlines	230		89	Sched.delivery
46	VT-	Indian Airlines	230		89	Sched.delivery
47	VT-	Indian Airlines	230		89	Sched.delivery
48	VT-	Indian Airlines	230		89	Sched.delivery
49	N	Pan American	210		89	Sched.delivery
50	VH-	Ansett	210			

ADDITIONAL ORDERS

C/N	Registration	Owner/Operator	Series	First Flight	Delivery	Remarks
	F-	Air France	110		89	Sched.delivery
	F-	Air France	110		89	Sched.delivery
	F-	Air France	110		89	Sched.delivery
	F-	Air France	110		90	Sched.delivery
	F-	Air France	110		90	Sched.delivery
	F-	Air France	110		90	Sched.delivery
	F-	Air France	110		90	Sched.delivery
	F-	Air France	110		90	Sched.delivery
	F-	Air France	110		90	Sched.delivery
	F-	Air France	110		91	Sched.delivery
	F-	Air France	110		91	Sched.delivery
	F-	Air France	110		91	Sched.delivery
	F-	Air France	110		91	Sched.delivery
	F-	Air France	110		91	Sched.delivery
	F-	Air France	110		91	Sched.delivery

AIRBUS INDUSTRIE A320

C/N	Registration	Owner/Operator	Series	First Flight	Delivery	Remarks
	F-	Air France	110		92	Sched.delivery
	F-	Air France	110		92	Sched.delivery
	F-	Air France	110		92	Sched.delivery
	VT-	Indian Airlines	230		89	Sched.delivery
	VT-	Indian Airlines	230		89	Sched.delivery
	VT-	Indian Airlines	230		89	Sched.delivery
	VT-	Indian Airlines	230		89	Sched.delivery
	VT-	Indian Airlines	230		89	Sched.delivery
	VT-	Indian Airlines	230		89	Sched.delivery
	VT-	Indian Airlines	230		89	Sched.delivery
	VT-	Indian Airlines	230		89	Sched.delivery
	VT-	Indian Airlines	230		89	Sched.delivery
	VT-	Indian Airlines	230		89	Sched.delivery
	VT-	Indian Airlines	230		90	Sched.delivery
	VT-	Indian Airlines	230		90	Sched.delivery
	VT-	Indian Airlines	230		90	Sched.delivery
	VT-	Indian Airlines	230		90	Sched.delivery
	JY-	Alia	200		90	Sched.delivery
	JY-	Alia	200		90	Sched.delivery
	JY-	Alia	200		90	Sched.delivery
	JY-	Alia	200		91	Sched.delivery
	JY-	Alia	200		91	Sched.delivery
	JY-	Alia	200		91	Sched.delivery
	YU-	Adria Airways	230		MAR/90	Sched.delivery
	YU-	Adria Airways	230		APR/90	Sched.delivery
	YU-	Adria Airways	230		MAR/91	Sched.delivery
	YU-	Adria Airways	230		APR/91	Sched.delivery
	D-	Lufthansa	200		OCT/89	Sched.delivery
	D-	Lufthansa	200			
	D-	Lufthansa	200			
	D-	Lufthansa	200			
	D-	Lufthansa	200			
	D-	Lufthansa	200			
	D-	Lufthansa	200			
	D-	Lufthansa	200			
	D-	Lufthansa	200			
	D-	Lufthansa	200			
	D-	Lufthansa	200			
	D-	Lufthansa	200			
	D-	Lufthansa	200			
	D-	Lufthansa	200		MAY/90	Sched.delivery
	VH-TAS	Australian Airlines	230		SEP/89	Sched.delivery
	VH-	Australian Airlines	230		90	Sched.delivery
	VH-	Australian Airlines	230		90	Sched.delivery
	VH-	Australian Airlines	230		90	Sched.delivery
	N	GATX Air	200		90	Sched.delivery
	N	GATX Air	200		90	Sched.delivery
	N	GATX Air	200		90	Sched.delivery
	N	GATX Air	200		90	Sched.delivery
	N	GATX Air	200		91	Sched.delivery
	N	GATX Air	200		91	Sched.delivery
	N	GATX Air	200		91	Sched.delivery
	N	GATX Air	200		91	Sched.delivery
	N	GATX Air	200		92	Sched.delivery
	N	GATX Air	200		92	Sched.delivery
	N	Pan American	210			
	N	Pan American	210			
	N	Pan American	210			
	N	Pan American	210			
	N	Pan American	210			
	N	Pan American	210			
	N	Pan American	210			
	N	Pan American	210			
	N	Pan American	210			
	N	Pan American	210			
	N	Pan American	210			
	N	Pan American	210			
	N	Pan American	210			
	N	Pan American	210			
	N	Pan American	210		92	Sched.delivery

BRITISH AEROSPACE/ROMBAC ONE-ELEVEN

Twin-jet short/medium range airliner. Originally launched in 1961, the prototype 111-200 flew for the first time on 20 August 1963 and entered service with British United Airways on 9 April 1965. Steady developments led to the more powerful Series 300, and the Series 400 to meet US requirements. The enlarged Series 500 with accommodation for up to 119 passengers first appeared in June 1967, and the final variant, the 475, in August 1970. A total of 230 aircraft were completed at Weybridge by July 1980, but production of the final two versions continues by ROMBAC in Romania.

Dimensions :	Wing span: 88ft 6in (26.97m) Length: 93ft 6in (28.50m) Height: 24ft 6in (7.47m) (200/300/400)
	: Wing span: 92ft 6in (28.50m) Length: 93ft 6in (28.50m) Height: 24ft 6in (7.47m) (475)
	: Wing span: 92ft 6in (28.50m) Length: 107ft 0in (32.61m) Height: 24ft 6in (7.47m) (500)
Powerplant :	Two Rolls Royce Spey 506 turbofans (200), two Rolls Royce Spey 511 turbofans (300/400), two Rolls Royce Spey 512-DW turbofans (475/500)
Performance :	Max cruising speed 470 knots (871 km/h) Range: with max fuel (3,430km) (200)
	Range: with max fuel (3,677km) (475)
	Range: with max fuel (3,458m) (500)
Accommodation:	89 passengers (200/300/400/475), 119 passengers (500)
Manufacturer :	British Aerospace - Weybridge/Bristol Division, Brooklands Road, Weybridge, Surrey KT12 ORN, England Telephone: (97) 45522 Telex: 27111

C/N	Registration	Owner/Operator	Series	First Flight	Delivery	Remarks
4	G-ASHG	BAC	200AB	29/AUG/63		W/O 22/OCT/63, Chicklade, Wilts
5	G-ASJA	British United Airlines	201AC	19/DEC/63	11/NOV/65	
	N734EB	Barwick Industries			OCT/69	
	XB-MUO	Senor Rane Mexicano			17/APR/75	
	XB-MUO	Comte Oumpico Mexicano				
	XB-MUO	Estado Mayor Presidencial			JUN/76	
	XB-MUO	Mario Vasquez Rano				
	TP-0201	Mexican Government			01/OCT/76	
	VR-CAQ	Omni International			04/SEP/78	
	N3756F					
	N97KR	Kenny Rogers			80	
	N97KR	Tracinda Investment Co.			APR/84	
	N88NB	Continental Broadcasting			MAR/85	
6	G-ASJB	BAC	201AC	14/FEB/64		W/O 18/MAR/64, Wisley
7	G-ASJC	British United Airlines	201AC	01/APR/64	06/NOV/65	
	G-ASJC	British Caledonian			30/NOV/70	
	N101EX	Pacific Express			DEC/81	WFU 02/FEB/84, stored Las Vegas
	N101EX	British Aerospace			84	
	N101EX	Air Wisconsin			84	Leased
	N101EX	Florida Express			04/APR/86	
8	G-ASJD	British United Airlines	201AC	06/JUL/64	05/AUG/65	
	G-ASJD	British Caledonian			30/NOV/70	
	XX105	Royal Aircraft Establishment			21/SEP/71	
9	G-ASJE	British United Airlines	201AC	05/MAY/64	23/JUL/65	
	G-ASJE	British Caledonian			30/NOV/70	
	N102EX	Pacific Express			82	WFU 02/FEB/84, stored Las Vegas
	N102EX	Cascade Airways			84	
	N102EX	Florida Express			JAN/86	
10	G-ASJF	British United Airlines	201AC	28/JUL/64	22/MAY/65	
	G-ASJF	British Caledonian			30/NOV/70	
	N103EX	Pacific Express			82	WFU 02/FEB/84, stored Las Vegas
	N103EX	Cascade Airways			84	
	N103EX	Florida Express			JAN/86	WFU JAN/86 for spares
11	G-ASJG	British United Airlines	201AC	31/OCT/64	06/JUL/65	
	G-ASJG	British Caledonian			30/NOV/70	
	N104EX	Pacific Express			82	WFU 02/FEB/84, stored Las Vegas
	N104EX	British Aerospace			84	
	N104EX	Air Wisconsin			84	Leased
	N104EX	British Aerospace			APR/86	
	N104EX	Florida Express			03/MAY/86	Leased
12	G-ASJH	British United Airlines	201AC	17/SEP/64	12/APR/65	
	G-ASJH	British Caledonian			30/NOV/70	
	N105EX	Pacific Express			82	WFU 02/FEB/84, stored Las Vegas
	N105EX	British Aerospace			84	
	N105EX	Air Wisconsin			84	Leased
	N105EX	British Aerospace			APR/86	
	N105EX	Florida Express			02/MAY/86	Leased
13	G-ASJI	British United Airlines	201AC	22/DEC/64	15/APR/65	
	G-ASJI	British Caledonian			30/NOV/70	
	N106EX	Pacific Express			82	WFU 02/FEB/84, stored Las Vegas
	N106EX	Cascade Airways			84	
	N106EX	Florida Express			JAN/86	
14	G-ASJJ	British United Airlines	201AC	17/SEP/64	06/APR/65	W/O 14/JAN/69, nr. Linate, Milan
15	N1541	Braniff	203AE	09/JUN/64	10/AUG/65	
	N111QA	Braniff				
	N5LC	Stewart Lumber Co.			09/NOV/72	
	N523AC	Amway Corp.			20/DEC/75	
16	N1542	Braniff	203AE	30/OCT/64	20/APR/65	
	N1542	Allegheny			18/AUG/72	
	N1542	US Air			28/OCT/79	
	N1542	Air Illinois			83	
	N1542	Wright Airlines			84	Op. by Air Illinois
	N1542	Atlantic Gulf			MAR/85	
17	N1543	Braniff	203AE	10/FEB/65	11/MAR/65	
	N1543	Flamingo			JUL/71	Leased
	N1543	Braniff			MAY/72	
	N1543	McCulloch			31/MAR/77	
	N1543	Jet Aviation			AUG/77	

C/N	Registration	Owner/Operator	Series	First Flight	Delivery	Remarks
	N1543	Omni International			11/FEB/78	
	VR-BAC	Bermuda Learjet			JUN/78	
	N1543	Spacetronics Inc.				
	N1543	Florida Express			84	
18	N1544	Braniff	203AE	26/MAR/65	06/APR/65	
	N1544	Allegheny			03/MAR/72	
	N1544	US Air			28/OCT/79	
	N1544	Florida Express			JAN/84	
19	N1545	Braniff	203AE	10/MAY/65	12/MAY/65	
	N1545	Allegheny			24/JUL/72	
	N1545	US Air			28/OCT/79	
	N1545	Florida Express			84	
20	N1546	Braniff	203AE	30/MAY/65	02/JUN/65	
	N1546	Allegheny			07/SEP/72	
	N1546	US Air			28/OCT/79	
	N1546	Florida Express				
29	N2111J	Mohawk	204AF	04/MAY/65	15/MAY/65	
	N2111J	Allegheny			12/APR/72	
	N2111J	US Air			28/OCT/79	
30	N1112J	Mohawk	204AF	19/JUN/65	25/JUN/65	
	N1112J	Allegheny			12/APR/72	
	N1112J	US Air			28/OCT/79	
31	N1113J	Mohawk	204AF	03/AUG/65	10/AUG/65	
	N1113J	Allegheny			12/APR/72	
	N1113J	US Air			28/OCT/79	
32	N1114J	Mohawk	204AF	29/SEP/65	29/SEP/65	
	N1114J	Allegheny			12/APR/72	
	N1114J	US Air			28/OCT/79	
33	G-ATPJ	Kuwait Finance Co.	301AG	19/APR/66		Not operated
	G-ATPJ	British Eagle			08/JUN/66	
	G-ATPJ	KLM			29/FEB/68	Leased
	G-ATPJ	British Eagle			AUG/68	
	G-ATPJ	Kuwait Finance Co.			23/NOV/68	
	G-ATPJ	Dan Air			20/MAR/70	
34	G-ATPK	Kuwait Finance Co.	301AG	14/JUN/66		Not operated
	G-ATPK	British Eagle			24/JUN/66	
	G-ATPK	Swissair			DEC/67	Leased
	G-ATPK	British Eagle			APR/68	
	G-ATPK	Kuwait Finance Co.			NOV/68	
	VP-BCP	Bahamas Airways			15/APR/70	
	VP-BCP	Hong Kong Banking Co.			16/OCT/70	
	G-ATPK	Laker Airways			18/FEB/71	
	G-ATPK	Hughes International			22/FEB/81	
	G-ATPK	Bryan Aviation			83	
	G-ATPK	Chemco			APR/85	
	G-ATPK	Dan Air			APR/85	Leased
35	G-ATPL	Kuwait Finance Co.	301AG	13/JUL/66		Not operated
	G-ATPL	British Eagle			22/JUL/66	
	G-ATPL	SAS			AUG/67	Leased
	G-ATPL	British Eagle			FEB/68	
	G-ATPL	Kuwait Finance Co.			NOV/68	
	G-ATPL	Dan Air			SEP/69	
39	VP-YXA	Central African Airways	207AJ	19/FEB/66		Not taken-up
	G-ATTP	BAC				
	G-ATTP	British Eagle			22/APR/66	Leased
	9J-RCH	Zambia Airways			15/DEC/67	
	7Q-YKE	Air Malawi			NOV/70	Leased
	9J-RCH	Zambia Airways			APR/72	
	G-ATTP	Dan Air			31/MAR/75	
40	VP-YXB	Central African Airways	207AJ	16/APR/66		Not taken-up
	9J-RCI	Zambia Airways				Not taken-up
	G-ATVH	British Eagle			27/APR/66	Leased
	G-ATVH	Swissair			01/APR/67	Sub-Leased
	G-ATVH	British Eagle			NOV/67	Leased
	9J-RCI	Zambia Airways			15/DEC/67	
	G-ATVH	Dan Air			31/MAR/75	
41	N1547	Braniff	203AE	18/JUL/65	20/JUL/65	
	N1547	Allegheny			06/APR/72	
	N1547	US Air			28/OCT/79	
	N1547	Air Illinois			82	
	N1547	US Air				
	N1547	Florida Express			JUN/85	
42	N1548	Braniff	203AE	15/AUG/65	18/AUG/65	
	N1548	Allegheny			04/MAY/72	
	N1548	US Air			28/OCT/79	
	N1548	Pacific Express			83	Leased
	N1548	US Air			JAN/84	
	N1548	Florida Express			JAN/84	
43	N1549	Braniff	203AE	20/SEP/65	24/SEP/65	
	N1549	Allegheny			17/APR/72	
	N1549	US Air			28/OCT/79	
	N1549	Florida Express			28/JUN/85	
44	N1550	Braniff	203AE	01/OCT/65	05/OCT/65	
	N1550	Allegheny			MAR/72	W/O 09/JUL/78, Rochester Ap., NY
45	N1551	Braniff	203AE	03/NOV/65	08/NOV/65	
	N1134J	Mohawk			SEP/70	
	N1134J	Allegheny			12/APR/72	
	N1134J	US Air			28/OCT/79	
46	N1552	Braniff	203AE	22/NOV/65	24/NOV/65	
	N1135J	Mohawk			SEP/70	
	N1135J	Allegheny			12/APR/72	
	N1135J	US Air			28/OCT/79	
	N1135J	Florida Express			FEB/85	
49	EI-ANE	Aer Lingus	208AL	28/APR/65	16/MAY/65	
50	EI-ANF	Aer Lingus	208AL	09/JUN/65	12/JUN/65	
	AN-BBS	Lanica			NOV/66	Leased
	EI-ANF	Aer Lingus			APR/67	
51	EI-ANG	Aer Lingus	208AL	25/JUL/65	31/JUL/65	
52	EI-ANH	Aer Lingus	208AL	27/AUG/65	09/SEP/65	
53	G-ASYD	BAC	400	13/JUL/65		
	G-ASYD	BAC	500		05/FEB/68	Converted
	G-ASYD	BAC	475	27/AUG/70		Converted
	G-ASYD	British Aerospace	670			
54	G-ASYE	BAC	410AQ	16/SEP/65		
	N3939V	Victor Comtometer			08/SEP/66	

C/N	Registration	Owner/Operator	Series	First Flight	Delivery	Remarks
	N77CS	Chesapeake & Ohio Railway			26/OCT/72	
	HZ-AMK	Sheikh Abdul Maksoud Khotah			JAN/79	
	N77QS	Concord Promotions			MAY/85	
55	N5015	American Airlines	401AK	04/NOV/65	23/DEC/65	
	N111NA	National Aircraft Leasing			24/JAN/73	
	N1JR	Ryder Systems			26/FEB/74	Leased
	N56B	Sharon Steel			23/JAN/75	Leased
56	N5016	American Airlines	401AK	08/DEC/65	22/JAN/66	
	N5016	National Aircraft Leasing			02/APR/75	
	N5016	Aero America				Leased
	N5016	National Aircraft Leasing			OCT/76	
	N5016	Pacific American Airlines			JAN/77	Leased
	N5016	National Aircraft Leasing			07/JUL/77	
	N5016	Tigerair			JUL/77	
	N120TA	Tigerair				
	N12CZ	Congoleum Aviation			SEP/82	
57	N5017	American Airlines	401AK	03/JAN/66	29/JAN/66	
	N5017	National Aircraft Leasing			15/APR/73	
	N277NS	Executive Air Fleet			01/DEC/73	
	N277NS	Norton Simon			DEC/74	Leased
	N277NS	Executive Air Fleet				
	N277NS	Tigerair				
	N277NS	Executive Air Fleet				
	N277NS	Bryan Aviation			83	
	VR-CBI	Bryan Aviation			83	
	N170FE	Florida Express			20/MAR/86	
58	N5018	American Airlines	401AK	15/JAN/66	15/FEB/66	
	N711ST	Jet Travel			05/APR/73	
	N711ST	National Aircraft Leasing				
	N711ST	Jet Travel				W/O 09/FEB/75, Lake Tahoe
	N128GA	Gulfstream American				Used to Rebuild C/N 117
59	N5019	American Airlines	401AK	29/JAN/66	24/FEB/66	
	N112NA	National Aircraft Leasing			02/JUL/73	
	N5019	1st National Bank of Chicago			18/FEB/74	
	N5019	Hilton Hotels			01/JAN/76	
	N5019	National Aircraft Leasing			21/OCT/76	
	N100CC	Luqa Inc.			13/MAY/77	
	N100CC	Trinity Jet			JUL/82	
	N8JA	Janmar Aviation Corp.				
	N700JA	Janmar Aviation Corp.				
	N700JA	Dee Howard Co.			DEC/84	Tay Test Aircraft
60	N5020	American Airlines	401AK	06/FEB/66	13/MAR/66	
	N5020	National Aircraft Leasing			15/APR/74	
	N102GP	Oceanic Air			20/OCT/75	Leased
	N111NA	National Aircraft Leasing			75	
	HZ-GRP	Saudi REDEC Aviation			24/DEC/75	Leased
	HZ-GP2	Saudi REDEC Aviation			FEB/77	Leased
	HZ-NB3	Saudi Commercial Bank			AUG/79	
	HZ-MAA	Sheikh Al Amudi			OCT/79	
61	N5021	American Airlines	401AK	16/FEB/66	04/MAR/66	
	N5021	Tristar Western			08/AUG/73	
	N5021	The Williams Co.			01/JAN/77	
	N5021	Omnia Aircraft Sales			11/JAN/78	
	N5021	Hustler Magazine			FEB/78	
	N40AS	American Standard Oil Inc.			07/FEB/79	
	N40AS	Florida Express			02/MAY/86	
62	N5022	American Airlines	401AK	03/MAR/66	17/MAR/66	
	VP-BDN	Bahamasair			29/NOV/73	
	C6-BDN	Bahamasair			FEB/75	
	N5022	Dresser Industries			05/OCT/76	
	N5022	Jet Fleet Corporation				
	N800MC	Personal Way Aviation			MAY/84	
63	N5023	American Airlines	401AK	05/MAR/66	21/MAR/66	
	VP-BDP	Bahamasair			20/DEC/73	
	C6-BDP	Bahamasair			FEB/75	
	N217CA	Cascade Airways			84	
	N217CA	Beech Aircraft			JAN/86	Stored Seattle
64	N5024	American Airlines	401AK	23/MAR/66	15/APR/66	
	N5024	National Aircraft Leasing			28/FEB/75	
	N5024	TAG International			29/AUG/76	
	HZ-NB2	National Commercial Bank			17/FEB/78	
65	N5025	American Airlines	401AK	25/MAR/66	07/APR/66	
	N111NA	National Aircraft Leasing			09/SEP/74	
	N111NA	1st National Bank of Chicago			01/OCT/75	
	N825AC	Allis Chalmers Corp.			JUN/76	
	N825AQ	Allis Chalmers Corp.			80	
	N117MR	McMoran Properties Inc.			MAR/82	
66	N5026	American Airlines	401AK	08/SPR/66	23/APR/66	
	G-AZMI	Orientair			20/JAN/72	Leased
	N5026	American Airlines			DEC/72	
	G-BBME	British Airways			09/APR/74	
67	N5027	American Airlines	401AK	16/APR/66	29/APR/66	
	N5027	National Aircraft Leasing			05/AUG/75	Leased
	N5027	National Aircraft Leasing			27/SEP/75	Purchased
	N5027	Oceanic Air			APR/77	Leased
	N5027	Tigerair Inc.			JUL/77	
	HZ-GRP	Saudi REDEC Aviation			77	Leased
	N909CH	Hemmeter Investment Corp.			83	
	N102ME	American Continental Corp.			AUG/83	
68	N5028	American Airlines	401AK	26/APR/66	10/MAY/66	
	N5028	National Aircraft Leasing			73	Leased
	N5028	National Aircraft Leasing			16/DEC/75	Purchased
	N3E	Cameron Iron Inc.			01/MAY/76	
	N200CC	Luqa Corp.			NOV/78	
	N18HH	Helmsley Spear Inc.			APR/80	
69	N5029	American Airlines	401AK	03/MAY/66	21/MAY/66	
	N5029	National Aircraft Leasing			01/APR/74	Leased
	N5029	National Aircraft Leasing			DEC/75	Purchased
	3D-LLG	Louis Luyt Group			01/SEP/76	Leased
	3D-LLG	Tigerair Inc.			77	
	VR-CAM	Omni Aircraft Sales			AUG/77	
	VR-CAM	Eurofinance			OCT/77	
	HZ-AMB	Baroom Aviation			29/APR/78	
70	N1553	Braniff	203AE	05/DEC/65	08/DEC/65	W/O 06/AUG/66, Falls City, Nb.
71	N1554	Braniff	203AE	19/DEC/65	22/DEC/65	

BAe/ROMBAC ONE-ELEVEN

C/N	Registration	Owner/Operator	Series	First Flight	Delivery	Remarks
	N1136J	Mohawk			SEP/70	
	N1136J	Allegheny			12/APR/72	
	N1136J	US Air			28/OCT/79	
	N1136J	Florida Express			FEB/85	
72	N5030	American Airlines	401AK	12/MAY/66	27/MAY/66	
	N5030	National Aircraft Leasing			25/OCT/73	Leased
	N5030	National Aircraft Leasing			25/OCT/75	Purchased
	N310EL	Eli Lilly International			25/APR/77	
73	N5031	American Airlines	401AK	21/MAY/66	09/JUN/66	
	N5031	Bankers Leasing			21/APR/69	
	N111FL	Farmland Co.			APR/69	
	N111FL	Stewart Lumber Co.			29/OCT/75	
	N5LC	James Stewart			APR/77	
	N5LC	Lone Star Industries			APR/84	
74	N5032	American Airlines	401AK	06/JUN/66	21/JUN/66	
	AN-BHN	Lanica			MAR/72	Leased
	VP-BDI	Bahamasair			17/MAR/73	
	G-BBMF	British Airways			18/DEC/73	
75	N5033	American Airlines	401AK	10/JUN/66	27/JUN/66	
	N55JT	Jet Travel			16/JAN/74	
	N5033	Dresser Industries			09/MAR/75	
	A6-SHJ	Government of Ras Al Khaimah			08/MAY/84	
76	N5034	American Airlines	401AK	25/JUN/66	09/JUL/66	
	N5034	National Aircraft Leasing			16/APR/75	Leased
	N5034	National Aircraft Leasing			DEC/75	Purchased
	N5034	Tigerair			JUL/77	
	N5034	TAG International			22/JUL/77	Leased
	N5034	Tigerair				
	VR-BHS	Air St.George			83	
	N333GB	HM Holdings Inc.			MAR/86	
77	N5035	American Airlines	401AK	01/JUL/66	22/JUL/66	
	YR-BCG	Tarom			20/JUN/72	
78	N5036	American Airlines	401AK	23/JUL/66	04/AUG/66	
	N5036	National Aircraft Leasing			08/AUG/73	Leased
	N5036	National Aircraft Leasing			09/AUG/75	Purchased
	N5036	Commonwealth Oil			18/JUL/74	Leased
	N5036	National Aircraft Leasing				
	N9WP	Walter F.Probst			03/DEC/76	
	N9WP	Jet Fleet Corporation				
	N800PW	Personal Way Aviation			FEB/84	
79	N5037	American Airlines	401AK	06/AUG/66	19/AUG/66	
	N5037	Dresser Industries			04/NOV/73	
	N800DM	Jet Fleet Corporation				
	N800DM	Personal Way Aviation			JAN/83	
80	N5038	American Airlines	401AK	23/AUG/66	08/SEP/66	
	N10HM	Jet Travel			19/JAN/73	
	N22RB	Rogers Brothers			JUN/74	
	N90TF	Omni Aircraft			24/MAR/77	
	HZ-MFA	Prince M.F. bin Abdul Aziz			05/AUG/77	
	HZ-BL1	Sheikh Bin Laden				
	HZ-BL1	Sheikh Salem			NOV/80	
81	N5039	American Airlines	401AK	01/OCT/66	13/OCT/66	
	N5039	National Aircraft Leasing			17/JUN/75	Leased
	N5039	National Aircraft Leasing			DEC/75	Purchased
	N5039	Austral			23/DEC/76	Leased
	N5039	Tigerair			JUL/77	
	HZ-RH1	Civil Construction Est.			80	
	HZ-RH1	Al Jabalain Trading Inc.				
	HZ-RH1	Saudi Oger Ltd.				
	VR-CTM	ATM Aviation			SEP/85	
82	N1115J	Mohawk	204AF	19/NOV/65	21/NOV/65	
	N1115J	Allegheny			12/APR/72	
	N1115J	US Air			28/OCT/79	
	N1115J	Florida Express			JAN/84	Leased
	N1115J	US Air			84	
83	N502T	Tenneco	212AR	02/MAR/66	04/APR/66	
84	D-ABHH	Helmut Horten	211AH	15/JAN/66	29/JAN/66	
	N504T	Omni Aircraft			03/JUL/75	
	N504T	Tenneco			13/SEP/75	
85	G-ASTJ	British United Airlines	201AC	25/OCT/65	09/NOV/65	
	G-ASTJ	British Caledonian			30/NOV/70	
	N107EX	Pacific Express			DEC/81	WFU 02/FEB/84, stored Las Vegas
	N107EX	Air Wisconsin				
	N107EX	Florida Express			28/MAR/86	
86	N5040	American Airlines	401AK	14/OCT/66	28/OCT/66	
	N5040	National Aircraft Leasing			05/MAR/74	Leased
	N5040	National Aircraft Leasing			DEC/75	Purchased
	N111NA	National Aircraft Leasing				
	N500CS	Coastal States Gas Corp.			14/DEC/76	Leased
	N500CS	Abco Aviation				
87	N5041	American Airlines	401AK	29/OCT/66	10/NOV/66	
	G-AXCP	Dan Air			14/MAR/69	
88	N5042	American Airlines	401AK	09/NOV/66	19/NOV/66	
	N5042	National Aircraft Leasing			11/FEB/74	Leased
	N5042	National Aircraft Leasing			DEC/75	Purchased
	N112NA	1st National Bank of Chicago			MAY/74	Leased
	N5042	National Aircraft Leasing				
	N5042	Austral			23/DEC/76	
	N5042	Tigerair			JUL/77	
	HZ-NIR	Rashid Engineering			FEB/79	
	HZ-MAJ	Jarallah Corp.			AUG/82	
89	N5043	American Airlines	401AK	21/NOV/66	10/DEC/66	
	VP-BDJ	Out Island Airways			01/JUL/73	Leased
	N5043	American Airlines				
	VP-BDJ	Bahamasair			20/DEC/73	
	C6-BDJ	Bahamasair			FEB/75	
	N218CA	Cascade Airways			84	
	N218CA	Beech Aircraft Corp.			JAN/86	
	N218CA	Atlantic Gulf			APR/86	Leased
	N218CA	Challenge International			MAY/86	Sub-leased
90	N5044	American Airlines	401AK	06/DEC/66	16/DEC/66	
	G-AXCK	Dan-Air			26/MAR/69	
	G-AXCK	British Midland Airways			23/OCT/82	Leased
	G-AXCK	Dan-Air			DEC/82	
	N164W	Westinghouse Electric Corp.			MAR/83	Radar Test Aircraft

C/N	Registration	Owner/Operator	Series	First Flight	Delivery	Remarks
91	PI-C1121	Philippine Airlines	402AP	07/APR/66	19/APR/66	
	PI-C1121	BAC			DEC/71	
	XX919	Royal Aircraft Establishment			16/MAY/74	
92	PI-C1131	Philippine Airlines	402AP	17/SEP/66	24/SEP/66	W/O 12/SEP/69, Manila
93	YS-17C	TACA	407AW	05/DEC/66	14/DEC/66	
94	PI-C1141	Philippine Airlines	402AP	03/JAN/67	16/FEB/67	
	G-AVEJ	Bavaria			23/MAR/67	Leased
	PI-C1141	Philippine Airlines			30/OCT/67	
	PI-C1141	BAC			DEC/71	
	CF-QBR	Quebecair			12/MAR/73	
	5N-AOW	Okada Air			OCT/85	
95	G-ASVT	BAC	200			Not completed
96	N11181	Aloha	215AU	06/APR/66	15/APR/66	
	N1130J	Mohawk			13/MAR/69	
	N1130J	Allegheny			12/APR/72	
	N1130J	US Air			28/OCT/79	
97	N11182	Aloha	215AU	30/MAY/66	07/JUN/66	
	N1131J	Mohawk			27/MAR/69	
	N1131J	Allegheny			12/APR/72	
	N1131J	US Air			28/OCT/79	
98	N1116J	Mohawk	204AF	01/AUG/66	05/AUG/66	
						W/O 23/JUN/67, Nr. Blossburg, Pa
99	N1117J	Mohawk	204AF	26/AUG/66	30/AUG/66	
	N1117J	Allegheny			12/APR/72	
	N1117J	US Air			28/OCT/79	
	N1117J	Quebecair			82	Leased
	N1117J	US Air			DEC/82	
100	N1118J	Mohawk	204AF	20/SEP/66	26/SEP/66	
	N1118J	Allegheny			12/APR/72	
	N1118J	US Air			28/OCT/79	
101	N1119J	Mohawk	204AF	11/OCT/66	15/OCT/66	
	N1119J	Allegheny			12/APR/72	
	N1119J	US Air			28/OCT/79	
102	N1120J	Mohawk	204AF	06/JAN/67	24/JAN/67	
	N1120J	Allegheny			12/APR/72	
	N1120J	US Air			28/OCT/79	WFU, stored Las Vegas
	N1120J	Pacific Express			83	Leased
	N1120J	US Air			02/FEB/84	
103	N1122J	Mohawk	204AF	10/AUG/67	17/AUG/67	
	N1122J	Allegheny			12/APR/72	
	N1122J	US Air			28/OCT/79	
104	N1123J	Mohawk	204AF	19/DEC/67	30/DEC/67	
	N1123J	Allegheny			12/APR/72	
	N1123J	US Air			28/OCT/79	
105	N11183	Aloha	215AU	26/MAY/67	31/MAY/67	
	N1132J	Mohawk			15/APR/69	Leased
	N1132J	Aloha				
	N1132J	Allegheny			APR/72	Leased
	N1132J	US Air			28/OCT/79	Leased
106	YS-18C	TACA	407AW	03/FEB/67	21/FEB/67	
107	G-AVBW	Laker Airways	320AZ	17/FEB/67	25/FEB/67	
	G-AVBW	Air Congo			FEB/68	Leased
	G-AVBW	Laker Airways			MAY/68	
	G-BKAU	Nordic Finance			31/MAR/82	
	G-BKAU	British Caledonian			31/MAR/82	Leased
	G-BKAU	Air Manchester			27/JUN/82	
	G-BKAU	Nordic Finance			JUL/82	
	G-BKAU	British Caledonian			JUL/82	
	5N-AOZ	Okada Air			NOV/83	
108	TI-1056C	Lacsa	409AY	06/MAR/67	14/APR/67	
	YS-01C	TACA			12/APR/73	
	G-BGTU	British Aerospace				
	G-BGTU	Turbo Union			DEC/78	
109	G-AVBX	Laker Airways	320AZ	28/MAR/67	08/APR/67	
	G-BKAV	Nordic Finance			31/MAR/82	
	G-BKAV	British Caledonian			31/MAR/82	Leased
	5N-AOP	Okada Air			SEP/83	
110	G-ATPH	British Eagle	304AX	19/APR/67	28/APR/67	
	G-ATPH	BAC			NOV/68	
	CF-QBN	Quebecair			15/APR/69	
	G-YMRU	Airways International Cymru			APR/84	
111	AN-BBI	Lanica	412EB	08/APR/67	20/APR/67	
	N221CN	Int. Chemical and Nuclear Co			10/OCT/72	
	N767RV	Revlon Corp.			JUN/77	
	N767RV	Executive Air Fleet				
	N90AM	AMM Inc.				
	HZ-JAM	Sheikh Abdul Moumena			OCT/79	
112	G-ATPI	British Eagle	304AX	12/MAY/67	25/MAY/67	
	G-ATPI	BAC			NOV/68	
	CF-QBO	Quebecair			15/APR/69	
	G-WLAD	Airways International Cymru			05/NOV/84	
	G-WLAD	British Midland			01/NOV/85	Leased
	G-WLAD	Airways International Cymru			01/FEB/87	Sched.return
113	G-AVBY	Laker Airways	320AZ	01/MAY/67	09/MAY/67	
	G-AVBY	Air Congo			MAY/67	Leased
	G-AVBY	Laker Airways			FEB/68	
	G-BKAW	Nordic Finance			31/MAR/82	
	G-BKAW	British Caledonian			31/MAR/82	Leased
	5N-AOK	Okada Air			DEC/83	
114	G-AVGP	Channel Airways	408EF	09/JUN/67	14/JUN/67	
	G-AVGP	Bavaria			MAY/68	Leased
	G-AVGP	BAC			JUN/68	
	G-AVGP	Autair			DEC/68	Leased
	G-AVGP	BAC			FEB/70	
	G-AVGP	Cambrian Airways			04/APR/70	
	G-AVGP	British Airways			01/APR/72	
115	G-AWEJ	Channel Airways	408EF	30/APR/68	10/MAY/68	
	G-BBMG	British Airwcys			01/APR/72	
116	G-AWGG	Bavaria	413FA	20/APR/68	25/JUN/68	
	G-AWGG	Export Refinancing Corp.			NOV/68	
	G-AWGG	Austral			DEC/68	Leased
	D-ALLI	Bavaria			26/FEB/69	
	D-ALLI	Gulf-Air			NOV/75	Leased
	D-ALLI	Bavaria				
	DQ-FCR	Air Pacific			25/JUN/78	

BAe/ROMBAC ONE-ELEVEN

C/N	Registration	Owner/Operator	Series	First Flight	Delivery	Remarks
117	LV-JGX	Austral	420EL	10/AUG/68	25/SEP/68	W/O 27/JAN/78, Buenos Aires
	N97GA	Gulfstream American				Rebuilt using C/N 54
118	VC92-2111	Forca Aerea Brasileira	423ET	12/OCT/67	10/OCT/67	
	G-BEJM	Ford Motor Co.			08/DEC/76	
119	PP-SRT	VASP	423ET	19/OCT/67	19/DEC/67	
	N18814	Carver Aero			04/DEC/74	
	N18814	Summit Aero Inc.				
	N18814	Carver Aero			13/AUG/76	
	N114M	Moncrief Oil Co.			20/JAN/77	
	N114M	Moncrief Oil/Montex Drilling			80	
120	N270E	Engelhard Industries	419EP	08/AUG/67	21/SEP/67	
	N44R	Rockwell Manufacturing			14/MAR/73	
	N524AC	Amway Corp.			30/MAR/77	
121	VP-BCY	Bahamas Airways	432FD	28/AUG/68	11/NOV/68	
	G-AXOX	BAC			AUG/69	
	G-AXOX	Gulf-Air			NOV/69	
	A40-BX	Gulf-Air			02/OCT/75	
	G-AXOX	British Island Airways			JUN/78	
	G-AXOX	Air UK			16/JAN/80	
	G-AXOX	British Island Airways			82	Leased
	G-AXOX	Air UK			NOV/85	
122	LV-IZR	Austral	420EL	21/JUL/67	12/OCT/67	
	N3126H				NOV/82	
	C-GQBP	Quebecair			NOV/82	
	5N-AOM	Okada Air			06/FEB/86	
123	LV-IZS	Austral	420EL	05/SEP/67	08/NOV/67	
	N3126Q				NOV/82	
	C-GQBV	Quebecair			NOV/82	
	5N-AOS	Okada Air			OCT/85	
124	A12-124	Royal Australian Air Force	217EA	03/NOV/67	12/JAN/68	
125	A12-125	Royal Australian Air Force	217EA	10/JAN/68	08/FEB/68	
126	PP-SRU	VASP	422EQ	08/NOV/67	19/DEC/67	
	N18813	Carver Aero			04/DEC/74	
	N80GM	Groves Manufacturing			03/AUG/76	
	N18813	Kidde Credit			07/SEP/76	
	N809M	Air Chariot			07/FEB/78	
	N341TC	Tracinda Investment Corp.			08/JAN/79	
	N111GS	Geosource Aviation			80	
	A6-RKT	Government of Ras Al Khaimah			OCT/84	
127	D-ANDY	Bavaria	414EG	06/DEC/67	29/DEC/67	
	G-AZED	Dan Air			21/DEC/71	
128	G-AWKJ	Channel Airways	408EF	29/JAN/69	31/MAR/69	
	G-AWKJ	British United Airlines			03/APR/69	Leased
	G-AWKJ	Channel Airways			08/OCT/69	
	G-AWKJ	BAC			FEB/72	
	G-BIII	Hanson Trust			16/FEB/74	
	RP-C1	Philippine National Bank			JUL/74	
	RP-C1	Philippine Govt.				Stored Gatwick Airport
	G-NIII	Bac One Ltd.			FEB/85	
129	G-AVOE	Autair	416EK	08/MAR/68	19/MAR/68	
	G-AVOE	Cambrian Airways			DEC/69	
	G-AVOE	British Airways			01/APR/72	WFU 30/JUN/80
	G-AVOE	British Aerospace			05/AUG/80	
	G-SURE	Air Manchester			MAR/82	
	G-SURE	British Air Ferries			01/SEP/82	WFU 21/JAN/83, Lasham
	G-AVOE	Dan Air			83	Leased
	G-AVOE	British Aerospace			26/SEP/83	
	N390BA	Britt Airways			11/MAY/84	Not taken-up
130	G-16-4	BAC	424EU	23/JAN/68		
	YR-BCA	Tarom			14/JUN/68	W/O 07/DEC/70, Constanta
131	G-AVOF	Autair	416EK	18/JAN/68	08/FEB/68	
	G-AVOF	Courtline				
	G-AVOF	Cambrian Airways			19/DEC/69	
	G-AVOF	British Airways			01/APR/72	
	G-AVOF	British Aerospace			20/SEP/80	
	G-BMAN	Air Manchester			SEP/82	
	G-AVOF	British Aerospace			83	
	G-AVOF	British Island Airways			83	Leased
	G-AVOF	British Aerospace			04/NOV/83	
	G-AVOF	British Caledonian			DEC/83	Leased
	G-AVOF	British Aerospace			84	
	N492BA	Britt Airways			APR/84	Not taken-up
	G-AVOF	Dan Air			MAY/84	Leased
	G-AVOF	British Aerospace			84	
	N392BA	Britt Airways			MAR/85	
132	G-AWBL	Autair	416EK	22/APR/68	01/MAY/68	
	G-AWBL	Courtline			DEC/69	
	G-AWBL	Cambrian Airways			20/JAN/71	
	G-AWBL	British Airways			01/APR/72	
133	G-AVYZ	Laker Airways	320AZ	08/APR/68	11/APR/68	
	G-BKAX	Nordic Finance			31/MAR/82	
	G-BKAX	British Caledonian			31/MAR/82	Leased
	5N-AOT	Okada Air			SEP/83	
134	N1124J	Mohawk	204AF	04/MAR/68	25/MAR/68	
	N1124J	Allegheny			12/APR/72	
	N1124J	US Air			28/OCT/79	
135	N1125J	Mohawk	204AF	11/JUN/68	17/JUN/68	
	N1125J	Allegheny			12/APR/72	
	N1125J	US Air			28/OCT/79	
	N1125J	O & A International Inc.			MAY/80	
	HZ-MO1	Mohammed Othman			83	
	N4550T	First United Air Inc.			NOV/83	
136	G-AVMH	BEA	510ED	07/FEB/68	12/JUN/69	
	G-AVMH	British Airways			01/APR/72	
137	G-AVMI	BEA	510ED	13/MAY/68	02/APR/69	
	G-AVMI	British Airways			01/APR/72	
138	G-AVMJ	BEA	510ED	15/JUL/68	29/AUG/68	
	G-AVMJ	British Airways			01/APR/72	
139	G-AVMK	BEA	510ED	08/AUG/68	16/SEP/68	
	G-AVMK	British Airways			01/APR/72	
140	G-AVML	BEA	510ED	30/AUG/68	04/OCT/68	
	G-AVML	British Airways			01/APR/72	
141	G-AVMM	BEA	510ED	28/SEP/68	25/OCT/68	
	G-AVMM	British Airways			01/APR/72	
142	G-AVMN	BEA	510ED	14/OCT/68	25/NOV/68	

C/N	Registration	Owner/Operator	Series	First Flight	Delivery	Remarks
	G-AVMN	British Airways			01/APR/72	
143	G-AVMO	BEA	510ED	29/OCT/68	27/NOV/68	
	G-AVMO	British Airways			01/APR/72	
144	G-AVMP	BEA	510ED	15/NOV/68	11/DEC/68	
	G-AVMP	British Airways			01/APR/72	
145	G-AVMR	BEA	510ED	28/NOV/68	05/MAY/70	
	G-AVMR	British Airways			01/APR/72	
146	G-AVMS	BEA	510ED	14/DEC/68	13/JAN/69	
	G-AVMS	British Airways			01/APR/72	
147	G-AVMT	BEA	510ED	10/JAN/69	28/MAR/69	
	G-AVMT	British Airways			01/APR/72	
148	G-AVMU	BEA	510ED	29/JAN/69	19/MAR/69	
	G-AVMU	British Airways			01/APR/72	
149	G-AVMV	BEA	510ED	21/MAR/69	21/APR/69	
	G-AVMV	British Airways			01/APR/72	
150	G-AVMW	BEA	510ED	27/APR/69	02/MAY/69	
	G-AVMW	British Airways			01/APR/72	
151	G-AVMX	BEA	510ED	02/JUN/69	20/JUN/69	
	G-AVMX	British Airways			01/APR/72	
152	G-AVMY	BEA	510ED	09/JUL/69	21/JUL/69	
	G-AVMY	British Airways			01/APR/72	
153	G-AVMZ	BEA	510ED	05/AUG/69	15/AUG/69	
	G-AVMZ	British Airways			01/APR/72	
154	VC92-2110	Forca Aerea Brasileira	423ET	09/OCT/68	13/MAY/69	
	G-BEJW	Ford Motor Co.			08/DEC/76	
155	LV-JGY	Austral	420EL	08/NOV/68	17/DEC/68	W/O 21/NOV/77, San Carlos de Bariloche.
156	YR-BCB	Tarom	424EU	11/DEC/68	17/DEC/68	
157	VP-BCZ	Bahamas Airways	432FD	27/NOV/68	04/DEC/68	
	G-AXMU	Laker Airways			21/AUG/69	
	G-AXMU	BAC			SEP/69	
	PI-C1151	Philippine Airlines			09/OCT/69	Leased
	G-16-14	BAC			19/FEB/71	
	G-AXMU	Gulf-Air			03/NOV/71	
	A40-BU	Gulf-Air			02/OCT/75	
	A40-BU	British Airways			AUG/77	Leased
	G-AXMU	British Island Airways			JUN/78	
	G-AXMU	Air UK			16/JAN/80	
	G-AXMU	British Island Airways			82	
	G-AXMU	Air Ecosse			FEB/84	Leased
	G-AXMU	British Island Airways			FEB/84	
	G-AXMU	Airways International Cymru			A?R/84	Leased
	G-AXMU	British Island Airways			85	
	G-AXMU	Virgin Atlantic			85	Leased
	G-AXMU	British Island Airways			FEB/85	
	G-AXMU	Air UK			10/MAY/85	Leased
	G-AXMU	British Island Airways			MAY/88	Sched.return
158	D-AISY	Bavaria	414EG	17/APR/70	22/APR/70	
	D-AISY	Bavaria-Germanair			01/JAN/77	
	D-AISY	BAC			28/NOV/77	
	HZ-MF1	ARAVCO			MAR/78	
	HZ-AMH	ARAVCO			OCT/78	
	HZ-AB1	Abdul Aziz Al-Ibrahim			SEP/82	
159	YR-BCD	Tarom	424EU	22/JUL/69	30/JUL/69	
	YR-BCD	LAR			15/DEC/75	
160	D-ANNO	Bavaria	414EG	19/DEC/70	22/DEC/70	
	D-ANNO	Bavaria-Germanair			01/JAN/77	
	G-BFMC	Ford Motor Co.			15/NOV/77	
161	PI-C1151	Philippine Airlines	402AP	20/SEP/68		Not delivered
	EC-BQF	TAE			01/MAR/69	
	G-AYHM	Export Refinancing Corp.			FEB/70	
	G-AYHM	Bavaria			01/AUG/70	Leased
	G-AYHM	Export Refinancing Corp			04/JAN/71	
	YR-BCH	Tarom			11/AUG/72	
162	TI-1055C	Lacsa	409AY	14/FEB/69	MAR/69	
	G-AXBB	Quebecair			13/MAR/69	Leased
	G-AXBB	Export Refinancing Corp.			11/APR/69	
	YR-BCB	Tarom			MAY/69	Leased
	G-AXBB	Germanair			14/AUG/69	Leased
	TI-1055C	Lacsa			13/NOV/69	
	G-AXBB	Gulf-Air			07/AUG/74	
	A40-BB	Gulf-Air			02/OCT/75	
	G-AXBB	British Island Airways			JUN/78	
	G-AXBB	Air UK			16/JAN/80	
	G-AXBB	British Island Airways			82	
	G-AXBB	Air UK			OCT/85	Leased
	G-AXBB	British Island Airways			OCT/88	Sched.return
163	D-AILY	Bavaria	414EG	26/JAN/70	26/FEB/70	
	N123H	Hilton Hotels			14/APR/76	
165	YR-BCE	Tarom	424EU	29/SEP/69	23/NOV/69	
166	G-AWXJ	Autair	416EK	27/FEB/69	20/MAR/69	
	G-AWXJ	BAC			NOV/69	
	HB-ITK	Aeroleasing			SEP/70	
	9V-BEF	Robinair			04/NOV/71	
	9V-BEF	Air Siam			MAY/72	Leased
	PK-PJC	Pelita Air Service			02/FEB/73	
	G-AWXJ	British Island Airways				
	G-CBIA	British Island Airways				
	G-CBIA	Air UK			16/JAN/80	
	G-CBIA	British Island Airways			MAY/82	
167	YR-BCC	Tarom	424EU	26/JUN/69	03/JUL/69	
	YR-BCC	LAR			15/DEC/75	
168	YR-BCF	Tarom	424EU	18/NOV/69	13/DEC/69	
	YR-BCF	LAR			APR/76	
174	G-AWYR	British United Airlines	501EX	25/MAR/69	11/APR/69	
	G-AWYR	British Caledonian			30/NOV/70	
175	G-AWYS	British United Airlines	501EX	16/APR/69	24/APR/69	
	G-AWYS	Swissair			23/APR/70	Leased
	G-AWYS	British United Airlines			31/OCT/70	
	G-AWYS	British Caledonian			30/NOV/70	
176	G-AWYT	British United Airlines	501EX	06/MAY/69	13/MAY/69	
	G-AWYT	British Caledonian			30/NOV/70	
177	G-AWYU	British United Airlines	501EX	10/JUN/69	17/JUN/69	
	G-AWYU	British Caledonian			30/NOV/70	
178	G-AWYV	British United Airlines	501EX	20/JUN/69	26/JUN/69	

BAe/ROMBAC ONE-ELEVEN

C/N	Registration	Owner/Operator	Series	First Flight	Delivery	Remarks
	G-AWYV	British Caledonian			30/NOV/70	
179	N1126J	Mohawk	204AF	15/JUL/68	02/AUG/68	
	N1126J	Allegheny			12/APR/72	
	N1126J	US Air			28/OCT/79	
180	N1127J	Mohawk	204AF	19/DEC/68	31/DEC/68	
	N1127J	Allegheny			12/APR/72	
	N1127J	US Air			28/OCT/79	
181	N1128J	Mohawk	204AF	10/JAN/69	21/JAN/69	
	N1128J	Allegheny			12/APR/72	
	N1128J	US Air			28/OCT/79	
182	N1129J	Mohawk	204AF	12/MAY/69	17/MAY/69	
	N1129J	Allegheny			12/APR/72	
	N1129J	US Air			28/OCT/79	
183	N503T	Tenneco	212AR	07/JUN/69	08/JUL/69	
184	G-AWWX	Caledonian	509EW	11/FEB/69	29/MAR/69	
	G-AWWX	British Caledonian			30/NOV/70	
	G-AWWX	Dan Air			03/OCT/75	
185	G-AWWY	Caledonian	509EW	11/MAR/69	31/MAR/69	
	G-AWWY	British Caledonian			30/NOV/70	
	LV-JNU	Austral			FEB/74	Leased
	LV-JNU	Austral			OCT/75	Purchased
	LV-LHT	Austral				
186	G-AWWZ	Caledonian	509EW	18/APR/69	28/APR/69	
	G-AWWZ	British Caledonian			30/NOV/70	
	G-AWWZ	Monarch			OCT/75	Leased
	G-AWWZ	Monarch			14/JAN/77	Purchased
	G-AWWZ	British Island Airways			OCT/85	
187	D-ALAT	Paninternational	515FB	22/MAY/69	13/JUN/69	
	G-AZPY	BAC			MAR/72	
	D-AMAS	Germanair			10/MAY/72	
	D-AMAS	Bavaria-Germanair			01/JAN/77	
	LV-PEW	Austral			NOV/79	
	LV-MZM	Austral				
188	VP-BCN	Bahamas Airways	517FE	17/JUL/69	23/JUL/69	
	VP-BCN	Hong Kong Bank			16/SEP/70	
	G-AZEB	Courtline			08/DEC/71	
	VP-LAP	LIAT			01/DEC/72	
	G-AZEB	Courtline			03/MAR/74	Leased
	RP-C1186	Philippine Airlines			27/SEP/75	
189	VP-BCO	Bahamas Airways	517FE	21/JUL/69	29/JUL/69	
	VP-BCO	Hong Kong Bank			18/OCT/70	
	G-AZEC	Courtline			24/SEP/71	
	VP-LAR	LIAT			01/DEC/73	
	G-AZEC	Courtline			05/APR/74	
	RP-C1187	Philippine Airlines			25/NOV/75	
190	D-AMIE	Germanair	534FF	02/SEP/69	17/OCT/69	
	RP-C1184	Philippine Airlines			12/APR/74	
191	G-AXJK	British United Airlines	501EX	14/AUG/69	05/MAR/70	
	G-AXJK	British Caledonian			30/NOV/70	
	G-AXJK	Austral			DEC/75	Leased
	G-AXJK	British Caledonian			APR/76	
	G-AXJK	Austrian Airlines			MAY/81	Leased
	G-AXJK	British Caledonian			81	
192	LV-JNR	Austral	521FH	15/OCT/69	21/NOV/69	
	PP-SDP	Sadia			17/SEP/70	Leased
	LV-JNR	Austral			JAN/71	
	G-AYXB	Courtline			17/APR/71	Leased
	LV-JNR	Austral			14/OCT/71	W/O 04/DEC/73, Bahia Blanca.
193	G-AXLL	British Midland Airways	523FJ	25/SEP/69	17/FEB/70	
	PP-SDT	TransBrasil			05/MAY/73	
	OB-R-1137	Faucett			08/AUG/77	Leased
	OB-R-1173	Faucett				
	G-AXLL	British Aerospace			09/OCT/83	
	G-AXLL	British Caledonian			DEC/83	
194	LV-JNS	Austral	521H	08/OCT/69	18/NOV/69	
195	D-AMUR	Germanair	534FF	20/OCT/69	16/DEC/69	
	RP-C1185	Philippine Airlines			DEC/74	
196	LV-JNT	Austral	521FH	06/NOV/69	25/NOV/69	
197	D-AMOR	Germanair	534FF	09/DEC/69	20/MAR/70	
	D-AMOR	Bavaria-Germanair			01/JAN/77	
	D-AMOR	Hapag Lloyd			JAN/79	
	LV-PFR	Austral			DEC/79	
	LV-OAX	Austral			81	
198	VP-BCQ	Bahamas Airways	517FE	12/JAN/70		Not delivered
	G-16-12	BAC				
	VP-LAN	LIAT			20/JUN/72	
	G-BCCV	Courtline			03/APR/74	
	G-BCXR	Monarch			20/FEB/75	
	G-BCXR	British Aerospace			23/MAR/83	
	G-BCXR	Dan Air			23/MAR/83	
199	G-AXLM	British Midland Airways	523FJ	22/DEC/69	05/MAR/70	
	G-AXLM	Courtline			26/SEP/73	
	PP-SDV	TransBrasil			05/APR/74	
	G-AXLM	Cyprus Airways			27/FEB/77	
	4X-BAS	Arkia			20/MAY/78	
	RP-C1193	Philippine Airlines			JUL/80	
200	G-AXMF	Courtline	518FG	25/NOV/69	05/DEC/69	
	G-AXMF	BAC			SEP/74	
	PP-TYV	TransBrasil			10/DEC/74	Leased
	G-AXMF	BAC			28/JAN/78	
	LV-MEX	Austral			28/JAN/78	
201	G-AXMG	Courtline	518FG	08/DEC/69	18/DEC/69	
	G-AXMG	BAC			SEP/74	
	5B-DAF	Cyprus Airways			74	Leased
	G-AXMG	BAC			11/DEC/75	
	G-AXMG	Bavaria			MAY/76	Leased
	G-AXMG	BAC				
	G-AXMG	Monarch			OCT/76	Leased
	G-AXMG	British Island Airways			MAY/85	Sub-leased
202	G-AXMH	Courtline	518FG	12/JAN/70	11/FEB/70	
	G-AXMH	BAC			SEP/74	
	G-BDAS	Dan Air			21/FEB/75	Leased
203	G-AXMI	Courtline	518FG	01/JAN/70	24/MAR/70	
	G-AXMI	BAC			SEP/74	
	G-BDAE	Dan Air			21/FEB/75	Leased

C/N	Registration	Owner/Operator	Series	First Flight	Delivery	Remarks
204	G-AXMJ	Courtline	518FG	17/FEB/70	12/MAR/70	
	G-AXMJ	BAC			SEP/74	
	G-BCWG	Monarch			03/FEB/75	Leased
	G-BCWG	BAC			76	
	G-BCWG	Cyprus Airways			30/OCT/76	Leased
	G-BCWG	BAC			04/FEB/78	
	RP-C1189	Philippine Airlines			11/AUG/78	
205	G-AXMK	Courtline	518FG	07/APR/70	17/APR/70	
	TG-ARA	Aviateca			23/NOV/70	Leased
	G-AXMK	Courtline			06/APR/71	
	VP-LAK	LIAT			22/NOV/71	Leased
	G-AXMK	Courtline			02/JUL/72	
	G-AXMK	BAC			74	
	G-AXMK	Germanair			MAY/74	Leased
	G-BCWA	Dan Air			29/JAN/76	
206	G-AXML	Courtline	518FG	22/APR/70	30/APR/70	
	AN-BHJ	Lanica			22/DEC/71	Leased
	G-AXML	Courtline			17/MAR/72	
	G-AXML	BAC			SEP/74	
	PT-TYW	Transbrasil			10/OCT/74	
	TG-AVA	Aviateca			04/SEP/75	
	LV-MRZ	Austral			MAR/79	
207	D-ALAR	Paninternational	515FB	01/MAY/70	13/MAY/70	W/O 06/SEP/71, Hamburg
208	D-ALAS	Paninternational	515FB	13/MAR/70	20/MAY/70	
	G-AZPE	BAC			18/MAR/72	
	G-AZPE	British Caledonian			14/AUG/72	
	G-AZPE	BAC			20/OCT/72	
	TI-LRK	Lacsa			20/DEC/73	
	G-BJYL	Dan Air			MAY/82	
209	G-AXJL	British United Airlines	501EX	20/FEB/70	03/MAR/70	
	G-AXJL	British Caledonian			30/NOV/70	
	RP-C1188	Philippine Airlines			01/JUL/77	
210	G-AXYD	Caledonian	509EW	06/MAR/70	18/MAR/70	
	G-AXYD	British Caledonian			30/NOV/70	
	G-AXYD	Dan-Air			APR/76	
	G-AXYD	British Caledonian			31/JAN/84	Leased
	G-AXYD	Dan Air			MAR/84	
211	G-AXLN	British Midland Airways	523FJ	04/FEB/70	12/MAR/70	
	G-AXLN	Courtline			MAR/72	Leased
	G-AXLN	British Midland Airways			26/AUG/73	
	PP-SDU	TransBrasil			26/SEP/73	
	PP-SDU	BAC			78	
	TG-AYA	Aviateca			20/APR/78	
	VR-CAL	Cayman Airways			27/JUN/78	
	VR-CAL	Interlease			OCT/82	
	G-AXLN	British Island Airways			17/APR/84	
212	HB-ITL	Phoenix	529FR	14/MAY/70	01/APR/71	
	G-16-13	BAC			APR/74	
	LV-LOX	Austral			15/JAN/75	W/O 07/MAY/81, River de la Plata
213	PI-C1161	Philippine Airlines	527FK	30/SEP/70	26/OCT/71	
	RP-C1161	Philippine Airlines			01/JUL/74	W/O 23/MAY/76, Zamboanga
214	G-AXJM	British United Airlines	501EX	17/MAR/70	25/MAR/70	
	G-AXJM	British Caledonian			30/NOV/70	
	7Q-YKI	Air Malawi				Leased
	G-AXJM	British Caledonian				
215	PI-C1171	Philippine Airlines	527FK	09/OCT/70	29/OCT/71	
	RP-C1171	Philippine Airlines			01/JUL/74	
226	PI-C1181	Philippine Airlines	527FL	03/NOV/70	03/NOV/71	
	RP-C1181	Philippine Airlines			01/JUL/74	
227	D-AMUC	Bavaria	528L	28/OCT/70	03/DEC/70	
	D-AMUC	Bavaria-Germanair			01/JAN/77	
	D-AMUC	Hapag Lloyd			JAN/79	
	LV-OAY	Austral			JAN/80	
228	PP-SDQ	Sadia	520FN	21/SEP/70	15/OCT/70	
	PP-SDQ	TransBrasil				W/O 01/FEB/74, Sao Paulo
229	D-ALAQ	Paninternational	515FB	04/DEC/70	12/MAR/71	
	G-AZPZ	BAC			MAR/72	
	D-AMAM	Germanair			25/MAY/72	
	D-AMAM	Bavaria-Germanair			01/JAN/77	
	D-AMAM	Hapag Lloyd			JAN/79	
	G-AZPZ	Dan Air			01/MAY/81	Leased
	D-AMAM	Hapag Lloyd			FEB/82	
	G-AZPZ	British Caledonian			MAR/82	
230	PP-SDR	Sadia	520FN	11/NOV/70	31/DEC/70	
	PP-SDR	TransBrasil			72	
	G-BEKA	BAC			DEC/76	
	4X-BAR	Arkia			16/AUG/77	Leased
	G-BEKA	BAC			78	
	G-BEKA	British Airways			78	
	G-BEKA	Dan Air			01/OCT/79	
231	TG-AZA	Aviateca	516FP	16/DEC/70	25/MAR/71	
	RP-C1194	Philippine Airlines			JUL/80	
232	G-AYOR	British Caledonian	518FG	29/JAN/71	18/MAR/71	
	G-AYOR	Courtline			18/MAR/71	Leased
	G-BDAT	Dan Air			31/JAN/75	
233	G-AYOP	British Caledonian	530FX	03/MAR/71	31/MAR/71	
	G-AYOP	Courtline			31/MAR/71	Leased
	G-AYOP	British Caledonian			15/MAR/73	
234	D-ALFA	Bavaria	528FL	08/FEB/71	26/FEB/71	
	D-ALFA	Bavaria-Germanair			01/JAN/77	
	D-ALFA	Hapag Lloyd			JAN/79	
	D-ALFA	British Aerospace			81	
	G-BJRT	British Caledonian			OCT/81	
235	D-AMAT	Germanair	524FF	17/APR/71	08/MAY/71	
	D-AMAT	Bavaria-Germanair			01/JAN/77	
	D-AMAT	Hapag Lloyd			JAN/79	
	7Q-YKK	Air Malawi			NOV/82	
236	PP-SDS	TransBrasil	531FS	13/MAY/70	20/MAY/71	W/O 04/JAN/77, Vira Copos Ap., Campinos
237	G-AYWB	British Caledonian	531FS	13/MAY/71	20/MAY/71	
	TI-1084C	Lacsa			26/MAY/71	Reg not taken-up
	TI-LRF	Lacsa			DEC/71	
	TI-LRL	Lacsa			14/OCT/75	
	VR-CAB	Cayman Airways			01/NOV/79	
	VR-CAB	Interlease			OCT/82	

Airliner Production List 1987

C/N	Registration	Owner/Operator	Series	First Flight	Delivery	Remarks
	G-AYWB	British Island Airways			MAY/84	
238	D-ANUE	Bavaria	528FL	28/FEB/72	15/MAR/72	
	D-ANUE	Bavaria-Germanair			01/JAN/77	
	D-ANUE	Hapag Lloyd			JAN/79	
	D-ANUE	British Aerospace			81	
	G-BJRU	British Caledonian			OCT/81	
239	G-AYUW	BAC	476FM	05/APR/71		
	OB-R-953	Faucett			20/JUL/71	
	OB-R-953	Aircraft Investment Corp.			JAN/83	
240	G-AZMF	British Caledonian	30FX	04/MAR/72	14/MAR/72	
	PP-TYY	TransBrasil			16/FEB/74	Leased
	G-AZMF	British Caledonian			30/NOV/74	Leased
	G-AZMF	Austrian Airlines			01/APR/75	Leased
	G-AZMF	British Caledonian				
	G-AZMF	British Airways			27/OCT/78	Leased
	G-AZMF	British Caledonian			30/APR/79	
	7Q-YKJ	Air Malawi			80	Leased
	G-AZMF	British Caledonian			APR/80	
241	G-16-16	BAC	76FM	07/JUL/71		
	G-AZUK	BAC				
	OB-R-1080	Faucett			20/JUL/74	
	OB-R-1080	Aircraft Investment Corp.			JAN/83	
242	TI-1059C	Lacsa	31FS			Reg. not taken-up
	TI-LRI	Lacsa			07/NOV/72	
	G-BJYM	Dan Air			MAY/82	Leased
243	7Q-YKF	Air Malawi	81FW		26/FEB/72	
244	TI-1096C	Lacsa	31FS			Reg. not taken-up
	TI-LRJ	Lacsa			15/MAY/73	
	TI-LRJ	Cayman Airways				Leased
	TI-LRJ	Lacsa				
	G-BJMV	Dan Air			11/NOV/81	Leased
	G-BJMV	Dan Air			OCT/82	Purchased
245	DQ-FBQ	Air Pacific	79FU	08/FEB/72	04/MAR/72	
	7Q-YKG	Air Malawi			05/JUL/74	Leased
	DQ-FBQ	Air Pacific			NOV/75	
	ZE433	Royal Aircraft Establishment			22/MAR/84	
246	RP-C1182	Philippine Airlines	27FK		14/JUN/74	W/O AUG/84
247	1001	Oman Air Force	85GD		28/DEC/74	
	551	Oman Air Force			01/JUL/76	
248	RP-C1183	Philippine Airlines	27FK		JUN/74	
249	1002	Oman Air Force	85GD		25/JAN/75	
	552	Oman Air Force			01/JUL/76	
250	DQ-FBV	Air Pacific	79FU		04/AUG/73	
	ZE432	Royal Aircraft Establishment			12/MAR/84	
251	1003	Oman Air Force	485GD		01/NOV/75	
	553	Oman Air Force			01/JUL/76	
252	YR-BCI	Tarom	525FT	20/DEC/76	21/MAR/77	
253	YR-BCJ	Tarom	525FT	17/MAR/77	05/APR/77	
	TC-JCP	Mamara Hava Yollari			MAY/86	Leased
	YR-BCJ	Tarom			JUN/86	
254	YR-BCK	Tarom	525FT		14/MAY/77	
255	YR-BCL	Tarom	525FT	17/MAY/77	09/JUL/77	
	OE-ILC	Lauda Air			85	Leased
	YR-BCL	Tarom			85	
	TC-AKA	Istanbul Hava Yollari			MAY/86	Leased
256	YR-BCM	Tarom	525FT	08/AUG/77	25/AUG/77	
	OE-ILD	Lauda Air			85	Leased
	YR-BCM	Tarom			MAR/86	
257	5B-DAG	Cyprus Airways	537GF	16/NOV/77	09/DEC/77	
258	5B-DAH	Cyprus Airways	537GF	18/JAN/78	28/JAN/78	
259	HZ-MAM	Sheikh M. Al Midani	488GH		15/MAY/78	
	LX-MAM	Sheikh M. Al Midani			MAR/86	
260	G-BLHD	British Aerospace	492GM			
	G-BLHD	McAlpine Aviation			APR/84	Stored
261	5B-DAJ	Cyprus Airways	537GF		06/OCT/78	
	G-BFWN	British Airways			07/OCT/78	Leased
	5A-DAJ	Cyprus Airways			APR/80	
262	G-BLDH	British Aerospace	475			
	G-BLDH	McAlpine Aviation			MAY/84	
263	G-BGKE	British Airways	539		22/FEB/80	
264	G-BGKF	British Airways	539	29/MAY/80	12/JUN/80	
265	G-BGKG	British Airways	539		AUG/80	
266	YR-BCN	Tarom	525FT	13/NOV/80	19/JAN/81	
	YU-AKN	Inex Adria			APR/85	Leased
	YR-BCN	Tarom			85	
	YU-ANM	Adria Airways			MAY/86	Leased
267	YR-BCR	Tarom	487GK	26/JUN/81	JUL/81	
	YR-BCR	Anglo Cargo			17/MAR/86	Leased
272	YR-BCQ	Tarom	525RC		82	
	G-TARO	Dan Air			16/MAR/84	Leased
	YR-BCQ	Tarom			28/DEC/85	
	YU-ANN	Adria Airways			MAY/86	Leased
274	YR-BCO	Tarom	525FT	15/FEB/82	15/MAR/82	
401	YR-BRA	RomBac	561RC	18/SEP/82		Assembled by RomBac
	YR-BRA	Tarom			24/DEC/82	
402	YR-BRB	RomBac	561RC		83	Assembled by RomBac
	YR-BRB	Tarom			SEP/83	
	EI-BSS	Ryan Air			JUL/86	
403	YR-BRC	RomBac	561RC		84	Assembled by RomBac
	YR-BRC	Tarom			JAN/86	
404	YR-BRD	RomBac	561RC		85	Assembled by RomBac
	YR-BRD	Tarom			MAR/86	

3D- Swaziland

69	3D-LLG

4X- Israel

230	4X-BAR
199	4X-BAS

5B- Cyprus

201	5B-DAF
257	5B-DAG
258	5B-DAH
261	5B-DAJ

5N- Nigeria

113	5N-AOK
122	5N-AOM
109	5N-AOP
123	5N-AOS
133	5N-AOT
94	5N-AOW
107	5N-AOZ

7Q- Malawi

39	7Q-YKE
243	7Q-YKF
245	7Q-YKG
214	7Q-YKI
240	7Q-YKJ
235	7Q-YKK

9J- Zambia

39	9J-RCH
40	9J-RCI

9V- Singapore

166	9V-BEF

A40- Oman

162	A40-BB
157	A40-BU
121	A40-BX

A6- United Arab Emirates

126	A6-RKT
75	A6-SHJ

AN- Nicaragua

111	AN-BBI
50	AN-BBS
206	AN-BHJ
74	AN-BHN

C- Canada

122	C-GQBP
123	C-GQBV

C6- Bahamas

89	C6-BDJ
62	C6-BDN
63	C6-BDP

CF- Canada

110	CF-QBN
112	CF-QBO
94	CF-QBR

D- West Germany

84	D-ABHH
163	D-AILY
158	D-AISY
229	D-ALAQ
207	D-ALAR
208	D-ALAS
187	D-ALAT
234	D-ALFA
116	D-ALLI
229	D-AMAM
187	D-AMAS
235	D-AMAT
190	D-AMIE
197	D-AMOR
227	D-AMUC
195	D-AMUR
127	D-ANDY
160	D-ANNO
238	D-ANUE

DQ- Fiji

245	DQ-FBQ
250	DQ-FBV
116	DQ-FCR

EC- Spain

161	EC-BQF

EI- Eire

49	EI-ANE
50	EI-ANF
51	EI-ANG
52	EI-ANH
402	EI-BSS

G- United Kingdom

198	G-16-12
212	G-16-13
157	G-16-14
241	G-16-16
130	G-16-4
4	G-ASHG
5	G-ASJA
6	G-ASJB
7	G-ASJC
8	G-ASJD
9	G-ASJE
10	G-ASJF
11	G-ASJG
12	G-ASJH
13	G-ASJI
14	G-ASJJ
85	G-ASVT
95	G-ASVT
53	G-ASYD
54	G-ASYE
110	G-ATPH
112	G-ATPI
33	G-ATPJ
34	G-ATPK
35	G-ATPL
39	G-ATTP
39	G-ATTP
40	G-ATVH
107	G-ATVW
109	G-AVBX
113	G-AVBY
94	G-AVEJ
114	G-AVGP
136	G-AVMH
137	G-AVMI
138	G-AVMJ
139	G-AVMK
140	G-AVML
141	G-AVMM
142	G-AVMN
143	G-AVMO
144	G-AVMP
145	G-AVMR
146	G-AVMS
147	G-AVMT
148	G-AVMU
149	G-AVMV
150	G-AVMW
151	G-AVMX
152	G-AVMY
153	G-AVMZ
129	G-AVOE
131	G-AVOF
133	G-AVYZ
132	G-AWBL
115	G-AWEJ
116	G-AWGG
128	G-AWKJ
184	G-AWWX
185	G-AWWX
186	G-AWWZ
166	G-AWXJ
174	G-AWYR
175	G-AWYS
176	G-AWYT
177	G-AWYU
178	G-AWYV
162	G-AXBB
90	G-AXCK
87	G-AXCP
191	G-AXJK
209	G-AXJL
214	G-AXJM
193	G-AXLL
199	G-AXLM
211	G-AXLN
200	G-AXMF
201	G-AXMG
202	G-AXMH
203	G-AXMI
204	G-AXMJ
205	G-AXMK
206	G-AXML
157	G-AXMU
121	G-AXOX
210	G-AXYD
161	G-AYHM
233	G-AYOP
232	G-AYOR
239	G-AYUW
237	G-AYWB
192	G-AYXB
188	G-AZEB
189	G-AZEC
127	G-AZED
240	G-AZMF
66	G-AZMI
208	G-AZPE
187	G-AZPY
229	G-AZPZ
241	G-AZUK
66	G-BBMF
115	G-BBMG
198	G-BCCV
205	G-BCWA
204	G-BCWG
198	G-BCXR
203	G-BDAE
202	G-BDAS
232	G-BDAT
118	G-BEJM
154	G-BEJW
230	G-BEKA
160	G-BFMC
261	G-BFWN
263	G-BGKE
264	G-BGKF
265	G-BGKG
108	G-BGTU
128	G-BIII
244	G-BJMV
234	G-BJRT
238	G-BJRU
208	G-BJYL
242	G-BJYM
107	G-BKAU
109	G-BKAV
113	G-BKAW
133	G-BKAX
262	G-BLDH
260	G-BLHD
131	G-BMAN
166	G-CBIA
128	G-NIII
128	G-SURE
272	G-TARO
112	G-WEAD
110	G-YMRU

HB- Switzerland

166	HB-ITK
212	HB-ITL

HZ- Saudi Arabia

158	HZ-AB1
69	HZ-AMB
158	HZ-AMH
54	HZ-AMK
80	HZ-BL1
60	HZ-GP2
60	HZ-GRP
67	HZ-GRP
111	HZ-JAM
60	HZ-MAA
88	HZ-MAJ
259	HZ-MAM
158	HZ-MF1
80	HZ-MFA
135	HZ-MO1
64	HZ-NB2
60	HZ-NB3
88	HZ-NIR
81	HZ-RH1

LV- Argentina

122	LV-IZR
123	LV-IZS
117	LV-JGX
155	LV-JGY
192	LV-JNR
194	LV-JNS
196	LV-JNT
185	LV-JNU
185	LV-LHT
212	LV-LOX
200	LV-MEX
206	LV-MRZ
187	LV-MZM
197	LV-OAX
227	LV-OAY
187	LV-PEW
197	LV-PFR

LX- Luxembourg

259	LX-MAM

N United States

59	N100CC
7	N101EX
9	N102EX
60	N102GP
67	N102ME
10	N103EX
11	N104EX
12	N105EX
13	N106EX
85	N107EX
30	N10HM
30	N1112J
31	N1113J
32	N1114J
82	N1115J
98	N1116J
99	N1117J
96	N11181
97	N11182
105	N11183
100	N1118J
101	N1119J
73	N111FL
126	N111GS
55	N111NA
60	N111NA
65	N111NA
86	N111NA
15	N111QA
102	N1120J
103	N1122J
104	N1123J
134	N1124J
135	N1125J
179	N1126J
180	N1127J
181	N1128J
182	N1129J
59	N112NA
88	N112NA
96	N1130J
97	N1131J
105	N1132J
45	N1134J
46	N1135J
71	N1136J
90	N114M
65	N114MR
56	N1201A
163	N123H
58	N128GA
56	N12CZ
15	N1541
16	N1542
17	N1543
18	N1544
19	N1545
20	N1546
41	N1547
42	N1548
43	N1549
44	N1550
45	N1551
46	N1552
70	N1553
71	N1554
90	N164W
57	N170FE
126	N18813
119	N18814
68	N18HH
55	N1JR
68	N200CC
29	N2111J
63	N217CA
89	N218CA
111	N221CN
80	N22RB
120	N270E
57	N277NS
72	N310EL
122	N3126H
123	N3126Q
76	N333GB
126	N341TC
5	N3756F
129	N390BA
131	N392BA
54	N3939V
68	N3E
61	N40AS
120	N44R
135	N4550T
131	N492BA
86	N500CS
55	N5015
56	N5016
57	N5017
58	N5018
59	N5019
60	N5020
61	N5021
62	N5022
63	N5023
64	N5024
65	N5025
66	N5026
67	N5027
68	N5028
69	N5029
83	N502T
72	N5030
73	N5031
74	N5032
75	N5033
76	N5034
77	N5035
78	N5036
79	N5037
80	N5038
81	N5039
183	N503T
86	N5040
87	N5041
88	N5042
89	N5043
90	N5044
84	N504T
15	N523AC
120	N524AC
55	N55JT
55	N568B
15	N5LC
73	N5LC
59	N700JA
58	N711ST
5	N734EB
111	N767RV
54	N77CS
54	N77QS
79	N800DM
62	N800MC
78	N800PW
126	N809M
126	N80GM
65	N825AC
65	N825AQ
5	N88NB
59	N8JA
67	N909CH
111	N90AAM
80	N90TF
117	N97GA
5	N97KR
78	N9WP

OB- Peru

241	OB-R-1080
193	OB-R-1137
193	OB-R-1173
239	OB-R-953

OE- Austria

255	OE-ILC
256	OE-ILD

PI- Philippines

91	PI-C1121
92	PI-C1131
94	PI-C1141
94	PI-C1141
157	PI-C1151
161	PI-C1151
213	PI-C1161
215	PI-C1171
226	PI-C1181

PK- Indonesia

166	PK-PJC

PP/PT- Brasil

192	PP-SDP
228	PP-SDQ
230	PP-SDR
236	PP-SDS
193	PP-SDT
211	PP-SDU
199	PP-SDV
119	PP-SRT
126	PP-SRU
200	PP-TYV
240	PP-TYY
206	PT-TYW

RP- Philippines

128	RP-C1
213	RP-C1161
215	RP-C1171
226	RP-C1181
246	RP-C1182
248	RP-C1183
190	RP-C1184

British Aerospace/RomBac One-eleven cross-reference index

195	RP-C1185
188	RP-C1186
189	RP-C1187
209	RP-C1188
204	RP-C1189
199	RP-C1193
231	RP-C1194

TC- Turkey

255	TC-AKA
253	TC-JCP

TG- Guatemala

205	TG-ARA
206	TG-AVA
211	TG-AYA
231	TG-AZA

TI- Costa Rica

162	TI-1055C
108	TI-1056C
242	TI-1059C
237	TI-1084C
244	TI-1096C
237	TI-LRF

242	TI-LRI
244	TI-LRJ
208	TI-LRK
237	TI-LRL

VP- Bahamas

188	VP-BCN
189	VP-BCO
34	VP-BCP
198	VP-BCQ
121	VP-BCY
157	VP-BCZ
74	VP-BDI
89	VP-BDJ
62	VP-BDN
63	VP-BDP

VP- Antigua

205	VP-LAK
198	VP-LAN
188	VP-LAP
189	VP-LAR

VP- Zimbabwe

39	VP-YXA

40	VP-YXB

VR- Bermuda

17	VR-BAC
76	VR-BHS

VR- Cayman Islands

237	VR-CAB
211	VR-CAL
69	VR-CAM
5	VR-CAQ
57	VR-CBI
81	VR-CTM

XB- Mexico

5	XB-MUO

YR- Romania

130	YR-BCA
156	YR-BCB
162	YR-BCB
167	YR-BCC
159	YR-BCD
165	YR-BCE

168	YR-BCF
77	YR-BCG
161	YR-BCH
252	YR-BCI
253	YR-BCJ
254	YR-BCK
255	YR-BCL
256	YR-BCM
266	YR-BCN
274	YR-BCO
272	YR-BCQ
267	YR-BCR
401	YR-BRA
402	YR-BRB
403	YR-BRC
404	YR-BRD

YS- El Salvador

108	YS-01C
93	YS-17C
106	YS-18C

YU- Yugoslavia

266	YU-AKN
266	YU-ANM
272	YU-ANN

Military operated

Australia

124	A12-124
125	A12-125

Brasil

154	VC92-2110
118	VC92-2111

Mexico

5	TP-0201

Oman

247	1001
249	1002
251	1003
247	551
249	552
251	553

United Kingdom

8	XX105
91	XX919
250	ZE432
245	ZE433

BRITISH AEROSPACE 146

Ultra-quiet short-haul regional airliner, powered by four AVCO Lycoming ALF502 high by-pass ratio turbofans. A high wing cantilever monoplane, the 146 is presently being built in two versions, the Series 100, seating 82-93 passengers in wide-body comfort and the longer fuselage series 200 for up to 111 passengers. A stretched 120-seat derivative, the 146-300, is due to fly in 1987, with deliveries planned for early 1988. The 146 made its first flight on 3 September 1981, and entered service with Dan-Air, the British independent airline, on May 27th 1983. To date 66 aircraft have been delivered and a further 22 are on order with the production rate currently two aircraft per month.

Dimensions :	Wing span 86ft 5in (26.34m) Length: 85ft 10in (26.16m) Height: 28ft 3in (8.61m) (100)
	: Wing span 86ft 5in (26.34m) Length: 93ft 8in (28.55m) Height: 28ft 3in (8.61m) (200)
	: Wing span 86ft 5in (26.34m) Length: 104ft 2in (31.75m) Height 28ft 1in (8.56m) (300)
Powerplant :	Four Avco Lycoming ALF 502R-5 turbofans (100/200) Four Avco Lycoming ALF-502R-7 (300)
	Performance : Max cruising speed 423 knots (784km/h) Range: with max payload 1,367nm (2,533km)(100)
	Range: with max payload 1,612nm (2,987km) (200)
	Range: with max payload 1,659nm (3,074km) (300)
Accommodation:	88 passengers in a six abreast layout (100), 106 passengers in a six abreast layout (200), 122 passenger in a six abreast layout (300)
Manufacturer :	British Aerospace - Hatfield/Chester Division, Hatfield, Hertfordshire, England
	Telephone: (30) 62345 Telex: 22411

C/N	Registration	Owner/Operator	Series	First Flight	Delivery	Remarks
E.1001	G-BIAD	British Aerospace	100			Reg. not taken-up
	G-SSSH	British Aerospace		03/SEP/81		
	G-SSSH	British Aerospace	300	Spring/87		Sched. first flight following conversion to -300 series
E.1002	G-BIAE	British Aerospace	100			Reg. not taken-up
	G-SSHH	British Aerospace		25/JAN/82		
	G-SSHH	British Aerospace				
	G-OPSA	British Aerospace			JAN/84	
	N5828B	Pacific Southwest Airlines			12/OCT/84	Leased
	N300PS	Pacific Southwest Airlines			85	Leased
	G-SSHH	British Aerospace			17/MAR/85	Demonstrator
	N801RW	Royal West Airlines			JUN/86	
E.1003	G-BIAF	British Aerospace	100			Reg. not taken-up
	G-SSCH	British Aerospace		22/APR/82		
	N346SS	British Caribbean Airways	100		NOV/86	Sched.delivery
E.1004	G-BIAG	British Aerospace	100			Reg. not taken-up
	G-SCHH	British Aerospace		29/AUG/82		
	G-OBAF	British Air Ferries			82	Route-proving trials
	G-OBAF	British Aerospace			83	
	ZD695	Royal Air Force	C1		16/SEP/83	Leased
	G-BRJS	British Aerospace	100		85	
	G-BRJS	Dan Air			26/APR/84	Leased
	G-BRJS	British Aerospace			85	
	N246SS	British Caribbean Airways			21/MAR/86	
E.1005	G-BIAJ	British Aerospace	100			
	G-SCHH	British Aerospace		19/OCT/82		
	ZK-CHH	British Aerospace			82	Demonstrator
	G-SCHH	British Aerospace			82	
	ZD696	Royal Air Force	C1		14/MAY/83	Leased
	G-SCHH	British Aerospace	100		JUL/84	
	G-SCHH	Dan Air			10/JUL/84	Leased
	G-SCHH	Dan Air			JAN/85	Purchased
E.1006	G-ODAN	Dan Air	100			Reg. Not taken-up
	G-BKMN	Dan Air		05/MAY/83	23/MAY/83	
E.1007	G-BKHT	Dan Air	100	02/JUN/83	18/JUN/83	
E.2008	G-WISC	British Aerospace	200	01/AUG/82		Series 200 development aircraft
	G-WISC	British Aerospace				
	G-WAUS	British Aerospace			AUG/84	Demonstrator
	G-BMYE	British Aerospace			AUG/86	Demonstrator
E.1009	TZ-ADT	Mali Government	100	05/OCT/83	15/OCT/83	
E.1010	PT-LEP	TABA	100	08/NOV/83	07/DEC/83	
	PT-LEP	British Aerospace			06/NOV/85	
	N802RW	Royal West Airlines			JUN/86	
E.1011	PT-LEQ	TABA	100	17/DEC/83	21/DEC/83	
	PT-LEQ	British Aerospace			30/DEC/85	
	N803RW	Royal West Airlines			JUL/86	
E.2012	N601AW	Air Wisconsin	200	25/MAY/83	16/JUN/83	
E.1013	N146AP	Air Pac	100	21/FEB/84	03/MAR/84	
	N146AP	British Aerospace			86	
E.2014	N602AW	Air Wisconsin	200	17/SEP/83	29/SEP/83	
E.1015	N461AW	Aspen Airways	100	16/APR/84	14/DEC/84	
E.2016	N605AW	Air Wisconsin	200	03/MAY/84	22/JUL/84	
E.1017	N462AP	Aspen Airways	100	03/OCT/84	07/JUN/85	
E.2018	N603AW	Air Wisconsin	200	09/DEC/83	17/DEC/83	
E.1019	G-XIAN	British Aerospace	100			
	B-2701	CAAC			10/SEP/86	
E.2020	N604AW	Air Wisconsin	200	09/FEB/84	23/FEB/84	
E.1021	ZE700	RAF/Queens Flight	100	23/NOV/84	MAY/86	
E.2022	N346PS	Pacific Southwest Airlines	200	16/MAY/84	13/JUN/84	
E.2023	N347PS	Pacific Southwest Airlines	200	31/MAY/84	13/JUN/84	
E.2024	N348PS	Pacific Southwest Airlines	200	06/JUL/84	14/JUL/84	
E.2025	N349PS	Pacific Southwest Airlines	200	22/OCT/84	09/NOV/84	
E.1026	B-2702	CAAC	100		OCT/86	Sched.delivery
E.2027	N350PS	Pacific Southwest Airlines	200	24/NOV/84	07/DEC/84	
E.2028	N351PS	Pacific Southwest Airlines	200	06/DEC/84	19/DEC/84	
E.1029	ZE701	RAF/Queens Flight	100	12/APR/85	86	
E.2030	N352PS	Pacific Southwest Airlines	200	07/MAR/85	27/MAR/85	
E.2031	N353PS	Pacific Southwest Airlines	200	07/FEB/85	29/MAR/85	

BRITISH AEROSPACE 146

C/N	Registration	Owner/Operator	Series	First Flight	Delivery	Remarks
E.1032	B-2703	CAAC	100		NOV/86	Sched.delivery
E.2033	N606AW	Air Wisconsin	200	19/FEB/85	27/FEB/85	
E.2034	N354PS	Pacific Southwest Airlines	200	09/MAY/85	24/MAY/85	
E.1035	B-2704	CAAC	100		DEC/86	Sched.delivery
E.2036	N355PS	Pacific Southwest Airlines	200	24/MAY/85	08/JUN/85	
E.2037	VH-JJP	Airline of Western Australia	200	26/MAR/85	21/APR/85	
E.2038	VH-JJQ	Airline of Western Australia	200	07/JUN/85	22/JUN/85	
E.2039	N356PS	Pacific Southwest Airlines	200	03/JUL/85	08/AUG/85	
E.2040	N357PS	Pacific Southwest Airlines	200	18/JUL/85	20/AUG/85	
E.2041	N358PS	Pacific Southwest Airlines	200	07/AUG/85	SEP/85	
E.2042	G-BMFM	British Aerospace	200		SEP/85	
	N359PS	Pacific Southwest Airlines			OCT/85	
E.2043	N360PS	Pacific Southwest Airlines	200		OCT/85	
E.2044	N361PS	Pacific Southwest Airlines	200		OCT/85	
E.2045	N362PS	Pacific Southwest Airlines	200		NOV/85	
E.2046	N363PS	Pacific Southwest Airlines	200		DEC/85	
E.2047	N364PS	Pacific Southwest Airlines	200		DEC/85	
E.2048	N365PS	Pacific Southwest Airlines	200		DEC/85	
E.2049	N608AW	Air Wisconsin	200		APR/86	
E.2050	PK-PJP	Pelita Air Services	200		JUL/86	
E.2051	N141AC	Air Cal	200		06/MAR/86	
E.2052	N607AW	Air Wisconsin	200		JAN/86	
E.2053	N142AC	Air Cal	200		24/MAR/86	
E.2054	N144AC	Air Cal	200		MAY/86	
E.2055	N145AC	Air Cal	200		JUN/86	
E.2056	N146QT	British Aerospace	200QT		86	'Quiet Trader' demonstrator
E.2057	N146AC	Air Cal	200		86	Sched.delivery
E.2058	G-ECAL	British Aerospace	200		AUG/86	
	N148AC	Air Cal			SEP/86	Sched.delivery
E.2059	N401XV	Presidential Airways	200		05/AUG/86	
E.2060	N402XV	Presidential Airways	200		AUG/86	
E.2061	G-OHAP	British Aerospace	200			
	N403XV	Presidential Airways			OCT/86	Sched.delivery
E.2064	N404XV	Presidential Airways	200		NOV/86	Sched.delivery
E.2066	N405XV	Presidential Airways	200		DEC/86	Sched.delivery
E.1068	B-2705	CAAC	100		87	Sched.delivery
E.1071	B-2706	CAAC	100		87	Sched.delivery
E.2072	N	Pacific Southwest Airlines	200		JAN/87	Sched.delivery
E.2073	N	Pacific Southwest Airlines	200		JAN/87	Sched.delivery
E.2074	N	Pacific Southwest Airlines	200		MAR/87	Sched.delivery
E.2075	N	Pacific Southwest Airlines	200		MAR/87	Sched.delivery
E.1076	B-2707	CAAC	100		87	Sched.delivery
E.1081	B-2708	CAAC	100		87	Sched.delivery
E.1083	B-2709	CAAC	100		87	Sched.delivery
E.1085	B-2710	CAAC	100		87	Sched.delivery

ADDITIONAL ORDERS

	N	Aspen Airways	100		86	Sched.delivery
	N	Presidential Airways	200		87	Sched.delivery
	N609AW	Air Wisconsin	200		SEP/87	Sched.delivery

British Aerospace 146 cross-reference index

B- China

E.1019	B-2701
E.1026	B-2702
E.1032	B-2703
E.1035	B-2704
E.1068	B-2705
E.1071	B-2706
E.1076	B-2707
E.1081	B-2708
E.1083	B-2709
E.1085	B-2710

G- United Kingdom

E.1001	G-BIAD
E.1002	G-BIAE
E.1003	G-BIAF
E.1004	G-BIAG
E.1005	G-BIAJ
E.1007	G-BKHT
E.1006	G-BKMN
E.2042	G-BMFM
E.2008	G-BMYE

E.1004	G-BRJS
E.2058	G-ECAL
E.1004	G-OBAF
E.1006	G-ODAN
E.2061	G-OHAP
E.1002	G-OPSA
E.1004	G-SCHH
E.1005	G-SCHH
E.1003	G-SSCH
E.1002	G-SSHH
E.1001	G-SSSH
E.2008	G-WAUS
E.2008	G-WISC
E.1019	G-XIAN

N United States

E.2051	N141AC
E.2053	N142AC
E.2054	N144AC
E.2055	N145AC
E.2057	N146AC
E.1013	N146AP
E.2056	N146QT

E.2058	N148AC
E.1004	N246SS
E.1002	N300PS
E.2022	N346PS
E.1003	N346SS
E.2023	N347PS
E.2024	N348PS
E.2025	N349PS
E.2027	N350PS
E.2028	N351PS
E.2030	N352PS
E.2031	N353PS
E.2034	N354PS
E.2036	N355PS
E.2039	N356PS
E.2040	N357PS
E.2041	N358PS
E.2042	N359PS
E.2043	N360PS
E.2044	N361PS
E.2045	N362PS
E.2046	N363PS
E.2047	N364PS
E.2048	N365PS
E.2059	N401XV

E.2060	N402XV
E.2061	N403XV
E.2064	N404XV
E.2066	N405XV
E.1015	N461AP
E.1017	N462AP
E.1002	N582BB
E.2012	N601AW
E.2014	N602AW
E.2018	N603AW
E.2020	N604AW
E.2016	N605AW
E.2033	N606AW
E.2052	N607AW
E.2049	N608AW
E.1002	N801RW
E.1010	N802RW
E.1011	N803RW

PK- Indonesia

E.2050	PK-PJP

PT- Brasil

E.1010	PT-LEP
E.1011	PT-LEQ

TZ- Mali

E.1009	TZ-ADT

VH- Australia

E.2037	VH-JJP
E.2038	VH-JJQ

ZK- New Zealand

E.1005	ZK-CHH

Military operated

United Kingdom

E.1004	ZD695
E.1005	ZD696
E.1021	ZE700
E.1029	ZE701

BOEING 727

Short/medium range commercial airliner, with three rear-mounted Pratt & Whitney JT8D turbofans. The world's most successful airliner by far, the Boeing 727 first flew on 9 February 1963 and by the time production ceased 21 years later in 1984, a total of 1,832 aircraft had been produced. The basic version, the 727-100, entered service on 1 February 1964, and this was followed two years later by convertible (-100C) and quick change (-100QC) options. The main production model was the 727-200 which had a lengthened fuselage and accommodation for up to 189 passengers. Further development resulted in a higher gross weight -200 Advanced, and an all-cargo -200F was also produced. A total of 1,831 aircraft were delivered before production was completed in August 1984.

Dimensions :	Wing span: 108ft 0in (32.92m) Length: 133ft 2in (40.59m) Height: 34ft 0in (10.36m) (100) Wing span: 108ft 0in (32.92m) Length: 153ft 2in (46.69m) Height: 34ft 0in (10.36m) (200)
Powerplants :	Three Pratt & Whitney JT8D-1, JT8D-7 or JT8D-9 turbofans (100), three Pratt & Whitney JT8D-9, JT8D-11, JT8D-15 or JT8D-17 turbofans (200)
Performance :	Max cruising speed 527 knots (977km/h) (100) Range: with max payload 1,760nm (3,260km) (100) Max cruising speed 520 knots (964km/h) (200) Range: with max payload 1,603nm (2,970km) (200) Range: with max payload 2,429nm (4,500km) (200 Advc)
Accommodation:	125 passengers in a six abreast layout (100), 189 passengers in a six abreast layout (200)
Manufacturer :	Boeing - PO Box 3707, Seattle, Washington 98124, USA Telephone: (206) 237-2121 Telex: 32 94 30

BOEING

C/N	Registration	Owner/Operator	Series	First Flight	Delivery	Remarks
18252	N8101N	Eastern Airlines	025	13/AUG/63	28/FEB/64	
	HK-2717	ACES Colombia			OCT/81	Leased
	N8101N	Eastern Airlines			DEC/81	
	N8101N	Air Niagara			01/AUG/82	
	N8101N	Eastern Airlines			JUL/83	
18253	N8102N	Eastern Airlines	025	10/SEP/63	15/NOV/63	
	N8102N	Aeronica			28/DEC/81	Leased
	N8102N	Eastern Airlines			02/MAR/82	
	N8102N	World Jet Aircraft Ind.			AUG/82	
	EL-GOL	Republic of Liberia Govt.			NOV/82	
18254	N8103N	Eastern Airlines	025	01/OCT/63	13/DEC/63	
18255	N8104N	Eastern Airlines	025	09/OCT/63	28/FEB/64	
	N8104E	Eastern Airlines			75	
	N8104N	Eastern Airlines			82	
	N8104N	Air Niagara			JUN/82	
	N8104N	Eastern Airlines			JUL/83	
18256	N8105N	Eastern Airlines	025	07/NOV/63	13/MAR/64	
18257	N8106N	Eastern Airlines	025	18/NOV/63	30/JAN/64	
18258	N8107N	Eastern Airlines	025	17/DEC/63	21/JAN/64	
18259	N8108N	Eastern Airlines	025	24/JAN/64	12/MAR/64	
	N8108N	Aviation Sales			APR/82	WFU APR/82, scrapped
18260	N8109N	Eastern Airlines	025	13/FEB/64	27/MAR/64	
	N8109N	Aviation Sales			15/JAN/82	WFU 15/JAN/82, scrapped
18261	N8110N	Eastern Airlines	025	17/FEB/64	26/MAR/64	
	N8110E	Charlotte Aircraft			JUL/81	WFU JUL/81, scrapped
18262	N8111N	Eastern Airlines	025	17/APR/64	30/APR/64	
	N8111N	Aviation Sales			JUN/82	WFU JUN/82, scrapped
18263	N8112N	Eastern Airlines	025	05/MAY/64	29/MAY/64	
	N8112N	Aviation Sales			15/JAN/82	WFU 15/JAN/82, scrapped
18264	N8113N	Eastern Airlines	025	11/JUN/64	23/JUN/64	
	N8113N	Aviation Sales			JUN/82	WFU MAR/82, scrapped
18265	N8114N	Eastern Airlines	025	16/JUN/64	26/JUN/64	
	N8114N	Aviation Sales			29/JAN/82	WFU 29/JAN/82, scrapped
18266	N8115N	Eastern Airlines	025	16/JUL/64	28/JUL/64	
	N8115N	Aviation Sales			JUN/82	WFU JUN/82, scrapped
18267	N8116N	Eastern Airlines	025	17/JUL/64	07/AUG/64	
18268	N8117N	Eastern Airlines	025	24/AUG/64	02/SEP/64	
18269	N8118N	Eastern Airlines	025	03/SEP/64	14/SEP/64	
	OB-R-1081	Aero Peru			MAY/74	WFU 16/SEP/83, Scrapped
18270	N8119N	Eastern Airlines	025	25/SEP/64	07/OCT/64	
	N8119N	Monarch Aviation	025F		SEP/82	Converted
	VH-LAP	Bloodstock Air Service			06/MAR/83	Leased
	VH-LAP	Trans Australia Airlines			06/JUN/83	Sub-leased
	VH-LAP	Ansett Industries			MAR/84	
	N8119N	IASCO			20/DEC/84	Leased
	N8119N	Spirit of America Airlines			MAY/86	Sub-leased
18271	N8120N	Eastern Airlines	025	05/OCT/64	28/OCT/64	
18272	N8121N	Eastern Airlines	025	30/OCT/64	12/NOV/64	
18273	N8122N	Eastern Airlines	025	05/NOV/64	13/NOV/64	
18274	N8123N	Eastern Airlines	025	24/NOV/64	04/DEC/64	
18275	N8124N	Eastern Airlines	025	14/DEC/64	18/DEC/64	
	N8124N	Eastern Airlines			FEB/82	Converted
	N8124N	Monarch Aviation	025F		SEP/82	Leased
	N8124N	United Parcel Services			05/APR/83	
	N8124N	Monarch Aviation			APR/83	Leased
	N8124N	Interstate Airlines			SEP/84	
	N8124N	Aircraft Sales Co.			SEP/84	Leased
	N8124N	DHL Airways			JAN/85	
	N8124N	Aviation Sales			JAN/85	
	N8124N	DHL Airways			JAN/85	Leased
18276	N8125N	Eastern Airlines	025	23/DEC/64	06/JAN/65	
18277	N8126N	Eastern Airlines	025	12/JAN/65	22/JAN/65	
	N8126N	United Technologies			15/JAN/84	Leased
	N8126N	Eastern Air Lines			84	
18278	N8127N	Eastern Airlines	025	01/FEB/65	12/FEB/65	
18279	N8128N	Eastern Airlines	025	01/MAR/65	10/MAR/65	
18280	N8129N	Eastern Airlines	025	24/MAR/65	07/APR/65	
18281	N8130N	Eastern Airlines	025	11/MAY/65	25/MAY/65	
	HK-2541	ACES Colombia			02/MAR/81	
18282	N8131N	Eastern Airlines	025	02/JUN/65	09/JUN/65	

C/N	Registration	Owner/Operator	Series	First Flight	Delivery	Remarks
	HK-2705	ACES Colombia			01/NOV/81	
	N4556W	Eastern Airlines			26/NOV/83	
18283	N8132N	Eastern Airlines	025	21/JUN/65	16/JUL/65	
18284	N8133N	Eastern Airlines	025	14/JUL/65	28/JUL/65	
	YN-BXW	Aeronica			28/AUG/81	
18285	N8134N	Eastern Airlines	025	06/AUG/65	25/AUG/65	
18286	N8135N	Eastern Airlines	025	09/SEP/65	24/SEP/65	
	N8135N	Aerostar			JUL/82	
	N8135N	Eastern Airlines			AUG/83	
18287	N8136N	Eastern Airlines	025	24/SEP/65	13/OCT/65	
	HK-2604	ACES Colombia			15/MAY/81	
	N8136N	Eastern Airlines			01/APR/84	
18288	N8137N	Eastern Airlines	025	19/OCT/65	27/OCT/65	
18289	N8138N	Eastern Airlines	025	28/OCT/65	10/NOV/65	
	N8138N	Aerostar Airlines			09/DEC/81	
	N8138N	Eastern Airlines			AUG/83	
18290	N8139N	Eastern Airlines	025	16/NOV/65	30/NOV/65	
	N8139N	Aviation Sales			FEB/82	WFU FEB/82, scrapped
18291	N8140N	Eastern Airlines	025	29/NOV/65	10/DEC/65	
	N8140N	Aerostar			15/MAY/81	
	N8140N	Eastern Airlines			AUG/83	
18293	N7001U	United Airlines	022	09/JAN/63	06/OCT/64	
18294	N7002U	United Airlines	022	10/APR/63	24/APR/64	
18295	N7003U	United Airlines	022			Not taken-up
	N68650	Boeing		22/MAY/63		
	N68650	All Nippon Airways			30/APR/64	Leased
	N68650	Boeing			07/APR/65	
	N68650	Iran Air			30/JUN/65	Leased
	N68650	Boeing			01/NOV/66	
	N68650	Piedmont			25/FEB/67	Leased
						W/O 19/JUL/67, Hendersonville
18296	N7004U	United Airlines	022	12/JUN/63	29/OCT/63	
18297	N68644	Boeing	022	28/JUN/63		
	N7005U	United Airlines			27/NOV/63	
18298	N7006U	United Airlines	022	16/JUL/63	23/NOV/63	
18299	N7007U	United Airlines	022	15/AUG/63	18/DEC/63	
18300	N7008U	United Airlines	022	04/SEP/63	22/JAN/64	
18301	N7009U	United Airlines	022	18/SEP/63	11/MAR/64	
18302	N7010U	United Airlines	022	10/DEC/63	20/JAN/64	
18303	N7011U	United Airlines	022	31/DEC/63	07/FEB/64	
18304	N7012U	United Airlines	022	10/JAN/64	13/FEB/64	
18305	N7013U	United Airlines	022	04/FEB/64	20/MAR/64	
18306	N7014U	United Airlines	022	10/MAR/64	07/APR/64	
18307	N7015U	United Airlines	022	01/APR/64	16/APR/64	
18308	N7016U	United Airlines	022	09/APR/64	01/MAY/64	
18309	N7017U	United Airlines	022	14/MAY/64	27/MAY/64	
18310	N7018U	United Airlines	022	21/MAY/64	08/JUN/64	
18311	N7019U	United Airlines	022	17/JUN/64	29/JUN/64	
18312	N7020U	United Airlines	022	07/JUL/64	16/JUL/64	
18313	N7021U	United Airlines	022	30/JUL/64	07/AUG/64	
18314	N7022U	United Airlines	022	01/SEP/64	16/SEP/64	
18315	N7023U	United Airlines	022	17/SEP/64	24/SEP/64	
	N7023U	Alaska Airlines			16/OCT/80	Leased
	N7023U	United Airlines			30/OCT/80	
18316	N7024U	United Airlines	022	29/SEP/64	07/OCT/64	
	N7024U	Alaska Airlines			80	Leased
	N7024U	United Airlines			05/SEP/80	
18317	N7025U	United Airlines	022	22/OCT/64	04/NOV/64	
18318	N7026U	United Airlines	022	23/NOV/64	03/DEC/64	
18319	N7027U	United Airlines	022	19/JAN/65	27/JAN/65	
	N7027U	Alaska Airlines			29/FEB/80	Leased
	N7027U	United Airlines			25/SEP/80	
18320	N7028U	United Airlines	022	17/FEB/65	11/MAY/65	
	N7028U	Allegheny Airlines			28/AUG/78	
	N7028U	US Air			28/OCT/79	
	N7028U	Key Airlines			26/SEP/83	
	N28KA	Key Airlines			84	
18321	N7029U	United Airlines	022	26/FEB/65	25/MAR/65	
	N7029U	Omni Aircraft			21/APR/78	
	HL7336	Korean Airlines			08/AUG/78	
	HK-2833	Aerotal			17/JUN/82	WFU NOV/83, stored Bogota
18322	N7030U	United Airlines	022	25/MAR/65	07/APR/65	W/O 11/NOV/65, Salt Lake City
18323	N7031U	United Airlines	022	12/APR/65	22/APR/65	
	N7031U	Omni Aircraft			21/APR/78	
	HL7337	Korean Airlines			18/AUG/78	
	N1187Z	ATASCO			SEP/85	
	N1187Z	Skybus			JAN/86	Leased
	N1187Z	Air Atlanta			07/MAY/86	Sub-leased
18324	N7032U	United Airlines	022	20/APR/65	28/APR/65	
	N7032U	Omni Aircraft			27/APR/78	
	N841N	Piedmont			31/JUL/78	
	N841N	Air 1			25/FEB/83	
	N841N	Aviation Sales			29/JUN/84	Leased
	N841N	Air 1			29/JUN/84	Leased
	N841N	Aviation Sales			DEC/84	
	N841N	Key Airlines			SEP/85	Leased
18325	N7033U	United Airlines	022	29/APR/65	12/MAY/65	
	N7033U	Omni Aircraft			14/APR/78	
	N7033U	Allegheny Airlines			15/MAY/78	
	N7033U	US Air			28/OCT/79	
	YV-82C	Avensa			08/APR/83	
18326	N7034U	United Airlines	022	05/MAY/65	21/MAY/65	
	N7034U	Allegheny Airlines			27/JUN/78	
	N7034U	US Air			28/OCT/79	
	YV-80C	Avensa			24/FEB/83	
18327	N7035U	United Airlines	022	11/MAY/65	24/MAY/65	
	N7035U	Allegheny Airlines			03/JUL/78	
	N7035U	US Air			28/OCT/79	
	YV-81C	Avensa			10/MAR/83	
18328	N7036U	United Airlines	022	18/MAY/65	03/JUN/65	W/O 16/AUG/65, Lake Michigan
18329	N7037U	United Airlines	022	14/JUN/65	24/JUN/65	
	N40481	Continental Airlines			06/JUL/78	
	N40481	Wien Air Alaska			22/MAY/84	Leased
	N40481	Continental Airlines			14/SEP/84	
18330	N7038U	United Airlines	022	22/JUN/65	02/JUL/65	

C/N	Registration	Owner/Operator	Series	First Flight	Delivery	Remarks
	N40482	Continental Airlines			JUL/78	
18331	N7039U	United Airlines	022	30/JUN/65	13/JUL/65	
	N40483	Continental Airlines			JUL/78	
	N483AS	Alaska Airlines			19/MAY/84	Leased
	N40483	Continental Airlines			15/FEB/85	
18332	N7040U	United Airlines	022	20/JUL/65	04/AUG/65	
	N40485	Continental Airlines			05/AUG/78	
18360	N68649	Boeing	030	14/JAN/64		
	D-ABIB	Lufthansa			22/FEB/64	
	N78649	Air Finance International			24/JUL/74	
	N77	FAA			MAR/76	
18361	D-ABIC	Lufthansa	030	04/FEB/64	19/MAR/64	
	N16765	Air Finance International			25/FEB/75	
	N18477	Continental Airlines			08/MAR/76	
	N18477	Air Micronesia			JUN/84	Leased
18362	D-ABID	Lufthansa	030	05/MAR/64	01/APR/64	
	N90558	Air Finance International			13/AUG/74	
	N78	FAA			MAR/76	
	84-0193	United States Air Force	C-22A		05/DEC/83	
18363	D-ABIF	Lufthansa	030	13/MAR/64	07/APR/64	
	N16768	Boeing			21/MAY/75	
	N16768	Omni Aircraft			14/JUN/76	
	EP-SHP	Iranian Government			JUL/76	
	EP-PLN	Iran Air			01/JUL/82	
	EP-PLN	Iranian Government			83	
18364	D-ABIG	Lufthansa	030	27/MAR/64	09/APR/64	
	N16766	Boeing			08/APR/75	
	N18478	Continental Airlines			08/APR/76	
18365	D-ABIH	Lufthansa	030	04/JUN/64	19/JUN/64	
	N16767	Boeing			05/MAY/75	
	HZ-TA1	Prince Talud Bin Abdul Aziz			21/APR/76	
18366	D-ABIK	Lufthansa	030	04/DEC/64	28/DEC/64	
	D-ABIK	Condor			06/APR/66	
	N9233Z	Boeing			15/JAN/76	
	N9233Z	Olympic Airways			10/APR/76	Leased
	N9233Z	Boeing			31/OCT/76	
	N44R	Rockwell Inc.			16/NOV/76	
	VR-BGW	Sigair			12/OCT/79	
18367	D-ABIL	Lufthansa	030	19/JAN/65	03/FEB/65	
	D-ABIL	Condor			14/JAN/69	Leased
	N2703J	Jet Aviation			15/JAN/82	Reg. not taken-up
	N727UD	Omni International			15/JAN/82	
	9Q-CBG	Scibe Airlift			JUL/84	
18368	D-ABIM	Lufthansa	030	11/FEB/65	26/FEB/65	
	D-ABIM	Condor			26/FEB/65	Leased
	N9234Z	Boeing			21/JAN/76	
	N9234Z	Olympic Airways			APR/76	Leased
	N9234Z	Boeing			31/OCT/76	
	N72700	Boeing			MAY/77	
18369	D-ABIN	Lufthansa	030	10/MAR/65	19/MAR/65	
	D-ABIN	Condor			15/APR/70	Leased
	D-ABIN	Jet Aviation			02/OCT/80	
	A40-CF	Oman Police Air Wing			JAN/81	
18370	D-ABIP	Lufthansa	030	08/APR/65	17/APR/65	
	D-ABIP	Condor			02/FEB/68	Leased
	N26565	Jet Aviation			04/FEB/82	
	VR-BHN	Jet Aviation			82	
	VR-BHN	Kuwait Real Estate			DEC/83	
18371	D-ABIQ	Lufthansa	030	14/MAY/65	26/MAY/65	
	D-ABIQ	Condor			27/MAR/68	Leased
	N727CH	Jet Aviation			28/JUN/82	
	VR-BHP	Jet Aviation			83	
	VR-BHP	Government of Brunei			OCT/83	
	VS-UHM	Government of Brunei			01/JAN/84	
	V8-UHM	Royal Brunei Airlines			SEP/85	
	V8-BG1	Government of Brunei			JAN/86	
18426	N1970	American Airlines	023	23/OCT/63	26/FEB/64	
18427	N1971	American Airlines	023	27/NOV/63	25/JAN/64	
18428	N1972	American Airlines	023	27/DEC/63	21/FEB/64	
18429	N1973	American Airlines	023	28/JAN/64	27/MAR/64	
	N1973	Frontier Horizon			05/OCT/83	
	N1973	International Air Leases			14/JAN/85	
	N1973	Frontier Horizon			14/JAN/85	Leased
	N1973	International Air Leases			MAY/85	
	N1973	Fairview Leasing			MAY/85	
	N1973	Flying Tigers			MAY/85	Leased
	N1973	Skybus			MAY/85	Sub-leased
	N1973	Continental Airlines			MAY/86	Sub-leased
18430	N1974	American Airlines	023	25/FEB/64	14/APR/64	
18431	N1975	American Airlines	023	27/FEB/64	31/MAR/64	
18432	N1976	American Airlines	023	21/APR/64	14/MAY/64	
18433	N1977	American Airlines	023	28/APR/64	26/MAY/64	
18434	N1978	American Airlines	023	27/MAY/64	17/JUN/64	
18435	N1979	American Airlines	023	03/JUN/64	29/JUN/64	
	N1979	Frontier Horizon			08/JAN/84	
	N1979	International Air Leases			14/JAN/85	
	N1979	Frontier Horizon			14/JAN/85	Leased
	N1979	International Air Leases			MAY/85	
	N1979	Fairview Leasing	023F		MAY/85	Converted
	N1979	Flying Tigers			JUN/85	Leased
	N1979	Skybus			JUN/85	Sub-leased
18436	N1980	American Airlines	023	30/JUN/64	17/JUL/64	
18437	N1981	American Airlines	023	08/JUL/64	27/JUL/64	
18438	N1982	American Airlines	023	04/AUG/64	21/AUG/64	
18439	N1983	American Airlines	023	07/AUG/64	24/AUG/64	
18440	N1984	American Airlines	023	14/AUG/64	28/AUG/64	
18441	N1985	American Airlines	023	25/NOV/64	18/DEC/64	
18442	N1986	American Airlines	023	31/DEC/64	22/JAN/65	
	N1986	Global International			14/DEC/82	
	N1986	American International			OCT/83	Leased
	N1986	Aviation Leasing			FEB/84	
	N1986	American Airlines			FEB/84	Leased
18443	N1987	American Airlines	023	25/JAN/65	10/FEB/65	
18444	N1988	American Airlines	023	02/FEB/65	24/FEB/65	
18445	N1989	American Airlines	023	09/FEB/65	24/FEB/65	
18446	N1990	American Airlines	023		18/MAR/65	

BOEING 727

C/N	Registration	Owner/Operator	Series	First Flight	Delivery	Remarks
18447	N1991	American Airlines	023	16/MAR/65	03/APR/65	
18448	N1992	American Airlines	023	26/MAR/65	12/APR/65	
18449	N1993	American Airlines	023	30/MAR/65	27/APR/65	
18450	N1994	American Airlines	023	27/APR/65	15/MAY/65	
18464	N72700	Boeing	022	12/MAR/63		Prototype
	N1784B	Boeing			77	
	N72700	Boeing			MAY/75	WFU APR/78, Derelict Everett
18569	N850TW	Trans World Airlines	031	25/MAR/64	29/APR/64	
18570	N851TW	Trans World Airlines	031	07/APR/64	25/APR/64	
18571	N852TW	Trans World Airlines	031	21/APR/64	02/MAY/64	
18572	N853TW	Trans World Airlines	031	06/MAY/64	21/MAY/64	
18573	N854TW	Trans World Airlines	031	23/MAY/64	05/JUN/64	
18574	N855TW	Trans World Airlines	031	23/JUN/64	10/JUL/64	
18575	N856TW	Trans World Airlines	031	29/JUN/64	14/JUL/64	
18576	N857TW	Trans World Airlines	031	23/JUL/64	11/AUG/64	
18577	N858TW	Trans World Airlines	031	23/JUL/64	31/JUL/64	
18578	N859TW	Trans World Airlines	031	06/AUG/64	18/AUG/64	
18741	VH-TJA	Trans Australia Airlines	176	25/AUG/64	28/SEP/64	
	N91891	Compania Inter-Americana			07/OCT/76	
	N91891	International Air Leases			14/NOV/76	
	N40AF	Air Florida			13/DEC/76	Leased
	N40AF	International Air Leases			19/JUL/77	
	N18480	Continental Airlines			19/JUL/77	
18742	VH-TJB	Trans Australia Airlines	176	01/OCT/64	28/OCT/64	
	VH-TJB	Australian Aircraft Sales			11/APR/80	
	VH-TJB	International Air Leases			15/APR/80	
	YN-BWX	Lanica			15/AUG/80	Leased
	YN-BWX	International Air Leases			FEB/81	
	PT-TCF	Transbrasil			28/JAN/82	Leased
	PT-TCF	Transbrasil			JUN/86	Purchased
18743	VH-RME	Ansett Airlines	177	21/SEP/64	29/SEP/64	
	VH-RME	Skyways Air International			22/DEC/78	
	VH-RME	International Air Leases			20/JAN/79	
	XA-MEG	Mexicana			18/JUN/79	Leased
	XA-MEG	International Air Leases			06/NOV/81	
	PT-TCE	Transbrasil			20/DEC/81	Leased
	PT-TCE	Transbrasil			JUN/86	Purchased
18744	VH-RMF	Ansett Airlines	177	18/OCT/64	01/NOV/64	
	VH-RMF	Skyways Air International			25/SEP/79	
	VH-RMF	International Air Leases			30/SEP/79	
	PT-TCD	Transbrasil			30/SEP/79	Leased
	PT-TCD	Transbrasil			MAR/82	Purchased
18750	N849TW	Trans World Airlines	031	14/AUG/64	03/SEP/64	
18751	N848TW	Trans World Airlines	031	09/SEP/64	18/SEP/64	
18752	N847TW	Trans World Airlines	031	10/SEP/64	21/SEP/64	
18753	N846TW	Trans World Airlines	031	08/OCT/64	26/OCT/64	
18754	N845TW	Trans World Airlines	031	13/OCT/64	28/OCT/64	
18755	N844TW	Trans World Airlines	031	22/OCT/64	09/NOV/64	
18791	N7003U	United Airlines	022	23/JUL/65	03/AUG/65	
	N40484	Continental Airlines			04/AUG/78	
18794	9Y-TCO	BWIA	078	10/DEC/64	22/DEC/64	
	N305BN	Braniff			08/JUL/71	
	PT-TYR	Transbrasil			06/AUG/76	
	PT-TYR	Evergreen International			15/APR/84	
	PT-TYR	Transbrasil			15/APR/84	Leased
	N728EV	Evergreen International			15/JUN/84	
	N728EV	Evergreen International	078F		DEC/84	Converted
18795	9Y-TCP	BWIA	078	05/JAN/65	13/JAN/65	
	N306BN	Braniff			10/APR/71	
	CP-1223	Lloyd Aero Boliviano			07/MAR/75	
18796	9Y-TCQ	BWIA	078	13/JAN/65	28/JAN/65	
	N307BN	Braniff			28/MAR/71	
	CC-CFG	Ladeco			06/JAN/76	
18797	N461US	Northwest Orient	051	03/NOV/64	12/NOV/64	
	N973PS	Pacific Southwest Airlines			MAY/77	
	XA-MEN	Mexicana			01/SEP/80	Leased
	N973PS	Pacific Southwest Airlines			28/OCT/82	
	N461US	Northwest Orient			MAR/83	
18798	N462US	Northwest Orient	051	11/NOV/64	24/NOV/64	
	N974PS	Pacific Southwest Airlines			24/MAR/77	
	N974PS	Continental Airlines			28/MAY/79	Leased
	N974PS	Pacific Southwest Airlines			31/MAR/81	
	N462US	Northwest Orient			04/OCT/82	
18799	N463US	Northwest Orient	051	17/DEC/64	23/DEC/64	
	N976PS	Pacific Southwest Airlines			15/MAY/77	
	N976PS	Continental Airlines			01/JUN/79	Leased
	N976PS	Pacific Southwest Airlines			15/MAR/81	
	N463US	Northwest Orient			30/NOV/82	
18800	N464US	Northwest Orient	051	11/FEB/65	17/FEB/65	
	N977PS	Pacific Southwest Airlines			10/JUN/77	
	XA-MEP	Mexicana			31/AUG/80	Leased
	N977PS	Pacific Southwest Airlines			30/OCT/82	
	YV-79C	Avensa			13/DEC/82	
18801	N465US	Northwest Orient	051	17/FEB/65	02/MAR/65	
	N978PS	Pacific Southwest Airlines			19/APR/77	WFU SEP/80
	N465US	Northwest Orient			29/OCT/82	
18802	N466US	Northwest Orient	051	17/MAR/65	31/MAR/65	
	N837N	Piedmont			20/JAN/78	
	N837N	Air 1			05/APR/83	Leased
	N837N	Aviation Sales			29/JUN/84	
	N837N	Air 1			29/JUN/84	Leased
	N837N	Aviation Sales			DEC/84	
	N837N	Southair Leasing			11/APR/85	
	N837N	Jetair			11/APR/85	Leased
	N837N	Havelet Leasing			18/DEC/85	WFU 18/DEC/85, stored Hurn
18803	N467US	Northwest Orient	051	13/APR/65	22/APR/65	
	N838N	Piedmont			06/JUN/78	
	N838N	United Technologies			01/DEC/82	Leased
	N838N	Piedmont			83	
	N838N	Flight Dynamics			01/MAY/83	Leased
	N838N	Piedmont			20/JAN/84	
	N838N	Key Airlines			SEP/84	
	N29KA	Key Airlines			84	
18804	N468US	Northwest Orient	051	13/JUL/65	23/JUL/65	
	N468US	National Airlines			15/JUN/78	
	N5607	National Airlines			JUN/78	

C/N	Registration	Owner/Operator	Series	First Flight	Delivery	Remarks
	N5607	Pan American			07/JAN/80	
	N157FN	Flight International			20/FEB/85	
	N5607	Intercredit			JUN/85	
	N5607	Amerijet International	051F		21/JUN/85	
	N5607	DHL Airways			21/JUN/85	Leased
18805	N469US	Northwest Orient	051	31/AUG/65	10/SEP/65	
	N469US	National Airlines			22/JUN/78	
	N5608	National Airlines			78	
	N5608	Pan American			07/JAN/80	
	N151FN	Flight International			14/JUN/84	
	N287AT	American Transair			NOV/84	
18806	N470US	Northwest Orient	051	14/SEP/65	07/OCT/65	
	N470US	National Airlines			22/JUN/78	
	N5609	National Airlines			78	
	N5609	Pan American			07/JAN/80	
	N5609	Pacific Interstate			20/MAR/84	
	N5609	Aerostar			21/MAR/84	Leased
	N5609	Pacific Interstate			84	
18807	N471US	Northwest Orient	051	18/OCT/65	22/OCT/65	
18811	N4610	National Airlines	035	15/OCT/64	20/OCT/64	
	N4610	Pan American			07/JAN/80	
	N4610	Intercredit			DEC/84	
	N4610	Boeing			15/JAN/85	
	83-4610	United States Air Force	C22B		APR/86	
18812	N4611	National Airlines	035	11/NOV/64	19/NOV/64	
	N4611	Pan American			07/JAN/80	
	N158FN	Flight International			17/OCT/84	
	N290AT	American Transair			NOV/84	
18813	N4612	National Airlines	035	18/NOV/64	03/DEC/64	
	N4612	Pan American			07/JAN/80	
	N4612	Air 1			JAN/83	Leased
	N4612	Aviation Sales			JUN/84	
	N4612	Air 1			JUN/84	Leased
	N4612	Aviation Sales			DEC/84	
	N4612	Boeing			JAN/85	
	83-4612	United States Air Force			OCT/86	Sched.delivery
18814	N4613	National Airlines	035	08/DEC/64	16/DEC/64	
	N4613	Pan American			07/JAN/80	
	N149FN	Intercredit			26/APR/84	
	N149FN	Flight International			JUN/84	Leased
	N149FN	Pride Air			28/JUN/85	Sub-leased
	N149FN	Intercredit			DEC/85	
	HK-3229X	Avianca			27/MAR/86	Leased
18815	N4614	National Airlines	035	04/JAN/65	18/JAN/65	
	N4614	Pan American			07/JAN/80	
	N154FN	Flight International			NOV/84	
	N154FN	Pride Air			28/JUN/85	Leased
	N154FN	Intercredit			DEC/85	
	N154FN	Independent Air			29/MAY/86	
18816	N4615	National Airlines	035	25/JAN/65	10/FEB/65	
	N4615	Pan American			07/JAN/80	
	N4615	Intercredit			DEC/84	
	N4615	Boeing			15/JAN/85	
	83-4615	United States Air Force	C22B		AUG/86	
18817	N4616	National Airlines	035	16/FEB/65	26/FEB/65	
	N4616	Pan American			07/JAN/80	
	N4616	Air 1			06/JAN/83	Leased
	N4616	Aviation Sales			JUN/84	
	N4616	Air 1			JUN/84	Leased
	N4616	Aviation Sales			DEC/84	
	N4616	Boeing			JAN/85	
	83-4616	United States Air Force			OCT/86	Sched.delivery
18821	JA8301	All Nippon Airways	081	04/MAR/65	18/MAR/65	
	N124	Pacific Southwest Airlines			29/MAY/71	
		Trans Australia Airlines	176	11/AUG/65	20/AUG/65	
	N124AS	Alaska Airlines			22/JUN/72	Leased
	XA-SEB	Mexicana			30/NOV/72	Sub-leased
	N124AS	Alaska Airlines			10/JAN/74	Leased
	N124AS	Alaska Airlines			14/DEC/75	Purchased
						W/O 05/APR/76,Ketchikan,Alaska
18822	JA8302	All Nippon Airways	081	11/MAR/65	27/MAR/65	W/O 04/FEB/66,Tokyo Bay
18823	JA8303	All Nippon Airways	081	09/APR/65	21/APR/65	
	D-AHLL	Hapag Lloyd			12/FEB/73	
	D-AHLL	JAT			APR/80	Leased
	D-AHLL	Hapag Lloyd			DEC/80	
	D-AHLL	Palenque Investment Co.			DEC/81	
	HR-SHE	SAHSA			28/DEC/81	
18843	VH-TJC	Trans Austra				
	VH-TJC	International Air Leases			29/APR/77	
	AN-BSQ	Lanica			31/MAY/77	Leased
	AN-BSQ	International Air Leases			MAY/79	
	YN-BSQ	Lanica			FEB/80	Leased
	YN-BSQ	International Air Leases			FEB/81	
	N4602D	Jet East International			DEC/83	
	N721JE	Jet East International	176F		APR/84	Converted
	N721JE	Purolator Courier			SEP/85	Leased, Op. by Orion Air
18844	VH-RMD	Ansett Airlines	177	06/AUG/65	20/AUG/65	
	VH-RMD	International Air Leases			25/JUL/79	
	PT-TCC	Transbrasil			30/SEP/79	Leased
	PT-TCC	Transbrasil			MAR/82	Purchased
18845	N4617	National Airlines	035	18/AUG/65	02/SEP/65	
	N4617	Pan American			07/JAN/80	
	N4617	ATASCO			24/FEB/84	
	N4617	Northeastern International			24/FEB/84	Leased
	N4617	ATASCO			NOV/84	
	N4617	International Air Leases			DEC/84	
	N4617	Pride Air			JUN/85	Leased
	N4617	International Air Leases			NOV/85	
	HK-3203X	Avianca			DEC/85	Leased

C/N	Registration	Owner/Operator	Series	First Flight	Delivery	Remarks
18846	N4618	National Airlines	035	10/SEP/65	25/SEP/65	
	N4618	Pan American			07/JAN/80	
	N153FN	Intercredit			JUN/84	
	N153FN	Flight International			JUN/84	Leased
	N153FN	Intercredit			SEP/85	
	N153FN	Pride Air			SEP/85	Leased
	N153FN	Intercredit			DEC/85	
	N153FN	Avianca			MAY/86	Leased
18847	N4619	National Airlines	035	12/SEP/65	11/NOV/65	
	N4619	Pan American			07/JAN/80	
	N4619	Air 1			MAR/83	Leased
	N4619	Aviation Sales			JUN/84	
	N4619	Air 1			JUN/84	Leased
	N4619	Aviation Sales			DEC/84	
	N937FT	Flying Tigers	035F		JUN/85	Converted, Leased
18848	N7041U	United Airlines	022	27/AUG/65	14/SEP/65	
	N40486	Continental Airlines			13/SEP/78	
18849	N7042U	United Airlines	022	30/AUG/65	16/SEP/65	
	N40487	Continental Airlines			15/SEP/78	
	N40487	Wien Air Alaska			22/MAY/84	Leased
	N40487	Continental Airlines			17/SEP/84	
	N727CD	NMB Singapore			17/SEP/84	
18850	N7043U	United Airlines	022	02/SEP/65		
	N1631	Northeast Airlines			07/OCT/65	
	N1631	Delta Airlines			01/AUG/72	
	N836N	Piedmont			21/SEP/77	
	N836N	Air 1			03/MAR/83	Leased
	N836N	Aviation Sales			29/JUN/84	
	N836N	Air 1			9/JUN/84	Leased
	N836N	Aviation Sales			DEC/84	
	N836N	Key Airlines			FEB/85	Leased
18851	N7044U	United Airlines	022	07/SEP/65	22/SEP/65	
	N7044U	Allegheny Airlines			21/SEP/78	
	N7044U	US Air			28/OCT/79	
	N7044U	Ryan Aviation			30/SEP/83	Leased
	N7044U	Ryan Aviation			21/NOV/84	Purchased
	YV-89C	Avensa			27/AUG/85	
18852	N7045U	United Airlines	022	22/SEP/65	05/OCT/65	
	N40488	Continental Airlines			OCT/78	
	N488AS	Alaska Airlines			25/MAY/84	Leased
	N40488	Continental Airlines			30/SEP/84	
18853	N7046U	United Airlines	022	14/SEP/65	14/OCT/65	
	N7046U	Allegheny Airlines			OCT/78	
	N7046U	US Air			28/OCT/79	
	C-GVCH	Vancouver Hockey Club			21/OCT/83	
	C-GVCH	Interjet Inc.			21/OCT/83	Leased
	C-GVCH	Vancouver Hockey Club			83	
	YV-87C	Avensa			MAR/85	
18854	N7047U	United Airlines	022	12/OCT/65	28/OCT/65	
	N40489	Continental Airlines			OCT/78	
18855	N7048U	United Airlines	022	22/OCT/65	03/NOV/65	
	N7048U	Allegheny Airlines			04/NOV/78	
	N7048U	US Air			28/OCT/79	
	N7048U	Ryan Aviation			13/SEP/83	Leased
	N7048U	Ryan Aviation			06/DEC/84	Purchased
	YV-88C	Avensa			27/AUG/85	
18856	N7049U	United Airlines	022	22/OCT/65	21/DEC/65	
	N7049U	Allegheny Airlines			27/JAN/79	
	N7049U	US Air			28/OCT/79	
	N7049U	Key Airlines			26/SEP/83	
	N31KA	Key Airlines			84	
	N300AA	Avensa Leasing			14/FEB/86	
	N300AA	Gulf Air Transport			APR/86	Leased
18857	N7050U	United Airlines	022	12/NOV/65	18/NOV/65	
	N7050U	Allegheny Airlines			21/NOV/78	
	N7050U	US Air			28/OCT/79	
	N7050U	Key Airlines			28/SEP/83	
	N30KA	Key Airlines			84	
18858	N7051U	United Airlines	022	09/DEC/65		
	N1632	Northeast Airlines			17/DEC/65	
	N1632	Delta Airlines			01/AUG/72	
	N834N	Piedmont			14/JUN/77	
	N834N	Air 1			09/MAR/83	Leased
	N834N	Aviation Sales			29/JUN/84	
	N834N	Air 1			29/JUN/84	Leased
	N834N	Aviation Sales			DEC/84	
	N834N	Key Airlines			AUG/85	
18859	N7052U	United Airlines	022	04/DEC/65	14/DEC/65	
	N7052U	Allegheny Airlines			12/JAN/79	
	N7052U	US Air			28/OCT/79	
	N7052U	Key Airlines			13/JUL/83	
	N27KA	Key Airlines			84	
18860	N7053U	United Airlines	022	09/DEC/65	16/DEC/65	
	N40490	Continental Airlines			14/DEC/78	
18861	N7054U	United Airlines	022	13/DEC/65	28/DEC/65	
	N7054U	Alaska Airlines			11/NOV/80	Leased
	N7054U	United Airlines			11/SEP/81	
18862	N7055U	United Airlines	022	29/DEC/65	12/JAN/66	
18863	N7056U	United Airlines	022	26/JAN/66	03/FEB/66	
18864	N7057U	United Airlines	022	09/FEB/66	22/FEB/66	
18865	N7058U	United Airlines	022	10/FEB/66	18/FEB/66	
18866	N7059U	United Airlines	022	04/MAR/66	13/MAR/66	
18867	N7060U	United Airlines	022	22/MAR/66	30/MAR/66	
18868	N7061U	United Airlines	022	25/MAR/66	01/APR/66	
18869	N7062U	United Airlines	022	05/APR/66	15/APR/66	
18870	N7063U	United Airlines	022	19/APR/66	27/APR/66	
18871	N7064U	Boeing	022	18/APR/66		
	N7064U	United Airlines			29/APR/66	Leased
	N7064U	United Airlines			09/DEC/80	Purchased
18872	N7065U	United Airlines	022	22/APR/66	30/MAR/66	
	N7065U	Alaska Airlines			30/OCT/80	Leased
	N7065U	United Airlines			31/MAY/81	
18874	JA8307	Japan Airlines	046	09/JUL/65	15/JUL/65	
	HL7308	Korean Airlines			01/AUG/72	
	HK-2420X	Aeronautics Services			08/MAR/80	

C/N	Registration	Owner/Operator	Series	First Flight	Delivery	Remarks
	HK-2420X	Avianca			08/MAR/80	Leased
	HK-2420X	SAM-Colombia			08/MAR/80	Sub-leased
18875	JA8308	Japan Airlines	046	15/NOV/65	19/NOV/65	
	HL7307	Korean Airlines			13/JUL/72	
	HK-2421X	Aeronautics Services			08/MAR/80	
	HK-2421X	Avianca			08/MAR/80	Leased
	HK-2421X	SAM-Colombia			08/MAR/80	Sub-leased
18876	JA8309	Japan Airlines	046	30/DEC/65	07/JAN/66	
	HL7309	Korean Airlines			13/NOV/72	
	HL7309	Aeronautics Services			09/NOV/80	
	HK-2420X	Avianca			09/NOV/80	Leased
	HK-2422X	SAM-Colombia			09/NOV/80	
18877	JA8310	Japan Airlines	046	21/JAN/66	31/JAN/66	
	G-BAFZ	Dan Air			15/DEC/72	
	G-BAFZ	Aeron Aviation			23/NOV/85	
	HK-3201X	Avianca			23/NOV/85	Leased
	HK-3201X	Aeron AViation			05/MAR/86	
	G-BAFZ	Dan Air			05/MAR/86	Leased
	G-BAFZ	Aeron Aviation			OCT/86	Sched.return
18878	JA8311	Japan Airlines	046	21/FEB/66	02/MAR/66	
	G-BAJW	Dan Air			06/APR/73	
	G-BAJW	Gas Air			OCT/83	Leased
	G-BAJW	Dan Air			APR/84	
	9N-ABW	Royal Nepal Airlines			15/OCT/85	Leased
	G-BAJW	Dan Air			04/APR/86	
18879	JA8312	Japan Airlines	046	07/APR/66	16/APR/66	
	G-BAEF	Dan Air			30/SEP/72	
	9N-ABV	Royal Nepal Airlines			OCT/84	Leased
	G-BAEF	Dan Air			23/APR/85	
18892	ZS-DYM	South African Airways	044	26/MAY/65	03/JUN/65	
	ZS-SBA	South African Airways			68	
	EL-AIY	Pan Aviation			JUN/82	
	EL-AIY	Liberia World			JUN/82	Leased
	N92GS	Pan Aviation			DEC/82	
	N92GS	Air Atlanta			AUG/86	Leased
18893	ZS-DYN	South African Airways	044	25/JUN/65	08/JUL/65	
	ZS-SBB	South African Airways			68	
	N93GS	Pan Aviation			17/SEP/82	
	TF-VLS	Eagle Air			FEB/84	Leased
	TF-VLS	Pan Aviation			DEC/84	
	N188CL	Cam Leasing			DEC/84	
	N188CL	Cam Air International	044F		MAR/85	Converted
18894	ZS-DYO	South African Airways	044	02/AUG/65	10/AUG/65	
	ZS-SBC	South African Airways			68	
	N727CR	Deutsche Aviation			MAR/83	
	HP-500A	Panamanian Air Force			FEB/84	
18895	ZS-DYP	South African Airways	044	13/AUG/65	23/AUG/65	
	ZS-SBD	South African Airways			68	
	EL-AIZ	Pan Aviation			20/DEC/81	
	EL-AIZ	Liberia World Airways			JAN/82	Leased
	N95GS	Pan Aviation			JUN/83	
	HK-3133X	Aeron Aviation			30/MAY/84	Leased
	HK-3133X	Avianca			30/MAY/84	Sub-leased
18896	ZS-DYR	South African Airways	044	10/SEP/65	30/SEP/65	
	ZS-SBE	South African Airways			68	
	HK-2957X	Aeronautics Services			19/NOV/82	
	HK-2957X	Aerotal			19/NOV/82	Leased
	HK-2957X	Aeronautics Services			19/NOV/83	
	N5458F	Jet East International			AUG/84	
	N723JE	Jet East International	044F		JAN/85	Converted, Op. for Emery
18897	N2977G	Boeing	051C	30/DEC/65		Prototype Cargo Convertible
	N7270C	Piedmont			06/APR/66	Leased
	N2977G	Boeing			24/SEP/68	
	N303BN	Braniff			29/MAY/69	Leased
	N15512	Boeing			07/JAN/70	
	N15512	Dominicana			29/MAR/72	Leased
	N15512	Boeing			15/MAY/75	
	N15512	Intl. Flight Research			29/JUL/76	
	OB-R-1115	Faucett			30/JUL/76	Leased
	OB-R-1115	Faucett			NOV/79	Purchased
	N721EV	Evergreen International			01/MAY/84	
18898	N490US	Northwest Orient	051C	29/MAR/66	15/APR/66	
	N434EX	Emery Worldwide	051F		29/NOV/82	Converted, Op. by Ryan Aviation
18899	N491US	Northwest Orient	051C	22/APR/66	09/MAY/66	
	N414EX	Emery Worldwide	051F		01/FEB/81	Converted. Op. by Orion Air
18900	N1995	American Airlines	023	04/JUN/65	23/JUN/65	
18901	N1996	American Airlines	023	15/JUN/65	28/JUN/65	W/O 01/NOV/65, Cincinnati Ap.
18902	N831TW	Trans World Airlines	031	23/APR/65	20/MAY/65	
18903	N833TW	Trans World Airlines	031	24/MAY/65	16/JUN/65	
18904	N839TW	Trans World Airlines	031	10/JUN/65	24/JUN/65	
18905	N840TW	Trans World Airlines	031	02/JUL/65	12/JUL/65	
18906	N841TW	Trans World Airlines	031	24/AUG/65	09/SEP/65	
18907	N842TW	Trans World Airlines	031	22/JAN/66	29/JAN/66	
18908	N970PS	Pacific Southwest Airlines	014	01/APR/65	05/APR/65	
	XA-SER	Mexicana			27/SEP/69	Leased
	XA-SER	Mexicana			30/NOV/71	Purchased
	TP-10503	Mexican Air Force			09/SEP/81	
18909	N971PS	Pacific Southwest Airlines	014	19/MAY/65	22/MAY/65	
	XA-SEU	Mexicana			16/JUN/69	Leased
	XA-SEU	Mexicana			30/NOV/71	Purchased
	TP-10504	Mexican Air Force			09/SEP/81	
	TP-10504	Mexican Air Force	014F		MAY/83	Converted
18910	N972PS	Pacific Southwest Airlines	014	23/JUN/65	27/JUN/65	
	N972PS	Alaska Airlines			29/MAY/69	Leased
	N972PS	Pacific Southwest Airlines				
	N972PS	All Nippon			18/JAN/73	Leased
	N972PS	Pacific Southwest Airlines			MAR/74	
	XA-IUP	Mexicana			23/MAY/79	Leased
	N972PS	Pacific Southwest Airlines			27/OCT/82	
	N460US	Northwest Orient			31/MAR/83	
18911	N973PS	Pacific Southwest Airlines	014	28/JUL/65	01/AUG/65	
	XA-SEA	Mexicana			06/AUG/69	
	TP-10505	Mexican Air Force			09/SEP/81	
18912	N974PS	Pacific Southwest Airlines	014	03/AUG/65	10/AUG/65	
	N974PS	All Nippon Airways			FEB/69	Leased

BOEING 727

C/N	Registration	Owner/Operator	Series	First Flight	Delivery	Remarks
	N974PS	Pacific Southwest Airlines			14/JAN/70	
	XA-SEK	Mexicana			03/MAR/70	Leased
	N974PS	Pacific Southwest Airlines			30/AUG/70	
	N974PS	Lockheed			15/JAN/71	
	XA-SEP	Mexicana			06/JAN/72	Leased
	XA-SEP	Mexicana			DEC/74	Purchased
	TP-10501	Mexican Air Force			29/MAY/81	
18919	JA8305	All Nippon Airways	081	19/JUL/65	26/JUL/65	
	D-AHLM	Hapag Lloyd			05/FEB/73	
	D-AHLM	JAT			APR/80	Leased
	D-AHLM	Hapag Lloyd			DEC/80	
	D-AHLM	Palenque Investments			DEC/81	
	HR-SHF	SAHSA			28/DEC/81	Leased
	D-AHLM	Hapag Lloyd			01/JUN/83	
	D-AHLM	Gas Air			01/JUN/83	Leased
	D-AHLM	Hapag Lloyd			14/FEB/84	
18920	JA8306	All Nippon Airways	081	16/AUG/65	22/AUG/65	
	HP-619	Air Panama			03/NOV/72	
18933	D-ABIR	Lufthansa	030	11/SEP/65	29/SEP/65	
	D-ABIR	Condor			08/JAN/67	Leased
	N727CH	Private Jet Services			15/JUN/81	
	VR-BHK	Sheikh Mohanna			22/DEC/82	
18934	D-ABIS	Lufthansa	030	12/JAN/66	21/JAN/66	
	N62219	Air Finance International			20/AUG/74	
	JY-HMH	Jordanian Royal Flight			05/AUG/75	
	JY-AHS	HMS Aviation			AUG/81	
	VR-CHS	HMS Aviation				
18935	D-ABIT	Lufthansa	030	18/FEB/66	24/FEB/66	
	N90557	Air Finance International			29/JUL/74	
	N833N	Piedmont			15/JAN/77	
	VR-CBA	Kuwait Real Estate			MAY/82	
18936	D-ABIV	Lufthansa	030	30/MAR/66	07/APR/66	
	N16764	Boeing			06/FEB/75	
	N33UT	United Technologies Corp.			OCT/75	
	N5073L	United Technologies Corp.			76	
18942	N472US	Northwest Orient	051	05/NOV/65	09/NOV/65	
	N3605	National Airlines			07/OCT/79	
	N3605	Pan American			07/JAN/80	
	N160FN	Flight International			20/SEP/84	
	N289AT	American Trans Air			FEB/85	
18943	N473US	Northwest Orient	051	24/NOV/65	02/DEC/65	
	N3606	National Airlines			31/AUG/79	
	N3606	Pan American			07/JAN/80	
	N156FN	Flight International			NOV/84	
	N290AT	American Trans Air			FEB/85	
18944	N474US	Northwest Orient	051	10/DEC/65	17/DEC/65	
18945	N492US	Northwest Orient	051C	02/MAY/66	12/MAY/66	
	N415EX	Emery Worldwide	051F		17/APR/81	Converted, Op. by Orion Air
18946	N493US	Northwest Orient	051C	19/MAY/66	27/MAY/66	
	N418EX	Emery Worldwide	051F		SEP/81	Converted, Op. by Orion Air
18947	N494US	Northwest Orient	051C	20/JUN/66	13/AUG/66	
	N419EX	Emery Worldwide	051F		OCT/81	Converted, Op. by Orion Air
18951	JA8316	All Nippon Airways	081	23/FEB/66	04/MAR/66	
	HP-620	Air Panama			26/MAY/73	
	N500JJ	IASCO			23/SEP/78	
	N50AJ	International Air Leases			01/AUG/79	
	HP-620	Air Panama			SEP/79	
	D-AJAA	Jetair			JUL/84	
	OO-JAA	Sobelair			JUL/84	Op. for Jetair
	D-AJAA	Jetair			17/OCT/84	
	D-AJAA	Havelet Leasing			18/DEC/85	WFU 18/DEC/85, stored Hurn
18952	JA8317	All Nippon Airways	081	19/AUG/66	30/AUG/66	
	D-AHLN	Hapag Lloyd			12/DEC/72	
	D-AHLN	Air Djibouti			27/MAR/82	Leased
	D-AHLN	Hapag Lloyd			82	
	D-AHLN	SAT Flug			01/APR/83	
	D-AHLN	Hapag Lloyd			01/APR/83	Leased
	D-AHLN	Gas Air			01/APR/83	Sub-leased
	D-AHLN	Hapag Lloyd			01/JUN/83	Leased
	D-AHLN	SAT Flug			NOV/85	
18965	N8141N	Eastern Airlines	025	03/DEC/65	15/DEC/65	
	N8141N	Aerostar			APR/82	Leased
	N8141N	Eastern Airlines			83	
18966	N8142N	Eastern Airlines	025	14/DEC/65	22/DEC/65	
18967	N8143N	Eastern Airlines	025	07/JAN/66	15/JAN/66	
18968	N8144N	Eastern Airlines	025	18/JAN/66	25/JAN/66	
	PP-CJL	Cruzeiro			01/AUG/74	
18969	N8145N	Eastern Airlines	025	20/JAN/66	29/JAN/66	
	N8145N	Alaska Airlines			17/SEP/71	Leased
	N8145N	Eastern Airlines			26/OCT/71	
	PP-CJK	Cruzeiro			04/JUL/74	
18970	N8146N	Eastern Airlines	025	02/FEB/66	10/FEB/66	
	C-GQBE	Quebecair			29/JUL/74	
	C-GQBE	Westburne Enterprises			09/JAN/80	
18971	N8147N	Eastern Airlines	025	04/FEB/66	15/FEB/66	
18972	N8148N	Eastern Airlines	025	10/MAR/66	18/MAR/66	
18973	N8149N	Eastern Airlines	025	17/MAR/66	25/MAR/66	
18974	N8150N	Eastern Airlines	025	06/APR/66	15/APR/66	
18990	N975PS	Pacific Southwest Airlines	014	25/FEB/66	07/MAR/66	
	N975PS	All Nippon Airways			05/APR/69	Leased
	N975PS	Pacific Southwest Airlines			05/FEB/70	
	N975PS	Lockheed			28/FEB/71	
	N975PS	Pacific Southwest Airlines			03/MAR/72	Leased
	N975PS	All Nippon Airways			18/APR/73	Sub-leased
	N975PS	Pacific Southwest Airlines			15/MAR/74	Leased
	D-AHLP	Hapag Lloyd			15/MAR/74	
	N2471A	Intl. Executive Aircraft			24/MAY/82	
	N21UC	United Coal			DEC/83	
18992	N314PA	Pan American	021	06/DEC/65	18/DEC/65	
	N314AS	Alaska Airlines			31/AUG/75	
	N314AS	ARCO			JAN/85	Leased
18993	N315PA	Pan American	021	29/DEC/65	14/JAN/66	
	HK-1717	Avianca			09/OCT/74	
18994	N316PA	Pan American	021	06/JAN/66	15/JAN/66	
	N316AS	Alaska Airlines			20/OCT/75	

C/N	Registration	Owner/Operator	Series	First Flight	Delivery	Remarks
	N316AS	Aeronautics Services			12/DEC/80	
	HK-2559X	Aerotal			12/DEC/80	Leased, W/O 04/AUG/82
						Simon Bolivar Ap.
18995	N317PA	Pan American	021	11/JAN/66	20/JAN/66	W/O 15/NOV/66, Berlin-Tegel
18996	N318PA	Pan American	021	14/FEB/66	19/FEB/66	
	N318AS	Alaska Airlines			17/SEP/75	
	N318AS	Aeronautics Services			05/NOV/80	
	HK-2560X	Aerotal			05/NOV/80	Leased, W/O NOV/82
18997	N319PA	Pan American	021	18/FEB/66	28/FEB/66	
	N721PC	Ports Of Call			21/JUL/81	
	N721PC	Skyworld Airlines			SEP/85	
18998	N320PA	Pan American	021	02/MAR/66	13/MAR/66	
	N320AS	Alaska Airlines			30/SEP/75	
	N1CC	Luqa Inc.			27/DEC/79	
	N727S	Signal Company			11/MAY/84	
	N300DK	TDK Leasing Inc.			06/MAY/86	
18999	N321PA	Pan American	021	08/MAR/66	16/MAR/66	
	HK-1716	Avianca			20/SEP/74	
19005	N323PA	Pan American	021	17/APR/66	28/APR/66	
	N323PA	ATASCO			29/JUN/82	
	HK-2845	Avianca			29/JUN/82	Leased
	HK-2845	ATASCO			SEP/85	
	N358QS	Emery Worldwide			SEP/85	
	N358QS	Emery Worldwide	021F		JAN/86	Converted, Op. by Cam Air
19006	N324PA	Pan American	021	26/APR/66	04/MAY/66	
	N324AS	Alaska Airlines			05/NOV/75	
	N2CC	Luqa Corp.			20/MAR/80	
	HZ-TFA	HRH Turki Faisal Al Aziz			19/NOV/83	
19007	N325PA	Pan American	021	10/MAY/66	18/MAY/66	
	N325PA	ATASCO			29/JUN/82	
	HK-2846	Avianca			29/JUN/82	Leased
	HK-2846	ATASCO			SEP/85	
	N359QS	Emery Worldwide			SEP/85	
19008	D-ABIW	Lufthansa	030QC	09/FEB/67	22/FEB/67	
	N310BN	Evergreen International			31/MAY/79	
	N310BN	Braniff			31/MAY/79	Leased
	N310BN	Evergreen International			08/APR/82	
	N918UP	UPS			JUN/82	Op. by Orion Air
19009	D-ABIX	Lufthansa	030QC	20/FEB/67	06/MAR/67	
	N705EV	Evergreen International			01/AUG/79	
	PP-VLV	Varig			29/DEC/79	
	PP-VLV	Cruzeiro			JAN/80	Leased
	PP-VLV	Varig			80	
19010	D-ABIZ	Lufthansa	030QC	28/FEB/67	17/MAR/67	
	CX-BKB	Pluna			OCT/78	
	CX-BKB	Nordstress Hong Kong			22/NOV/83	
	N4585L	Integrity Aircraft	030F		JAN/84	Converted
	N4585L	Camair International			JAN/84	
	N4585L	Flying Tigers			13/FEB/84	Leased
	N4585L	Camair International			29/APR/85	
	N724JE	Jet East			17/AUG/85	
19011	D-ABIA	Lufthansa	030QC	23/FEB/67	31/MAR/67	
	EP-AMU	ATASCO			DEC/78	
	EP-AMU	Projects & Technology			DEC/78	Leased
	EP-AMU	Air Service Co.			DEC/78	Sub-leased
	D-ABIA	ATASCO			APR/79	
	D-ABIA	Lufthansa			APR/79	Leased
	4X-AGJ	ATASCO			29/NOV/79	
	OO-ATJ	Transjet			17/NOV/80	
	N727JE	Integrity Aircraft			JAN/84	
	N727JE	Jet East	030F		MAY/86	Converted
	N727JE	DHL Airways			MAY/86	Leased
19012	D-ABIE	Lufthansa	030QC	06/APR/67	10/APR/67	
	N311BN	Evergreen International			31/MAY/79	
	N311BN	Braniff			JUN/79	Leased
	N311BN	Evergreen International			02/APR/82	
	N919UP	United Parcel Service	030F		JUL/82	Converted, Op. by Orion Air
19035	N326PA	Pan American	021	19/MAY/66	28/MAY/66	
	HK-1803	Avianca			15/NOV/75	
19036	N327PA	Pan American	021	27/MAY/66	24/JUN/66	W/O 03/SEP/80, San Jose,
						Costa Rica
19037	N328PA	Pan American	021	15/JUN/66	22/JUN/66	
	HK-1804	Avianca			21/NOV/75	
19038	N329PA	Pan American	021	18/JUN/66	29/JUN/66	
	N349PA	ATASCO			14/JAN/83	
	N329QS	Northeastern International			14/JAN/83	Leased
	N329QS	ATASCO			NOV/84	
	N329QS	Emery Worldwide	021F		FEB/85	Converted, Op. by Cam Air
19079	N7066U	United Airlines	022	08/MAY/66	17/MAY/66	
	N7066U	Wien Air Alaska			81	Leased
	N7066U	United Airlines			24/OCT/81	
19080	N7067U	Boeing	022	11/MAY/66		
	N7067U	United Airlines			18/MAY/66	Leased
	N7067U	Boeing			01/MAY/81	
	N7067U	General Electric Credit			27/JAN/84	
	N7067U	Air Atlanta			27/JAN/84	Leased
19081	N7068U	United Airlines	022	20/MAY/66	06/JUN/66	
19082	N7069U	United Airlines	022	27/MAY/66	09/JUN/66	
19083	N7070U	Boeing	022	13/JUN/66		
	N7070U	United Airlines			21/JUN/66	Leased
	N7070U	United Airlines			13/JAN/81	Purchased
19084	N7071U	Boeing	022	08/DEC/66		
	N7071U	United Airlines			21/DEC/66	Leased
	N7071U	United Airlines			JUL/81	Purchased
19085	N7072U	Boeing	022	16/DEC/66		
	N7072U	United Airlines			22/DEC/66	Leased
	N7072U	United Airlines			JUL/81	Purchased
19086	N7073U	Boeing	022	14/JAN/67		
	N7073U	United Airlines			23/JAN/67	Leased
	N7073U	Boeing			JUL/81	WFU JUL/81, Las Vegas
	N7073U	General Electric Credit			27/DEC/83	
	N7073U	Air Atlanta			27/DEC/83	Leased
19087	N7074U	Boeing	022	20/JAN/67		
	N7074U	United Airlines			27/JAN/67	Leased
	N7074U	Boeing			13/SEP/81	WFU 13/SEP/81

BOEING 727

C/N	Registration	Owner/Operator	Series	First Flight	Delivery	Remarks
	N7074U	General Electric Credit			27/DEC/83	
	N7074U	Air Atlanta			27/DEC/83	Leased
19088	N7075U	Boeing	022	26/JAN/67		
	N7075U	United Airlines			09/FEB/67	Leased
	N7075U	Boeing			16/SEP/81	
	PT-TCH	Transbrasil			07/DEC/82	Leased
19089	N7401U	Boeing	022QC	07/APR/66		
	N7401U	United Airlines			14/MAY/66	Leased
	N7401U	Boeing			21/NOV/80	
	N426EX	Emery Worldwide	022F		AUG/81	Converted. Op. by Jet East
19090	N7402U	Boeing	022QC	02/JUN/66		
	N7402U	United Airlines			29/JUN/66	Leased
	N7402U	Boeing			07/NOV/80	WFU 07/NOV/80, Las Vegas
	N427EX	Emery Worldwide	022F		AUG/81	Converted. Op. by Cam Air
19091	N7403U	Boeing	022QC	03/JUN/66		
	N7403U	United Airlines			01/JUL/66	Leased
	N7403U	Boeing			12/NOV/80	
	N498WC	Wien Air Alaska			10/APR/81	
	N928UP	United Parcel Service	022F		14/SEP/82	Converted, Op. by Evergreen
19092	N7404U	Boeing	022QC	08/JUL/66		
	N7404U	United Airlines			20/JUL/66	Leased
	N7404U	Boeing			15/JAN/81	
	N495WC	Wien Air Alaska			18/MAR/81	
	N929UP	United Parcel Service	022F		08/SEP/82	Converted, Op. by Evergreen
19093	N7405U	Boeing	022QC	15/JUL/66		
	N7405U	United Airlines			19/AUG/66	Leased
	N7405U	Boeing			02/DEC/80	
	N498WC	Wien Air Alaska			30/MAR/81	
	N498WC	United Parcel Service			14/SEP/82	Leased
	N498WC	Wien Air Alaska			DEC/83	
	N498WC	Flying Tigers			83	Leased
	N498WC	Wien Air Alaska			83	
	N831RV	Reeve Aleutian			08/AUG/83	
19094	N7406U	Boeing	022QC	18/JUL/66		
	N7406U	United Airlines			23/SEP/66	Leased
	N7406U	Boeing			19/DEC/80	
	HK-2475	Avianca			14/APR/81	
	N422EX	Emery Worldwide	022F		10/NOV/81	Converted. Op. by Ryan Aviation
19095	N7407U	Boeing	022QC	09/AUG/66		
	N7407U	United Airlines			09/SEP/66	Leased
	N7407U	Boeing			31/OCT/80	WFU 31/OCT/80, Las Vegas
	N425EX	Emery Worldwide	022F		AUG/81	Converted. Op by Jet East
	N425EX	Emery Worldwide			01/SEP/84	Op. by Cam Air
19096	N7408U	Boeing	022QC	19/AUG/66		
	N7408U	United Airlines			14/SEP/66	Leased
	N7408U	Boeing			12/DEC/80	
	N497WC	Wien Air Alaska			30/MAR/81	
	N930UP	United Parcel Service	022F		14/SEP/82	Converted, Op. by Evergreen.
19097	N7409U	Boeing	022QC	23/AUG/66		
	N7409U	United Airlines			01/SEP/66	Leased
	N7409U	Boeing			04/NOV/80	WFU 04/NOV/80, Las Vegas
	N428EX	Emery Worldwide	022F		AUG/81	Converted, Op. by Ryan Aviation
19098	N7410U	Boeing	022QC	18/SEP/66		
	N7410U	United Airlines			10/OCT/66	Leased
	N7410U	Boeing			04/DEC/80	
	N496WC	Wien Air Alaska			27/MAR/81	
	N496WC	United Parcel Service			14/SEP/82	Leased
	N4ʳ 6WC	Wien Air Alaska			26/APR/83	
	N496WC	Flying Tigers			27/MAY/83	Leased
	N496WC	Wien Air Alaska			83	
	N832RV	Reeve Aleutian			08/AUG/83	
19099	N7411U	Boeing	022QC	30/SEP/66		
	N7411U	United Airlines			27/OCT/66	Leased
	N7411U	Boeing			08/JAN/81	
	HK-247	Avianca			13/APR/81	Leased
	N421EX	Emery Worldwide	022F		18/NOV/81	Converted, Op. by Ryan Aviation
19100	N7412U	Boeing	022QC	06/OCT/66		
	N7412U	United Airlines			31/OCT/66	Leased
	N7412U	Boeing			23/JAN/81	
	N429EX	Emery Worldwide	022F		OCT/81	Converted, Op. by Interstate
	N429EX	Emery Worldwide			01/SEP/84	Op. by Camair
19101	N7413U	Boeing	022QC	04/NOV/66		
	N7413U	United Airlines			21/NOV/66	Leased
	N7413U	Boeing			30/JAN/81	
	N430EX	Emery Worldwide	022F		OCT/81	Converted, Op. by Interstate
	N430EX	Emery Worldwide			01/SEP/85	Op. by Camair
19102	N7414U	Boeing	022QC	14/NOV/66		
	N7414U	United Airlines			07/DEC/66	Leased
	N7414U	Boeing			13/JAN/81	
	HK-2476	Avianca			29/APR/81	
	N420EX	Emery Worldwide	022F		19/NOV/81	Converted, Op. by Ryan Aviation
19103	N7415U	Boeing	022QC	30/NOV/66		
	N7415U	United Airlines			17/DEC/66	Leased
	N7415U	Boeing			08/MAY/81	WFU 08/MAY/81, Las Vegas
	N431EX	Emery Worldwide	022F		OCT/81	Converted, Op. by Interstate
	N431EX	Emery Worldwide			01/SEP/84	Op. by Camair
19109	N7270	Braniff	027C	22/MAY/66	27/MAY/66	
	N7270	American Flyers Airlines			01/NOV/67	Leased
	N7270	Braniff			01/MAY/68	
	PT-TYU	Transbrasil			28/NOV/75	
	N724EV	Evergreen International	027F		15/APR/84	Converted
19110	N7271	Braniff	027C	15/JUN/66	24/JUN/66	
	N7271	Transbrasil			25/SEP/76	
	PT-TYQ	Transbrasil			26/DEC/77	
	N730EV	Evergreen International			18/APR/85	
	HP-1063	COPA Panama			27/DEC/85	Leased
19111	N7272	Braniff	027C	21/JUL/66	14/AUG/66	
	PT-TYS	Transbrasil			07/JUN/76	
19112	N7273	Braniff	027C	29/JUL/66	26/AUG/66	W/O 12/APR/80, Florianopolis Ap.
	PT-TYT	Transbrasil			15/OCT/76	
	N725EV	Evergreen International			01/MAY/84	
19113	N7274	Braniff	027C	26/AUG/66	14/SEP/66	
	N7274	Transbrasil			22/DEC/76	
	PT-TYP	Transbrasil			27/DEC/77	
	N731EV	Evergreen International			23/JUL/85	
	N731EV	Pride Air			SEP/85	Leased

C/N	Registration	Owner/Operator	Series	First Flight	Delivery	Remarks
	N731EV	Evergreen International			NOV/85	
	9N-ABY	Royal Nepal Airlines			16/MAY/86	Leased
19114	N7275	Braniff	027C	01/SEP/66	21/SEP/66	
	N908UP	United Parcel Service	027F		11/MAR/82	Converted, Op. by Orion Air
19115	N7276	Braniff	027C	16/OCT/66	29/SEP/66	
	N909UP	United Parcel Service	027F		05/OCT/81	Converted, Op. by Orion Air
19116	N7277	Braniff	027C	22/OCT/66	04/NOV/66	
	OB-R-1115	Faucett			JUN/75	Leased
	N7277	Braniff			27/SEP/75	
	N7277	Transbrasil			26/APR/77	
	PT-TYO	Transbrasil			26/DEC/77	
	N729EV	Evergreen International	027F		01/APR/85	Converted
	N729EV	Pride Air			JUN/85	Leased
	N729EV	Evergreen International			85	
19117	N7278	Braniff	027C	16/FEB/67	28/FEB/67	
	N910UP	United Parcel Service	027F		OCT/81	Converted, Op. by Orion Air
19118	N7279	Braniff	027C	21/FEB/67	01/MAR/67	
	N907UP	United Parcel Service	027F		05/OCT/81	Converted, Op. by Orion Air
19119	N7280	Braniff	027C	29/MAR/67	07/APR/67	
	N911UP	United Parcel Service	027F		OCT/81	Converted, Op. by Orion Air
19120	N7281	Braniff	027C	06/APR/67	17/APR/67	
	3X-GCA	Air Guinee			22/MAY/80	
	5N-AWH	Kabo Air			JAN/86	
19121	N475US	Northwest Orient	051	30/APR/66	05/MAY/66	
	TP-02	Mexican Government			24/SEP/77	
19122	N476US	Northwest Orient	051	19/SEP/66	28/SEP/66	
	N105RK	San Diego Padres			FEB/78	
	N105RK	Thunderbird Airways			03/SEP/81	
	N727TA	Thunderbird Airways			FEB/82	
	N727TA	Aeron Aviation			SEP/84	
	HK-3151X	Avianca			08/NOV/84	Leased
19123	N477US	Northwest Orient	051	04/NOV/66	13/NOV/66	
	TP-01	Mexican Government			11/SEP/77	
19124	N478US	Northwest Orient	051	09/DEC/66	16/DEC/66	
	N5604	National Airlines				Not taken-up
	N604NA	National Airlines			30/NOV/79	
	N604NA	Pan American			07/JAN/80	
	N604NA	Intl. Executive Aircraft			25/JAN/82	
19125	N479US	Northwest Orient	051	17/JAN/67	25/JAN/67	
19126	N480US	Northwest Orient	051	21/JAN/67	30/JAN/67	
19127	HK-727	Avianca	059	16/MAR/66	26/MAR/66	
19128	N1997	American Airlines	023	29/OCT/65	24/NOV/65	
19129	N1998	American Airlines	023	03/NOV/65	19/NOV/65	
19130	N1901	American Airlines	023	14/DEC/65	21/DEC/65	
19131	N1902	American Airlines	023	04/JAN/66	18/JAN/66	
	N1902	Frontier Horizon			DEC/83	
	N1902	International Air Leases			JAN/85	
	N1902	Frontier Horizon			JAN/85	Leased
	N1902	International Air Leases			APR/85	
	N1902	Fairview Leasing	023F		MAY/85	Converted
	N938FT	Flying Tigers			JUL/85	Leased
19132	N1903	American Airlines	023	31/JAN/66	16/FEB/66	
19134	N339PA	Pan American	021C	29/JUN/66	21/JUL/66	
	N1186Z	Integrity Aircraft	021F		09/AUG/82	Converted
	N1186Z	Camair International			09/AUG/82	
	N1186Z	Integrity Aircraft			NOV/85	
	N1186Z	Burlington Northern	021C		NOV/85	Op. by Cam Air
19135	N340PA	Pan American	021C	01/AUG/66	02/SEP/66	
	J2-KAD	Air Djibouti			10/MAY/82	
	N47142	Air Traffic Service	021F		16/FEB/84	Converted
	N724PL	Interstate Airlines			16/FEB/84	Leased
	N724PL	Air Traffic Service			AUG/84	
	N724PL	United Parcel Service			AUG/84	Leased
	N934UP	United Parcel Service			MAY/85	Purchased, Op. by Interstate
19136	N341PA	Pan American	021C	29/AUG/66	27/SEP/66	
	PT-TCA	Transbrasil			02/OCT/74	
	PT-TCA	Aerobrasil			JUL/80	Leased
	PT-TCA	Transbrasil			80	
	PT-TCA	International Air Leases			29/DEC/81	
	PT-TCG	Transbrasil			29/DEC/81	Leased
	N727GB	International Air Leases			23/JUL/82	
	N727GB	Arrow Air			OCT/82	Leased
	N727GB	International Air Leases			01/APR/84	
	N722EV	Evergreen International	021F		01/APR/84	Converted
19137	N342PA	Pan American	021C	09/SEP/66	07/OCT/66	
	PT-TCB	Transbrasil			02/OCT/74	
	PT-TCB	International Air Leases			DEC/81	
	PT-TCB	Transbrasil			DEC/81	Leased
	N2969V	International Air Leases			19/MAR/82	
	N727LJ	Arrow Air			OCT/83	Leased
	N727LJ	International Air Leases			01/MAR/84	
	N723EV	Evergreen International	021F		01/MAR/84	Converted
19138	JA8314	Japan Domestic Airlines	089	18/MAR/66	29/MAR/66	
	JA8314	Japan Air Lines			JUL/66	Leased
	JA8314	Toa Domestic Airways			01/APR/72	
	D-AHLR	Hapag Lloyd			29/NOV/75	
	D-AHLR	Condor			01/JUN/82	Leased
	D-AHLR	Hapag Lloyd			01/JUL/82	
	9Q-CBT	Scibe-Airlift			05/MAY/83	
19139	JA8315	Japan Domestic Airlines	089	13/APR/66	19/APR/66	
	JA8315	Japan Air Lines			JUL/66	Leased
	JA8315	Toa Domestic Airways			01/APR/72	
	D-AHLS	Hapag Lloyd			MAR/76	
	D-AHLS	Gas Air			MAY/83	Leased
	D-AHLS	Hapag Lloyd			83	
	D-AHLS	SAT Flug			12/JAN/84	
	D-AHLS	Hapag Lloyd			12/JAN/84	Leased
	D-AHLS	SAT Flug			13/DEC/85	
19140	N7076U	Boeing	022	27/JAN/67		
	N7076U	United Airlines			12/FEB/67	Leased
	N7076U	Boeing			29/SEP/81	
	PT-TCI	Transbrasil			08/DEC/82	Leased
19141	N7077U	Boeing	022	10/FEB/67		
	N7077U	United Airlines			18/FEB/67	Leased
	N7077U	Boeing			09/OCT/81	

C/N	Registration	Owner/Operator	Series	First Flight	Delivery	Remarks
	N7077U	General Electric Credit			09/DEC/83	
	N7077U	Air Atlanta			09/DEC/83	Leased
19142	N7078U	United Airlines	022	24/JUL/67	30/JUL/67	
19143	N7079U	United Airlines	022	04/AUG/67	17/AUG/67	
19144	N7080U	United Airlines	022	11/AUG/67	29/AUG/67	
19145	N7081U	United Airlines	022	11/AUG/67	31/AUG/67	
	N7081U	Mexicana			07/SEP/78	Leased
	N7081U	United Airlines			12/DEC/78	
19146	N7082U	United Airlines	022	18/AUG/67	05/SEP/67	
19147	N7083U	Boeing	022	02/OCT/67		
	N7083U	United Airlines			11/OCT/67	Leased
	N7083U	Boeing			MAY/81	
	N7083U	General Electric Credit			09/DEC/83	
	N7083U	Air Atlanta			09/DEC/83	Leased
19148	N7084U	Boeing	022	02/OCT/67		
	N7084U	United Airlines			17/OCT/67	Leased
	N7084U	Boeing			18/NOV/80	
	N341TC	Tracinda Corp.			JUL/81	
19149	N7085U	Boeing	022	18/OCT/67		
	N7085U	United Airlines			31/OCT/67	Leased
	N7085U	Boeing			06/MAY/81	
	N400RG	Reliance Group			07/MAY/81	Op. by Executive Air
19150	N7086U	Elk Grove	022	25/OCT/67		
	N7086U	United Airlines			08/DEC/67	Leased
	N7086U	Elk Grove			DEC/82	
	N7086U	American Trans Air			DEC/83	
	N283AT	American Trans Air			FEB/85	
19151	N7087U	Buffalo Grove	022	03/DEC/67		
	N7087U	United Airlines			20/DEC/67	Leased
	N7087U	Buffalo Grove			DEC/82	
	N7087U	American Trans Air			DEC/83	
	N284AT	American Trans Air			FEB/85	
19152	N7088U	Buffalo Grove	022	11/DEC/67		
	N7088U	United Airlines			20/DEC/67	Leased
	N7088U	Buffalo Grove			DEC/82	
	N7088U	American Trans Air			DEC/83	
	N285AT	American Trans Air			FEB/85	
19153	N7089U	Buffalo Grove	022	12/DEC/67		
	N7089U	United Airlines			20/DEC/67	Leased
	N7089U	Buffalo Grove			DEC/82	
	N7089U	American Trans Air			DEC/83	
	N286AT	American Trans Air			FEB/85	
19154	N7090U	United Airlines	022	18/DEC/67	29/DEC/67	
19155	N7091U	United Airlines	022QC			Cancelled order
19156	N7092U	United Airlines	022QC			Cancelled order
19157	N7093U	United Airlines	022QC			Cancelled order
19158	N7094U	United Airlines	022QC			Cancelled order
19159	N7095U	United Airlines	022QC			Cancelled order
19165	N4620	National Airlines	035	12/JUL/66	23/JUL/66	
	N4620	Pan American			07/JAN/80	
	N4620	Air 1			83	Leased
	N4620	Pan American			FEB/84	
	N4620	Gulf Air Transport			24/FEB/84	
19166	N4621	National Airlines	035	12/AUG/66	31/AUG/66	
	N4621	Pan American			07/JAN/80	
	N150FN	Intercredit			01/JUN/84	
	N150FN	Intercredit	035F		DEC/84	Converted
	N150FN	Flying Tigers			JAN/85	Leased
	N150FN	Kalitta Services			MAR/86	Sub-leased
19167	N4622	National Airlines	035	08/OCT/66	18/SEP/66	
	N4622	Pan American			07/JAN/80	
	N152FN	Intercredit			AUG/84	
	N152FN	Intercredit	035F		OCT/84	Converted
	N152FN	Flying Tigers			DEC/84	Leased
	N152FN	Kalitta Services			MAR/86	Sub-leased
19169	N797AS	Alaska Airlines	090C	25/SEP/66	27/OCT/66	
	N797AS	SOHIO			23/SEP/75	Leased
	N797AS	Alaska Airlines			SEP/77	
	C-FRST	Bradley Air Service			31/DEC/85	
19170	N798AS	Alaska Airlines	090C	21/OCT/66	18/NOV/66	
	N798AS	SOHIO			SEP/79	Leased
19171	EP-IRA	Iran Air	086	25/MAY/66	17/JUN/66	W/O 07/JAN/83, Tehran
19172	EP-IRB	Iran Air	086	01/OCT/66	13/OCT/66	
19173	N5055	Air Asia	092C	09/SEP/66	03/OCT/66	
	N5055	China Airlines			22/MAY/70	Leased
	N5055	Air Asia			08/JUN/70	
	N2476	Continental Airlines			03/OCT/72	
	N18476	Continental Airlines			20/NOV/72	
	N18476	Air Micronesia			SEP/73	Op. by Continental
19174	N5092	Air Asia	092C	29/SEP/66	11/OCT/66	
	CF-PXB	Pacific Western			26/OCT/72	
	N18479	Continental Airlines			17/JUL/77	
	N18479	Air Micronesia			JAN/79	W/O 21/NOV/80, Yap Island
19175	N5093	Air America	092C	19/NOV/66	10/DEC/66	
	B-1018	Civil Air Transport			03/JAN/68	W/O 16/FEB/68, Taipei, Formosa
19176	N127	FAA	061	01/HJUL/66	13/JUL/66	
	N27	FAA			NOV/76	
	N2777	US Marshalls Service			JUN/85	
19180	N1905	American Airlines	023	30/MAR/66	15/APR/66	
	N935FT	Aviation Sales			14/MAR/84	
	N935FT	Aviation Sales	023F		JUN/84	Converted
	N935FT	Flying Tigers			JUN/84	Leased
19181	N1906	American Airlines	023	03/MAY/66	24/JUN/66	
19182	N1907	American Airlines	023	05/MAY/66	13/MAY/66	
	N933FT	Aviation Sales			18/JAN/84	
	N933FT	Aviation Sales	023F		MAY/84	Converted
	N933FT	Flying Tigers			MAY/84	Leased
19183	N1908	American Airlines	023	06/MAY/66	19/MAY/66	
	N1908	Global International			22/DEC/82	
	N1908	Aviation Leasing			JAN/84	
	N1908	American Airlines			JAN/84	Leased
19184	N1909	American Airlines	023	10/JUN/66	24/JUN/66	
19191	N7416U	United Airlines	022C	09/MAR/67	31/MAR/67	
	C-GAGX	Air Canada			29/SEP/78	
	N725PL	Plymouth Leasing	022F		NOV/81	Converted

C/N	Registration	Owner/Operator	Series	First Flight	Delivery	Remarks
	N725PL	Interstate Airlines			NOV/81	Leased
	N725PL	Air Traffic Service			AUG/82	
	N725PL	Interstate Airlines			AUG/82	
	N725PL	DHL Airways			31/MAR/84	
19192	N7417U	United Airlines	022C	10/MAR/67	10/APR/67	
	C-GAGY	Air Canada			26/JAN/79	
	N726PL	Plymouth Leasing	022F		NOV/81	Converted
	N726PL	Interstate Airlines			NOV/81	Leased
	N726PL	Air Traffic Service			AUG/82	
	N726PL	Interstate Airlines			AUG/82	
	N726PL	DHL Airways			31/MAR/84	
19193	N7418U	United Airlines	022C	23/MAR/67	17/APR/67	
	N102FE	Federal Express	022F		14/MAR/78	Converted
19194	N7419U	United Airlines	022C	03/APR/67	25/APR/67	
	N105FE	Federal Express	022F		01/JUN/78	Converted
19195	N7420U	United Airlines	022C	28/APR/67	11/MAY/67	
	C-GAGZ	Air Canada			FEB/79	WFU 25/APR/81
	N727PL	Plymouth Leasing	022F		NOV/81	Converted
	N727PL	Interstate Airlines			NOV/81	Leased
	N727PL	Air Traffic Service			AUG/82	
	N727PL	Interstate Airlines			AUG/82	
19196	N7421U	United Airlines	022C	03/MAY/67	16/MAY/67	
	N7421U	Dominicana			AUG/80	Leased
	N7421U	United Airlines			OCT/80	
	N7421U	Boeing			13/JAN/81	
	901	Chilean Air Force			14/JAN/81	
	CC-CLB	Ladeco			24/APR/86	
19197	N7422U	United Airlines	022C	09/MAY/67	23/MAY/67	
	N101FE	Federal Express	022F		11/JAN/78	Converted
19198	N7423U	United Airlines	022C	17/MAY/67	05/JUN/67	
	N104FE	Federal Express	022F		APR/78	Converted
19199	N7424U	United Airlines	022C	19/MAY/67	12/JUN/67	
	N103FE	Federal Express	022F		APR/78	Converted
19200	N7425U	United Airlines	022C	25/MAY/67	19/JUN/67	W/O 21/MAR/68, Chicago
19201	N7426U	United Airlines	022C	13/JUN/67	27/JUN/67	
	N106FE	Federal Express	022F		17/APR/78	Converted
19202	N7427U	United Airlines	022C	16/JUN/67	30/JUN/67	
	N107FE	Federal Express	022F		23/AUG/78	Converted
19203	N7428U	United Airlines	022C	07/JUL/67	30/JUL/67	
	N753AL	Allegheny Airlines			04/AUG/78	
	N753AL	US Air			28/OCT/79	
	N753AS	Alaska Airlines			26/JUL/82	
	N753AS	ARCO			83	Leased
19204	N7429U	United Airlines	022C	11/JUL/67	25/JUL/67	
	N108FE	Federal Express	022F		02/OCT/78	Converted
19205	N7430U	United Airlines	022C	18/JUL/67	03/AUG/67	
	N109FE	Federal Express	022F		25/SEP/78	Converted
19206	N495US	Northwest Orient	051C	05/AUG/66	24/AUG/66	
	N413EX	Emery Worldwide	051F		01/FEB/81	Converted, Op. by Orion Air
19228	N889TW	Trans World Airlines	031	18/DEC/66	29/DEC/66	
19229	N890TW	Trans World Airlines	031QC	23/MAR/67	16/APR/67	
	N923UP	United Parcel Service	031F		25/MAY/82	Converted, Op. by Evergreen
19230	N891TW	Trans World Airlines	031QC	19/APR/67	03/MAY/67	
	N925UP	United Parcel Service	031F		22/APR/82	Converted. Op. by Evergreen
19231	N892TW	Trans World Airlines	031QC	25/APR/67	08/MAY/67	
	N922UP	United Parcel Service	031F		25/MAY/82	Converted. Op. by Evergreen
19232	N893TW	Trans World Airlines	031QC	16/JUN/67	30/JUN/67	
	N927UP	United Parcel Service	031F		23/MAR/82	Converted. Op. by Evergreen
19233	N894TW	Trans World Airlines	031QC	01/SEP/67	16/SEP/67	
	N926UP	United Parcel Service	031F		23/MAR/82	Converted. Op. by Evergreen
19234	N895TW	Trans World Airlines	031QC	14/SEP/67	26/SEP/67	
	N924UP	United Parcel Service			06/APR/82	Converted. Op. by Evergreen
19242	CF-FUN	Wardair	011	20/APR/66	25/APR/66	
	N4509	National Airlines			15/NOV/66	Leased
	CF-FUN	Wardair			31/MAR/67	
	N302BN	Braniff			15/APR/69	Leased
	CF-FUN	Wardair			26/MAR/70	
	PP-CJI	Cruzeiro			28/MAY/73	
19243	N7271P	Pacific Northern	162		20/MAY/66	Not taken-up
	N7282	Braniff		19/MAY/66	20/MAY/66	
	N7282	Transbrasil			23/SEP/77	
	PT-TYN	Transbrasil			21/OCT/77	
19244	N2727	Pacific Northern	162			Not taken-up
	N7284	Braniff		18//NOV/66	24/NOV/66	
	N912UP	United Parcel Service	162F		OCT/81	Converted, Op. by Orion Air
19245	N3727	Pacific Northern	162			Not taken-up
	N7286	Braniff		30/NOV/66	12/DEC/66	
	N913UP	United Parcel Service	162F		05/OCT/81	Converted, Op. by Orion Air
19246	N4727P	Pacific Northern	162			Not taken-up
	N7287	Braniff		05/JUN/67	08/JUN/67	
	N914UP	United Parcel Service			OCT/81	Converted, Op. by Orion Air
19249	N1633	Northeast Airlines	095	16/AUG/66	25/AUG/66	
	N1633	Delta Air Lines			01/AUG/72	
	G-BFGM	Dan Air			02/DEC/77	
	HK-2960X	Aeron Aviation			DEC/82	
	HK-2960X	Avianca			DEC/82	Leased
	HK-2960X	Aeron Aviation			01/MAY/84	
	4X-BAE	Arkia			01/MAY/84	Leased
	4X-BAE	Aeron Aviation			30/APR/85	
	N727ZV	Skybus			JUN/85	Leased
	N727ZV	World Airways			85	Sub-leased
	N727ZV	Skybus			18/MAR/86	Leased
	N727ZV	Aeron Aviation			18/MAR/86	
	N727ZV	Key Airlines			18/MAR/86	Leased
19250	N1634	Northeast Airlines	095	01/SEP/66	16/SEP/66	
	N1634	Delta Air Lines			01/AUG/72	
	PP-VLT	Varig			04/JUN/74	
19251	N1635	Northeast Airlines	095	10/SEP/66	29/SEP/66	
	N1635	Delta Air Lines			01/AUG/72	
	G-BFGN	Dan Air			01/DEC/77	
	N29895	EBM Group Inc.			OCT/81	
	VR-BHO	Omni International			NOV/85	
19252	N1636	Northeast Airlines	095	13/OCT/66	22/OCT/66	
	N1636	Delta Airlines			01/AUG/72	
	C2-RN5	Air Nauru			25/DEC/77	WFU JUL/83 to JUN/85

C/N	Registration	Owner/Operator	Series	First Flight	Delivery	Remarks
	N740EV	Evergreen International			JUN/85	
	N740EV	Pride Air			JUN/85	Leased
	N740EV	Evergreen International			NOV/85	
	N740EV	Suncoast Airlines			JAN/86	Leased
	N740EV	Evergreen International			86	
	N740EV	Prince Alwaleed			APR/86	
19253	VH-RMR	Ansett Airlines	177	20/JUL/66	09/AUG/66	
	N110AC	International Air Leases			23/SEP/76	
	VR-CKL	Handlingair			NOV/77	
	N111EK	Handlingair			78	
	N111EK	Sudan Government			08/SEP/78	Leased
	N111EK	Handlingair			OCT/78	
	N111EK	GATX Leasing			APR/86	
19254	VH-TJD	Trans Australia Airlines	176	20/APR/66	09/AUG/66	
	N8043B	Interedec			18/AUG/79	
	N10XY	Occidental Petroleum Co.			JUL/80	
19255	XA-SEJ	Mexicana	064	26/OCT/66	08/NOV/66	W/O 21/SEP/69, Mexico City
19256	XA-SEL	Mexicana	064	06/JAN/67	17/JAN/67	W/O 04/JUN/69, Monterrey Ap.
19257	N355PA	Pan American	021	04/MAR/67	17/MAR/67	
	N355PA	ATASCO			05/DEC/82	
	N355QS	Northeastern International			05/DEC/82	Leased
	N355QS	ATASCO			NOV/84	
	N355QS	Emery Worldwide	021F		FEB/85	Converted, Op. by Cam Air
19258	N356PA	Pan American	021	06/APR/67	13/APR/67	
	N356PA	ATASCO			21/JUL/83	
	N356QS	Northeastern International			21/JUL/83	Leased
	N356QS	ATASCO			NOV/84	
	N356QS	Emery Worldwide	021F		MAR/85	Converted, Op. by Cam Air
19259	N357PA	Pan American	021	02/MAY/67	10/MAY/67	
	N357PA	ATASCO			29/JUN/83	
	N357QS	Northeastern International			29/JUN/83	Leased
	N357QS	ATASCO			NOV/84	
	N357QS	Emery Worldwide	021F		FEB/85	Converted
19260	N358PA	Pan American	021	12/MAY/67	21/MAY/67	
	N727SG	Intl. Executive Aircraft			AUG/81	
	N727SG	Beneficial Leasing			FEB/84	
	N727SG	Funair Corp.			09/MAY/84	
19261	N359PA	Pan American	021	07/JUN/67	17/JUN/67	
	N727DG	Intl. Executive Aircraft			14/AUG/81	
	N727DG	Beneficial Leasing			FEB/84	
	N727RF	R & F 727 Inc.			01/OCT/84	
19262	N360PA	Pan American	021	16/JUN/67	28/JUN/67	
	N727WE	Intl. Executive Aircraft			14/APR/81	
	N199AM	Jetex International			FEB/82	
	N199AM	Abdul Mahdi			83	Leased
	N199AM	Jetex International			83	
19279	JA8318	Japan Air Lines	046	24/JUN/66	14/JUL/66	
	JA8318	Toa Domestic Airways			MAR/72	
	G-BDAN	Dan Air			21/AUG/74	W/O 25/APR/80, Nr.Los Rodeos Ap. Tenerife
19280	JA8319	Japan Air Lines	046	10/FEB/67	17/FEB/67	
	HP-661	Air Panama			04/MAR/75	
	HP-661	Aeronautics & Astronautics			JUL/86	
	HP-661	Aces Colombia			86	Sched.lease
19281	JA8320	Japan Air Lines	046	17/FEB/67	25/FEB/67	
	G-BCDA	Dan Air			22/APR/74	
19282	JA8325	Japan Air Lines	046	13/NOV/67	05/DEC/67	
	D-AHLQ	Hapag Lloyd			21/SEP/75	
	N4245S	Dee Howard Sales			22/MAY/81	
	VR-CBE	Resebury Corp.			MAY/81	
19283	JA8326	Japan Air Lines	046	30/NOV/67	11/DEC/67	
19287	N496US	Northwest Orient	051C	01/MAR/67	12/MAR/67	
	N416EX	Emery Worldwide	051F		JUN/81	Converted, Op. by Orion Air
19288	N497US	Northwest Orient	051C	13/MAR/67	28/MAR/67	
	N435EX	Emery Worldwide	051F		29/OCT/82	Converted, Op. by Ryan Aviation
19289	N498US	Northwest Orient	051C	18/APR/67	22/APR/67	
	N436EX	Emery Worldwide	051F		01/OCT/82	Converted, Op. by Orion Air
19290	N499US	Northwest Orient	051C	20/MAY/67	27/MAY/67	
	N417EX	Emery Worldwide	051F		01/JUL/81	Converted, Op. by Orion Air
19298	N8151G	Eastern Airlines	025C	10/NOV/66	08/DEC/66	
	N116FE	Federal Express	025F		JUN/82	Converted
19299	N8152G	Eastern Airlines	025C	04/DEC/66	18/DEC/66	
	N8152G	Air Panama			81	Leased
	N8152G	Eastern Airlines			81	
	HK-2717	ACES			81	Leased
	N8152G	Eastern Airlines			82	
	N117FE	Federal Express	025F		22/MAY/82	Converted
19300	N8153G	Eastern Airlines	025C	12/DEC/66	21/DEC/66	
	N118FE	Federal Express	025F		01/MAY/81	Converted
19301	N8154G	Eastern Airlines	025C	03/JAN/67	27/JAN/67	
	N119FE	Federal Express	025F		01/MAY/81	Converted
19302	N8155G	Eastern Airlines	025C	12/JAN/67	02/FEB/67	
	N8155G	Gateway Leasing			25/JAN/79	
	TG-ALA	Aviateca			10/FEB/79	Leased
	TG-ALA	Aviateca			24/SEP/81	Purchased
19303	HK-1337	Avianca	059	03/JAN/67	16/JAN/67	
19304	N2969G	Boeing	193	24/JUN/66		
	N2969G	Pacific Airlines			01/NOV/67	Leased
	N2969G	BWIA			01/NOV/67	Sub-leased
	N2969G	Hughes Airwest			01/NOV/68	Leased
	N2969G	Braniff			15/MAR/69	Sub-leased
	N2969G	Hughes Airwest			27/FEB/70	Leased
	N2969G	Boeing			APR/70	
	N2969G	Hughes Airwest			APR/70	
	N2969G	Alaska Airlines			01/SEP/70	Leased
						W/O 04/SEP/71, Juneau, Alaska
19305	N2979G	Boeing	193	28/JUL/66		
	N2979G	Pacific Airlines			05/AUG/66	Leased
	N2979G	Hughes Airwest			18/APR/68	Leased
	N2979G	Braniff			01/MAR/69	Sub-leased
	N2979G	Hughes Airwest			06/MAR/70	Leased
	N2979G	Alaska Airlines			01/SEP/70	Sub-leased
	N2979G	Hughes Airwest			16/SEP/72	Leased
	N2979G	Boeing			06/NOV/72	
	PP-CJH	Cruzeiro			06/NOV/72	
	PP-CJH	Union of Burma Airways			74	Leased

C/N	Registration	Owner/Operator	Series	First Flight	Delivery	Remarks
	PP-CJH	Cruzeiro			74	
	OB-R-1256	Aero Peru			19/AUG/82	Leased
19310	D-ABII	Lufthansa	030QC	06/APR/67	18/APR/67	
	N701EV	Evergreen International			20/FEB/79	
	PP-SRY	Vasp			20/FEB/79	Leased
	N701EV	Evergreen International			18/OCT/80	
	N917UP	United Parcel Service	030F		FEB/82	Converted, Op. by Orion Air
19311	D-ABIO	Lufthansa	030QC	13/APR/67	28/APR/67	
	N703EV	Evergreen International			08/FEB/79	
	PP-SRZ	Vasp			08/FEB/79	Leased
	N703EV	Evergreen International			18/FEB/81	
	T3-ATB	Air Tungaru			JUN/81	
	N726EV	Evergreen International	030F		MAR/84	
19312	D-ABIU	Lufthansa	030QC	05/MAY/67	18/MAY/67	
	OB-R-1141	Aero Peru			09/MAR/78	
19313	D-ABIY	Lufthansa	030QC	11/MAY/67	20/MAY/67	
	D-ABIY	Evergreen International			21/FEB/79	
	SE-DDD	Transair			21/FEB/79	
	SE-DDD	Transadria			80	Leased
	SE-DDD	Transair			80	
	N727M	Nomads			OCT/81	
19314	D-ABIJ	Lufthansa	030QC	14/JUL/67	28/JUL/67	
	EP-AMV	ATASCO			10/JUN/78	
	EP-AMV	Projects & Technology			10/JUN/78	Leased
	EP-AMV	Air Service Co.			10/JUN/78	Sub-leased
	D-AFGK	ATASCO			JUL/79	
	CX-BNT	Pluna			20/NOV/80	Leased
	N423EX	ATASCO			OCT/81	
	N423EX	Emery Worldwide	030F		OCT/81	Converted, Op. by Ryan Aviation
19318	ZS-EKW	South African Airways	044	21/DEC/66	06/JAN/67	
	ZS-SBF	South African Airways			68	
	N2689E	International Executive			12/DEC/81	
	N727MB	International Executive				
	N727EC	Scimitair Inc.			JUN/84	
19319	ZS-EKX	South African Airways	044C	24/JUL/67	18/AUG/67	
	ZS-SBG	South African Airways			68	
	N2689S	United Air Leasing			82	
	9Q-CBS	SBZ Scibe Cargo			02/APR/82	
	N750UA	IASCO			28/NOV/84	
	N750UA	Federal Express	044F		JUN/86	Converted
19356	N8156G	Eastern Airlines	025QC	10/JAN/67	10/FEB/67	
	N120FE	Federal Express	025F		OCT/81	Converted
19357	N8157G	Eastern Airlines	025QC	20/JAN/67	06/FEB/67	
	N121FE	Federal Express	025F		JUL/81	Converted
19358	N8158G	Eastern Airlines	025QC	16/FEB/67	18/MAR/67	
	N122FE	Federal Express	025F		SEP/81	Converted
19359	N8159G	Eastern Airlines	025QC	31/JAN/67	24/FEB/67	
	N123FE	Federal Express	025F		JUL/81	Converted
19360	N8160G	Eastern Airlines	025QC	03/FEB/67	09/MAR/67	
	N124FE	Federal Express	025F		05/NOV/81	Converted
19385	N1910	American Airlines	023	27/AUG/66	09/SEP/66	
19386	N1928	American Airlines	023	25/SEP/66	08/OCT/66	
19387	N1929	American Airlines	023	20/OCT/66	27/OCT/66	
	N930FT	Aviation Sales			09/NOV/83	
	N930FT	Aviation Sales	023F		MAY/84	Converted
	N930FT	Flying Tigers			MAY/84	Leased
19388	N1930	American Airlines	023	16/NOV/66	02/DEC/66	
	N1930	Frontier Horizon			02/FEB/84	
	N1930	International Air Leases			14/JAN/85	
	N1930	Frontier Horizon			14/JAN/85	Leased
	N1930	International Air Leases			01/MAY/85	
	N939FT	Fairview Leasing	023F		JUL/85	Converted
	N939FT	Flying Tigers			JUL/85	Leased
19389	N1931	American Airlines	023	01/DEC/66	13/DEC/66	
	N1931	Frontier Horizon			15/NOV/83	
	N1931	International Air Leases			14/JAN/85	
	N1931	Frontier Horizon			14/JAN/85	Leased
	N1931	International Air Leases			01/MAY/85	
	N940FT	Fairview Leasing	023F		JUL/85	Converted
	N940FT	Flying Tigers			JUL/85	Leased
19390	N1932	American Airlines	023	19/DEC/67	06/JAN/67	
	N931FT	Aviation Sales			31/DEC/83	
	N931FT	Flying Tigers	023F		APR/84	Converted
19391	N7270F	Frontier Airlines	191	25/AUG/66	08/SEP/66	
	N297BN	Ledbetter Leasing			16/DEC/69	
	N297BN	Braniff			16/DEC/69	Leased
	N297BN	Ledbetter Leasing			28/DEC/81	
	N297BN	Prestige Aircraft			AUG/82	
	N502RA	Regent Air			AUG/82	Leased
	N502RA	Prestige Aircraft			MAR/86	
19392	N7271F	Frontier Airlines	191	15/SEP/66	04/OCT/66	
	N298BN	Ledbetter Leasing			03/DEC/69	
	N298BN	Braniff			03/DEC/69	Leased
	N298BN	Ledbetter Leasing			06/JAN/82	
	N503RA	Prestige Aircraft			AUG/82	
	N503RA	Regent Air			AUG/82	Leased
	N503RA	Prestige Aircraft			MAR/86	
19393	N7272F	Frontier Airlines	191	14/APR/67	19/APR/67	
	N299BN	Braniff			17/APR/69	
	PT-TYJ	Transbrasil			14/MAR/80	
19394	N7273F	Frontier Airlines	191	26/MAY/67	02/JUN/67	
	N300BN	Ledbetter Leasing			05/NOV/69	
	N300BN	Braniff			05/NOV/69	Leased
	N300BN	Ledbetter Leasing			04/JAN/82	
	N3946A	Burlington Northern			04/JAN/82	
19395	N7274F	Frontier Airlines	191	29/JUN/67	08/JUL/67	
	N301BN	Ledbetter Leasing			16/NOV/69	
	N301BN	Braniff			16/NOV/69	Leased
	N301BN	Ledbetter Leasing			06/JAN/82	
	N504RA	Prestige Aircraft			AUG/82	
	N504RA	Regent Air			AUG/82	Leased
	N504RA	Prestige Aircraft			MAY/86	
	N504RA	Suncoast Airlines			MAY/86	Leased
19396		Japan Domestic Airlines	089			Cancelled order
19397		Japan Domestic Airlines	089			Cancelled order
19398	N976PS	Pacific Southwest Airlines	014	10/DEC/66	16/DEC/66	

BOEING 727

C/N	Registration	Owner/Operator	Series	First Flight	Delivery	Remarks
	XA-SEN	Mexicana			10/JUN/69	Leased
	XA-SEN	Mexicana			30/NOV/71	Purchased
						W/O 20/OCT/73,Mazatlan
19399	B-1818	China Airlines	109	24/FEB/67	03/MAR/67	
	2721	Taiwan Air Force			31/AUG/82	
19400	OO-STA	Sabena	029	16/APR/67	25/APR/67	
	PP-CJJ	Cruzeiro			12/JUL/74	
	OB-R-1277	Aero Peru			01/SEP/83	
19401	OO-STC	Sabena	029	01/JUN/67	09/JUN/67	
	D-AHLO	Hapag Lloyd			28/FEB/74	
	N577JB	Eagle Aviation			11/JUL/81	
	N577JB	Golden Nugget			OCT/83	
	N711GN	Golden Nugget			84	
	N711GN	Jet East			AUG/84	
	N711GN	Jet East	029F		AUG/85	Converted
19402	OO-STB	Sabena	029QC	22/MAY/67	06/JUN/67	
	CB-01	Royal Belgian Air Force			10/JAN/76	
	TG-AVA	Aviateca			15/JUL/79	
19403	OO-STD	Sabena	029QC	11/JUL/67	22/JUL/67	
	CB-02	Royal Belgian Air Force			MAR/76	
19404	CS-TBK	TAP Air Portugal	082	06/MAR/67	12/MAR/67	
19405	CS-TBL	TAP Air Portugal	082	10/APR/67	24/APR/67	
	CS-TBL	Air Atlantis			86	Leased
19406	CS-TBM	TAP Air Portugal	082	28/JUN/67	11/JUL/67	
19427	XA-SEM	Mexicana	064	07/FEB/67	14/MAR/67	
	TP-10502	Mexican Air Force			JUN/81	
19428	N1933	American Airlines	023	12/JAN/67	20/JAN/67	
	N1933	Frontier Horizon			24/FEB/84	
	N1933	International Air Leases			14/JAN/85	
	N1933	Frontier Horizon			14/JAN/85	Leased
	N1933	International Air Leases			20/FEB/85	
	N1933	Fairview Leasing	023F		JUN/85	Converted
	N1933	Flying Tigers			JUN/85	Leased
	N1933	Skybus			JUN/85	Sub-leased
19429	N1934	American Airlines	023	20/JAN/67	31/JAN/67	WFU SEP/83
19430	N1935	American Airlines	023	26/JAN/67	03/FEB/67	
	N934FT	Aviation Sales	023F		08/FEB/84	Converted
	N934FT	Flying Tigers			08/FEB/84	Leased
19431	N1955	American Airlines	023	03/FEB/67	12/FEB/67	
	N1955	Frontier Horizon			03/NOV/83	
	N1955	International Air Leases			14/JAN/85	
	N1955	Frontier Horizon			20/FEB/85	Leased
	N1955	International Air Leases			01/APR/85	
	N1955	Fairview Leasing	023F		MAY/85	Converted
	N1955	Flying Tigers			MAY/85	Leased
19432	N1956	American Airlines	023	27/FEB/67	10/MAR/67	
19444	N1639	American Airlines	295	16/AUG/67	29/JAN/68	
	N1639	Trans World Airlines			20/APR/68	Leased
	N1639	Northeast Airlines			30/SEP/68	
	N1639	Delta Air Lines			01/AUG/72	
	N1639	Piedmont Airlines			02/DEC/82	
19445	N1640	Northeast Airlines	295	01/SEP/67	18/DEC/67	
	N1640	Delta Air Lines			01/AUG/72	
	N1640	Piedmont Airlines			23/NOV/82	
19446	N1641	Northeast Airlines	295	20/NOV/67	11/DEC/67	
	N1641	Delta Air Lines			01/AUG/72	
	N1641	Piedmont Airlines			DEC/82	
19447	N1642	Northeast Airlines	295	29/NOV/67	15/DEC/67	
	N1642	Delta Air Lines			01/AUG/72	
	N1642	Piedmont Airlines			DEC/82	
19448	N1643	Northeast Airlines	295	19/DEC/67	08/JAN/68	
	N1643	Delta Air Lines			01/AUG/72	
	N1643	Piedmont Airlines			16/FEB/83	
19449	N1644	Northeast Airlines	295	28/DEC/67	01/JAN/68	
	N1644	Delta Air Lines			01/AUG/72	
	N1644	Piedmont Airlines			83	
19450	N4730	National Airlines	235	17/NOV/67	12/DEC/67	
	N4730	Trans World Airlines			25/APR/67	Leased
	N4730	National Airlines			25/SEP/68	
	N4730	Pan American			07/JAN/80	
19451	N4731	National Airlines	235	04/DEC/67	19/DEC/67	
	N4731	Pan American			07/JAN/80	
19452	N4732	National Airlines	235	14/DEC/67	26/DEC/67	
	N4732	Trans World Airlines			15/JUN/68	Leased
	N4732	National Airlines			26/OCT/68	
	N4732	Pan American			07/JAN/80	
19453	N4733	National Airlines	235	05/JAN/68	19/JAN/68	
	N4733	Trans World Airlines			15/JUN/68	Leased
	N4733	National Airlines			27/OCT/68	
	N4733	Pan American			07/JAN/80	
19454	N4734	National Airlines	235	09/JAN/68	23/JAN/68	
	N4734	Pan American			07/JAN/80	
19455	N4735	National Airlines	235	12/JAN/68	25/JAN/68	
	N4735	Pan American			07/JAN/80	
19456	N4736	National Airlines	235	21/JAN/68	30/JAN/68	
	N4736	Pan American			07/JAN/80	
19457	N4737	National Airlines	235	24/JAN/68	31/JAN/68	
	N4737	Pan American			07/JAN/80	W/O 09/JUL/82, New Orleans Intl. Ap.
19458	N4738	National Airlines	235	02/FEB/68	16/FEB/68	
	N4738	Pan American			07/JAN/80	
19459	N4739	National Airlines	235	14/FEB/68	23/FEB/68	
	N4739	Pan American			07/JAN/80	
19460	N4740	National Airlines	235	16/FEB/68	27/FEB/68	
	N4740	Pan American			07/JAN/80	
19461	N4741	National Airlines	235	27/FEB/68	08/MAR/68	
	N4741	Pan American			07/JAN/80	
19462	N4742	National Airlines	235	29/MAR/68	23/MAR/68	
	N4742	Pan American			07/JAN/80	
19463	N4743	National Airlines	235	20/MAR/68	29/MAR/68	
	N4743	Pan American			07/JAN/80	
19464	N4744	National Airlines	235	20/MAR/68	27/MAR/68	W/O MAY/78 Pensacola Bay
19465	N4745	National Airlines	235	22/MAR/68	03/APR/68	
	N4745	Pan American			07/JAN/80	
19466	N4746	National Airlines	235	05/APR/68	18/APR/68	
	N4746	Trans World Airlines			01/MAY/68	Leased

C/N	Registration	Owner/Operator	Series	First Flight	Delivery	Remarks
	N4746	National Airlines			01/OCT/68	
	N4746	Pan American			07/JAN/80	
19467	N4747	National Airlines	235	19/APR/68	26/APR/68	
	N4747	Pan American			07/JAN/80	
19468	N4748	National Airlines	235	20/APR/68	30/APR/68	
	N4748	Trans World Airlines			27/APR/69	Leased
	N4748	National Airlines			01/OCT/69	
	N4748	Pan American			07/JAN/80	
19469	N4749	National Airlines	235	24/APR/68	29/APR/68	
	N4749	Pan American			07/JAN/80	
19470	N4750	National Airlines	235	24/APR/68	03/MAY/68	
	N4750	Trans World Airlines			27/APR/69	Leased
	N4750	National Airlines			01/OCT/69	
	N4750	Pan American			07/JAN/80	
19471	N4751	National Airlines	235	06/JUN/68	18/JUN/68	
	N4751	Pan American			07/JAN/80	
19472	N4752	National Airlines	235	11/JUN/68	20/JUN/68	
	N4752	Pan American			07/JAN/80	
19473	N4753	National Airlines	235	09/JUL/68	23/JUL/68	
	N4753	Pan American			07/JAN/80	
19474	N4754	National Airlines	235	12/JUL/68	25/JUL/68	
	N4754	Pan American			07/JAN/80	
19475	N6800	American Airlines	223	20/JAN/68	01/FEB/68	
19476	N6801	American Airlines	223	03/FEB/68	19/FEB/68	
19477	N6802	American Airlines	223	16/FEB/68	29/FEB/68	
19478	N6803	American Airlines	223	21/FEB/68	05/MAR/68	
19479	N6804	American Airlines	223	08/MAR/68	18/MAR/68	
19480	N6805	American Airlines	223	12/FEB/68	25/MAR/68	
19481	N6806	American Airlines	223	13/MAR/68	02/APR/68	
19482	N6807	American Airlines	223	02/APR/68	17/APR/68	
19483	N6808	American Airlines	223	04/APR/68	11/APR/68	
19484	N6809	American Airlines	223	08/APR/68	23/APR/68	
19485	N6810	American Airlines	223	01/MAY/68	11/MAY/68	
19486	N6811	American Airlines	223	14/MAY/68	27/MAY/68	
19487	N6812	American Airlines	223	14/MAY/68	29/MAY/68	
19488	N6813	American Airlines	223	04/JUN/68	12/JUN/68	
19489	N6814	American Airlines	223	14/JUN/68	28/JUN/68	
19490	N6815	American Airlines	223	02/JUL/68	15/JUL/68	
19491	N6816	American Airlines	223	19/JUL/68	31/JUL/68	
19492	N6817	American Airlines	223	23/OCT/68	01/NOV/68	
19493	N6818	American Airlines	223	06/NOV/68	19/NOV/68	
19494	N6819	American Airlines	223	12/NOV/68	22/NOV/68	
19495	N6820	American Airlines	223	19/NOV/68	03/DEC/68	
19496	N6821	American Airlines	223	04/DEC/68	17/DEC/68	
19497	N7288	Braniff	027QC	23/JUN/67	30/JUN/67	
	PT-TYH	Transbrasil			06/JUN/80	Leased
19499	N7289	Braniff	027	29/JUL/67	10/AUG/67	
	PT-TYK	Transbrasil			08/APR/80	Leased
19500	N7290	Braniff	027	04/AUG/67	14/AUG/67	
	PT-TYM	Transbrasil			29/SEP/78	Leased
	PT-TYM	Evergreen International			15/APR/84	
	PT-TYM	Transbrasil			15/APR/84	Leased
	N727EV	Evergreen International			15/JUN/84	
	N727EV	Evergreen International	027F		OCT/84	Converted
19501	N7292	Braniff	027	19/AUG/67	31/AUG/67	
	PT-TYL	Transbrasil			10/DEC/79	
19503	TF-FIE	Icelandair	108C	06/JUN/67	22/JUN/67	
	TF-FLH	Icelandair			01/OCT/79	
	TF-FLH	Aviateca			01/NOV/79	Leased
	TF-FLH	Icelandair			FEB/80	
	TF-FLH	Kabo Travels			15/APR/81	Leased
	TF-FLH	Icelandair			81	
	TF-FLH	TAG Aviation			27/JAN/84	
	TF-FLH	Icelandair			27/JAN/84	Leased
	N727TG	TAG Aviation			01/JAN/85	
	N727TG	TAG Aviation	108F		MAR/85	Converted
	N727TG	Orion Air			MAR/85	Op. for Burlington Northern
19504	N690WA	World Airways	173C	27/JUN/67	12/JUL/67	
	N690WA	Ariana			15/JUL/69	Leased
	N690WA	World Airways			17/JAN/70	
	N690WA	Japan Air Lines			28/FEB/70	Leased
	N690WA	World Airways			01/SEP/70	
	N690WA	Japan Air Lines			01/FEB/73	Leased
	N690WA	World Airways			31/MAR/74	
	N690WA	Air Algerie			17/FEB/76	Leased
	N690WA	World Airways			76	
	N690WA	Yemen Airways			31/MAY/76	Leased
	N690WA	World Airways			31/DEC/79	
	N690WA	Toyomenka America			31/DEC/79	
	N690WA	Northern Pacific Airlines			NOV/80	Leased
	N690WA	Toymenka America			81	
	N690WA	Integrity Aircraft Sales	173F		23/OCT/81	Converted
	N690WA	Cam Air			23/OCT/81	
	N690WA	Integrity Aircraft Sales			NOV/85	
	N690WA	Burlington Northern			NOV/85	Op. by Cam Air
19505	N691WA	World Airways	173C	05/JUL/67	15/JUL/67	
	N691WA	Japan Air Lines			21/MAR/69	Leased
	N691WA	World Airways			19/AUG/69	
	N691WA	Japan Air Lines			03/JUL/70	Leased
	N691WA	World Airways			13/JAN/73	
	N691WA	Pacific Southwest Airlines			01/JUN/76	Leased
	N691WA	World Airways			27/MAY/77	
	HI-312	Dominicana			30/JUL/77	
19506	N692WA	World Airways	173C	04/AUG/67	20/AUG/67	
	N692WA	Japan Air Lines			14/AUG/69	Leased
	N692WA	World Airways			11/JUL/70	
	N692WA	Braniff			06/APR/72	Leased
	N692WA	World Airways			07/JUN/73	
	N692WA	Air Algerie			JUN/75	Leased
	N692WA	World Airways			JAN/76	
	N692WA	Air Malta			APR/76	Leased
	N692WA	World Airways			NOV/76	
	N692WA	Yemen Airways			DEC/76	Leased
	N692WA	World Airways			77	
	OB-R-1135	Faucett			FEB/77	

C/N	Registration	Owner/Operator	Series	First Flight	Delivery	Remarks
	N692WA	World Airways			27/AUG/77	
	PJ-BOA	ALM			31/OCT/77	
	TG-AYA	Aviateca			15/JUL/79	
19507	N693WA	World Airways	173C	25/AUG/67	06/SEP/67	
	N693WA	United Airlines			08/OCT/67	Leased
	N693WA	World Airways			25/JUN/68	
	N693WA	Japan Air Lines			02/AUG/69	Leased
	N693WA	World Airways			16/JUN/70	
	N693WA	Toa Domestic Airways			09/OCT/72	Leased
	N693WA	World Airways			28/MAR/75	
	N693WA	Pacific Southwest Airlines			03/MAY/76	Leased
	N693WA	World Airways			30/MAY/77	
	N693WA	Yemen Airways			20/JUL/77	Leased
	N693WA	World Airways			31/DEC/79	
	N693WA	Toyomenka America			31/DEC/79	
	PP-VLW	Varig			12/MAR/80	
19508	N694WA	World Airways	173C	30/AUG/67	22/SEP/67	
	N694WA	United Airlines			08/OCT/67	Leased
	N694WA	World Airways			27/JUN/68	
	N694WA	Japan Air Lines			21/MAR/69	Leased
	N694WA	World Airways			31/MAR/70	
	N694WA	Japan Air Lines			17/JUN/70	Leased
	N694WA	World Airways			09/MAR/71	
	PP-VLS	Varig			04/JAN/74	
19509	N695WA	World Airways	173C	06/SEP/67	14/SEP/67	
	N695WA	United Airlines			06/OCT/67	Leased
	N695WA	World Airways			30/JUN/68	
	N695WA	Ariana			03/FEB/69	Leased
	N695WA	World Airways			18/JUL/69	
	N695WA	Japan Air Lines			08/AUG/70	Leased
	N695WA	World Airways			31/MAR/71	
	N695WA	Air Mali			JUL/71	Leased
	TZ-ADR	Air Mali			15/SEP/74	Purchased
19510	N88701	Continental Airlines	224	11/MAY/68	21/MAY/68	
19511	N88702	Continental Airlines	224	17/MAY/68	28/MAY/68	
19512	N88703	Continental Airlines	224	20/MAY/68	29/MAY/68	
19513	N88704	Continental Airlines	224	18/JUN/68	26/JUN/68	
19514	N88705	Continental Airlines	224	21/JUN/68	01/JUL/68	
19520	B-1820	China Airlines	109	16/SEP/67	27/SEP/67	
	2722	Taiwan Air Force			24/AUG/82	
19524	N2471	Boeing	024C	23/JUN/67		
	N2471	Continental Airlines			30/JUN/67	Leased
	N2471	Boeing			02/AUG/68	
	N1781B	Boeing			FEB/70	
	N5475	Boeing			18/OCT/71	
	HK-1271	Avianca			17/NOV/71	
	HK-1271	SAM Colombia			DEC/81	
19525	N2472	Boeing	024C	20/JUL/67		
	N2472	Continental Airlines			27/JUL/67	Leased
	N2472	Boeing			07/AUG/68	
	N5472	Boeing			68	
	N1781B	Boeing			70	
	HK-1272	Avianca			17/NOV/71	W/O 30/SEP/75, Barranquila
19526	N2473	Boeing	024C	25/JUL/67		
	N2473	Continental Airlines			01/AUG/67	Leased
	N2473	Boeing			14/AUG/68	
	N5473	Boeing			FEB/69	
	N1781B	Boeing			70	
	N8320	Continental Airlines			27/JAN/71	Leased
	N8320	Boeing			03/MAR/71	
	HK-1273	Avianca			17/NOV/71	
	HK-1273	SAM Colombia			DEC/81	
19527	N2474	Boeing	024C	07/SEP/67		
	N2474	Continental Airlines			16/SEP/67	Leased
	N5474	Boeing			20/AUG/68	
	N1781B	Boeing			70	
	N1355B	Boeing			72	
	CC-CAN	LAN Chile			27/MAY/72	
	N114FE	Federal Express	024F		25/APR/79	Converted
19528	N2475	Boeing	024C	16/SEP/67		
	N2475	Continental Airlines			23/SEP/67	Leased
	N2475	Air Micronesia			MAR/68	Sub-leased
	N2475	Continental Airlines			30/JUN/69	Purchased
	N2475	Air Micronesia			30/JUN/69	Op. by Continental
19532	N7295	Braniff	027QC	22/SEP/67	05/OCT/67	
	CC-CGD	Ladeco			SEP/78	
19533	N7296	Braniff	027QC	06/OCT/67	20/OCT/67	
	N915UP	United Parcel Service	027F		15/JAN/82	Converted, Op. by Orion Air
19534	N7293	Braniff	027QC	29/AUG/67	06/SEP/67	
	N293AS	Alaska Airlines			17/MAY/67	
	N293AS	McClain Airlines			14/AUG/86	
19535	N7294	Braniff	027QC	25/AUG/67	31/AUG/67	
	N60FM	Forbes Inc.			29/JUN/83	
19536	N7270L	Boeing	2C8	27/JUL/67		Prototype -200
	N3182B	Boeing			22/OCT/70	
	SX-CBF	Olympic Airways	284		28/JUN/71	
19537	N7620U	United Airlines	222	18/APR/68	03/MAY/68	
19538	N7621U	United Airlines	222	17/MAY/68	31/MAY/68	
19539	N7622U	United Airlines	222	28/MAY/68	09/JUN/68	
19540	N7623U	United Airlines	222	31/MAY/68	12/JUN/68	
19541	N7624U	United Airlines	222	08/JUN/68	15/JUN/68	
19542	N7625U	United Airlines	222	08/JUN/68	19/JUN/68	
19543	F-BOJA	Air France	228	09/MAR/68	24/MAR/68	
19544	F-BOJB	Air France	228	10/APR/68	23/APR/68	
	F-BOJB	Air Afrique			01/JUN/86	Leased
	F-BOJB	Air France			01/NOV/86	Sched.return
19545	F-BOJC	Air France	228	19/APR/68	02/MAY/68	
19546	F-BOJD	Air France	228	03/MAY/68	21/MAY/68	
19557	JA8321	All Nippon Airways	081	25/APR/67	04/MAY/67	
	N329K	Ford Motor Co.			29/AUG/72	
	EP-MRP	Shah of Iran			26/JUN/74	
	1002	Iranian Air Force				
	EP-GDS	Iran Air			01/JUL/82	
19558	N12301	Trans World Airlines	231	16/FEB/68	06/MAR/68	
19559	N12302	Trans World Airlines	231	16/MAR/68	02/APR/68	
19560	N12303	Trans World Airlines	231			

C/N	Registration	Owner/Operator	Series	First Flight	Delivery	Remarks
19561	N12304	Trans World Airlines	231	06/MAY/68	18/MAY/68	
	N12304	National Airlines			15/DEC/68	Leased
	N12304	Trans World Airlines			16/APR/69	
19562	N12305	Trans World Airlines	231	10/MAY/68	25/MAY/68	
19563	N12306	Trans World Airlines	231	03/JUN/68	17/JUN/68	
19564	N12307	Trans World Airlines	231	28/AUG/68	19/JUL/68	
19565	N12308	Trans World Airlines	231	09/JUL/68	22/JUL/68	
19595	N1637	Northeast Airlines	095	14/SEP/67	27/SEP/67	
	N530EJ	Alaska Airlines				
	N1637	Delta Air Lines		01/AUG/72		
	PP-VLQ	Varig			11/MAY/73	
19596	N1638	Northeast Airlines	095		OCT/67	
	N1638	Delta Air Lines			AUG/72	
	PP-VLR	Varig			MAY/73	
	HC-BLJ	Saeta			30/SEP/81	
19597	CS-TBN	TAP Air Portugal	082	24/JAN/68	08/FEB/68	
	N4564U	Purolator Courier	082F		29/NOV/83	Converted
	N528PC	Purolator Courier				Op. by Orion Air
19618	N530EJ	Executive Jet Aviation	155C	08/SEP/67	29/SEP/67	
	N530EJ	United Airlines			13/OCT/67	Leased
	N530EJ	Executive Jet Aviation			15/MAY/68	
	N530EJ	Trans Caribbean			15/MAY/68	Leased
	N530EJ	Executive Jet Aviation			10/MAY/69	
	N530EJ	CIT Corp.			08/MAY/71	
	N530EJ	Braniff			08/MAY/71	Leased
	N530EJ	CIT Corp.			10/APR/72	
	N530EJ	National Aircraft Leasing			APR/72	
	N530EJ	Alaska Airlines			10/APR/74	Leased
	N530EJ	National Aircraft Leasing			74	
	N530EJ	Continental Airlines			21/SEP/74	Leased
	N530EJ	National Aircraft Leasing			20/NOV/74	
	N530EJ	Alaska Airlines			21/NOV/74	Leased
	N530EJ	National Aircraft Leasing			APR/77	
	N530EJ	Alaska Airlines			APR/78	
	N530EJ	Omni International			10/APR/78	
	CS-TBV	TAP Air Portugal			06/MAY/78	Leased
	CS-TBV	Omni International			JUN/81	
	CS-TBV	United Coal			JUN/81	
	CS-TBV	TAP Air Portugal			JUN/81	Leased
	N3254D	United Coal			OCT/82	
	N720JE	Jet East			MAR/83	
	N720JE	Jet East	155F		MAY/86	
	N720JE	DHL Airways			MAY/86	Leased
19619	N531EJ	Executive Jet Aviation	155C	26/SEP/67	27/OCT/67	
	N531EJ	United Airlines			27/OCT/67	Leased
	N531EJ	Executive Jet Aviation			09/JUN/68	
	N531EJ	Trans Caribbean			09/JUN/68	Leased
	N531EJ	Executive Jet Aviation			07/JUL/69	
	N531EJ	World Airways			15/JUL/69	Leased
	N531EJ	Executive Jet Aviation			69	
	YA-FAW	Ariana			24/APR/71	
	G-BIUR	Dan Air			MAR/81	Leased
	YA-FAW	Ariana			31/OCT/81	
	TF-FLJ	Icelandair			31/OCT/81	Leased
	TF-FLJ	Kabo Air			31/OCT/81	Sub-leased
	TF-FLJ	Icelandair			22/APR/82	Leased
	TF-FLJ	Ariana			22/APR/82	
	G-BIUR	Dan Air			22/APR/82	Leased
	YA-FAW	Ariana			01/NOV/82	
	TF-FLJ	Icelandair			JUL/83	Leased
	YA-FAW	Ariana			83	
	YA-FAW	Bakhtar Afghan			NOV/85	
19620	N898PC	Pacific Airlines	193	17/FEB/67	10/MAR/67	
	N898PC	Hughes Airwest			18/APR/68	
	N898PC	Braniff			01/FEB/69	Leased
	N898PC	Hughes Airwest			05/FEB/70	
	XY-ADR	Union of Burma Airways			09/JUL/70	
	XY-ADR	Fokker			JUL/76	
	G-BEGZ	Dan Air			23/OCT/76	
	VR-CBG	Kuwait Real Estate			04/FEB/82	
	HZ-AMH	Kuwait Real Estate				
19662	HK-1400	Avianca	059	20/OCT/67	03/NOV/67	
19663	HK-1401	Avianca	059	06/NOV/67	15/NOV/67	
19665	N725AL	Airlift International	172C	06/OCT/67	23/OCT/67	
	N725AL	Air Mali			01/MAR/71	Leased
	N725AL	Airlift International			15/MAY/72	
	CS-TBQ	TAP Air Portugal			10/MAR/73	
	N444CM	Purolator Courier			24/NOV/83	
	N45498	Purolator Courier	172F		DEC/83	Converted
	N527PC	Purolator Courier				Op. by Orion Air
19666	N726AL	Airlift International	172C	17/OCT/67	30/OCT/67	
	N726AL	ALM			71	Leased
	N726AL	Airlift International			73	
	PP-VLE	Varig			02/APR/73	
19683	N528PS	Pacific Southwest Airlines	214	07/DEC/67	18/DEC/67	
	F-BPJU	Air Charter International			26/MAY/72	
	F-BPJU	Tunis Air			26/JUN/72	Leased
	F-BPJU	Air Charter International			SEP/72	
19684	N529PS	Pacific Southwest Airlines	214	03/JAN/68	12/JAN/68	
	F-BPJV	Air Charter International			22/NOV/72	
19685	N530PS	Pacific Southwest Airlines	214	27/MAR/68	02/APR/68	
	N530PS	Eastern Airlines			22/SEP/80	Leased
	N530PS	Eastern Airlines			DEC/85	Purchased
19686	N531PS	Pacific Southwest Airlines	214	25/APR/68	03/MAY/68	
	N531PS	Eastern Airlines			07/OCT/80	Leased
	N531PS	Eastern Airlines			DEC/85	Purchased
19687	N532PS	Pacific Southwest Airlines	214	02/MAY/68	10/MAY/68	
	N532PS	Eastern Airlines			16/OCT/80	Leased
	N532PS	Eastern Airlines			DEC/85	Purchased
19688	N533PS	Pacific Southwest Airlines	214	04/JUN/68	11/JUN/68	W/O 25/SEP/78, San Diego
19689	N534PS	Pacific Southwest Airlines	214	16/JUL/68	20/JUL/68	
	N534PS	Eastern Airlines			07/OCT/80	Leased
	N534PS	Eastern Airlines			DEC/85	Purchased
19690	YA-FAR	Ariana	113C	22/FEB/68	25/MAR/68	W/O 05/JAN/69, Gatwick Ap.
19691	SE-DDA	Transair	134	02/NOV/67	13/NOV/67	

BOEING 727

C/N	Registration	Owner/Operator	Series	First Flight	Delivery	Remarks
	SE-DDA	Scanair			01/OCT/69	
	SE-DDA	Transair			81	
	RP-C1240	Philippine Airlines			10/SEP/81	
	HC-BLE	TAME			30/JUN/84	
19692	SE-DDB	Transair	134	20/NOV/67	30/NOV/67	
	SE-DDB	Scanair			01/OCT/69	
	SE-DDB	Central Airways			OCT/80	Leased
	SE-DDB	Transair			81	
	RP-C1241	Philippine Airlines			05/OCT/81	
	HC-BLF	TAME			JUL/84	
19700	N6822	American Airlines	223	14/DEC/68	02/JAN/69	
19701	N6823	American Airlines	223	06/JAN/69	14/JAN/69	
19702	N6824	American Airlines	223	08/JAN/69	17/JAN/69	
19703	N6825	American Airlines	223	21/JAN/69	30/JAN/69	
19704	N6826	American Airlines	223	31/JAN/69	13/FEB/69	
19717	N8161G	Eastern Airlines	025QC	19/SEP/67	30/SEP/67	
	N125FE	Federal Express	025F		DEC/82	Converted
19718	N8162G	Eastern Airlines	025QC	04/OCT/67	15/OCT/67	
	N126FE	Federal Express	025F		08/OCT/82	Converted
19719	N8163G	Eastern Airlines	025QC	11/OCT/67	27/OCT/67	
	N127FE	Federal Express	025F		15/DEC/82	Converted
19720	N8164G	Eastern Airlines	025QC	19/OCT/67	09/NOV/67	
	N128FE	Federal Express	025F		04/NOV/82	Converted
19721	N8165G	Eastern Airlines	025QC	03/NOV/67	14/NOV/67	
	N130FE	Federal Express	025F		22/AUG/80	Converted
19722	N8166G	Eastern Airlines	025QC	09/NOV/67	20/NOV/67	
	N131FE	Federal Express	025F		16/AUG/82	Converted
19728	N766AS	Alaska Airlines	090QC	17/FEB/68	07/MAR/68	
	N766AS	SOHIO			SEP/77	Leased
	N766AS	Alaska Airlines			SEP/79	
19778	CF-	Nordair	142C			Cancelled order
19793	D-ABBI	Lufthansa	030QC	10/JAN/68	20/JAN/68	
	CX-BKA	Pluna			11/AUG/78	
	N4555W	Integrity Aircraft	030F		DEC/83	Converted
	N4555W	Flying Tigers			06/FEB/84	Leased
	N4555W	Cam Air			29/APR/85	
	N725JE	Jet East			29/APR/85	
19797	N88706	Continental Airlines	224	20/JUN/68	03/JUL/68	
19798	N88707	Continental Airlines	224	16/JUL/68	25/JUL/68	
	N88777	Continental Airlines			06/JAN/69	W/O 07/AUG/75,Denver
19799	N88708	Continental Airlines	224	23/JUL/68	02/AUG/68	
19800	N88709	Continental Airlines	224	31/JUL/68	02/AUG/68	
19801	N88710	Continental Airlines	224	01/AUG/68	07/AUG/68	
19802	N88711	Continental Airlines	224	07/AUG/68	14/AUG/68	
19803	N88712	Continental Airlines	224	13/AUG/68	20/AUG/68	
19804	N88713	Continental Airlines	224	15/AUG/68	28/AUG/68	
19805	N7431U	United Airlines	022QC	01/MAR/68	14/MAR/68	
	N111FE	Federal Express	022F		09/APR/79	Converted
19806	N7432U	United Airlines	022QC	14/MAR/68	25/MAR/68	
	N110FE	Federal Express	022F		20/FEB/79	Converted
19807	N727AL	Airlift International	172QC	07/MAY/68	31/MAY/68	
	N727AL	Jet Freight Cargo Enterprise			JUL/76	Leased
	N727AL	Airlift International			MAY/78	
	N727AL	MCA Leasing			03/AUG/80	
	N727AL	Southeast Airlines			03/AUG/80	Leased
	N727AL	MCA Leasing			81	
	N727AL	Fleming International			OCT/81	
	N727AL	Flying Tigers			08/FEB/84	Leased
	N727AL	Jet East International			JUL/84	
	N722JE	Jet East International			JAN/85	Op. for Emery Worldwide
19808	N732AL	Airlift International	172QC	29/JUL/68	09/AUG/68	
	N309BN	Braniff			21/MAR/72	Leased,
	N916UP	United Parcel Service	172F		26/MAY/82	Converted, Op by Orion Air
19811	CC-CAG	LAN Chile	116	12/JAN/68	06/FEB/68	
	CC-CAG	Ladeco			21/AUG/79	
19812	CC-CAQ	LAN Chile	116	02/FEB/68	07/FEB/68	W/O 28/APR/69, Santiago de Chile
19813	CC-CFD	LAN Chile	116C	13/JUN/68	11/JUL/68	
	N70708	International Air Leases			15/SEP/77	
	9N-ABN	Royal Nepal Airlines			14/MAY/78	
19814	CC-CFE	LAN Chile	116C	25/JUN/68	11/JUL/68	
	N115FE	Federal Express	116F		19/JUL/79	Converted
19815	N977PS	Pacific Southwest Airlines	114	28/JUL/68	03/AUG/68	
	XA-TUY	Mexicana			02/DEC/68	Leased
	XA-TUY	Mexicana			12/NOV/69	Purchased
	XA-TUY	Aeronautics Services			15/JUN/81	
	HK-2637X	Aerotal			15/JUN/81	Leased
	HK-2637X	Aeronautics Services			19/JUL/83	
	HP-1001	Panamanian Air Force			DEC/83	Leased
	HP-1001	Aeronautics Services			MAY/85	
	N726JE	Jet East			AUG/85	
	N726JE	Avensa			JUN/86	
19816	EP-IRC	Iran Air	086	07/DEC/67	19/DEC/67	
19817	EP-IRD	Iran Air	086	17/FEB/68	09/MAR/68	W/O 21/JAN/80, Nr. Tehran
19818	N388PA	Pan American	121C	09/SEP/67	25/SEP/67	
	XV-NJB	Air Vietnam			02/JAN/68	
	B-188	Taiwan Government			FEB/76	
	B-188	China Airlines			77	
	2724	Taiwan Air Force			OCT/82	
19819	N389PA	Pan American	121C	04/JAN/68	16/JAN/68	
	XV-NJC	Air Vietnam			23/JAN/68	W/O 15/SEP/74, Phan Rang AFB
19826	N12826	American Flyers Airline	185	05/MAR/68	01/APR/68	
	TF-FIA	Icelandair			18/MAY/71	
	TF-FLG	Icelandair			01/OCT/79	
19827	N12827	American Flyers Airlines	185C	26/JAN/68	20/FEB/68	
	N12827	Universal Airlines			27/MAY/71	
	N308BN	Braniff			30/JUN/71	
	PT-TYI	Transbrasil			02/MAY/80	Leased
19828	N52309	Trans World Airlines	231	17/JUL/68	29/JUL/68	
19829	N52310	Trans World Airlines	231	29/AUG/68	17/SEP/68	
19830	N52311	Trans World Airlines	231	06/SEP/68	20/SEP/68	
19831	N52312	Trans World Airlines	231	13/SEP/68	27/SEP/68	
19832	N52313	Trans World Airlines	231	27/SEP/68	11/OCT/68	
	N52313	National Airlines			10/NOV/68	Leased
	N52313	Trans World Airlines			26/APR/69	
19833	N1957	American Airlines	035	26/OCT/67	07/NOV/67	

C/N	Registration	Owner/Operator	Series	First Flight	Delivery	Remarks
19834	N1958	American Airlines	035	01/NOV/67	14/NOV/67	
	N932FT	Aviation Sales			16/DEC/83	
	N932FT	Aviation Sales	035F		FEB/84	Converted
	N932FT	Flying Tigers			MAR/84	Leased
19835	N1959	American Airlines	035	29/NOV/67	28/DEC/67	
	N727HC	Hardesty Co.			02/MAR/81	
19836	N1962	American Airlines	035	13/NOV/67	05/DEC/67	
	N936FT	Aviation Sales	035F		28/MAR/84	Converted
	N936FT	Flying Tigers			28/MAR/84	Leased
19837	N1963	American Airlines	035	22/NOV/67	19/DEC/67	W/O 26/APR/76, St Thomas, USVI
19838	N1964	American Airlines	123	18/MAR/68	29/MAR/68	
19839	N1965	American Airlines	123	23/FEB/68	08/MAR/68	
19846	OB-R-902	Faucett	063	26/MAR/68	09/APR/68	
	N32720	Boeing			15/MAY/85	
	N32720	General Electric Credit Co.			AUG/85	Leased
19850	N8167G	Eastern Airlines	025QC	17/NOV/67	02/DEC/67	
	N132FE	Federal Express	025F		14/SEP/82	Converted
19851	N8168G	Eastern Airlines	025QC	19/DEC/67	09/JAN/68	
	N133FE	Federal Express	025F		23/MAY/80	Converted
19852	N8169G	Eastern Airlines	025QC	10/JAN/68	23/JAN/68	
	N134FE	Federal Express	025F		JUL/80	Converted
19853	N8170G	Eastern Airlines	025QC	20/JAN/68	31/JAN/68	
	N135FE	Federal Express	025F		29/MAY/80	Converted
19854	N8171G	Eastern Airlines	025QC	27/AUG/68	10/SEP/68	
	N40	FAA			19/OCT/77	
19855	N8172G	Eastern Airlines	025QC	04/SEP/68	20/SEP/68	
	N136FE	Federal Express	025F		30/JUL/82	Converted
19856	N8173G	Eastern Airlines	025QC	12/SEP/68	03/OCT/68	
	N8173G	Federal Express	025F		24/SEP/80	Converted, leased
	N8173G	Morgan Guarantee			03/OCT/83	
	N8173G	Air Traffic Service			03/OCT/83	
	N8173G	Interstate Airlines			03/OCT/83	Leased
	N8173G	Air Traffic Service			MAY/85	
	N932UP	United Parcel Service			MAY/85	Op. by Interstate
19857	N8174G	Eastern Airlines	025QC	24/SEP/68	15/OCT/68	
	N8174G	Federal Express	025F		04/NOV/80	Converted, leased
	N8174G	Morgan Guarantee			14/OCT/83	
	N8174G	Air Traffic Service			14/OCT/83	
	N8174G	Interstate Airlines			14/OCT/83	Leased
	N8174G	Air Traffic Service			MAY/85	
	N933UP	United Parcel Service			MAY/85	Op. by Interstate
19858	N8175G	Eastern Airlines	025QC	01/OCT/68	18/OCT/68	
	N8175G	Federal Express	025F		23/DEC/80	Converted, leased
	N8175G	Morgan Guarantee			17/OCT/83	
	N8175G	Interstate Airlines			17/OCT/83	Leased
	N931UP	United Parcel Service			AUG/84	Op. by Interstate
19859	N1727T	Transamerica	171C		APR/68	
	C-FPXD	Pacific Western			DEC/73	
	C-FPXD	Panarctic Oil			FEB/76	Leased
	C-FPXD	Pacific Western			MAY/84	
	C-FPXD	Echo Bay Mining Co.			19/AUG/84	
19860	N1728T	Trans International	171C	22/JUN/68	05/JUL/68	
	N1728T	Braniff			27/NOV/72	Leased
	N1728T	Trans International			07/MAY/74	
	CP-1070	Lloyd Aero Boliviano			MAY/74	
19861	F-BOJE	Air France	228	15/JAN/69	28/JAN/69	
19862	F-BOJF	Air France	228	23/JAN/69	06/FEB/69	
19863	F-BPJG	Air France	228	06/FEB/69	19/FEB/69	
19864	F-BPJH	Air France	228	19/FEB/69	28/FEB/69	
19865	F-BPJI	Air France	228	13/MAR/69	27/MAR/69	
19867	N488US	Northwest Orient	151C	29/DEC/67	11/JAN/68	
	N432EX	Emery Worldwide	151F		04/JAN/82	Converted, Op. by Orion Air
19868	N489US	Northwest Orient	151C	11/JAN/68	29/JAN/68	
	N489US	Union of Burma Airways			11/JUL/69	Leased
	N489US	Northwest Orient			10/JUL/70	
	N433EX	Emery Worldwide	151F		05/MAY/82	Converted, Op. by Orion Air
19873	N9516T	Trans World Airlines	180C	08/JUL/68	23/JUL/68	
	N920UP	United Parcel Service	180F		13/JUL/82	Converted, Op. by Evergreen
19874	N9515T	Trans World Airlines	180C	07/FEB/68	19/FEB/68	
	N921UP	United Parcel Service	180F		13/JUL/82	Converted, Op. by Evergreen
19890	N7433U	United Airlines	022QC	30/AUG/68	19/SEP/68	
	N112FE	Federal Express	022F		27/AUG/79	Converted
19891	N7434U	United Airlines	022QC	04/SEP/68	20/SEP/68	W/O 18/JAN/69, Los Angeles Intl.
19892	N7435U	United Airlines	022QC	24/SEP/68	14/OCT/68	
	N7435U	Boeing			JUL/81	
	NZ7271	Royal New Zealand Air Force			JUL/81	
19893	N7436U	United Airlines	022QC	28/SEP/68	15/OCT/68	
	N7436U	Boeing			09/DEC/80	
	NZ7273	Royal New Zealand Air Force			29/APR/81	
19894	N7437U	United Airlines	022QC	04/OCT/68	25/OCT/68	
	N113FE	Federal Express	022F		20/SEP/79	Converted
19895	N7438U	United Airlines	022QC	06/NOV/68	19/NOV/68	
	N7438U	Boeing			JUL/81	
	NZ7272	Royal New Zealand Air Force			JUL/81	
19899	N7626U	United Airlines	222	29/JUL/68	16/AUG/68	
19900	N7627U	United Airlines	222	06/AUG/68	13/AUG/68	
19901	N7628U	United Airlines	222	09/AUG/68	06/AUG/68	
19902	N7629U	United Airlines	222	22/AUG/68	02/OCT/68	
19903	N7630U	United Airlines	222	28/AUG/68	04/OCT/68	
19904	N7631U	United Airlines	222	24/SEP/68	04/NOV/68	
19905	N7632U	United Airlines	222	30/SEP/68	08/NOV/68	
19906	N7633U	United Airlines	222	10/OCT/68	15/NOV/68	
19907	N7634U	United Airlines	222	30/OCT/68	21/NOV/68	
19908	N7635U	United Airlines	222	11/NOV/68	05/DEC/68	
19909	N7636U	United Airlines	222	11/NOV/68	12/DEC/68	
19910	N7637U	United Airlines	222	04/DEC/68	27/DEC/68	
19911	N7638U	United Airlines	222	12/DEC/68	27/DEC/68	
19912	N7639U	United Airlines	222	18/DEC/68	06/JAN/69	
19913	N7640U	United Airlines	222	19/DEC/68	10/FEB/69	
19914	N7641U	United Airlines	222	03/JAN/69	15/JAN/69	
19915	N7642U	United Airlines	222	17/JAN/69	03/MAR/69	
19968	CS-TBO	TAP Air Portugal	082C	12/NOV/68	21/NOV/68	
19970	N251US	Northwest Orient	251	11/OCT/68	19/OCT/68	
19971	N252US	Northwest Orient	251	26/OCT/68	21/NOV/68	
19972	N253US	Northwest Orient	251	15/NOV/68	21/NOV/68	

BOEING 727

C/N	Registration	Owner/Operator	Series	First Flight	Delivery	Remarks
19973	N254US	Northwest Orient	251	19/NOV/68	27/NOV/68	
19974	N255US	Northwest Orient	251	27/NOV/68	07/DEC/68	
19975	N256US	Northwest Orient	251	18/DEC/68	04/JAN/69	
19976	N257US	Northwest Orient	251	16/JAN/69	24/JAN/69	
19977	N258US	Northwest Orient	251	05/FEB/69	14/FEB/69	
19978	N259US	Northwest Orient	251	11/FEB/69	21/FEB/69	
19979	N260US	Northwest Orient	251	21/FEB/69	05/MAR/69	
19980	N261US	Northwest Orient	251	10/MAR/69	28/MAR/69	
19981	N262US	Northwest Orient	251	30/JUN/69	11/JUL/69	
19982	N263US	Northwest Orient	251	07/JUL/69	15/JUL/69	
19983	N264US	Northwest Orient	251	18/JUL/69	01/AUG/69	
19984	N265US	Northwest Orient	251	28/JUL/69	05/AUG/69	
19985	N266US	Northwest Orient	251	01/AUG/69	08/AUG/69	
19987	OO-STE	Sabena	029C	11/SEP/68	01/OCT/68	
	N696WA	World Airways			21/APR/76	
	N696WA	Yemen Airways			MAY/76	Leased
	N696WA	World Airways			31/DEC/79	
	N696WA	Toyomenka America			31/DEC/79	
	N696WA	International Air Leases			FEB/80	
	N444SA	FAMCO Aviation			20/NOV/80	Leased
	HZ-HE4	FAMCO Aviation			82	Leased
19991	N7276F	Frontier Airlines	291	27/JAN/68	08/FEB/68	
	N406BN	Braniff			01/MAR/72	
	N406BN	Southwest Airlines			01/MAR/79	Leased
	N406BN	Braniff			11/JAN/80	
	N406BN	Braniff Liquidating Trust			MAY/82	
	N406BN	Braniff (Hyatt)			DEC/83	Leased
	N406BN	Braniff Liquidating Trust			19/FEB/85	
	N406BN	International Air Leases			30/MAY/85	
	N406BN	Pride Air			01/AUG/85	Leased
	N406BN	International Air Leases			NOV/85	
	N406BN	Braniff			FEB/86	Leased
19992	N7277F	Frontier Airlines	291	09/FEB/68	18/FEB/68	
	N407BN	Braniff			06/APR/72	
	N407BN	Thomas Investment Corp.			28/DEC/83	
	N407BN	Air 1			28/DEC/83	Leased
	N407BN	Thomas Investment Corp.			OCT/84	
	N407BN	Skybus			17/JAN/86	Leased
	N407BN	World Airways			30/APR/86	Sub-leased
19993	N7278F	Frontier Airlines	291	13/MAR/68	23/MAR/68	
	N408BN	Braniff			13/MAR/72	
	N408BN	Braniff Liquidating Trust			MAY/82	
	N408BN	Braniff (Hyatt)			DEC/83	
	N408BN	Braniff Liquidating Trust			19/FEB/85	
	N408BN	International Air Leases			30/MAY/85	
	N408BN	Pride Air			01/AUG/85	Leased
	N408BN	International Air Leases			NOV/85	
	N408BN	Skybus			10/MAR/86	Leased
	N408BN	World Airways			10/MAR/86	Sub-leased
19994	N7279F	Frontier Airlines	291	10/JAN/69		Not taken-up
	N1784B	GATX Leasing			30/JAN/69	
	N1648	Northeast Airlines			30/JAN/69	Leased
	N1648	Delta Air Lines			01/AUG/72	
	N1648	Piedmont Airlines			16/JUN/83	
19995	N7275F	Frontier Airlines	291	13/JAN/69		Not taken-up
	N1785B	GATX Leasing			31/JAN/69	
	N1649	Northeast Airlines			31/JAN/69	Leased
	N1649	Delta Air Lines			01/AUG/72	
	N1649	Piedmont Airlines			23/JUN/83	
20003	SX-CBA	Olympic Airways	284	11/DEC/68	19/DEC/68	
20004	SX-CBB	Olympic Airways	284	04/JAN/69	16/JAN/69	
20005	SX-CBC	Olympic Arways	284	28/JAN/69	07/FEB/69	
20006	SX-CBD	Olympic Airways	284	30/JAN/69	07/FEB/69	
20037	N7643U	United Airlines	222	07/MAR/69	19/MAR/69	
20038	N7644U	United Airlines	222	20/APR/69	14/MAY/69	
20039	N7645U	United Airlines	222	13/MAY/69	26/MAY/69	
20040	N7646U	United Airlines	222	06/JUN/69	17/JUN/69	
20041	N7647U	United Airlines	222	19/JUN/69	30/JUN/69	
20042	SE-DDC	Transair	134C	22/AUG/68	05/SEP/68	
	SE-DDC	Scanair			01/OCT/69	Leased
	SE-DDC	Transair			81	
	N424EX	Emery Worldwide	134F		23/SEP/81	Converted, Op. by Ryan Aviation
20044	N1969	American Airlines	023	13/JUN/68	24/JUN/68	
20045	N2913	American Airlines	023	25/JUN/68	09/JUL/68	
	N2913	Parker Drilling Co.			24/DEC/80	
	N2913	Parker Aviation			DEC/81	
20046	N2914	American Airlines	023	10/JUL/68	23/JUL/68	
	N927DS	Diamond Shamrock Corp.			16/DEC/81	
20047	N94314	Trans World Airlines	231	30/DEC/68	03/FEB/69	
20048	N64315	Trans World Airlines	231	09/JAN/69	11/FEB/69	
20049	N44316	Trans World Airlines	231	14/FEB/69	27/FEB/69	
	N44316	Aviation Sales			JUL/84	
	N44316	Trans World Airlines			JUL/84	Leased
20050	N74317	Trans World Airlines	231	28/FEB/69	07/MAR/69	
	N74317	Aviation Sales			JUL/84	
	N74317	Trans World Airlines			JUL/84	Leased
20051	N74318	Trans World Airlines	231	01/APR/69	16/APR/69	
	N74318	Aviation Sales			JUL/84	
	N74318	Trans World Airlines			JUL/84	Leased
20052	N64319	Trans World Airlines	231	03/APR/69	18/APR/69	
	N64319	Aviation Sales			JUL/84	
	N64319	Trans World Airlines			JUL/84	Leased
20053	N64320	Trans World Airlines	231	21/APR/69	28/APR/69	
	N64320	Aviation Sales			JUL/84	
	N64320	Trans World Airlines			JUL/84	Leased
20054	N64321	Trans World Airlines	231	29/APR/69	15/MAY/69	
	N64321	Aviation Sales			JUL/84	
	N64321	Trans World Airlines			JUL/84	Leased
20055	N64322	Trans World Airlines	231	06/MAY/69	28/MAY/69	
	N64322	Aviation Sales			JUL/84	
	N64322	Trans World Airlines			JUL/84	Leased
20075	F-BPJJ	Air France	228	14/MAR/69	28/MAR/69	
20078	JA8327	Japan Air Lines	046	22/JAN/69	31/JAN/69	
20079	JA8328	Japan Air Lines	046			Cancelled order
20098	N64323	Trans World Airlines	231	12/JUN/69	25/JUN/69	

C/N	Registration	Owner/Operator	Series	First Flight	Delivery	Remarks
	N64323	Aviation Sales			JUL/84	
	N64323	Trans World Airlines			JUL/84	Leased
20099	N64324	Trans World Airlines	231	20/JUN/69	02/JUL/69	
	N64324	Aviation Sales			JUL/84	
	N64324	Trans World Airlines			JUL/84	Leased
20111	B-1822	China Airlines	109C	18/FEB/69	28/FEB/69	82
	2723	Taiwan Air Force			82	
20112	N7890	Trans World Airlines	031	14/APR/69	01/MAY/69	
20113	N7891	Trans World Airlines	031	18/APR/69	07/MAY/69	
20114	N7892	Trans World Airlines	031	09/APR/69	21/MAY/69	
20115	N7893	Trans World Airlines	031	25/JUN/69	07/JUL/69	
	N505T	Tenneco			12/SEP/80	
20139	N1645	Northeast Airlines	295	30/SEP/68	09/OCT/68	
	N1645	Delta Air Lines			01/AUG/72	
	N1645	Piedmont Airlines			25/MAR/83	
20140	N1646	Northeast Airlines	295	14/OCT/68	28/OCT/68	
	N1646	Delta Air Lines			01/AUG/72	
	N1646	Piedmont Airlines			24/MAY/83	
20141	N1647	Northeast Airlines	295	05/NOV/68	15/NOV/68	
	N1647	Delta Air Lines			01/AUG/72	
	N1647	Piedmont Airlines			16/MAY/83	
20143	N8789R	Trans Caribbean	1A7C	06/AUG/68	16/AUG/68	
	N2915	American Airlines			02/MAR/71	
	N2915	Walter E. Heller & Co.			15/AUG/83	
	N2915	TAG Leasing	1A7F		OCT/83	Converted
	N2915	Orion Air			OCT/83	Leased
20144	N8825E	Eastern Airlines	225	22/JUL/69	22/AUG/69	
20145	N8826E	Eastern Airlines	225	18/AUG/69	29/AUG/69	
20146	N8827E	Eastern Airlines	225	29/AUG/69	10/SEP/69	
20147	N8828E	Eastern Airlines	225	23/OCT/69	31/OCT/69	
20148	N8829E	Eastern Airlines	225	30/OCT/69	07/NOV/69	
20149	N8830E	Eastern Airlines	225	31/OCT/69	12/NOV/69	
20150	N8831E	Eastern Airlines	225	05/NOV/69	14/NOV/69	
20151	N8832E	Eastern Airlines	225	17/NOV/69	21/NOV/69	
20152	N8833E	Eastern Airlines	225	17/NOV/69	26/NOV/69	
20153	N8834E	Eastern Airlines	225	02/DEC/69	12/DEC/69	
20154	N8835E	Eastern Airlines	225	05/DEC/69	16/DEC/69	
20161	N535PS	Pacific Southwest Airlines	214	14/APR/69	17/APR/69	
	N535PS	All Nippon Airways			10/SEP/69	Leased
	N535PS	Pacific Southwest Airlines			19/JAN/70	
	N858N	Piedmont Airlines			OCT/81	
20162	N536PS	Pacific Southwest Airlines	214	18/APR/69		Not taken-up
	N7279F	GATX Leasing			24/APR/69	
	N7279F	Frontier Airlines			24/APR/69	Leased
	N7279F	Frontier Airlines			31/DEC/69	Purchased
	N499BN	Braniff			20/JUL/71	Leased
	N499BN	Frontier Airlines			01/DEC/71	
	N409BN	Braniff			01/FEB/72	
	N409BN	Braniff Liquidating Trust			MAY/82	
	N409BN	Braniff (Hyatt)			DEC/83	Leased
	N409BN	Braniff Liquidating Trust			19/FEB/85	
	N409BN	International Air Leases			30/MAY/85	
	N409BN	Pride Air			01/AUG/85	Leased
	N409BN	International Air Leases			NOV/85	
	N409BN	Braniff			FEB/86	Leased
20163	N537PS	Pacific Southwest Airlines	214	14/MAY/69	19/MAY/69	
	N855N	Piedmont Airlines			JUL/81	
20164	N538PS	Pacific Southwest Airlines	214	19/MAY/69	23/MAY/69	
	N856N	Piedmont Airlines			JUN/81	
20165	N539PS	Pacific Southwest Airlines	214	21/MAY/69	27/MAY/69	
	N857N	Piedmont Airlines			OCT/81	
20166	N540PS	Pacific Southwest Airlines	214	28/MAY/69	04/JUN/69	
	N860N	Piedmont Airlines			17/MAY/82	
20167	N541PS	Pacific Southwest Airlines	214	02/JUN/69	04/JUN/69	
	N861N	Piedmont Airlines			11/JUN/82	
20168	N542PS	Pacific Southwest Airlines	214	14/JUL/69	17/JUL/69	
	N895N	Piedmont Airlines			02/JUL/82	
20169	N545PS	GATX Leasing	214	22/JUL/69	31/JUL/69	
	N545PS	Pacific Southwest Airlines			31/JUL/69	Leased
	N545PS	Overseas National			MAY/81	
	N545PS	Pacific Southwest Airlines			MAY/81	Leased
	N545PS	Overseas National			30/JUL/82	
	N545PS	C & S Air Inc.			DEC/82	
	N545PS	Air National			DEC/82	Leased
	N545PS	C & S Air Inc.			DEC/83	
	N545PS	Thomas Investment Corp.			DEC/83	
	N545PS	Air 1			DEC/83	Leased
	N545PS	Thomas Investment Corp.			OCT/84	
	N545PS	Skybus			03/JAN/86	Leased
	N545PS	World Airways			30/APR/86	Sub-leased
20180	N6827	American Airlines	223	27/FEB/69	21/MAR/69	
20181	N6828	American Airlines	223	28/FEB/69	24/MAR/69	
20182	N6829	American Airlines	223	11/MAR/69	31/MAR/69	
20183	N6830	American Airlines	223	21/MAR/69	07/APR/69	
20184	N6831	American Airlines	223	24/MAR/69	15/APR/69	
20185	N6832	American Airlines	223	02/APR/69	18/APR/69	
20186	N6833	American Airlines	223	13/MAY/69	21/MAY/69	
20187	N6834	American Airlines	223	15/MAY/69	26/MAY/69	
20188	N6835	American Airlines	223	01/JUN/69	20/JUN/69	
20189	N6836	American Airlines	223	19/JUN/69	26/JUN/69	
20190	N6837	American Airlines	223	09/JUL/69	22/JUL/69	
20191	N6838	American Airlines	223	14/JUL/69	28/JUL/69	
20192	N6839	American Airlines	223	28/AUG/69	22/SEP/69	
20193	N6841	American Airlines	223	11/SEP/69	26/SEP/69	
20201	SX-CBE	Olympic Airways	284	15/OCT/69	24/OCT/69	
20202	F-BPJK	Air France	228	17/NOV/69	26/NOV/69	
20203	F-BPJL	Air France	228	27/NOV/69	06/DEC/69	
20204	F-BPJM	Air France	228	01/DEC/69	16/DEC/69	
20217		LAN Chile	116			Not taken-up
	N1780B	Boeing		20/AUG/68		
	N304BN	Braniff			28/MAY/69	Leased
	N1780B	Boeing			19/DEC/69	
	XA-SEW	Mexicana			24/JUL/70	
	HK-2605X	Aerotal			APR/81	WFU NOV/83, stored Bogota
20228	VH-TJE	Trans Australia Airlines	076	16/OCT/69	27/OCT/69	

BOEING 727

C/N	Registration	Owner/Operator	Series	First Flight	Delivery	Remarks
	N8043E	Interedec			21/AUG/79	
	HZ-GP2	Saudi REDEC			SEP/80	
	HZ-GRP	Saudi REDEC			81	
	N727RE	Interedec			DEC/84	
20232	N54325	Trans World Airlines	231	08/JAN/70	03/FEB/70	
20233	N54326	Trans World Airlines	231	15/JAN/70	05/FEB/70	
20234	N54327	Trans World Airlines	231	04/FEB/70	17/FEB/70	
20240	N8790R	GATX Leasing	2A7	24/APR/69	30/APR/69	
	N8790R	Trans Caribbean			30/APR/69	Leased
						W/O 28/DEC/70, St.Thomas, USVI
20241	N8791R	GATX Leasing	2A7	20/MAY/69	27/MAY/69	
	N8791R	Trans Caribbean			27/MAY/69	Leased
	N8791R	GATX Leasing			02/MAR/71	
	N6842	American Airlines			02/MAR/71	Leased
	N6842	American Airlines			19/MAY/82	Purchased
20243	N1781B	Boeing	224	11/OCT/68		
	N88714	Continental Airlines			24/APR/69	Leased
20244	N1782B	Boeing	224	16/OCT/68		
		Continental Airlines				Not taken-up
	5A-DAH	Libyan Arab Airlines			28/DEC/70	W/O 21/FEB/73, Sinai Desert
20245	N1783B	Boeing	224	13/JUN/69		
		Continental Airlines				Not taken-up
	5A-DAI	Libyan Arab Airlines			27/JUL/71	
20248	N11650	Northeast Airlines	295	30/SEP/69	10/OCT/69	
	N11650	Delta Air Lines			01/AUG/72	
	N11650	Bankers Trust			10/OCT/82	
	N371PA	Pan American			16/NOV/83	
20249	N11651	Northeast Airlines	295	06/OCT/69	17/OCT/69	
	N11651	Delta Air Lines			01/AUG/72	
	N11651	Bankers Trust			17/OCT/82	
	N372PA	Pan American			30/NOV/83	
20250	N7270Q	Mohawk Airlines	254			Not taken-up
	N547PS	Pacific Southwest Airlines		10/DEC/69	12/DEC/69	
	N547PS	All Nippon Airways			22/DEC/69	Leased
	N547PS	Jet Air Leasing			12/DEC/75	
	N547PS	Pacific Southwest Airlines			12/DEC/75	Leased
	N547PS	Jet Air Leasing			01/MAY/81	
	N547PS	Eastern Airlines			JUN/81	
20251	N7271Q	Mohawk Airlines	254			Not taken-up
	N548PS	Pacific Southwest Airlines		15/DEC/69	29/DEC/69	
	N548PS	All Nippon Airways			04/JAN/70	Leased
	N548PS	Jet Air Leasing			10/JAN/76	
	N548PS	Pacific Southwest Airlines			10/JAN/76	Leased
	N548PS	Jet Air Leasing			01/MAY/81	
	N548PS	Eastern Airlines			JUN/81	
20252	N7272Q	Mohawk Airlines	254			Not taken-up
	N549PS	Pacific Southwest Airlines		23/DEC/69	06/JAN/70	
	N549PS	All Nippon Airways			19/JAN/70	Leased
	N549PS	Jet Air Leasing			21/JAN/76	
	N549PS	Pacific Southwest Airlines			21/JAN/76	Leased
	N549PS	Jet Air Leasing			01/MAY/81	
	N549PS	Eastern Airlines			JUN/81	
20263	N2801W	Western Airlines	247	21/AUG/69	16/OCT/69	
	N2801W	International Air Leases			JUN/85	
	N2801W	Western Airlines			JUN/85	Leased
20264	N2802W	Western Airlines	247	11/SEP/69	16/OCT/69	
	N2802W	International Air Leases			JUN/85	
	N2802W	Western Airlines			JUN/85	Leased
20265	N2803W	Western Airlines	247	23/SEP/69	16/OCT/69	
	N2803W	International Air Leases			JUN/85	
	N2803W	Western Airlinea			JUN/85	Leased
20266	N2804W	Western Airlines	247	24/OCT/69	14/NOV/69	
	N2804W	International Air Leases			JUN/85	
	N2804W	Western Airlines			JUN/85	Leased
20267	N2805W	Western Airlines	247	29/OCT/69	14/NOV/69	
	N2805W	International Air Leases			JUN/85	
	N2805W	Western Airlines			JUN/85	Leased
20268	N2806W	Western Airlins	247	30/OCT/69	14/NOV/69	
	N2806W	International Air Leases			JUN/85	
	N2806W	Western Airlines			JUN/85	Leased
20278	VH-RMS	Ansett Airlines	077C	20/OCT/69	31/OCT/69	
	C2-RN7	Air Nauru			16/MAY/80	WFU SEP/83
	C2-RN7	Trans Australia Airlines			MAR/84	Leased
20279	CP-861	Lloyd Aero Boliviano	293	12/AUG/69	17/FEB/70	
20285		Air West	293			Not taken-up
	JA8335	All Nippon Airways	281	06/AUG/71	17/AUG/71	
	JA8335	Nissho Iwai			23/FEB/82	
	JA8335	All Nippon Airways			23/FEB/82	Leased
	JA8335	Nissho Iwai			31/JUL/84	
	N870N	Piedmont Airlines			01/AUG/84	
20286		Air West	293			Not taken-up
	N1780B	Boeing	281	01/DEC/71		
	JA8336	All Nippon Airways			10/MAY/72	
	JA8336	Nissho Iwai			23/FEB/82	
	JA8336	All Nippon Airways			23/FEB/82	Leased
	JA8336	Nissho Iwai			04/JAN/84	
	N864N	Piedmont Airlines			05/JAN/84	
20289	N267US	Northwest Orient	251	05/AUG/69	12/AUG/69	
20290	N268US	Northwest Orient	251	07/AUG/69	15/AUG/69	
20291	N269US	Northwest Orient	251	03/SEP/69	12/SEP/69	
20292	N270US	Northwest Orient	251	05/SEP/69	22/SEP/69	
20293	N271US	Northwest Orient	251	12/SEP/69	26/SEP/69	
20294	N272US	Northwest Orient	251	19/SEP/69	03/OCT/69	
20295	N273US	Northwest Orient	251	06/NOV/69	18/NOV/69	
20296	N274US	Northwest Orient	251	25/NOV/69	10/DEC/69	W/O 01/DEC/74, Bear Mountain, State Park, Ny.
20302	N750VJ	GATX Leasing	2B7	27/JAN/70	28/MAY/70	
	N750VJ	Allegheny Airlines			28/MAY/70	Leased
	N750VJ	GATX Leasing			30/NOV/71	
	N404BN	Braniff			30/NOV/71	Leased
	N404BN	GATX Leasing			12/MAR/82	
	N207US	Northwest Orient			15/JUN/83	
20303	N751VJ	GATX Leasing	2B7	17/APR/70	21/APR/70	
	N751VJ	Allegheny Airlines			21/APR/70	Leased
	N751VJ	GATX Leasing			27/NOV/71	

C/N	Registration	Owner/Operator	Series	First Flight	Delivery	Remarks
	N405BN	Braniff			27/NOV/71	Leased
	N405BN	GATX Leasing			13/MAR/82	
	N208US	Northwest Orient			15/JUN/83	
20304	CN-CCF	Royal Air Maroc	2B6	17/APR/70	24/APR/70	
20306	N54328	Trans World Airlines	231	13/FEB/70	03/MAR/70	W/O 01/DEC/74,Nr.Washington
20307	N54329	Trans World Airlines	231	24/FEB/70	10/MAR/70	
20308	N54330	Trans World Airlines	231	19/MAR/70	02/APR/70	
20309	N54331	Trans World Airlines	231	20/MAR/70	07/APR/70	
20310	N54332	Trans World Airlines	231	30/MAR/70	04/MAY/70	
20311	N2807W	Western Airlines	247			Cancelled order
20312	N2808W	Western Airlines	247			Cancelled order
20313	N2809W	Western Airlines	247			Cancelled order
20314	N2810W	Western Airlines	247			Cancelled order
20327	CF-CPN	CP Air	017	26/FEB/70	11/MAR/70	
	N115TA	National Aircraft Leasing			APR/77	
	N115TA	Nigeria Airways			10/MAY/77	Leased
	N115TA	National Aircraft Leasing			26/OCT/77	
	N4002M	Fluor Corp. USA			DEC/77	
	N529AC	Amway Corp.			NOV/82	
20328	CF-CPK	CP Air	017	08/APR/70	20/APR/70	
	N116TA	National Aircraft Leasing			APR/77	
	XA-GUU	Mexicana			JUN/77	Leased
	N116TA	Tigerair			01/NOV/80	
	XA-GUU	Mexicana			01/FEB/81	
	XA-GUU	Aeronautics Services			10/MAR/81	
	HC-BIC	SAN Ecuador			JUN/81	Leased
	HC-BIC	Aeronautics Services			03/MAY/82	
	G-BKCG	Dan Air			03/MAY/82	Leased
	HC-BIC	Aeronautics Services			DEC/84	
	HC-BLV	TAME			16/APR/85	
20343	YA-FAU	Ariana	113C	30/DEC/69	25/JAN/70	
	YA-FAU	Royal Nepal Airlines			08/SEP/79	Leased
	YA-FAU	Ariana			08/OCT/79	
	YA-FAU	Bakhtar Afghan Airlines			NOV/85	
20366	N564PS	Pacific Southwest Airlines	214	09/NOV/70	24/NOV/70	
	N859N	Piedmont Airlines			26/JAN/82	
20367	N544PS	Pacific Southwest Airlines	214	25/NOV/70	27/MAY/71	
	N544PS	Piedmont Airlines			23/JUL/82	
	N896N	Piedmont Airlines			30/MAY/83	
20370	VH-RMT	Ansett Airlines	077C	24/JUN/70	08/JUL/70	
	C2-RN4	Air Nauru			16/JUN/76	
	N555BN	World Jet Aircraft			06/SEP/83	
	N555BN	Purolator Courier			06/SEP/83	
	N526PC	Purolator Courier	077F		DEC/83	Converted, Op. by Orion Air
20371	VH-TJF	Trans Australia Airlines	076	30/JUN/70	09/JUL/70	
	VR-BAT	Constance Leasing			23/JAN/79	
	N727KA	Kirby Leasing			80	
	N888VT	View Top Corp.			JUN/84	
20379	N8836E	Eastern Airlines	225	08/JUN/70	17/JUN/70	
20380	N8837E	Eastern Airlines	225	19/JUN/70	30/JUN/70	
20381	N8838E	Eastern Airlines	225	02/JUL/70	14/JUL/70	
20382	N8839E	Eastern Airlines	225	13/JUL/70	21/JUL/70	
20383	N8840E	Eastern Airlines	225	11/AUG/70	20/AUG/70	
20384	N88715	Continental Airlines	224	01/FEB/70	12/FEB/70	
20385	N32716	Continental Airlines	224	10/MAR/70	16/MAR/70	
20386	N32717	Continental Airlines	224	16/MAR/70	27/MAR/70	
20387	N32718	Continental Airlines	224	31/MAR/70	08/APR/70	
20388	N32719	Continental Airlines	224	03/APR/70	15/APR/70	
20392	N401BN	Braniff	227	04/MAY/70	30/JUN/70	
	N205US	Northwest Orient			28/OCT/82	
20393	N402BN	Braniff	227	12/MAY/70	30/JUN/70	
	N206US	Northwest Orient			28/OCT/82	
20394	N403BN	Braniff	227	17/JUN/70	30/JUN/70	
	YV-76C	Avensa			20/FEB/81	
20409	F-BPJN	Air France	228	17/NOV/70	07/DEC/70	
20410	F-BPJO	Air France	228	25/NOV/70	11/DEC/70	
20411	F-BPJP	Air France	228	03/DEC/70	22/DEC/70	
20415	N8841E	Eastern Airlines	225	24/AUG/70	01/SEP/70	
20416	N8842E	Eastern Airlines	225	25/AUG/70	01/SEP/70	
20418	PP-CJE	Cruzeiro	1C3	20/OCT/70	29/JAN/71	
20419	PP-CJF	Cruzeiro	1C3	27/OCT/70	29/JAN/71	
20420	PP-CJG	Cruzeiro	1C3	02/NOV/70	29/JAN/71	
20421	PP-CJH	Cruzeiro	1C3	19/MAR/71		Not taken-up
	N1781B	Boeing				
	9N-ABD	Royal Nepal Airlines	1F8		16/AUG/72	
20422	PP-VLA	Varig	041	23/SEP/70		Not taken-up
	PP-VLF	Varig			10/OCT/70	
20423	PP-VLB	Varig	041	25/SEP/70		Not taken-up
	PP-VLG	Varig			10/OCT/70	
20424	PP-VLH	Varig	041	05/OCT/70	16/OCT/70	
20425	PP-VLD	Varig	041	14/OCT/70	23/OCT/70	
20426	PP-VLE	Varig	041	19/MAR/71		Not taken-up
	N1781B	Boeing				
	HI-212	Dominicana	1J1		18/OCT/72	
20430	N1785B	Boeing	230	11/SEP/70		
	D-ABCI	Lufthansa			27/JAN/71	
20431	D-ABDI	Lufthansa	230	26/FEB/71	11/MAR/71	
20432	N1780B	Boeing	264	24/JUL/70		
	XA-TAA	Mexicana			17/OCT/70	
20433	XA-TAB	Mexicana	264	12/OCT/70	26/OCT/70	
20434	XA-TAC	Mexicana	264	23/OCT/70	09/NOV/70	
20435	JA8328	All Nippon Airways	281	15/FEB/71	22/FEB/71	
	HL7348	Korean Airlines			10/FEB/80	
20436	JA8329	All Nippon Airways	281	02/MAR/71	12/MAR/71	W/O 30/JUL/71, nr.Shizukuishi
20437	N384PS	Pacific Southwest Airlines	254	02/MAR/70	17/MAR/70	
	N384PS	All Nippon Airways			17/MAR/70	Leased
	N384PS	Pacific Southwest Airlines			19/MAY/75	
	N384PS	Jetair Leasing			JUN/81	
	N384PS	Eastern Airlines			JUN/81	
20438	N536PS	Pacific Southwest Airlines	254	25/MAR/70	09/APR/70	
	N536PS	All Nippon Airways			21/APR/70	Leased
	N536PS	Pacific Southwest Airlines			13/APR/75	
	N536PS	Eastern Airlines			16/OCT/80	Leased
	N536PS	Eastern Airlines			DEC/85	Purchased
20441	N8843E	Eastern Airlines	225	28/AUG/70	04/SEP/70	

BOEING 727

C/N	Registration	Owner/Operator	Series	First Flight	Delivery	Remarks
20442	N8844E	Eastern Airlines	225	04/SEP/70	28/SEP/70	
20443	N8845E	Eastern Airlines	225	23/OCT/70	10/NOV/70	W/O 24/JUN/75,J.F.Kennedy Intl.
20444	N8846E	Eastern Airlines	225	27/OCT/70	16/NOV/70	
20445	N8847E	Eastern Airlines	225	29/OCT/70	18/NOV/70	
20446	N8848E	Eastern Airlines	225	02/NOV/70	19/NOV/70	
20447	N8849E	Eastern Airlines	225	04/NOV/70	20/NOV/70	
20448	N8850E	Eastern Airlines	225	11/NOV/70	23/NOV/70	
20460	N54333	Trans World Airlines	231	19/MAR/71	31/MAR/71	
20461	N54334	Trans World Airlines	231	25/MAR/71	06/APR/71	
20462	N54335	Trans World Airlines	231	23/APR/71	01/MAY/71	
20463	TC-JBA	Turk Hava Yollari	2FC			Not taken-up
	N1781B	Boeing		16/OCT/70		
	N32721	Continental Airlines	224		06/MAR/72	
20464	TC-JBB	Turk Hava Yollari	2F2			Not taken-up
	N1781B	Boeing		22/OCT/70		
	N32722	Continental Airlines	224		03/MAR/72	
20465	TC-JBC	Turk Hava Yollari	2F2	28/OCT/70		Not taken-up
	N1781B	Boeing			01/AUG/71	
	N1335B	Boeing			09/MAR/72	
	N32723	Continental Airlines	224			
20466	JA8332	All Nippon Airways	281	07/JUN/71	15/JUN/71	
	HL7355	Korean Airlines			12/NOV/80	
20467	JA8333	All Nippon Airways	281	18/JUN/71	25/JUN/71	
	JA8333	Nissho Iwai			23/FEB/82	
	JA8333	All Nippon Airways			23/FEB/82	Leased
	JA8333	Nissho Iwai			02/JUL/84	
	N869N	Piedmont Airlines			03/JUL/84	
20468	N1781B	Boeing	281	09/DEC/70		
	JA8330	All Nippon Airways			25/JUN/71	
	HL7349	Korean Airlines			17/FEB/80	
20469	N1781B	Boeing	281	29/DEC/70		
	JA8331	All Nippon Airways			10/MAY/71	
	HL7350	Korean Airlines			17/DEC/80	
20470	F-BPJQ	Air France	228	17/FEB/71	12/MAR/71	
20471	CN-CCG	Royal Air Maroc	2B6	24/NOV/70	01/FEB/71	
20472	7T-VEA	Air Algerie	2D6	14/JAN/71	12/FEB/71	
20473	7T-VEB	Air Algerie	2D6	03/MAR/71	12/MAR/71	
20475	ZS-SBH	South African Airways	044C	26/JAN/71	09/FEB/71	
	N26879	United Air Leasing Corp.			19/JAN/82	
	N26879	IASCO			MAY/82	
	N26879	Purolator Courier			MAY/82	Leased
	N26879	IASCO			OCT/82	
	N26879	Federal Express			OCT/82	Leased
	N26879	IASCO			31/DEC/82	
	N26879	Federal Express	044F		JUN/86	Converted
20476	ZS-SBI	South African Airways	044C	18/FEB/71	09/MAR/71	
	N2688Z	United Air Leasing Corp.			19/MAR/82	
	N2688Z	IASCO			MAY/82	
	N2688Z	Purolator Courier			MAY/82	Leased
	N2688Z	IASCO			82	
	N2688Z	Federal Express	044F		JUN/86	Converted
20489	CS-TBP	TAP Air Portugal	082	22/FEB/71	04/MAR/71	
	CS-TBP	Dominicana			01/NOV/83	Leased
	CS-TBP	TAP Air Portugal			DEC/83	
	N727KS	Kalair USA Corp.			03/FEB/84	
20490	N54336	Trans World Airlines	231	03/MAY/71	11/MAY/71	
20491	N54337	Trans World Airlines	231	18/MAY/71	26/MAY/71	
20509	JA8334	All Nippon Airways	281	07/JUL/71	15/JUL/71	
	JA8334	Nissho Iwai			23/FEB/82	
	JA8334	All Nippon Airways			23/FEB/82	Leased
	JA8334	Nissho Iwai			01/APR/84	
	N867N	Piedmont Airlines			02/APR/84	
20510	JA8337	All Nippon Airways	281	17/DEC/71	24/MAY/72	
	JA8337	Nissho Iwai			23/FEB/82	
	JA8337	All Nippon Airways			23/FEB/82	Leased
	JA8337	Nissho Iwai			30/NOV/83	
	N863N	Piedmont Airlines			01/DEC/83	
20511		All Nippon Airways	281			Cancelled order
20512	CF-CUR	CP Air	017	26/FEB/71	10/MAR/71	
	N99548	Boeing			17/MAR/77	
	CP-1339	Lloyd Aero Boliviano			14/APR/77	
	N99548	Boeing			16/OCT/78	
	N767RV	Asterion Inc.			OCT/78	
	N767RV	Baker Corp.			MAY/86	
	N767RV	Vallejo Corp.			MAY/86	
20513	CF-CUS	CP Air	017	08/APR/71	23/APR/71	
	N117TA	National Aircraft Leasing			06/JUN/77	
	XA-GUV	Mexicana			JUN/77	Leased
	N117TA	Tigerair			JUN/80	
	N117TA	Tenneco			JUN/80	Leased
	N117TA	Tigerair			80	
	XA-GUV	Mexicana			01/FEB/81	
	HC-BIB	SAN Ecuador			10/MAR/81	
20524	XA-TAY	Mexicana	264			Cancelled order
20525	N1779B	Boeing	230	03/SEP/71		
	D-ABFI	Lufthansa			12/DEC/71	
20526	D-ABGI	Lufthansa	230	19/OCT/71	25/NOV/71	
20533	N320HG	Intl.Telephone and Telegraph	1H2	23/AUG/71	03/NOV/71	
	N228G	W.R. Grace & Co.			08/OCT/81	
20538	F-BPJR	Air France	228	07/OCT/71	11/FEB/72	
20539	N1790B	Boeing	228	22/OCT/71		
	F-BPJS	Air France			18/JAN/72	
20540	N1781B	Boeing	228	05/NOV/71		
	N1788B	Boeing			13/MAR/72	
	F-BPJT	Air France				
20545	TS-JHN	Tunis Air	2HJ	29/JAN/72	14/FEB/72	
	TS-JHN	Saudia			APR/78	Leased
	TS-JHN	Tunis Air			11/MAR/79	
20548	VH-RMU	Ansett Airlines	277	10/NOV/72	20/NOV/72	
	VH-RMU	NASA			20/NOV/72	Leased
	VH-RMU	Ansett Airlines			19/FEB/73	
	N274WC	Wien Air Alaska			16/DEC/83	
	N274WC	Republic Airlines			FEB/85	Leased
20549	VH-RMV	Ansett Airlines	277	05/NOV/73	7/NOV/73	
	N275WC	Wien Air Alaska			16/DEC/83	

C/N	Registration	Owner/Operator	Series	First Flight	Delivery	Remarks
	N275WC	Republic Airlines			FEB/85	Leased
20550	VH-RMW	Ansett Airlines	277	01/APR/74	05/APR/74	
	N276WC	Wien Air Alaska			16/DEC/83	
	N276WC	Republic Airlines			FEB/85	Leased
20551	VH-RMX	Ansett Airlines	277	03/JUL/74	18/JUL/74	
	VH-RMX	Ansett Airlines	277F		DEC/83	Converted
20552	N1779B	Boeing	276	02/NOV/72		
	VH-TBG	Trans Australia Airlines			07/DEC/72	
20553	N1787B	Boeing	276	18/NOV/73		
	VH-TBH	Trans Australia Airlines			20/NOV/73	
20554	VH-TBI	Trans Australia Airlines	276	27/MAR/74	04/APR/74	
20555	VH-TBJ	Trans Australia Airlines	276	12/JUL/74	27/JUL/74	
20560	D-ABHI	Lufthansa	230	12/MAY/72	23/MAY/72	
20564	JA8418	All Nippon Airways	281			Cancelled order
20565	JA8419	All Nippon Airways	281			Cancelled order
20566	JA8420	All Nippon Airways	281			Cancelled order
20567	JA8421	All Nippon Airways	281			Cancelled order
20568	N1788B	Boeing	281	28/JAN/72		
	JA8338	All Nippon Airways			17/APR/72	
	JA8338	Nissho Iwai			23/FEB/83	
	JA8338	All Nippon Airways			23/FEB/83	Leased
	JA8338	Nissho Iwai			31/OCT/83	
	N862N	Piedmont Airlines			01/NOV/83	
20569	JA8339	All Nippon Airways	281	15/MAR/72	24/MAR/72	
	JA8339	Nissho Iwai			23/FEB/82	
	JA8339	All Nippon Airways			23/FEB/82	Leased
	JA8339	Nissho Iwai			29/FEB/84	
	N866N	Piedmont Airlines			01/MAR/84	
20570	JA8340	All Nippon Airways	281	01/MAR/72	10/MAR/72	
	JA8340	Nissho Iwai			23/FEB/82	
	JA8340	All Nippon Airways			23/FEB/82	Leased
	JA8340	Nissho Iwai			31/JAN/84	
	N865N	Piedmont Airlines			01/FEB/84	
20571	JA8341	All Nippon Airways	281	18/APR/72	28/APR/72	
	JA8341	Nissho Iwai			MAR/82	
	JA8341	All Nippon Airways			MAR/82	
	HL7367	Korean Air Lines			21/NOV/84	
20572	N1790B	Boeing	281	29/FEB/72		Not taken-up
	JA8342	All Nippon Airways				
	JA8343	All Nippon Airways			30/JUN/72	
20573	JA8343	All Nippon Airways	281			Not taken-up
	JA8344	All Nippon Airways		15/JUN/72	23/JUN/72	
20579	N2807W	Western Airlines	247	04/MAY/72	12/MAY/72	
20580	N2808W	Western Airlines	247	05/JUN/72	13/JUN/72	
	N2808W	Guinness Peat Aviation			MAY/84	
	N2808W	Northeastern Airlines			MAY/84	Leased
	EI-BRD	Guinness Peat Aviation			MAR/85	
	EI-BRD	Western Airlines			04/APR/85	Leased
20581	N2809W	Western Airlines	247	09/JUN/72	16/JUN/72	
20592	N1791B	Boeing	256	13/MAR/72		
	EC-CAI	Iberia			29/APR/72	
20593	EC-CAJ	Iberia	256	31/MAR/72	20/APR/72	
20594	EC-CAK	Iberia	256	26/APR/72	06/MAY/72	
20595	N1787B	Boeing	256	23/OCT/72		
	EC-CBA	Iberia			12/MAY/73	
	N1788B	Boeing				
20596	N1786B	Boeing	256	30/NOV/72		
	N1788B	Boeing				
	EC-CBB	Iberia			01/MAY/73	
20597	N1788B	Boeing	256	16/NOV/72		
	EC-CBC	Iberia			14/APR/73	
20598	N1788B	Boeing	256	21/NOV/72		
	EC-CBD	Iberia			03/APR/73	
20599	N1788B	Boeing	256	29/NOV/72		
	EC-CBE	Iberia			23/MAR/73	
20600	N1789B	Boeing	256	07/DEC/72		
	EC-CBF	Iberia			15/MAR/73	
20601	EC-CBG	Iberia	256	14/DEC/72	01/MAR/73	
20602	EC-CBH	Iberia	256	19/DEC/72	06/JAN/73	
20603	N1788B	Boeing	256	21/DEC/72		
	EC-CBI	Iberia			02/FEB/73	
20604	EC-CBJ	Iberia	256	05/JAN/73	17/JAN/73	
20605	EC-CBK	Iberia	256	02/FEB/73	14/FEB/73	
20606	N1788B	Boeing	256	12/APR/73		
	EC-CBL	Iberia			20/APR/73	
20607	N1788B	Boeing	256	08/MAY/73		
	EC-CBM	Iberia			21/MAY/73	
20608	N410BN	Braniff	227	20/JUN/72	03/JUL/72	
	N716AA	American Airlines			09/MAR/81	
20609	N411BN	Braniff	227	24/JUN/72	11/JUL/72	
	F-GCGQ	Europe Aero Serevices			16/APR/80	
20610	N412BN	Braniff	227	10/JUL/72	19/JUL/72	
	N717AA	American Airlines			24/DEC/80	
20611	N413BN	Braniff	227	20/JUL/72	01/AUG/72	
	N718AA	American Airlines			09/JAN/81	
20612	N414BN	Braniff	227	05/MAR/73	13/MAR/73	
	N719AA	American Airlines			20/FEB/81	
2C613	N415BN	Braniff	227	07/MAR/73	14/MAR/73	
	N720AA	American Airlines			17/MAR/81	
20614	N8851E	Eastern Airlines	225	14/SEP/72	27/SEP/72	
20615	N8852E	Eastern Airlines	225	19/SEP/72	29/SEP/72	
20616	N8853E	Eastern Airlines	225	27/SEP/72	06/OCT/72	
20617	N8855E	Eastern Airlines	225	04/OCT/72	11/OCT/72	
20618	N8856E	Eastern Airlines	225	05/OCT/72	16/OCT/72	
20619	N8857E	Eastern Airlines	225	10/OCT/72	19/OCT/72	
20620	N8858E	Eastern Airlines	225	13/OCT/72	24/OCT/72	
20621	N8859E	Eastern Airlines	225	27/OCT/72	03/NOV/72	
20622	N8860E	Eastern Airlines	225	27/MAR/73	06/APR/73	
20623	N8861E	Eastern Airlines	225	20/APR/73	01/MAY/73	
20624	N8862E	Eastern Airlines	225	25/APR/73	04/MAY/73	
20625	N8863E	Eastern Airlines	225	30/APR/73	08/MAY/73	
20626	N8864E	Eastern Airlines	225	21/MAY/73	30/MAY/73	
20627	N8865E	Eastern Airlines	225	24/MAY/73	05/JUN/73	
20628	N8866E	Eastern Airlines	225	30/MAY/73	06/JUN/73	
20634	N452DA	Delta Air Lines	232	15/JAN/73	23/JAN/73	

C/N	Registration	Owner/Operator	Series	First Flight	Delivery	Remarks
	N511PE	People Express			29/DEC/83	
20635	N453DA	Delta Air Lines	232	17/JAN/73	26/JAN/73	
	N512PE	People Express			30/JAN/84	
20636	N454DA	Delta Air Lines	232	22/JAN/73	02/FEB/73	
	N513PE	People Express			15/NOV/84	
20637	N455DA	Delta Air Lines	232	26/JAN/73	08/FEB/73	
	N514PE	People Express			13/FEB/84	
20638	N456DA	Delta Air Lines	232	14/MAR/73	12/APR/73	
	N515PE	People Express			29/MAY/84	
20639	N457DA	Delta Air Lines	232	16/MAR/73	04/APR/73	
	N516PE	People Express			08/FEB/84	
20640	N458DA	Delta Air Lines	232	20/APR/73	02/MAY/73	
	N517PE	People Express			01/JUN/84	
20641	N459DA	Delta Air Lines	232	24/APR/73	11/MAY/73	
	N518PE	People Express			30/APR/84	
20642	N460DA	Delta Air Lines	232	18/MAY/73	01/JUN/73	
	N519PE	People Express			29/JUN/84	
20643	N461DA	Delta Air Lines	232	14/JUN/73	23/JUN/73	
	N520PE	People Express			31/AUG/83	
20644	N462DA	Delta Air Lines	232	18/JUL/73	27/JUL/73	
	N521PE	People Express			11/OCT/84	
20645	N463DA	Delta Air Lines	232	21/JUL/73	27/JUL/73	
	N522PE	People Express			13/SEP/84	
20646	N464DA	Delta Air Lines	232	10/AUG/73	16/AUG/73	
	N523PE	People Express			28/DEC/84	
20647	N465DA	Delta Air Lines	232	22/AUG/73	31/AUG/73	
	N524PE	People Express			01/SEP/84	
20648	N2810W	Western Airlines	247	26/JUL/72	04/AUG/72	
20649	N2811W	Western Airlines	247	07/AUG/72	16/AUG/72	
20654	N32724	Continental Airlines	224	19/MAR/73	28/MAR/73	
20655	N32725	Continental Airlines	224	30/MAR/73	10/APR/73	
20656	N66726	Continental Airlines	224	18/APR/73	27/APR/73	
20657	N24728	Continental Airlines	224	29/AUG/73	07/SEP/73	
20658	N25729	Continental Airlines	224	24/SEP/73	08/OCT/73	
20659	N29730	Continental Airlines	224	03/OCT/73	15/OCT/73	
20660	N66731	Continental Airlines	224	16/OCT/73	31/OCT/73	
20661	N66732	Continental Airlines	224	22/AUG/74	05/SEP/74	
	N66732	Air Micronesia			DEC/81	Op. by Continental
20662	N66733	Continental Airlines	224	21/SEP/74	07/OCT/74	
20663	N66734	Continental Airlines	224	20/SEP/74	02/OCT/74	
20664	N69735	Continental Airlines	224	16/OCT/74	25/OCT/74	
20665	N69736	Continental Airlines	224	18/AUG/75	26/AUG/75	
20666	N93738	Continental Airlines	224	27/AUG/75	08/SEP/75	
20667	N69739	Continental Airlines	224	26/SEP/75	07/OCT/75	
	N69739	Air Micronesia			AUG/83	Op. by Continental
20668	N69740	Continental Airlines	224	03/OCT/75	14/OCT/75	
20673	D-ABKI	Lufthansa	230	05/FEB/73	16/FEB/73	
20674	D-ABLI	Lufthansa	230	13/FEB/73	24/FEB/73	
20675	D-ABYL	Condor	230			Not taken-up
	D-ABMI	Condor		19/FEB/73	04/MAR/73	
	D-ABMI	Lufthansa			74	Leased
	D-ABMI	Condor			75	
	D-ABMI	Nigeria Airways			DEC/76	Leased
	D-ABMI	Condor			15/MAR/77	
	D-ABMI	Nigeria Airways			DEC/77	Leased
	D-ABMI	Condor			MAR/78	
	D-ABMI	Nigeria Airways			NOV/78	Leased
	D-ABMI	Condor				
20676	D-ABYM	Condor	230			Not taken-up
	D-ABNI	Condor		22/FEB/73	07/MAR/73	
	D-ABNI	Lufthansa			80	Leased
	D-ABNI	Condor				
	D-ABNI	Lufthansa			MAR/85	
20677	D-ABYN	Condor	230			Not taken-up
	D-ABPI	Condor		23/MAR/73	02/APR/73	
	D-ABPI	Lufthansa			NOV/76	Leased
	D-ABPI	Condor			APR/79	
	D-ABPI	Lufthansa			MAR/85	Leased
20678	N550PS	Pacific Southwest Airlines	214	21/MAR/73	30/MAR/73	
	N550PS	Continental Airlines			04/JUN/79	Leased
	N550PS	Pacific Southwest Airlines			23/MAR/81	
	N373PA	Pan American			01/NOV/84	
20679	N551PS	Pacific Southwest Airlines	214	03/MAY/73	11/MAY/73	
	N374PA	Pan American			27/DEC/84	
20705	CN-CCH	Royal Air Maroc	2B6	07/MAY/73	18/MAY/73	
20706	N552PS	National Aircraft Leasing	2J7	04/JUN/73		
	N552PS	Pacific Southwest Airlines			14/JUN/73	Leased
	N552NA	National Aircraft Leasing			13/JUN/75	
	OY-SBA	Sterling Airways			08/JUL/75	Leased
	N552NA	National Aircraft Leasing			15/JUN/76	
	N552NA	Mexicana			15/JUN/76	Leased
20707	N553PS	National Aircraft Leasing	2J7	13/JUN/73		
	N553PS	Pacific Southwest Airlines			21/JUN/73	Leased
	N553NA	National Aircraft Leasing			20/JUN/75	
	OY-SBB	Sterling Airways			07/JUL/75	Leased
	N553NA	National Aircraft Leasing			20/JUN/76	
	N553NA	Mexicana			20/JUN/76	Leased
20709	XA-CUB	Mexicana	264	06/JUN/73	18/JUN/73	
20710	XA-CUE	Mexicana	264	14/SEP/73	25/SEP/73	WFU 09/AUG/83, damaged
	N788BR	World Jet Aircraft			15/OCT/83	
	N788BR	Aircraft Sales Co.			JUL/83	
	N788BR	Guinness Peat Aviation			01/FEB/84	
	N788BR	Northeastern International			01/FEB/84	Leased
	EI-BRF	Guinness Peat Aviation			MAR/85	
	N728ZV	Sun Country			JUN/85	Leased
	N728ZV	Guinness Peat Aviation			SEP/85	
	N728ZV	Aeron Aviation			SEP/85	
	N728ZV	Sun Country			SEP/85	Leased
	N728ZV	Aeron Aviation			04/APR/86	
	G-BMLP	Dan Air			04/APR/86	Leased
20724	JA8345	All Nippon Airways	281	25/JUN/73	06/JUL/73	
20725	JA8346	All Nippon Airways	281	07/JUL/73	16/JUL/73	
	HL7366	Korean Air Lines			SEP/84	
20726	JA8347	All Nippon Airways	281	31/JUL/73	09/AUG/73	
20727	JA8348	All Nippon Airways	281	17/AUG/73	23/AUG/73	

C/N	Registration	Owner/Operator	Series	First Flight	Delivery	Remarks
20728	JA8349	All Nippon Airways	281	24/AUG/73	07/SEP/73	
20729	N416BN	Braniff	227	28/JUN/73	10/JUL/73	
	N721AA	American Airlines			11/DEC/80	
20730	N417BN	Braniff	227	03/JUL/73	12/JUL/73	
	N722AA	American Airlines			25/MAR/81	
20731	N418BN	Braniff	227	09/JUL/73	16/JUL/73	
	N723AA	American Airlines			16/JAN/81	
20732	N419BN	Braniff	227	02/AUG/73	10/AUG/73	
	N725AA	American Airlines			17/NOV/80	
20733	N420BN	Braniff	227	09/AUG/73	16/AUG/73	
	N726AA	American Airlines			26/NOV/80	
20734	N421BN	Braniff	227	13/AUG/73	21/AUG/73	
	N727AA	American Airlines			22/JAN/81	
20735	N422BN	Braniff	227	10/SEP/73	18/SEP/73	
	N728AA	American Airlines			02/FEB/81	
20736	N423BN	Braniff	227	12/SEP/73	24/SEP/73	
	N729AA	American Airlines			11/FEB/81	
20737	N424BN	Braniff	227	20/SEP/73	28/SEP/73	
	N730AA	American Airlines			02/MAR/81	
20738	N425BN	Braniff	227	21/SEP/73	05/OCT/73	
	N731AA	American Airlines			31/MAR/81	
20739	TS-JHO	Tunis Air	2H3	14/JUN/73	25/JUN/73	
	N189CB	Air 1			MAR/84	
	N189CB	Leslie Leasing			OCT/84	
	PH-AHB	Air Holland			28/MAR/85	
	PH-AHB	PK Finans			DEC/85	
	PH-AHB	Air Holland			DEC/85	Leased
	PH-AHB	Worldwide Airlines			DEC/85	Sub-leased
	PH-AHB	Air Holland			MAR/86	Leased
20743	N466DA	Delta Air Lines	232	28/AUG/73	06/SEP/73	
20744	N467DA	Delta Air Lines	232	07/SEP/73	14/SEP/73	
20745	N468DA	Delta Air Lines	232	27/SEP/73	07/OCT/73	
20746	N469DA	Delta Air Lines	232	08/OCT/73	18/OCT/73	
20747	N470DA	Delta Air Lines	232	25/OCT/73	01/NOV/73	
20748	N471DA	Delta Air Lines	232	29/OCT/73	15/NOV/73	
20749	N472DA	Delta Air Lines	232	05/NOV/73	22/NOV/73	
20750	N473DA	Delta Air Lines	232	16/NOV/73	30/NOV/73	
20751	N474DA	Delta Air Lines	232	18/DEC/73	04/JAN/74	
20752	N475DA	Delta Air Lines	232	14/DEC/73	09/JAN/74	
20753	N1785B	Boeing	232	01/FEB/74		For JT8D-17 Tests
	N476DA	Delta Air Lines			29/APR/74	
20754	N477DA	Delta Air Lines	232	04/FEB/74	08/FEB/74	
20755	N478DA	Delta Air Lines	232	08/FEB/74	28/FEB/74	
20756	N479DA	Delta Air Lines	232	03/APR/74	12/APR/74	
20757	D-ABQI	Lufthansa	230	21/DEC/73	11/JAN/74	
20764	N1779B	Boeing	2J4	26/JUL/73		
	OY-SAU	Sterling Airways			15/NOV/73	
	N727BE	Boeing			13/JUN/84	
	N221FE	Federal Express			10/DEC/85	
	OY-SAU	Sterling Airways			11/FEB/86	
20765	OY-SAS	Sterling Airways	2J4	23/OCT/73	03/NOV/73	
	OY-SAS	Egyptair			AUG/74	Leased
	OY-SAS	Sterling Airways			DEC/74	
	OY-SAS	Laker Airways			79	Leased
	OY-SAS	Sterling Airways			79	
	N728BE	Boeing			03/DEC/84	
	N728BE	Sterling Airways			25/MAY/85	Leased
	N728BE	Boeing			OCT/85	
	N222FE	Federal Express			26/NOV/85	
	OY-SAS	Sterling Airways			11/FEB/86	
20766	OY-SAT	Sterling Airways	2J4	16/NOV/73	03/DEC/73	
	N729BE	Boeing			15/MAY/84	
	N223FE	Federal Express			08/FEB/86	
	OY-SAT	Sterling Airways			11/FEB/86	
20772	N426BN	Braniff	227	08/OCT/73	23/OCT/73	WFU MAY/82
	N551PE	People Express			15/FEB/84	
	N551PE	Southwest Airlines			15/FEB/84	Leased
	N551PE	People Express			FEB/85	
20773	N427BN	Braniff	227	10/OCT/73	25/OCT/73	WFU MAY/82
	N552PE	People Express			08/AUG/83	
20774	N428BN	Braniff	227	20/NOV/73	14/DEC/73	WFU MAY/82
	N553PE	People Express			27/JUN/83	
20775	N429BN	Braniff	227	11/DEC/73	04/JAN/74	WFU MAY/82
	N554PE	People Express			03/NOV/83	
20780	XA-CUN	Mexicana	264	22/OCT/73	02/NOV/73	
20787	XA-DAT	Mexicana	264	05/DEC/73	14/DEC/73	
20788	D-ABRI	Lufthansa	230	01/FEB/74	11/FEB/74	
20789	D-ABSI	Lufthansa	230	14/FEB/74	25/FEB/74	
20790	D-ABTI	Lufthansa	230	05/MAR/74	19/MAR/74	
	N1787B	Boeing			17/JUL/74	
	D-ABTI	Condor			15/NOV/74	
20791	D-ABVI	Condor	230	08/MAR/74	22/MAR/74	
20792	D-ABWI	Condor	230	15/MAR/74	25/MAR/74	
20811	EC-CFA	Iberia	256	21/DEC/73	15/JAN/74	
20812	EC-CFB	Iberia	256	11/JAN/74	22/JAN/74	
20813	EC-CFC	Iberia	256	08/JAN/74	29/JAN/74	
20814	EC-CFD	Iberia	256	11/JAN/74	06/FEB/74	
20815	EC-CFE	Iberia	256	17/JAN/74	15/FEB/74	
20816	EC-CFF	Iberia	256	18/JAN/74	25/FEB/74	
20817	EC-CFG	Iberia	256	22/JAN/74	07/MAR/74	
20818	EC-CFH	Iberia	256	25/JAN/74	20/MAR/74	
20819	EC-CFI	Iberia	256	26/JAN/74	02/APR/74	
20820	EC-CFJ	Iberia	256	01/MAR/74	16/APR/74	W/O 07/DEC/83, Madrid Ap.
20821	EC-CFK	Iberia	256	26/MAR/74	09/MAY/74	
20822	TS-JHP	Tunis Air	2H3	28/NOV/73	13/DEC/73	
	N191CB	Air One			MAR/84	
	N191CB	Walker Leasing			OCT/84	
	PH-AHD	Air Holland			17/MAY/85	
	PH-AHD	PK Finans			DEC/85	
	PH-AHD	Air Holland			DEC/85	Leased
20823	N8867E	Eastern Airlines	225	28/NOV/73	13/DEC/73	
20824	N8869E	Eastern Airlines	225	21/NOV/73	07/DEC/73	
20837	N430BN	Braniff	227	18/FEB/74	27/FEB/74	WFU MAY/82
	N555PE	People Express			30/JAN/84	
20838	N431BN	Braniff	227	20/FEB/74	06/MAR/74	WFU MAY/82

C/N	Registration	Owner/Operator	Series	First Flight	Delivery	Remarks
	N556PE	People Express			10/JAN/84	
20839	N432BN	Braniff	227	09/APR/74	19/APR/74	WFU MAY/82
	N557PE	People Express			08/JUL/83	
20840	N433BN	Braniff	227	30/APR/74	09/MAY/74	WFU MAY/82
	N558PE	People Express			09/AUG/83	
20843	N54338	Trans World Airlines	231	20/AUG/74	31/AUG/74	
20844	N64339	Trans World Airlines	231	27/AUG/74	05/SEP/74	
20845	N54340	Trans World Airlines	231	29/AUG/74	10/SEP/74	
20846	N54341	Trans World Airlines	231			Cancelled order
20847	N54342	Trans World Airlines	231			Cancelled order
20848	N54343	Trans World Airlines	231			Cancelled order
20850	N54345	Trans World Airlines	231			Cancelled order
20851	N54346	Trans World Airlines	231			Cancelled order
20852	N54367	Trans World Airlines	231			Cancelled order
20853	N54348	Trans World Airlines	231			Cancelled order
20854	N54349	Trans World Airlines	231			Cancelled order
20855	N54350	Trans World Airlines	231			Cancelled order
20856	N54351	Trans World Airlines	231			Cancelled order
20857	N54352	Trans World Airlines	231			Cancelled order
20858	N54353	Trans World Airlines	231			Cancelled order
20859	N54354	Trans World Airlines	231			Cancelled order
20860	N480DA	Delta Air Lines	232	07/MAY/74	16/MAY/74	
20861	N481DA	Delta Air Lines	232	15/MAY/74	30/MAY/74	
20862	N482DA	Delta Air Lines	232	24/MAY/74	17/JUN/74	
20863	N483DA	Delta Air Lines	232	26/JUN/74	12/JUL/74	
20864	N484DA	Delta Air Lines	232	08/AUG/74	21/AUG/74	
20865	N485DA	Delta Air Lines	232	16/AUG/74	28/AUG/74	
20866	N486DA	Delta Air Lines	232	03/SEP/74	13/SEP/74	
20867	N487DA	Delta Air Lines	232	06/SEP/74	19/SEP/74	
	N487DA	Charlotte Aerospace			15/JUN/86	
20868	N2812W	Western Airlines	247	20/MAR/74	29/MAR/74	
20869	N2813W	Western Airlines	247	22/MAR/74	02/APR/74	
20870	N2814W	Western Airlines	247	11/APR/74	26/APR/74	
20871	N2815W	Western Airlines	247	17/MAY/74	29/MAY/74	
20872	N2816W	Western Airlines	247	10/MAY/74	25/MAY/74	
20873	N2817W	Western Airlines	247	21/MAY/74	05/JUN/74	
20874	N2818W	Western Airlines	247	16/JUL/74	25/JUL/74	
	N2818W	Gulf Air Transport			23/JAN/85	
20875	N554PS	Pacific Southwest Airlines	214	06/MAR/74	15/MAR/74	
	N375PA	Pan American			NOV/84	
20876	JA8350	All Nippon Airways	281	26/MAR/74	04/APR/74	
20877	JA8351	All Nippon Airways	281	02/APR/74	16/APR/74	
20878	JA8352	All Nippon Airways	281	23/APR/74	02/MAY/74	
20879	N128NA	National Aircraft Leasing	2J7	22/APR/74	04/NOV/74	
	N128NA	Air Jamaica			07/NOV/74	Leased
	N128NA	National Aircraft Leasing			19/OCT/75	
	N128NA	Mexicana			20/OCT/75	Leased
20880	N129NA	National Aircraft Leasing	2J7	02/MAY/74	07/NOV/74	
	N129NA	Air Jamaica			07/NOV/74	Leased
	N129NA	National Aircraft Leasing			07/NOV/75	
	N129NA	Mexicana			31/DEC/75	Leased
20885	JY-ADR	Alia	2D3	28/JUN/74	30/JUL/74	
20886	JY-ADU	Alia	2D3	26/JUL/74	14/AUG/74	W/O 14/MAR/79, Doha
20894	XA-DUI	Mexicana	264	05/JUN/74	25/JUN/74	
20895	XA-DUJ	Mexicana	264	11/JUN/74	25/JUN/74	
20896	XA-DUK	Mexicana	264	18/JUN/74	25/JUN/74	
20899	D-ABKA	Lufthansa	230	06/JUN/74	17/JUN/74	
20900	D-ABKB	Lufthansa	230	19/JUN/74	28/JUN/74	
20901	D-ABKC	Lufthansa	230	18/JUL/74	26/JUL/74	
20902	D-ABKD	Lufthansa	230	23/JUL/74	02/AUG/74	
20903	N8293V	Boeing	230	21/NOV/74		
	N87790	Boeing			JAN/75	AWACS support Aircraft
	D-ABKE	Lufthansa			02/MAY/75	
20904	D-ABKF	Lufthansa	230	05/DEC/74	06/JAN/75	
20905	D-ABKG	Lufthansa	230	28/JAN/75	07/FEB/75	
20906	D-ABKH	Lufthansa	230	26/FEB/75	07/MAR/75	
20918	D-ABKJ	Lufthansa	230	26/MAR/75	04/APR/75	
20930	YU-AKA	JAT	2H9	31/MAY/74	07/JUN/74	
20931	YU-AKB	JAT	2H9	29/MAY/74	12/JUN/74	
20932	C-GAAA	Air Canada	233	16/SEP/74	30/SEP/74	
20933	C-GAAB	Air Canada	233	19/SEP/74	13/OCT/74	
20934	C-GAAC	Air Canada	233	02/OCT/74	17/OCT/74	
	N220FE	Federal Express	233F		31/MAR/85	Converted
20935	C-GAAD	Air Canada	233	08/OCT/74	22/OCT/74	
20936	C-GAAE	Air Canada	233	16/OCT/74	23/OCT/74	
	6Y-JMH	Air Jamaica			JAN/82	Leased
	C-GAAE	Air Canada			DEC/82	
20937	C-GAAF	Air Canada	233	21/FEB/75	06/MAR/75	
20938	C-GAAG	Air Canada	233	03/MAR/75	13/MAR/75	
20939	C-GAAH	Air Canada	233	24/MAR/75	04/APR/75	
20940	C-GAAI	Air Canada	233	31/MAR/75	10/APR/75	
20941	C-GAAJ	Air Canada	233	08/APR/75	08/MAY/75	
20942	C-GAAK	Air Canada	233	05/MAY/75	15/MAY/75	
20945	EP-IRP	Iran Air	286	12/JUN/74	29/JUL/74	Impounded at Baghdad 08/SEP/84 following hijack, still WFU
20946	EP-IRR	Iran Air	286	24/JUN/74	09/JUL/74	
20947	EP-IRS	Iran Air	286	12/SEP/74	25/SEP/74	
20948	TS-JHQ	Tunis Air	2H3	04/NOV/74	13/NOV/74	
20950	VH-TBK	Trans Australia Airlines	276	22/OCT/74	31/OCT/74	
20951	VH-TBL	Trans Australia Airlines	276	04/APR/75	24/APR/75	
	VH-TBL	Iran Air			26/JUL/76	Leased
	VH-TBL	Trans Australia Airlines			01/AUG/77	
	VH-TBL	Australian Airlines			04/AUG/86	
20955	7T-VEH	Air Algerie	2D6	27/SEP/74	27/OCT/74	
20972	CS-TBR	TAP Air Portugal	282	07/JAN/75	22/JAN/75	W/O 19/NOV/77, Funchal-Madeira
20973	CS-TBS	TAP Air Portugal	282	14/JAN/75	06/FEB/75	
20974	EC-CID	Iberia	256	11/OCT/74	24/OCT/74	
20975	EC-CIE	Iberia	256	18/OCT/74	30/OCT/74	
20978	VH-RMY	Ansett Airlines	277	29/OCT/74	07/NOV/74	
	6Y-JML	Air Jamaica			22/OCT/85	Leased
20979	VH-RMZ	Ansett Airlines	277	03/APR/75	30/APR/75	WFU JUL/83, stored
20980	TC-JBF	Turk Hava Yollari	2F2	31/OCT/74	27/NOV/74	
20981	TC-JBG	Turk Hava Yollari	2F2	11/NOV/74	21/NOV/74	
20982	TC-JBH	Turk Hava Yollari	2F2	11/NOV/74	21/NOV/74	W/O 19/SEP/76, Mt. Karatepe, Turkey

C/N	Registration	Owner/Operator	Series	First Flight	Delivery	Remarks
20983	TC-JBJ	Turk Hava Yollari	2F2	18/NOV/74	26/NOV/74	
20984	N843AA	American Airlines	223	26/MAR/75	09/MAY/75	
20985	N844AA	American Airlines	223	18/APR/75	13/MAY/75	
20986	N845AA	American Airlines	223	06/MAY/75	15/MAY/75	
20987	N846AA	American Airlines	223	07/MAY/75	16/MAY/75	
20988	N847AA	American Airlines	223	04/JUN/75	13/JUN/75	
20989	N848AA	American Airlines	223	13/JUN/75	25/JUN/75	
20990	N849AA	American Airlines	223	27/APR/76	26/MAY/76	
20991	N850AA	American Airlines	223	23/APR/76	26/MAY/76	
20992	N851AA	American Airlines	223	29/APR/76	26/MAY/76	
20993	N852AA	American Airlines	223	05/MAY/76	26/MAY/76	
20994	N853AA	American Airlines	223	06/MAY/76	26/MAY/76	
20995	N854AA	American Airlines	223	27/MAY/76	22/JUN/76	
20996	N855AA	American Airlines	223	04/JUN/76	22/JUN/76	
20997	N856AA	American Airlines	223	10/JUN/76	22/JUN/76	
21010	N111AK	American Capital Aviation	2L4	07/JAN/75	25/JAN/75	
	VS-HB1	Brunei Government			MAY/84	
21018	N488DA	Delta Air Lines	232	17/JAN/75	21/FEB/75	
21019	N489DA	Delta Air Lines	232	14/FEB/75	20/MAR/75	
21020	N490DA	Delta Air Lines	232	07/APR/75	17/APR/75	
21021	JY-ADV	Alia	2D3	25/OCT/74	05/NOV/74	
	JY-ADV	Dominicana			21/DEC/84	
	HI-452	Dominicana			JUN/85	
21036	HI-242	Dominicana	2J1	23/APR/75	07/MAY/75	
21037	YU-AKE	JAT	2H9	10/DEC/74	20/DEC/74	
21038	YU-AKF	JAT	2H9	20/DEC/74	14/MAR/75	
21039	YU-AKG	JAT	2H9	19/MAR/75	28/MAR/75	
21040	YU-AKD	Yugoslav Government	2HP	18/JUN/75	26/JUN/75	
	YU-AKD	JAT			81	Leased
	YU-AKD	Yugoslav Government			82	
	YU-AKD	Aviogenex			04/FEB/83	
21041	N434BN	Braniff	227	24/JAN/75	04/FEB/75	
	N559PE	People Express			30/SEP/83	
21042	N435BN	Braniff	227	29/JAN/75	20/FEB/75	
	N560PE	People Express			27/OCT/83	
21043	N436BN	Braniff	227	27/FEB/75	13/MAR/75	
	N561PE	People Express			26/AUG/83	
	N561PE	Southwest Airlines			26/AUG/83	Leased
	N561PE	People Express			SEP/85	
21044	N437BN	Braniff	227	03/MAY/75	14/MAY/75	
	N562PE	People Express			15/JUN/83	
21045	N438BN	Braniff	227	05/MAY/75	15/MAY/75	
	N563PE	People Express			17/MAY/84	
21050	5A-DIA	Libyan Arab Airlines	2L5	07/FEB/75	19/FEB/75	
21051	5A-DIB	Libyan Arab Airlines	2L5	14/FEB/75	26/FEB/75	
21052	5A-DIC	Libyan Arab Airlines	2L5	26/FEB/75	06/MAR/75	
21053	7T-VEI	Air Algerie	2D6	20/FEB/75	04/MAR/75	
21055	C-GCPA	CP Air	217	12/MAR/75	20/MAR/75	
	G-BKAG	Dan Air			01/APR/82	Leased
	G-BKAG	Dan Air			30/MAR/84	Purchased
	G-BKAG	Sun Country			02/DEC/84	Leased
	G-BKAG	Dan Air			03/MAY/85	
	G-BKAG	Sun Country			DEC/85	Leased
	G-BKAG	Dan Air			16/APR/86	
21056	C-GCPB	CP Air	217	31/MAR/75	08/APR/75	
	C-GCPB	Alaska Airlines			20/MAY/82	Leased
	C-GCPB	CP Air			24/SEP/82	
	G-NROA	Dan Air			01/FEB/83	Leased
21057	N2819W	Western Airlines	247	09/MAY/75	23/MAY/75	
21058	N2820W	Western Airlines	247	16/JUL/75	29/JUL/75	
21059	N2821W	Western Airlines	247	22/MAY/75	03/JUN/75	
21060	N491DA	Delta Air Lines	232	21/MAR/75	04/APR/75	
21061	N492DA	Delta Air Lines	232	12/MAR/75	26/MAR/75	
21062	N493DA	Delta Air Lines	232	11/APR/75	01/MAY/75	
21068	CN-CCW	Royal Air Maroc	2B6	05/FEB/75	28/FEB/75	
21071	XA-FID	Mexicana	264	04/JUN/75	23/JUN/75	
21072	XA-FIE	Mexicana	264	09/JUN/75	23/JUN/75	
21074	N494DA	Delta Air Lines	232	16/JUN/75	23/JUN/75	
21075	N495DA	Delta Air Lines	232	06/JUN/75	25/JUN/75	
21076	N496DA	Delta Air Lines	232	29/MAY/75	11/JUN/75	
21077	N497DA	Delta Air Lines	232	28/MAY/75	18/JUN/75	
21078	EP-IRT	Iran Air	276	11/JUN/75	02/JUL/75	
21079	EP-IRU	Iran Air	276	23/JUN/75	10/JUL/75	
21080	YU-AKH	Yugoslav Government	2L8	14/JUL/75	31/JUL/75	
	YU-AKH	Aviogenex			04/FEB/83	
21082	N48054	Boeing	2K3	02/APR/75		
	CP-1276	Lloyd Aero Boliviano			08/OCT/75	
21084	N857AA	American Airlines	223	13/APR/76	27/APR/75	
21085	N858AA	American Airlines	223	17/APR/76	27/APR/76	
21086	N859AA	American Airlines	223	15/FEB/77	07/MAR/77	
21087	N860AA	American Airlines	223	24/FEB/77	07/MAR/77	
21088	N861AA	American Airlines	223	21/MAR/77	07/APR/77	
21089	N862AA	American Airlines	223	04/MAY/77	13/MAY/77	
21090	N863AA	American Airlines	223	19/MAY/77	01/JUN/77	
21091	PK-PJP	Pertamina	2M1			Not taken-up
	N40104	Boeing		14/JUN/75		Executive demonstrator
	6V-AEF	Senegal Government			02/NOV/76	
21100	C-GAAL	Air Canada	233	23/JUL/75	21/AUG/75	
21101	C-GAAM	Air Canada	233	31/JUL/75	28/AUG/75	
	N218FE	Federal Express	233F		29/OCT/84	Converted
21102	C-GAAN	Air Canada	233	25/AUG/75	05/SEP/75	
	N219FE	Federal Express	233F		28/SEP/84	Converted
21105	6Y-JIP	Air Jamaica	2J0			Not taken-up
	6Y-JMA	Air Jamaica		22/AUG/75	29/AUG/75	
	VR-JMA	Guinness Peat Aviation			JAN/85	
	VR-JMA	Air Jamaica			JAN/85	Leased
21106	6Y-JIQ	Air Jamaica	2J0			Not taken-up
	6Y-JMB	Air Jamaica		09/SEP/75	10/OCT/75	
	VR-JMB	Guinness Peat Aviation			JAN/85	
	VR-JMB	Air Jamaica			JAN/85	Leased
21107	6Y-JIR	Air Jamaica	2J0			Not taken-up
	6Y-JMC	Air Jamaica		31/OCT/75	12/NOV/75	
	VR-JMC	Guinness Peat Aviation			JAN/85	
	VR-JMC	Air Jamaica			JAN/85	Leased
21108	6Y-JIS	Air Jamaica	2J0			Not taken-up

BOEING 727

C/N	Registration	Owner/Operator	Series	First Flight	Delivery	Remarks
	6Y-JMD	Air Jamaica		11/NOV/75	19/NOV/75	
	VR-JMD	Guinness Peat Aviation			JAN/85	
	VR-JMD	Air Jamaica			JAN/85	Leased
21113	D-ABKK	Condor	230	20/NOV/75	02/DEC/75	
21114	D-ABKL	Condor	230	05/DEC/75	12/DEC/75	
21118	N439BN	Braniff	227	24/SEP/75	01/OCT/75	
	N564PE	People Express			26/AUG/83	
	N564PE	Southwest Airlines			26/AUG/83	Leased
	N564PE	People Express			SEP/85	
21119	N440BN	Braniff	227	19/NOV/75	02/DEC/75	
	N565PE	People Express			12/JUL/83	
21142	N498DA	Delta Air Lines	232	18/AUG/75	28/AUG/75	
21143	N499DA	Delta Air Lines	232	21/AUG/75	04/SEP/75	
21144	N400DA	Delta Air Lines	232	30/JUL/75	12/SEP/75	
21145	N401DA	Delta Air Lines	232	25/AUG/75	17/SEP/75	
21146	N402DA	Delta Air Lines	232	23/SEP/75	02/OCT/75	
21147	N403DA	Delta Air Lines	232	30/SEP/75	09/OCT/75	
21148	N404DA	Delta Air Lines	232	23/OCT/75	05/NOV/75	
21149	N405DA	Delta Air Lines	232	17/OCT/75	12/NOV/75	
21150	N406DA	Delta Air Lines	232	18/NOV/75	03/DEC/75	
21151	N407DA	Delta Air Lines	232	25/NOV/75	10/DEC/75	
21152	N408DA	Delta Air Lines	232	07/JAN/76	25/JAN/76	
21153	N409DA	Delta Air Lines	232	19/JAN/76	28/JAN/76	
21154	N275US	Northwest Orient	251	05/OCT/75	20/OCT/75	
21155	N276US	Northwest Orient	251	16/OCT/75	27/OCT/75	
21156	N277US	Northwest Orient	251	22/OCT/75	31/OCT/75	
21157	N278US	Northwest Orient	251	07/NOV/75	18/NOV/75	
21158	N279US	Northwest Orient	251	03/DEC/75	11/DEC/75	
21159	N280US	Northwest Orient	251	06/DEC/75	17/DEC/75	
21160	N281US	Northwest Orient	251	13/DEC/75	19/DEC/75	
21161	N282US	Northwest Orient	251	14/DEC/75	22/DEC/75	
21171	VH-TBM	Trans Australia Airlines	276	04/NOV/76	18/NOV/76	
	VH-TBM	Australian Airlines			04/AUG/86	
21178	VH-RMK	Ansett Airlines	277	03/DEC/76	10/DEC/76	
21179	TS-JHR	Tunis Air	2H3	28/OCT/75	06/NOV/75	
21197	YI-AGK	Iraqi Airways	270	03/FEB/76	08/MAR/76	
21198	YI-AGL	Iraqi Airways	270	26/FEB/76	24/MAR/76	
21199	YI-AGM	Iraqi Airways	270	07/MAY/76	18/MAY/76	
21200	N721RW	Hughes Airwest	2M7	27/FEB/76	19/AUG/76	
	N721RW	Republic			01/OCT/80	
21201	N722RW	Hughes Airwest	2M7	19/OCT/76	01/NOV/76	
	N722RW	Republic			01/OCT/80	
21202	N723RW	Hughes Airwest	2M7	20/NOV/76	01/DEC/76	
	N723RW	Republic			01/OCT/80	
21203	YK-AGA	Syrianair	294	20/FEB/76	27/MAR/76	
21204	YK-AGB	Syrianair	294	24/DEC/76	31/MAR/76	
21205	YK-AGC	Syrianair	294	09/APR/76	27/MAY/76	
21210	7T-VEM	Air Algerie	2D6	13/MAY/76	26/MAY/76	
21222	N410DA	Delta Air Lines	232	14/MAY/76	08/JUL/76	
21223	N411DA	Delta Air Lines	232	21/MAY/76	21/OCT/76	
21229	5A-DID	Libyan Arab Airlines	2L5	02/JUL/76	19/JUL/76	
21230	5A-DIE	Libyan Arab Airlines	2L5	16/JUL/76	30/JUL/76	
21232	N412DA	Delta Air Lines	232	15/JUL/76	19/AUG/76	
21233	N413DA	Delta Air Lines	232	28/JUL/76	25/AUG/76	
21234	TS-JHS	Tunis Air	2H3	08/JUN/76	18/JUN/76	
21235	TS-JHT	Tunis Air	2H3	11/JUN/76	23/JUN/76	
	TS-JHT	Sudan Airways			JAN/83	Leased
	TS-JHT	Tunis Air			MAR/84	
21242	N441BN	Braniff	227	31/MAR/76	22/APR/76	WFU MAY/82
	N566PE	People Express			22/MAY/84	
	N566PE	Southwest Airlines			MAY/84	Leased
	N566PE	People Express			OCT/85	
21243	N442BN	Braniff	227	08/APR/76	23/APR/76	WFU MAY/82
	N567PE	People Express			14/OCT/83	
21244	N443BN	Braniff	227	21/APR/76	29/APR/76	WFU MAY/82
	N568PE	People Express			27/SEP/83	
21245	N444BN	Braniff	227	27/APR/76	04/MAY/76	WFU MAY/82
	N569PE	People Express			02/MAY/84	
	N569PE	Southwest Airlines			02/MAY/84	Leased
	N569PE	People Express			30/SEP/85	
21246	N445BN	Braniff	227	17/JUL/76	30/JUL/76	WFU MAY/82
	N570PE	People Express			22/NOV/83	
21247	N446BN	Braniff	227	22/JUL/76	27/JUL/76	WFU MAY/82
	N446BN	Braniff Liquidating Trust			MAY/82	
	N446BN	Braniff (Hyatt)			DEC/83	Leased
	N446BN	Braniff Liquidating Trust			19/FEB/85	
	N446BN	Texas Air Corporation			30/MAY/85	
	N73751	Continental Airlines			30/MAY/85	
21248	N447BN	Braniff	227	14/OCT/76	29/OCT/76	WFU MAY/82
	N447BN	Braniff Liquidating Trust			MAY/82	
	N447BN	Braniff (Hyatt)			DEC/83	Leased
	N447BN	Braniff Liquidating Trust			19/FEB/85	
	N447BN	Texas Air Corporation			30/MAY/85	
	N76752	Continental Airlines			30/MAY/85	
21249	N448BN	Braniff	227	18/SEP/76	28/OCT/76	WFU MAY/82
	N448BN	Braniff Liquidating Trust			MAY/82	
	N448BN	Braniff (Hyatt)			DEC/83	Leased
	N448BN	Braniff Liquidating Trust			12/MAR/85	
	N448BN	Texas Air Corporation			30/MAY/85	
	N76753	Continental Airlines			30/MAY/85	
21256	N414DA	Delta Air Lines	232	13/OCT/76	27/OCT/76	
21257	N415DA	Delta Air Lines	232	14/OCT/76	28/OCT/76	
21258	N416DA	Delta Air Lines	232	21/SEP/76	01/DEC/76	
21259	N417DA	Delta Air Lines	232	24/NOV/76	08/DEC/76	
21260	TC-JBM	Turk Hava Yollari	2F2	09/SEP/76	08/OCT/76	
21264	N1787B	Boeing	243	24/SEP/76		
	I-DIRA	Alitalia			06/OCT/76	
	N571PE	People Express			06/JAN/84	
21265	I-DIRI	Alitalia	243	04/OCT/76	18/OCT/76	
	N572PE	People Express			28/JUL/84	
21266	I-DIRO	Alitalia	243	07/OCT/76	18/OCT/76	
	N573PE	People Express			21/JUN/84	
21267	I-DIRU	Alitalia	243	08/DEC/76	20/DEC/76	
	N574PE	People Express			26/JUL/84	
21268	I-DIRB	Alitalia	243	09/DEC/76	20/DEC/76	

C/N	Registration	Owner/Operator	Series	First Flight	Delivery	Remarks
	N575PE	People Express			26/AUG/84	
21269	N40133	Boeing	243	01/NOV/76		
	I-DIRC	Alitalia			19/NOV/76	
	N576PE	People Express			AUG/84	
21270	I-DIRJ	Alitalia	243	04/NOV/76	19/NOV/76	
	I-DIRJ	Douglas			03/APR/84	
	N577PE	People Express			03/APR/84	
21271	N418DA	Delta Air Lines	232	19/JAN/77	27/JAN/77	
21272	N419DA	Delta Air Lines	232	19/JAN/77	28/JAN/77	
21273	N420DA	Delta Air Lines	232	21/JAN/77	02/FEB/77	
21274	N421DA	Delta Air Lines	232	28/JAN/77	09/FEB/77	
21284	7T-VEP	Air Algerie	2D6	10/NOV/76	19/NOV/76	
21288	N8870Z	Eastern Airlines	225	16/NOV/76	23/NOV/76	
21289	N8871Z	Eastern Airlines	225	22/NOV/76	03/DEC/76	
21290	N8872Z	Eastern Airlines	225	08/DEC/76	16/DEC/76	
21291	N8873Z	Eastern Airlines	225	08/DEC/76	20/DEC/76	
21292	N8874Z	Eastern Airlines	225	11/DEC/76	21/DEC/76	
21293	N8875Z	Eastern Airlines	225	16/DEC/76	23/DEC/76	
21297	CN-RMO	Royal Air Maroc	2B6	24/NOV/76	09/DEC/76	
21298	CN-RMP	Royal Air Maroc	2B6	04/FEB/77	16/MAR/77	
21299	CN-RMQ	Royal Air Maroc	2B6	02/MAR/77	22/MAR/77	
21303	N501DA	Delta Air Lines	232	23/APR/77	03/MAY/77	
21304	N502DA	Delta Air Lines	232	03/MAY/77	10/MAY/77	
21305	N503DA	Delta Air Lines	232	20/MAY/77	03/JUN/77	
21306	N504DA	Delta Air Lines	232	03/JUN/77	15/JUN/77	
21307	N505DA	Delta Air Lines	232	13/JUN/77	22/JUN/77	
21308	N506DA	Delta Air Lines	232	07/SEP/77	16/SEP/77	
21309	N507DA	Delta Air Lines	232	15/SEP/77	24/OCT/77	
21310	N508DA	Delta Air Lines	232	29/SEP/77	26/OCT/77	
21311	N509DA	Delta Air Lines	232	11/OCT/77	21/OCT/77	
21312	N510DA	Delta Air Lines	232	22/MAR/78	31/MAR/78	
21313	N511DA	Delta Air Lines	232	15/MAY/78	24/JUN/78	
21314	N512DA	Delta Air Lines	232	06/JUN/78	28/JUN/78	
21315	N513DA	Delta Air Lines	232	21/JUN/78	30/JUN/78	
21318	TS-JHU	Tunis Air	2H3	08/MAR/77	17/MAR/77	
21319	TS-JHV	Tunis Air	2H3	31/MAY/77	10/JUN/77	
21320	TS-JHW	Tunis Air	2H3	03/JUN/77	17/JUN/77	
21322	N283US	Northwest Orient	251	12/MAY/77	24/MAY/77	
21323	N284US	Northwest Orient	251	29/JUL/77	09/AUG/77	
21324	N285US	Northwest Orient	251	11/AUG/77	22/AUG/77	
21325	N286US	Northwest Orient	251	19/AUG/77	30/AUG/77	
21327	N2822W	Western Airlines	247	18/FEB/77	09/MAR/77	
21328	N2823W	Western Airlines	247	25/FEB/77	09/MAR/77	
21329	N2824W	Western Airlines	247	15/MAR/77	29/MAR/77	
21330	N2825W	Western Airlines	247	18/APR/77	03/MAY/77	
21331	N2826W	Western Airlines	247	11/MAY/77	24/MAY/77	
21332	5A-DIF	Libyan Arab Airlines	2L5	05/APR/77	21/APR/77	
21333	5A-DIG	Libyan Arab Airlines	2L5	15/APR/77	25/APR/77	
21341	PP-SNE	Vasp	2A1	17/MAR/77	19/APR/77	
	PP-SNE	Guinness Peat Aviation			15/JUN/84	Leased
	PP-SNE	Northeastern			15/JUN/84	Sub-leased
	PP-SNE	Guinness Peat Aviation			28/JUN/85	Purchased
	N213UP	United Parcel Service			28/JUN/85	
	N213UP	United Parcel Service	2A1F		OCT/85	Converted, Op. by Ryan Aviation
21342	PP-SNF	Vasp	2A1	29/MAR/77	29/APR/77	
	PP-SNF	Guinness Peat Aviation			15/JUN/84	Leased
	PP-SNF	Northeastern			15/JUN/84	Sub-leased
	PP-SNF	Guinness Peat Aviation			28/JUN/85	Purchased
	N214UP	United Parcel Service			28/JUN/85	
	N214UP	United Parcel Service	2A1F		NOV/85	Converted
21343	HK-2151X	Boeing	2A1	13/FEB/78		
	HK-2151X	Avianca			12/OCT/78	Leased
21344	HK-2152X	Boeing	2A1	22/SEP/78		
	HK-2152X	Avianca			02/NOV/78	Leased
21345	PP-SNG	Vasp	2A1	07/OCT/80	16/OCT/80	
	PP-SNG	Capital Air			OCT/84	Leased
	PP-SNG	Vasp			21/NOV/84	
	PP-SNG	Arrow Air			08/JUN/85	Leased
	PP-SNG	Vasp			MAR/86	
21346	PP-SNH	Vasp	2A1	07/OCT/80	21/OCT/80	
	XA-MXF	Mexicana			10/OCT/85	Leased
	PP-SNH	Vasp			OCT/88	Sched.return
21347	9V-SGA	Singapore Airlines	212	23/JUL/77	30/JUL/77	
	9V-SGA	International Lease Finance			06/JUN/80	
	PP-SRK	Vasp			06/JUN/80	Leased, W/O 08/JUN/82
21348	9V-SGB	Singapore Airlines	212	14/SEP/77	26/SEP/77	
	9V-SGB	International Lease Finance			17/JUN/80	
	PP-SMK	Vasp			17/JUN/80	Leased
	PP-SMK	International Lease Finance			07/MAR/82	
	N26729	Alaska Airlines			08/MAR/82	Leased
	N293AS	Alaska Airlines			DEC/82	Purchased
21349	9V-SGC	Singapore Airlines	212	03/OCT/77	21/OCT/77	
	G-BHVT	Dan Air			25/MAY/80	
	G-BHVT	LACSA			11/NOV/81	Leased
	G-BHVT	Dan Air			21/APR/82	
	TI-LRR	LACSA			15/OCT/82	
	G-BHVT	Dan Air			22/APR/83	Leased
	TI-LRR	LACSA			01/NOV/83	
	G-BHVT	Dan Air			30/APR/84	Leased
	G-BHVT	Dan Air			SEP/84	Purchased
	G-BHVT	Sun Country			31/DEC/84	Leased
	G-BHVT	Dan Air			01/MAY/85	
	G-BHVT	Sun Country			01/DEC/85	Leased
	G-BHVT	Dan Air			30/APR/86	
21363	N449BN	Braniff	227	11/APR/77	20/APR/77	WFU MAY/82
	N449BN	Braniff Liquidating Trust			MAY/82	
	N449BN	Braniff (Hyatt)			DEC/83	Leased
	N449BN	Braniff Liquidating Trust			17/FEB/85	
	N449BN	Texas Air Corporation			30/MAY/85	
	N79754	Continental Airlines			30/MAY/85	
21364	N450BN	Braniff	227	06/MAY/77	19/MAY/77	WFU MAY/82
	N450BN	Braniff Liquidating Trust			MAY/82	
	N450BN	Braniff (Hyatt)			DEC/83	Leased
	N450BN	Braniff Liquidating Trust			12/MAR/85	
	N322AS	Alaska Airlines			APR/85	

C/N	Registration	Owner/Operator	Series	First Flight	Delivery	Remarks
21365	N451BN	Braniff	227	13/JUN/77	08/JUL/77	WFU MAY/82
	N451BN	Braniff Liquidating Trust			MAY/82	
	N451BN	Braniff (Hyatt)			DEC/83	Leased
	N323AS	Alaska Airlines			APR/85	
21366	N452BN	Braniff	227	24/JUN/77	07/JUL/77	WFU MAY/82
	N452BN	Braniff Liquidating Trust			MAY/82	
	N452BN	Braniff (Hyatt)			DEC/83	Leased
	N452BN	Texas Air Corporation			30/MAY/85	
	N70755	Continental Airlines			30/MAY/85	
21369	N864AA	American Airlines	223	17/JUN/77	28/JUN/77	
21370	N865AA	American Airlines	223	29/JUN/77	12/JUL/77	
21371	N866AA	American Airlines	223	01/JUL/77	15/JUL/77	
21372	N867AA	American Airlines	223	08/JUL/77	20/JUL/77	
21373	N868AA	American Airlines	223	08/JUL/77	22/JUL/77	
21374	N869AA	American Airlines	223	13/JUL/77	02/AUG/77	
21375	N287US	Northwest Orient	251	26/AUG/77	08/SEP/77	
21376	N288US	Northwest Orient	251	07/SEP/77	21/SEP/77	
21377	N289US	Northwest Orient	251	14/SEP/77	17/NOV/77	
21378	N290US	Northwest Orient	251	21/SEP/77	05/OCT/77	
21379	N291US	Northwest Orient	251	27/SEP/77	19/OCT/77	
21382	N870AA	American Airlines	223	04/NOV/77	17/NOV/77	
21383	N871AA	American Airlines	223	24/FEB/78	10/MAR/78	
21384	N872AA	American Airlines	223	08/MAR/78	23/MAR/78	
21385	N873AA	American Airlines	223	15/MAR/78	04/APR/78	
21386	N874AA	American Airlines	223	04/APR/78	13/APR/78	
21387	N875AA	American Airlines	223	04/APR/78	18/APR/78	
21388	N876AA	American Airlines	223	05/MAY/78	17/MAY/78	
21389	N877AA	American Airlines	223	16/MAY/78	31/MAY/78	
21390	N878AA	American Airlines	223	20/JUN/78	07/JUL/78	
21391	N879AA	American Airlines	223	13/JUL/78	25/JUL/78	
21392	N2827W	Western Airlines	247	02/DEC/77	15/DEC/77	
	N212UP	United Parcel Service	247F		22/OCT/85	Converted, op. By Ryan Aviation
21393	N2828W	Western Airlines	247	13/DEC/77	21/DEC/77	
	N2828W	Piedmont Airlines			11/OCT/84	
21394	N453BN	Braniff	227	15/JUL/77	27/JUL/77	
	N453BN	Braniff (Hyatt)			DEC/83	
21395	N454BN	Braniff	227	24/JUL/77	01/AUG/77	
	N454BN	Braniff (Hyatt)			DEC/83	
21398	N7251U	United Airlines	222	29/SEP/77	21/OCT/77	
21399	N7252U	United Airlines	222	27/OCT/77	08/NOV/77	
21400	N7253U	United Airlines	222	23/DEC/77	16/JAN/78	
21401	N7254U	United Airlines	222	11/JAN/78	24/JAN/78	
21402	N7255U	United Airlines	223	16/JAN/78	21/JAN/78	
21403	N7256U	United Airlines	222	21/JAN/78	25/JAN/78	
21404	N7257U	United Airlines	222	20/JAN/78	01/MAR/78	
21405	N7258U	United Airlines	222	24/FEB/78	07/MAR/78	
21406	N7259U	United Airlines	222	03/MAR/78	14/MAR/78	
21407	N7260U	United Airlines	222	28/MAR/78	04/APR/78	
21408	N7261U	United Airlines	222	04/APR/78	12/APR/78	
21409	N7262U	United Airlines	222	11/APR/78	20/APR/78	
21410	N7263U	United Airlines	222	03/MAY/78	16/MAY/78	
21411	N7264U	United Airlines	222	08/MAY/78	23/MAY/78	
21412	N7265U	United Airlines	222	17/MAY/78	30/MAY/78	
21413	N7266U	United Airlines	222	24/MAY/78	05/JUN/78	
21414	N7267U	United Airlines	222	31/MAY/78	14/JUN/78	
21415	N7268U	United Airlines	222	06/JUN/78	20/JUN/78	
21416	N7269U	United Airlines	222	06/JUL/78	20/JUL/78	
21417	N7270U	United Airlines	222	12/JUL/78	27/JUL/78	
21418	N7271U	United Airlines	222	18/JUL/78	04/AUG/78	
21419	N7272U	United Airlines	222	09/AUG/78	16/AUG/78	
21420	N7273U	United Airlines	222	10/AUG/78	21/AUG/78	
21421	N7274U	United Airlines	222	25/AUG/78	06/SEP/78	
21422	N7275U	United Airlines	222	31/AUG/78	12/SEP/78	
21423	N7276U	United Airlines	222	06/SEP/78	18/SEP/78	
21424	N7277U	United Airlines	222	15/SEP/78	02/OCT/78	
21425	N7278U	United Airlines	222	21/SEP/78	05/OCT/78	
21426	5N-ANP	Nigeria Airways	2F9	09/AUG/77	19/AUG/77	
	N528D	Charlotte Aviation			JUL/85	
	N298AS	Alaska Airlines			SEP/85	
21427	5N-ANQ	Nigeria Airways	2F9	31/AUG/77	23/SEP/77	
	N528E	Charlotte Aviation			JUL/85	
	N299AS	Alaska Airlines			SEP/85	
21430	N514DA	Delta Air Lines	232	27/JUL/78	12/AUG/78	
21431	N515DA	Delta Air Lines	232	04/AUG/78	18/AUG/78	
21432	N516DA	Delta Air Lines	232	22/AUG/78	31/AUG/78	
21433	N517DA	Delta Air Lines	232	24/AUG/78	08/SEP/78	
21438	OY-SBC	Sterling Airways	2J4	21/OCT/77	27/OCT/77	
	G-BHNF	Dan Air			08/APR/80	
	G-BHNF	Sun Country Airlines			30/NOV/83	Leased
	G-BHNF	Dan Air			16/APR/84	
21442	D-ABKM	Lufthansa	230	03/MAR/78	17/MAR/78	
21449	N8876Z	Eastern Airlines	225	11/NOV/77	18/NOV/77	
21450	N8877Z	Eastern Airlines	225	30/NOV/77	07/DEC/77	
21451	N8878Z	Eastern Airlines	225	12/JAN/78	20/JAN/78	
21452	N8879Z	Eastern Airlines	225	19/JAN/78	27/JAN/78	
21453	N8880Z	Eastern Airlines	225	26/JAN/78	02/FEB/78	
21455	JA8353	All Nippon Airways	281	28/JAN/78	01/FEB/78	
21456	JA8354	All Nippon Airways	281	02/FEB/78	10/FEB/78	
21457	N724RW	Hughes Airwest	2M7	19/OCT/77	01/NOV/77	
	LV-MCD	Aerolineas Argentinas			01/DEC/77	Leased
	N724RW	Republic			28/APR/81	
	YV-77C	Avensa			OCT/81	
	XA-MXE	Mexicana			DEC/84	Leased
21458	9V-SGD	Singapore Airlines	212	13/MAR/78	22/MAR/78	
	N292AS	Alaska Airlines			27/APR/81	
21459	9V-SGE	Singapore Airlines	212	11/MAR/78	31/MAR/78	
	N296AS	Alaska Airlines			27/APR/81	
21460	9V-SGF	Singapore Airlines	212	18/APR/78	04/MAY/78	
	HZ-DA5	Dallah AVCO			22/APR/81	
	VR-CBQ	Mezel Ltd.			05/AUG/84	
21461	N455BN	Braniff	227	18/APR/78	27/APR/78	WFU MAY/82
	N455BN	Braniff (Hyatt)			DEC/83	
21462	N456BN	Braniff	227	01/MAY/78	10/MAY/78	WFU MAY/82
	N456BN	Braniff (Hyatt)			DEC/83	
21463	N457BN	Braniff	227	02/JUN/78	13/JUN/78	WFU MAY/82

C/N	Registration	Owner/Operator	Series	First Flight	Delivery	Remarks
	N457BN	Braniff (Hyatt)			DEC/83	
21464	N458BN	Braniff	227	06/JUN/78	15/JUN/78	WFU MAY/82
	N458BN	Braniff (Hyatt)			DEC/83	
21465	N459BN	Braniff	227	30/JUN/78	17/JUL/78	WFU MAY/82
	N459BN	Braniff (Hyatt)			DEC/83	
21466	N460BN	Braniff	227	28/JUL/78	09/AUG/78	WFU MAY/82
	N460BN	Braniff (Hyatt)			DEC/83	
21469	N518DA	Delta Air Lines	232	26/SEP/78	24/OCT/78	
21470	N519DA	Delta Air Lines	232	04/OCT/78	18/OCT/78	
21471	N520DA	Delta Air Lines	232	22/NOV/78	10/NOV/78	
21472	N521DA	Delta Air Lines	232	04/NOV/78	17/NOV/78	
21474	JA8355	All Nippon Airways	281	09/AUG/78	18/AUG/78	
21479	VH-TBN	Trans Australia Airlines	276	09/JUN/78	26/JUN/78	
21480	VH-RML	Ansett Airlines	277	23/MAY/78	08/JUN/78	
21481	N2829W	Western Airlines	247	20/APR/78	20/JUN/78	
21482	N830WA	Western Airlines	247	24/APR/78	09/MAY/78	
21483	N831WA	Western Airlines	247	19/MAY/78	31/MAY/78	
21484	N282WA	Western Airlines	247	28/JUN/78	12/JUL/78	
21485	N283WA	Western Airlines	247	26/JUN/78	13/JUL/78	
21488	N461BN	Braniff	227	11/SEP/78	21/SEP/78	WFU MAY/82
	N461BN	Braniff (Hyatt)			DEC/83	
21489	N462BN	Braniff	227	18/SEP/78	27/SEP/78	WFU MAY/82
	N462BN	Braniff (Hyatt)			DEC/83	
21490	N463BN	Braniff	227	28/SEP/78	11/OCT/78	WFU MAY/82
	N463BN	Braniff (Hyatt)			DEC/83	
21491	N464BN	Braniff	227	17/OCT/78	26/OCT/78	WFU MAY/82
	N464BN	Braniff (Hyatt)			DEC/83	
21492	N465BN	Braniff	227	30/JAN/78	07/FEB/79	WFU MAY/82
	N465BN	Braniff (Hyatt)			DEC/83	
21493	N466BN	Braniff	227	02/FEB/79	09/FEB/79	WFU MAY/82
	N466BN	Braniff (Hyatt)			DEC/83	
21494	CP-1366	Lloyd Aero Boliviano	2K3	24/JUL/78	04/AUG/78	
21495	CP-1367	Lloyd Aero Boliviano	2K3	11/OCT/78	25/OCT/78	
21502	N725RW	Hughes Airwest	2H7	20/APR/78	02/MAY/78	
	N725RW	Philippine Airlines			15/JUL/79	Leased
	N725RW	Republic			OCT/81	
21503	N292US	Northwest Orient	251	02/FEB/78	13/FEB/78	
21504	N293US	Northwest Orient	251	08/SEP/78	17/FEB/78	
21505	N294US	Northwest Orient	251	12/SEP/78	26/SEP/78	
21506	N295US	Northwest Orient	251	13/SEP/78	28/SEP/78	
21510	N290AS	Alaska Airlines	290	14/JUN/78	28/JUN/78	
21511	N291AS	Alaska Airlines	290	23/JAN/79	02/MAR/79	
21512	N555PS	Pacific Southwest Airlines	214	04/MAY/78	16/MAY/78	
	N555PS	Piedmont			30/OCT/84	Leased
	N555PS	Piedmont			NOV/85	Purchased
21513	N556PS	Pacific Southwest Airlines	214	07/JUL/78	18/JUL/78	
	N556PS	Piedmont			18/OCT/84	Leased
	N556PS	Piedmont			NOV/85	Purchased
21519	N880AA	American Airlines	223	07/MAR/79	23/MAR/79	
21520	N881AA	American Airlines	223	20/MAR/79	29/MAR/79	
21521	N882AA	American Airlines	223	22/MAR/79	03/APR/79	
21522	N883AA	American Airlines	223	29/MAR/79	10/APR/79	
21523	N884AA	American Airlines	223	03/APR/79	12/APR/79	
21524	N885AA	American Airlines	223	18/APR/79	27/APR/79	
21525	N886AA	American Airlines	223	23/APR/79	02/MAY/79	
21526	N887AA	American Airlines	223	19/APR/79	04/MAY/79	
21527	N889AA	American Airlines	223	27/APR/79	08/MAY/79	
21529	N467BN	Braniff	227	08/FEB/79	17/FEB/79	WFU MAY/82
	N467BN	Braniff (Hyatt)			DEC/83	
21530	N468BN	Braniff	227	14/FEB/79	22/FEB/79	WFU MAY/82
	N468BN	Braniff (Hyatt)			DEC/83	
21531	N469BN	Braniff	227	21/FEB/79	02/MAR/79	WFU MAY/82
	N469BN	Braniff (Hyatt)			DEC/83	
21532	N470BN	Braniff	227	01/MAR/79	10/MAR/79	WFU MAY/82
	N470BN	Braniff (Hyatt)			DEC/83	
21539	5A-DIH	Libyan Arab Airlines	2L5	19/JUL/78	07/NOV/78	
21540	5A-DII	Libyan Arab Airlines	2L5	29/SEP/78	03/NOV/78	
21557	N7279U	United Airlines	222	03/OCT/78	12/OCT/78	
21558	N7280U	United Airlines	222	06/OCT/78	17/OCT/78	
21559	N7281U	United Airlines	222	11/OCT/78	31/OCT/78	
21560	N7282U	United Airlines	222	19/OCT/78	02/NOV/78	
21561	N7283U	United Airlines	222	24/OCT/78	08/NOV/78	
21562	N7284U	United Airlines	222	30/OCT/78	13/NOV/78	
21563	N7285U	United Airlines	222	17/NOV/78	11/DEC/78	
21564	N7286U	United Airlines	222	22/NOV/78	06/DEC/78	
21565	N7287U	United Airlines	222	07/DEC/78	14/DEC/78	
21566	N7288U	United Airlines	222	14/DEC/78	08/JAN/79	
21567	N7289U	United Airlines	222	20/DEC/78	20/JAN/79	
21568	N7290U	United Airlines	222	21/DEC/78	25/JAN/79	
21569	N7291U	United Airlines	222	25/JAN/79	06/FEB/79	
21570	N7292U	United Airlines	222	30/JAN/79	13/FEB/79	
21571	N7293U	United Airlines	222	05/FEB/79	19/FEB/79	
21572	N7294U	United Airlines	222	08/FEB/79	22/FEB/79	
21573	N7295U	United Airlines	222	14/FEB/79	01/MAR/79	
21574	N7296U	United Airlines	222	19/FEB/79	05/MAR/79	
21577	XA-HOH	Mexicana	264	11/AUG/78	18/AUG/78	
21578	N8881Z	Eastern Airlines	225	01/NOV/78	10/NOV/78	
21579	N8882Z	Eastern Airlines	225	08/NOV/78	17/NOV/78	
21580	N8883Z	Eastern Airlines	225	16/JAN/79	25/JAN/79	
21581	N8884Z	Eastern Airlines	225	22/JAN/79	31/JAN/79	
21582	N522DA	Delta Air Lines	232	30/NOV/78	13/DEC/78	
21583	N523DA	Delta Air Lines	232	06/DEC/78	15/DEC/78	
21584	N524DA	Delta Air Lines	232	24/APR/79	10/MAY/79	
21585	N525DA	Delta Air Lines	232	01/MAY/79	11/MAY/79	
21586	N526DA	Delta Air Lines	232	25/MAY/79	06/JUN/79	
21587	N527DA	Delta Air Lines	232	05/JUN/79	14/JUN/79	
21595	A7-AAB	Qatar Government	2P1	09/JAN/79	01/FEB/79	
21600	PP-SNI	Vasp	2A1	23/OCT/80	03/NOV/80	
	XA-MXG	Mexicana			26/AUG/85	Leased
	PP-SNI	Vasp			AUG/88	Sched.return
21601	PP-SNJ	Vasp	2A1	25/NOV/80	12/DEC/80	
21603	TC-JBR	Turk Hava Yollari	2F2	08/SEP/78	19/DEC/78	W/O 16/JAN/83, Ankara
21608	N791L	International Lease Finance	2Q8	08/DEC/78	20/DEC/78	
	N791L	Pacific Southwest Airlines			20/DEC/78	Leased
	N791L	International Lease Finance			06/OCT/83	

BOEING 727

C/N	Registration	Owner/Operator	Series	First Flight	Delivery	Remarks
	N297AS	Alaska Airlines			06/OCT/83	Leased
21609	EC-DCC	Iberia	256	19/JUL/78	28/JUL/78	
21610	EC-DCD	Iberia	256	16/AUG/78	30/AUG/78	
21611	EC-DCE	Iberia	256	21/AUG/78	05/SEP/78	
21617	XA-HON	Mexicana	264	16/NOV/78	29/NOV/78	
21618	D-ABKN	Lufthansa	230	13/OCT/78	30/OCT/78	
21619	D-ABKP	Lufthansa	230	20/OCT/78	03/NOV/78	
21620	D-ABKQ	Lufthansa	230	28/NOV/78	07/DEC/78	
21621	D-ABKR	Lufthansa	230	11/DEC/78	20/DEC/78	
21622	D-ABKS	Lufthansa	230	03/JAN/79	12/JAN/79	
21623	D-ABKT	Lufthansa	230	10/JAN/79	19/JAN/79	
21624	C-GAAO	Air Canada	233	02/APR/79	17/APR/79	
21625	C-GAAP	Air Canada	233	06/APR/79	24/APR/79	
21626	C-GAAQ	Air Canada	233	11/APR/79	26/APR/79	
21628	N54341	Trans World Airlines	231	27/FEB/79	13/MAR/79	
21629	N54342	Trans World Airlines	231	02/MAR/79	20/MAR/79	
21630	N54343	Trans World Airlines	231	08/MAR/79	22/MAR/79	
21631	N54344	Trans World Airlines	231	13/MAR/79	28/MAR/79	
21632	N54345	Trans World Airlines	231	19/MAR/79	02/APR/79	
21633	N64646	Trans World Airlines	231	22/MAR/79	05/APR/79	
21634	N64647	Trans World Airlines	231	28/MAR/79	11/APR/79	
21636	TJ-AAM	Cameroon Government	2R1		NOV/78	
21637	XA-HOV	Mexicana	264	15/DEC/78	10/JAN/79	
21638	XA-HOX	Mexicana	264	09/MAR/79	20/MAR/79	
21646	VH-TBO	Trans Australia Airlines	276	10/JAN/79	25/JAN/79	
	VH-TBO	Australian Airlines			04/AUG/86	
21647	VH-RMM	Ansett Airlines	277	12/JAN/79	29/JAN/79	
21655	N726RW	Hughes Airwest	2M7	23/FEB/79	07/MAR/79	
	N726RW	Philippine Airlines			15/AUG/79	
	N726RW	Republic			82	
	N726RW	AirResearch			04/JUN/82	
	TN-AEB	Congo Government			09/JUN/82	
21656	N727RW	Hughes Airwest	2M7	02/MAR/79	12/MAR/79	
	N727RW	Republic			01/OCT/80	
21661	I-DIRD	Alitalia	243	25/SEP/78	05/OCT/78	
	N578PE	People Express			03/AUG/84	
21662	I-DIRF	Alitalia	243	01/DEC/78	12/DEC/78	
	N579PE	People Express			14/JAN/84	
21663	I-DIRG	Alitalia	243	15/JAN/79	01/JUL/78	
	N580PE	People Express			17/JUL/84	
21664	I-DIRL	Alitalia	243	12/FEB/79	27/FEB/79	
	I-DIRL	ATASCO			30/NOV/83	
	TC-JCK	THY			05/JAN/84	
21669	N471BN	Braniff	227	16/MAY/79	25/MAY/79	WFU MAY/82
	N471BN	Braniff (Hyatt)			DEC/83	
21670	N472BN	Braniff	227	21/MAY/79	31/MAY/79	WFU MAY/82
	N472BN	Braniff (Hyatt)			DEC/83	
21671	C-GAAR	Air Canada	233	06/SEP/79	27/SEP/79	
21672	C-GAAS	Air Canada	233	09/OCT/79	01/NOV/79	
21673	C-GAAT	Air Canada	233	16/OCT/79	02/NOV/79	
21674	C-GAAU	Air Canada	233	19/OCT/79	30/NOV/79	
21675	C-GAAV	Air Canada	233	19/NOV/79	06/DEC/79	
21676	OY-SBD	Sterling Airways	254	15/NOV/78	30/NOV/78	
	G-BHNE	Dan Air			20/MAR/80	
21688	LV-MIM	Aerolineas Argentinas	287	10/NOV/78	01/DEC/78	
	LV-MIM	Wien Air Alaska			18/APR/84	Leased
	LV-MIM	Aerolineas Argentinas			21/NOV/85	
21689	LV-MIN	Aerolineas Argentinas	287	12/DEC/79	21/DEC/78	
21690	LV-MIO	Aerolineas Argentinas	287	09/APR/79	18/APR/79	
21691	N557PS	Pacific Southwest Airlines	214	04/MAY/79	15/MAY/79	
	N557PS	Piedmont			19/APR/84	Leased
21692	N558PS	Pacific Southwest Airlines	214	07/MAY/79	21/MAY/79	
	N558PS	Piedmont			23/APR/84	Leased
21695	VH-RMN	Ansett Airlines	277	08/MAY/79	17/MAY/79	
21696	VH-TBP	Trans Australia Airlines	276	11/MAY/79	22/MAY/79	
	VH-TBP	Australian Airlines			04/AUG/86	
21697	N284WA	Western Airlines	247	12/APR/79	24/APR/79	
	N210UP	United Parcel Service	247F		SEP/85	Converted, Op. by Ryan Aviation
21698	N286WA	Western Airlines	247	16/APR/79	01/MAY/79	
	N209UP	United Parcel Service	247F		AUG/85	Converted, Op. by Ryan Aviation
21699	N287WA	Western Airlines	247	14/MAY/79	22/MAY/79	
	N207UP	United Parcel Service	247F		06/JUN/85	Converted, Op. by Ryan Aviation
21700	N288WA	Western Airlines	247	23/MAY/79	07/JUN/79	
	N211UP	United Parcel Service	247F		02/OCT/85	Converted, Op. by Ryan Aviation
21701	N289WA	Western Airlines	247	01/JUN/79	19/JUN/79	
	N208UP	United Parcel Service			02/JUL/85	Converted, Op. by Ryan Aviation
21702	N528DA	Delta Air Lines	232	29/AUG/79	25/OCT/79	
21703	N529DA	Delta Air Lines	232	06/NOV/79	21/NOV/79	
21741	N728RW	Hughes Airwest	2M7		JUL/79	
	N728RW	Republic			01/OCT/80	
21742	N729RW	Hughes Airwest	2M7	26/JUL/79	10/AUG/79	
	N729RW	Republic			01/OCT/80	
21777	EC-DDU	Iberia	256	18/MAY/79	13/FEB/79	W/O 19/FEB/85, Nr. Bilbao Ap.
21778	EC-DDV	Iberia	256	31/MAY/79	12/JUN/79	
21779	EC-DDX	Iberia	256	20/JUN/79	28/JUN/79	
21780	EC-DDY	Iberia	256	18/JUN/79	03/JUL/79	
21781	EC-DDZ	Iberia		22/JUN/79	09/JUL/79	
21788	N296US	Northwest Orient	251	06/JUN/79	15/JUN/79	
21789	N297US	Northwest Orient	251	08/JUN/79	20/JUN/79	
21813	N530DA	Delta Air Lines	232	09/NOV/79	30/NOV/79	
21814	N531DA	Delta Air Lines	232	28/NOV/79	07/DEC/79	
21823	N730RW	Hughes Airwest	2M7	27/FEB/80	21/MAR/80	
	LV-ODY	Aerolines Argentinas			26/MAY/80	Leased
21824	N740RW	Hughes Airwest	2M7	13/MAR/80	24/MAR/80	
	N740RW	Charlotte Aircraft			AUG/80	
	A9C-BA	Bahrain Government			AUG/81	
21826	N831L	International Lease Finance	2Q8	13/JUL/79	26/JUL/79	
	N831L	Western Airlines			26/JUL/79	Leased
21836	XA-IEU	Mexicana	264	13/JUN/79	27/JUN/79	
21837	XA-MEB	Mexicana	264	25/OCT/79	13/NOV/79	
21838	XA-MEC	Mexicana	264	29/OCT/79	13/NOV/79	
21842	4W-ACJ	Yemen Airways	2N8	20/JUL/79	05/SEP/79	Op. by Yemen Govt.
21844	4W-ACF	Yemen Airways	2N8	06/AUG/79	22/AUG/79	
21845	4W-ACG	Yemen Airways	2N8	17/SEP/79	01/OCT/79	
21846	4W-ACH	Yemen Airways	2N8	02/NOV/79	29/NOV/79	

C/N	Registration	Owner/Operator	Series	First Flight	Delivery	Remarks
21847	4W-ACI	Yemen Airways	2N8	27/NOV/79	13/DEC/79	
21849	N720ZK	Ozark Airlines	2D4	12/SEP/79	11/OCT/79	
	N361PA	Pan American			27/OCT/79	
21850	N721ZK	Ozark Airlines	2D4		OCT/79	
	N362PA	Pan American			80	
	N362PA	Boeing			80	Leased
	N362PA	Pan American			80	
21851	D-AHLT	Hapag Lloyd	2K5	13/NOV/79	30/NOV/79	
21852	D-AHLU	Hapag Lloyd	2K5	19/NOV/79	29/NOV/79	
	D-AHLU	Tunis Air			01/APR/83	Leased
	D-AHLU	Hapag Lloyd			OCT/83	
21853	N8290V	Boeing	2K5			
	D-AHLV	Hapag Lloyd		27/JUN/80	18/JUL/80	
	LX-MJM	Al Tass Hell Liltijara			04/AUG/82	
	LX-MMM	Omar S.A.R.L.			JUL/84	
21854	N8885Z	Eastern Airlines	225	28/SEP/79	17/OCT/79	
21855	N8886Z	Eastern Airlines	225	09/OCT/79	23/OCT/79	
21856	N8887Z	Eastern Airlines	225	11/OCT/79	01/NOV/79	
21857	N8888Z	Eastern Airlines	225	17/OCT/79	05/NOV/79	
21858	N8889Z	Eastern Airlines	225	23/OCT/79	04/DEC/79	
21859	N8890Z	Eastern Airlines	225	30/OCT/79	30/NOV/79	
21860	N8891Z	Eastern Airlines	225	01/NOV/79	27/NOV/79	
21861	N8892Z	Eastern Airines	225	21/NOV/79	07/DEC/79	
21892	N7297U	United Airlines	222	19/JUN/79	02/JUL/79	
	N7297U	Northeastern International			MAY/85	Leased
	N7297U	United Airlines			85	
21893	N7298U	United Airlines	222	02/JUL/79	11/JUL/79	
21894	N7299U	United Airlines	222		JUL/79	
21895	N7441U	United Airlines	222		JUL/79	
21896	N7442U	United Airlines	222		AUG/79	
21897	N7443U	United Airlines	222		AUG/79	
21898	N7444U	United Airlines	222		AUG/79	
21899	N7445U	United Airlines	222	07/AUG/79	28/AUG/79	
21900	N7446U	United Airlines	222	10/AUG/79	04/SEP/79	
21901	N7447U	United Airlines	222	30/AUG/79	11/SEP/79	
21902	N7448U	United Airlines	222	10/SEP/79	21/SEP/79	
21903	N7449U	United Airlines	222	13/SEP/79	24/SEP/79	
21904	N7450U	United Airlines	222	18/SEP/79	01/OCT/79	
21905	N7451U	United Airlines	222	21/SEP/79	04/OCT/79	
21906	N7452U	United Airlines	222	05/NOV/79	19/NOV/79	
21907	N7453U	United Airlines	222	04/DEC/79	13/DEC/79	
21908	N7454U	United Airlines	222	07/DEC/79	17/DEC/79	
21909	N7455U	United Airlines	222	13/DEC/79	21/DEC/79	
21910	N7456U	United Airlines	222	10/JAN/80	07/FEB/80	
21911	N7457U	United Airlines	222	21/FEB/80	03/MAR/80	
21912	N7458U	United Airlines	222	15/FEB/80	05/MAR/80	
21913	N7459U	United Airlines	222	10/MAR/80	19/MAR/80	
21914	N7460U	United Airlines	222	18/MAR/80	31/MAR/80	
21915	N7461U	United Airlines	222	16/APR/80	28/APR/80	
21916	N7462U	United Airlines	222	21/APR/80	30/APR/80	
21917	N7463U	United Airlines	222	30/APR/80	12/MAY/80	
21918	N7464U	United Airlines	222	28/MAY/80	11/JUN/80	
21919	N7465U	United Airlines	222	16/JUN/80	27/JUN/80	
21920	N7466U	United Airlines	222	19/JUN/80	30/JUN/80	
21921	N7467U	United Airlines	222	02/JUL/80	25/JUL/80	
21930	N1273E	Boeing	2A7			
	N200AV	ITEL			DEC/79	
	N200AV	Bank of America			DEC/79	
	N200AV	Avianca			DEC/79	Leased
21931	N202AV	ITEL	2Q9		DEC/79	
	N202AV	Bank of America			DEC/79	
	N202AV	Avianca			DEC/79	Leased
21945	9V-SGG	Singapore Airlines	212	27/JUN/79	10/JUL/79	
	TI-LRQ	LACSA			27/APR/82	
21946	9V-SGH	Singapore Airlines	212	06/JUL/79	17/JUL/79	
	9V-WGA	Age of Enlightenment Trust			19/JAN/83	
	N48054	Rolls Royce Credit			APR/84	
	N48054	Citicorp.			NOV/84	
	N48054	Ryan Aviation			NOV/84	Leased
	N48054	Citicorp.			MAY/86	
	N48054	E-Systems			MAY/86	
	N48054	Ryan Aviation			MAY/86	Leased
21947	9V-SGI	Singapore Airlines	212	06/JUL/79	20/JUL/79	
	N309AS	Alaska Airlines			22/JAN/85	
21948	9V-SGJ	Singapore Airlines	212	17/JUL/79	01/AUG/79	
	N310AS	Alaska Airlines			06/MAR/85	
	N310AS	TAG Aeronautics			DEC/85	
21949	CS-TBW	TAP Air Portugal	282	11/JUN/79	28/JUN/79	
21950	CS-TBX	TAP Air Portugal	282	29/JAN/80	03/MAR/80	
21951	N741RW	Republic	2M7	28/OCT/80	07/NOV/80	
	A6-HRR	Dubai Air Wing			07/NOV/80	
	A6-EMA	Emirates Airlines			DEC/85	
21952	N742RW	Republic	2M7	03/DEC/80	18/DEC/80	WFU 18/DEC/80 Las Vegas
21953	N760AL	US Air	2B7	31/JUL/79	30/AUG/79	
21954	N761AL	US Air	2B7	04/SEP/79	27/SEP/79	
21958	N559PS	Pacific Southwest Airlines	214	25/SEP/79	10/OCT/79	
	N559PS	Piedmont			FEB/84	Leased
21967	N54348	Trans World Airlines	231	11/DEC/79	18/MAR/80	
21968	N54349	Trans World Airlines	231	17/DEC/79	26/FEB/80	
21969	N54350	Trans World Airlines	231	20/DEC/79	29/FEB/80	
21971	N1289E	LACSA	2Q6			Not taken-up
	N1279E	LACSA		12/OCT/79	01/NOV/79	
21972	N1290E	LACSA	2Q6			Not taken-up
	N1280E	LACSA		27/JUN/80	10/JUL/80	
21978	ET-AHL	Ethiopian Airlines	260	24/AUG/79	18/SEP/79	
21979	ET-AHM	Ethiopian Airlines	260	28/SEP/79	17/OCT/79	
21983	N54351	Trans World Airlines	231	04/JAN/80	13/FEB/80	
21984	N54352	Trans World Airlines	231	17/JAN/80	20/FEB/80	
21985	N54353	Trans World Airlines	231	22/JAN/80	21/FEB/80	
21986	N54354	Trans World Airlines	231	31/JAN/80	06/MAR/80	
21987	N84355	Trans World Airlines	231	06/FEB/80	11/MAR/80	
21988	N84356	Trans World Airlines	231	15/FEB/80	20/MAR/80	
21989	N84357	Trans World Airlines	231	12/MAR/80	03/APR/80	
21996	N473BN	Braniff	227	12/JAN/80	22/JAN/80	WFU MAY/82
	N473BN	Bankers Trust			23/JUL/82	

C/N	Registration	Owner/Operator	Series	First Flight	Delivery	Remarks
	N782AL	US Air			14/DEC/83	
21997	N474BN	Braniff	227	17/JAN/80	29/JAN/80	WFU MAY/82
	N474BN	Bankers Trust			23/JUL/82	
	N474BN	Alaska Airlines			25/MAY/83	Leased
	N306AS	Alaska Airlines			85	Leased
21998	N475BN	Braniff	227	28/JAN/80	07/FEB/80	WFU MAY/82
	N475BN	Bankers Trust			23/JUL/82	
	N783AL	US Air			14/DEC/83	
21999	N476BN	Braniff	227	08/FEB/80	24/FEB/80	WFU MAY/82
	N476BN	Bankers Trust			23/JUL/82	
	N780AL	US Air			JUL/83	
22000	N477BN	Braniff	227	11/FEB/80	21/FEB/80	WFU MAY/82
	N477BN	Bankers Trust			23/JUL/82	
	N477BN	Alaska Airlines			22/APR/83	Leased
	N307AS	Alaska Airlines			85	Leased
22001	N478BN	Braniff	227	19/FEB/80	28/FEB/80	WFU MAY/82
	N478BN	Bankers Trust			23/JUL/82	
	N781AL	US Air			JUL/83	
22002	N479BN	Braniff	227	03/JUN/80	06/JUN/80	WFU MAY/82
	N479BN	Bankers Trust			23/JUL/82	
	N479BN	Alaska Airlines			26/MAY/83	Leased
	N308AS	Alaska Airlines			85	Leased
22003	N480BN	Braniff	227			Stored Seattle
	N271AF	Air Florida			SEP/81	
	N271AF	Cayman Airways			20/NOV/82	
22004	N481BN	Braniff	227			Stored Seattle
	N272AF	Air Florida			SEP/81	
	N272AF	Cayman Airways			20/NOV/82	
22005	N482BN	Braniff	227			Stored Seattle
	N273AF	Air Florida			NOV/81	
	N273AF	General Electric Credit			29/JUN/83	
	N273AF	Alaska Airlines			29/JUN/83	Leased
	N304AS	Alaska Airlines			15/AUG/83	Leased
22006	N890AA	American Airlines	223	18/JUN/80	16/JUL/80	
22007	N891AA	American Airlines	223	11/JUL/80	22/JUL/80	
22008	N892AA	American Airlines	223	15/JUL/80	31/JUL/80	
22009	N893AA	American Airlines	223	29/JUL/80	07/AUG/80	
22010	N894AA	American Airlines	223	07/AUG/80	22/AUG/80	
22011	N895AA	American Airlines	223	19/AUG/80	28/AUG/80	
22012	N896AA	American Airlines	223	18/AUG/80	04/SEP/80	
22013	N897AA	American Airlines	223	28/AUG/80	15/SEP/80	
22014	N898AA	American Airlines	223	09/SEP/80	23/SEP/80	
22015	N899AA	American Airlines	223	22/SEP/80	01/OCT/80	
22016	VH-RMO	Ansett Airlines	277	02/JAN/80	15/JAN/80	
22017	VH-TBQ	Trans Australia Airlines	276	13/DEC/79	14/JAN/80	
	VH-TBQ	Australian Airlines			04/AUG/86	
22019	N711RC	Republic	257			Not taken-up
	N715RC	Republic		11/FEB/80	28/FEB/80	
22020	N712RC	Republic	257	05/MAR/80	14/MAR/80	
22021	N713RC	Republic	257			Not taken-up
	N716RC	Republic		06/MAY/80	02/JUN/80	
22035	C-GAAW	Air Canada	233	28/JAN/80	14/FEB/80	
22036	C-GAAX	Air Canada	233	11/MAR/80	27/MAR/80	
22037	C-GAAY	Air Canada	233	20/MAR/80	10/APR/80	
22038	C-GAAZ	Air Canada	233	24/APR/80	09/MAY/80	
22039	C-GYNA	Air Canada	233	29/APR/80	15/MAY/80	
22040	C-GYNB	Air Canada	233	23/MAY/80	11/JUN/80	
22041	C-GYNC	Air Canada	233	29/MAY/80	13/JUN/80	
22042	C-GYND	Air Canada	233	04/JUN/80	19/JUN/80	
22043	YV-74C	International Lease Finance	294	29/NOV/79	10/DEC/79	
	YV-74C	Avensa			10/DEC/79	Leased
22044	YV-75C	International Lease Finance	294	07/DEC/79	14/DEC/79	Leased
	YV-75C	Avensa			14/DEC/79	Leased
22045	N532DA	Delta Air Lines	232	31/MAR/80	09/APR/80	
22046	N533DA	Delta Air Lines	232	03/APR/80	16/APR/80	
22047	N534DA	Delta Air Lines	232	04/APR/80	23/APR/80	
22048	N535DA	Delta Air Lines	232	09/APR/80	07/MAY/80	
22049	N536DA	Delta Air Lines	232	15/APR/80	09/MAY/80	
22052	I-DIRM	Alitalia	243	07/JAN/80	17/JAN/80	
	N581PE	People Express			20/DEC/84	
22053	I-DIRN	Alitalia	243	13/MAY/80	23/MAY/80	
	N582PE	People Express			25/JAN/85	
22068	VH-RMP	Ansett Airlines	277	02/SEP/80	10/SEP/80	
22069	VH-TBR	Trans Australia Airlines	276	06/SEP/80	19/SEP/80	
	VH-TBR	Australian Airlines			04/AUG/86	
22073	N537DA	Delta Air Lines	232		MAY/80	
22076	N1786B	Boeing	232			
	N538DA	Delta Air Lines		21/AUG/80	01/OCT/80	
22078	N1293E	Boeing	2T3			
	N710EV	Evergreen International				Not taken-up
	HC-BHM	TAME		28/AUG/80	30/SEP/80	
22079	OY-SBE	Sterling Airways	2J4	21/FEB/80	11/MAR/80	
22080	OY-SBF	Sterling Airways	2J4	19/MAR/80	26/MAR/80	
22081	F-GCDA	Air France	228	07/MAR/80	26/MAR/80	
22082	F-GCDB	Air France	228	27/MAR/80	11/APR/80	
22083	F-GCDC	Air France	228	08/APR/80	17/APR/80	
22084	F-GCDD	Air France	228	24/JUN/80	09/JUL/80	
22085	F-GCDE	Air France	228	15/SEP/80	30/SEP/80	
22091	N483BN	Braniff	227			
	N274AF	Air Florida			NOV/81	
	N274AF	General Electric Credit			29/JUN/83	
	N274AF	Alaska Airlines			29/JUN/83	Leased
	N305AS	Alaska Airlines			15/AUG/83	Leased
22092	N484BN	Braniff	227			
	N275AF	Air Florida		09/FEB/81	20/NOV/81	
	N275AF	General Electric Credit			OCT/82	
	N275AF	Sun Country Airlines			DEC/82	Leased
22093	N485BN	Braniff	227			Cancelled order
22094	N486BN	Braniff	227			Cancelled order
22095	N487BN	Braniff	227			Cancelled order
22096	N488BN	Braniff	227			Cancelled order
22097	N489BN	Braniff	227			Cancelled order
22098	N490BN	Braniff	227			Cancelled order
22099	N491BN	Braniff	227			Cancelled order
22100	N492BN	Braniff	227			Cancelled order

C/N	Registration	Owner/Operator	Series	First Flight	Delivery	Remarks
22101	N493BN	Braniff	227			Cancelled order
22102	N494BN	Braniff	227			Cancelled order
22103	N495BN	Braniff	227			Cancelled order
22104	N496BN	Braniff	227			Cancelled order
22108	N290WA	Western Airlines	247	22/FEB/80	05/MAR/80	
22109	N291WA	Western Airlines	247	26/FEB/80	11/MAR/80	
22110	N292WA	Western Airlines	247	22/APR/80	06/MAY/80	
22111	N293WA	Western Airlines	247	25/APR/80	09/MAY/80	
22112	N294WA	Westen Airlines	247	05/MAY/80	19/MAY/80	
22146	N294AS	Alaska Airlines	290	09/MAY/80	30/MAY/80	
22147	N295AS	Alaska Airlines	290	14/MAY/80	29/MAY/80	
22152	N298US	Northwest Orient	251	15/MAR/80	01/APR/80	
22153	N299US	Northwest Orient	251	26/MAR/80	11/APR/80	
22154	N201US	Northwest Orient	251	16/JUL/80	25/JUL/80	
22155	N202US	Northwest Orient	251	24/JUL/80	04/AUG/80	
22156	XA-MED	Mexicana	264	04/APR/80	18/APR/80	
22157	XA-MEE	Mexicana	264	08/MAY/80	16/MAY/80	
22158	N1786B	Boeing	264	03/JUL/80		
	XA-MEF	Mexicana			18/JUL/80	
22162	N770AL	US Air	2B7	12/FEB/80	20/FEB/81	
22163	N771AL	US Air	2B7	27/MAR/81	10/APR/81	
22164	N772AL	US Air	2B7	20/APR/81	05/MAY/81	
22165	I-DIRP	Alitalia	243	19/JUN/80	02/JUL/80	
	N583PE	People Express			24/FEB/85	
22166	I-DIRQ	Alitalia	243	27/FEB/80	17/MAR/81	
	N584PE	People Express			19/NOV/84	
22167	N8280V	Boeing	243	20/MAY/81		
	I-DIRR	Alitalia			01/JUN/81	
	N585PE	People Express			16/APR/85	
22168	I-DIRS	Alitalia	243		SEP/81	
	N586PE	People Express			04/MAY/85	
22240	EC-	Iberia	256			Cancelled order
22241	EC-	Iberia	256			Cancelled order
22242	EC-	Iberia	256			Cancelled order
22243	EC-	Iberia	256			Cancelled order
22244	EC-	Iberia	256			Cancelled order
22250	N69741	Continental Airlines	224	30/OCT/80	18/NOV/80	
22251	N69742	Continental Airlines	224	11/NOV/80	09/DEC/80	
22252	N79743	Continental Airlines	224	09/DEC/80	04/FEB/81	
22253	N79744	Continental Airlines	224	23/DEC/80	04/FEB/81	
22261	N8284V	Boeing	270	05/AUG/80		
	YI-AGQ	Iraqi Airways			12/MAY/81	
22262	N8286V	Boeing	270	05/NOV/80		
	YI-AGR	Iraqi Airways			14/MAY/81	
22263	YI-AGS	Iraqi Airways	270	15/JUL/82	29/JUL/82	
22268	JY-AFT	Alia	203	03/JUL/80	22/JUL/80	
22269	JY-AFU	Alia	203	18/DEC/80	16/JAN/81	
22270	N57001	Boeing	203			
	JY-AFV	Alia			JUN/81	
22271	N8286V	Boeing	203	28/JAN/81		
	JY-AFW	Alia			10/FEB/81	W/O 16/JUN/85, Beirut
22287	F-GCDF	Air France	228	20/JAN/81	28/JAN/81	
22288	F-GCDG	Air France	228	22/JAN/81	06/FEB/81	
22289	F-GCDH	Air France	228	16/FEB/81	26/FEB/81	
22290	F-GCDI	Air France	228	25/FEB/81	10/MAR/81	
22295	TF-FLI	Icelandair	208	15/MAY/80	30/MAY/80	
22344	N714RC	Republic	257			Not taken-up
	N718RC	Republic		18/AUG/80	02/SEP/80	
22345	C-GABE	Air Canada	233			Reg.not taken-up
	C-GYNE	Air Canada	233	09/DEC/80	19/DEC/80	
22346	C-GABF	Air Canada	233			Reg.not taken-up
	C-GYNF	Air Canada	233	08/JAN/81	22/JAN/81	
22347	C-GABG	Air Canada	233			Reg.not taken-up
	C-GYNG	Air Canada	233	16/JAN/81	29/JAN/81	
22348	C-GABH	Air Canada	233			Reg.not taken-up
	C-GYNH	Air Canada	233	03/FEB/81	13/FEB/81	
22349	C-GABI	Air Canada	233	23/FEB/81		Reg.not taken-up
	N8278V	Boeing			16/MAR/81	
	C-GYNI	Air Canada				
22350	C-GABJ	Air Canada	233			Reg.not taken-up
	C-GYNJ	Air Canada		24/APR/81	14/MAY/81	
22359	N8291V	Boeing	269	14/AUG/80	05/SEP/80	
	9K-AFA	Kuwait Airways	269			
22360	9K-AFB	Kuwait Airways	269	26/SEP/80	09/OCT/80	
22361	9K-AFC	Kuwait Airways	269	06/FEB/81	26/FEB/81	
22362	JY-HNH	King Hussein	2U5	28/AUG/80	16/SEP/80	
	VB-HM1	Brunei Government			JUN/85	
22372	7T-VET	Air Algerie	2D6	09/SEP/80	18/SEP/80	
22373	7T-VEU	Air Algerie	2D6	13/SEP/80	22/SEP/80	
22374	N8292V	Boeing	2D6	20/JAN/81		
	7T-VEV	Air Algerie			09/MAR/81	
22375	7T-VEW	Air Algerie	2D6	27/FEB/81	11/MAR/81	
22377	CN-RMR	Royal Air Maroc	2B6	11/JUN/80	30/JUN/80	
22385	N539DA	Delta Air Lines	232	19/SEP/80	08/OCT/80	
22386	N540DA	Delta Air Lines	232	24/SEP/80	15/OCT/80	
22387	N541DA	Delta Air Lines	232		OCT/80	
22391	N542DA	Delta Air Lines	232	06/JAN/81	21/JAN/81	
22392	N543DA	Delta Air Lines	232	08/JAN/81	28/JAN/81	
22393	YU-AKI	JAT	2H9	23/OCT/80	15/DEC/80	
22394	YU-AKJ	JAT	2H9	17/NOV/80	15/DEC/80	
22409	XA-MEH	Mexicana	264	10/OCT/80	27/OCT/80	
22410	XA-MEI	Mexicana	264	14/OCT/80	27/OCT/80	
22411	XA-MEJ	Mexicana	264	03/DEC/80	12/DEC/80	
22412	XA-MEK	Mexicana	264	20/FEB/81	27/FEB/81	
22413	XA-MEL	Mexicana	264	09/MAR/81	27/MAR/81	
22414	XA-MEM	Mexicana	264	04/MAY/81	18/MAY/81	W/O 31/MAR/86, nr. Maravaito
22417	N497BN	Braniff	227			Cancelled order
22418	N498BN	Braniff	227			Cancelled order
22419	N499BN	Braniff	227			Cancelled order
22420	N	Braniff	227			Cancelled order
22421	N	Braniff	227			Cancelled order
22422	N	Braniff	227			Cancelled order
22423	N	Braniff	227			Cancelled order
22424	PT-TCE	TransBrasil	2Q4			Not taken-up
	XA-MEQ	Mexicana		28/OCT/80	05/DEC/80	

BOEING 727

C/N	Registration	Owner/Operator	Series	First Flight	Delivery	Remarks
22425	PT-TCF	TransBrasil	2Q4			Not taken-up
	XA-MER	Mexicana		08/DEC/80	22/DEC/80	
22430	N8285V	Boeing	282	30/JAN/81		
	CS-TBY	TAP Air Portugal			02/MAR/81	
22432	N801EA	Eastern Airlines	225	02/SEP/80	06/OCT/80	
22433	N802EA	Eastern Airlines	225	29/SEP/80	08/OCT/80	
22434	N803EA	Eastern Airlines	225	17/OCT/80	03/NOV/80	
22435	N804EA	Eastern Airlines	225	29/OCT/80	07/NOV/80	
22436	N805EA	Eastern Airlines	225	03/NOV/80	12/NOV/80	
22437	N806EA	Eastern Airlines	225	06/NOV/80	17/NOV/80	
22438	N807EA	Eastern Airlines	225	07/NOV/80	21/NOV/80	
22439	N808EA	Eastern Airlines	225	18/NOV/80	02/DEC/80	
22440	N809EA	Eastern Airlines	225	21/NOV/80	08/DEC/80	
22441	N810EA	Eastern Airlines	225	03/DEC/80	15/DEC/80	
22448	N79745	Continental Airlines	224	09/APR/81	21/MAY/81	
22449	N79746	Continental Airlines	224	02/JUN/81	11/JUN/81	
22450	N79748	Continental Airlines	224		JUN/81	
22451	N79749	Continental Airlines	224		JUL/81	
22452	N79750	Continental Airlines	224		SEP/81	
22459	N701AA	American Airlines	223	21/APR/81	30/APR/81	
22460	N702AA	American Airlines	223	01/MAY/81	11/MAY/81	
22461	N703AA	American Airlines	223	13/MAY/81	26/MAY/81	
22462	N705AA	American Airlines	223	12/MAY/81	02/JUN/81	
22463	N706AA	American Airlines	223	18/MAY/81	12/JUN/81	
22464	N707AA	American Airlines	223	02/JUN/81	18/JUN/81	
22465	N708AA	American Airlines	223		JUN/81	
22466	N709AA	American Airlines	223		JUL/81	
22467	N710AA	American Airlines	223		JUL/81	
22468	N712AA	American Airlines	223		JUL/81	
22469	N713AA	American Airlines	223		AUG/81	
22470	N715AA	American Airlines	223		SEP/81	
22474	HK-2474	Avianca	259			Reg.not taken-up
	N203AV	Avianca		11/NOV/80	04/DEC/80	
22475	HK-2475	Avianca	259			Reg.not taken-up
	N204AV	Avianca		14/NOV/80	04/DEC/80	
22476	HK-2476	Avianca	259			Reg.not taken-up
	N205AV	Avianca			JUN/81	
22490	N719RC	Republic	257	12/FEB/81	26/FEB/81	
22491	N720RC	Republic	257	06/MAR/81	17/MAR/81	
22492	N721RC	Republic	257	17/MAR/81	26/MAR/81	
22493	N544DA	Delta Air Lines	232	14/APR/81	01/MAY/81	
22494	N545DA	Delta Air Lines	232	11/MAY/81	20/MAY/81	
22532	N295WA	Western Airlines	247	13/MAY/81	29/MAY/81	
22533	N296WA	Western Airlines	247	08/APR/81	05/JUN/81	
22534	N297WA	Western Airlines	247	02/APR/81	22/MAY/81	
22535	N363PA	Pan American	221	23/JUN/81	22/APR/82	
22536	N364PA	Pan American	221	26/AUG/81	29/DEC/81	
22537	N365PA	Pan American	221	23/SEP/81	29/DEC/81	
22538	N366PA	Pan American	221	08/DEC/81	22/APR/82	
22539	N367PA	Pan American	221	26/JAN/81	22/APR/82	
22540	N368PA	Pan American	221	16/APR/82	26/MAY/82	
22541	N369PA	Pan American	221	16/APR/82	26/MAY/82	
22542	N370PA	Pan American	221	16/APR/82	26/MAY/82	
22543	N203US	Northwest Orient	251	11/DEC/80	07/JAN/81	
22544	N204US	Northwest Orient	251	18/DEC/80	13/JAN/81	
22548	N811EA	Eastern Airlines	225	31/MAR/81	09/APR/81	
22549	N812EA	Eastern Airlines	225	09/APR/81	20/APR/81	
22550	N813EA	Eastern Airlines	225	16/APR/81	27/APR/81	
22551	N814EA	Eastern Airlines	225	27/APR/81	07/MAY/81	
22552	N815EA	Eastern Airlines	225	19/AUG/81	02/OCT/81	
22553	N816EA	Eastern Airlines	225	31/AUG/81	02/OCT/81	
22554	N817EA	Eastern Airlines	225		NOV/81	
22555	N818EA	Eastern Airlines	225	15/OCT/81	01/DEC/81	
22556	N819EA	Eastern Airlines	225	12/MAR/82	07/APR/82	
22557	N820EA	Eastern Airlines	225	17/MAR/82	07/APR/82	
22558	N821EA	Eastern Airlines	225	09/APR/82	03/MAY/82	
22559	N822EA	Eastern Airlines	225	13/APR/82	03/MAY/82	
22560	N823EA	Eastern Airlines	225			Cancelled order
22561	N824EA	Eastern Airlines	225			Cancelled order
22562	N8893Z	Eastern Airlines	225			Cancelled order
22563	N8894Z	Eastern Airlines	225			Cancelled order
22574	OY-SBG	Sterling Airways	2J4	20/MAR/81	03/APR/81	
22603	LV-OLN	Aerolineas Argentinas	287	25/MAR/81	09/APR/81	
22604	LV-OLO	Aerolineas Argentinas	287	11/SEP/81	15/OCT/81	
22605	LV-OLP	Aerolineas Argentinas	287	06/NOV/81	08/JAN/82	
22606	LV-OLR	Aerolineas Argentinas	287	01/SEP/82	23/DEC/82	
22608	F-GCMV	Air Charter International	2X3	04/MAR/81	20/MAR/81	
22609	F-GCMX	Air Charter International	2X3	20/MAR/81	31/MAR/81	
22621	C-GYNK	Air Canada	233	25/JAN/82	04/FEB/82	
22622	C-GYNL	Air Canada	233	08/FEB/82	09/MAR/82	
22623	C-GYNM	Air Canada	233	12/MAY/82	17/JUN/82	
22641	VH-ANA	Ansett	277	29/MAY/81	11/JUN/81	
22642	VH-ANB	Ansett	277		30/AUG/81	
22643	VH-ANE	Ansett	277		03/JUL/81	
22644	VH-ANF	Ansett	277		24/JUL/81	
22661	XA-MXA	Mexicana	264	29/MAY/81	11/JUN/81	
22662	XA-MXB	Mexicana	264		NOV/81	
22663	XA-MXC	Mexicana	264		NOV/81	
22664	XA-MXD	Mexicana	264		NOV/81	
22665	YU-AKK	JAT	2H9	02/NOV/81	30/DEC/81	
	YU-AKK	Air Afrique			JUL/83	Leased
	YU-AKK	JAT			01/JUN/86	
22666	YU-AKL	JAT	2H9	08/DEC/81	30/DEC/81	
	YU-AKL	Air Afrique			JUL/83	Leased
	YU-AKL	JAT			MAR/87	Sched.return
22676	XA-MXA	Mexicana	264	20/MAY/81	04/JUN/81	
22677	N546DA	Delta	232		NOV/81	
22677	XA-MXF	Mexicana	264			
22678	XA-MXG	Mexicana	264			
22679	XA-MXH	Mexicana	264			
22680	XA-MXI	Mexicana	264			
22681	XA-MXJ	Mexicana	264			
22682	XA-MXK	Mexicana	264			
22687	N721MF	Wedge Aviation	2X8		NOV/81	
22702	I-DIRT	Alitalia	243	09/NOV/82	15/MAR/83	

C/N	Registration	Owner/Operator	Series	First Flight	Delivery	Remarks
	YU-AKM	Aviogenex			09/MAY/85	
22759	ET-AHK	Ethiopian Airlines	260	18/NOV/81	21/DEC/81	
22763	9K-AFD	Kuwait Airways	269	12/NOV/81	10/DEC/81	
22765	7T-VEX	Air Algerie	2D6	20/APR/82	05/MAY/82	
22770	CP-1741	Lloyd Aereo Boliviano	2K3			Cancelled order
	N776AL	US Air		28/JUN/82	15/MAR/83	
22825	5N-AGY	Nigerian Government	2N6	09/JUN/82	14/JUL/82	
22924	N201FE	Federal Express	2S2F	28/APR/83	27/JUN/83	
22925	N203FE	Federal Express	2S2F	24/MAY/83	01/AUG/83	
22926	N204FE	Federal Express	2S2F	08/JUL/83	01/AUG/83	
22927	N205FE	Federal Express	2S2F	05/AUG/83	01/SEP/83	
22928	N206FE	Federal Express	2S2F	01/SEP/83	16/SEP/83	
22929	N207FE	Federal Express	2S2F	07/OCT/83	17/OCT/83	
22930	N208FE	Federal Express	2S2F	09/NOV/83	17/NOV/83	
22931	N209FE	Federal Express	2S2F	19/DEC/83	11/JAN/84	
22932	N210FE	Federal Express	2S2F	30/JAN/84	17/FEB/84	
22933	N211FE	Federal Express	2S2F	02/MAR/84	23/MAR/84	
22934	N212FE	Federal Express	2S2F	04/APR/84	20/APR/84	
22935	N213FE	Federal Express	2S2F	09/MAY/84	24/MAY/84	
22936	N215FE	Federal Express	2S2F	12/JUN/84	29/JUN/84	
22937	N216FE	Federal Express	2S2F	24/JUL/84	14/AUG/84	
22938	N217FE	Federal Express	2S2F	28/AUG/84	18/SEP/84	Last Boeing 727 built
22968	HZ-RH3	Rafic Hariri	2Y4		JAN/83	
	HZ-HR3	Saudi Oger Ltd.			21/JUL/83	
22982	XA-	Mexicana	264			Cancelled order
	A6-HHM	Government of Dubai		05/MAY/82	17/JUL/82	
22983	XA-	Mexicana	264			Cancelled order
	N773AL	US Air		18/NOV/82	03/DEC/82	
22984	XA-	Mexicana	264			Cancelled order
	N774AL	US Air		19/NOV/82	13/DEC/82	
22992	TC-JCA	Turk Hava Yollari	2F2	24/MAY/82	16/JUN/82	
22993	TC-JCB	Turk Hava Yollari	2F2	08/JUL/82	19/JUL/82	
22998	TC-JCE	Turk Hava Yollari	2F2	10/AUG/82	23/AUG/82	
22999	TC-JCF	Turk Hava Yollari	2F2	25/AUG/82	03/SEP/82	
23014	XA-	Mexicana	264			Cancelled order
	N775AL	US Air		26/JAN/83	15/FEB/83	
23015	XA-	Mexicana	264			Cancelled order
23052	N779AL	US Air	270	23/MAR/83	06/APR/83	

Boeing 727 cross-reference index

3X- Guinea

19120	3X-GCA

4W- North Yemen

21844	4W-ACF
21845	4W-ACG
21846	4W-ACH
21847	4W-ACI
21842	4W-ACJ

4X- Israel

19011	4X-AGJ
19249	4X-BAE

5A- Libyan

20244	5A-DAH
20245	5A-DAI
21050	5A-DIA
21051	5A-DIB
21052	5A-DIC
21229	5A-DID
21230	5A-DIE
21332	5A-DIF
21333	5A-DIG
21539	5A-DIH
21540	5A-DII

5N- Nigeria

22825	5N-AGY
21426	5N-ANP
21427	5N-ANQ
19120	5N-AWH

6V- Senegal

21091	6V-AEF

6Y- Jamaica

21105	6Y-JIP
21106	6Y-JIQ
21107	6Y-JIR
21108	6Y-JIS
21105	6Y-JMA
21106	6Y-JMB
21107	6Y-JMC
21108	6Y-JMD
20936	6Y-JMH
20978	6Y-JML

7T- Algerie

20472	7T-VEA
20473	7T-VEB
20955	7T-VEH
21053	7T-VEI
21210	7T-VEM
21284	7T-VEP
22372	7T-VET
22373	7T-VEU
22374	7T-VEV
22375	7T-VEW
22765	7T-VEX

9K- Kuwait

22359	9K-AFA
22360	9K-AFB
22361	9K-AFC
22763	9K-AFD

9N- Nepal

20421	9N-ABD
19813	9N-ABN
18879	9N-ABV
18878	9N-ABW
19113	9N-ABY

9Q- Zaire

18367	9Q-CBG
19319	9Q-CBS
19138	9Q-CBT

9V- Singapore

21347	9V-SGA
21348	9V-SGB
21349	9V-SGC
21458	9V-SGD
21459	9V-SGE
21460	9V-SGF
21945	9V-SGG
21946	9V-SGH
21947	9V-SGI
21948	9V-SGJ
21946	9V-WGA

9Y- Trinidad & Tobago

18794	9Y-TCO
18795	9Y-TCP
18796	9Y-TCQ

A40- Oman

18369	A40-CF

A6- United Arab Emirates

21951	A6-EMA
22982	A6-HHM
21951	A6-HRR

A7- Qatar

21595	A7-AAB

A9C- Bahrain

21824	A9C-BA

AN- Nicaragua

18843	AN-BSQ

B- Taiwan

19175	B-1018
19399	B-1818
19520	B-1820
20111	B-1822
19818	B-188

C- Canada

19859	C-FPXD
19169	C-FRST
20932	C-GAAA
20933	C-GAAB
20934	C-GAAC
20935	C-GAAD
20936	C-GAAE
20937	C-GAAF
20938	C-GAAG
20939	C-GAAH
20940	C-GAAI
20941	C-GAAJ
20942	C-GAAK
21100	C-GAAL
21101	C-GAAM
21102	C-GAAN
21624	C-GAAO
21625	C-GAAP
21626	C-GAAQ
21671	C-GAAR
21672	C-GAAS
21673	C-GAAT
21674	C-GAAU
21675	C-GAAV
22035	C-GAAW
22036	C-GAAX
22037	C-GAAY
22038	C-GAAZ
22345	C-GABE
22346	C-GABF
22347	C-GABG
22348	C-GABH
22349	C-GABI
22350	C-GABJ
19191	C-GAGX
19192	C-GAGY
19195	C-GAGZ
21055	C-GCPA
21056	C-GCPB
18970	C-GQBE
18853	C-GVCH
22039	C-GYNA
22040	C-GYNB
22041	C-GYNC
22042	C-GYND
22345	C-GYNE
22346	C-GYNF
22347	C-GYNG
22348	C-GYNH
22349	C-GYNI
22350	C-GYNJ
22621	C-GYNK
22622	C-GYNL
22623	C-GYNM

C2- Nauru

20370	C2-RN4
19252	C2-RN5
20278	C2-RN7

CC- Chile

19811	CC-CAG
19527	CC-CAN
19812	CC-CAQ
19813	CC-CFD
19814	CC-CFE
18796	CC-CFG
19532	CC-CGD
19196	CC-CLB

CF- Canada

20328	CF-CPK
20327	CF-CPN
20512	CF-CUR
20513	CF-CUS
19242	CF-FUN
19242	CF-FUN
19174	CF-PXB

CN- Morocco

20304	CN-CCF
20471	CN-CCG
20705	CN-CCH
21068	CN-CCW
21297	CN-RMQ
21298	CN-RMP
21299	CN-RMQ
22377	CN-RMR

CP- Bolivia

19860	CP-1070
18795	CP-1223
21082	CP-1276
20512	CP-1339
21494	CP-1366
21495	CP-1367
22770	CP-1741
20279	CP-861

CS- Portugal

19404	CS-TBK
19405	CS-TBL
19405	CS-TBL
19406	CS-TBM
19597	CS-TBN
19968	CS-TBO
20489	CS-TBP
19665	CS-TBQ
20972	CS-TBR
20973	CS-TBS
19618	CS-TBV
21949	CS-TBW
21950	CS-TBX
22430	CS-TBY

CX- Uruguay

19793	CX-BKA
19010	CX-BKB
19314	CX-BNT

D- West Germany

19793	D-ABBI
20430	D-ABCI
20431	D-ABDI
20525	D-ABFI
20526	D-ABGI
20560	D-ABHI
19011	D-ABIA
19011	D-ABIA
18360	D-ABIB
18361	D-ABIC
18362	D-ABID
19012	D-ABIE
18363	D-ABIF
18364	D-ABIG
18365	D-ABIH
19310	D-ABII
19314	D-ABIJ
18366	D-ABIK
18367	D-ABIL
18368	D-ABIM
18369	D-ABIN
19311	D-ABIO
18370	D-ABIP
18371	D-ABIQ
18933	D-ABIR
18934	D-ABIS
18935	D-ABIT
19312	D-ABIU
18936	D-ABIV
19008	D-ABIW
19009	D-ABIX
19313	D-ABIY
19010	D-ABIZ
20899	D-ABKA
20900	D-ABKB
20901	D-ABKC
20902	D-ABKD
20903	D-ABKE
20904	D-ABKF
20905	D-ABKG
20906	D-ABKH
20673	D-ABKI
20918	D-ABKJ
21113	D-ABKK
21114	D-ABKL
21442	D-ABKM
21618	D-ABKN
21619	D-ABKP
21620	D-ABKQ
21621	D-ABKR
21622	D-ABKS
21623	D-ABKT
20674	D-ABLI
20675	D-ABMI
20676	D-ABNI
20677	D-ABPI
20757	D-ABQI
20788	D-ABRI
20789	D-ABSI
20790	D-ABTI
20791	D-ABVI
20792	D-ABWI
20675	D-ABYL
20676	D-ABYM
20677	D-ABYN
19314	D-AFGK
18823	D-AHLL
18919	D-AHLM
18952	D-AHLN
19401	D-AHLO
18990	D-AHLP
19282	D-AHLQ
19138	D-AHLR
19139	D-AHLS
21851	D-AHLT
21852	D-AHLU
21853	D-AHLV
18951	D-AJAA

EC- Spain

20592	EC-CAI
20593	EC-CAJ
20594	EC-CAK
20595	EC-CBA
20596	EC-CBB
20597	EC-CBC
20598	EC-CBD
20599	EC-CBE
20600	EC-CBF
20601	EC-CBG
20602	EC-CBH
20603	EC-CBI
20604	EC-CBJ
20605	EC-CBK
20606	EC-CBL
20607	EC-CBM
20811	EC-CFA
20812	EC-CFB
20813	EC-CFC
20814	EC-CFD
20815	EC-CFE
20816	EC-CFF
20817	EC-CFG
20818	EC-CFH
20819	EC-CFI
20820	EC-CFJ
20821	EC-CFK
20974	EC-CID
20975	EC-CIE
21609	EC-DCC
21610	EC-DCD
21611	EC-DCE
21777	EC-DDU
21778	EC-DDV
21779	EC-DDX
21780	EC-DDY
21781	EC-DDZ

EI- Eire

20580	EI-BRD
20710	EI-BRF

EL- Liberia

18892	EL-AIY
18895	EL-AIZ
18253	EL-GOL

EP- Iran

19011	EP-AMU
19314	EP-AMV
19557	EP-GDS
19171	EP-IRA
19172	EP-IRB
19816	EP-IRC
19817	EP-IRD
20945	EP-IRP
20946	EP-IRR
20947	EP-IRS
21078	EP-IRT
21079	EP-IRU
19557	EP-MRP
18363	EP-PLN
18363	EP-SHP

ET- Ethiopia

22759	ET-AHK
21978	ET-AHL
21979	ET-AHM

F- France

19543	F-BOJA
19544	F-BOJB
19545	F-BOJC
19546	F-BOJD
19861	F-BOJE
19862	F-BOJF
19863	F-BPJG
19864	F-BPJH
19865	F-BPJI
20075	F-BPJJ
20202	F-BPJK
20203	F-BPJL
20204	F-BPJM
20409	F-BPJN
20410	F-BPJO
20411	F-BPJP
20470	F-BPJQ
20538	F-BPJR
20539	F-BPJS
20540	F-BPJT
19683	F-BPJU
19684	F-BPJV
22081	F-GCDA
22082	F-GCDB
22083	F-GCDC
22084	F-GCDD
22085	F-GCDE
22287	F-GCDF
22288	F-GCDG
22289	F-GCDH
22290	F-GCDI
20609	F-GCGQ
22608	F-GCM/
22609	F-GCMX

G- United Kingdom

18879	G-BAEF
18877	G-BAFZ
18878	G-BAJW
19281	G-BCDA
19279	G-BDAN
19620	G-BEGZ
19249	G-BFGM
19251	G-BFGN
21676	G-BHNE
21438	G-BHNF
21349	G-BHVT
19619	G-BIUR
21055	G-BKAG
20328	G-BKCG
20710	G-BMLP
21056	G-NROA

HC- Ecuador

22078	HC-BHM
20513	HC-BIB
20328	HC-BIC
19691	HC-BLE
19692	HC-BLF
19596	HC-BLJ
20328	HC-BLV

HI- Dominican Republic

20426	HI-212
21036	HI-242
19505	HI-312
21021	HI-452

HK- Colombia

19524	HK-1271
19525	HK-1272
19529	HK-1273
19303	HK-1337
19662	HK-1400
19663	HK-1401
18999	HK-1716
18993	HK-1717
19035	HK-1803
19037	HK-1804
21343	HK-2151X
21344	HK-2152X
18874	HK-2420X
18876	HK-2420X
18875	HK-2421X
18876	HK-2422X
19099	HK-2474
22474	HK-2474
19094	HK-2475
22475	HK-2475
19102	HK-2476
22476	HK-2476
18281	HK-2541
18994	HK-2559X
18996	HK-2560X
18287	HK-2604
20217	HK-2605X
19815	HK-2637X
18282	HK-2705
18252	HK-2717
19299	HK-2717
18321	HK-2833

19005	HK-2845				
19007	HK-2846				
18896	HK-2957X				
19249	HK-2960X				
18895	HK-3133X				
19122	HK-3151X				
18877	HK-3201X				
18845	HK-3203X				
18814	HK-3229X				
19127	HK-727				

HL South Korea

18875	HL7307
18874	HL7308
18876	HL7309
18321	HL7336
18323	HL7337
20435	HL7348
20468	HL7349
20469	HL7350
20466	HL7355
20725	HL7366
20571	HL7367

HP- Panama

19815	HP-1001
19110	HP-1063
18894	HP-500A
18920	HP-619
18951	HP-620
18951	HP-620
19280	HP-661

HR- Honduras

18823	HR-SHE
18919	HR-SHF

HZ- Saudi Arabia

19620	HZ-AMH
21460	HZ-DA5
20228	HZ-GP2
20228	HZ-GRP
19987	HZ-HE4
22968	HZ-HR3
22968	HZ-RH3
18365	HZ-TA1
19006	HZ-TFA

I- Italy

21264	I-DIRA
21268	I-DIRB
21269	I-DIRC
21661	I-DIRD
21662	I-DIRF
21663	I-DIRG
21265	I-DIRI
21270	I-DIRJ
21664	I-DIRL
22052	I-DIRM
22053	I-DIRN
21266	I-DIRO
22165	I-DIRP
22166	I-DIRQ
22167	I-DIRR
22168	I-DIRS
22702	I-DIRT
21267	I-DIRU

J2- Djibouti

19135	J2-KAD

JA Japan

18821	JA8301
18822	JA8302
18823	JA8303
18919	JA8305
18920	JA8306
18874	JA8307
18875	JA8308
18876	JA8309
18877	JA8310
18878	JA8311
18879	JA8312
19138	JA8314
19139	JA8315
18951	JA8316
18952	JA8317
19279	JA8318
19280	JA8319
19281	JA8320
19557	JA8321
19282	JA8325
19283	JA8326
20078	JA8327
20079	JA8328
20435	JA8328
20436	JA8329
20468	JA8330
20469	JA8331
20466	JA8332
20467	JA8333
20509	JA8334
20285	JA8335
20286	JA8336
20510	JA8337
20568	JA8338
20569	JA8339
20570	JA8340
20571	JA8341
20572	JA8342
20573	JA8343
20573	JA8344
20724	JA8345
20725	JA8346
20726	JA8347
20727	JA8348
20728	JA8349
20876	JA8350
20877	JA8351
20878	JA8352
21455	JA8353
21456	JA8354
21474	JA8355
20564	JA8418
20565	JA8419
20566	JA8420
20567	JA8421

JY- Jordan

20885	JY-ADR
20886	JY-ADU
21021	JY-ADV
22268	JY-AFT
22269	JY-AFU
22270	JY-AFV
22271	JY-AFW
18934	JY-AHS
18934	JY-HMH
22362	JY-HNH

LV- Argentina

21457	LV-MCD
21688	LV-MIM
21689	LV-MIN
21690	LV-MIO
21823	LV-ODY
22603	LV-OLN
22604	LV-OLO
22605	LV-OLP
22606	LV-OLR

LX- Luxembourg

21853	LX-MJM
21853	LX-MMM

N United States

19197	N101FE
19193	N102FE
19199	N103FE
19198	N104FE
19194	N105FE
19122	N105RK
19201	N106FE
19202	N107FE
19204	N108FE
19205	N109FE
19254	N10XY
19253	N110AC
19806	N110FE
21010	N111AK
19253	N111EK
19890	N111FE
19894	N113FE
19527	N114FE
19814	N115FE
20327	N115TA
20248	N11650
20249	N11651
19298	N116FE
20328	N116TA
19299	N117FE
20513	N117TA
20513	N117TA
19134	N1186Z
18323	N1187Z
19300	N118FE
19301	N119FE
19356	N120FE
19357	N121FE
19358	N122FE
19558	N12301
19559	N12302
19560	N12303
19561	N12304
19562	N12305
19563	N12306
19564	N12307
19565	N12308
19359	N123FE
18821	N124
18821	N124AS
18821	N124AS
19360	N124FE
19717	N125FE
19718	N126FE
19176	N127
21930	N1273E
21971	N1279E
19719	N127FE
2172	N1280E
19826	N12826
19827	N12827
21971	N129FE
19720	N128FE
20879	N128NA
21972	N1290E
22078	N1293E
20880	N129NA
19721	N130FE
19722	N131FE
19850	N132FE
20465	N1335B
19851	N133FE
19852	N134FE
19527	N1355B
19853	N135FE
19855	N136FE
18814	N149FN
19166	N150FN
18805	N151FN
19167	N152FN
18846	N153FN
18815	N154FN
18897	N15512
18943	N156FN
18804	N157FN
18812	N158FN
18942	N160FN
18850	N1631
18858	N1632
19249	N1633
19250	N1634
19251	N1635
19252	N1636
19595	N1637
19596	N1638
19444	N1639
19445	N1640
19446	N1641
19447	N1642
19448	N1643
19449	N1644
20139	N1645
20140	N1646
20141	N1647
19994	N1648
19995	N1649
18936	N16764
18361	N16765
18364	N16766
18365	N16767
18363	N16768
18959	N1727T
19860	N1728T
20525	N1779B
20552	N1779B
20764	N1779B
20217	N1780B
20286	N1780B
20432	N1780B
19524	N1781B
19525	N1781B
19526	N1781B
19527	N1781B
20243	N1781B
20421	N1781B
20426	N1781B
20463	N1781B
20464	N1781B
20465	N1781B
20468	N1781B
20469	N1781B
20540	N1781B
20244	N1782B
20245	N1783B
18464	N1784B
19994	N1784B
19995	N1785B
20430	N1785B
20753	N1785B
22076	N1786B
22158	N1786B
20596	N1786B
20553	N1787B
20595	N1787B
20790	N1787B
21264	N1787B
20540	N1788B
20568	N1788B
20595	N1788B
20596	N1788B
20597	N1788B
20598	N1788B
20599	N1788B
20603	N1788B
20606	N1788B
20607	N1788B
20600	N1789B
20539	N1790B
20572	N1790B
20592	N1791B
19173	N18476
18361	N18477
18364	N18478
19174	N18479
18741	N18480
18893	N188CL
20739	N189CB
19130	N1901
19131	N1902
19132	N1903
19180	N1905
19181	N1906
19182	N1907
19183	N1908
19184	N1909
19385	N1910
20822	N191CB
19386	N1928
19387	N1929
19388	N1930
19389	N1931
19390	N1932
19428	N1933
19429	N1934
19430	N1935
19431	N1955
19432	N1956
19833	N1957
19834	N1958
19835	N1959
19836	N1962
19837	N1963
19838	N1964
19839	N1965
20044	N1969
18426	N1970
18427	N1971
18428	N1972
18429	N1973
18430	N1974
18431	N1975
18432	N1976
18433	N1977
18434	N1978
18435	N1979
18436	N1980
18437	N1981
18438	N1982
18439	N1983
18440	N1984
18441	N1985
18442	N1986
18443	N1987
18444	N1988
18445	N1989
18446	N1990
18447	N1991
18448	N1992
18449	N1993
18450	N1994
18900	N1995
18901	N1996
19128	N1997
19129	N1998
19262	N199AM
18998	N1CC
21930	N200AV
22924	N201FE
22154	N201US
21931	N202AV
22155	N202US
22474	N203AV
22925	N203FE
22543	N203US
22475	N204AV
22926	N204FE
22544	N204US
22476	N205AV
22927	N205FE
22392	N205US
22928	N206FE
22393	N206US
22929	N207FE
21699	N207UP
20302	N207US
22930	N208FE
21701	N208UP
20303	N208US
22931	N209FE
21698	N209UP
22932	N210FE
21697	N210UP
22933	N211FE
21700	N211UP
22934	N212FE
21392	N212UP
22935	N213FE
21341	N213UP
21342	N214UP
22936	N215FE
22937	N216FE
22938	N217FE
21101	N218FE
21102	N219FE
18990	N21UC
20934	N220FE
20764	N221FE
20765	N222FE
20766	N223FE
20533	N228G
19524	N2471
18990	N2471A
19525	N2472
20657	N24728
19526	N2473
19527	N2474
19528	N2475
19173	N2476
19970	N251US
19971	N252US
19972	N253US
19973	N254US
19974	N255US
19975	N256US
20658	N25729
19976	N257US
19977	N258US
19978	N259US
19979	N260US
19980	N261US
19981	N262US
19982	N263US
19983	N264US
18370	N26565
19984	N265US
19985	N266US
21348	N26729
20289	N267US
20475	N26879
20476	N2688Z
19318	N2689E
19319	N2689S
20290	N268US
20291	N269US
19176	N27
18367	N2703J
20292	N270US
22003	N271AF
20293	N271US
19244	N2727
22004	N272AF
20294	N272US
22005	N273AF
20295	N273US
22091	N274AF
20296	N274US
20548	N274WC
22092	N275AF
21154	N275US
20549	N275WC
22155	N276US
20550	N276WC
19176	N2777
21356	N277US
21157	N278US
21158	N279US
18859	N27KA
20263	N2801W
20264	N2802W
20265	N2803W
20266	N2804W
20267	N2805W
20268	N2806W
20311	N2807W
20579	N2807W
20312	N2808W
20580	N2808W
20313	N2809W
20581	N2809W
21159	N280US
20314	N2810W
20648	N2810W
20649	N2811W
20868	N2812W
20869	N2813W
20870	N2814W
20871	N2815W
20872	N2816W
20873	N2817W
20874	N2818W
21057	N2819W
21160	N281US
21058	N2820W
21059	N2821W
21327	N2822W
21328	N2823W
21329	N2824W
21330	N2825W
21331	N2826W
21392	N2827W
21393	N2828W
21481	N2829W
21161	N282US
21484	N282WA
19150	N283AT
21322	N283US
21485	N283WA
19151	N284AT
21323	N284US
21697	N284WA
19152	N285AT
21324	N285US

Boeing 727 Cross-reference index

19153	N286AT
21325	N286US
21698	N286WA
18805	N287AT
21375	N287US
21699	N287WA
21376	N288US
21700	N288WA
18942	N289AT
21377	N289US
21701	N289WA
18320	N28KA
21510	N290AS
18812	N290AT
18943	N290AT
21378	N290US
22108	N290WA
20045	N2913
20046	N2914
20143	N2915
21511	N291AS
21379	N291US
22109	N291WA
21458	N292AS
21503	N292US
22110	N292WA
19534	N293AS
21348	N293AS
21504	N293US
22111	N293WA
22146	N294AS
21505	N294US
22112	N294WA
22147	N295AS
21506	N295US
22532	N295WA
19304	N2969G
19137	N2969V
21459	N296AS
21788	N296US
22533	N296WA
20659	N29730
18897	N2977G
19305	N2979G
21608	N297AS
19391	N297BN
21789	N297US
22534	N297WA
19251	N29895
21426	N298AS
19392	N298BN
22152	N298US
21427	N299AS
19393	N299BN
22153	N299US
18803	N29KA
19006	N2CC
18856	N300AA
19394	N300BN
18998	N300DK
19395	N301BN
19242	N302BN
18897	N303BN
22005	N304AS
20217	N304BN
22091	N305AS
18794	N305BN
21997	N306AS
18795	N306BN
22000	N307AS
18796	N307BN
22002	N308AS
19827	N308BN
21947	N309AS
19808	N309BN
18857	N30KA
21948	N310AS
19008	N310BN
19012	N311BN
18992	N314AS
18992	N314PA
18993	N315PA
18994	N316AS
18994	N316PA
18995	N317PA
19536	N3182B
18996	N318AS
18996	N318PA
18997	N319PA
18856	N31KA
18998	N320AS
20533	N320HG
18998	N320PA
18999	N321PA
21364	N322AS
21365	N323AS
19005	N323PA
19006	N324AS
19006	N324PA
19618	N3254D
19007	N325PA
19035	N326PA
20385	N32716
20386	N32717
20387	N32718
20388	N32719
19846	N32720
20463	N32721
20464	N32722
20465	N32723
20654	N32724
20655	N32725
19036	N327PA
19037	N328PA
19557	N329K
19038	N329PA
19038	N329QS
19134	N339PA
18936	N33UT
19135	N340PA
19136	N341PA
19148	N341TC
19137	N342PA
19038	N349PA
19257	N355PA
19257	N355QS
19258	N356PA
19258	N356QS
19259	N357PA
19259	N357QS
19260	N358PA
19005	N358QS
19261	N359PA
19007	N359QS
18942	N3605
18943	N3606
19262	N360PA
21849	N361PA
21850	N362PA
22535	N363PA
22536	N364PA
22537	N365PA
22538	N366PA
22539	N367PA
22540	N368PA
22541	N369PA
22542	N370PA
20248	N371PA
19245	N3727
20249	N372PA
20678	N373PA
20679	N374PA
20875	N375PA
20437	N384PS
19818	N388PA
19819	N389PA
19394	N3946A
19854	N40
20327	N4002M
21144	N400DA
19149	N400RG
21091	N40104
21269	N40133
20392	N401BN
21145	N401DA
20393	N402BN
21146	N402DA
20394	N403BN
21147	N403DA
18329	N40481
18330	N40482
18331	N40483
18791	N40484
18332	N40485
18848	N40486
18849	N40487
18852	N40488
18854	N40489
18860	N40490
20302	N404BN
21148	N404DA
20303	N405BN
21149	N405DA
19991	N406BN
21150	N406DA
19992	N407BN
21151	N407DA
19993	N408BN
21152	N408DA
20162	N409BN
21153	N409DA
18741	N40AF
20608	N410BN
21222	N410DA
20609	N411BN
21223	N411DA
20610	N412BN
21232	N412DA
20611	N413BN
21233	N413DA
19206	N413EX
20612	N414BN
21256	N414DA
18899	N414EX
20613	N415BN
21257	N415DA
18945	N415EX
20729	N416BN
21258	N416DA
19287	N416EX
20730	N417BN
21259	N417DA
19290	N417EX
20731	N418BN
21271	N418DA
18946	N418EX
20732	N419BN
21272	N419DA
18947	N419EX
20733	N420BN
21273	N420DA
19102	N420EX
20734	N421BN
21274	N421DA
19099	N421EX
20735	N422BN
19094	N422EX
20736	N423BN
19314	N423EX
19282	N4245S
20737	N424BN
20042	N424EX
20738	N425BN
19095	N425EX
20772	N426BN
19089	N426EX
20773	N427BN
19090	N427EX
20774	N428BN
19097	N428EX
20775	N429BN
19100	N429EX
20837	N430BN
19101	N430EX
20838	N431BN
19103	N431EX
20839	N432BN
19867	N432EX
20840	N433BN
19868	N433EX
21041	N434BN
18898	N434EX
21042	N435BN
19288	N435EX
21043	N436BN
19289	N436EX
21044	N437BN
21045	N438BN
21118	N439BN
21119	N440BN
21242	N441BN
21243	N442BN
20049	N44316
21244	N443BN
21245	N444BN
19665	N444CM
19987	N444SA
21246	N445BN
21247	N446BN
21248	N447BN
21249	N448BN
21363	N449BN
18366	N44R
19242	N4509
21364	N450BN
21365	N451BN
21366	N452BN
20634	N452DA
21394	N453BN
20635	N453DA
19665	N45498
21395	N454BN
20636	N454DA
19793	N4555W
18282	N4556W
21461	N455BN
20637	N455DA
19597	N4564U
21462	N456BN
20638	N456DA
21463	N457BN
20639	N457DA
19010	N4585L
21464	N458BN
20640	N458DA
21465	N459BN
20641	N459DA
18843	N4602D
21466	N460BN
20642	N460DA
18910	N460US
18811	N4610
18812	N4611
18813	N4612
18814	N4613
18815	N4614
18816	N4615
18817	N4616
18845	N4617
18846	N4618
18847	N4619
21488	N461BN
20643	N461DA
18797	N461US
18797	N461US
19165	N4620
19166	N4621
19167	N4622
21489	N462BN
20644	N462DA
18798	N462US
18798	N462US
21490	N463BN
20645	N463DA
18799	N463US
18799	N463US
21491	N464BN
20646	N464DA
18800	N464US
21492	N465BN
20647	N465DA
18801	N465US
21493	N466BN
20743	N466DA
18802	N466US
21529	N467BN
20744	N467DA
18803	N467US
21530	N468BN
20745	N468DA
18804	N468US
21531	N469BN
20746	N469DA
18805	N469US
21532	N470BN
20747	N470DA
18806	N470US
19135	N47142
21669	N471BN
20748	N471DA
18807	N471US
19246	N4727P
21670	N472BN
20749	N472DA
18942	N472US
19450	N4730
19451	N4731
19452	N4732
19453	N4733
19454	N4734
19455	N4735
19456	N4736
19457	N4737
19458	N4738
19459	N4739
21996	N473BN
20750	N473DA
18943	N473US
19460	N4740
19461	N4741
19462	N4742
19463	N4743
19464	N4744
19465	N4745
19466	N4746
19467	N4747
19468	N4748
19469	N4749
21997	N474BN
20751	N474DA
18944	N474US
19470	N4750
19471	N4751
19472	N4752
19473	N4753
19474	N4754
21998	N475BN
20752	N475DA
19121	N475US
21999	N476BN
20753	N476DA
19122	N476US
22000	N477BN
20754	N477DA
19123	N477US
22001	N478BN
20755	N478DA
19124	N478US
22002	N479BN
20756	N479DA
19125	N479US
21946	N48054
21082	N48054
22003	N480BN
20860	N480DA
19126	N480US
22004	N481BN
20861	N481DA
22005	N482BN
20862	N482DA
18331	N483AS
22091	N483BN
20863	N483DA
22092	N484BN
20864	N484DA
22093	N485BN
20865	N485DA
22094	N486BN
20866	N486DA
22095	N487BN
20867	N487DA
18852	N488AS
22096	N488BN
21018	N488DA
19867	N488US
22097	N489BN
21019	N489DA
19868	N489US
22098	N490BN
21020	N490DA
18898	N490US
22099	N491BN
21060	N491DA
18899	N491US
22100	N492BN
21061	N492DA
18945	N492US
22101	N493BN
21062	N493DA
18946	N493US
22102	N494BN
21074	N494DA
18947	N494US
22103	N495BN
21075	N495DA
19206	N495US
19092	N495WC
22104	N496BN
21076	N496DA
19287	N496US
19098	N496WC
22417	N497BN
21077	N497DA
19288	N497US
19096	N497WC
22418	N498BN
21142	N498DA
19289	N498US
19091	N498WC
19093	N498WC
20162	N499BN
22419	N499BN
21143	N499DA
19290	N499US
18951	N500JJ
21303	N501DA
21304	N502DA
19391	N502RA
21305	N503DA
19392	N503RA
21306	N504DA
19395	N504RA
19173	N5055
21307	N505DA
20115	N505T
21308	N506DA
18936	N5073L
21309	N507DA
21310	N508DA
19174	N5092
19175	N5093
21311	N509DA
18951	N50AJ
21312	N510DA
21313	N511DA
20634	N511PE
21314	N512DA
20635	N512PE
21315	N513DA
20636	N513PE
21430	N514DA
20637	N514PE
21431	N515DA
20638	N515PE
21432	N516DA
20639	N516PE
21433	N517DA
20640	N517PE
21469	N518DA
20641	N518PE
21470	N519DA
20642	N519PE
21471	N520DA
20643	N520PE
21472	N521DA
20644	N521PE
21582	N522DA
20645	N522PE
19828	N52309
19829	N52310
19830	N52311
19831	N52312
19832	N52313
21583	N523DA
20646	N523PE
21584	N524DA
21585	N525DA
21586	N526DA
20370	N526PC
21587	N527DA
19665	N527PC
21426	N528D
21702	N528DA
21427	N528E
19597	N528PC
19683	N528PS
20327	N529AC
21703	N529DA
19684	N529PS
21813	N530DA
19618	N530EJ
19685	N530PS
21814	N531DA
19619	N531EJ
19686	N531PS

c/n	reg	c/n	reg	c/n	reg	c/n	reg	c/n	reg
22045	N532DA	20366	N564PS	18298	N7006U	22468	N712AA	21557	N7279U
19687	N532PS	21119	N565PE	18299	N7007U	22020	N712RC	20734	N727AA
22046	N533DA	21242	N566PE	18300	N7008U	22469	N713AA	19807	N727AL
19688	N533PS	21243	N567PE	18301	N7009U	22021	N713RC	20764	N727BE
22047	N534DA	21244	N568PE	18302	N7010U	22344	N714RC	18849	N727CD
19689	N534PS	21245	N569PE	18303	N7011U	22470	N715AA	18371	N727CH
22048	N535DA	22270	N57001	18304	N7012U	22019	N715RC	18933	N727CH
20161	N535PS	21246	N570PE	18305	N7013U	20608	N716AA	18894	N727CR
22049	N536DA	21264	N571PE	18306	N7014U	22021	N716RC	19261	N727DG
20162	N536PS	21265	N572PE	18307	N7015U	20610	N717AA	19318	N727EC
20438	N536PS	21266	N573PE	18308	N7016U	20611	N718AA	19500	N727EV
22073	N537DA	21267	N574PE	18309	N7017U	22344	N718RC	19136	N727GB
20163	N537PS	21268	N575PE	18310	N7018U	20612	N719AA	19835	N727HC
22076	N538DA	21269	N576PE	18311	N7019U	22490	N719RC	19011	N727JE
20164	N538PS	19401	N577JB	22459	N701AA	20613	N720AA	2021	N727KA
22385	N539DA	21270	N577PE	19310	N701EV	19618	N720JE	20489	N727KS
20165	N539PS	21661	N578PE	18312	N7020U	22491	N720RC	19137	N727LJ
22386	N540DA	21662	N579PE	18313	N7021U	21849	N720ZK	19313	N727M
20166	N540PS	21663	N580PE	18314	N7022U	20729	N721AA	19318	N727MB
22387	N541DA	22052	N581PE	18315	N7023U	18897	N721EV	19195	N727PL
20167	N541PS	22053	N582PE	18316	N7024U	18843	N721JE	20228	N727RE
22391	N542DA	22165	N583PE	18317	N7025U	22687	N721MF	19261	N727RF
20168	N542PS	22166	N584PE	18318	N7026U	18997	N721PC	21656	N727RW
22232	N54326	22167	N585PE	18319	N7027U	22492	N721RC	18998	N727S
20233	N54326	22168	N586PE	18320	N7028U	21200	N721RW	19260	N727SG
22234	N54327	19124	N604NA	18321	N7029U	21850	N721ZK	19122	N727TA
20306	N54328	19535	N60FM	22460	N702AA	20730	N722AA	19503	N727TG
20307	N54329	18934	N62219	18322	N7030U	19136	N722EV	18367	N727UD
20308	N54330	20048	N64315	18323	N7031U	19807	N722JE	19262	N727WE
20309	N54331	20052	N64319	18324	N7032U	21201	N722RW	19249	N727ZV
20310	N54332	20053	N64320	18325	N7033U	20731	N723AA	19119	N728
20460	N54333	20054	N64321	18326	N7034U	19137	N723EV	21558	N728OU
20461	N54334	20055	N64322	18327	N7035U	18896	N723JE	19120	N7281
20462	N54335	20098	N64323	18328	N7036U	21202	N723RW	21559	N7281U
20490	N54336	20099	N64324	18329	N7037U	19109	N724EV	19243	N7282
20491	N54337	20844	N64339	18330	N7038U	19010	N724JE	21560	N7282U
20843	N54338	21633	N64646	18331	N7039U	19135	N724PL	21561	N7283U
20845	N54340	21634	N64647	22461	N703AA	21457	N724RW	19244	N7284
20846	N54341	20656	N66726	19311	N703EV	21398	N7251U	21562	N7284U
21628	N54341	20660	N66731	18332	N7040U	21399	N7252U	21563	N7285U
20847	N54342	20661	N66732	18848	N7041U	21400	N7253U	19245	N7286
21629	N54342	20662	N66733	18849	N7042U	21401	N7254U	21564	N7286U
20848	N54343	20663	N66734	18850	N7043U	21402	N7255U	19246	N7287
21630	N54343	19475	N6800	18851	N7044U	21403	N7256U	21565	N7287U
21631	N54344	19476	N6801	18852	N7045U	21404	N7257U	19497	N7288
20850	N54345	19477	N6802	18853	N7046U	21405	N7258U	21566	N7288U
21632	N54345	19478	N6803	18854	N7047U	21406	N7259U	19499	N7289
20851	N54346	19479	N6804	18855	N7048U	20732	N725AA	21567	N7289U
21967	N54348	19480	N6805	18856	N7049U	19665	N725AL	20735	N728AA
20853	N54348	19481	N6806	18857	N7050U	19112	N725EV	20765	N728BE
21968	N54349	19482	N6807	18858	N7051U	19793	N725JE	18794	N728EV
20854	N54349	19483	N6808	18859	N7052U	19191	N725PL	21741	N728RW
21969	N54350	19484	N6809	18860	N7053U	21502	N725RW	20710	N728ZV
20855	N54350	19485	N6810	18861	N7054U	21407	N7260U	19500	N7290
21983	N54351	19486	N6811	18862	N7055U	21408	N7261U	21568	N7290U
20856	N54351	19487	N6812	18863	N7056U	21409	N7262U	21569	N7291U
21984	N54352	19488	N6813	18864	N7057U	21410	N7263U	19501	N7292
20857	N54352	19489	N6814	18865	N7058U	21411	N7264U	21570	N7292U
21985	N54353	19490	N6815	18866	N7059U	21412	N7265U	19534	N7293
20858	N54353	19491	N6816	22462	N705AA	21413	N7266U	21571	N7293U
21986	N54354	19492	N6817	19009	N705EV	21414	N7267U	19535	N7294
20859	N54354	19493	N6818	18867	N7060U	21415	N7268U	21572	N7294U
20852	N54367	19494	N6819	18868	N7061U	21416	N7269U	19532	N7295
22392	N543DA	19495	N6820	18869	N7062U	20733	N726AA	21573	N7295U
22493	N544DA	19496	N6821	18870	N7063U	19666	N726AL	19533	N7296
20367	N544PS	19700	N6822	18871	N7064U	19311	N726EV	21574	N7296U
18896	N545BF	19701	N6823	18872	N7065U	19815	N726JE	21892	N7297U
22494	N545DA	19702	N6824	19079	N7066U	19192	N726PL	21893	N7298U
20169	N545PS	19703	N6825	19080	N7067U	21655	N726RW	21894	N7299U
22677	N546DA	19704	N6826	19081	N7068U	19109	N7270	20736	N729AA
19526	N5473	20180	N6827	19082	N7069U	18368	N72700	20766	N729BE
19527	N5474	20181	N6828	22463	N706AA	18464	N72700	19116	N729EV
19524	N5475	20182	N6829	19813	N70708	18897	N7270C	21742	N729RW
20250	N547PS	20183	N6830	19083	N7070U	19391	N7270F	20737	N730AA
20251	N548PS	20184	N6831	19084	N7071U	19536	N7270L	19110	N730EV
20252	N549PS	20185	N6832	19085	N7072U	20250	N7270Q	21823	N730RW
20678	N550PS	20186	N6833	19086	N7073U	21417	N7270U	20738	N731AA
20772	N551PE	20187	N6834	19087	N7074U	19110	N7271	19113	N731EV
20679	N551PS	20188	N6835	21366	N70755	19392	N7271F	19808	N732AL
20706	N552NA	20189	N6836	19088	N7075U	19243	N7271P	21247	N73751
20773	N552PE	20190	N6837	19140	N7076U	20251	N7271Q	19089	N7401U
20706	N552PS	20191	N6838	19141	N7077U	21418	N7271U	19090	N7402U
20707	N553NA	20192	N6839	19142	N7078U	19111	N7272	19091	N7403U
20774	N553PE	20193	N6841	19143	N7079U	19393	N7272F	19092	N7404U
20707	N553PS	20241	N6842	22464	N707AA	20253	N7272Q	19093	N7405U
20775	N554PE	18297	N68644	19144	N7080U	21419	N7272U	19094	N7406U
20875	N554PS	18360	N68649	19145	N7081U	19112	N7273	19095	N7407U
20370	N555BN	18295	N68650	19146	N7082U	19394	N7273F	19096	N7408U
20837	N555PE	19504	N690WA	19147	N7083U	21420	N7273U	19097	N7409U
21512	N555PS	19505	N691WA	19148	N7084U	19113	N7274	19252	N740EV
20838	N556PE	19506	N692WA	19149	N7085U	19395	N7274F	21824	N740RW
21513	N556PS	19507	N693WA	19150	N7086U	21421	N7274U	19098	N7410U
20839	N557PE	19508	N694WA	19151	N7087U	19114	N7275	19099	N7411U
21691	N557PS	19509	N695WA	19152	N7088U	19995	N7275F	19100	N7412U
20840	N558PE	19987	N696WA	19153	N7089U	21422	N7275U	19101	N7413U
21692	N558PS	20664	N69735	22465	N708AA	19115	N7276	19102	N7414U
21041	N559PE	20665	N69736	19154	N7090U	19991	N7276F	19103	N7415U
21958	N559PS	20667	N69739	19155	N7091U	21423	N7276U	19191	N7416U
19124	N5604	20668	N69740	19156	N7092U	19116	N7277	19192	N7417U
18804	N5607	22250	N69741	19157	N7093U	19992	N7277F	19193	N7418U
18805	N5608	22251	N69742	19158	N7094U	21424	N7277U	19194	N7419U
18806	N5609	18293	N7001U	19159	N7095U	19117	N7278	21951	N741RW
21042	N560PE	18294	N7002U	22466	N709AA	19993	N7278F	19195	N7420U
21043	N561PE	18295	N7003U	22467	N710AA	21425	N7278U	19196	N7421U
21044	N562PE	18791	N7003U	19401	N710EV	19118	N7279	19197	N7422U
21045	N563PE	18296	N7004U	22078	N711GN	19994	N7279F	19198	N7423U
21118	N564PE	18297	N7005U	22019	N711RC	20162	N7279F	19199	N7424U

Boeing 727 Cross-reference index

c/n	Reg	c/n	Reg	c/n	Reg	c/n	Reg
19200	N7425U	22449	N79746	22559	N822EA	21520	N881AA
19201	N7426U	22450	N79748	22560	N823EA	20144	N8825E
19202	N7427U	22451	N79749	22561	N824EA	20145	N8826E
19203	N7428U	22452	N79750	22349	N8278V	20146	N8827E
19204	N7429U	21363	N79754	22167	N8280V	20147	N8828E
21952	N742RW	19169	N797AS	22261	N8284V	20148	N8829E
19205	N7430U	19170	N798AS	22430	N8285V	21521	N882AA
20050	N74317	22432	N801EA	22262	N8286V	20149	N8830E
20051	N74318	22433	N802EA	22271	N8286V	20150	N8831E
19805	N7431U	22434	N803EA	21853	N8290V	20151	N8832E
19806	N7432U	19254	N8043B	22359	N8291V	20152	N8833E
19890	N7433U	20228	N8043E	22374	N8292V	20153	N8834E
19891	N7434U	22435	N804EA	20903	N8293V	20154	N8835E
19892	N7435U	22436	N805EA	21482	N830WA	20379	N8836E
19893	N7436U	22437	N806EA	21826	N831L	20380	N8837E
19894	N7437U	22438	N807EA	19093	N831RV	20381	N8838E
19895	N7438U	22439	N808EA	18902	N831TW	20382	N8839E
21895	N7441U	22440	N809EA	21483	N831WA	21522	N883AA
21896	N7442U	18252	N8101N	19529	N8320	20383	N8840E
21897	N7443U	18253	N8102N	19098	N832RV	20415	N8841E
21898	N7444U	18254	N8103N	18935	N833N	20416	N8842E
21899	N7445U	18255	N8104E	18903	N833TW	20441	N8843E
21900	N7446U	18255	N8104N	18858	N834N	20442	N8844E
21901	N7447U	18256	N8105N	18850	N836N	20443	N8845E
21902	N7448U	18257	N8106N	18802	N837N	20444	N8846E
21903	N7449U	18258	N8107N	18803	N838N	20445	N8847E
21904	N7450U	18259	N8108N	18904	N839TW	20446	N8848E
21905	N7451U	18260	N8109N	18905	N840TW	20447	N8849E
21906	N7452U	22441	N810EA	18324	N841N	21523	N884AA
21907	N7453U	18261	N8110E	18906	N841TW	20448	N8850E
21908	N7454U	18261	N8110N	18907	N842TW	20614	N8851E
21909	N7455U	18262	N8111N	21987	N84355	20615	N8852E
21910	N7456U	18263	N8112N	21988	N84356	20616	N8853E
21911	N7457U	18264	N8113N	21989	N84357	20617	N8855E
21912	N7458U	18265	N8114N	20984	N843AA	20618	N8856E
21913	N7459U	18266	N8115N	20985	N844AA	20619	N8857E
21914	N7460U	18267	N8116N	18755	N844TW	20620	N8858E
21915	N7461U	18268	N8117N	20986	N845AA	20621	N8859E
21916	N7462U	18269	N8118N	18754	N845TW	21524	N885AA
21917	N7463U	18270	N8119N	20987	N846AA	20622	N8860E
21918	N7464U	22548	N811EA	18753	N846TW	20623	N8861E
21919	N7465U	18271	N8120N	20988	N847AA	20624	N8862E
21920	N7466U	18272	N8121N	18752	N847TW	20625	N8863E
21921	N7467U	18273	N8122N	20989	N848AA	20626	N8864E
19319	N750UA	18274	N8123N	18751	N848TW	20627	N8865E
20302	N750VJ	18275	N8124N	20990	N849AA	20628	N8866E
20303	N751VJ	18276	N8125N	18750	N849TW	20823	N8867E
19203	N753AL	18277	N8126N	20991	N850AA	20824	N8869E
19203	N753AS	18278	N8127N	18569	N850TW	21525	N886AA
21953	N760AL	18279	N8128N	20992	N851AA	19510	N88701
21954	N761AL	18280	N8129N	18570	N851TW	19511	N88702
19537	N7620U	22549	N812EA	20993	N852AA	19512	N88703
19538	N7621U	18281	N8130N	18571	N852TW	19513	N88704
19539	N7622U	18282	N8131N	20994	N853AA	19514	N88705
19540	N7623U	18283	N8132N	18572	N853TW	19797	N88706
19541	N7624U	18284	N8133N	20995	N854AA	19798	N88707
19542	N7625U	18285	N8134N	18573	N854TW	19799	N88708
19899	N7626U	18286	N8135N	20996	N855AA	19800	N88709
19900	N7627U	18287	N8136N	20163	N855N	21288	N8870Z
19901	N7628U	18288	N8137N	18574	N855TW	19801	N88710
19902	N7629U	18289	N8138N	20997	N856AA	19802	N88711
19903	N7630U	18290	N8139N	20164	N856N	19803	N88712
19904	N7631U	22550	N813EA	18575	N856TW	19804	N88713
19905	N7632U	18291	N8140N	21084	N857AA	20243	N88714
19906	N7633U	18965	N8141N	20165	N857N	20384	N88715
19907	N7634U	18966	N8142N	18576	N857TW	21289	N8871Z
19908	N7635U	18967	N8143N	21085	N858AA	21290	N8872Z
19909	N7636U	18968	N8144N	20161	N858N	21291	N8873Z
19910	N7637U	18969	N8145N	18577	N858TW	21292	N8874Z
19911	N7638U	18970	N8146N	21086	N859AA	21293	N8875Z
19912	N7639U	18971	N8147N	20366	N859N	21449	N8876Z
19913	N7640U	18972	N8148N	18578	N859TW	19798	N88777
19914	N7641U	18973	N8149N	21087	N860AA	21450	N8877Z
19915	N7642U	22551	N814EA	20166	N860N	21451	N8878Z
20037	N7643U	18974	N8150N	21088	N861AA	21452	N8879Z
20038	N7644U	19298	N8151G	20167	N861N	21526	N887AA
20039	N7645U	19299	N8152G	21089	N862AA	21453	N8880Z
20040	N7646U	19300	N8153G	20568	N862N	21578	N8881Z
20041	N7647U	19301	N8154G	21090	N863AA	21579	N8882Z
19728	N766AS	19302	N8155G	20510	N863N	21580	N8883Z
21248	N76752	19356	N8156G	21369	N864AA	21581	N8884Z
21249	N76753	19357	N8157G	20286	N864N	21854	N8885Z
20512	N767RV	19358	N8158G	21370	N865AA	21855	N8886Z
18360	N77	19359	N8159G	20570	N865N	21856	N8887Z
22162	N770AL	22552	N815EA	21371	N866AA	21857	N8888Z
22163	N771AL	19360	N8160G	20569	N866N	21858	N8889Z
22164	N772AL	19717	N8161G	21372	N867AA	20371	N888VT
22983	N773AL	19718	N8162G	20509	N867N	21859	N8890Z
22984	N774AL	19719	N8163G	21373	N868AA	21860	N8891Z
23014	N775AL	19720	N8164G	20467	N869N	21861	N8892Z
22770	N776AL	19721	N8165G	21374	N869AA	22562	N8893Z
23052	N779AL	19722	N8166G	21382	N870AA	22563	N8894Z
18362	N78	19850	N8167G	20285	N870N	21527	N889AA
21999	N780AL	19851	N8168G	21383	N871AA	19228	N889TW
22001	N781AL	19852	N8169G	21384	N872AA	22006	N890AA
21996	N782AL	22553	N816EA	21385	N873AA	19229	N890TW
21998	N783AL	19853	N8170G	21386	N874AA	22007	N891AA
18360	N78649	19854	N8171G	21387	N875AA	19230	N891TW
20710	N788BR	19855	N8172G	21388	N876AA	22008	N892AA
20112	N7890	19856	N8173G	20903	N87790	19231	N892TW
20113	N7891	19857	N8174G	21389	N877AA	22009	N893AA
20114	N7892	19858	N8175G	20143	N8789R	19232	N893TW
20115	N7893	22554	N817EA	21390	N878AA	22010	N894AA
21608	N791L	22555	N818EA	20240	N8790R	19233	N894TW
22252	N79743	22556	N819EA	20241	N8791R	22011	N895AA
22253	N79744	22557	N820EA	21391	N879AA	20168	N895N
22448	N79745	22558	N821EA	21519	N880AA	19234	N895TW

c/n	Reg
22012	N896AA
20367	N896N
22013	N897AA
22014	N898AA
19620	N898PC
19620	N898PC
22015	N899AA
18935	N90557
18362	N90558
19118	N907UP
19114	N908UP
19115	N909UP
19117	N910UP
19119	N911UP
19244	N912UP
19245	N913UP
19246	N914UP
19533	N915UP
19808	N916UP
19310	N917UP
18741	N91891
19008	N918UP
19012	N919UP
19873	N920UP
19874	N921UP
19231	N922UP
18366	N9233Z
18368	N9234Z
19229	N923UP
19234	N924UP
19230	N925UP
19233	N926UP
20046	N927DS
19232	N927UP
19091	N928UP
19092	N929UP
18892	N92GS
19387	N930FT
19096	N930UP
19390	N931FT
19858	N931UP
19834	N932FT
19856	N932UP
19182	N933FT
19857	N933UP
19430	N934FT
19135	N934UP
19180	N935FT
19836	N936FT
20666	N93738
18847	N937FT
19131	N938FT
19388	N939FT
18893	N93GS
19389	N940FT
20047	N94314
19874	N9515T
19873	N9516T
18895	N95GS
19908	N970PS
19909	N971PS
19910	N972PS
18797	N973PS
19911	N973PS
18798	N974PS
19912	N974PS
18990	N975PS
18799	N976PS
19398	N976PS
19815	N977PS
18800	N977PS
18801	N978PS
20512	N99548

OB- Peru

c/n	Reg
18269	OB-R-1081
18897	OB-R-1115
19116	OB-R-1115
19506	OB-R-1135
19312	OB-R-1141
19306	OB-R-1256
19400	OB-R-1277
19846	OB-R-902

OO- Belgium

c/n	Reg
19011	OO-ATJ
18951	OO-JAA
19400	OO-STA
19402	OO-STB
19401	OO-STC
19403	OO-STD
19987	OO-STE

OY- Denmark

c/n	Reg
20765	OY-SAS
20766	OY-SAT
20764	OY-SAU
20706	OY-SBA
20707	OY-SBB
21438	OY-SBC
21676	OY-SBD
22079	OY-SBE
22080	OY-SBF
22574	OY-SBG

PH- Netherlands

20739	PH-AHB
20822	PH-AHD

PJ- Netherlands Antilles

19506	PJ-BOA

PK- Indonesia

21091	PK-PJP

PP/PT- Brasil

20418	PP-CJE
20419	PP-CJF
20420	PP-CJG
19305	PP-CJH
20421	PP-CJH
19242	PP-CJI
19400	PP-CJJ
18969	PP-CJK
18968	PP-CJL
21348	PP-SMK
21341	PP-SNE
21342	PP-SNF
21345	PP-SNG
21346	PP-SNH
21600	PP-SNI
21601	PP-SNJ
21347	PP-SRK
19310	PP-SRY
19311	PP-SRZ
20422	PP-VLA
20423	PP-VLB
20425	PP-VLD
19666	PP-VLE
20426	PP-VLE
20422	PP-VLF
20423	PP-VLG
20424	PP-VLH
19595	PP-VLQ
19596	PP-VLR
19508	PP-VLS
19250	PP-VLT
19009	PP-VLV
19507	PP-VLW
19136	PT-TCA
19137	PT-TCB
18844	PT-TCC
18744	PT-TCD
18743	PT-TCE
18742	PT-TCF
22425	PT-TCF
19136	PT-TCG
19088	PT-TCH
19140	PT-TCI
19497	PT-TYH
19827	PT-TYI
19393	PT-TYJ
19499	PT-TYK
19501	PT-TYL
19500	PT-TYM
19243	PT-TYN
19116	PT-TYO
19113	PT-TYP
19110	PT-TYQ
18794	PT-TYR
19111	PT-TYS
19112	PT-TYT
19109	PT-TYU

New Zealand

19892	NZ7271
19895	NZ7272
19893	NZ7273

Taiwan

19399	2721
19520	2722
20111	2723
1v818	2724

RP- Philippines

19691	RP-C1240
19692	RP-C1241

SE- Sweden

19691	SE-DDA
19692	SE-DDB
20042	SE-DDC
19313	SE-DDD

SX- Greece

20003	SX-CBA
20004	SX-CBB
20005	SX-CBC
20006	SX-CBD
20201	SX-CBE
19536	SX-CBF

T3- Kiribati

19311	T3-ATB

TC- Turkey

20463	TC-JBA
20463	TC-JBB
20465	TC-JBC
20980	TC-JBF
20981	TC-JBG
20982	TC-JBH
20983	TC-JBJ
21260	TC-JBM
21603	TC-JBR
22992	TC-JCA
22993	TC-JCB
22998	TC-JCE
22999	TC-JCF
21664	TC-JCK

TF- Iceland

19826	TF-FIA
19503	TF-FIE
19826	TF-FLG
19503	TF-FLH
22295	TF-FLI
19619	TF-FLJ
18893	TF-VLS

TG- Guatemala

19302	TG-ALA
19402	TG-AVA
19506	TG-AYA

TI- Costa Rica

21945	TI-LRQ
21349	TI-LRR

TJ- Cameroon

21636	TJ-AAM

TN- Congo

21655	TN-AEB

TS- Tunisia

20545	TS-JHN
20739	TS-JHO
20822	TS-JHP
20948	TS-JHQ
21179	TS-JHR
21234	TS-JHS
21235	TS-JHT
21318	TS-JHU
21319	TS-JHV
21320	TS-JHW

TZ- Mali

19509	TZ-ADR

V8- Brunei

18371	V8-BG1
22362	V8-HM1
18371	V8-UHM

VH- Australia

22641	VH-ANA
22642	VH-ANB
22643	VH-ANE
22644	VH-ANF
18270	VH-LAP
18844	VH-RMD
18743	VH-RME
18744	VH-RMF
21178	VH-RMK
21480	VH-RML
21647	VH-RMM
21695	VH-RMN
22016	VH-RMO
22068	VH-RMP
19253	VH-RMR
20278	VH-RMS
20370	VH-RMT
20548	VH-RMU
20549	VH-RMV
20550	VH-RMW
20551	VH-RMX
20978	VH-RMY
20979	VH-RMZ
20552	VH-TBG
20553	VH-TBH
20554	VH-TBI
20555	VH-TBJ
20950	VH-TBK
20951	VH-TBL
21171	VH-TBM
21479	VH-TBN
21646	VH-TBO
21696	VH-TBP
22017	VH-TBQ
22069	VH-TBR
18741	VH-TJA
18742	VH-TJB
18843	VH-TJC
19254	VH-TJD
20228	VH-TJE
20371	VH-TJF

VR- Bermuda

20371	VR-BAT
18366	VR-BGW
18933	VR-BHK
18370	VR-BHN
19251	VR-BHO
18371	VR-BHP

VR- Cayman Islands

18935	VR-CBA
19282	VR-CBE
19620	VR-CBG
21460	VR-CBQ
18934	VR-CHS
19253	VR-CKL

VR- Jamaica

21105	VR-JMA
21106	VR-JMB
21107	VR-JMC
21108	VR-JMD

VS- Brunei

21010	VS-HB1
18371	VS-UHM

XA- Mexico

20709	XA-CUB
20710	XA-CUE
20780	XA-CUN
20787	XA-DAT
20894	XA-DUI
20895	XA-DUJ
20896	XA-DUK
21071	XA-FID
21072	XA-FIE
20328	XA-GUU
20513	XA-GUV
20513	XA-GUV
21577	XA-HOH
21617	XA-HON
21637	XA-HOV
21638	XA-HOX
21836	XA-IEU
18910	XA-IUP
21837	XA-MEB
21838	XA-MEC
22156	XA-MED
22157	XA-MEE
22158	XA-MEF
18743	XA-MEG
22409	XA-MEH
22410	XA-MEI
22411	XA-MEJ
22412	XA-MEK
22413	XA-MEL
22414	XA-MEM
18797	XA-MEN
18800	XA-MEP
22424	XA-MEQ
22425	XA-MER
22676	XA-MXA
22661	XA-MXA
22662	XA-MXB
22663	XA-MXC
22664	XA-MXD
21457	XA-MXE
22677	XA-MXF
21346	XA-MXF
22678	XA-MXG
21600	XA-MXG
22679	XA-MXH
22680	XA-MXI
22681	XA-MXJ
22682	XA-MXK
18911	XA-SEA
18821	XA-SEB
19255	XA-SEJ
18912	XA-SEK
19256	XA-SEL
19427	XA-SEM
19398	XA-SEN
18908	XA-SER
18909	XA-SEU
20217	XA-SEW
20432	XA-TAA
20433	XA-TAB
20434	XA-TAC
20524	XA-TAY
19815	XA-TUY

XV- Vietnam

19818	XV-NJB
19819	XV-NJC

XY- Burma

19620	XY-ADR

YA- Afghanistan

19690	YA-FAR
20343	YA-FAU
19619	YA-FAW

YI- Iraq

21197	YI-AGK
21198	YI-AGL
21199	YI-AGM
22261	YI-AGQ
22262	YI-AGR
22263	YI-AGS

YK- Syria

21203	YK-AGA
21204	YK-AGB
21205	YK-AGC

YN- Nicaragua

18843	YN-BSQ
18742	YN-BWX
18284	YN-BXW

YU- Yugoslavia

20930	YU-AKA
20931	YU-AKB
21040	YU-AKD
21037	YU-AKE
21038	YU-AKF
21039	YU-AKG
21080	YU-AKH
22393	YU-AKI
22394	YU-AKJ
22665	YU-AKK
22666	YU-AKL
22702	YU-AKM

YV- Venezuela

22043	YV-74C
22044	YV-75C
20394	YV-76C
21457	YV-77C
18800	YV-79C
18326	YV-80C
18327	YV-81C
18325	YV-82C
18853	YV-87C
18855	YV-88C
18851	YV-89C

ZS- South Africa

18892	ZS-DYM
18893	ZS-DYN
18894	ZS-DYO
18895	ZS-DYP
18896	ZS-DYR
19318	ZS-EKW
19319	ZS-EKX
18892	ZS-SBA
18893	ZS-SBB
18894	ZS-SBC
18895	ZS-SBD
18896	ZS-SBE
18818	ZS-SBF
19319	ZS-SBG
20475	ZS-SBH
20476	ZS-SBI

Military operated

Belgium

19402	CB-01
19403	CB-02

Chile

19196	901

Iran

19557	1002

Mexico

19123	TP-01
19121	TP-02
18712	TP-10501
19427	TP-10502
18908	TP-10503
18909	TP-10504
18911	TP-10505

New Zealand

19892	NZ7271
19895	NZ7272
19893	NZ7273

Taiwan

19399	2721
19520	2722
20111	2723
19818	2724

United States

18811	83-4610
18813	83-4612
18816	83-4615
18817	83-4616
18362	84-0193

Yugoslavia

21080	14301
21040	14302

BOEING 737

Short-range commercial airliner with wing-mounted twin Pratt & Whitney JT8D turbofans. A smaller brother to the 727, with accomodation for 115 passengers, the 737-100 first flew on 9 April 1967 and entered service with Lufthansa on 10 February 1968. This was followed a year later by the larger 737-200 for 130 passengers, also available in 200C convertible and 200QC quick-change variants, and new technology produced advanced versions in later years. The latest model is the 737-300 which first flew on 24 February 1984. It has a lengthened fuselage for a maximum 149 passengers, and new-generation CFMI CFM56-3 turbofans. Versions currently available are the 737-200 and 737-300 with 1278 aircraft of all models delivered and a further 403 on order. Current production rates are one and a half per month for the 737-200 and eleven per month for the 737-300.

Dimensions :	Wing span: 93ft 0in (28.35m) Length: 94ft 0in (28.65m) Height: 37ft 0in (11.28m) (100)
	Wing span: 93ft 0in (28.35m) Length: 100ft 0in (30.48m) Height: 37ft 0in (11.28m) (200)
	Wing span: 94ft 9in (28.90m) Length: 109ft 7in (33.40m) Height: 36ft 6in (11.10m) (300)
	Powerplants : Two Pratt & Whitney JT8D-7, JT8D-9 or JT8D-15 turbofans (100/200), two CFMI CFM56-3B1 or CFM56-3B2 turbofans (300)
Performance :	Max cruising speed 526 knots (974km/h) (100) Range: with max payload 1,598nm (2,960km) (100)
	Max cruising speed 488 knots (903km/h) (200) Range: with max payload 1,550nm (2,868km) (200)
	Max cruising speed 491 knots (897km/h) (300) Range: with max payload 1,580nm (2,923km) (300)
Accommodation:	115 passengers (100), 130 passengers (200), 149 passengers (300)
Manufacturer :	Boeing - PO Box 3707, Seattle, Washington 98124, USA
	Telephone: (206) 237-2121 Telex: 32 94 30

BOEING

C/N	Registration	Owner/Operator	Series	First Flight	Delivery	Remarks
19013	N2282C	Boeing	130	13/MAY/67		
	D-ABEA	Lufthansa			29/DEC/67	
	D-ABEA	Asia Aviation Services			NOV/82	
	N701AW	America West			06/APR/84	
19014	N2286C	Boeing	130	12/JUN/67		
	D-ABEB	Lufthansa			29/DEC/67	
	B-2621	Far Eastern Air Transport			20/AUG/81	
19015	N2289C	Boeing	130	05/JUL/67		
	D-ABEC	Lufthansa			28/DEC/67	
	D-ABEC	Asia Aviation Services			NOV/82	
	N702AW	America West			06/APR/84	
19016	D-ABED	Lufthansa	130	20/JAN/68	02/FEB/68	
	D-ABED	Far Eastern Air Transport			FEB/82	
	YV-406C	Asia Aviation Services			22/NOV/82	
	YV-406C	SAVAR			22/NOV/82	Leased
	YV-406C	Asia Aviation Services			JUN/83	
	N703AW	America West			06/APR/84	
19017	D-ABEF	Lufthansa	130	15/FEB/68	29/FEB/68	
	B-2623	Far Eastern Air Transport			14/JUL/81	
19018	D-ABEG	Lufthansa	130	02/MAR/68	12/MAR/68	
	N401PE	People Express			30/MAY/81	
19019	D-ABEH	Lufthansa	130	09/APR/68	25/APR/68	
	N402PE	People Express			19/NOV/81	
19020	D-ABEI	Lufthansa	130	03/APR/68	14/APR/68	
	N403PE	People Express			19/NOV/81	
19021	D-ABEK	Lufthansa	130	20/MAR/68	05/APR/68	
	D-ABEK	Condor			JAN/69	Leased
	D-ABEK	Lufthansa			70	
	N404PE	People Express			AUG/81	
19022	D-ABEL	Lufthansa	130	24/MAR/68	06/APR/68	
	D-ABEL	Condor			69	Leased
	D-ABEL	Lufthansa			20/MAR/71	
	N405PE	People Express			OCT/81	
19023	D-ABEM	Lufthansa	130	16/APR/68	29/APR/68	
	D-ABEM	Condor			69	Leased
	D-ABEM	Lufthansa			18/APR/70	
	N406PE	People Express			AUG/81	
19024	D-ABEN	Lufthansa	130	05/MAY/68	19/MAY/68	
	N407PE	People Express			24/APR/81	
19025	D-ABEO	Lufthansa	130	01/JUN/68	10/JUN/68	
	N408PE	People Express			25/APR/81	
19026	D-ABEP	Lufthansa	130	15/JUN/68	24/JUN/68	
	N409PE	People Express			15/DEC/81	
19027	D-ABEQ	Lufthansa	130	28/JUL/68	02/AUG/68	
	N410PE	People Express			03/MAR/81	
19028	D-ABER	Lufthansa	130	21/NOV/68	27/NOV/68	
	N411PE	People Express			25/APR/81	
19029	D-ABES	Lufthansa	130	07/DEC/68	14/DEC/68	
	N412PE	People Express			30/MAY/81	
19030	D-ABET	Lufthansa	130	18/DEC/68	01/JAN/69	
	N413PE	People Express			29/JUL/81	
19031	D-ABEU	Lufthansa	130	06/JAN/69	09/JAN/69	
	N414PE	People Express			30/SEP/81	
19032	D-ABEV	Lufthansa	130	08/JAN/69	14/JAN/69	
	N415PE	People Express			24/JUN/81	
19033	D-ABEW	Lufthansa	130	10/JAN/69	24/JAN/69	
	N416PE	People Express			11/MAR/82	
19039	N9001U	United Airlines	222	08/AUG/67	09/SEP/67	
19040	N9002U	United Airlines	222	31/AUG/67	29/DEC/67	
	N9002U	America West			25/JUN/85	Leased
	N9002U	United Airlines			15/OCT/85	
19041	N9003U	United Airlines	222	30/JAN/68	23/FEB/68	
19042	N9004U	United Airlines	222	02/FEB/68	02/MAR/68	
19043	N9005U	United Airlines	222	29/FEB/68	16/MAR/68	W/O 19/JUL/70, Philadelphia, Pa.
19044	N9006U	United Airlines	222	11/MAR/68	25/MAR/68	
19045	N9007U	United Airlines	222	10/APR/68	29/APR/68	
19046	N9008U	United Airlines	222	15/APR/68	03/MAY/68	
	N9008U	Air Florida			80	Leased
	N9008U	United Airlines			OCT/80	

C/N	Registration	Owner/Operator	Series	First Flight	Delivery	Remarks
19047	N9009U	United Airlines	222	22/APR/68	10/MAY/68	
	N9009U	Wien Air Alaska			APR/80	Leased
	N9009U	United Airlines			80	
19048	N9010U	United Airlines	222	24/APR/68	14/MAY/68	
19049	N9011U	United Airlines	222	01/MAY/68	24/MAY/68	
19050	N9012U	United Airlines	222	08/MAY/68	26/MAY/68	
	N9012U	Air California			20/OCT/80	Leased
	N9012U	United Airlines			05/JAN/81	
19051	N9013U	United Airlines	222	12/MAY/68	29/MAY/68	
19052	N9014U	United Airlines	222	16/MAY/68	26/JUN/68	
	N9014U	Air California			FEB/80	Leased
	N9014U	United Airlines			28/APR/81	
19053	N9015U	United Airlines	222	01/JUN/68	10/JUN/68	
19054	N9016U	United Airlines	222	12/JUN/68	23/JUN/68	
	N9016U	America West			25/JUN/85	Leased
	N9016U	United Airlines			15/SEP/85	
19055	N9017U	United Airlines	222	18/JUN/68	26/JUN/68	
19056	N9018U	United Airlines	222	28/JUN/68	13/JUL/68	
19057	N9019U	United Airlines	222	15/JUL/68	27/JUL/68	
	N9019U	Aloha Airlines				Leased
	N9019U	United Airlines			04/APR/72	
19058	N9020U	United Airlines	222	23/JUL/68	02/AUG/68	
	N9020U	Wien Air Alaska			01/AUG/79	Leased
	N9020U	United Airlines			13/OCT/79	
	N9020U	Heleasco			25/APR/80	
	N9020U	Air Florida			25/APR/80	Leased
	N9020U	Air Berlin			27/APR/80	Sub-leased
	N68AF	Air Florida			30/AUG/80	Leased
	N68AF	Pan American			16/MAY/82	Sub-leased
	N68AF	Air Florida			JUL/84	Leased
	N68AF	Heleasco			JUL/84	
	N68AF	Pan American			JUL/84	Leased
19059	N9021U	United Airlines	222	23/JUL/68	31/JUL/68	
	N9021U	Heleasco			25/APR/80	
	N9021U	Air Florida			25/APR/80	Leased
	N9021U	Air Berlin			29/AUG/80	Sub-leased
	N69AF	Air Florida			01/OCT/80	Leased
	N69AF	Pan American			28/MAY/82	Leased
	N69AF	Air Florida			JUL/84	Leased
	N69AF	Heleasco			JUL/84	
	N69AF	Pan American			JUL/84	Leased
19060	N9022U	United Airlines	222	07/AUG/68	16/AUG/68	
19061	N9023U	United Airlines	222	15/AUG/68	27/AUG/68	
19062	N9024U	United Airlines	222	15/AUG/68	26/AUG/68	
	PH-TVH	Transavia			75	Leased
	N9024U	United Airlines			75	
19063	N9025U	United Airlines	222	24/AUG/68	04/SEP/68	
	N9025U	Wien Air Alaska			MAY/80	Leased
	N9025U	United Airlines			80	
	N9025U	America West			15/JUN/85	Leased
	N9025U	United Airlines			15/SEP/85	
19064	N9026U	United Airlines	222	29/AUG/68	06/SEP/68	
	F-GCLL	Euralair			22/FEB/80	
19065	N9027U	United Airlines	222	09/SEP/68	14/SEP/68	
	N9027U	Air Florida			29/OCT/79	Leased
	N9027U	Air Florida			16/APR/80	
	N9027U	Wien Air Alaska			MAY/80	Leased
	N9027U	United Airlines			80	
19066	N9028U	United Airlines	222	14/SEP/68	23/SEP/68	
	F-GCSL	Euralair			17/APR/80	
	F-GCSL	Air Berlin			27/APR/80	Leased
	F-GCSL	Euralair			01/MAR/81	
19067	N9029U	United Airlines	222	15/SEP/68	23/SEP/68	
	N9029U	Aloha Airlines			SEP/76	Leased
	N9029U	United Airlines			08/SEP/77	
	F-GCJL	Euralair			08/FEB/80	
	F-GCJL	Air Florida			NOV/81	Leased
	F-GCJL	Euralair			MAR/82	
19068	N9030U	United Airlines	222	27/SEP/68	03/OCT/68	
19069	N9031U	United Airlines	222	24/SEP/68	30/SEP/68	W/O 08/DEC/72, Chicago
19070	N9032U	United Airlines	222	01/OCT/68	08/OCT/68	
19071	N9033U	United Airlines	222	19/OCT/68	23/OCT/68	
19072	N9034U	United Airlines	222	21/JAN/68	28/OCT/68	
	N73714	Aloha Airlines			12/JUN/71	
	N73714	Air California			01/DEC/80	Leased
	N73714	AirCal			06/APR/81	Purchased
	N459AC	AirCal			13/JAN/82	
19073	N9035U	United Airlines	222	27/OCT/68	04/NOV/68	
	N752N	Piedmont			08/JUN/73	
19074	N9036U	United Airlines	222	15/NOV/68	23/NOV/68	
	G-AZNZ	Britannia Airways			01/MAR/73	
	G-AZNZ	Guinness Peat			01/APR/85	
	N144AW	America West			01/APR/85	Leased
19075	N9037U	United Airlines	222	17/NOV/68	24/NOV/68	
	N7383F	Frontier Airlines			19/MAR/73	
	N7383F	Air Florida			OCT/79	Leased
	N7383F	Frontier Airlines			MAY/80	
	N7383F	E.G & G			01/OCT/84	Leased
19076	N9038U	United Airlines	222	22/NOV/68	27/NOV/68	
19077	N9039U	United Airlines	222	30/NOV/68	06/DEC/68	WFU NOV/80, stored Denver
19078	N9040U	United Airlines	222	08/DEC/68	13/DEC/68	
19306	N831PC	Pacific Airlines	293			Not taken-up
	N461GB	GATX Leasing		22/MAR/68	03/MAY/68	
	N461GB	Wien Consolidated			23/MAY/68	Leased
	N461GB	GATX Leasing			NOV/68	
	N461GB	Air California			29/NOV/68	Leased
	N461GB	Air Cal			06/APR/81	Leased
	N461GB	Air Cal			MAR/84	Purchased
19307	N832PC	Pacific Airlines	293			Not taken-up
	N462GB	GATX Leasing		09/APR/68	18/SEP/68	Leased
	N462GB	Air California			18/SEP/68	Leased
	N462GB	Pacific Southwest Airlines			08/SEP/72	Sub-leased
	N462GB	Air California			MAY/74	Leased
	N462AC	Air California			JUN/78	Purchased
	N462AC	Air Cal			06/APR/81	

BOEING 737

C/N	Registration	Owner/Operator	Series	First Flight	Delivery	Remarks
19308	N833PC	Pacific Airlines	293			Not taken-up
	N463GB	GATX Leasing		28/JUN/68	10/JUL/68	
	N463GB	Air California			10/JUL/68	Leased
	N463GB	Air California			FEB/84	Purchased
	N463GB	Air Cal			06/APR/81	
19309	N834PC	Pacific Airlines	293			Not taken-up
	N464GB	GATX Leasing		13/JUL/68	31/JUL/68	
	N464GB	Air California			31/JUL/68	Leased
	N464AC	Air California			SEP/77	Purchased
	N464AC	Air Cal			06/APR/81	
19408	LN-SUS	Braathens Safe	205	15/DEC/68	02/JAN/69	
19409	LN-SUP	Braathens Safe	205	25/JAN/69	31/JAN/69	
19418	N734N	Piedmont	201	24/MAY/68	30/MAY/68	
19419	N735N	Piedmont	201	27/JUN/68	03/JUL/68	
19420	N736N	Piedmont	201	05/JUL/68	15/JUL/68	
19421	N737N	Piedmont	201	20/JUL/68	08/AUG/68	
19422	N738N	Piedmont	201	22/AUG/68	29/AUG/68	
19423	N740N	Piedmont	201	09/SEP/68	16/SEP/68	
19424	EI-APP	Aer Lingus	248	15/MAR/69		Not taken-up
	EI-ASA	Aer Lingus			28/MAR/69	
	EI-ASA	Air Algerie			01/JUN/70	Leased
	EI-ASA	Aer Lingus			70	
	EI-ASA	Cameroon Airlines			30/OCT/71	Leased
	EI-ASA	Aer Lingus			31/AUG/72	
	9J-ADZ	Zambia Airways			30/MAR/75	Leased
	EI-ASA	Aer Lingus			19/JUN/76	
	EI-ASA	Guinness Peat Aviation			NOV/83	Leased
	EI-ASA	Nigeria Airways			NOV/83	Sub-leased
	EI-ASA	Guinness Peat Aviation			DEC/83	Leased
	EI-ASA	Aer Lingus			DEC/83	
19425	EI-APS	Aer Lingus	248	02/APR/69		Not taken-up
	EI-ASB	Aer Lingus			15/APR/69	
	EI-ASB	Air Algerie			14/DEC/69	Leased
	EI-ASB	Aer Lingus			MAR/71	
	EI-ASB	Nigerian Airways			20/OCT/71	Leased
	EI-ASB	Aer Lingus			02/APR/73	
	EI-ASB	Cameroon Airlines			28/SEP/75	Leased
	EI-ASB	Aer Lingus			26/OCT/75	
	SU-AYK	Egyptair			01/DEC/75	Leased
	EI-ASB	Aer Lingus			31/MAR/76	
	PP-SRX	Vasp			21/NOV/76	Leased
	EI-ASB	Aer Lingus			30/APR/77	
19426	N2711R	Wien Consolidated	202C	18/SEP/68	30/OCT/68	
	N2711R	Wien Air Alaska			01/JUL/73	
	N2711R	Quebecair			28/JUN/84	
	N2711R	Wien Air Alaska			28/JUN/84	Leased
	C-GQBC	Quebecair			07/SEP/84	
	N801AL	CIS Corp.			10/MAR/86	
	N801AL	Aloha			10/MAR/86	Leased
19437	N73700	Boeing	130	09/APR/67	Prototype	
	N515NA	NASA			26/JUL/73	
19547	N9041U	United Airlines	222	13/DEC/68	30/DEC/68	
	N749N	Piedmont			14/SEP/72	
19548	N9042U	United Airlines	222	22/DEC/68	31/DEC/68	
	N751N	Piedmont			30/NOV/72	
19549	N9043U	United Airlines	222	06/JAN/69	13/JAN/69	
	N9043U	Air Florida			01/OCT/80	
	N64AF	Air Florida			06/DEC/80	
	N64AF	Pan American			26/APR/82	Leased
	N64AF	Air Florida			AUG/84	
	N64AF	Interfirst Bank			AUG/84	
	N64AF	Aviation Sales			AUG/84	
	N64AF	Pan American			AUG/84	Leased
19550	N9044U	United Airlines	222	10/JAN/69	22/JAN/69	
19551	N9045U	United Airlines	222	13/JAN/69	23/JAN/69	
19552	N9046U	United Airlines	222	17/JAN/69	03/MAR/69	
	N61AF	Air Florida			14/JUL/80	
	N61AF	Pan American			82	Leased
	N61AF	Air Florida			84	
	N61AF	Air Lease			DEC/84	Leased
	N73714	Aloha Airlines			DEC/84	
19553	N9047U	United Airlines	222	01/FEB/69	10/FEB/69	
	N9047U	Air Florida			SEP/80	
	N63AF	Air Florida			07/DEC/80	
	N63AF	Pan American			12/APR/82	Leased
	N63AF	Air Florida			AUG/84	
	N63AF	Interfirst Bank			AUG/84	
	N63AF	Aviation Sales			AUG/84	
	N63AF	Pan American			AUG/84	Leased
19554	N9048U	United Airlines	222	09/FEB/69	17/FEB/69	
	N67AF	Air Florida			NOV/80	
	N67AF	Pan American			27/APR/82	Leased
	N67AF	Air Florida			AUG/84	
	N67AF	Interfirst Bank			AUG/84	
	N67AF	Aviation Sales			AUG/84	
	N67AF	Pan American			AUG/84	Leased
19555	N9049U	United Airlines	222	09/FEB/69	14/FEB/69	
	N9049U	GE Credit Corp.			23/FEB/72	
	N9049U	Piedmont			23/FEB/72	Leased
	N9049U	Piedmont			FEB/82	Purchased
19556	N9050U	United Airlines	222	15/FEB/69	25/FEB/69	
	N62AF	Air Florida			28/JUL/80	W/O 13/JAN/82, Washington DC
19591		Lake Central Airlines	215C			Cancelled order
19592		Lake Central Airlines	215			Cancelled order
19593		Lake Central Airlines	215C			Cancelled order
19594	N4907	Northern Consolidated	210C	27/NOV/68	05/DEC/68	
	N4907	Wien Consolidated			68	
	N4907	Wien Air Alaska			72	
	N4907	Quebecair			28/JUN/84	
	N4907	Wien Air Alaska			28/JUN/84	Leased
	C-GQBD	Quebecair			16/NOV/84	
19598	N4501W	Western Airlines	247	31/MAY/68	11/JUN/68	
	N4501W	Polaris Leasing			MAR/81	
	N4501W	Lockheed Aircraft Services			MAR/81	Leased
	N4501W	Polaris Leasing			DEC/84	

C/N	Registration	Owner/Operator	Series	First Flight	Delivery	Remarks
	N4501W	Air Cal			17/DEC/84	Leased
	N457AC	Air Cal			JAN/85	
19599	N4502W	Western Airlines	247	20/JUN/68	01/JUL/68	
	N4502W	Polaris Leasing			JAN/86	
	N4502W	Western Airlines			JAN/86	Leased
19600	N4503W	Western Airlines	247	01/JUL/68	13/JUL/68	
	N4503W	Polaris Leasing			OCT/80	
	N4503W	Lockheed Aircraft Services			OCT/80	Leased
	N4503W	Polaris Leasing			01/APR/85	
	N4503W	Western Airlines			01/APR/85	Leased
19601	N4504W	Western Airlines	247	12/JUL/68	17/JUL/68	
	N4504W	Westinghouse Leasing			JAN/74	
	N4504W	Air France			JAN/74	Leased
	N4504	Air France			OCT/76	Leased
	N4504W	Air France			FEB/77	Leased
	N4504W	Polaris Leasing			03/OCT/79	
	N4504W	Air France			03/OCT/79	Leased
	N4504W	Westinghouse Leasing			NOV/79	
	N466AC	Air California			JUN/80	
	N466AC	Air Cal			06/APR/81	
19602	N4505W	Western Airlines	247	12/JUL/68	22/JUL/68	
	N4505W	Polaris Leasing			JAN/86	
	N4505W	Western Airlines			JUL/68	Leased
19603	N4506W	Western Airlines	247	24/JUL/68	31/JUL/68	
	N758N	Piedmont			06/NOV/74	
19604	N4507W	Western Airlines	247	08/AUG/68	16/AUG/68	
	N4507W	Polaris Leasing			JAN/86	
	N4507W	Western Airlines			JAN/86	Leased
19605	N4508W	Western Airlines	247	12/AUG/68	20/AUG/68	
	N4508W	E.G. & G Inc.			04/DEC/80	
19606	N4509W	Western Airlines	247	04/SEP/68	13/SEP/68	
	N4509W	Polaris Leasing			JAN/86	
	N4509W	Western Airlines			JAN/86	Leased
19607	N4510W	Western Airlines	247	14/SEP/68	19/SEP/68	
	N4510W	E.G. & G Inc.			03/SEP/80	
19608	N4511W	Western Airlines	247	24/SEP/68	30/SEP/68	
	N4511W	Polaris Leasing			JAN/86	
	N4511W	Western Airlines			JAN/86	Leased
19609	N4512W	Western Airlines	247	09/OCT/68	16/OCT/68	
	N4512W	Polaris Leasing			JAN/86	
	N4512W	Western Airlines			JAN/86	Leased
19610	N4513W	Western Airlines	247	12/OCT/68	18/OCT/68	
	N4513W	International Air Leases			FEB/82	
	N4513W	Western Airlines			FEB/82	Leased
19611	N4514W	Western Airlines	247	02/NOV/68	07/NOV/68	
	N4514W	International Air Leases			FEB/82	
	N4514W	Western Airlines			FEB/82	Leased
19612	N4515W	Western Airlines	247	09/NOV/68	16/NOV/68	
	N4515W	E.G. & G Inc.			26/JUN/80	
19613	N4516W	Western Airlines	247		09/DEC/68	
	N4516W	Polaris Leasing			JAN/86	
	N4516W	Western Airlines			JAN/86	Leased
19614	N4517W	Western Airlines	247	05/DEC/68	10/DEC/68	
	N473AC	Polaris Leasing			31/MAR/81	
	N473AC	Air California			31/MAR/81	Leased
	N473AC	Air California			OCT/81	Purchased
	N473AC	Air Cal			06/APR/81	
19615	N4518W	Western Airlines	247	19/JAN/69	28/JAN/69	
	N4518W	Polaris Leasing			JAN/86	
	N4518W	Western Airlines			JAN/86	Leased
19616	N4519W	Western Airlines	247	20/OCT/69	29/JAN/69	
	N4519W	Polaris Leasing			JUN/81	
	N4519W	Lockheed Aircraft Services			JUN/81	Leased
	N4519W	E.G. & G Inc.			82	Sub-leased
	N4519W	Lockheed Aircraft Services			82	Leased
	N4519W	Polaris Leasing			01/APR/85	
	N4519W	Western Airlines			01/APR/85	Leased
19617	N4520W	Western Airlines	247	11/FEB/69	15/FEB/69	
	N4520W	Polaris Leasing			JAN/86	
	N4520W	Western Airlines			JAN/86	Leased
19679	HK-1403	Avianca	159	24/OCT/68	15/NOV/68	
	D-ABWA	West German Air Force				Not taken-up
	N1780B	Boeing			24/AUG/72	
	N73715	Aloha Airlines			15/MAR/73	
	N472GB	GATX Leasing			07/SEP/78	
	N472GB	Air California			07/SEP/78	
	N472GB	Aloha Airlines			78	Leased
	N472GB	Air California			02/APR/79	
	N472GB	Aloha Airlines			01/MAY/79	Leased
	N472GB	Air Cal			84	
19680	HK-1404	Avianca	159	14/NOV/68	21/NOV/68	
	D-ABWB	West German Air Force				Not taken-up
	N1781B	Boeing			05/SEP/72	
	N73717	Aloha Airlines			12/APR/73	
	N471GB	GATX Leasing			30/SEP/77	
	N471GB	Air California			30/SEP/77	
	N73717	Southwest Airlines			22/SEP/78	Leased
	N471GB	Air California			78	
	N471GB	Air Cal			06/APR/81	
19681	N378PS	Pacific Southwest Airlines	214	15/SEP/68	20/SEP/68	
	N7380F	Frontier Airlines			15/MAR/72	
	N7380F	E.G. & G			01/OCT/84	Leased
19682	N379PS	Pacific Southwest Airlines	214	02/OCT/68	05/OCT/68	
	N379PS	All Nippon Airways			10/APR/73	Leased
	N379PS	Pacific Southwest Airlines			09/MAY/74	
	N7387F	Frontier Airlines			31/MAR/76	
19707	ZS-EUY	South African Airways	244	15/OCT/68	29/OCT/68	
	ZS-SBL	South African Airways			68	
	ZS-SBL	South African Government			SEP/81	Leased
	ZS-SBL	South African Airways			AUG/85	
	N754UA	United Air Leasing			AUG/85	
	N754UA	Air Cal			AUG/85	
	N754UA	America West			17/MAR/86	Leased
	N754UA	Air Cal			31/MAY/86	
19708	ZS-EUZ	South African Airways	244	24/OCT/68	29/OCT/68	
	ZS-SBM	South African Airways			68	
	3D-ADA	Royal Swazi Airways			01/OCT/82	

BOEING 737

C/N	Registration	Owner/Operator	Series	First Flight	Delivery	Remarks
	N136AW	Guinness Peat			30/NOV/83	
	N136AW	America West			30/NOV/83	Leased
	N136AW	America West			OCT/85	Purchased
19709	G-AVRL	Britannia Airways	204	28/JUN/68	06/JUL/68	
	G-AVRL	Aerolineas Argentinas			24/JAN/70	Leased
	G-AVRL	Britannia Airways			28/APR/70	
	G-AVRL	Yemen Airways			11/DEC/73	Leased
	G-AVRL	Britannia Airways			74	
	N311XV	Presidential Airways			01/APR/86	
19710	G-AVRM	Britannia Airways	204	02/AUG/68	09/AUG/68	
	G-AVRM	Presidential Airways			04/NOV/85	Leased
	N312XV	Presidential Airways			30/JAN/86	Purchased
19711	G-AVRN	Britannia Airways	204	29/MAR/69	08/APR/69	
	PH-TVG	Transavia			30/NOV/74	Leased
	G-AVRN	Britannia Airways			25/MAR/75	
	N314XV	Presidential Airways			MAY/86	
19712	G-AVRO	Britannia Airways	204	23/APR/69	26/APR/69	
	B-2605	Far Eastern Air Transport			26/NOV/76	Leased
	G-AVRO	Britannia Airways			15/APR/77	
	B-2605	Far Eastern Air Transport			01/NOV/77	Leased
	G-AVRO	Britannia Airways			24/APR/78	
	N313XV	Presidential Airways			01/MAY/86	
19713	N835PC	Pacific Airlines	293			Not taken-up
	N465GB	GATX Leasing		10/OCT/68	14/OCT/68	
	N465GB	Air California			14/OCT/68	Leased
	N465AC	Air California			DEC/77	Purchased
	N465AC	Air Cal			06/APR/81	
19714	N836PC	Pacific Airlines	293			Not taken-up
	N467GB	GATX Leasing		27/OCT/68	31/OCT/68	
	N467GB	Air California			31/OCT/68	Leased
	N467GB	Air California			MAY/81	Purchased
	N467GB	Air Cal			06/APR/81	
19742	CF-PWD	Pacific Western	275	16/NOV/68	26/NOV/68	
	EI-BJE	Guinness Peat Aviation			16/MAY/80	Leased
	EI-BJE	Nigeria Airways			16/MAY/80	Sub-leased
	EI-BJE	Guinness Peat Aviation			MAY/85	Purchased
	4R-ULH	Air Lanka			15/JUN/85	Leased
19743	CF-PWE	Pacific Western	275C	04/MAR/69	12/MAR/69	
	EI-BJP	Guinness Peat Aviation			FEB/83	
	EI-BJP	Nigeria Airways			FEB/83	Leased
	EI-BJP	Guinness Peat Aviation			DEC/85	
	EI-BJP	Presidential Airways			DEC/85	Leased
19758	N737Q	Boeing	222	09/MAR/68		
	N1359B	Boeing			01/JUL/70	
	ZK-NAM	National Airways Corp.			15/FEB/74	
	ZK-NAM	Air New Zealand			01/APR/78	
	ZK-NAM	International Lease Finance			18/APR/86	
	N7302F	Frontier Airlines			APR/86	Leased
19759		Braathens Safe	205			Cancelled order
19768	9M-AOU	Malaysian Singapore Airlines	112	26/JUN/69	16/JUL/69	
	9V-BFD	Singapore Airlines			30/JUN/72	
	N46AF	Air Florida			26/OCT/79	
	HP-873	COPA Panama			05/DEC/80	
19769	9V-BBC	Malaysian Singapore Airlines	112	25/JUL/69	31/JUL/69	
	9V-BBC	Singapore Airlines			01/OCT/72	
	N40AF	Christina Leasing			16/MAY/79	
	N40AF	Air Florida			16/MAY/79	Leased
	N40AF	COPA Panama			15/AUG/80	Sub-leased
	N40AF	Air Florida			80	
	N40AF	Christina Leasing			03/JUL/84	
	N40AF	Sunbank			DEC/84	
	N40AF	Aviation Sales			MAY/85	
	OB-R-1288	Faucett			JUN/85	Leased
19770	9M-AOV	Malaysian Singapore Airlines	112	28/AUG/69	03/SEP/69	
	9V-BFE	Singapore Airlines			02/SEP/72	
	N42AF	Greyhound Leasing			JUN/79	
	N42AF	Air Florida			19/JUN/79	Leased
	N42AF	COPA Panama			23/AUG/80	Sub-leased
	N42AF	Air Florida			07/NOV/80	Leased
	N42AF	Greyhound Leasing			AUG/84	
	N709AW	America West			12/FEB/85	Leased
19771	9V-BBE	Malaysian Singapore Airlines	112	08/OCT/69	10/OCT/69	
	9V-BBE	Singapore Airlines			01/OCT/72	
	N47AF	Air Florida			05/AUG/80	Leased
	N47AF	Air Florida			29/SEP/80	Purchased
	YV-405C	SAVAR			05/FEB/82	
	HP-1038	Chapter International			FEB/84	
	N708AW	America West			OCT/85	
19772	9M-AOW	Malaysian Singapore Airlines	112	28/OCT/69	02/NOV/69	
	9V-BFF	Singapore Airlines			15/AUG/72	
	N48AF	Air Florida			15/AUG/80	Leased
	TP-04	Mexican Government			JUN/81	
19794	D-ABEY	Lufthansa	130	25/JAN/69	06/FEB/69	
	N417PE	People Express			31/MAR/82	
19795	D-ABEZ	Lufthansa	130			Cancelled order
19796	D-ABEJ	Lufthansa	130			Cancelled order
19847	N6241	Boeing	242C	18/OCT/68		
	CF-NAB	Nordair			27/NOV/68	
19848	CF-NAH	Nordair	242C	15/APR/69	18/APR/69	
	CF-NAH	Eastern Provincial Airways			69	Leased
	CF-NAH	Nordair			69	
19849	CF-NAF	Nordair	242C			Cancelled order
19884	CF-CPB	CP Air	217	12/OCT/68	21/OCT/68	
	N431PE	People Express			10/NOV/82	
19885	CF-CPC	CP Air	217	02/NOV/68	09/NOV/68	
	N432PE	People Express			23/NOV/82	
19886	CF-CPD	CP Air	217	25/NOV/68	01/DEC/68	
	N433PE	People Express			21/DEC/82	
19887	CF-CPE	CP Air	217	13/DEC/68	20/DEC/68	
	N434PE	People Express			10/MAR/83	
19888	CF-CPU	CP Air	217	19/DEC/68	27/DEC/68	
	N435PE	People Express			23/MAY/83	
19889	CF-CPV	CP Air	217			Cancelled order
19920	N380PS	Pacific Southwest Airlines	214	24/NOV/68	25/NOV/68	
	N7388F	Frontier Airlines			05/MAR/76	

C/N	Registration	Owner/Operator	Series	First Flight	Delivery	Remarks
19921	N381PS	Pacific Southwest Airlines	214	14/DEC/68	17/DEC/68	
	CF-PWM	Pacific Western			17/JUL/69	
	C6-BES	Bahamasair			APR/82	Leased
	CF-PWM	Pacific Western			82	
	N382PA	ATASCO			15/SEP/82	
	N382PA	Pan American			15/SEP/82	Leased
	N382PA	ATASCO			APR/86	
	N382PA	Panco Corp.			APR/86	
	N382PA	Guinness Peat			APR/86	Leased
	N382PA	Pan American			APR/86	Sub-leased
19929	ZK-NAC	National Airways Corp.	219	20/AUG/68	30/AUG/68	
	ZK-NAC	Air New Zealand			01/APR/78	
	N321XV	Presidential Airways			24/APR/86	
19930	ZK-NAD	National Airways Corp.	219	07/SEP/68	12/SEP/68	
	ZK-NAD	Air New Zealand			01/APR/78	
	N322XV	Presidential Airways			28/FEB/86	
19931	ZK-NAE	National Airways Corp.	219	27/SEP/68	07/OCT/68	
	ZK-NAE	Air New Zealand			01/APR/78	
	ZK-NAE	Integrated Aircraft			27/MAR/86	
	N453AC	Air Cal			APR/86	Leased
19932	N9051U	United Airlines	222	26/FEB/69	10/MAR/69	
19933	N9052U	United Airlines	222	01/MAR/69	07/MAR/69	
19934	N9053U	United Airlines	222	06/MAR/69	11/MAR/69	
19935	N9054U	United Airlines	222	20/MAR/69	31/MAR/69	
19936	N9055U	United Airlines	222	22/MAR/69	02/APR/69	
	B-2601	Far Eastern Air Transport			01/MAR/76	
19937	N9056U	United Airlines	222	28/MAR/69	09/APR/69	
	N7389F	Frontier Airlines			15/JUL/76	
19938	N9057U	United Airlines	222	29/APR/69	01/MAY/69	
	N9057U	Eastern Provincial Airways			31/MAY/69	Leased
	N9057U	United Airlines			70	
19939	N9058U	United Airlines	222	30/APR/69	05/MAY/69	
	B-2603	Far Eastern Air Transport			03/APR/76	W/O AUG/81
19940	N9059U	United Airlines	222	21/MAY/69	27/MAY/69	
	N9059U	International Lease Finance			07/MAY/75	
	PH-TVI	Transavia			07/MAY/75	Leased
	PH-TVI	British Airways			03/NOV/77	Sub-leased
	PH-TVI	Transavia			OCT/78	Leased
	PH-TVI	British Airways			27/JAN/79	Sub-leased
	PH-TVI	Transavia			31/MAR/80	Leased
	N842L	Air Florida			19/DEC/80	Sub-leased
	PH-TVI	Transavia			30/APR/81	Leased
	PH-TVI	International Lease Finance			01/NOV/83	
	N135AW	America West			22/DEC/83	
19941	N9060U	United Airlines	222	24/MAY/69	29/MAY/69	
19942	N9061U	United Airlines	222	03/JUN/69	10/JUN/69	
19943	N9062U	United Airlines	222	11/JUN/69	19/JUN/69	
19944	N9063U	United Airlines	222	21/JUN/69	30/JUN/69	
19945	N9064U	United Airlines	222	27/JUN/69	08/JUL/69	
	CF-NAI	Nordair			08/JUL/69	Leased
	N9064U	United Airlines			09/MAY/70	
	N9064U	Frontier Airlines			SEP/76	
19946	N9065U	United Airlines	222	02/JUL/69	09/JUL/69	
	CF-NAP	Nordair			13/JUL/69	Leased
	N9065U	United Airlines			MAY/70	
19947	N9066U	United Airlines	222	03/JUL/69	15/JUL/69	
	EI-ASK	Aer Lingus			30/MAY/74	Leased
	N9066U	United Airlines			01/OCT/76	
19948	N9067U	United Airlines	222	18/JUL/69	28/JUL/69	
19949	N9068U	United Airlines	222	05/AUG/69	12/AUG/69	
19950	N9069U	United Airlines	222	11/AUG/69	29/AUG/69	
	N9069U	Air Florida			26/SEP/79	Leased
	N9069U	United Airlines			17/OCT/80	
19951	N9070U	Unitred Airlines	222	19/AUG/69	28/AUG/69	
19952	N9071U	United Airlines	222	25/AUG/69	02/SEP/69	
	N9071U	Air Florida			26/SEP/79	Leased
	N9071U	United Airlines			01/NOV/80	
19953	N9072U	United Airlines	222	02/SEP/69	12/SEP/69	
19954	N9073U	United Airlines	222	15/SEP/69	22/SEP/69	
	N759N	Piedmont			APR/76	Leased
19955	N9074U	United Airlines	222	30/SEP/69	07/OCT/69	
	N9074U	International Lease Finance			26/MAR/75	
	PH-TVH	Transavia			26/MAR/75	Leased
	PH-TVH	British Airways			03/NOV/78	Sub-leased
	PH-TVH	Transavia			31/MAY/79	Leased
	PH-TVH	British Airways			79	Sub-Leased
	PH-TVH	Transavia			31/MAR/80	Leased
	N841L	Air Florida			31/OCT/80	Sub-leased
	PH-TVH	Transavia			NOV/81	Leased
	PH-TVH	Air Florida			NOV/81	Sub-Leased
	PH-TVH	Transavia			MAY/82	Leased
	PH-TVH	Transavia			OCT/82	Purchased
	PH-TVH	Air Florida			25/OCT/83	Leased
	PH-TVH	Transavia			APR/84	
	PH-TVH	Challenge Air Transport			09/DEC/84	Leased
	PH-TVH	Transavia			30/APR/85	
	PH-TVH	Challenge Air Transport			11/NOV/85	Leased
	PH-TVH	Transavia			Spring/86	Sched.return
19956	N9075U	United Airlines	222	03/OCT/69	10/OCT/69	
19989	CF-QBK	Quebecair	296			Cancelled order
19990	CF-QBN	Quebecair	296			Cancelled order
20070	N7371F	Frontier Airlines	2C0			Not taken-up
	N570GB	GATX Leasing		17/JAN/69	31/JAN/69	
	N570GB	Aloha Airlines			31/JAN/69	Leased
	N570GB	GATX Leasing			JAN/70	
	N7378F	Frontier Airlines			27/JAN/70	Leased
20071	N7372F	Frontier Airlines	2C0			Not taken-up
	N571GB	GATX Leasing		07/FEB/69	11/FEB/69	
	N571GB	Aloha Airlines			11/FEB/69	Leased
	N571GB	GATX Leasing			JAN/70	
	N7379F	Frontier Airlines			20/JAN/70	Leased
20072	N572GB	GATX Leasing	2C0	20/FEB/69	04/MAR/69	
	N7372F	Frontier Airlines			26/JUN/69	Leased
20073	N7374F	Frontier Airlines	2C0			Not taken-up
	N573GB	GATX Leasing		06/MAR/69	13/MAR/69	
	N7370F	Frontier Airlines			10/DEC/69	Leased

BOEING 737

C/N	Registration	Owner/Operator	Series	First Flight	Delivery	Remarks
20074	N574GB	GATX Leasing	2C0	19/MAY/69	26/MAY/69	
	N7371F	Frontier Airlines			26/MAY/69	Leased
20090		British Caledonian	299			Cancelled order
20091		British Caledonian	299			Cancelled order
20092	PP-SMA	Vasp	2A1	21/APR/69	18/JUL/69	
20093	PP-SMB	Vasp	2A1	14/MAY/69	18/JUL/69	
20094	PP-SMC	Vasp	2A1	18/JUN/69	18/JUL/69	
20095	PP-SMD	Vasp	2A1	08/JUL/69	18/JUL/69	
	N25SW	Southwest Airlines			01/OCT/74	
	N767N	Piedmont			18/DEC/78	
20096	PP-SME	Vasp	2A1	16/JUL/69	25/JUL/69	W/O 28/JAN/85, Sao Paulo Ap.
20125	N4521W	Western Airlines	247	12/FEB/69	18/FEB/69	
	N4521W	Polaris Leasing			JAN/86	
	N4521W	Western Airlines			JAN/86	Leased
20126	N4522W	Western Airlines	247	22/FEB/69	04/MAR/69	
	N4522W	Westinghouse Leasing			OCT/73	
	N4522W	Air France			OCT/73	Leased
	N4522	Air France			76	Leased
	N4522W	Air France			FEB/77	Leased
	N4522W	Westinghouse Leasing			08/APR/80	
	N470AC	Air California			MAY/80	
	N470AC	Air Cal			06/APR/81	
20127	N4523W	Western Airlines	247	08/MAR/69	17/MAR/69	
	TP-03	Mexican Government			27/JUN/80	
20128	N4524W	Western Airlines	247	13/MAR/69	17/MAR/69	
	N73718	Aloha Airlines			13/MAR/76	
	N73718	International Lease Finance			01/APR/80	
	N73718	Air Belgium			25/APR/80	Leased
	C6-BEI	Bahamasair			25/APR/80	Sub-leased
	OO-PLH	Air Belgium			25/APR/82	Leased
	OO-PLH	America West			14/NOV/85	Sub-leased
	OO-PLH	Air Belgium			22/APR/86	Leased
	OO-PLH	Britannia Airways			24/APR/86	Sub-leased
20129	N4525W	Wesetern Airlines	247	01/APR/69	14/APR/69	
	N7384F	Frontier Airlines			26/JUL/74	
20130	N4526W	Western Airlines	247	02/APR/69	15/APR/69	
	B-2617	Far Eastern Air Transport			18/MAR/80	
20131	N4527W	Western Airlines	247	07/MAY/69	12/MAY/69	W/O 31/MAR/75, Casper
20132	N4528W	Western Airlines	247	09/MAY/69	20/MAY/69	
	B-2607	Far Eastern Air Transport			30/JUN/77	
20133	N4529W	Western Airlines	247	02/JUN/69	09/JUN/69	
	N7363F	International Lease Finance			19/MAY/78	
	N7363F	Frontier Airlines			19/MAY/78	Leased
	N7363F	Frontier Airlines			27/NOV/79	Purchased
20134	N4530W	Western Airlines	247	05/JUN/69	15/JUN/69	
	B-2613	Far Eastern Air Transport			19/JAN/79	
20138	N4906	Wien Consolidated	210C	24/MAY/68	29/MAY/68	
	N4906	Wien Air Alaska			01/JUL/73	
	N4906	Mark Air			17/MAY/84	Leased
	N4906	Wien Air Alaska			18/JUL/85	
	N4906	Polaris Leasing			04/AUG/85	
	N4906	Aloha Airlines			04/AUG/85	Leased
20142	CF-PWC	Pacific Western	275		01/MAY/70	W/O 12/FEB/78, Cranbrook, B.C.
20155	N382PS	Pacific Southwest Airlines	214	12/JUN/69	18/JUN/69	
	PP-SMQ	Vasp			16/MAY/74	
20156	N983PS	Pacific Southwest Airlines	214	16/JUN/69	19/JUN/69	
	ZK-NAK	National Airways Corp.			13/SEP/73	
	ZK-NAK	Air New Zealand			01/APR/78	
	N323XV	Presidential Airways			FEB/86	
20157	N984PS	Pacific Southwest Airlines	214	11/JUL/69	17/JUL/69	
	PP-SMR	Vasp			16/MAY/74	
20158	N985PS	Pacific Southwest Airlines	214	18/JUL/69	24/JUL/69	
	ZK-NAL	National Airways Corp.			15/SEP/74	
	ZK-NAL	Air New Zealand			01/APR/78	
	N4264Y	Polaris Leasing			01/APR/78	
	N4264Y	Air Cal			06/APR/81	Leased
	N460AC	Air Cal			OCT/81	Purchased
20159	N986PS	Pacific Southwest Airlines	214	22/JUL/69	29/JUL/69	
	PP-SMS	Vasp			16/MAY/74	
20160	N987PS	Pacific Southwest Airlines	214	31/JUL/69	06/AUG/69	
	PP-SMT	Vasp			16/MAY/74	W/O 17/NOV/85, Eurico Sales Ap., Victoria, Brasil.
20194	N520L	GATX Leasing	2A6	31/JUL/69	25/AUG/69	
	N520L	LTV Aerospace Corp.			25/AUG/69	Leased
	N520L	GATX Leasing			27/APR/72	
	VR-BEH	Maritime Investment Corp.			27/APR/72	
	N8527S	John W.Mecom Co.			17/OCT/80	
	N3333M	John W.Mecom Co.			81	
	N145AW	America West			10/JUN/85	
20195	N1288	Essex Wire Co.	2A6		16/SEP/69	
	N1288	United Technologies			MAR/79	
	N1288	Corsair			09/JAN/86	
	N146AW	America West			09/JAN/86	Leased
20196	CF-CPV	CP Air	217	19/MAR/69	24/MAR/69	
20197	CF-CPZ	CP Air	217	21/MAR/69	28/MAR/69	
20205	CF-TAO	Transair	2A9C		13/MAR/70	
	C-FTAO	Pacific Western			DEC/79	
	N383PA	ATASCO			30/AUG/82	
	N383PA	Pan American			30/SEP/82	Leased
20206	CF-TAN	Transair	2A9C		14/APR/70	
	C-FTAN	Pacific Western			DEC/79	
	C-FTAN	Markair			18/APR/84	Leased
	C-FTAN	Pacific Western			05/SEP/84	
20209	N73711	GATX Leasing	297	28/MAR/69	09/APR/69	
	N73711	Aloha Airlines			09/APR/69	Leased
	N73711	Air California			26/FEB/81	Sub-leased
	N73711	Aloha Airlines			10/JAN/82	Leased
	N73711	GATX Leasing			17/APR/82	
	N73711	Air Cal			13/MAY/82	Leased
	N73711	GATX Leasing			SEP/83	
	N73711	Aloha Airlines			06/NOV/83	Leased
20210	N73712	GATX Leasing	297	02/MAY/69	07/MAY/69	
	N73712	Aloha Airlines			07/MAY/69	Leased
	N73712	GATX Leasing			25/JUL/82	
	N73712	Aloha Airlines			06/NOV/83	Leased
20211	N741N	Piedmont	201	23/FEB/69	04/MAR/69	

C/N	Registration	Owner/Operator	Series	First Flight	Delivery	Remarks
20212	N743N	Piedmont	201	17/APR/69	22/APR/69	
20213	N744N	Piedmont	201	18/APR/69	29/APR/69	
20214	N745N	Piedmont	201	21/MAY/69	29/MAY/69	
20215	N746N	Piedmont	201		19/SEP/69	
20216	N747N	Piedmont	201	09/OCT/69	14/OCT/69	
20218	EI-ASC	Aer Lingus	248C	21/AUG/69	09/SEP/69	
	EI-ASC	Cameroon Airlines			25/JAN/76	Leased
	EI-ASC	Aer Lingus			07/FEB/76	
	EI-ASC	Guinness Peat			AUG/85	Leased
	EI-ASC	Nigeria Airways			AUG/85	Sub-leased
	EI-ASC	Guinness Peat			DEC/85	Leased
	PP-SNY	Vasp			DEC/85	Sub-leased
	EI-ASC	Guinness Peat			MAR/86	Leased
	EC-DZB	Hispania			MAY/86	Sub-leased
20219	EI-ASD	Aer Lingus	248C	26/SEP/69	24/OCT/69	
20220	EI-ASE	Aer Lingus	248C	16/OCT/69	17/NOV/69	
20221	EI-ASF	Aer Lingus	248	07/JAN/70	19/JUL/70	
	EI-ASF	Guinness Peat			MAR/83	Leased
	EI-ASF	Air Florida			MAR/83	Sub-leased
	EI-ASF	Guinness Peat			03/JUL/84	Leased
	C6-BFB	Bahamasair			11/JUL/84	Sub-leased
	EI-ASF	Guinness Peat			MAY/85	Leased
	EI-ASF	Aer Lingus			MAY/85	
20222	EI-ASG	Aer Lingus	248		22/FEB/70	
	SU-AYT	Egyptair			28/OCT/75	Leased
	EI-ASG	Aer Lingus			24/MAR/76	
	N7360F	Frontier Airlines			16/OCT/77	Leased
	EI-ASG	Aer Lingus			15/MAY/78	
	HR-SHD	SAHSA			20/NOV/79	Leased
	EI-ASG	Aer Lingus			10/MAR/80	
	EI-ASG	Air California			04/JAN/81	Leased
	EI-ASG	Aer Lingus			29/APR/81	
20223	EI-ASH	Aer Lingus	248		25/APR/70	
	CF-TAR	Transair			16/NOV/73	Leased
	EI-ASH	Aer Lingus			15/MAY/74	
	C-GTAR	Transair			16/NOV/74	Leased
	EI-ASH	Aer Lingus			01/APR/75	
	C-GTAR	Transair			15/DEC/75	Leased
	EI-ASH	Aer Lingus			14/APR/76	
	N7361F	Frontier Airlines			10/NOV/77	Leased
	EI-ASH	Aer Lingus			31/MAR/78	
	N80AF	Air Florida			15/NOV/78	Leased
	EI-ASH	Aer Lingus			15/MAR/79	
	C-GTAR	Pacific Western			15/OCT/79	Leased
	EI-ASH	Aer Lingus			30/APR/80	
	HR-TNS	TAN			20/NOV/80	Leased
	EI-ASH	Aer Lingus			27/MAR/82	
	EI-ASH	Southwest Airlines			20/SEP/83	Leased
	EI-ASH	Aer Lingus			31/MAR/84	
	EI-ASH	Guinness Peat			31/OCT/84	Leased
	EI-ASH	Nigeria Airways			31/OCT/84	Sub-leased
	EI-ASH	Guinness Peat			DEC/84	Leased
	EI-ASH	Aerolineas Argentinas			19/DEC/84	Sub-leased
	EI-ASH	Guinness Peat			15/MAR/85	Leased
	EI-ASH	Air Cal			AUG/85	Leased
20226	JA8401	All Nippon Airways	281	12/MAY/69	22/MAY/69	
	B-1870	China Airlines			16/APR/76	W/O 16/FEB/86, Makung, P'enju Island, Taiwan.
20227	JA8402	All Nippon Airways	281	06/JUN/69	17/JUN/69	
	B-1872	China Airlines			09/APR/76	
20229	ZS-FKH	South African Airways	244			Not taken-up
	ZS-SBN	South African Airways		07/AUG/69	28/AUG/69	
20231	5R-MFA	Air Madagascar	2B2	05/SEP/69	19/SEP/69	
20236	G-AWSY	Britannia Airways	204	08/MAY/69	12/MAY/69	
	G-AWSY	Yemen Airways			NOV/75	Leased
	G-AWSY	Britannia Airways			JAN/76	
20242	N73713	GATX Leasing	297	11/NOV/69	24/NOV/69	
	N73713	Aloha Airlines			24/NOV/69	Leased
	N73713	GATX Leasing			19/NOV/82	
	N73713	Air Cal			DEC/82	Leased
	N73713	GATX Leasing			SEP/83	
	N73713	Aloha Airlines			06/NOV/83	
20253	D-ABBE	Lufthansa	230C	10/DEC/69	17/DEC/69	
	N301XV	Presidential Airways			19/AUG/85	
20254	D-ABCE	Lufthansa	230C	07/JAN/70	12/JAN/70	
	N302XV	Presidential Airways			05/SEP/85	
20255	D-ABDE	Lufthansa	230C	23/JAN/70	29/JAN/70	
	N303XV	Presidential Airways			AUG/85	
20256	D-ABFE	Lufthansa	230C		14/FEB/70	
	N304XV	Presidential Airways			OCT/85	
20257	D-ABGE	Lufthansa	230C		20/JAN/71	
	D-ABGE	Lufthansa	230F		JUN/85	Converted
20258	D-ABHE	Lufthansa	230C	12/FEB/71	20/FEB/71	
	D-ABHE	Lufthansa	230F		AUG/85	Converted
20276	JA8403	All Nippon Airways	281	09/JAN/70	15/JAN/70	
	JA8403	Aer Lingus			09/FEB/76	
	9Q-CNL	Air Zaire			29/FEB/76	Leased
	EI-BCR	Aer Lingus			01/APR/76	
	EI-BCR	Nigeria Airways			18/SEP/80	Leased
	EI-BCR	Aer Lingus			31/OCT/80	
20277	JA8405	All Nippon Airways	281	24/JAN/70	30/JAN/70	
	B-1874	China Airlines			23/APR/76	
20280	CR-BAA	DETA	2B1	04/DEC/69	10/DEC/69	
	C9-BAA	DETA				
	C9-BAA	LAM			MAY/80	
20281	CR-BAB	DETA	2B1	16/DEC/69	21/DEC/69	
	C9-BAB	DETA				
	C9-BAB	LAM			MAY/80	
	C9-BAB	Royal Swazi			03/MAY/82	Leased
	C9-BAB	LAM			30/SEP/82	W/O 27/MAR/83, Quelimane
20282	G-AXNA	Britannia Airways	204C		18/MAR/70	
	PH-TVF	Transavia			13/DEC/74	Leased
	G-AXNA	Britannia Airways			08/MAY/75	
20299	N1787B	Boeing	2A3	16/APR/69		
	N1797B	Boeing				

C/N	Registration	Owner/Operator	Series	First Flight	Delivery	Remarks
	CX-BHM	Pluna			31/DEC/69	
	HR-TNR	TAN			08/MAY/74	
20300	N1788B	Boeing	2A3	14/MAY/69		
	N1733B	Boeing				
	CF-EPO	Eastern Provincial Airways			17/JUL/70	
	C-FEPO	CP Air			JAN/86	
20329	ZS-SBO	South African Airways	244		20/APR/70	
20330	ZS-SBP	South African Airways	244		27/MAY/70	
20331	ZS-SBR	South African Airways	244		29/JUN/70	
20334	N468AC	Air California	293		15/SEP/70	W/O 17/FEB/81, John Wayne Ap.
20335	N469AC	Air California	293		25/MAY/71	
	N469AC	Pacific Southwest Airlines			05/APR/73	Leased
	N469AC	Air California			73	
	N469AC	Aloha Airlies			13/JUN/74	Leased
	N469AC	Air California			27/MAR/76	
	N469AC	Air Cal			06/APR/81	
20336	N470AC	Air California	203			Not taken-up
	N22SW	Southwest Airlines	2H4		15/JUN/71	
	N22SW	ITEL			21/JUL/78	
	EI-BFC	Guinness Peat			21/JUL/78	Leased
	EI-BFC	Nigeria Airways			27/AUG/78	Sub-leased
	EI-BFC	ITEL			DEC/80	
	EI-BFC	GATX Leasing			DEC/80	
	EI-BFC	Guinness Peat			DEC/80	Leased
	EI-BFC	Nigeria Airways			DEC/80	Sub-leased
	EI-BFC	Guinness Peat			28/FEB/86	Purchased
	N332XV	Presidential Airways			28/FEB/86	Leased
	EI-BFC	Guinness Peat			MAY/86	
	EC-DZH	Spantax			MAY/86	Leased
20344	N73714	Boeing	297	15/DEC/69		
	N73714	Aloha Airlines			27/MAY/70	Leased
	N73714	Boeing			24/NOV/70	
	ZK-NAJ	National Airways Corp.			18/JUL/71	
	ZK-NAJ	Air New Zealand			01/APR/78	
	ZK-NAJ	International Lease Finance			24/APR/86	
	N7310F	Frontier Airlines			23/MAY/86	Leased
20345	N21SW	Southwest Airlines	297	20/JAN/70	10/JUN/71	
	N73717	ITEL			21/JUL/78	
	N73717	Aloha Airlines			27/JUL/78	Leased
	N73717	ITEL			DEC/80	
	N73717	GATX Leasing			DEC/80	
	N73717	Aloha Airlines			DEC/80	Leased
	N73717	Air California			FEB/81	Sub-leased
	N73717	Air Cal			06/APR/81	
	N73717	Aloha Airlines			27/JUL/82	
20346	N23SW	Southwest Airlines	2H4C	23/SEP/71	29/SEP/71	
	PP-SMW	Vasp			27/SEP/74	
20361	N7373F	GATX Leasing	291	23/SEP/69		
	N7373F	Frontier Airlines			07/OCT/69	Leased
20362	N7374F	GATX Leasing	291	23/OCT/69	27/OCT/69	Leased
	N7374F	Frontier Airlines			27/OCT/69	
20363	N7375F	Frontier Airlines	291	05/NOV/69	07/NOV/69	
20364	N7376F	Frontier Airlines	291	12/NOV/69	14/NOV/69	
	N7376F	E.G. & G			09/OCT/84	Leased
	N7376F	Frontier Airlines			86	
	N802AL	Aloha Airlines			24/JUN/86	Leased
20365	N7377F	Frontier Airlines	291	24/NOV/69	05/DEC/69	
20368	N988PS	Pacific Southwest Airlines	214	20/AUG/70	01/MAR/71	
	N7386F	Frontier Airlines			07/NOV/75	
20369	N989PS	Pacific Southwest Ailines	214			Not taken-up
	N20SW	Southwest Airlines	2H4		02/JUN/71	
	N7381F	Frontier Airlines			23/NOV/72	
20389	G-AXNB	Britannia Airways	204C		18/APR/70	
	G-AXNB	Pelican Air Cargo			01/NOV/80	Leased
	G-AXNB	Britannia Airways			MAR/81	
20396	N1785B	Boeing	2E1	19/NOV/69		
	CF-EPL	Eastern Provincial Airways			25/NOV/69	
	C-FEPL	CP Air			JAN/86	
20397	N1786B	Boeing	2E1	09/DEC/69		
	CF-EPR	Eastern Provincial Airways			15/DEC/69	
	C-FEPR	CP Air			JAN/86	
20403	LV-JMW	Aerolineas Argentinas	287		27/FEB/70	
20404	LV-JMX	Aerolineas Argentinas	287		25/MAR/70	
20405	LV-JMY	Aerolineas Argentinas	287		09/APR/70	
20406	LV-JMZ	Aerolineas Argentinas	287		31/JUL/70	
20407	LV-JND	Aerolineas Argentinas	287C		04/SEP/70	
20408	LV-JNE	Aerolineas Argentinas	287C		02/OCT/70	
20412	N1787B	Boeing	205	15/DEC/69		
	LN-SUG	Braathens Safe			03/AUG/71	
20413	JA8406	All Nippon Airways	281		22/JUN/70	
	JA8406	Guinness Peat			28/MAY/79	
	C6-BEC	Bahamasair			28/MAY/79	Leased
	EI-BEE	Guinness Peat			03/MAY/80	
	EI-BEE	Aer Lingus			SEP/80	
	EI-BEE	Southwest Airlines			08/OCT/83	Leased
	EI-BEE	Aer Lingus			31/MAR/84	
20414	JA8407	All Nippon Airways	281		10/MAR/70	
	N776N	Piedmont			31/OCT/79	
20417	G-AXNC	Britannia Airways	204		12/MAY/70	
20440	N4902W	ARMCO	210C		15/MAY/70	
	N4902W	Wien Consolidated			15/MAY/70	Leased
	N4902W	Wien Air Alaska			01/JUL/73	Leased
	N4902W	ARMCO			MAY/81	
	N4902W	Overseas National			MAY/81	
	N4902W	Wien Air Alaska			MAY/81	Leased
	N4902W	Overseas National			MAY/82	
	N4902W	Pan American			25/MAY/82	Leased
	N4902W	Overseas National			MAY/84	
	N4902W	United Aviation			MAY/84	
	N4902W	Pan American			MAY/84	Leased
20449	JA8408	All Nippon Airways	281		22/JUN/70	
	EI-BEF	Guinness Peat			07/AUG/79	
	EI-BEF	Nigeria Airways			13/AUG/79	Leased
	EI-BEF	Guinness Peat			NOV/82	
	OB-R-1263	Faucett			20/DEC/82	Leased
	EI-BEF	Guinness Peat			MAY/84	

C/N	Registration	Owner/Operator	Series	First Flight	Delivery	Remarks
	N142AW	GE Credit Corp.			20/JUL/84	
	N142AW	America West			20/JUL/84	Leased
20450	JA8409	All Nippon Airways	281		27/JUL/70	
20451	JA8410	All Nippon Airways	281		22/SEP/70	
20452	JA8411	All Nippon Airways	281		16/NOV/70	
20453	N1790B	Boeing	201	25/AUG/71		
	LN-MTC	Mey-Air			03/SEP/71	
	LN-MTC	Boeing			07/MAR/74	
	N753N	Piedmont			14/MAY/74	
20454	N1791B	Boeing	201			
	LN-MTD	Mey-Air			06/NOV/71	
	LN-MTD	Boeing			07/MAR/74	
	N754N	Piedmont			16/MAY/74	
20455	CF-NAQ	Nordair	242C		13/MAY/70	
	C-FNAQ	Guinness Peat			31/JAN/83	
	EI-BOC	Wien Air Alaska			17/MAY/83	Leased
	EI-BOC	Guinness Peat			NOV/83	
	C-FNAQ	Nordair			NOV/83	
20458	LN-SUA	Braathens Safe	205C	09/MAR/71	17/MAR/71	
	LN-SUA	International Lease Finance			21/FEB/84	
	TF-VLT	Eagle Air			21/FEB/84	Leased
20480	VT-EAG	Indian Airlines	2A8		09/NOV/70	
20481	VT-EAH	Indian Airlines	2A8		03/DEC/70	
20482	VT-EAI	Indian Airlines	2A8	15/DEC/70	21/DEC/70	
20483	VT-EAJ	Indian Airlines	2A8		12/JAN/71	
20484	VT-EAK	Indian Airlines	2A8		16/FEB/71	
20485	VT-EAL	Indian Airlines	2A8	25/FEB/71	09/MAR/71	W/O 17/DEC/78, Hyderabad Ap.
20486	VT-EAM	Indian Airlines	2A8	26/MAR/71	10/APR/71	W/O MAY/83
20492	9V-BCR	Malaysian Singapore Airlines	212	11/MAY/71	05/JUN/71	
	9V-BCR	Singapore Airlines			01/OCT/72	
	N7382F	Frontier Airlines			18/DEC/72	
	N7382F	Air Florida			01/OCT/79	Leased
	N7382F	Frontier Airlines			01/OCT/80	
20496	N1788B	Boeing	242C	13/OCT/70		
	CF-NAP	Nordair			16/JUN/71	
20498	EP-IRF	Iran Air	286	18/JUN/71	02/JUL/71	
20499	EP-IRG	Iran Air	286	08/JUL/71	17/JUL/71	
20500	EP-IRH	Iran Air	286	13/AUG/71	02/SEP/71	
20506	JA8412	All Nippon Airways	281	15/APR/71	20/MAY/71	
20507	JA8413	All Nippon Airways	281	27/MAY/71	04/JUN/71	
	JA8413	Nihon Kinkyori Airways			15/MAR/83	
20508	JA8414	All Nippon Airways	281	23/SEP/71	04/OCT/71	
20521	9M-AQC	Malaysian Singapore Airlines	212	10/NOV/71	18/NOV/71	
	9M-AQC	Singapore Airlines			01/OCT/72	
	CF-NAW	Nordair			31/MAR/73	
	CF-NAW	Air France			23/SEP/76	Leased
	CF-NAW	Nordair			27/OCT/76	
	C-FNAW	Guinness Peat			FEB/82	
	C-FNAW	Nordair			FEB/82	Leased
	EI-BNS	Guinness Peat			08/APR/83	
	EI-BNS	Nigeria Airways			08/APR/83	Leased
	EI-BNS	Guinness Peat			AUG/83	
	N130AW	America West			13/OCT/83	
20523	LV-PRQ	Aerolineas Argentinas	287	26/JUL/71	08/OCT/71	
	LV-JTD	Aerolineas Argentinas			OCT/71	
20536	CR-BAC	DETA	2B1C	22/OCT/71	28/OCT/71	
	C9-BAC	DETA				
	C9-BAC	LAM			MAY/80	
20537	LV-JTO	Aerolineas Argentinas	287	11/DEC/71	23/DEC/71	
20544	7T-VEC	Air Algerie	206	19/NOV/71	17/DEC/71	
	TZ-ADL	Air Mali			SEP/82	
	TZ-ADL	Aerolineas Argentinas			01/JAN/85	Leased
	TZ-ADL	Air Mali			19/MAR/85	
	G-BMMZ	Britannia Airways			27/MAR/86	Leased
	TZ-ADL	Air Mali			OCT/86	Sched.return
20561	N1788B	Boeing	281	05/JAN/72		
	JA8415	All Nippon Airways			13/APR/72	
20562	JA8416	All Nippon Airways	281	22/MAR/72	03/APR/72	
20563	JA8417	All Nippon Airways	281	08/MAR/72	17/MAR/72	
20564	JA8418	All Nippon Airways	281			Cancelled order
20565	JA8419	All Nippon Airways	281			Cancelled order
20566	JA8420	All Nippon Airways	281			Cancelled order
20567	JA8421	All Nippon Airways	281			Cancelled order
20574	HZ-AGA	Saudia	268C		15/MAR/72	
20575	HZ-AGB	Saudia	268C	30/MAR/72	07/APR/72	
20576	HZ-AGC	Saudia	268	25/MAY/72	05/MAY/72	
20577	HZ-AGD	Saudia	268	12/MAY/72	19/MAY/72	
20578	HZ-AGE	Saudia	268	18/MAY/72	26/MAY/72	
20582	9M-AQL	Malaysian Airline System	2H6	23/SEP/72	06/OCT/72	
	9M-MBA	Malaysian Airline System			75	
20583	9M-AQM	Malaysian Airline System	2H6	31/JUL/72	07/AUG/72	
	9M-MBB	Malaysian Airline System			75	
20584	9M-AQN	Malaysian Airline System	2H6	17/JUL/72	31/JUL/72	
	9M-MBC	Malaysian Airline System			75	
20585	9M-AQO	Malaysian Airline System	2H6	12/SEP/72	21/SEP/72	
	9M-MBD	Malaysian Airline System			75	W/O 04/DEC/77,Nr. Johore Bharu
20586	9M-AQP	Malaysian Airline System	2H6	24/AUG/72	01/SEP/72	
	9M-MBE	Malaysian Airline System			75	
20587	9M-AQQ	Malaysian Airline System	2H6	01/SEP/72	13/SEP/72	
	9M-MBF	Malaysian Airline System			75	
20588	CF-PWP	Pacific Western	275	20/APR/72	27/APR/72	
	N381PA	ATASCO			30/JUN/82	
	N381PA	Pan American			30/JUN/82	Leased
20589	PP-SMF	Vasp	2A1	21/JUN/72	14/JUL/72	
20590	TJ-CBA	Cameroon Airlines	2H7C	11/JUL/72	14/JUL/72	
20591	TJ-CBB	Cameroon Airlines	2H7C	21/SEP/72	28/SEP/72	
20631	9M-ARG	Malaysian Airline System	2H6	10/OCT/72	16/OCT/72	
	9M-MBG	Malaysian Airline System			75	
20632	G-BADP	Britannia Airways	204	04/JAN/73	10/JAN/73	
20633	G-BADR	Britannia Airways	204	16/FEB/73	12/MAR/73	
20650	7T-VED	Air Algerie	2D6C	24/OCT/72	14/NOV/72	
20670	CF-PWW	Pacific Western	275	13/DEC/72	20/DEC/72	
	C-FPWW	ATASCO			27/MAY/82	
	N380PA	Pan American			27/MAY/82	Leased
20671	5N-ANC	Nigeria Airways	2F9	03/NOV/72	16/JAN/73	
20672	5N-AND	Nigeria Airways	2F9	29/NOV/72	16/JAN/73	

BOEING 737

C/N	Registration	Owner/Operator	Series	First Flight	Delivery	Remarks
20680	5R-MFB	Air Madagascar	2B2	05/DEC/72	14/DEC/72	
20681	CF-EPP	Eastern Provincial Airways	2E1		12/MAR/73	
	C-FEPP	CP Air			JAN/86	
20685	71-1403	United States Air Force	T43A	10/APR/73	31/JUL/73	
20686	71-1404	United States Air Force	T43A	11/SEP/73	27/SEP/73	
20687	71-1405	United States Air Force	T43A	19/OCT/73	31/OCT/73	
20688	71-1406	United States Air Force	T43A	07/NOV/73	16/NOV/73	
20689	72-0282	United States Air Force	T43A	12/DEC/73	21/DEC/73	
20690	72-0283	United States Air Force	T43A	15/JAN/74	23/JAN/74	
20691	72-0284	United States Air Force	T43A	24/JAN/74	30/JAN/74	
20692	72-0285	United States Air Force	T43A	06/FEB/74	13/FEB/74	
20693	72-0286	United States Air Force	T43A	07/FEB/74	21/FEB/74	
20694	72-0287	United States Air Force	T43A	28/FEB/74	15/MAR/74	
20695	72-0288	United States Air Force	T43A	13/MAR/74	28/MAR/74	
20696	72-1149	United States Air Force	T43A	27/MAR/74	11/APR/74	
20697	73-1150	United States Air Force	T43A	12/APR/74	25/APR/74	
20698	73-1151	United States Air Force	T43A	19/APR/74	03/MAY/74	
20699	73-1152	United States Air Force	T43A	18/MAY/74	31/MAY/74	
20700	73-1153	United States Air Force	T43A	01/JUN/74	14/JUN/74	
20701	73-1154	United States Air Force	T43A	14/JUN/74	26/JUN/74	
20702	73-1155	United States Air Force	T43A	02/JUL/74	12/JUL/74	
20703	73-1156	United States Air Force	T43A	09/JUL/74	19/JUL/74	
20711	LN-SUD	Braathens Safe	205	02/APR/73	10/APR/73	
20740	EP-IRI	Iran Air	286C	23/APR/73	01/MAY/73	
20758	7T-VEE	Air Algerie	2D6C	17/MAY/73	25/MAY/73	
20759	7T-VEF	Air Algerie	2D6	09/NOV/73	21/NOV/73	
20768	LV-LEB	Aerolineas Argentinas	287	26/OCT/73	14/NOV/73	
20769		Aerolineas Argentinas	287			Cancelled order
20776	CF-EPU	Eastern Provincial Airways	2E1	18/SEP/73	29/OCT/73	
	C-FEPU	CP Air			JAN/86	
20777	PP-SMG	Vasp	2A1	02/JUL/73	10/JUL/73	
20778	PP-SMH	Vasp	2A1	10/AUG/73	17/AUG/73	
20779	N1782B	Boeing	2A1	31/AUG/73		
	PP-SMP	Vasp			21/SEP/73	
20785	CF-PWB	Pacific Western	275	07/DEC/73	19/DEC/73	
	N4529W	E.G. & G.			MAR/83	
20786	CR-BAD	DETA	2B1	24/OCT/73	31/OCT/73	
	C9-BAD	DETA				
	C9-BAD	LAM			MAY/80	
20793	9Q-CNI	Air Zaire	298C	13/NOV/73	19/NOV/73	
20794	9Q-CNJ	Air Zaire	298C	14/MAR/74	30/APR/74	Damaged MAR/84
	9Q-CNJ	Waites Aviation			OCT/85	Under Repair
20795	9Q-CNK	Air Zaire	298C	29/MAR/74	01/MAY/74	
20796	9Q-CNL	Air Zaire	298C			Cancelled order
20797	9Q-CNM	Air Zaire	298C			Cancelled order
20806	G-BAZG	Britannia Airways	204	15/JAN/74	31/JAN/74	
	G-BAZG	Yemen Airways			17/JUN/74	Leased
	G-BAZG	Britannia Airways			29/MAY/76	
20807	G-BAZH	Britannia Airways	204	08/FEB/74	15/FEB/74	
20808	N1779B	Boeing	204	14/FEB/74		
	G-BAZI	Britannia Airways			18/MAR/74	
	G-BAZI	Airways International Cymru			28/MAR/85	
	G-BAZI	Air New Zealand			OCT/85	Leased
	G-BAZI	Airways International Cymru			30/APR/86	
20836	PH-TVC	Transavia	2K2C	09/MAY/74	02/JUN/74	
	PH-TVC	Sterling Airways			09/JUN/75	Leased
	PH-TVC	Transavia			13/JUN/75	
	PH-TVC	Saudia			18/OCT/77	Leased
	PH-TVC	Transavia			77	
	LV-MDB	Aerolineas Argentinas			12/DEC/77	Leased
	PH-TVC	Transavia			20/JUN/78	
	PH-TVC	British Airways				Leased
	PH-TVC	Transavia				
	PH-TVC	Austrian Airlines			22/JUN/80	Leased
	PH-TVC	Transavia			01/NOV/80	
	PH-TVC	Air Malta			01/APR/81	Leased
	PH-TVC	Transavia			31/MAR/83	
	PH-TVC	Air Florida			01/JUN/83	Leased
	PH-TVC	Mark Air			17/JAN/84	Sub-leased
	PH-TVC	Air Florida			23/MAY/84	Leased
	PH-TVC	Transavia			23/MAY/84	
20882	HZ-AGF	Saudia	268	22/MAY/74	31/MAY/74	
20883	HZ-AGG	Saudia	268	15/JUL/74	26/JUL/74	
20884	7T-VEG	Air Algerie	2D6	14/JUN/74	29/JUN/74	
20892	YI-AGH	Iraqi Airways	270C	26/JUL/74	07/OCT/74	
20893	YI-AGI	Iraqi Airways	270C	24/AUG/74	06/SEP/74	
20907	OO-SDA	Sabena	229	23/APR/74	29/APR/74	
20908	OO-SDB	Sabena	229	25/APR/74	06/MAY/74	
20909	OO-SDC	Sabena	229	01/MAY/74	08/MAY/74	
20910	OO-SDD	Sabena	229		06/JUN/74	
20911	OO-SDE	Sabena	229	12/JUN/74	20/JUN/74	
	OO-SDE	Camair			03/OCT/76	Leased
	OO-SDE	Sabena			19/NOV/76	
	OO-SDE	Nordair			08/OCT/83	Leased
	OO-SDE	Sabena			02/MAY/84	
	OO-SDE	Air Djibouti			AUG/84	Leased
	OO-SDE	Sabena			84	
	OO-SDE	Nordair			20/OCT/84	Leased
	OO-SDE	Sabena			03/MAY/85	
	C-GNDX	Nordair			15/OCT/85	
	OO-SDE	Sabena			02/MAY/86	
20912	OO-SDF	Sabena	229	09/JUL/74	21/JUL/74	
20913	OO-SDG	Sabena	229	12/FEB/75	26/FEB/75	
	VR-UEB	Royal Brunei	2M6	15/APR/75	24/APR/75	
	VR-UEB	Guinness Peat			24/APR/80	Leased
	4R-ALD	Air Lanka			24/APR/80	Sub-Leased
	4R-ALD	Guinness Peat			OCT/83	
	VR-UEB	Royal Brunei			OCT/83	
	VS-UEB	Royal Brunei			01/JAN/84	
	V8-UEB	Royal Brunei			20/FEB/84	
20914	OO-SDH	Sabena	229	25/FEB/75	07/MAR/75	W/O 04/APR/78, Chareloi, Belgium
20915	OO-SDJ	Sabena	229		11/MAR/75	
20916	OO-SDK	Sabena	229	07/MAR/75	22/MAR/75	
20917	N1786B	Boeing	210C	28/FEB/74		
	N4905W	Wien Air Alaska			08/APR/74	
	N4905W	Libyan Arab Airlines			15/DEC/79	Leased

C/N	Registration	Owner/Operator	Series	First Flight	Delivery	Remarks
	N4905W	Wien Air Alaska				
	N4905W	ARAMCO			29/FEB/80	Leased
	N4905W	Wien Air Alaska			MAY/80	
	N4905W	CPC Leasing			NOV/84	
	N4905W	TACA			NOV/84	Leased
20922	C-GAPW	Pacific Western	275	19/AUG/74	29/AUG/74	
	N127AW	Guinness Peat			15/JUL/83	
	N127AW	America West			15/JUL/83	Leased
20925	N24SW	Southwest Airlines	2H4	09/SEP/74	18/SEP/74	
20926	9M-ASR	Malaysian Airline System	2H6	28/AUG/74	09/SEP/74	
	9M-MBH	Malaysian Airline System			75	
20943	PH-TVD	Transavia	2K2C	19/MAR/75	31/MAR/75	
	PH-TVD	Saudia			14/DEC/75	Leased
	PH-TVD	Transavia			30/DEC/75	
	PH-TVD	Saudia			18/OCT/77	Leased
	PH-TVD	Transavia			20/DEC/77	
	PH-TVD	British Airways			SEP/78	Leased
	PH-TVD	Transavia			JUN/79	
	PH-TVD	Air Djibouti			APR/80	Leased
	PH-TVD	Transavia			81	
	G-BKBT	Britannia Airways			15/APR/82	Leased
	PH-TVD	Transavia			01/NOV/82	
	PH-TVD	Eagle Air			29/MAR/83	Leased
	PH-TVD	Transavia			SEP/83	
	G-BKBT	British Airtours			APR/84	Leased
	PH-TVD	Transavia			01/APR/85	
	PH-TVD	Challenge Air Transport			01/MAY/85	Leased
	PH-TVD	Transavia			13/MAR/86	
	VT-EKC	Indian Airlines			01/MAY/86	Leased
	PH-TVD	Transavia			MAY/89	Sched.return
20944	PH-TVE	Transavia	2K2C	04/APR/75	16/APR/75	
	PH-TVE	Saudia			23/NOV/77	Leased
	PH-TVE	Transavia			19/DEC/77	
	PH-TVE	British Airways			SEP/78	Leased
	PH-TVE	Transavia			01/APR/80	
	PH-TVE	Austrian Airlines			80	Leased
	PH-TVE	Transavia			80	
	PH-TVE	Air Malta			01/NOV/80	Leased
	PH-TVE	Transavia			31/MAR/83	
	PH-TVE	Transavia			DEC/83	Op. for KLM
	VT-	Indian Airlines			Summer/86	Sched.lease
20956	C-GTAQ	Transair	2A9	18/NOV/74	27/NOV/74	
	C-GTAQ	Pacific Western			79	
	C-GTAQ	Guinness Peat Aviation			01/APR/82	Leased
	C6-BEK	Bahamasair			01/APR/82	Sub-leased
	C6-BEK	Guinness Peat Aviation			28/NOV/83	Leased
	N131AW	America West			28/NOV/83	Sub-leased
20957	HR-SHA	SAHSA	2K6	26/SEP/74	01/OCT/74	
20958	C-GBPW	Pacific Western	275	03/JAN/75	13/JAN/75	
	N128AW	Guinness Peat			27/JUL/83	Leased
	N128AW	America West			27/JUL/83	Sub-leased
	C-GBPW	Pacific Western			JUN/85	
	N128AW	America West			28/FEB/86	Leased
	C-GBPW	Pacific Western			09/JUN/86	
20959	C-GCPW	Pacific Western	275	22/JAN/75	24/FEB/75	
	N126AW	Guinness Peat			20/JUN/83	
	N126AW	America West			20/JUN/83	Leased
20960	VT-ECP	Indian Airlines	2A8	13/SEP/74	26/SEP/74	
20961	VT-ECQ	Indian Airlines	2A8	18/SEP/74	26/SEP/74	
20962	VT-ECR	Indian Airlines	2A8	16/OCT/74	28/OCT/74	W/O APR/79 Madras Ap.
20963	VT-ECS	Indian Airlines	2A8		13/NOV/74	
20964	LV-LIU	Aerolineas Argentinas	287	10/OCT/74	10/DEC/74	
20965	LV-LIV	Aerolineas Argentinas	287	22/OCT/74	12/DEC/74	
20966	LV-LIW	Aerolineas Argentinas	287	25/NOV/74	11/DEC/74	
20967	N1799B	Boeing	2A1	02/JUL/74		
	PP-SMU	Vasp			04/SEP/74	
20968	PP-SMV	Vasp	2A1		09/AUG/74	
20969	PP-SMX	Vasp	2A1		28/AUG/74	W/O 02/APR/78, Sao Paulo
20970	PP-SMY	Vasp	2A1		04/OCT/74	W/O 24/MAY/82, Brasilia
20971	PP-SMZ	Vasp	2A1		07/NOV/74	
20976	C-GEPA	Eastern Provincial Airways	2E1	27/NOV/74	06/DEC/74	
	C-GEPA	CP Air			JAN/86	
21000	PP-VME	Varig	241	05/OCT/74	21/OCT/74	
21001	PP-VMF	Varig	241	07/NOV/74	19/NOV/74	
21002	PP-VMG	Varig	241	14/NOV/74	26/NOV/74	
21003	PP-VMH	Varig	241	09/DEC/74	19/DEC/74	
21004	PP-VMI	Varig	241	13/DEC/74	06/JAN/75	
21005	PP-VMJ	Varig	241	16/JAN/75	27/JAN/75	
21006	N87569	Boeing	241	07/FEB/75		
	PP-VMK	Varig			05/MAR/75	
21007	PP-VML	Varig	241	20/FEB/75	12/MAR/75	
21008	PP-VMM	Varig	241	03/MAR/75	12/MAR/75	
21009	PP-VMN	Varig	241	27/MAY/75	10/JUN/75	
21011	EI-ASL	Aer Lingus	248C	19/APR/75	02/MAY/75	
21012	PP-CJN	Cruzeiro	2C3	06/JAN/75	31/JAN/75	
21013	PP-CJO	Cruzeiro	2C3	10/JAN/75	31/JAN/75	
21014	PP-CJP	Cruzeiro	2C3	03/FEB/75	13/FEB/75	
21015	PP-CJR	Cruzeiro	2C3	13/MAR/75	25/MAr/75	
21016	PP-CJS	Cruzeiro	2C3	25/MAR/75	09/APr/75	
21017	PP-CJT	Cruzeiro	2C3	16/APR/75	01/MAY/75	
21063	7T-VEJ	Air Algerie	2D6	28/MAR/75	10/APR/75	
21064	7T-VEK	Air Algerie	2D6	10/APR/75	22/APR/75	
21065	7T-VEL	Air Algerie	2D6	20/MAY/75	04/JUN/75	
21066	N4951W	Wien Air Alaska	210C	02/MAY/75	14/MAY/75	
	N4951W	Wien Airlines			15/JUL/85	
	N4951W	Air Cal			20/NOV/85	Leased
21067	N4952W	Wien Air Alaska	210C	08/MAY/75	20/MAY/75	
	N4952W	Wien Airlines			28/JUN/85	
	N4952W	Air Cal			20/NOV/85	Leased
21069	N7385F	Frontier Airlines	291	13/MAY/75	27/MAY/75	
21073	C2-RN3	Air Nauru	2L7C	16/JUN/75	23/JUN/75	
21094	PP-SNA	Vasp	2A1	28/APR/75	20/AUG/75	
21095	PP-SNB	Vasp	2A1	12/SEP/75	02/OCT/75	
21109	9M-MBI	Malaysian Airline System	2H6C	14/OCT/75	30/OCT/75	
21112	C-GEPB	Eastern Provincial Airways	2E1	02/JUL/75	10/OCT/75	
	N4039W	Wien Air Alaska			16/MAY/76	Leased

BOEING 737

C/N	Registration	Owner/Operator	Series	First Flight	Delivery	Remarks
	C-GEPB	Eastern Provincial Airways			19/OCT/76	
	N70720	Aloha Airlines			15/JUN/77	Leased
	C-GEPB	Eastern Provincial Airways			13/DEC/77	
	EI-BDY	Guinness Peat			01/NOV/78	
	C-GNDD	Nordair			01/NOV/78	Leased
	C-GNDD	Royal Air Maroc			78	Sub-Leased
	C-GNDD	Nordair			78	Leased
	EI-BDY	Guinness Peat			02/APR/82	
	EI-BDY	Aer Lingus			04/APR/82	
	EI-BDY	Guinness Peat			01/MAY/84	Leased
	EI-BDY	Air Florida			01/MAY/84	Sub-leased
	EI-BDY	Guinness Peat			16/JUL/84	Leased
	EI-BDY	Air Cal			16/JUL/84	Sub-leased
21115	C-GEPW	Pacific Western	275C	31/OCT/75	12/DEC/75	
	C-GEPW	Guinness Peat			01/SEP/83	Leased
	N129AW	America West			01/SEP/83	Sub-leased
	C-GEPW	Pacific Western			FEB/85	
21116	C-GDPW	Pacific Western	275C	23/JUL/75	10/OCT/75	
21117	N26SW	Southwest Airlines	2H4	23/JUN/75	09/JUL/75	
21130	ZK-NAP	National Airways Corp.	219	21/JUL/75	04/SEP/75	
	ZK-NAP	Air New Zealand			01/JUN/78	
21131	ZK-NAQ	National Airways Corp.	219	01/AUG/75	20/NOV/75	
	PH-TVM	Transavia				Not taken-up
	EI-BCC	Guinness Peat			20/JUN/76	Leased
	EI-BCC	Nigeria Airways			20/JUN/76	Sub-leased
	EI-BCC	International Lease Finance			MAR/77	
	EI-BCC	Britannia Airways			APR/77	Leased
	N7362F	Frontier Airlines			01/NOV/77	Sub-leased
	N7362F	Britannia Airways			15/MAY/78	Leased
	OO-TEJ	TEA			18/MAY/78	Sub-leased
	G-BGNW	Britannia Airways			FEB/79	Leased
21135	OO-SDG	Sabena	229	31/MAY/75	12/JUN/75	
21136	OO-SDL	Sabena	229	12/JUN/75	25/JUN/75	
21137	OO-SDM	Sabena	229	18/JUN/75	01/JUL/75	
21138	OO-SDO	Sabena	229			
	VR-UEC	Royal Brunei	2M6	17/JUL/75	31/JUL/75	
	VS-UEC	Royal Brunei			01/JAN/84	
	V8-UEC	Royal Brunei			20/FEB/84	
21139	OO-SDP	Sabena	229	22/OCT/75	04/NOV/75	
21163	VT-EDR	Indian Airlines	2A8	26/SEP/75	08/OCT/75	
21164	VT-EDS	Indian Airlines	2A8	06/OCT/75	15/OCT/75	
21165	VC96-2115	Forca Aerea Brasiliera	2N3	05/MAR/76	18/MAR/76	
21166	VC96-2116	Forca Aerea Brasiliera	2N3	31/MAR/76	13/APR/76	
21167	0001	Venezuelan Government	2N1	09/JAN/76	30/JAN/76	
21169	ST-AFK	Sudan Airways	2J8C	29/AUG/75	15/SEP/75	
21170	ST-AFL	Sudan Airways	2J8C	11/SEP/75	18/SEP/75	
21172	CR-LOR	TAAG Angola	2M2C			Not taken-up
	D2-TAA	TAAG Angola		07/NOV/75	19/NOV/75	
	D2-TBA	TAAG Angola			NOV/80	W/O NOV/80
21173	CR-LOS	TAAG Angola	2M2C			Not taken-up
	D2-TAB	TAAG Angola		28/JAN/76	09/MAR/76	
	D2-TBC	TAAG Angola			80	
21176	OO-SDN	Sabena	229	03/SEP/75	03/DEC/75	
	OO-SDN	Gulf Air			22/OCT/77	Leased
	OO-SDN	Sabena			15/MAY/78	
	OO-SDN	Air Gabon			NOV/85	Leased
	OO-SDN	Sabena			DEC/85	
21177	OO-SDQ	Sabena	229	18/SEP/75	09/DEC/75	
21183	YI-AGJ	Iraqi Airways	270C	09/DEC/75	26/JAN/76	
21184	LN-SUI	Braathens Safe	205	14/NOV/75	26/NOV/75	
21186	C-GNDL	Nordair	242	30/OCT/75	12/NOV/75	
	N73AF	Air Florida			21/NOV/78	Leased
	C-GNDL	Nordair			31/JAN/79	
	C-GNDL	Guinness Peat			28/NOV/83	
	N132AW	America West			28/NOV/83	Leased
	N132AW	Guinness Peat			NOV/85	
	C-GNDL	Nordair			NOV/85	
21187	PP-SNC	Vasp	2A1C	12/DEC/75	29/JAN/76	W/O 22/FEB/83, Manaus
21188	PP-SND	Vasp	2A1C	22/DEC/75	29/JAN/76	
21191	SU-AYH	Egyptair	266	26/FEB/76	04/MAR/76	W/O 24/NOV/85, Luqa
21192	SU-AYI	Egyptair	266	02/MAR/76	26/MAR/76	
21193	SU-AYJ	Egyptair	266	18/MAR/76	30/MAR/76	
	PH-TVN	Transavia			23/MAR/77	Leased
	PH-TVN	Saudia			23/NOV/77	Sub-leased
	PH-TVN	Transavia			14/DEC/77	Leased
	SU-BBX	Egyptair			20/APR/80	
21194	SU-AYK	Egyptair	266	02/APR/76	21/APR/76	
21195	SU-AYL	Egyptair	266	20/APR/76	29/APR/76	
21196	SU-AYM	Egyptair	266	29/JUN/76	13/JUL/76	
	PH-TVO	Transavia			18/MAR/77	Leased
	PH-TVO	Saudia			18/OCT/77	Sub-leased
	PH-TVO	Transavia			19/NOV/77	Leased
	SU-BBW	Egyptair			20/APR/80	
21206	9K-ACV	Kuwait Airways	269	05/FEB/76	11/MAR/76	
	VR-BOX	Starjet Ltd			23/DEC/80	
	VR-BOX	Alghanim			23/DEC/80	Leased
	VR-BOX	Guinness Peat			DEC/85	
	PP-SNP	Vasp			DEC/85	Leased
21211	7T-VEN	Air Algerie	2D6	25/MAR/76	12/APR/76	
21212	7T-VEO	Air Algerie	2D6	06/MAY/76	19/MAY/76	
21214	CN-RMI	Royal Air Maroc	2B6	13/FEB/76	25/FEB/76	
21215	CN-RMJ	Royal Air Maroc	2B6	10/MAR/76	22/MAR/76	
21216	CN-RMK	Royal Air Maroc	2B6	06/APR/76	27/APR/76	
21219	LN-SUH	Braathens Safe	205	09/MAY/76	14/MAY/76	
21224	SX-BCA	Olympic Airways	284	16/JUN/76	23/JUN/76	
21225	SX-BCB	Olympic Airways	284	21/JUN/76	30/JUN/76	
21226	SU-AYN	Egyptian Government	200		28/MAY/76	
	SU-AYN	Egyptair			19/JUN/86	
21227	SU-AYO	Egyptair	266	08/JUL/76	20/JUL/76	
21231	OO-TEH	TEA	2M8	08/JUN/76	15/JUN/76	
	C6-BDZ	Bahamasair			14/DEC/78	Leased
	OO-TEH	TEA			10/JUN/79	
	C-GQBS	Quebecair			01/DEC/79	Leased
	OO-TEH	TEA			03/DEC/80	
	OO-TEH	Nigeria Airways			06/NOV/81	Leased
	OO-TEH	TEA			APR/82	

C/N	Registration	Owner/Operator	Series	First Flight	Delivery	Remarks
	C-GQBS	Quebecair			AUG/83	Leased
	OO-TEH	TEA			15/APR/85	
	OO-TEH	Kabo Air			MAY/85	Leased
	OO-TEH	TEA			15/MAR/86	
	OO-TEH	America West			15/MAR/86	Leased
21236	9J-AEA	Zambia Airways	2M9			Not taken-up
	9J-AEG	Zambia Airways		26/MAY/76	07/JUN/76	
21262	N27SW	Southwest Airlines	2H4	26/AUG/76	08/SEP/76	
21275	HZ-AGH	Saudia	268	16/JUL/76	30/JUL/76	
21276	HZ-AGI	Saudia	268	26/JUL/76	20/AUG/76	
21277	HZ-AGJ	Saudia	268	30/JUL/76	26/AUG/76	
21278	N1787B	Boeing	2L9	30/NOV/76		
	N8289V	Boeing				
	OY-APG	Maersk Air			10/DEC/76	
	OY-APG	Tunis Air			MAY/78	Leased
	OY-APG	Maersk Air			NOV/79	
	OY-APG	Guinness Peat			NOV/79	
	4R-ALC	Air Lanka			NOV/79	Leased
	4R-ALC	Guinness Peat			APR/80	
	F-GCGR	Aerotour			MAY/80	Leased
	F-GCGR	Guinness Peat			07/NOV/80	
	D2-TBT	TAAG Angola			31/JAN/81	Leased
	EI-BMY	Guinness Peat			31/MAY/82	
	EI-BMY	Nigeria Airways			DEC/82	Leased
	EI-BMY	Guinness Peat			APR/83	
	G-BKRO	Air Europe			25/APR/83	Leased
	EI-BMY	Guinness Peat			31/OCT/83	
	4R-ALC	Air Lanka			31/OCT/83	Leased
	4R-ALC	Guinness Peat			APR/85	
	C6-BFC	Bahamasair			JUL/85	Leased
21279	N1787B	Boeing	2L9	13/DEC/76		
	OY-APH	Maersk Air			22/DEC/76	
	OY-APH	Guinness Peat			NOV/79	
	OY-APH	Maersk Air			NOV/79	Leased
	EI-BII	Guinness Peat			04/JAN/80	
	F-GCGS	Aerotour			01/FEB/80	Leased
	F-GCGS	Guinness Peat			07/NOV/80	
	D2-TBU	TAAG Angola			24/JAN/81	Leased
	EI-BII	Guinness Peat			NOV/82	
	C6-BEQ	Bahamasair			DEC/82	Leased
21280	HZ-AGK	Saudia	268	01/SEP/76	01/NOV/76	
21281	HZ-AGL	Saudia	268	14/SEP/76	01/OCT/76	
21282	HZ-AGM	Saudia	268	20/OCT/76	04/NOV/76	
21283	HZ-AGN	Saudia	268	10/NOV/76	01/DEC/76	
21285	7T-VEQ	Air Algerie	2D6	20/SEP/76	13/OCT/76	
21286	7T-VER	Air Algerie	2D6	19/JAN/77	31/JAN/77	
21287	7T-VES	Air Algerie	2D6	21/MAR/77	01/APR/77	
21294	C-GFPW	Pacific Western	275C	19/DEC/76	23/DEC/76	
	C-GFPW	Mark Air			23/MAY/84	Leased
	C-GFPW	Pacific Western			08/AUG/84	
21295	TJ-CBD	Cameroon Airlines	2H7C	15/FEB/77	02/MAR/77	W/O AUG/84
21296	N1238E	Boeing	2N8	12/NOV/76		
	4W-ABZ	Yemen Airways			16/DEC/76	
	4W-ABZ	Guinness Peat			MAY/81	Leased
	4W-ABZ	Nigeria Airways			MAY/81	Sub-leased
	4W-ABZ	Yemen Airways			DEC/82	
21301	SX-BCC	Olympic Airways	284	29/SEP/76	13/OCT/76	
21302	SX-BCD	Olympic Airways	284	07/OCT/76	19/OCT/76	
21317	EP-AGA	Iran Air/Persepolis	286	25/FEB/77	12/MAR/77	
	EP-AGA	Iranian Government			80	
21335	G-BECG	Britannia Airways	204	31/MAR/77	14/APR/77	
21336	G-BECH	Britannia Airways	204	27/APR/77	06/MAY/77	
21337	N20SW	Southwest Airlines	2H4	06/MAY/77	16/MAY/77	
21338	N23SW	Southwest Airlines	2H4	15/JUN/77	27/JUN/77	
21339	N28SW	Southwest Airlines	2H4	28/JUN/77	11/JUL/77	
21340	N29SW	Southwest Airlines	2H4	19/AUG/77	01/SEP/77	
21355	A40-BC	Gulf Air	2P6	10/JUN/77	28/JUN/77	
21356	A40-BD	Gulf Air	2P6	06/JUL/77	15/JUL/77	
21357	A40-BE	Gulf Air	2P6	15/JUL/77	03/AUG/77	
21358	A40-BF	Gulf Air	2P6	28/JUL/77	09/AUG/77	
21359	A40-BG	Gulf Air	2P6	02/SEP/77	13/SEP/77	
	A40-BG	Britannia Airways			15/DEC/78	Leased
	A40-BG	Gulf Air			14/DEC/79	
	OO-ABB	Air Belgium			09/JAN/80	Leased
	OO-TYB	TEA			DEC/81	Sub-leased
	OO-TYB	Air Belgium			MAY/82	Leased
	A40-BG	Gulf Air			OCT/82	
21360	HZ-AGO	Saudia	268	02/MAR/77	20/MAR/77	
21361	HZ-AGP	Saudia	268	08/APR/77	29/APR/77	
21362	HZ-AGQ	Saudia	268	17/FEB/78	APR/78	
21397	PH-TVP	Transavia	2K2	06/JAN/78	19/JAN/78	
	PH-TVP	Air Malta			01/APR/81	Leased
	PH-TVP	Transavia			31/MAR/83	
	PH-TVP	Air Zaire			31/DEC/83	Leased
	PH-TVP	Transavia			31/MAR/84	
	G-BLEA	British Airtours			01/APR/84	Leased
	PH-TVP	Transavia			01/APR/85	
	C-GRCP	CP Air			01/OCT/85	Leased
21440	HS-TBA	Thai Airways	2P5	19/SEP/77	01/OCT/77	
21443	N8277V	Boeing	2C9	22/SEP/77		
	LX-LGH	Luxair			02/DEC/77	
21444	LX-LGI	Luxair	2C9		20/APR/78	
21445	LN-SUM	Braathens Safe	205	03/DEC/77	19/DEC/77	
21447	N50SW	Southwest Airlines	2H4	19/JAN/78	02/FEB/78	
21448	N51SW	Southwest Airlines	2H4	30/JAN/78	10/FEB/78	
21467	TR-LXL	Air Gabon	2Q2C	29/MAR/78	31/JUL/78	
21476	JA8443	Southwest Airlines	2Q3	09/MAY/78	26/MAY/78	
	JA8443	Japan Air Lines			AUG/78	Leased
	JA8443	Southwest Airlines			78	
21477	JA8444	Southwest Airlines	2Q3	01/DEC/78	18/JAN/79	W/O 26/AUG/82, Ishigaki
21478	JA8445	Southwest Airlines	2Q3	20/JUL/79	02/AUG/79	
21496	VT-EFK	Indian Airlines	2A8	30/SEP/77	10/NOV/77	
21497	VT-EFL	Indian Airlines	2A8	17/NOV/77	28/NOV/77	
	VT-EFL	Maldive Intl. Airlines			79	Leased
	VT-EFL	Indian Airlines			81	
	K-2371	Indian Air Force			12/OCT/81	Leased

BOEING 737

C/N	Registration	Owner/Operator	Series	First Flight	Delivery	Remarks
	VT-EFL	Indian Airlines			05/MAR/84	
21498	VT-EFM	Indian Airlines	2A8	02/DEC/77	08/DEC/77	
	K2370	Indian Air Force			11/APR/81	Leased
	VT-EFM	Indian Airlines			05/MAY/84	
21499	5U-MAF	Air Niger	2N9C			Not taken-up
	5U-BAG	Air Niger		24/MAR/78	28/APR/78	
21500	N70721	Aloha Airlines	284	18/MAY/77	15/SEP/77	
	N70721	Nigeria Airways			03/APR/82	Leased
	N70721	Aloha Airlines			16/APR/83	
	N70721	Western Airlines			MAY/83	Leased
21501	N70722	Aloha Airlines	284	14/JUN/77	31/AUG/77	
	N70722	Nigeria Airways			31/MAR/82	Leased
	N70722	Aloha Airlines			APR/83	
	N70722	Western Airlines			MAY/83	Leased
21508	N7391F	Frontier Airlines	291	27/APR/78	12/MAY/78	
	N7391F	United Airlines			13/JUN/85	
	N7391F	Frontier Airlines			13/JUN/85	Leased
	N977UA	United Airlines			SEP/85	
21509	N7392F	Frontier Airlines	291	26/MAY/78	09/JUN/78	
	N7392F	United Airlines			12/JUN/85	
	N7392F	Frontier Airlines			12/JUN/85	Leased
	N978UA	United Airlines			SEP/85	
21518	N977MP	International Lease Finance	2Q8	08/JUN/78	22/JUN/78	
	B-2611	Far Eastern Air Transport			22/JUN/78	Leased
	C-GNDS	Nordair			31/DEC/80	
21528	OY-API	Maersk Air	2L9	14/APR/78	28/APR/78	
	OY-API	Guinness Peat			22/OCT/80	
	G-BICV	Dan Air			23/OCT/80	Leased
	G-BICV	Nigeria Airways			01/DEC/80	Sub-leased
	G-BICV	Dan Air			15/JAN/81	Leased
	G-BICV	Transavia			02/APR/81	Sub-leased
	G-BICV	Dan Air			MAY/81	Leased
	G-BICV	Guinness Peat			01/NOV/83	
	C6-BEX	Bahamasair			01/NOV/83	Leased
21533	N52SW	Southwest Airlines	2H4	26/JUN/78	11/JUL/78	
21534	N53SW	Southwest Airlines	2H4	12/JUL/78	21/JUL/78	
21535	N54SW	Southwest Airlines	2H4	16/NOV/78	01/DEC/78	
21538	EL-AIL	Air Liberia	2Q5C	02/JUN/78	22/JUN/78	
	TN-AEE	LINA Congo			07/SEP/82	
21544	N7393F	Frontier Airlines	291	13/JUN/78	23/JUN/78	
	N7393F	United Airlines			12/JUN/85	
	N7393F	Frontier Airlines			12/JUN/85	Leased
	N979UA	United Airlines			SEP/85	
21545	N7394F	Frontier Airlines	291	06/JUL/78	19/JUL/78	
	N7394F	United Airlines			12/JUN/85	
	N7394F	Frontier Airlines			12/JUN/85	Leased
	N980UA	United Airlines			OCT/85	
21546	N7395F	Frontier Airlines	291	21/JUL/78	05/AUG/78	
	N7395F	Wien Air Alaska			20/MAY/82	Leased
	N7395F	Frontier Airlines			NOV/82	
	N7395F	Wien Air Alaska			30/OCT/83	Leased
	N7395F	Frontier Airlines			29/MAY/84	
	N7395F	United Airlines			13/JUN/85	
	N7395F	Frontier Airlines			13/JUN/85	Leased
	N981UA	United Airlines			OCT/85	
21593	N55SW	Southwest Airlines	2H4	27/NOV/78	08/DEC/78	
21596	OO-SBQ	Sobelair	229	16/AUG/78	25/AUG/78	
	OO-SBQ	Air Djibouti			DEC/83	Leased
	OO-SBQ	Sobelair			30/APR/86	
21597	N7340F	Frontier Airlines	2A1	21/MAR/78	30/AUG/78	
	N7340F	United Airlines			14/JUN/85	
	N7340F	Frontier Airlines			14/JUN/85	Leased
	N974UA	United Airlines			OCT/85	
21598	N7341F	Frontier Airlines	2A1	31/MAR/78	12/APR/78	
	N7341F	United Airlines			14/JUN/85	
	N7341F	Frontier Airlines			14/JUN/85	Leased
	N976UA	United Airlines			NOV/85	
21599	N1247E	Boeing	2A1			
	YS-08C	TACA			JUL/78	
	YS-08C	Braathens			26/SEP/85	Leased
	YS-08C	TACA			28/MAY/86	
	N171AW	Polaris Leasing			28 MAY/86	
	N171AW	America West			28/MAY/86	Leased
21612	A40-BH	Gulf Air	2P6	27/JUL/78	09/AUG/78	
21613	A6-AAA	UAE Government	2P6	20/OCT/78	06/NOV/78	
21616	C2-RN6	Air Nauru	2L7	18/SEP/78	29/SEP/78	
21639	C-GGPW	Pacific Western	275	29/OCT/78	10/NOV/78	
21640	N7396F	Frontier Airlines	291	06/OCT/78	19/OCT/78	
	N7396F	Air Florida			DEC/79	Leased
	N7396F	Frontier Airlines			24/JUN/80	
	N7396F	Wien Air Alaska			01/JUL/80	Leased
	N7396F	Frontier Airlines			15/JAN/81	
	N7396F	Sunland			24/JUN/81	Leased
	N7396F	Frontier Airlines			81	
	N7396F	United Airlines			13/JUN/85	
	N7396F	Frontier Airlines			13/JUN/85	Leased
	N982UA	United Airlines			OCT/85	
21641	N7397F	Frontier Airlines	291	13/OCT/78	26/OCT/78	
	N7397F	Wien Air Alaska			06/JAN/83	Leased
	N7397F	Frontier Airlines			11/SEP/83	
	N7397F	United Airlines			12/JUN/85	
	N7397F	Frontier Airlines			12/JUN/85	Leased
	N983UA	United Airlines			NOV/85	
21642	N7398F	Frontier Airlines	291	01/NOV/78	15/NOV/78	
	N7398F	United Airlines			14/JUN/85	
	N7398F	Frontier Airlines			14/JUN/85	Leased
	N984UA	United Airlines			15/NOV/85	
21645	ZK-NAR	Air New Zealand	219	29/MAY/78	12/OCT/78	
21653	HZ-AGR	Saudia	268	28/AUG/78	14/SEP/78	
21654	HZ-AGS	Saudia	268	08/SEP/78	26/SEP/78	
21665	N761N	Piedmont	201	15/SEP/78	11/OCT/78	
21666	N762N	Piedmont	201	11/DEC/78	21/DEC/78	
21667	N763N	Piedmont	201	18/DEC/78	10/JAN/79	
21677	A40-BI	Gulf Air	2P6	20/OCT/78	02/NOV/78	
21685	OY-APJ	Maersk Air	2L9	03/JAN/79	17/JAN/79	
	9M-MBZ	Malaysian Airline System			MAR/80	Leased

C/N	Registration	Owner/Operator	Series	First Flight	Delivery	Remarks
	OY-APJ	Maersk Air			82	
	G-BKAP	Dan Air			27/APR/82	Leased
	G-BKAP	Maersk Air			12/NOV/83	
	G-BKAP	Orion Airways			12/NOV/83	Leased
	G-BKAP	Wien Air Alaska			NOV/83	Sub-leased
	G-BKAP	Orion Airways			84	Leased
	OY-APJ	Maersk Air			31/OCT/84	
	OY-APJ	Guinness Peat			31/OCT/84	
	PP-SNO	VASP			17/DEC/84	Leased
21686	OY-APK	Maersk Air	2L9	09/JAN/79	22/JAN/79	
	OY-APK	Guyana Airways			01/SEP/80	Leased
	OY-APK	Maersk Air			81	
	9M-MBY	Malaysian Airline System			15/APR/81	Leased
	OY-APK	Maersk Air			10/JUN/82	
	PP-SNK	Vasp			17/AUG/82	Leased
	OY-APK	Guinness Peat			17/AUG/84	Purchased
	PP-SNK	Vasp			17/AUG/84	Leased
21687	N821L	International Lease Finance	2Q8	31/JAN/79	13/FEB/79	
	B-2615	Far Eastern Air Transport			13/FEB/79	Leased
21693	G-BFVA	Britannia Airways	204	07/NOV/78	20/NOV/78	
21694	G-BFVB	Britannia Airways	204	13/NOV/78	28/NOV/78	
	C-GNDW	Nordair			01/MAY/85	Leased
	G-BFVB	Britannia Airways			30/APR/86	
21710	5H-ATC	Air Tanzania	2R8C	05/DEC/78	15/DEC/78	
21711	5H-MRK	Air Tanzania	2R8C	03/MAY/79	16/MAY/79	
21712	C-GIPW	Pacific Western	275		FEB/79	
21713	C-GJPW	Pacific Western	275		SEP/79	
21714	EI-BEB	Aer Lingus	248		APR/79	
21715	EI-BEC	Aer Lingus	248		JUN/79	
	TF-VLM	Eagle Air			07/APR/82	Leased
	TF-VLM	Britannia			07/APR/82	Sub-leased
	TF-VLM	Eagle Air			OCT/82	Leased
	EI-BEC	Aer Lingus			MAR/83	
21716	N1262E	Boeing	217	09/MAR/79		
	C-GCPM	CP Air			22/MAY/79	
21717	C-GCPN	CP Air	217	07/JUN/79	20/JUN/79	
21718	C-GCPO	CP Air	217	20/JUN/79	03/JUL/79	
21719	C-GNDC	ITEL	2Q9	15/JAN/79	26/JAN/79	
	C-GNDC	Nordair			26/JAN/79	Leased
	C-GNDC	ITEL			JUN/79	
	OO-TEK	TEA			16/JUN/79	Leased
	C-GQBT	Quebecair			01/NOV/79	Sub-leased
	OO-TEK	TEA			31/MAY/80	Leased
	C-GQBT	Quebecair			31/OCT/80	Sub-leased
	C-GQBT	ITEL			DEC/80	
	C-GQBT	GATX Leasing			DEC/80	
	C-GQBT	TEA			DEC/80	Leased
	C-GQBT	Quebecair			DEC/80	Sub-leased
	OO-TEK	TEA			24/APR/81	Leased
	C-GQBT	Quebecair			01/NOV/81	Sub-leased
	OO-TEK	TEA			APR/82	Leased
	N385PA	Pan American			APR/83	Leased
	OO-TEK	TEA			SEP/85	
	C-GQBT	Quebecair			15/NOV/85	Leased
	OO-TEK	TEA			MAR/86	
	OO-TEK	Pan American			MAY/86	Leased
	OO-TEK	TEA			OCT/86	Sched.return
21720	N37AF	ITEL	2Q9	18/JAN/79	30/JAN/79	
	N37AF	Air Florida			30/JAN/79	Leased
	N37AF	ITEL			JUL/80	
	N37AF	Great American Insurance			JUL/80	
	N37AF	Air Florida			JUL/80	Leased
	N37AF	Transavia			01/MAY/81	Leased
	N37AF	Air Florida			29/OCT/81	
	N37AF	Transavia			15/APR/82	Leased
	N37AF	Britannia			82	Sub-leased
	N37AF	Transavia			30/OCT/82	Leased
	N37AF	Air Florida			30/OCT/82	
	N458AC	Air Cal			01/NOV/84	Leased
21721	N56SW	Southwest Airlines	2H4	25/JAN/79	08/FEB/79	
21722	N57SW	Southwest Airlines	2H4	12/APR/79	25/APR/79	
21723	D2-TAH	TAAG Angola	2M2	09/APR/79	27/APR/79	
	D2-TBD	TAAG Angola			80	
21728	C-GNDC	Nordair	242C	04/JUN/79	15/JUN/79	
21729	LN-SUK	Braathens Safe	205	30/APR/79	11/MAY/79	
21732	9M-MBJ	Malaysian Airline System	246	28/FEB/79	19/MAR/79	
21733	A40-BJ	Gulf Air	2P6	28/MAR/79	10/APR/79	
21734	A40-BK	Gulf Air	2P6	04/APR/79	18/APR/79	W/O 22/SEP/83, Nr. Dubai
21735	OO-TEM	International Lease Finance	2Q8	12/JUN/79	20/JUN/79	
	OO-TEM	TEA			20/JUN/79	Leased
	OO-TEM	Southwest Airlines			27/FEB/81	Sub-leased
	OO-TEM	TEA			30/APR/83	Leased
	OO-TEM	International Lease Finance			01/OCT/83	
	N133AW	America West			27/OCT/83	Leased
21736	OO-TEL	TEA	2M8	16/FEB/79	01/MAR/79	
	OO-TEL	Libyan Arab Airlines			08/OCT/79	Leased
	OO-TEL	TEA			25/MAR/80	
	4X-ABL	El Al			01/OCT/80	Leased
	OO-TEL	TEA			82	
	PH-RAL	Rotterdam Airlines			28/NOV/83	Leased
	OO-TEL	TEA			01/APR/84	
21738	OO-SDR	Sabena	229C	17/MAY/79	22/MAY/79	
21739	N70723	Aloha Airlines	297	09/MAR/79	28/MAR/79	
	N70723	Pan American			12/OCT/83	Leased
21740	N70724	Aloha Airlines	297	15/MAR/79	29/MAR/79	
	N70724	Pan American			22/SEP/83	Leased
21747	N7342F	Frontier Airlines	291	07/FEB/79	20/FEB/79	
	N7342F	United Airlines			18/JUL/85	
	N7342F	Frontier Airlines			18/JUL/85	Leased
	N985UA	United Airlines			19/FEB/86	
21748	N7343F	Frontier Airlines	291	22/FEB/79	07/MAR/79	
	N7343F	United Airlines			19/JUL/85	
	N7343F	Frontier Airlines			19/JUL/85	Leased
	N986UA	United Airlines			07/MAR/86	
21749	N7344F	Frontier Airlines	291	16/APR/79	30/APR/79	

BOEING 737

C/N	Registration	Owner/Operator	Series	First Flight	Delivery	Remarks
	N7344F	United Airlines			17/JUL/85	
	N7344F	Frontier Airlines			17/JUL/85	Leased
	N987UA	United Airlines			14/MAR/86	
21750	N7345F	Frontier Airlines	291	08/MAY/79	21/MAY/79	
	N7345F	United Airlines			17/JUL/85	
	N7345F	Frontier Airlines			17/JUL/85	Leased
	N988UA	United Airlines			MAR/86	
21751	N7346F	Frontier Airlines	291	11/MAY/79	24/MAY/79	
	N7346F	United Airlines			19/JUL/85	
	N7346F	Frontier Airlines			19/JUL/85	Leased
	N989UA	United Airlines			MAR/86	
21763	LN-NPB	Busy Bee	2R4C	25/APR/79	12/DEC/79	
21765	LN-SUB	Braathens Safe	2Q5	07/AUG/79	21/AUG/79	
21766	JA8452	All Nippon Airways	281		JUN/79	
21767	JA8453	All Nippon Airways	281		JUL/79	
21768	JA8454	All Nippon Airways	281		JUL/79	
21769	JA8455	All Nippon Airways	281	03/JUL/79	24/JUL/79	
21770	JA8456	All Nippon Airways	281	05/JUL/79	27/JUL/79	
21771	JA8457	All Nippon Airways	281	02/AUG/79	18/SEP/79	
21774	G-BMHG	Air Europe	2S3	22/MAR/79	05/APR/79	
	G-BMHG	British Airtours			01/NOV/84	Leased
	G-BMHG	Air Europe			23/APR/85	
	G-BMHG	Guinness Peat			23/APR/85	
	OO-TYD	TEA			10/MAY/85	Leased
	EI-BPY	Guinness Peat			16/SEP/85	
	EI-BPY	Western Airlines			28/SEP/85	Leased
21775	G-BMEC	Air Europe	2S3	20/APR/79	02/MAY/79	
	G-BMEC	British Airtours			01/MAY/83	Leased
	EI-BPR	Guinness Peat			28/APR/85	
	EI-BPR	Air Cal			05/MAY/85	Leased
21776	G-BMOR	Air Europe	2S3	18/MAY/79	31/MAY/79	
	G-BMOR	British Airtours			01/MAY/83	Leased
	G-BMOR	Air Europe			APR/85	
	G-BMOR	Guinness Peat			26/APR/85	
	G-BMOR	Midway Express			26/APR/85	Leased
	EI-BPW	Guinness Peat			85	
	EI-BPW	Western Airlines			JUN/85	Leased
21790	N1275E	Boeing	236	12/SEP/79		
	N1285E	Boeing			07/FEB/80	
	G-BGDA	British Airways			04/DEC/81	
21791	G-BGDB	British Airways	236	08/JAN/80	14/FEB/80	
21792	G-BGDC	British Airways	236	10/JAN/80	07/FEB/80	
21793	G-BGDD	British Airways	236	13/FEB/80	23/FEB/80	
21794	G-BGDE	British Airways	236	04/MAR/80	12/MAR/80	
21795	G-BGDF	British Airways	236	07/MAR/80	20/MAR/80	
21796	G-BGDG	British Airways	236	18/MAR/80	07/APR/80	
21797	G-BGDH	British Airways	236	01/APR/80	14/APR/80	
21798	G-BGDI	British Airways	236	18/APR/80	30/APR/80	
21799	G-BGDJ	British Airways	236	25/APR/80	07/APR/80	
21800	G-BGDK	British Airways	236	29/APR/80	16/MAY/80	
21801	G-BGDL	British Airways	236	28/MAY/80	09/JUN/80	
21802	G-BGDN	British Airways	236	31/MAY/80	11/JUN/80	
21803	G-BGDO	British Airways	236	24/JUN/80	25/JUL/80	
21804	G-BGDP	British Airways	236	04/AUG/80	13/AUG/80	
	G-BGDP	British Airtours			01/APR/82	Leased
21805	G-BGDR	British Airways	236	04/SEP/80	18/SEP/80	
	G-BGDR	British Airtours			01/APR/82	Leased
	G-BGDR	British Airways			03/NOV/84	
21806	G-BGDS	British Airways	236	11/SEP/80	26/SEP/80	
21807	G-BGDT	British Airways	236	21/OCT/80	04/NOV/80	
21808	G-BGDU	British Airways	236	04/NOV/80	13/NOV/80	
21809	VR-UED	Royal Brunei	2M6C	29/JAN/80	05/MAR/80	
	VS-UED	Royal Brunei			01/JAN/84	
	V8-UED	Royal Brunei			20/FEB/84	
21810	HS-TBB	Thai Airways	2P5	24/SEP/79	10/OCT/79	W/O 15/APR/85, Phuket.
21811	N59SW	Southwest Airlines	2H4	10/OCT/79	23/OCT/79	
21812	N60SW	Southwest Airlines	2H4	17/OCT/79	05/NOV/79	
21815	N768N	Piedmont	201	12/JUL/79	27/JUL/79	
21816	N769N	Piedmont	201	15/JUL/79	07/AUG/79	
21817	N772N	Piedmont	201	14/SEP/79	26/SEP/79	
21818	N773N	Piedmont	201	23/SEP/79	16/OCT/79	
21819	C-GKPW	Pacific Western	275	03/JAN/80	09/JAN/80	
21820	N491WC	Wien Air Alaska	210	24/MAY/79	11/JUN/79	
	N491WC	Arkia			08/MAY/81	
	N491WC	Air Berlin			08/MAY/81	Leased
	N491WC	Arkia			01/DEC/81	
	4X-BAA	Arkia			MAR/82	
	G-BKNH	IACO			01/APR/83	
	G-BKNH	Dan Air			01/APR/83	Leased
21821	N492WC	Wien Air Alaska	210C			
	N492WC	Alaska Airlines			SEP/84	
	N492WC	Wien Air Alaska			SEP/84	Leased
	N743AS	Alaska Airlines			OCT/84	
21822	N493WC	Wien Air Alaska	210C	26/SEP/79	23/OCT/79	
	N493WC	Alaska Airlines			29/NOV/84	
	N493WC	Wien Air Alaska			29/NOV/84	Leased
	N744AS	Alaska Airlines			JAN/85	
21839	OO-SBS	Sobelair	229	30/JUL/79	14/AUG/79	
	OO-SBS	America West			01/AUG/86	Leased
	OO-SBS	Sobelair			APR/87	Sched.return
21840	OO-SBT	Sobelair	229	07/NOV/79	20/NOV/79	
21926	N201FE	Federal Express	2S2C	14/AUG/79	29/AUG/79	
	N201FE	Sunland			13/MAY/81	Leased
	N201FE	Federal Express			81	
	N720A	ARAMCO			AUG/81	
21927	N203FE	Federal Express	2S2C	07/SEP/79	19/SEP/79	
	CC-CHU	LAN Chile			06/MAR/81	
21928	N204FE	Federal Express	2S2C	18/SEP/79	28/SEP/79	
	N715A	ARAMCO			27/DEC/80	
21929	N205FE	Federal Express	2S2C	08/OCT/79	12/OCT/79	
	N716A	ARAMCO			15/MAR/81	
21955	OO-TEN	TEA	2M8	15/APR/80	24/APR/80	
	G-BHCL	Orion Airways			24/APR/80	Leased
	OO-TEN	TEA			26/JAN/81	
	OO-TEN	Nigeria Airways			06/NOV/81	Leased
	OO-TEN	TEA			JUN/82	

C/N	Registration	Owner/Operator	Series	First Flight	Delivery	Remarks
	N141AW	America West			20/APR/84	
21957	VR-BEG	Maritime Investments	2S9	13/NOV/79	11/DEC/79	
21959	N206FE	International Lease Finance	2Q8C	12/OCT/79	26/OCT/79	
	N206FE	Federal Express			26/OCT/79	Leased
	N206FE	International Lease Finance			27/JAN/81	
	N206FE	Alaska Airlines			29/JAN/81	Leased
	N741AS	Alaska Airlines			MAY/81	Leased
21960	G-BGTY	International Lease Finance	2Q8	15/FEB/80	21/MAR/80	
	G-BGTY	Orion Airways			21/MAR/80	Leased
	G-BGTY	America West			10/OCT/85	Sub-leased
	G-BGTY	Orion Airways			11/MAR/86	Leased
21970	N61SW	Southwest Airlines	2H4	24/OCT/79	05/NOV/79	
21973	TS-IOC	Tunis Air	2H3	03/OCT/79	22/OCT/79	
21974	TS-IOD	Tunis Air	2H3C	31/OCT/79	14/NOV/79	
21975	N774N	ITEL	2Q9	19/OCT/79	07/NOV/79	
	N774N	Piedmont			07/NOV/79	Leased
21976	N775N	ITEL	2Q9	07/DEC/79	20/DEC/79	
	N775N	Piedmont			20/DEC/79	Leased
21980	N7347F	Frontier Airlines	291	10/AUG/79	21/SEP/79	
	N7347F	United Airlines			17/JUL/85	
	N7347F	Frontier Airlines			17/JUL/85	Leased
	N990UA	United Airlines			APR/86	
21981	N7348F	Frontier Airlines	291	11/SEP/79	02/OCT/79	
	N7348F	United Airlines			18/JUL/85	
	N7348F	Frontier Airlines			18/JUL/85	Leased
	N991UA	United Airlines			APR/86	
22018	N778N	Piedmont	2Q8	04/MAR/80	01/APR/80	
22022	LN-SUT	Braathens Safe	205	05/NOV/79	21/NOV/79	
22023	G-BGTW	Orion Airways	2T5	25/JAN/80	11/FEB/80	
	G-BGTW	International Lease Finance			07/MAR/85	
	G-BGTW	Orion Airways			DEC/84	Leased
	G-BGTW	International Lease Finance			14/MAR/85	
	PH-TVX	Transavia			14/MAR/85	
	OE-ILE	Lauda Air			15/DEC/85	Leased
	PH-TVX	Transavia			88	Sched.return
22024	G-BGTV	Orion Airways	2T5	12/FEB/80	27/FEB/80	
	EI-BPV	Guinness Peat			21/MAR/85	
	EI-BPV	Eastern Provincial			MAR/85	Leased
	EI-BPV	Guinness Peat			APR/85	
	EI-BPV	Haiti Air			APR/85	Leased
	EI-BPV	Guinness Peat			FEB/86	
	C-FHCP	CP Air			28/FEB/86	Leased
	C-FHCP	CP Air			24/APR/86	Purchased
22025	PH-TVR	Transavia	2K2	04/MAR/80	26/MAR/80	
22026	G-BGJE	British Airtours	236	07/MAR/80	21/MAR/80	
	G-BGJE	British Airways			23/OCT/82	Leased
	G-BGJE	British Airtours			MAR/84	
22027	G-BGJF	British Airtours	236	04/APR/80	17/APR/80	
	G-BGJF	British Airways			FEB/82	Leased
	G-BGJF	British Airtours			83	
22028	G-BGJG	British Airtours	236	14/APR/80	29/APR/80	
	G-BGJG	British Airways			FEB/82	Leased
	G-BGJG	British Airtours			83	
22029	G-BGJH	British Airtours	236	02/MAY/80	13/MAY/80	
	G-BGJH	British Airways			83	
22030	G-BGJI	British Airtours	236	21/AUG/80	01/OCT/80	
22031	N8293V	Boeing	236	03/DEC/80		
	G-BGJJ	British Airtours			18/DEC/80	
	G-BGJJ	British Airways			29/OCT/83	
	G-BGJJ	British Airtours			MAR/84	
22032	G-BGJK	British Airtours	236	25/FEB/81	10/MAR/81	
22033	G-BGJL	British Airtours	236	26/FEB/81	02/APR/81	W/O 22/AUG/85, Manchester Ap.
22034	G-BGJM	British Airtours	236	01/APR/81	08/APR/81	
22050	HZ-AGT	Saudia	268	28/NOV/79	14/DEC/79	
	HZ-HM4	Saudi Royal Flight			12/JAN/80	
22051	N725AL	Aloha Airlines	297	17/JAN/80	29/JAN/80	
	N725AL	Pacific Express			11/NOV/83	Leased
	N725AL	Air Cal			01/MAY/84	
22054	N53AF	Air Florida	2T4	05/DEC/79	17/DEC/79	
	G-BJXL	Air Europe			01/MAY/82	Leased
	N53AF	Air Florida			NOV/82	
	N53AF	GATX Leasing			05/MAY/83	
	G-BJXL	Air Europe			05/MAY/83	Leased
	G-BJXL	GATX Leasing			31/OCT/83	
	G-BJXL	Dan Air			31/OCT/83	Leased
	G-BJXL	Nordair			01/NOV/84	Sub-leased
	G-BJXL	Dan Air			03/MAY/85	Leased
	C-GNDG	Nordair			01/NOV/85	Sub-leased
	G-BJXL	Dan Air			29/APR/86	Leased
22055	N54AF	Air Florida	2T4	15/JAN/80	28/JAN/80	
	N54AF	Air Europe			30/APR/81	Leased
	N54AF	Air Florida			NOV/81	
	G-BJXM	Air Europe			01/MAY/82	Leased
	N54AF	Air Florida			NOV/82	
	N54AF	GATX Leasing			08/APR/83	
	N54AF	Wien Air Alaska			08/APR/83	Leased, WFU DEC/84
	N54AF	GATX Leasing			JUL/85	
	N54AF	Midway Airlines			JUL/85	Leased
22056	C-GDPA	Dome Petroleum	2T2C	02/APR/80	22/APR/80	
	C-GDPA	Pacific Western			01/JUN/84	
22057	G-BGRU	Britannia Airways	204			Not taken-up
	G-BGYJ	Britannia Airways		21/NOV/79	07/JAN/80	
	G-BGYJ	Royal Brunei			NOV/81	Leased
	G-BGYJ	Britannia Airways			08/DEC/81	
	G-BGYJ	Guinness Peat			17/OCT/84	Leased
	G-BGYJ	Midway Express			17/OCT/84	Sub-leased
	G-BGYJ	Britannia Airways			01/MAY/85	
22058	G-BGRV	Britannia Airways	204			Not taken-up
	G-BGYK	Britannia Airways			JAN/80	
22059	G-BGYL	Britannia Airways	204		FEB/80	
22060	N62SW	Southwest Airlines	2H4	31/JAN/80	27/MAR/80	
22061	N63SW	Southwest Airlines	2H4	05/FEB/80	27/MAR/80	
22062	N64SW	Southwest Airlines	2H4	25/FEB/80	27/MAR/80	
22070	OY-APL	Maersk Air	2L9	29/OCT/79	09/NOV/79	
	D-ADDA	Supair			80	Leased
	OY-APL	Maersk Air			NOV/80	

BOEING 737

C/N	Registration	Owner/Operator	Series	First Flight	Delivery	Remarks
	C-GQBQ	Quebecair			18/NOV/81	
	C2-RN8	Air Nauru			14/SEP/82	
22071	OY-APN	Maersk Air	2L9	16/NOV/79	04/DEC/79	
	OY-APN	Arab International Air			20/NOV/80	Leased
	SU-BCJ	Arab International Air			20/JAN/81	Purchased
	G-BJSO	Guinness Peat			28/NOV/81	
	G-BJSO	Monarch Airlines			04/DEC/81	Leased
	EI-BOJ	Guinness Peat			08/NOV/83	
	EI-BOJ	Nigeria Airways			08/NOV/83	Leased
	EI-BOJ	Guinness Peat			15/MAY/84	
	G-GPAB	Orion Airways			15/MAY/84	Leased
	EI-BOJ	Guinness Peat			15/NOV/84	
	EI-BOJ	Midway Express			15/NOV/84	Leased
	EI-BOJ	Guinness Peat			27/APR/85	
	VR-HKP	Dragon Air			14/JUN/85	Leased
22072	OY-APO	Maersk Air	2L9	30/NOV/79	14/DEC/79	
	OY-APO	Arab International Air			30/NOV/80	Leased
	OY-APO	Maersk Air			JUN/81	
	C-GQBA	Quebecair			26/AUG/82	
	C2-RN9	Air Nauru			SEP/83	
	C-FACP	Citibank Leasing Canada			OCT/85	
	C-FACP	CP Air			OCT/85	Leased
22074	C-GNDM	Nordair	242	14/NOV/79	30/NOV/79	
22075	N8536Z	Boeing	242	04/JAN/80		
	C-GNDR	Nordair			31/JAN/80	
22086	C-GLPW	Pacific Western	275	16/MAY/80	23/MAY/80	
22087	C-GMPW	Pacific Western	275	04/JUN/80	20/JUN/80	
22088	ZK-NAS	Air New Zealand	219	16/JUN/80	01/JUL/80	
22089	N7349F	Frontier Airlines	291	17/JAN/80	15/FEB/80	
	N7349F	United Airlines			18/JUL/85	
	N7349F	Frontier Airlines			18/JUL/85	
	N992UA	United Airlines			MAY/86	
22090	OO-TEO	TEA	2M8	02/MAY/80	19/MAY/80	
	4X-ABM	El Al			01/OCT/80	Leased
	OO-TEO	TEA			NOV/82	
	OO-TEO	Kabo Air			FEB/83	Leased
	OO-TEO	TEA			JUN/84	
	OO-TEO	Kabo Air			AUG/84	Leased
	OO-TEO	TEA			01/MAR/86	
	OO-TEO	LINA Congo			01/MAR/86	Leased
22113	N5573K	Boeing	230	10/MAR/81		
	D-ABFB	Lufthansa			15/APR/83	
22114	N1782B	Boeing	230			
	D-ABFA	Lufthansa		17/APR/81	28/MAY/81	
22115	D-ABFC	Lufthansa	230	20/SEP/80	19/DEC/80	
22116	D-ABFD	Lufthansa	230	13/OCT/80	16/JAN/81	
22117	D-ABFF	Lufthansa	230	22/DEC/80	27/JAN/81	
22118	D-ABFH	Lufthansa	230	09/JAN/81	30/JAN/81	
22119	N8298V	Boeing	230	15/JAN/81		
	D-ABFK	Lufthansa			02/FEB/81	
22120	N8296V	Boeing	230	20/JAN/81		
	D-ABFL	Lufthansa			06/FEB/81	
22121	D-ABFM	Lufthansa	230	30/JAN/81	13/FEB/81	
22122	D-ABFN	Lufthansa	230	04/FEB/81	19/FEB/81	
22123	D-ABFP	Lufthansa	230	13/FEB/81	05/MAR/81	
22124	D-ABFR	Lufthansa	230	20/FEB/81	12/MAR/81	
22125	D-ABFS	Lufthansa	230	16/MAR/81	02/APR/81	
22126	D-ABFU	Lufthansa	230	23/MAR/81	09/APR/81	
22127	N5573K	Boeing	230	27/MAR/81		
	D-ABFW	Lufthansa			16/APR/81	
22128	D-ABFX	Lufthansa	230	07/APR/81	23/APR/81	
22129	D-ABFY	Lufthansa	230	08/APR/81	14/MAY/81	
22130	D-ABFZ	Lufthansa	230	08/MAY/81	21/MAY/81	
22131	D-ABHA	Lufthansa	230	21/MAY/81	04/JUN/81	
22132	N8298V	Boeing	230	05/JUN/81		
	D-ABHB	Lufthansa			18/JUN/81	
22133	D-ABHC	Lufthansa	230	10/JUN/81	01/JUL/81	
22134	D-ABHF	Lufthansa	230	26/JUN/81	16/JUL/81	
	D-ABHF	Condor			JUL/81	Leased
22135	D-ABHH	Lufthansa	230	13/JUL/81	30/JUL/81	
22136	D-ABHK	Lufthansa	230	20/JUL/81	11/AUG/81	
	D-ABHK	Condor			AUG/81	Leased
22137	N8297V	Boeing	230			
	D-ABHL	Lufthansa			AUG/81	
22138	N1800B	Boeing	230			
	D-ABHM	Lufthansa			AUG/81	
22139	D-ABHN	Lufthansa	230		SEP/81	
22140	D-ABHP	Lufthansa	230		SEP/81	
22141	D-ABHR	Lufthansa	230	04/SEP/81	24/SEP/81	
22142	D-ABHS	Lufthansa	230	14/SEP/81	01/OCT/81	
22143	D-ABHU	Lufthansa	230	02/FEB/82	16/FEB/82	
22148	C-GENL	Eldorado Aviation	255C	30/APR/80	20/MAY/80	
	C-GENL	Esso Resources			15/MAR/83	
22159	C-GNPW	Pacific Western	275	15/JUL/80	28/JUL/80	
22160	C-GOPW	Pacific Western	275	05/AUG/80	30/SEP/80	
22161	G-BOSL	Owners Service	2U4	21/MAR/80	17/APR/80	
	G-BOSL	Britannia Airways			17/APR/80	Leased
	G-BOSL	International Lease Finance			01/JUL/83	
	G-BOSL	Owners Service			01/JUL/83	
	G-BOSL	Britannia Airways			01/JUL/83	Leased
	G-ILFC	International Lease Finance			01/NOV/83	
	G-ILFC	Dan Air			01/NOV/83	Leased
	G-ILFC	Wien Air Alaska			01/NOV/83	Sub-leased
	G-ILFC	Dan Air			MAY/84	Leased
22255	C-GCPP	CP Air	217	09/MAY/80	28/MAY/80	
22256	C-GCPQ	CP Air	217	02/JUN/80	18/JUN/80	
22257	C-GCPR	CP Air	217			Not taken-up
	C-GCPS	CP Air			APR/81	
22258	C-GCPS	CP Air	217			Not taken-up
	C-GCPT	CP Air		28/MAY/81	10/JUN/81	
22259	C-GCPU	CP Air	217	05/JUN/81	12/JUN/81	
22260	C-GCPV	CP Air	217	17/JUL/81	29/JUL/81	
22264	C-GPPW	Pacific Western	275	03/APR/81	10/APR/81	
22265	N56807	Boeing	275	03/APR/81		
	C-GQPW	Pacific Western			15/APR/81	W/O MAR/84

C/N	Registration	Owner/Operator	Series	First Flight	Delivery	Remarks
22266	C-GRPW	Pacific Western	275	08/MAY/81	28/MAY/81	
22267	HS-TBC	Thai Airways	2P5	25/JUL/80	18/AUG/80	
22273	N779N	Piedmont	201	08/JUL/80	17/JUL/80	
22274	N780N	Piedmont	201		22/JUL/80	
22275	N781N	Piedmont	201	24/JUL/80	27/OCT/80	
22276	C-GQBU	Quebecair	296			Not taken-up
	C-GQBB	Quebecair		06/MAY/80	21/MAY/80	
	N387PA	Pan American			09/MAY/83	Leased
	C-GQBB	Quebecair			10/MAY/85	
22277	C-GQBV	Quebecair	296			Not taken-up
	C-GQBJ	Quebecair		10/JUN/80	24/JUN/80	
	G-BJZV	Britannia			26/APR/82	Leased
	C-GQBJ	Quebecair			06/NOV/82	
	N388PA	Pan American			25/APR/83	Leased
	C-GQBJ	Quebecair			10/MAY/85	
22278	G-BJFH	Air Europe	2S3	29/FEB/80	18/MAR/80	
	G-BJFH	Air Florida			10/NOV/81	Leased
	G-BJFH	Air Europe			MAY/82	
	G-BJFH	Air Florida			NOV/82	Leased
	G-BJFH	Air Europe			18/APR/83	
22279	G-BMSM	Air Europe	2S3	14/MAR/80	27/MAR/80	
	G-BMSM	Air Florida			01/NOV/80	Leased
	G-BMSM	Air Europe			30/APR/81	
	G-BMSM	Air Florida			NOV/81	
	G-BMSM	Air Europe			MAY/82	
	G-BMSM	British Airtours			01/NOV/84	Leased
	G-BMSM	Air Europe			30/APR/85	
	EI-BRB	Guinness Peat			16/JUN/85	
	EI-BRB	Western Airlines			16/JUN/85	Leased
22280	VT-EGD	Indian Airlines	2A8	29/MAY/80	18/JUN/80	
22281	VT-EGE	Indian Airlines	2A8	25/JUN/80	16/JUL/80	
22282	VT-EGF	Indian Airlines	2A8	02/JUL/80	23/JUL/80	
22283	VT-EGG	Indian Airlines	2A8	31/JUL/80	12/AUG/80	
22284	VT-EGH	Indian Airlines	2A8	06/FEB/81	18/FEB/81	
22285	VT-EGI	Indian Airlines	2A8	04/SEP/81	23/SEP/81	
22286	VT-EGJ	Indian Airlines	2A8	16/SEP/81	30/SEP/81	
22296	PH-TVS	Transavia	2K2	16/MAY/80	05/JUN/80	
	EC-DVN	Hispania			01/APR/85	Leased
	PH-TVS	Transavia			01/APR/88	Sched.return
22300	SX-BCE	Olympic Airways	284	10/JUN/80	25/JUN/80	
22301	SX-BCF	Olympic Airways	284	10/JUL/80	24/JUL/80	
22338	SX-BCG	Olympic Airways	284	14/AUG/80	21/AUG/80	
22339	SX-BCH	Olympic Airways	284	12/AUG/80	26/AUG/80	
22340	HR-	SAHSA	2K6			Not taken-up
	CC-CIM	Ladeco		23/JUN/80	11/JUL/80	
	N148AW	America West			23/APR/86	
22341	C-GCPX	CP Air	217	24/JUL/81	06/AUG/81	
22342	C-GCPY	CP Air	217			
22343	SX-BCI	Olympic Airways	284	12/DEC/80	23/DEC/80	
22352	N782N	Piedmont	201	12/DEC/80	23/DEC/80	
22353	N783N	Piedmont	201	09/JAN/81	23/JAN/81	
22354	N784N	Piedmont	201	28/JAN/81	10/FEB/81	
22355	N785N	Piedmont	201	15/FEB/81	27/FEB/81	
22356	N67SW	Southwest Airlines	2H4	14/NOV/80	03/DEC/80	
22357	N68SW	Southwest Airlines	2H4	05/DEC/80	17/DEC/80	
22358	N71SW	Southwest Airlines	2H4	13/JAN/81	23/JAN/81	
22364	G-BHWE	Britannia Airways	204	26/AUG/80	09/SEP/80	
	G-BHWE	British Airtours			01/APR/85	Leased
22365	G-BHWF	Britannia Airways	204	10/SEP/80	01/DEC/80	
22367	JA8467	Southwest Airlines	2Q3	01/OCT/80	13/NOV/80	
22368	N52AF	Air Florida	2T4	03/OCT/80	23/OCT/80	
	G-GPAA	Guinness Peat			MAY/84	
	G-GPAA	Monarch Airlines			16/MAY/84	Leased
	EI-BOM	Guinness Peat			15/NOV/84	
	EI-BOM	Midway Express			15/NOV/84	Leased
	EI-BOM	Guinness Peat			19/AUG/85	
	EI-BOM	Western Airlines			28/AUG/85	Leased
22369	N56AF	Air Florida	2T4	08/OCT/80	23/OCT/80	
	N56AF	Guinness Peat			JUL/84	
	EC-DUL	Spantax			JUL/84	Leased
	EI-BON	Guinness Peat			22/MAR/85	
	EI-BON	Midway Express			22/MAR/85	Leased
	EI-BON	Guinness Peat			02/SEP/85	
	EI-BON	Western Airlines			13/SEP/85	Leased
22370	N57AF	Air Florida	2T4	05/NOV/80	20/NOV/80	
	N57AF	Guinness Peat			19/APR/84	
	N139AW	America West			19/APR/84	Leased
	N139AW	Guinness Peat			MAY/85	
	N139AW	GE Credit Corp.			MAY/85	
	N139AW	America West			MAY/85	Leased
22371	N58AF	Air Florida	2T4	07/NOV/80	20/NOV/80	
	N58AF	Guinness Peat			19/APR/84	
	N140AW	America West			19/APR/84	Leased
	N140AW	Guinness Peat			MAY/85	
	N140AW	GE Credit Corp.			MAY/85	
	N140AW	America West			MAY/85	Leased
22383	N1786B	Boeing	291	24/OCT/80		
	N7350F	Frontier Airlines			06/NOV/80	
	N7350F	United Airlines			19/JUL/85	
	N7350F	Frontier Airlines			19/JUL/85	Leased
	N993UA	United Airlines			MAY/86	
22384	N7351F	Frontier Airlines	291	13/NOV/80	26/NOV/80	
	N7351F	United Airlines			17/JUL/85	
	N7351F	Frontier Airlines			17/JUL/85	Leased
	N994UA	United Airlines			APR/86	
22395	G-BHVG	Orion Airways	2T5	23/DEC/80	12/JAN/81	
	C-GEPM	International Lease Finance			08/MAR/85	
	C-GEPM	Eastern Provincial			08/MAR/85	Leased
	C-GEPM	CP Air			JAN/86	Leased
22396	G-BHVH	Orion Airways	2T5	16/JAN/81	23/FEB/81	
	G-BHVH	America West			10/OCT/85	Leased
	G-BHVH	Orion Airways			08/MAR/86	
22397	G-BHVI	Orion Airways	2T5	30/JAN/81	30/MAR/81	
22398	C-GQBE	Quebecair	296			Not taken-up
	N789N	Piedmont		16/JAN/81	25/FEB/81	

BOEING 737

C/N	Registration	Owner/Operator	Series	First Flight	Delivery	Remarks
22399	N7352F	Frontier Airlines	291	02/DEC/80	15/DEC/80	
	N7352F	United Airlines			18/JUL/85	
	N7352F	Frontier Airlines			18/JUL/85	Leased
	N995UA	United Airlines			MAY/86	
22400	SX-BCK	Olympic Airways	284	20/MAY/81	10/JUN/81	
22401	SX-BCL	Olympic Airways	284		JUL/81	
22402	D-ABFT	Condor	230	09/MAR/81	19/MAR/81	
22406	N8295V	Boeing	2L9			
	OY-APP	Maersk Air		06/AUG/80	22/SEP/80	
22407	OY-APR	Maersk Air	2L9	03/SEP/80	06/OCT/80	
	OY-APR	Guyana Airways			06/OCT/80	Leased
	OY-APR	Maersk Air			31/MAR/82	
	OY-APR	Surinam Airways			13/MAY/83	Leased
	OY-APR	Maersk Air			MAY/84	
	TS-IEB	Tunis Air			MAY/84	Leased
	OY-APR	Maersk Air			19/NOV/85	
	OY-APR	Guinness Peat			19/NOV/85	
	EC-DXV	Hispania			19/NOV/85	Leased
22408	OY-APS	Maersk Air	2L9	26/SEP/80	10/NOV/80	
	OY-APS	Guinness Peat			13/SEP/85	
	Z-NAL	Air Zimbabwe			16/SEP/85	Leased
22415	G-DFUB	Bavaria	2K9	17/SEP/80	30/SEP/80	
	G-DFUB	Monarch			30/SEP/80	Leased
	G-DFUB	Guinness Peat			22/NOV/84	Sub-leased
	G-DFUB	Midway Express			22/NOV/84	Sub-leased
	G-DFUB	Monarch			MAR/85	Leased
22416	G-BMON	Bavaria	2K9	13/OCT/80	31/OCT/80	
	G-BMON	Monarch			14/FEB/81	Leased
	C-GPWC	Pacific Western			OCT/85	Sub-leased
	G-BMON	Monarch			24/APR/86	Leased
22426	N726AL	Aloha Airlines	297	06/FEB/81	18/FEB/81	
	N726AL	Pacific Express			11/NOV/83	Leased
	N726AL	Aloha Airlines			84	
	N726AL	Air Cal			01/MAY/84	Leased
22431	HB-IEH	Petrolair Systems	2V6		OCT/81	
22443	N786N	Piedmont	201		JUL/81	
22444	N787N	Piedmont	201	09/SEP/81	01/OCT/81	
22445	N788N	Piedmont	201	15/JAN/82	22/JAN/82	
22453	OO-RVM	International Lease Finance	2Q8	10/MAR/81	20/MAR/81	
	OO-RVM	Air Belgium			20/MAR/81	Leased
	OO-RVM	Bahamasair			MAR/81	Sub-leased
	OO-RVM	Air Belgium			APR/81	Leased
	TF-VLK	Eagle Air			21/APR/81	Sub-leased
	TF-VLK	Britannia Airways			21/APR/81	Sub-leased
	TF-VLK	Eagle Air			08/NOV/81	Sub-leased
	OO-RVM	Air Belgium			08/NOV/81	Leased
	OO-RVM	International Lease Finance			28/FEB/83	
	G-BKMS	Orion Airways			28/FEB/83	Leased
	G-BKMS	Wien Air Alaska			10/OCT/83	Sub-leased
	G-BKMS	Orion Airways			21/APR/84	Leased
	G-BKMS	International Lease Finance			12/NOV/84	
	N143AW	America West			12/NOV/84	Leased
22456	N7353F	Frontier Airlines	291	11/FEB/81	25/FEB/81	
	N7353F	United Airlines			17/JUL/85	
	N7353F	Frontier Airlines			17/JUL/85	Leased
	N996UA	United Airlines			APR/86	
22457	N7354F	Frontier Airlines	291	10/APR/81	22/APR/81	
	N7354F	United Airlines			17/JUL/85	
	N7354F	Frontier Airlines			17/JUL/85	Leased
	N997UA	United Airlines			MAY/86	
22458	OO-	TEA	2M8		APR/82	Cancelled order
22473	VT-EGM	Indian Airlines	2A8C	11/MAR/81	18/MAR/81	
22504	N4529W	Bavaria	2K9	28/SEP/81	17/MAY/82	Not taken-up
	PP-VNF	Bavaria			17/MAY/82	
	PP-VNF	Varig			17/MAY/82	Leased
22505	N4530W	Bavaria	2K9	04/NOV/81	17/MAY/82	Not taken-up
	PP-VNG	Bavaria			17/MAY/82	
	PP-VNG	Varig			17/MAY/82	Leased
22516	C-GQBH	Quebecair	296	14/APR/81	24/APR/81	
	G-BJZW	Britannia			27/APR/82	Leased
	C-GQBH	Quebecair			06/NOV/82	
	N389PA	Pan American			29/APR/83	Leased
	C-GQBH	Quebecair			27/APR/85	
22529	N51AF	Air Florida	2T4		30/MAR/81	
	N51AF	Transavia			01/MAY/81	Leased
	N51AF	Air Florida			01/NOV/81	
	N51AF	FAA			JUL/84	
	N51AF	Midway Express			OCT/84	
	EI-BRN	Guinness Peat			JUL/85	
	EI-BRN	Midway Airlines			JUL/85	Leased
22531	C6-BEH	Bahamasair	2V5	12/DEC/80	09/JAN/81	
22575	5W-PAL	Polynesian Airlines	2U9	13/MAR/81	31/MAR/81	
	5W-PAL	Air Vanuatu			82	Leased
	5W-PAL	Polynesian Airlines			82	
	5W-PAL	Ansett Airlines			JUN/85	
	5W-PAL	Polynesian Airlines			JUN/85	Leased
	5W-PAL	Ansett Airlines			12/NOV/85	
	N149AW	America West			12/NOV/85	Leased
	N149AW	Ansett Airlines			18/AUG/86	
	5W-	Polynesian Airlines			AUG/86	Sched.lease
22576	G-OSLA	Owners Service	2U4	24/APR/81	09/MAY/81	
	G-OSLA	Britannia Airways			09/MAY/81	Leased
	G-OSLA	International Lease Finance			01/NOV/83	
	N134AW	America West			22/NOV/83	Leased
22577	N730AS	Alaska Airlines	290C	24/APR/81	24/MAY/81	
22578	N740AS	Alaska Airlines	290C	15/MAY/81	02/JUN/81	
22580	ZS-SIA	South African Airways	244		23/AUG/81	
	PP-SNW	Vasp			22/NOV/85	Leased
	ZS-SIA	South African Airways			22/NOV/87	Sched.return
22581	ZS-SIB	South African Airways	244		SEP/81	
	D6-CAJ	Air Comores			05/NOV/84	Leased
	ZS-SIB	South African Airways			OCT/85	WFU OCT/85, stored Johannesburg
22582	ZS-SIC	South African Airways	244		OCT/81	
22583	ZS-SID	South African Airways	244		NOV/81	
22584	ZS-SIE	South African Airways	244	02/DEC/81	14/DEC/81	

C/N	Registration	Owner/Operator	Series	First Flight	Delivery	Remarks
22585	ZS-SIF	South African Airways	244	07/JAN/82	14/JAN/82	
22586	ZS-SIG	South African Airways	244	14/JAN/82	28/JAN/82	
22587	ZS-SIH	South African Airways	244		14/MAY/82	
22588	ZS-SII	South African Airways	244	28/JAN/82	17/FEB/82	
22589	ZS-SIJ	South African Airways	244	16/FEB/82	03/MAR/82	
	CC-CHK	Lan Chile			DEC/85	Leased
22590	ZS-SIK	South African Airways	244	16/MAR/82	01/APR/82	
22591	ZS-SIL	South African Airways	244	01/APR/82	15/APR/82	
22596	N8279V	Boeing	2K5	07/MAY/81		
	D-AHLD	Hapag Lloyd			29/MAY/81	
	N2941W	Air Berlin			26/MAR/82	Leased
	D-AHLD	Hapag Lloyd			MAY/86	
22597	D-AHLE	Hapag Lloyd	2K5	11/JUN/81	19/JUN/81	
	D-AHLE	Guinness Peat			01/NOV/83	
	EC-DTR	Spantax			01/NOV/83	Leased
	EC-DTR	Spantax			FEB/85	Purchased
22598	D-AHLF	Hapag Lloyd	2K5		SEP/81	
	EC-DUB	Spantax			01/APR/84	Leased
22599	D-AHLG	Hapag Lloyd	2K5	12/NOV/81	24/NOV/81	
22600	D-AHLH	Hapag Lloyd	2K5	18/NOV/81	08/JAN/82	
22601	D-AHLI	Hapag Lloyd	2K5	18/JAN/82	29/JAN/82	
22602	N8286V	Boeing	2A1	17/OCT/80		
	CC-CHJ	Lan-Chile			22/DEC/80	
22607	HC-BIG	TAME	2V2	11/JUN/81	05/OCT/81	W/O 11/JUL/83 Cuenca, Ecuador
22618	C-GSPW	Pacific Western	275			
	C-GSPW	Eastern Provincial			15/APR/82	Leased
	C-GSPW	Pacific Western			SEP/82	
22619	C-	Pacific Western	275C			Cancelled order
22620	9M-MBK	Malaysian Airline System	2H6	01/DEC/81	18/DEC/81	
22624	TS-IOE	Tunis Air	2H3	15/APR/81	27/APR/81	
22625	TS-IOF	Tunis Air	2H3			
22626	D2-TBV	TAAG Angola	2M2	21/SEP/81	14/OCT/81	
22627	3X-GCB	Air Guinee			AUG/81	
22628	N180RN	Chemco Leasing	2W8	01/DEC/81		
	N180RN	Noga S.A.			15/DEC/81	Leased
	N180RN	Chemco Leasing			MAR/85	
	A6-ESH	Government of Sharjah			15/MAY/85	
22629	N728AL	Aloha Airlines	297		23/FEB/82	
22630	N729AL	Aloha Airlines	297	30/MAR/82	26/MAY/82	
	N147AW	America West			29/AUG/85	Leased
22631	N730AL	Aloha Airlines	297	06/JUL/82	21/JUL/82	
22632	G-BJBJ	Orion Airways	2T5	22/FEB/82	22/MAR/82	
22633	G-BMMP	Air Europe	2S3			Reg. not taken-up
	G-DDDV	Air Europe		02/MAR/81	19/MAR/81	
	G-DDDV	Air Florida			03/NOV/82	Leased
	G-DDDV	Air Europe			13/APR/83	
	G-DDDV	British Airtours			01/NOV/84	Leased
	G-DDDV	Air Europe			30/APR/85	
	G-DDDV	Hafslund Transport			30/APR/85	
	G-DDDV	Air Europe			30/APR/85	Leased
	G-DDDV	British Airtours			30/APR/85	Sub-leased
	G-DDDV	Air Europe			30/APR/86	Leased
22634	D-ABHW	Lufthansa	230	05/FEB/82	19/FEB/82	
22635	N8279V	Boeing	230	15/JUN/81		
	D-ABHD	Condor			25/JUN/81	Leased
	D-ABHD	Lufthansa			OCT/82	
	D-ABHD	Condor			APR/83	
22636	D-ABHT	Condor	230		OCT/81	
22637	D-ABHX	Condor	230	02/MAR/82	17/MAR/82	
	D-ABHX	Lufthansa			17/MAR/82	Leased
	D-ABHX	Condor			APR/83	
22638	G-BJCT	Britannia Airways	204	23/MAR/82	06/APR/82	
	EC-DXK	Spantax			01/MAY/85	Leased
	G-BJCT	Britannia Airways			MAR/86	
22639	G-BJCU	Britannia Airways	204	07/APR/82	22/APR/82	
	EC-DVE	Spantax			01/NOV/84	Leased
	G-BJCU	Britannia Airways			01/NOV/85	
22640	G-BJCV	Britannia Airways	204	16/APR/82	01/MAY/82	
	C-GXCP	CP Air			NOV/85	Leased
	G-BJCV	Britannia Airways			30/APR/86	
22645	VH-CZM	Ansett	277	27/MAY/81	15/JUN/81	
22646	VH-CZN	Ansett	277		19/JUL/81	
22647	VH-CZO	Ansett	277		11/AUG/81	
22648	VH-CZP	Ansett	277		26/AUG/81	
22649	VH-CZQ	Ansett	277	18/SEP/81	13/OCT/81	
22650	VH-CZR	Ansett	277		30/OCT/81	
22651	VH-CZS	Ansett	277	24/NOV/81	09/DEC/81	
22652	VH-CZT	Ansett	277	18/JAN/82	26/JAN/82	
22653	VH-CZU	Ansett	277	13/JAN/82	17/FEB/82	
22654	VH-CZV	Ansett	277	15/APR/82	21/APR/82	
22655	VH-CZW	Ansett	277		17/MAY/82	
22656	VH-CZX	Ansett	277		02/JUN/82	
22657	ZK-NAT	Air New Zealand	219	23/FEB/82		Not taken-up
	N851L	International Lease Finance			05/MAR/82	
	G-BJXJ	Dan Air			05/MAR/82	Leased
22658	C-GCPZ	CP Air	217	06/APR/82	13/APR/82	
22659	C-GFCP	CP Air	217	19/MAY/82	20/MAY/82	
22660	G-BMSP	Air Europe	2S3	26/FEB/82		Reg. not taken-up
	G-BRJP	Air Europe			11/MAR/82	
	G-BRJP	British Airtours			01/NOV/83	Leased
	G-BRJP	Air Europe			84	
	G-BRJP	British Airtours			MAR/85	Leased
	G-BRJP	America West			30/APR/86	
	G-BRJP	Air Europe			30/APR/86	
	G-BRJP	Air Europe			30/APR/86	Leased
22667	N5573K	Boeing	2P5	21/AUG/81		
	HS-TBD	Thai Airways			25/SEP/81	
22673	N73SW	Southwest Airlines	2H4	11/DEC/81	18/DEC/81	
22674	N74SW	Southwest Airlines	2H4	11/DEC/81	23/DEC/81	
22675	N80SW	Southwest Airlines	2H4	01/FEB/82	12/FEB/82	
22679	DQ-FDM	Air Pacific	2X2		OCT/81	
22697	N81AF	Air Florida	2T4	10/NOV/81	25/NOV/81	
	N81AF	FAA			JUL/84	
	N81AF	Midway Express			OCT/84	
	N81AF	Guinness Peat			JUL/85	
	N81AF	Midway Airlines			JUL/85	Leased

BOEING 737

C/N	Registration	Owner/Operator	Series	First Flight	Delivery	Remarks
22698	N82AF	Air Florida	2T4	04/DEC/81	18/DEC/81	
	N82AF	FAA			JUL/84	
	N82AF	Midway Express			OCT/84	
	N82AF	Guinness Peat			JUL/85	
	N82AF	Midway Airlines			JUL/85	Leased
22699	N83AF	Interfirst Bank	2T4	12/MAR/82		
	N83AF	Air Florida			13/MAY/82	Leased
	N83AF	Interfirst Bank			FEB/83	
	N83AF	Southwest Airlines			15/AUG/83	Leased
	N130SW	Southwest Airlines			01/NOV/84	Purchased
22700	N84AF	Air Florida	2T4	09/JUN/82		Cancelled order
	7T-VEZ	Air Algerie			08/DEC/83	
22701	N85AF	Air Florida	2T4		82	Cancelled order
	N4569N	Alaska International Air		10/JUN/82	30/DEC/82	
	N4569N	Western Airlines			30/DEC/82	Leased
22703	CC-CIN	Ladeco	2K6		07/DEC/81	
	EI-BRZ	Guinness Peat			31/MAR/86	Leased
	EC-DYZ	Spantax			31/MAR/86	
22726	D-ADDB	Supair	2X4			Cancelled order
22727	D-ADDC	Supair	2X4			Cancelled order
22728	C-GJCP	CP Air	217	10/SEP/82	01/OCT/82	
22729	C-GKCP	CP Air	217	23/SEP/82	01/NOV/82	
22730	N81SW	Southwest Airlines	2H4	04/FEB/82	17/FEB/82	
22731	N82SW	Southwest Airlines	2H4	15/APR/82	23/APR/82	
22732	N83SW	Southwest Airlines	2H4	21/MAY/82	28/MAY/82	
22733	OY-MBZ	Maersk	2L9		NOV/81	
22734	OY-MBW	Maersk	2L9	13/NOV/81	25/NOV/81	
	OY-MBW	Midway Express			11/SEP/85	Leased
	OY-MBW	Maersk			SEP/88	Sched.return
22735	OY-MBV	Maersk	2L9	08/DEC/81	23/DEC/81	
22736	JA8475	Southwest	2Q3	15/JUL/82	08/OCT/82	
22737	CX-BON	Pluna	2A3	05/JAN/82	18/JAN/82	
	PH-TSI	Transavia			23/APR/86	Leased
	CX-BON	Pluna			Autumn/86	Sched.return
22738	CX-BOO	Pluna	2A3	12/JAN/82	25/JAN/82	
	PH-TSA	Transavia			28/MAR/84	Leased
	CX-BOO	Pluna			31/OCT/84	
22739	N8295V	Boeing	2A3			
	CX-BOP	Pluna		17/FEB/82	25/FEB/82	
	PH-TSD	Transavia			01/MAY/85	Leased
	CX-BOP	Pluna			31/OCT/85	
22741	N7355F	Frontier Airlines	291	05/MAY/82	12/MAY/82	
	N7355F	United Airlines			17/JUL/85	
	N7355F	Frontier Airlines			17/JUL/85	Leased
	N998UA	United Airlines			MAY/86	
22742	N7356F	Frontier Airlines	291	11/MAY/82	24/MAY/82	
	N7356F	United Airlines			17/JUL/85	
	N7356F	Frontier Airlines			17/JUL/85	Leased
	N999UA	United Airlines			JUN/86	
22743	N7357F	Frontier Airlines	291	03/SEP/82	28/OCT/82	
22744	N7358F	Frontier Airlines	291	27/OCT/82	10/DEC/82	
22751	N798N	Piedmont	201	19/MAR/82	02/APR/82	
22752	N791N	Piedmont	201	13/FEB/82	02/MAR/82	
22753	N792N	Piedmont	201	27/APR/82	11/MAY/82	
22754	N793N	Piedmont	201		MAY/82	
22755	N794N	Piedmont	201	10/MAY/82	17/MAY/82	
22756	N795N	Piedmont	201	27/MAY/82	08/JUN/82	
22757	N796N	Piedmont	201	02/JUN/82	15/JUN/82	
22758	N797N	Piedmont	201	21/JUN/82	02/JUL/82	
22760	N861L	International Lease Finance	2Q8	08/MAR/82	06/APR/82	
	N861L	TACA			06/APR/82	Leased
22761	G-DWHH	Monarch Airlines	2T7	03/MAR/82	16/MAR/82	
	C-FPWD	Pacific Western			15/NOV/83	Leased
	G-DWHH	Monarch Airlines			01/MAY/84	
	C-FPWD	Pacific Western			26/NOV/84	Leased
	G-DWHH	Monarch Airlines			01/MAY/85	
	C-FPWD	Pacific Western			28/NOV/85	Leased
	G-DWHH	Monarch Airlines			08/APR/86	
22762	G-DGDP	Monarch Airlines	2T7	20/MAR/82	26/MAR/82	
	C-FPWE	Pacific Western			22/NOV/83	Leased
	G-DGDP	Monarch Airlines			01/MAY/84	
	C-FPWE	Pacific Western			19/NOV/84	Leased
	G-DGDP	Monarch Airlines			02/MAY/85	
	C-FPWE	Pacific Western			NOV/85	Leased
	G-DGDP	Monarch Airlines			28/APR/86	
	G-DGDP	Guinness Peat			28/APR/86	
	C-FCPN	CP Air			01/JUL/86	
22766	7T-VEY	Air Algerie	2D6	11/MAR/82	25/MAR/82	
22767	CN-RML	Royal Air Maroc	2B6	03/MAR/82	19/MAR/82	
22771	5N-ANW	Nigeria Airways	2F9	20/APR/82	11/OCT/82	
22772	5N-ANX	Nigeria Airways	2F9	07/JUN/82	11/OCT/82	
22773	5N-ANY	Nigeria Airways	2F9	01/JUL/82	09/FEB/83	
22774	5N-ANZ	Nigeria Airways	2F9	08/JUL/82	09/FEB/83	
22775	D2-TBN	TAAG Angola	2M2	29/APR/82	06/MAY/82	W/O NOV/83
22776	D2-TBO	TAAG Angola	2M2	25/JUN/82	01/NOV/82	
22777	AI-7301	Indonesian Air Force	2X9	21/APR/82	20/MAY/82	
22778	N8288V	Boeing	2X9	24/FEB/83		
	AI-7302	Indonesian Air Force			30/JUN/83	
22779	AI-7303	Indonesian Air Force	2X9	25/AUG/83	03/OCT/83	
22792	CC-CIY	Ladeco	2E3	14/JUN/82	29/JUN/82	
	N138AW	America West			15/MAR/84	
22793	N4571M	Alaska International Air	2T2	07/JUL/82	30/DEC/82	
	N4571M	Western Airlines			30/DEC/82	
22795	N799N	Piedmont	201	08/SEP/82	27/SEP/82	
22796	N802N	Piedmont	201	20/SEP/82	01/OCT/82	
22797	N803N	Piedmont	201	06/OCT/82	15/OCT/82	
22798	N804N	Piedmont	201	29/OCT/82	06/JAN/83	
22799	N805N	Piedmont	201	15/DEC/82	01/FEB/83	
22800	N86AF	Air Florida	2T4	28/OCT/82		Cancelled Order
	7T-VJA	Air Algerie			12/DEC/83	
22801	N87AF	Air Florida	2T4	05/APR/83		Cancelled Order
	7T-VJB	Air Algerie			14/DEC/83	
22802	N88AF	Air Florida	2T4			Cancelled Order
	N6009U	Boeing		22/DEC/82		
	B-2501	CAAC			22/FEB/83	

C/N	Registration	Owner/Operator	Series	First Flight	Delivery	Remarks
22803	N89AF	Air Florida	2T4			Cancelled Order
	N6018N	Boeing		07/JAN/83		
	B-2502	CAAC			22/FEB/83	
22804	N90AF	Air Florida	2T4		MAR/83	Cancelled Order
	N6038E	Boeing		27/JAN/83		
	B-2503	CAAC			01/MAR/83	
22806	N806N	Piedmont	201	10/JAN/83	28/FEB/83	
22807	C-GTPW	Pacific Western	275	10/DEC/81	18/DEC/81	
	C-GTPW	Eastern Provincial			82	Leased
	C-GTPW	Pacific Western			82	
22826	N85SW	Southwest Airlines	2H4	19/MAY/82	03/JUN/82	
22827	N86SW	Southwest Airlines	2H4	23/MAY/82	04/JUN/82	
22828	ZS-SIM	South African Airways	244	03/JUN/82	17/JUN/82	
22856	4X-ABN	El Al	258	02/SEP/82	30/SEP/82	Stored Seattle
22857	4X-ABO	El Al	258	11/OCT/82	09/NOV/82	Stored Seattle
22859	ST-AIB	Sudan Airways	2J8	23/JUL/82		Cancelled order
	N235WA	Western Airlines			01/MAY/84	
22860	VT-EHE	Indian Airlines	2A8	20/JUL/82	04/AUG/82	
22861	VT-EHF	Indian Airlines	2A8	28/JUL/82	11/AUG/82	
22862	VT-EHG	Indian Airlines	2A8	30/JUL/82	18/AUG/82	
22863	VT-EHH	Indian Airlines	2A8	30/AUG/82	08/SEP/82	
22864	C-GMCP	CP Air	217	16/FEB/83	01/MAR/83	
22865	C-GQCP	CP Air	217	11/APR/83	22/APR/83	
22866	N807N	Piedmont	201	23/FEB/83	01/APR/83	
22867	N809N	Piedmont	201	15/APR/83	27/APR/83	
22868	N810N	Piedmont	201	22/APR/83	02/MAY/83	
22869	N811N	Piedmont	201	29/APR/83	10/JUN/83	
22873	C-GUPW	Pacific Western	275	16/JUL/82	23/JUL/82	
22874	C-GVPW	Pacific Western	275	20/AUG/82	27/AUG/82	
22875	N45708	Boeing	2E7	01/OCT/82		
	4X-BAB	Arkia			02/MAR/83	
	G-BMDF	IACO			22/MAR/84	
	G-BMDF	Dan Air			22/MAR/84	Leased
22876	N4571A	Boeing	2E7	22/OCT/82		
	4X-BAC	Arkia			15/MAR/83	
	G-BLDE	IACO			01/JAN/84	
	G-BLDE	Dan Air			01/JAN/84	Leased
22877	C-GNDU	Nordair	242C	28/MAY/82	06/JUN/82	
22878	N320AU	US Air	2B7	26/OCT/82	15/NOV/82	
22879	N321AU	US Air	2B7	12/NOV/82	22/NOV/82	
22880	N322AU	US Air	2B7	19/NOV/82	01/DEC/82	
22881	N323AU	US Air	2B7	03/DEC/82	16/DEC/82	
22882	N314AU	US Air	2B7	09/DEC/82	22/DEC/82	
22883	N315AU	US Air	2B7	10/DEC/82	22/DEC/82	
22884	N316AU	US Air	2B7	28/MAR/83	04/APR/83	
22885	N317AU	US Air	2B7	03/MAY/83	13/MAY/83	
22886	N318AU	US Air	2B7	07/JUN/83	14/JUN/83	
22887	N319AU	US Air	2B7	24/JUN/83	11/JUL/83	
22888	N320AU	US Air	2B7	18/JUL/83	11/AUG/83	
22889	N321AU	US Air	2B7	11/AUG/83	15/SEP/83	
22890	N322AU	US Air	2B7	25/AUG/83	20/SEP/83	
22891	N323AU	US Air	2B7	27/SEP/83	20/OCT/83	
22892	N324AU	US Air	2B7	30/SEP/83	01/DEC/83	
22903	N87SW	Southwest Airlines	2H4	19/AUG/82	16/SEP/82	
22904	N89SW	Southwest Airlines	2H4	10/SEP/82	30/SEP/82	
22905	N90SW	Southwest Airlines	2H4	29/SEP/82	18/OCT/82	
22906	PH-TVU	Transavia	2K2		21/JUN/82	
	PH-TVU	Air Florida			18/JAN/84	Leased
	PH-TVU	Transavia			01/APR/84	
	PH-TVU	Aerolineas Argentinas			10/DEC/84	Leased
	PH-TVU	Transavia			29/MAR/85	
22940	N300SW	Southwest Airlines	3H4	15/AUG/84	30/NOV/84	
22941	N301SW	Southwest Airlines	3H4		20/DEC/84	
22942	N302SW	Southwest Airlines	3H4		20/DEC/84	
22943	N303SW	Southwest Airlines	3H4	29/MAR/85	15/APR/85	
22944	N304SW	Southwest Airlines	3H4	05/AUG/85	22/AUG/85	
22945	N305SW	Southwest Airlines	3H4	07/AUG/85	28/AUG/85	
22946	N306SW	Southwest Airlines	3H4	30/AUG/85	30/SEP/85	
22947	N307SW	Southwest Airlines	3H4	24/SEP/85	30/OCT/85	
22948	N309SW	Southwest Airlines	3H4	11/OCT/85	30/OCT/85	
22949	N310SW	Southwest Airlines	3H4	15/OCT/85	30/OCT/85	
22950	N73700	Boeing	3B7	24/FEB/84		Prototype
	N350AU	US Air			30/APR/85	
22951	N351AU	Boeing	3B7			Development aircraft
	N351AU	US Air			NOV/85	
22952	N352AU	Boeing	3B7	04/MAY/84		Development aircraft
	N352AU	US Air			11/APR/85	
22953	N353AU	US Air	3B7	25/JUN/84	28/NOV/84	
22954	N354AU	US Air	3B7		05/DEC/84	
22955	N355AU	US Air	3B7		11/DEC/84	
22956	N356AU	US Air	3B7		19/DEC/84	
22957	N357AU	US Air	3B7	21/JUN/85	28/JUN/85	
22958	N358AU	US Air	3B7	18/JUL/85	31/JUL/85	
22959	N359AU	US Air	3B7	09/AUG/85	23/AUG/85	
22961	N813N	Piedmont	201	23/AUG/83	30/AUG/83	
22962	N814N	Piedmont	201	08/SEP/83	22/SEP/83	
22963	N91SW	Southwest Airlines	2H4	22/NOV/82	13/DEC/82	
22964	N92SW	Southwest Airlines	2H4	15/DEC/82	04/JAN/83	
22965	N93SW	Southwest Airlines	2H4	22/MAR/83	07/APR/83	
22966	G-BKHE	Britannia	204	11/FEB/83	25/FEB/83	
22967	G-BKHF	Britannia	204	15/MAR/83	22/MAR/83	
22979	G-BKHO	Orion Airways	2T5	01/MAR/83	14/MAR/83	
	G-BKHO	America West			06/NOV/84	Leased
	G-BKHO	Orion Airways			19/MAR/86	
22985	5N-AUA	Nigeria Airways	2F9	14/OCT/82	09/FEB/83	
22986	5N-AUB	Nigeria Airways	2F9	01/NOV/82	09/FEB/83	
22987	5N-AUC	Nigeria Airways	2F9			Cancelled Order
22988	5N-AUD	Nigeria Airways	2F9			Cancelled Order
22994	ZK-NQC	Air New Zealand	219C	17/NOV/82	02/DEC/82	
23000	F-GBYA	Air France	228	29/NOV/82	15/DEC/82	
23001	F-GBYB	Air France	228	11/JAN/83	21/JAN/83	
23002	F-GBYC	Air France	228	13/JAN/83	26/JAN/83	
23003	F-GBYD	Air France	228	19/JAN/83	04/FEB/83	
23004	F-GBYE	Air France	228	31/JAN/83	10/FEB/83	
23005	F-GBYF	Air France	228	04/FEB/83	18/FEB/83	
23006	F-GBYG	Air France	228	09/FEB/83	23/FEB/83	

BOEING 737

C/N	Registration	Owner/Operator	Series	First Flight	Delivery	Remarks
23007	F-GBYH	Air France	228	25/FEB/83	10/MAR/83	
23008	F-GBYI	Air France	228	14/MAR/83	24/MAR/83	
23009	F-GBYJ	Air France	228	07/APR/83	27/APR/83	
23010	F-GBYK	Air France	228	12/APR/83	02/MAY/83	
23011	F-GBYL	Air France	228	27/MAY/83	13/JUN/83	
23023	N7359F	Frontier Airlines	291	30/MAR/83	27/APR/83	
23024	N7399F	Frontier Airlines	291	03/MAY/83	09/MAY/83	
23036	VT-EHW	Indian Airlines	2A8	01/JUL/83	20/JUL/83	
	K-2412	Indian Air Force			15/JUN/84	
23037	VT-EHX	Indian Airlines	2A8	03/AUG/83	17/AUG/83	
	VT-EHX	Indian Government			OCT/83	Leased
	VT-EHX	Indian Airlines			84	
	K-2413	Indian Air Force			05/MAY/84	
23038	9H-ABA	Air Malta	2Y5	01/MAR/83	11/MAR/83	
23039	9H-ABB	Air Malta	2Y5	17/MAR/83	31/MAR/83	
23040	9H-ABC	Air Malta	2Y5	23/MAR/83	30/MAR/83	
23041	CS-TEK	TAP Air Portugal	282	25/APR/83	03/JUN/83	
23042	CS-TEL	TAP Air Portugal	282	13/MAY/83	03/JUN/83	
23043	CS-TEM	TAP Air Portugal	282	01/JUN/83	30/JUN/83	
23044	CS-TEN	TAP Air Portugal	282	08/JUN/83	30/JUN/83	
	CS-TEN	Air Atlantis			APR/85	Leased
	CS-TEN	TAP Air Portugal			85	
23045	CS-TEO	TAP Air Portugal	282	11/JUL/83	22/JUL/83	
	CS-TEO	Air Atlantis			APR/85	Leased
	CS-TEO	TAP Air Portugal			85	
23046	CS-TEP	TAP Air Portugal	282	05/AUG/83	12/AUG/83	
23049	CN-RMM	Royal Air Maroc	2B6C	04/MAR/83	25/MAR/83	
23050	CN-RMN	Royal Air Maroc	2B6C	15/JUN/83	28/JUN/83	
23051	CS-TEQ	TAP Air Portugal	282QC	09/DEC/83	29/DEC/83	
23053	N94SW	Southwest	2H4	12/MAY/83	25/MAY/83	
23054	N95SW	Southwest	2H4	19/MAY/83	25/MAY/83	
23055	N96SW	Southwest	2H4	26/MAY/83	30/JUN/83	
23059	N45733	Boeing	2Z6	21/JUL/83		
	22-222	Royal Thai Air Force			15/DEC/83	
23060	G-BLKB	Orion Airways	3T5	12/DEC/84	29/JAN/85	
23061	G-BLKC	Orion Airways	3T5	04/FEB/85	11/FEB/85	
23062	G-BLKD	Orion Airways	3T5	07/FEB/85	18/MAR/85	
23063	G-BLKE	International Lease Finance	3T5	01/MAR/85	25/MAR/85	
	G-BLKE	Orion Airways			25/MAR/85	Leased
	G-BLKE	International Lease Finance			MAR/86	
	G-BLKE	Midland Montague			MAR/86	
	G-BLKE	Orion Airways			MAR/86	Leased
23064	G-	Orion Airways	3T5		10/MAR/86	
23065	B-2504	CAAC	2T6C	29/SEP/83	14/OCT/83	
23066	B-2505	CAAC	2T6C	24/OCT/83	08/DEC/83	
23073	N301DL	Delta Air Lines	232	14/OCT/83	25/OCT/83	
23074	N302DL	Delta Air Lines	232	02/NOV/83	10/NOV/83	
23075	N303DL	Delta Air Lines	232	01/NOV/83	22/NOV/83	
23076	N304DL	Delta Air Lines	232	08/NOV/83	02/DEC/83	
23077	N305DL	Delta Air Lines	232	15/NOV/83	07/DEC/83	
23078	N306DL	Delta Air Lines	232	13/DEC/83	22/DEC/83	
23079	N307DL	Delta Air Lines	232	09/JAN/84	09/MAY/84	
23080	N308DL	Delta Air Lines	232	11/JAN/84	30/JAN/84	
23081	N309DL	Delta Air Lines	232	18/JAN/84	01/FEB/84	
23082	N310DA	Delta Air Lines	232	24/JAN/84	08/FEB/84	
23083	N311DL	Delta Air Lines	232	27/JAN/84	14/FEB/84	
23084	N312DL	Delta Air Lines	232	10/FEB/84	01/MAR/84	
23085	N313DL	Delta Air Lines	232	21/FEB/84	14/MAR/84	
23086	N314DA	Delta Air Lines	232	27/FEB/84	21/MAR/84	
23087	N315DL	Delta Air Lines	232	06/MAR/84	03/APR/84	
23088	N316DL	Delta Air Lines	232	29/MAR/84	11/APR/84	
23089	N317DL	Delta Air Lines	232	30/MAR/84	09/MAY/84	
23090	N318DL	Delta Air Lines	232	11/APR/84	16/MAY/84	
23091	N319DL	Delta Air Lines	232	17/APR/84	14/NOV/84	
23092	N320DL	Delta Air Lines	232	20/APR/84	01/JUN/84	
23093	N321DL	Delta Air Lines	232	01/MAY/84	05/SEP/84	
23094	N322DL	Delta Air Lines	232	09/MAY/84	10/AUG/84	
23095	N323DL	Delta Air Lines	232	15/MAY/84	06/JUN/84	
23096	N324DL	Delta Air Lines	232	23/MAY/84	03/JUL/84	
23097	N325DL	Delta Air Lines	232	22/MAY/84	10/JUL/84	
23098	N326DL	Delta Air Lines	232	26/SEP/84	10/OCT/84	
23099	N327DL	Delta Air Lines	232	16/JUL/84	02/AUG/84	
23100	N328DL	Delta Air Lines	232	27/AUG/84	12/SEP/84	
23101	N329DL	Delta Air Lines	232	05/SEP/84	01/NOV/84	
23102	N330DL	Delta Air Lines	232	19/SEP/84	03/OCT/84	
23103	N331DL	Delta Air Lines	232	01/NOV/84	13/NOV/84	
23104	N332DL	Delta Air Lines	232		04/DEC/84	
23105	N334DL	Delta Air Lines	232		13/DEC/84	
23108	N102SW	Southwest Airlines	2H4	02/MAR/84	15/MAR/84	
23109	N103SW	Southwest Airlines	2H4	12/MAR/84	23/MAR/84	
23110	N104SW	Southwest Airlines	2H4	19/MAR/84	26/MAR/84	
23113	HS-TBE	Thai Airways	2P5	15/FEB/84	22/FEB/84	
23114	N325AU	US Air	2B7	21/NOV/83	08/DEC/83	
23115	N326AU	US Air	2B7	05/DEC/83	12/DEC/83	
23116	N327AU	US Air	2B7	08/DEC/83	19/DEC/83	
23117	JA8492	Southwest Air Lines	2Q3	11/JUN/84	19/JUN/84	
23121	N122NA	Northair	2X6C			Reg. Not taken-up
	N670MA	Mark Air		02/MAY/84	11/MAY/84	
	N670MA	Skybus			19/AUG/85	Leased
	N670MA	Mark Air			85	
23122	N133NA	Northair	2X6C			Reg. Not taken-up
	N671MA	Avery Leasing		15/JUN/84	22/JUN/84	
	N671MA	Mark Air			22/JUN/84	Leased
	N671MA	Skybus			SEP/85	Leased
	N671MA	Mark Air			85	
	N671MA	Avery Leasing			FEB/85	
	N170AW	America West				Leased
23123	N144NA	Northair	2X6C			Reg. Not taken-up
	N672MA	Mark Air		19/JUL/84	14/AUG/84	
23124	N155NA	Northair	2X6C			Reg. Not taken-up
	N673MA	Mark Air		01/AUG/84	28/AUG/84	
23129	7O-ACQ	Alyemda	2R4C	14/JUN/84	21/JUN/84	
23130	7O-ACR	Alyemda	2R4C	06/JUL/84	18/JUL/84	
23131	N328AU	US Air	2B7	17/JUL/84	24/JUL/84	
23132	N329AU	US Air	2B7	17/AUG/84	30/AUG/84	
23133	N330AU	US Air	2B7	14/SEP/84	25/SEP/84	

C/N	Registration	Owner/Operator	Series	First Flight	Delivery	Remarks
23134	N331AU	US Air	2B7	01/OCT/84	23/OCT/84	
23135	N332AU	US Air	2B7	04/OCT/84	20/NOV/84	
23136	N742AS	Alaska Airlines	290C	31/MAY/84	15/JUN/84	
23148	N137AW	International Lease Finance	2Q8	19/OCT/84	25/OCT/84	
	N137AW	America West			25/OCT/84	Leased
	N137AW	International Lease Finance			95	Sched.return
23152	85101	South Korean Government	3Z8	07/JAN/85	30/JAN/85	
23153	D-ABMA	Lufthansa	230	18/DEC/84	17/JAN/85	
23154	D-ABMB	Lufthansa	230	07/JAN/85	24/JAN/85	
23155	D-ABMC	Lufthansa	230	10/JAN/85	31/JAN/85	
23156	D-ABMD	Lufthansa	230	22/JAN/85	07/FEB/85	
23157	D-ABME	Lufthansa	230	21/JAN/85	21/FEB/85	
23158	D-ABMF	Lufthansa	230	14/FEB/85	07/MAR/85	
23159	G-BKYA	British Airways	236	29/AUG/84	20/SEP/84	Leased
23160	G-BKYB	British Airways	236	02/SEP/84	27/SEP/84	Leased
23161	G-BKYC	British Airways	236	12/SEP/84	01/OCT/84	Leased
23162	G-BKYD	British Airways	236	28/SEP/84	11/OCT/84	Leased
23163	G-BKYE	British Airways	236	16/OCT/84	01/NOV/84	Leased
23164	G-BKYF	British Airways	236	24/OCT/84	19/NOV/84	Leased
23165	G-BKYG	British Airways	236		06/DEC/84	Leased
23166	G-BKYH	British Airways	236		13/DEC/84	Leased
23167	G-BKYI	British Airways	236	13/DEC/84	07/JAN/84	Leased
23168	G-BKYJ	British Airways	236	09/JAN/85	28/JAN/84	Leased
23169	G-BKYK	British Airways	236	16/JAN/85	01/FEB/85	Leased
23170	G-BKYL	British Airways	236	04/FEB/85	22/FEB/85	Leased
23171	G-BKYM	British Airways	236	11/FEB/85	01/MAR/85	Leased
23172	G-BKYN	British Airways	236	21/FEB/85	21/MAR/85	Leased
23173	C-FCPG	CP Air	317	18/MAR/85	12/APR/85	
	C-FCPG	Guinness Peat			28/APR/86	
	PP-SNQ	Vasp			30/APR/86	Leased
23174	C-FCPI	CP Air	317	09/APR/85	26/APR/85	
	C-FCPI	Guinness Peat			03/JUL/86	
	PP-SNR	Vasp			04/JUL/86	Leased
23175	C-FCPJ	CP Air	317	25/APR/85	07/MAY/85	
	C-FCPJ	Guinness Peat			18/APR/86	
	PP-SNS	Vasp			29/APR/86	Leased
23176	C-FCPK	CP Air	317	18/MAR/86	02/APR/86	
	C-FCPK	Guinness Peat			OCT/86	Sched.delivery
23177	C-FCPL	CP Air	317	25/MAR/86	09/APR/86	
	C-FCPL	Guinness Peat			OCT/86	Sched.delivery
23181	N3301	Western	347	07/MAR/85	29/MAR/85	
23182	N302WA	Western	347	12/APR/85	26/APR/85	
23183	N303WA	Western	347	19/APR/85	07/MAY/85	
23184	N236WA	Western	247	26/OCT/84	19/NOV/84	
23185	N237WA	Western	247	16/NOV/84	28/NOV/84	
23186	N238WA	Western	247	14/NOV/84	28/NOV/84	
23187	N239WA	Western	247		13/DEC/84	
23188	N240WA	Western	247		28/DEC/84	
	B-2509	CAAC			JAN/85	
23189	N241WA	Western	247		28/DEC/84	
	B-2510	CAAC			JAN/85	
23218	N150AW	America West	3G7	18/JAN/85	20/FEB/85	
23219	N151AW	America West	3G7	22/FEB/85	13/MAY/85	
23220	D2-TBP	TAAG Angola	2M2	28/JAN/85	15/FEB/85	
23225	G-BKYO	British Airways	236	01/APR/85	12/APR/85	
23226	G-BKYP	British Airways	236	10/APR/85	24/APR/85	
23228	N301P	Piedmont	301	04/APR/85	19/APR/85	
23229	N303P	Piedmont	301	01/MAY/85	20/MAY/85	
23230	N304P	Piedmont	301	15/MAY/85	23/MAY/85	
23231	N313P	Piedmont	301	06/NOV/85	04/DEC/85	
23232	N314P	Piedmont	301	25/NOV/85	12/DEC/85	
23233	N315P	Piedmont	301	07/FEB/86	04/MAR/86	
23234	N316P	Piedmont	301	03/MAR/86	14/MAR/86	
23235	N317P	Piedmont	301		APR/86	
23236	N319P	Piedmont	301	02/APR/86	01/MAY/86	
23237	N320P	Piedmont	301	17/APR/86	01/MAY/86	
23238	N	Piedmont	301			Re-assigned
23239	N	Piedmont	301			Re-assigned
23240	N	Piedmont	301			Re-assigned
23241	N	Piedmont	301			Re-assigned
23242	N	Piedmont	301			Re-assigned
23249	N105SW	Southwest Airlines	2H4	07/MAR/85	15/MAR/85	
23251	N307AC	International Lease Finance	3A4	19/DEC/84	01/FEB/85	
	N307AC	Air Cal			01/FEB/85	Leased
23252	N308AC	International Lease Finance	3A4	12/MAR/85	01/APR/85	
	N308AC	Air Cal			01/APR/85	Leased
23253	N309AC	International Lease Finance	3A4	07/MAR/85	27/MAR/85	
	N309AC	Air Cal			27/MAR/85	Leased
23254	G-SCUH	International Lease Finance	3Q8	18/APR/85		
	G-SCUH	Dan Air			02/MAY/85	Leased
23255	N841L	International Lease Finance	3Q8	12/JUN/85	26/JUN/85	
	N841L	Sunworld International			26/JUN/85	Leased
23256	N871L	International Lease Finance	3Q8	25/JUN/85	11/JUL/85	
	N871L	Sunworld International			11/JUL/85	Leased
	N871L	International Lease Finance			13/MAY/86	
	G-PROC	Airways International Cymru			13/MAY/86	Leased
	N871L	International Lease Finance			31/OCT/86	Sched.return
23257	N305P	Piedmont	301	06/JUN/85	20/JUN/85	
23258	N306P	Piedmont	301	12/JUN/85	25/JUN/85	
23259	N307P	Piedmont	301	28/JUN/85	15/JUL/85	
23260	N309P	Piedmont	301	22/AUG/85	05/SEP/85	
	N309P	Boeing			05/SEP/85	Leased for demonstration
	N309P	Piedmont			20/SEP/85	
23261	N312P	Piedmont	301	06/JUN/85	11/OCT/85	
23272	B-2506	CAAC	2T4	01/MAR/85	25/MAR/85	
23273	B-2507	CAAC	2T4	18/MAR/85	02/APR/85	
23274	B-2508	CAAC	2T4	20/MAR/85	09/APR/85	
23283	C-GWPW	Pacific Western	275	25/APR/85	01/MAY/85	
23284	C-GYPW	Pacific Western	275			
23285	C-GZPW	Pacific Western	275			
23288	N301AC	Air Cal	3A4	25/MAR/85	15/MAY/85	
23289	N303AC	Air Cal	3A4	07/DEC/85	19/DEC/85	
23290	N304AC	Air Cal	3A4	21/FEB/86	13/MAR/86	
23291	N306AC	Air Cal	3A4	07/MAR/86	02/APR/86	
23292	N674MA	Mark Air	2X6C	06/MAY/85	05/JUL/85	
23294	AP-BCA	PIA	340	06/MAY/85	31/MAY/85	

BOEING 737

C/N	Registration	Owner/Operator	Series	First Flight	Delivery	Remarks
23295	AP-BCB	PIA	340	15/MAY/85	06/JUN/85	
23296	AP-BCC	PIA	340	30/MAY/85	18/JUN/85	
23297	AP-BCD	PIA	340	03/JUN/85	21/JUN/85	
	AP-BCD	Emirates Airlines			25/NOV/85	Leased
23298	AP-BCE	PIA	340	06/JUN/85	25/JUN/85	
23299	AP-BCF	PIA	340	16/MAY/86	20/JUN/86	
23302	N1792B	Boeing	3J6	16/APR/86		
	B-2531	CAAC			15/MAY/86	
23303	N5573B	Boeing	3J6	22/MAY/86		
	B-2532	CAAC			19/JUN/86	
23310	N360AU	US Air	3B7	23/AUG/85	13/SEP/85	
23311	N361AU	US Air	3B7	04/SEP/85	18/SEP/85	
23312	N362AU	US Air	3B7		NOV/85	
23313	N363AU	US Air	3B7	11/DEC/85	20/DEC/85	
23314	N364AU	US Air	3B7	09/DEC/85	20/DEC/85	
23315	N365AU	US Air	3B7	07/MAR/86	24/MAR/86	
23316	N366AU	US Air	3B7	13/MAR/86	31/MAR/86	
23317	N367AU	US Air	3B7	08/APR/86	23/APR/86	
23318	N368AU	US Air	3B7	14/MAY/86	30/MAY/86	
23319	N369AU	US Air	3B7	27/JUN/86	17/JUL/86	
23320	9M-MBL	Malaysian Airlines System	2H6	23/MAY/85	07/JUN/85	
23329	YU-AND	JAT	3H9	12/JUL/85	31/JUL/85	
23330	YU-ANF	JAT	3H9	31/JUL/85	15/AUG/85	
23331	OY-MMK	Maersk	3L9	03/MAY/85	24/MAY/85	
23332	OY-MML	Maersk	3L9	22/MAY/85	10/JUN/85	
23333	N311SW	Southwest Airlines	3H4	02/JAN/86	13/MAR/86	
23334	N312SW	Southwest Airlines	3H4	28/JAN/86	14/MAR/86	
23335	N313SW	Southwest Airlines	3H4	11/FEB/86	17/MAR/86	
23336	N314SW	Southwest Airlines	3H4	30/APR/86	19/MAY/86	
23337	N315SW	Southwest Airlines	3H4	06/MAY/86	30/MAY/86	
23338	N316SW	Southwest Airlines	3H4	08/MAY/86	30/MAY/86	
23339	N318SW	Southwest Airlines	3H4	15/JUL/86	11/AUG/86	
23340	N319SW	Southwest Airlines	3H4		86	Sched.delivery
23341	N320SW	Southwest Airlines	3H4		86	Sched.delivery
23342	N321SW	Southwest Airlines	3H4		86	Sched.delivery
23343	N322SW	Southwest Airlines	3H4		86	Sched.delivery
23344	N323SW	Southwest Airlines	3H4		86	Sched.delivery
23345	N304WA	Western Airlines	347		MAR/86	Sched.delivery
23346	N305WA	Western Airlines	347	08/NOV/85	03/DEC/85	
23347	N306WA	Western Airlines	347	18/NOV/85	06/DEC/85	
23349	F-GBYM	Air France	228	09/JUL/85	23/JUL/85	
23351	D2-TBX	TAAG Angola	2M2	16/MAY/85	14/JUN/85	
23352	N16301	Texas Air Corporation	3T0	29/MAY/85	17/JUN/85	
	N16301	Continental Airlines			17/JUN/85	
23353	N59302	Texas Air Corporation	3T0	02/JUL/85	19/JUL/85	
	N59302	Continental Airlines			19/JUL/85	
23354	N77303	Texas Air Corporation	3T0	09/JUL/85	24/JUL/85	
	N77303	Continental Airlines			24/JUL/85	
23355	N61304	Texas Air Corporation	3T0	15/JUL/85	30/JUL/85	
	N61304	Continental Airlines			30/JUL/85	
23356	N63305	Texas Air Corporation	3T0	29/JUL/85	13/AUG/85	
	N63305	New York Air			13/AUG/85	
23357	N17306	Texas Air Corporation	3T0	13/AUG/85	28/AUG/85	
	N17306	Continental West			28/AUG/85	
	N17306	Continental Airlines			MAY/86	
23358	N14307	Texas Air Corporation	3T0	14/AUG/85	27/AUG/85	
	N14307	Continental West			27/AUG/85	
	N14307	Continental Airlines			MAY/86	
23359	N14308	Texas Air Corporation	3T0	20/AUG/85	05/SEP/85	
	N14308	New York Air			05/SEP/85	
23360	N17309	Texas Air Corporation	3T0	28/AUG/85	13/SEP/85	
	N17309	Continental West			13/SEP/85	
	N17309	Continental Airlines			MAY/86	
23361	N16310	Texas Air Corporation	3T0	06/SEP/85	24/SEP/85	
	N16310	New York Air			24/SEP/85	
23362	N69311	Texas Air Corporation	3T0	12/SEP/85	30/SEP/85	
	N69311	New York Air			30/SEP/85	
23363	N60312	Texas Air Corporation	3T0	16/SEP/85	03/OCT/85	
	N60312	Continental Airlines			03/OCT/85	
23364	N12313	Texas Air Corporation	3T0	30/SEP/85	16/OCT/85	
	N12313	Continental Airlines			16/OCT/85	
23365	N71314	Texas Air Corporation	3T0	03/OCT/85	24/OCT/85	
	N71314	Continental Airlines			24/OCT/85	
23366	N34315	Texas Air Corporation	3T0		NOV/85	
	N34315	Continental Airlines			NOV/85	
23367	N17316	Texas Air Corporation	3T0	03/DEC/85	18/DEC/85	
	N17316	New York Air			18/DEC/85	
23368	N17317	Texas Air Corporation	3T0	05/DEC/85	19/DEC/85	
	N17317	New York Air			19/DEC/85	
23369	N12318	Texas Air Corporation	3T0	08/JAN/86	15/JAN/86	
	N12318	Continental Airlines			15/JAN/86	
23370	N12319	Texas Air Corporation	3T0	09/JAN/86	22/JAN/86	
	N12319	Continental Airlines			22/JAN/86	
23371	N14320	Texas Air Corporation	3T0	15/JAN/86	30/JAN/86	
	N14320	Continental Airlines			30/JAN/86	
23372	N17321	Texas Air Corporation	3T0	17/JAN/86	05/FEB/86	
	N17321	Continental Airlines			05/FEB/86	
23373	N12322	Texas Air Corporation	3T0	14/FEB/86	27/FEB/86	
	N12322	Continental Airlines			27/FEB/86	
23374	N10323	Texas Air Corporation	3T0	19/FEB/86	10/MAR/86	
	N10323	Continental Airlines			10/MAR/86	
23375	N14324	Texas Air Corporation	3T0	27/FEB/86	17/MAR/86	
	N14324	Continental Airlines			17/MAR/86	
23376	N370AU	US Air	3B7		JAN/87	Sched.delivery
23377	N371AU	US Air	3B7		FEB/87	Sched.delivery
23378	N372AU	US Air	3B7		MAR/87	Sched.delivery
23379	N373AU	US Air	3B7		APR/87	Sched.delivery
23380	N374AU	US Air	3B7		MAY/87	Sched.delivery
23381	N375AU	US Air	3B7		JUN/87	Sched.delivery
23382	N376AU	US Air	3B7		JUL/87	Sched.delivery
23383	N377AU	US Air	3B7		AUG/87	Sched.delivery
23384	N378AU	US Air	3B7		SEP/87	Sched.delivery
23385	N379AU	US Air	3B7		OCT/87	Sched.delivery
23386	TJ-CBE	Cameroon Airlines	2K9	14/AUG/85	30/AUG/85	
23387	N781L	International Lease Finance	3Q8		NOV/85	
	N152AW	America West			NOV/85	Leased
23388	N891L	International Lease Finance	3Q8	13/JAN/86		

C/N	Registration	Owner/Operator	Series	First Flight	Delivery	Remarks
	N891L	Sunworld International			28/JAN/86	
23396	N5573K	Boeing	3WO	05/NOV/85		
	B-2517	CAAC/Yunnan Province			12/DEC/85	
23397	N1791B	Boeing	3WO	20/JAN/86		
	B-2518	CAAC/Yunnan Province			08/MAR/86	
23401	OO-ILF	International Lease Finance	3Q8	06/MAR/86	17/MAR/86	
	OO-ILF	Air Belgium			17/MAR/86	Leased
23404	N700ML	Bavaria	2K9	15/NOV/85	03/DEC/85	
	N700ML	Midway Airlines			03/DEC/85	Leased
23405	N701ML	Bavaria	2K9	20/NOV/85	05/DEC/85	
	N701ML	Midway Airlines			05/DEC/85	Leased
23406	N153AW	International Lease Finance	3Q8	21/MAR/86	08/APR/86	
	N153AW	America West			08/APR/86	Leased
23411	PH-HVF	Transavia	3K2	27/JAN/86	28/FEB/86	
23412	PH-HVG	Transavia	3K2		04/MAR/86	
23414	N324SW	Southwest Airlines	3H4		88	Sched.delivery
23415	YU-ANH	JAT	3H9	22/NOV/85	10/DEC/85	
23416	YU-ANI	JAT	3H9	26/NOV/85	17/DEC/85	
23440	N307WA	Western Airlines	347	31/MAR/86	16/APR/86	
23441	N308WA	Western Airlines	347	04/APR/86	22/APR/86	
23442	N309WA	Western Airlines	347	29/MAY/86	13/JUN/86	
23443	N1785B	Boeing	2T4	09/SEP/85		
	B-2511	CAAC Southwest			05/OCT/85	
23444	N1790B	Boeing	2T4	16/SEP/85		
	B-2512	CAAC Southwest			12/OCT/85	
23445	N1791B	Boeing	2T4	18/SEP/85		
	B-2514	CAAC Southwest			18/OCT/85	
23446	B-2515	CAAC Southwest	2T4		85	
23447	B-2516	CAAC Southwest	2T4		19/NOV/85	
23448	N5573P	Boeing	3ZO	01/NOV/85		
	B-2519	CAAC Southwest			17/DEC/85	
23449	N1789B	Boeing	3ZO	16/DEC/85		
	B-2520	CAAC Southwest			25/JAN/86	
23450	N1790B	Boeing	3ZO	28/JAN/86		
	B-2521	CAAC Southwest			26/FEB/86	
23451	N5573K	Boeing	3ZO	10/JUL/86		
	B-2522	CAAC Southwest			10/JUL/86	
23455	N14325	Texas Air Corporation	3TO	28/APR/86	19/MAY/86	
	N14325	New York Air			19/MAY/86	
23456	N17326	Texas Air Corporation	3TO	02/MAY/86	20/MAY/86	
	N17326	New York Air			20/MAY/86	
23457	N12327	Texas Air Corporation	3TO	27/MAY/86	12/JUN/86	
	N12327	Continental Airlines			12/JUN/86	
23458	N17328	Texas Air Corporation	3TO	12/JUN/86	10/JUL/86	
	N17328	Continental Airlines			10/JUL/86	
23459	N17329	Texas Air Corporation	3TO	20/JUN/86	15/JUL/86	
	N17329	Continental Airlines			15/JUL/86	
23460	N70330	Texas Air Corporation	3TO	09/JUL/86	25/JUL/86	
	N70330	Continental Airlines			25/JUL/86	
23462	C-FCPM	CP Air	317		APR/87	Cancelled order
23463	C-FCPN	CP Air	317		APR/87	Cancelled order
23464	LN-SUA	Braathens SAFE	205	10/APR/86	28/APR/86	
23465	LN-SUU	Braathens SAFE	205	18/APR/86	06/MAY/86	
23466	LN-SUZ	Braathens SAFE	205	16/MAY/86	04/JUN/86	
23467	LN-SUQ	Braathens SAFE	205	12/JUN/86	27/JUN/86	
23468	LN-SUJ	Braathens SAFE	205	30/JUL/86	12/AUG/86	
23469	LN-SUV	Braathens SAFE	205	06/AUG/86	26/AUG/86	
23470	ZK-NAT	Air New Zealand	219	02/JAN/86	16/JAN/86	
23471	ZK-NAU	Air New Zealand	219	06/JAN/86	21/JAN/86	
23472	ZK-NAV	Air New Zealand	219	20/JAN/86	10/FEB/86	
23473	ZK-NAW	Air New Zealand	219	28/JAN/86	13/FEB/86	
23474	ZK-NAX	Air New Zealand	219	03/FEB/86	18/FEB/86	
23475	ZK-NAY	Air New Zealand	219	14/FEB/86	05/MAR/86	
23477	VH-TAF	Trans Australia Airlines	376		JUL/86	Sched.delivery
23478	VH-TAG	Trans Australia Airlines	376	03/JUL/86	25/JUL/86	
23479	VH-TAH	Trans Australia Airlines	376	25/JUL/86	11/AUG/86	
23481	JA8250	Southwest Air Lines	2Q3	03/JUN/86	17/JUN/86	
23483	VH-TAI	Trans Australia Airlines	376	06/AUG/86	22/AUG/86	
23484	VH-TAJ	Trans Australia Airlines	376		NOV/86	Sched.delivery
23485	VH-TAK	Trans Australia Airlines	376		DEC/86	Sched.delivery
23486	VH-TAU	Trans Australia Airlines	376		JAN/87	Sched.delivery
23487	VH-TAV	Trans Australia Airlines	376		FEB/87	Sched.delivery
23488	VH-TAW	Trans Australia Airlines	376		MAR/87	Sched.delivery
23489	VH-TAX	Trans Australia Airlines	376		APR/87	Sched.delivery
23490	VH-TAY	Trans Australia Airlines	376		MAY/87	Sched.delivery
23491	VH-TAZ	Trans Australia Airlines	376		JUN/87	Sched.delivery
23495	G-DWHH	GPA Group	3Y0	26/FEB/86	13/MAR/86	
	G-DWHH	Monarch Airlines			13/MAR/86	Leased
23496	N67AB	GPA Group	3Y0	27/MAR/86	11/APR/86	
	N67AB	Air Berlin			11/APR/86	Leased
23497	G-MONF	GPA Group	3Y0	24/APR/86	13/MAY/86	
	G-MONF	Monarch Airlines			13/MAY/86	Leased
23498	G-MONG	GPA Group	3Y0	12/MAY/86	28/MAY/86	
	G-MONG	Monarch Airlines			28/MAY/86	Leased
23499	PT-TEA	GPA Group	3Y0	05/JUN/86	23/JUN/86	
	PT-TEA	TransBrasil			23/JUN/86	Leased
23500	PT-TEB	GPA Group	3Y0	10/JUN/86	25/JUN/86	
	PT-TEB	Transbrasil			25/JUN/86	Leased
23503	F-GBYN	Air France	228	17/JUL/86	03/AUG/86	
23504	F-GBYO	Air France	228	16/AUG/86	28/AUG/86	
23505	N310AC	Air Cal	3A4		86	Sched.delivery
23506	N781L	International Lease Finance	3Q8	20/JUN/86	02/JUL/86	
	N781L	Sunworld International			02/JUL/86	Leased
	N781L	America West			02/JUL/86	Sub-leased
	N781L	Sunworld International			JUN/87	Sched.return
23507	N751L	International Lease Finance	3Q8	03/JUL/86	18/JUL/86	
	N751L	Sunworld International			18/JUL/86	Leased
23510	N321P	Piedmont	301	23/JUN/86	09/JUL/86	
23511	N322P	Piedmont	301		AUG/86	Sched.delivery
23512	N323P	Piedmont	301		NOV/86	Sched.delivery
23513	N324P	Piedmont	301		DEC/86	Sched.delivery
23514	N325P	Piedmont	301		FEB/87	Sched.delivery
23515	N326P	Piedmont	301		FEB/87	Sched.delivery
23516	N242WA	Western	247	21/JUL/86	04/AUG/86	
23517	N243WA	Western	247	29/JUL/86	13/AUG/86	

BOEING 737

C/N	Registration	Owner/Operator	Series	First Flight	Delivery	Remarks
23518	N244WA	Western	247	08/AUG/86	22/AUG/86	
23519	N245WA	Western	247		APR/87	Sched.delivery
23520	N246WA	Western	247		MAY/87	Sched.delivery
23521	N247WA	Western	247		MAY/87	Sched.delivery
23522	D-ABXA	Lufthansa	330	23/JUN/86	16/AUG/86	
23523	D-ABXB	Lufthansa	330		86	Sched.delivery
23524	D-ABXC	Lufthansa	330		86	Sched.delivery
23525	D-ABXD	Lufthansa	330		86	Sched.delivery
23526	D-ABXE	Lufthansa	330		86	Sched.delivery
23527	D-ABXF	Lufthansa	330		86	Sched.delivery
23528	D-ABXH	Lufthansa	330		86	Sched.delivery
23529	D-ABXI	Lufthansa	330		86	Sched.delivery
23530	D-ABXK	Lufthansa	330		86	Sched.delivery
23531	D-ABXL	Lufthansa	330		DEC/86	Sched.delivery
23535		International Lease Finance	3Q8		JUL/86	Sched.delivery
23536		International Lease Finance	3Q8		NOV/86	Sched.delivery
		Air Europe			NOV/86	Sched.lease
		Air Europa			NOV/86	Sched.sub-lease
23537	PH-BDA	KLM	306		SEP/86	
23538	PH-BDB	KLM	306			
23539	PH-BDC	KLM	306			
23540	PH-BDD	KLM	306			
23541	PH-BDE	KLM	306			
23542	PH-BDG	KLM	306			
23543	PH-BDH	KLM	306			
23544	PH-BDI	KLM	306			
23545	PH-BDK	KLM	306			
23546	PH-BDL	KLM	306		MAR/87	
23550	N	Piedmont	301		MAR/87	Sched.delivery
23551	N	Piedmont	301		MAR/87	Sched.delivery
23552	N	Piedmont	301		87	Sched.delivery
23553	N	Piedmont	301		87	Sched.delivery
23554	N	Piedmont	301		87	Sched.delivery
23555	N	Piedmont	301		87	Sched.delivery
23556	N	Piedmont	301		87	Sched.delivery
23557	N	Piedmont	301		87	Sched.delivery
23558	N	Piedmont	301		87	Sched.delivery
23559	N	Piedmont	301		87	Sched.delivery
23560	N	Piedmont	301		87	Sched.delivery
23561	N	Piedmont	301		87	Sched.delivery
23562	N	Piedmont	301			Re-assigned
23563	N	Piedmont	301			Re-assigned
23564	N	Piedmont	301			Re-assigned
23565	N	Piedmont	301			Re-assigned
23569	N13331	Texas Air Corporation	3T0	23/JUL/86		
	N13331	Continental Airlines			11/AUG/86	
23570	N47332	Texas Air Corporation	3T0	04/AUG/86		
	N47332	Continental Airlines			21/AUG/86	
23571	N69333	Texas Air Corporation	3T0		86	Sched.delivery
	N69333	New York Air			86	Sched.delivery
23572	N14334	Texas Air Corporation	3T0		86	Sched.delivery
	N14334	New York Air			86	Sched.delivery
23573	N14335	Texas Air Corporation	3T0		86	Sched.delivery
	N14335	New York Air			86	Sched.delivery
23574	N14336	Texas Air Corporation	3T0		86	Sched.delivery
	N14336	New York Air			86	Sched.delivery
23575	N14337	Texas Air Corporation	3T0		86	Sched.delivery
	N14337	New York Air			86	Sched.delivery
23576	N59338	Texas Air Corporation	3T0		87	Sched.delivery
23577	N16339	Texas Air Corporation	3T0			
23578	N39340	Texas Air Corporation	3T0			
23579	N14341	Texas Air Corporation	3T0			
23580	N14342	Texas Air Corporation	3T0			
23581	N39343	Texas Air Corporation	3T0			
23582	N17344	Texas Air Corporation	3T0			
23583	N17345	Texas Air Corporation	3T0			
23584	N14346	Texas Air Corporation	3T0			
23585	N14347	Texas Air Corporation	3T0			
23586	N69348	Texas Air Corporation	3T0			
23587	N12349	Texas Air Corporation	3T0			
23588	N18350	Texas Air Corporation	3T0			
23589	N69351	Texas Air Corporation	3T0			
23590	N70352	Texas Air Corporation	3T0			
23591	N70353	Texas Air Corporation	3T0			
23592	N76354	Texas Air Corporation	3T0			
23593	N76355	Texas Air Corporation	3T0			
23594	N380AU	US Air	3B7		NOV/87	Sched.delivery
23595	N381AU	US Air	3B7		DEC/87	Sched.delivery
23596	N2310	Western Airlines	347	20/AUG/86	29/AUG/86	
23597	N311WA	Western Airlines	347		NOV/86	Sched.delivery
23598	N312WA	Western Airlines	347		DEC/86	Sched.delivery
23599	N313WA	Western Airlines	347		JAN/87	Sched.delivery
23601	OE-ILF	Lauda Air	3Z9	11/JUL/86	28/JUL/86	
23602	N248WA	Western Airlines	247		87	Sched.delivery
23603	N249WA	Western Airlines	247		87	Sched.delivery
23604	N254WA	Western Airlines	247		87	Sched.delivery
23605	N255WA	Western Airlines	247		87	Sched.delivery
23606	N256WA	Western Airlines	247		87	Sched.delivery
23607	N257WA	Western Airlines	247		87	Sched.delivery
23608	N258WA	Western Airlines	247		87	Sched.delivery
23609	N259WA	Western Airlines	247		87	Sched.delivery
23625	N3281V	Trans Pacific Enterprises	33A		OCT/86	Sched.delivery
23626	N3281W	Trans Pacific Enterprises	33A		NOV/86	Sched.delivery
23627	N3281Y	Trans Pacific Enterprises	33A		DEC/86	Sched.delivery
23628	N3282G	Trans Pacific Enterprises	33A		JAN/87	Sched.delivery
23629	N3282N	Trans Pacific Enterprises	33A		FEB/87	Sched.delivery
23630	N3282P	Trans Pacific Enterprises	33A		MAR/87	Sched.delivery
23631	N3282R	Trans Pacific Enterprises	33A		APR/87	Sched.delivery
23632	N3282V	Trans Pacific Enterprises	33A		MAY/87	Sched.delivery
23633	N3282W	Trans Pacific Enterprises	33A		JUN/87	Sched.delivery
23634	N3282X	Trans Pacific Enterprises	33A		JUL/87	Sched.delivery
23635	N3282Y	Trans Pacific Enterprises	33A		AUG/87	Sched.delivery
23636	N3283G	Trans Pacific Enterprises	33A		SEP/87	Sched.delivery
23642	N301UA	United Airlines	322		NOV/86	Sched.delivery
23643	N302UA	United Airlines	322		86	Sched.delivery
23644	N303UA	United Airlines	322		86	Sched.delivery

C/N	Registration	Owner/Operator	Series	First Flight	Delivery	Remarks
23646	N	Piedmont	301		87	Sched.delivery
23647	N	Piedmont	301		88	Sched.delivery
23648	N	Piedmont	301		88	Sched.delivery
23649	N	Piedmont	301		88	Sched.delivery
23650	N	Piedmont	301		88	Sched.delivery
23653	VH-CZA	Ansett Airlines	377	03/AUG/86	22/AUG/86	
23654	VH-CZB	Ansett Airlines	377		SEP/86	Sched.delivery
23655	VH-CZC	Ansett Airlines	377		SEP/86	Sched.delivery
23656	VH-CZD	Ansett Airlines	377		OCT/86	Sched.delivery
23657	VH-CZE	Ansett Airlines	377		OCT/86	Sched.delivery
23658	VH-CZF	Ansett Airlines	377		OCT/86	Sched.delivery
23659	VH-CZG	Ansett Airlines	377		NOV/86	Sched.delivery
23660	VH-CZH	Ansett Airlines	377		NOV/86	Sched.delivery
23661	VH-CZI	Ansett Airlines	377		DEC/86	Sched.delivery
23662	VH-CZJ	Ansett Airlines	377		DEC/86	Sched.delivery
23663	VH-CZK	Ansett Airlines	377		JAN/87	Sched.delivery
23664	VH-CZL	Ansett Airlines	377		JAN/87	Sched.delivery
23665	N304UA	United Airlines	322		JAN/87	Sched.delivery
23666	N305UA	United Airlines	322		87	Sched.delivery
23667	N306UA	United Airlines	322		87	Sched.delivery
23668	N307UA	United Airlines	322		87	Sched.delivery
23669	N308UA	United Airlines	322		87	Sched.delivery
23670	N309UA	United Airlines	322		87	Sched.delivery
23671	N310UA	United Airlines	322		MAY/87	Sched.delivery
23672	N311UA	United Airlines	322			
23673	N312UA	United Airlines	322			
23674	N313UA	United Airlines	322			
23675	N314UA	United Airlines	322			
23680	EI-	Guinness Peat	300			Re-assigned
23681	EI-	Guinness Peat	300			Re-assigned
23682	EI-	Guinness Peat	300			Re-assigned
23683	EI-	Guinness Peat	300			Re-assigned
23684	EI-	Guinness Peat	300		87	Sched.delivery
23685	EI-	Guinness Peat	300		87	Sched.delivery
23689	N325SW	Southwest Airlines	3H4		88	Sched.delivery
23690	N326SW	Southwest Airlines	3H4		88	Sched.delivery
23691	N327SW	Southwest Airlines	3H4		88	Sched.delivery
23692	N328SW	Southwest Airlines	3H4		88	Sched.delivery
23693	N329SW	Southwest Airlines	3H4		89	Sched.delivery
23694	N330SW	Southwest Airlines	3H4		89	Sched.delivery
23695	N331SW	Southwest Airlines	3H4		89	Sched.delivery
23696	N332SW	Southwest Airlines	3H4		89	Sched.delivery
23697	N	Southwest Airlines	3H4		89	Sched.delivery
23699	N382AU	US Air	3B7		JAN/88	Sched.delivery
23700	N383AU	US Air	3B7		FEB/88	Sched.delivery
23701	N384AU	US Air	3B7		MAR/88	Sched.delivery
23702	N385AU	US Air	3B7		APR/88	Sched.delivery
23703	N386AU	US Air	3B7		MAY/88	Sched.delivery
23704	N387AU	US Air	3B7		JUN/88	Sched.delivery
23705	N388AU	US Air	3B7		JUL/88	Sched.delivery
23706	N390AU	US Air	3B7		AUG/88	Sched.delivery
23712	G-BMTE	Air Europe	3S3		MAR/87	Sched.delivery
23713	G-BMTF	Air Europe	3S3		MAR/87	Sched.delivery
23714	YU-ANJ	JAT	3H9		NOV/86	Sched.delivery
23715	YU-ANK	JAT	3H9		NOV/86	Sched.delivery
23716	YU-ANL	JAT	3H9		DEC/86	Sched.delivery
23717	OY-MMM	Maersk Air	3L9		JUN/87	Sched.delivery
23718	OY-MMN	Maersk Air	3L9		JUN/87	Sched.delivery
23733	G-BMTG	Air Europe	3S3		APR/87	Sched.delivery
23734	G-BMTH	Air Europe	3S3		APR/87	Sched.delivery
23738	PH-HVJ	Transavia	3K2		MAR/87	Sched.delivery
23739	N	Piedmont	301		88	Sched.delivery
23740	N	Piedmont	301		88	Sched.delivery
23741	N	Piedmont	301		88	Sched.delivery
23742	N	Piedmont	301		88	Sched.delivery
23743	N	Piedmont	301		88	Sched.delivery
23747	EI-	Guinness Peat	3YO		87	Sched.delivery
23748	EI-	Guinness Peat	3YO		87	Sched.delivery
23749	EI-	Guinness Peat	3YO		87	Sched.delivery
23750	EI-	Guinness Peat	3YO		87	Sched.delivery
23752	N	Air Cal	3A4		87	Sched.delivery
23753	N	Air Cal	3A4		87	Sched.delivery
23754	N	Air Cal	3A4		87	Sched.delivery
23755	N	Air Cal	3A4		88	Sched.delivery
23766	N	International Air Lease	3Q8		APR/87	Sched.delivery
		Air Europe			APR/87	Sched.lease
	EC-	Air Europa			APR/87	Sched.sub-lease
23768	N	International Lease Finance	3Q8		MAY/87	Sched.delivery
23771	OO-SDV	Sabena	329		AUG/87	Sched.delivery
23772	OO-SDW	Sabena	329		AUG/87	Sched.delivery
23773	OO-SDX	Sabena	329		SEP/87	Sched.delivery
23774	OO-SDY	Sabena	329		SEP/87	Sched.delivery
23775	OO-SBZ	Sobelair	329		JUL/87	Sched.delivery
23776	N154AW	America West	3G7		JUN/87	Sched.delivery
23777	N155AW	America West	3G7			Sched.delivery
23778	N156AW	America West	3G7			Sched.delivery
23779	N157AW	America West	3G7			Sched.delivery
23780	N158AW	America West	3G7			Sched.delivery
23781	N159AW	America West	3G7			Sched.delivery
23782	N160AW	America West	3G7			Sched.delivery
23783	N161AW	America West	3G7			Sched.delivery
23784	N162AW	America West	3G7			Sched.delivery
23785	N163AW	America West	3G7		SEP/88	Sched.delivery
23787	N	International Lease Finance	3Q8		SEP/87	Sched.delivery
23788	N	International Lease Finance	3Q8		FEB/88	Sched.delivery
23789	N	Presidential Airways	25A		JUL/87	Sched.delivery
23790	N	Presidential Airways	25A		AUG/87	Sched.delivery
23791	N	Presidential Airways	25A		JAN/88	Sched.delivery
23797	D-	Bavaria Flug	3K9		JUL/87	Sched.delivery
23798	D-	Bavaria Flug	3K9		AUG/87	Sched.delivery
23809	EI-	Aer Lingus	348		NOV/87	Sched.delivery
23810	EI-	Aer Lingus	348		NOV/87	Sched.delivery
23811	N	International Lease Finance	3Q8		APR/88	Sched.delivery
23812	EI-	Guinness Peat Aviation	3YO		AUG/87	Sched.delivery

C/N	Registration	Owner/Operator	Series	First Flight	Delivery	Remarks

ADDITIONAL ORDERS

C/N	Registration	Owner/Operator	Series	First Flight	Delivery	Remarks
N		America West	3G7			
N		America West	3G7			
N		Piedmont	301		88	Sched.delivery
N		Piedmont	301		88	Sched.delivery
N		Piedmont	301		88	Sched.delivery
N		Piedmont	301		JAN/89	Sched.delivery
N		International Lease Finance	3Q8		MAY/88	Sched.delivery
OE-ILG		Lauda Air	300		MAR/88	Sched.delivery
D-		Condor	330		MAR/88	Sched.delivery
D-		Condor	330		MAR/88	Sched.delivery
D-		Condor	330		APR/88	Sched.delivery
D-		Condor	330		APR/88	Sched.delivery
D-		Condor	330		MAY/88	Sched.delivery
9M-		Malaysian Airline System	2H6		OCT/87	Sched.delivery
OO-		TEA	3M8		OCT/88	Sched.delivery
OO-		TEA	3M8			
OO-		TEA	3M8			
OO-		TEA	3M8			
OO-		TEA	3M8			
N		Piedmont	401		SEP/88	Sched.delivery
N		Piedmont	401			
N		Piedmont	401			
N		Piedmont	401			
N		Piedmont	401			
N		Piedmont	401			
N		Piedmont	401			
N		Piedmont	401			
N		Piedmont	401			
N		Piedmont	401			
N		Piedmont	401			
N		Piedmont	401			
N		Piedmont	401			
N		Piedmont	401			
N		Piedmont	401			
N		Piedmont	401			
N		Piedmont	401			
N		Piedmont	401			
N		Piedmont	401			
N		Piedmont	401			
N		Piedmont	401			
N		Piedmont	401			
N		Piedmont	401			
N		Piedmont	401		DEC/89	Sched.delivery
N		Interlease	4Q8		NOV/88	Sched.delivery
N		Interlease	4Q8		DEC/88	Sched.delivery
N		Interlease	4Q8		MAR/89	Sched.delivery
N		US Air	3B7		87	Sched.delivery
N		US Air	3B7			
N		US Air	3B7			
N		US Air	3B7			
N		US Air	3B7			
N		US Air	3B7			
N		US Air	3B7			
N		United Airlines	322			
N		United Airlines	322			
N		United Airlines	322			
N		United Airlines	322			
N		United Airlines	322			
N		United Airlines	322		JUN/88	Sched.delivery
YU-		Aviogenex	200		JUN/87	Sched.delivery
9H-		Air Malta	2Y5		JUL/87	Sched.delivery
9H-		Air Malta	2Y5		JUL/87	Sched.delivery

Plus : 90 further Boeing 737-322s for United Airlines for delivery by December 1990
: 50 further Boeing 737-3Y0s for Guinness Peat for delivery between August 1987 and May 1991
: 30 Boeing 737-4Y0s for Guinness Peat for delivery from October 1988

3D- Swaziland
19708 3D-ADA

3X- Guinea
22627 3X-GCB

4R- Sri Lanka
21278 4R-ALC
20913 4R-ALD
19742 4R-ULH

4W- North Yemen
21296 4W-ABZ

4X- Israel
21736 4X-ABL
22090 4X-ABM
22856 4X-ABN
22857 4X-ABO
21820 4X-BAA
22875 4X-BAB
22876 4X-BAC

5H- Tanzania
21710 5H-ATC
21711 5H-MRK

5N- Nigeria
20671 5N-ANC
20672 5N-AND
22771 5N-ANW
22772 5N-ANX
22773 5N-ANY
22774 5N-ANZ
22985 5N-AUA
22986 5N-AUB
22987 5N-AUC
22988 5N-AUD

5R- Madagascar
20231 5R-MFA
20680 5R-MFB

5U- Nigeria
21499 5U-BAG
21499 5U-MAF

5W- Western Samoa
22555 5W-PAL

70- South Yemen
23129 7O-ACQ
23130 7O-ACR

7T- Algeria
20544 7T-VEC
20650 7T-VED
20758 7T-VEE
20759 7T-VEF
20884 7T-VEG
21063 7T-VEJ
21064 7T-VEK
21065 7T-VEL
21211 7T-VEN
21212 7T-VEO
21285 7T-VEQ
21286 7T-VER
21287 7T-VES
22766 7T-VEY
22700 7T-VEZ
22800 7T-VJA
22801 7T-VJB

9H- Malta
23038 9H-ABA
23039 9H-ABB
23040 9H-ABC

9J- Zambia
19424 9J-ADZ
21236 9J-AEA
21236 9J-AEG

9K- Kuwait
21206 9K-ACV

9M- Malaysia
19768 9M-AOU
19770 9M-AOV
19772 9M-AOW
20521 9M-AQC
20582 9M-AQL
20583 9M-AQM
20584 9M-AQN
20585 9M-AQO
20586 9M-AQP
20587 9M-AQQ
20631 9M-ARG
20926 9M-ASR
20582 9M-MBA
20583 9M-MBB
20584 9M-MBC
20585 9M-MBD
20586 9M-MBE
20587 9M-MBF
20631 9M-MBG
20926 9M-MBH
21109 9M-MBI
21732 9M-MBJ
22620 9M-MBK
23320 9M-MBL
21686 9M-MBY
21685 9M-MBZ

9Q- Zaire
20793 9Q-CNI
20794 9Q-CNJ
20795 9Q-CNK
20276 9Q-CNL
20796 9Q-CNL
20797 9Q-CNM

9V- Singapore
19769 9V-BBC
19771 9V-BBE
20492 9V-BCR
19768 9V-BFD
19770 9V-BFE
19772 9V-BFF

A40- Oman
21355 A40-BC
21356 A40-BD
21357 A40-BE
21358 A40-BF
21359 A40-BG
21612 A40-BH
21677 A40-BI
21733 A40-BJ
21734 A40-BK

A6- United Arab Emirates
21613 A6-AAA
22628 A6-ESH

AP- Pakistan
23294 AP-BCA
23295 AP-BCB
23296 AP-BCC
23297 AP-BCD
23298 AP-BCE
23299 AP-BCF

B- Taiwan
20226 B-1870
20227 B-1872
20277 B-1874

B- China
22802 B-2501
22803 B-2502
22804 B-2503
23065 B-2504
23066 B-2505
23272 B-2506
23273 B-2507
23274 B-2508
23188 B-2509
23189 B-2510
23443 B-2511
23444 B-2512
23445 B-2514
23446 B-2515
23447 B-2516
23396 B-2517
23397 B-2518
23448 B-2519
23449 B-2520
23450 B-2521
23451 B-2522
23302 B-2531
23303 B-2532
19936 B-2601
19939 B-2603
19712 B-2605
20132 B-2607
21518 B-2611
20134 B-2613
21687 B-2615
20130 B-2617
19014 B-2621
19017 B-2623

C- Canada
22072 C-FACP
23173 C-FCPG
23174 C-FCPI
23175 C-FCPJ
23176 C-FCPK
23177 C-FCPL
23462 C-FCPM
22762 C-FCPN
23463 C-FCPN
20396 C-FEPL
20300 C-FEPO
20681 C-FEPP
20397 C-FEPR
20776 C-FEPU
22024 C-FHCP
20455 C-FNAQ
20521 C-FNAW
22761 C-FPWD
22762 C-FPWE
20670 C-FPWW
20206 C-FTAN
20205 C-FTAO
20922 C-GAPW
20958 C-GBPW
21716 C-GCPM
21717 C-GCPN
21718 C-GCPO
22255 C-GCPP
22256 C-GCPQ
22257 C-GCPR
22257 C-GCPS
22258 C-GCPS
22258 C-GCPT
22259 C-GCPU
22260 C-GCPV
20959 C-GCPW
22341 C-GCPX
22342 C-GCPY
22658 C-GCPZ
22056 C-GDPA
21116 C-GDPW
22148 C-GENL
20976 C-GEPA
21112 C-GEPB
22395 C-GEPM
21115 C-GEPW
22659 C-GFCP
21294 C-GFPW
21639 C-GGPW
21712 C-GIPW
22728 C-GJCP
21713 C-GJPW
22729 C-GKCP
21819 C-GKPW
22086 C-GLPW
22864 C-GMCP
22087 C-GMPW
21719 C-GNDC
21728 C-GNDC
21112 C-GNDD
22054 C-GNDG
21186 C-GNDL
22074 C-GNDM
22075 C-GNDR
21518 C-GNDS
22877 C-GNDU
21694 C-GNDW
20911 C-GNDX
22159 C-GNPW
22160 C-GOPW
22264 C-GPPW
22416 C-GPWC
22072 C-GQBA
22276 C-GQBB
19426 C-GQBC
19594 C-GQBD
22398 C-GQBE
22516 C-GQBH
22277 C-GQBJ
22070 C-GQBQ
21231 C-GQBS
21719 C-GQBT
22276 C-GQBU
22277 C-GQBV
22865 C-GQCP
22265 C-GQPW
21397 C-GRCP
22266 C-GRPW
22618 C-GSPW
20956 C-GTAQ
20223 C-GTAR
22807 C-GTPW
22873 C-GUPW
22874 C-GVPW
23283 C-GWPW
22640 C-GXCP
23284 C-GYPW
23285 C-GZPW

C2- Nauru
21073 C2-RN3
21616 C2-RN6
22070 C2-RN8
22072 C2-RN9

C6- Bahamas
21231 C6-BDZ
20413 C6-BEC
22531 C6-BEH
20128 C6-BEI
20956 C6-BEK
21279 C6-BEQ
19921 C6-BES
21528 C6-BEX
20221 C6-BFB
21278 C6-BFC

C9- Mozambique
20280 C9-BAA
20281 C9-BAB
20536 C9-BAC
20786 C9-BAD

CC- Chile
22602 CC-CHJ
22589 CC-CHK
21927 CC-CHU
22340 CC-CIM
22703 CC-CIN
22792 CC-CIY

CF- Canada
19884 CF-CPB
19885 CF-CPC
19886 CF-CPD
19887 CF-CPE
19888 CF-CPU
19889 CF-CPV
20196 CF-CPV
20197 CF-CPZ
20396 CF-EPL
20300 CF-EPO
20681 CF-EPP
20397 CF-EPR
20776 CF-EPU
19847 CF-NAB
19849 CF-NAF
19848 CF-NAH
19945 CF-NAI
19946 CF-NAP
20496 CF-NAP
20455 CF-NAQ
20521 CF-NAW
22785 CF-PWB
20142 CF-PWC
19742 CF-PWD
19743 CF-PWE
19921 CF-PWM
20588 CF-PWP
20670 CF-PWW
19989 CF-QBN
19990 CF-QBN
20206 CF-TAN
20205 CF-TAO
20223 CF-TAR

CN- Morocco
21214 CN-RMI
21215 CN-RMJ
21216 CN-RMK
22767 CN-RML
23049 CN-RMM
23050 CN-RMN

CR- Mozambique
20280 CR-BAA
20281 CR-BAB
20536 CR-BAC
20786 CR-BAD

CR- Angola
21172 CR-LOR
21173 CR-LOS

CS- Portugal
23041 CS-TEK
23042 CS-TEL
23043 CS-TEM
23044 CS-TEN
23045 CS-TEO
23046 CS-TEP
23051 CS-TEQ

CX- Uruguay
20299 CX-BHM
22737 CX-BON
22738 CX-BOO
22739 CX-BOP

D- West Germany
20253 D-ABBE
20254 D-ABCE
20255 D-ABDE
19013 D-ABEA
19014 D-ABEB
19015 D-ABEC
19016 D-ABED
19017 D-ABEF
19018 D-ABEG
19019 D-ABEH
19020 D-ABEI
19796 D-ABEJ
19021 D-ABEK
19022 D-ABEL
19023 D-ABEM
19024 D-ABEN
19025 D-ABEO
19026 D-ABEP
19027 D-ABEQ
19028 D-ABER
19029 D-ABES
19030 D-ABET
19031 D-ABEU
19032 D-ABEV
19033 D-ABEW
19794 D-ABEY
19795 D-ABEZ
22114 D-ABFA
22113 D-ABFB
22115 D-ABFC
22116 D-ABFD
20256 D-ABFE
22117 D-ABFF
22118 D-ABFH
22119 D-ABFK
22120 D-ABFL
22121 D-ABFM
22122 D-ABFN
22123 D-ABFP
22124 D-ABFR
22125 D-ABFS
22402 D-ABFT
22126 D-ABFU
22127 D-ABFW
22128 D-ABFX
22129 D-ABFY
22130 D-ABFZ
20257 D-ABGE
22131 D-ABHA
22132 D-ABHB
22133 D-ABHC
22635 D-ABHD
20258 D-ABHE
22134 D-ABHF
22135 D-ABHH
22136 D-ABHK
22137 D-ABHL
22138 D-ABHM
22139 D-ABHN
22140 D-ABHP
22141 D-ABHR
22142 D-ABHS
22636 D-ABHT
22143 D-ABHU
22634 D-ABHW
22637 D-ABHX
23153 D-ABMA
23154 D-ABMB
23155 D-ABMC
23156 D-ABMD
23157 D-ABME
23158 D-ABMF
19679 D-ABWA
19680 D-ABWB
23522 D-ABXA
23523 D-ABXB
23524 D-ABXC
23525 D-ABXD
23526 D-ABXE
23527 D-ABXF
23528 D-ABXH
23529 D-ABXI
23530 D-ABXK
23531 D-ABXL
20070 D-ADDA
22726 D-ADDB
22727 D-ADDC
22596 D-AHLD
22597 D-AHLE
22598 D-AHLF
22599 D-AHLG
22600 D-AHLH
22601 D-AHLI

D2- Angola
21172 D2-TAA
21172 D2-TAB
21723 D2-TBA
21172 D2-TBC
21723 D2-TBD

22775	D2-TBN	19710	G-AVRM	20544	G-BMMZ	21477	JA8444	23574 N14336
22776	D2-TBO	19711	G-AVRN	22416	G-BMON	21478	JA8445	23575 N14337
23220	D2-TBP	19712	G-AVRO	21776	G-BMOR	22766	JA8452	23579 N14341
21278	D2-TBT	20236	G-AWSY	22279	G-BMSM	21767	JA8453	23580 N14342
21279	D2-TBU	20282	G-AXNA	22660	G-BMSP	21768	JA8454	23584 N14346
22626	D2-TBV	20389	G-AXNB	23712	G-BMTE	21769	JA8455	23585 N14347
23351	D2-TBX	20417	G-AXNC	23713	G-BMTF	21770	JA8456	22453 N143AW
		19074	G-AZNZ	23733	G-BMTG	21771	JA8457	19074 N144AW

D6- Comores Islands

22581 D6-CAJ

DQ- Fiji

22679 DQ-FDM

EC- Spain

22597	EC-DTR
22598	EC-DUB
22369	EC-DUL
22639	EC-DVE
22296	EC-DVN
22638	EC-DXK
22407	EC-DXV
22703	EC-DYZ
20218	EC-DZB
20336	EC-DZH

EI- Eire

19424	EI-APP
19425	EI-APS
19424	EI-ASA
19425	EI-ASB
20218	EI-ASC
20219	EI-ASD
20220	EI-ASE
20221	EI-ASF
22222	EI-ASG
20223	EI-ASH
19947	EI-ASK
21011	EI-ASL
21131	EI-BCC
20276	EI-BCR
21112	EI-BDY
21714	EI-BEB
21715	EI-BEC
20413	EI-BEE
20449	EI-BEF
20336	EI-BFC
21279	EI-BII
19742	EI-BJE
19743	EI-BJP
21278	EI-BMY
20521	EI-BNS
20455	EI-BOC
22071	EI-BOJ
22368	EI-BOM
22369	EI-BON
21775	EI-BPR
22024	EI-BPV
21776	EI-BPW
21774	EI-BPY
22279	EI-BRB
22529	EI-BRN
22703	EI-BRZ

EL- Liberia

21538 EL-AIL

EP- Iran

21317	EP-AGA
20498	EP-IRF
20499	EP-IRG
20500	EP-IRH
20740	EP-IRI

F- France

23000	F-GBYA
23001	F-GBYB
23002	F-GBYC
23003	F-GBYD
23004	F-GBYE
23005	F-GBYF
23006	F-GBYG
23007	F-GBYH
23008	F-GBYI
23009	F-GBYJ
23010	F-GBYK
23011	F-GBYL
23349	F-GBYM
23503	F-GBYN
23504	F-GBYO
21278	F-GCGR
21279	F-GCGS
19067	F-GCJL
19064	F-GCLL
19066	F-GCSL

G- United Kingdom

19709	G-AVRL
20632	G-BADP
20633	G-BADR
20806	G-BAZG
20807	G-BAZH
20808	G-BAZI
21335	G-BECG
21336	G-BECH
21693	G-BFVA
21694	G-BFVB
21790	G-BGDA
21791	G-BGDB
21792	G-BGDC
21793	G-BGDD
21794	G-BGDE
21795	G-BGDF
21796	G-BGDG
21797	G-BGDH
21798	G-BGDI
21799	G-BGDJ
21800	G-BGDK
21801	G-BGDL
21802	G-BGDN
21803	G-BGDO
21804	G-BGDP
21805	G-BGDR
21806	G-BGDS
21807	G-BGDT
21808	G-BGDU
22026	G-BGJE
22027	G-BGJF
22028	G-BGJG
22029	G-BGJH
22030	G-BGJI
22031	G-BGJJ
22032	G-BGJK
22033	G-BGJL
22034	G-BGJM
21131	G-BGNW
22057	G-BGRU
22058	G-BGRV
22024	G-BGTV
22023	G-BGTW
21960	G-BGTY
22057	G-BGYJ
22058	G-BGYK
22059	G-BGYL
21955	G-BHCL
22395	G-BHVG
22396	G-BHVH
22397	G-BHVI
22364	G-BHWE
22365	G-BHWF
21528	G-BJCV
22632	G-BJBJ
22638	G-BJCT
22639	G-BJCU
22640	G-BJCV
22278	G-BJFH
22071	G-BJSO
22657	G-BJXJ
22054	G-BJXL
22055	G-BJXM
22277	G-BJZV
22516	G-BJZW
21685	G-BKAP
20943	G-BKBT
22966	G-BKHE
22967	G-BKHF
22979	G-BKHO
22453	G-BKMS
21820	G-BKNH
21278	G-BKRO
23159	G-BKYA
23160	G-BKYB
23161	G-BKYC
23162	G-BKYD
23163	G-BKYE
23164	G-BKYF
23165	G-BKYG
23166	G-BKYH
23167	G-BKYI
23168	G-BKYJ
23169	G-BKYK
23170	G-BKYL
23171	G-BKYM
23172	G-BKYN
23225	G-BKYO
23226	G-BKYP
22876	G-BLDE
21397	G-BLEA
23060	G-BLKB
23061	G-BLKC
23062	G-BLKD
23063	G-BLKE
22875	G-BMDF
21775	G-BMEC
21774	G-BMHG
22633	G-BMMP
23734	G-BMTH
22161	G-BOSL
22660	G-BRJP
22633	G-DDDV
22415	G-DFUB
22762	G-DGDP
22761	G-DWHH
23495	G-DWHH
22368	G-GPAA
22071	G-GPAB
22161	G-ILFC
23497	G-MONF
23498	G-MONG
22576	G-OSLA
23256	G-PROC
23254	G-SCUH

HB- Switzerland

22431 HB-IEH

HC- Ecuador

22607 HC-BIG

HK- Colombia

19679	HK-1403
19680	HK-1404

HP- Panama

19771	HP-1038
19768	HP-873

HR- Honduras

20957	HR-SHA
20222	HR-SHD
20299	HR-TNR
20223	HR-TNS

HS- Thailand

21440	HS-TBA
21810	HS-TBB
22267	HS-TBC
22667	HS-TBD
23113	HS-TBE

HZ- Saudi Arabia

20574	HZ-AGA
20575	HZ-AGB
20576	HZ-AGC
20577	HZ-AGD
20578	HZ-AGE
20882	HZ-AGF
20883	HZ-AGG
21275	HZ-AGH
21276	HZ-AGI
21277	HZ-AGJ
21280	HZ-AGK
21281	HZ-AGL
21282	HZ-AGM
21283	HZ-AGN
21360	HZ-AGO
21361	HZ-AGP
21362	HZ-AGQ
21653	HZ-AGR
21654	HZ-AGS
22050	HZ-AGT
22050	HZ-HM4

JA Japan

23481	JA8250
20226	JA8401
22227	JA8402
20276	JA8403
22277	JA8405
20413	JA8406
20414	JA8407
20449	JA8408
20450	JA8409
20451	JA8410
20452	JA8411
20506	JA8412
20507	JA8413
20508	JA8414
20561	JA8415
20562	JA8416
20563	JA8417
20564	JA8418
20565	JA8419
20566	JA8420
20567	JA8421
21476	JA8443
22367	JA8467
22736	JA8475
23117	JA8492

LN- Norway

20453	LN-MTC
20454	LN-MTD
21763	LN-NPB
20458	LN-SUA
23464	LN-SUA
21765	LN-SUB
20711	LN-SUD
20412	LN-SUG
21219	LN-SUH
21184	LN-SUI
23468	LN-SUJ
21729	LN-SUK
21445	LN-SUM
19409	LN-SUP
23467	LN-SUQ
19408	LN-SUS
22022	LN-SUT
23465	LN-SUU
23469	LN-SUV
23466	LN-SUZ

LV- Argentina

20403	LV-JMW
20404	LV-JMX
20405	LV-JMY
20406	LV-JMZ
20407	LV-JND
20408	LV-JNE
20523	LV-JTD
20537	LV-JTO
20768	LV-LEB
20964	LV-LIU
20965	LV-LIV
20966	LV-LIW
20836	LV-MDB
20523	LV-PRQ

LX- Luxembourg

21443	LX-LGH
21444	LX-LGI

N United States

23108	N102SW
23374	N10323
23109	N103SW
23110	N104SW
23249	N105SW
23121	N122NA
23364	N12313
23369	N12318
23370	N12319
23373	N12322
23457	N12327
23587	N12349
21296	N1238E
21599	N1247E
21716	N1262E
20959	N126AW
21790	N1275E
20922	N127AW
21790	N1285E
20195	N1288
20958	N128AW
21115	N129AW
20521	N130AW
22699	N130SW
20956	N131AW
21186	N132AW
23569	N13331
21735	N133AW
23122	N133NA
22576	N134AW
19758	N1359B
19940	N135AW
19708	N136AW
23148	N137AW
22792	N138AW
22370	N139AW
22371	N140AW
20370	N141AW
20449	N142AW
23358	N14307
23359	N14308
23371	N14320
23375	N14324
23455	N14325
23572	N14334
23573	N14335
23123	N144NA
20194	N145AW
20195	N146AW
22630	N147AW
22340	N148AW
22575	N149AW
23218	N150AW
23219	N151AW
23387	N152AW
23406	N153AW
22776	N154AW
23777	N155AW
23124	N155NA
23778	N156AW
23779	N157AW
23780	N158AW
23781	N159AW
23782	N160AW
23783	N161AW
23784	N162AW
23352	N16301
23361	N16310
23577	N16339
23785	N163AW
23122	N170AW
21599	N171AW
23357	N17306
23360	N17309
23367	N17316
23368	N17317
23372	N17321
23456	N17326
23458	N17328
23459	N17329
20300	N1733B
23582	N17344
23583	N17345
20808	N1779B
19679	N1780B
19680	N1781B
22114	N1782B
20779	N1782B
20396	N1785B
23443	N1785B
22383	N1785B
20397	N1786B
20917	N1786B
20299	N1787B
20412	N1787B
21278	N1787B
21279	N1787B
20300	N1788B
20396	N1788B
20561	N1788B
23449	N1789B
20453	N1790B
23444	N1790B
23450	N1790B
20454	N1791B
23397	N1791B
23445	N1791B
23302	N1792B
20299	N1797B
20967	N1799B
22138	N1800B
20369	N180RN
18350	N18350
21926	N201FE
21927	N203FE
21928	N204FE
21929	N205FE
21959	N206FE
21337	N20SW
20369	N20SW
20345	N21SW
22282C	N2282C
19013	N2282C
19014	N2286C
19015	N2289C
20336	N22SW
23596	N2310
22859	N235WA
23184	N236WA
23185	N237WA
23186	N238WA
23187	N239WA
21338	N23SW
20346	N23SW
23188	N240WA
23189	N241WA
23516	N242WA
23517	N243WA
23518	N244WA
23519	N245WA
23520	N246WA
23521	N247WA
23602	N248WA
23603	N249WA
20925	N24SW

23604	N254WA	22887	N319AU	23594	N380AU	20126	N470AC	22577	N730AS
23605	N255WA	23091	N319DL	20670	N380PA	20336	N470AC	20344	N7310F
23606	N256WA	23236	N319P	19920	N380PS	19680	N471GB	21597	N7340F
23607	N257WA	23340	N319SW	23595	N381AU	19679	N472GB	21598	N7341F
23608	N258WA	22878	N320AU	20588	N381PA	23570	N47332	21747	N7342F
23609	N259WA	22888	N320AU	19921	N381PS	19614	N473AC	21748	N7343F
20095	N255W	23092	N320DL	23699	N382AU	19771	N47AF	21749	N7344F
21117	N265W	23237	N320P	19921	N382PA	19772	N48AF	21750	N7345F
19426	N2711R	23341	N320SW	20155	N382PS	20440	N4902W	21751	N7346F
21262	N27SW	22879	N321AU	23700	N383AU	20917	N4905W	21980	N7347F
21339	N28SW	22889	N321AU	20205	N383PA	20138	N4906	21981	N7348F
22596	N2941W	23093	N321DL	23701	N384AU	19594	N4907	22089	N7349F
21340	N29SW	23510	N321P	23702	N385AU	21820	N491WC	19418	N734N
22940	N300SW	23342	N321SW	21719	N385PA	21821	N492WC	22383	N7350F
23288	N301AC	19929	N321XV	23703	N386AU	21822	N493WC	22384	N7351F
23073	N301DL	22880	N322AU	23704	N387AU	21066	N4951W	22399	N7352F
23228	N301P	22890	N322AU	22276	N387PA	21067	N4952W	22456	N7353F
22941	N301SW	23094	N322DL	23705	N388AU	21447	N50SW	22457	N7354F
23642	N301UA	23511	N322P	22277	N388PA	19437	N515NA	22741	N7355F
20253	N301XV	23343	N322SW	22516	N389PA	22529	N51AF	22742	N7356F
23074	N302DL	19930	N322XV	23706	N390AU	21448	N51SW	22743	N7357F
22942	N302SW	22881	N323AU	23578	N39340	20194	N520L	22744	N7358F
23643	N302UA	23095	N323DL	23581	N39343	22368	N52AF	23023	N7359F
23182	N302WA	23512	N323P	19018	N401PE	21533	N52SW	19419	N735N
20254	N302XV	23344	N323SW	19019	N402PE	22054	N53AF	20222	N7360F
23289	N303AC	20156	N323XV	21112	N403WV	21534	N53SW	20223	N7361F
23075	N303DL	22892	N324AU	19020	N403PE	22055	N54AF	21131	N7362F
23229	N303P	23096	N324DL	19021	N404PE	21535	N54SW	20133	N7363F
22943	N303SW	23513	N324P	19022	N405PE	23303	N5573B	19420	N736N
23644	N303UA	23414	N324SW	19023	N406PE	22113	N5573K	19437	N73700
23183	N303WA	23114	N325AU	19024	N407PE	22127	N5573K	22950	N73700
20255	N303XV	23097	N325DL	19025	N408PE	22667	N5573K	20073	N73700
23290	N304AC	23514	N325P	19026	N409PE	23396	N5573K	20209	N73711
23076	N304DL	23689	N325SW	19769	N40AF	23451	N5573S	20210	N73712
23230	N304P	23115	N326AU	19027	N410PE	23448	N5573P	20242	N73713
22944	N304SW	23098	N326DL	19028	N411PE	21593	N55SW	19072	N73714
23665	N304UA	23515	N326P	19029	N412PE	22265	N56807	19552	N73714
23345	N304WA	23690	N326SW	19030	N413PE	22389	N56AF	20344	N73714
20256	N304XV	23116	N327AU	19031	N414PE	21721	N56SW	19679	N73715
23077	N305DL	23099	N327DL	19032	N415PE	20070	N570GB	19680	N73717
23257	N305P	23691	N327SW	19033	N416PE	20071	N571GB	20345	N73717
22945	N305SW	23625	N3281V	19794	N417PE	20072	N572GB	20128	N73718
23666	N305UA	23626	N3281W	20158	N4264Y	20073	N573GB	20070	N7371F
23346	N305WA	23627	N3281Y	19770	N42AF	20074	N574GB	20074	N7371F
23291	N306AC	23628	N3282G	19884	N431PE	22370	N57AF	20071	N7372F
23078	N306DL	23629	N3282N	19885	N432PE	21722	N57SW	20072	N7372F
23258	N306P	23630	N3282P	19886	N433PE	22371	N58AF	20361	N7373F
22946	N306SW	23631	N3282R	19887	N434PE	23353	N59302	20073	N7374F
23667	N306UA	23632	N3282V	19888	N435PE	23576	N59338	20362	N7374F
23347	N306WA	23633	N3282W	19598	N4501W	21811	N59SW	20363	N7375F
23251	N307AC	23634	N3282X	19599	N4502W	22802	N6009F	20364	N7376F
23079	N307DL	23635	N3282Y	19600	N4503W	22803	N6018N	20365	N7377F
23259	N307P	23636	N3283G	19601	N4504	23363	N60312	20070	N7378F
22947	N307SW	23131	N328AU	19601	N4504W	22804	N603BE	20071	N7379F
23668	N307UA	23100	N328DL	19602	N4505W	21812	N60SW	19421	N737N
23440	N307WA	23692	N328SW	19603	N4506W	23355	N61304	19758	N737Q
23252	N308AC	23132	N329AU	19604	N4507W	19552	N61AF	19681	N7380F
23080	N308DL	23101	N329DL	19605	N4508W	21970	N61SW	20369	N7381F
23669	N308UA	23693	N329SW	19606	N4509W	19847	N6241	20492	N7382F
23441	N308WA	23181	N3301	19607	N4510W	19556	N62AF	19075	N7383F
23253	N309AC	23133	N330AU	19608	N4511W	22060	N625W	20129	N7384F
23081	N309P	23102	N330DL	19609	N4512W	23356	N63305	21069	N7385F
23260	N309P	23694	N330SW	19610	N4513W	19553	N63AF	20368	N7386F
22948	N309SW	23134	N331AU	19611	N4514W	22061	N63SW	19682	N7387F
23670	N309UA	23103	N331DL	19612	N4515W	19549	N64AF	19920	N7388F
23442	N309WA	23695	N331SW	19613	N4516W	22062	N64SW	19937	N7389F
23505	N310AC	23135	N332AU	19614	N4517W	23121	N670MA	19422	N738N
23082	N310DA	23104	N332DL	19615	N4518W	23122	N671MA	21508	N7391F
22949	N310SW	23696	N332SW	19616	N4519W	23123	N672MA	21509	N7392F
23671	N310UA	20336	N332XV	19617	N4520W	23124	N673MA	21544	N7393F
23083	N311DL	20194	N333AM	20125	N4521W	23292	N674MA	21545	N7394F
23333	N311SW	23105	N334DL	20126	N4522	23496	N67AB	21546	N7395F
23672	N311UA	23366	N34315	20126	N4522W	19554	N67AF	21640	N7396F
23597	N311WA	22950	N350AU	20127	N4523W	22356	N675W	21641	N7397F
19709	N311XV	22951	N351AU	20128	N4524W	19028	N68AF	21642	N7398F
23084	N312DL	22952	N352AU	20129	N4525W	22357	N68SW	23024	N7399F
23261	N312P	22953	N353AU	20130	N4526W	23362	N69311	21186	N73AF
23334	N312SW	22954	N354AU	20131	N4527W	23571	N69333	22673	N73SW
23673	N312UA	22955	N355AU	20132	N4528W	23586	N69348	22578	N740AS
23598	N312WA	22956	N356AU	20133	N4529W	23589	N69351	19423	N740N
19710	N312XV	22957	N357AU	22504	N4529W	19059	N69AF	21959	N741AS
23085	N313DL	22958	N358AU	20785	N4529W	23404	N700ML	20211	N741N
23231	N313P	22959	N359AU	20134	N4530W	19013	N701AW	23136	N742AS
23335	N313SW	23310	N360AU	22505	N4530W	23405	N701ML	21821	N743AS
23674	N313UA	23311	N361AU	19931	N453AC	19015	N702AW	20212	N743N
23599	N313WA	23312	N362AU	22701	N4569N	23460	N70330	21822	N744AS
19712	N313XV	23313	N363AU	22875	N45708	23590	N70353	20213	N744N
22882	N314AU	23314	N364AU	22876	N4571A	23591	N70353	20214	N745N
23086	N314DA	23315	N365AU	22793	N4571M	19016	N703AW	20215	N746N
23232	N314P	23316	N366AU	23059	N45733	21112	N70720	20216	N747N
23336	N314SW	23317	N367AU	19598	N457AC	21500	N70721	19547	N749N
23675	N314UA	23318	N368AU	21720	N458AC	21501	N70722	22674	N74SW
19711	N314XV	23319	N369AU	19072	N459AC	21739	N70723	23507	N751L
22883	N315AU	23376	N370AU	20158	N460AC	21740	N70724	19548	N751N
23087	N315DL	23377	N371AU	19306	N461GB	19771	N708AW	19073	N752N
23233	N315P	23378	N372AU	19307	N462AC	19770	N709AW	20453	N753N
23337	N315SW	23379	N373AU	19307	N462GB	23365	N71314	20454	N754N
22884	N316AU	23380	N374AU	19308	N463GB	21928	N715A	19707	N754UA
23088	N316DL	23381	N375AU	19309	N464AC	21929	N716A	19603	N758N
23234	N316P	23382	N376AU	19309	N464GB	22358	N71SW	19954	N759N
23338	N316SW	23383	N377AU	19713	N465AC	21926	N720A	21665	N761N
22885	N317AU	23384	N378AU	19713	N465GB	22051	N725AL	21666	N762N
23089	N317DL	19681	N378PS	19601	N466AC	22426	N726AL	23592	N76354
23235	N317P	23385	N379AU	19714	N467GB	22629	N728AL	23593	N76355
22886	N318AU	19682	N379PS	20334	N468AC	22630	N729AL	21667	N763N
23090	N318DL	21720	N37AF	20335	N469AC	19758	N7302F	20095	N767N
23339	N318SW			19768	N46AF	22631	N730AL		

c/n	reg	c/n	reg
21815	N768N	19054	N9016U
21816	N769N	19055	N9017U
21817	N772N	19056	N9018U
23354	N77303	19057	N9019U
21818	N773N	19058	N9020U
21975	N774N	19059	N9021U
21976	N775N	19060	N9022U
20414	N776N	19061	N9023U
22018	N778N	19062	N9024U
22273	N779N	19063	N9025U
22274	N780N	19064	N9026U
23387	N781L	19065	N9027U
23506	N781L	19066	N9028U
22275	N781N	19067	N9029U
22352	N782N	19068	N9030U
22353	N783N	19069	N9031U
22354	N784N	19070	N9032U
22355	N785N	19071	N9033U
22443	N786N	19072	N9034U
22444	N787N	19073	N9035U
22445	N788N	19074	N9036U
22398	N789N	19075	N9037U
22752	N791N	19076	N9038U
22753	N792N	19077	N9039U
22754	N793N	19078	N9040U
22755	N794N	19547	N9041U
22756	N795N	19548	N9042U
22757	N796N	19549	N9043U
22758	N797N	19550	N9044U
22751	N798N	19551	N9045U
22795	N799N	19552	N9046U
19426	N801AL	19553	N9047U
20364	N802AL	19554	N9048U
22796	N802N	19555	N9049U
22797	N803N	19556	N9050U
22798	N804N	19932	N9051U
22799	N805N	19933	N9052U
22806	N806N	19934	N9053U
22866	N807N	19935	N9054U
22867	N809N	19936	N9055U
20223	N80AF	19937	N9056U
22675	N80SW	19938	N9057U
22868	N810N	19939	N9058U
22869	N811N	19940	N9059U
22961	N813N	19941	N9060U
22962	N814N	19942	N9061U
22697	N81AF	19943	N9062U
22730	N81SW	19944	N9063U
21687	N821L	19945	N9064U
21443	N8277V	19946	N9065U
22596	N8279V	19947	N9066U
22635	N8279V	19948	N9067U
22602	N8286V	19949	N9068U
22778	N8288V	19950	N9069U
21278	N8289V	19951	N9070U
22031	N8293V	19952	N9071U
22406	N8295V	19953	N9072U
22739	N8295V	19954	N9073U
22120	N8296V	19955	N9074U
22137	N8297V	19956	N9075U
22119	N8298V	22804	N90AF
22132	N8298V	22905	N90SW
22698	N82AF	22963	N91SW
22731	N82SW	22964	N92SW
19306	N831PC	22965	N93SW
19307	N832PC	23053	N94SW
19308	N833PC	23054	N95SW
19309	N834PC	23055	N96SW
19713	N835PC	21597	N974UA
19714	N836PC	21598	N976UA
22699	N83AF	21518	N977MP
22732	N83SW	21508	N977UA
19955	N841L	21509	N978UA
23255	N841L	21544	N979UA
19940	N842L	21545	N980UA
22700	N84AF	21546	N981UA
22657	N851L	21640	N982UA
20194	N8527S	20156	N983PS
22075	N8536Z	21641	N983UA
22701	N85AF	20157	N984PS
22826	N85SW	21642	N984UA
22760	N861L	20158	N985PS
22800	N86AF	21747	N985UA
22827	N86SW	20159	N986PS
23256	N871L	21748	N986UA
21006	N87569	20160	N987PS
22801	N87AF	21749	N987UA
22903	N87SW	20368	N988PS
22802	N88AF	21750	N988UA
23388	N891L	20369	N989PS
22803	N89AF	21751	N989UA
22904	N89SW	21980	N990UA
19039	N9001U	21981	N991UA
19040	N9002U	22089	N992UA
19041	N9003U	22383	N993UA
19042	N9004U	22384	N994UA
19043	N9005U	22399	N995UA
19044	N9006U	22456	N996UA
19045	N9007U	22457	N997UA
19046	N9008U	22741	N998UA
19047	N9009U	22742	N999UA
19048	N9010U		
19049	N9011U		
19050	N9012U	**OB- Peru**	
19051	N9013U		
19052	N9014U	20449	OB-R-1263
19053	N9015U	19769	OB-R-1288

OE- Austria

c/n	reg
22023	OE-ILE
23601	OE-ILF

OO- Belgium

c/n	reg
21359	OO-ABB
23401	OO-ILF
20128	OO-PLH
22453	OO-RVM
21596	OO-SBQ
21839	OO-SBS
21840	OO-SBT
23775	OO-SBZ
20907	OO-SDA
20908	OO-SDB
20909	OO-SDC
20910	OO-SDD
20911	OO-SDE
20912	OO-SDF
20913	OO-SDG
21135	OO-SDG
20914	OO-SDH
20915	OO-SDJ
20916	OO-SDK
21136	OO-SDL
21137	OO-SDM
21176	OO-SDN
21138	OO-SDO
21139	OO-SDP
21177	OO-SDQ
21738	OO-SDR
23771	OO-SDV
23772	OO-SDW
23773	OO-SDX
23774	OO-SDY
21231	OO-TEH
21131	OO-TEJ
21719	OO-TEK
21736	OO-TEL
21735	OO-TEM
21955	OO-TEN
22090	OO-TEO
21359	OO-TYB
21774	OO-TYD

OY- Denmark

c/n	reg
21278	OY-APG
21279	OY-APH
21528	OY-API
21685	OY-APJ
21686	OY-APK
22070	OY-APL
22071	OY-APN
22072	OY-APO
22406	OY-APP
22407	OY-APR
22408	OY-APS
22735	OY-MBV
22734	OY-MBW
22733	OY-MBZ
23331	OY-MMK
23332	OY-MML
23717	OY-MMM
23718	OY-MMN

PH- Netherlands

c/n	reg
23537	PH-BDA
23538	PH-BDB
23539	PH-BDC
23540	PH-BDD
23541	PH-BDE
23542	PH-BDG
23543	PH-BDH
23544	PH-BDI
23545	PH-BDK
23546	PH-BDL
23411	PH-HVF
23412	PH-HVG
23738	PH-HVJ
21736	PH-RAL
22738	PH-TSA
22739	PH-TSD
22737	PH-TSI
20836	PH-TVC
20943	PH-TVD
20944	PH-TVE
20282	PH-TVF
19711	PH-TVG
19062	PH-TVH
19955	PH-TVH
19940	PH-TVI
21131	PH-TVM
21193	PH-TVN
21196	PH-TVO
21397	PH-TVP
22025	PH-TVR
22296	PH-TVS
22906	PH-TVU
22023	PH-TVX

PP/PT- Brasil

c/n	reg
21012	PP-CJN
21013	PP-CJO
21014	PP-CJP
21015	PP-CJR
21016	PP-CJS
21017	PP-CJT
20092	PP-SMA
20093	PP-SMB
20094	PP-SMC
20095	PP-SMD
20096	PP-SME
20589	PP-SMF
20777	PP-SMG
20778	PP-SMH
20779	PP-SMP
20155	PP-SMQ
20157	PP-SMR
20159	PP-SMS
20160	PP-SMT
20967	PP-SMU
20968	PP-SMV
20346	PP-SMW
20969	PP-SMX
20970	PP-SMY
20971	PP-SMZ
21094	PP-SNA
21095	PP-SNB
21187	PP-SNC
21188	PP-SND
21686	PP-SNK
21685	PP-SNO
21206	PP-SNP
23173	PP-SNQ
23174	PP-SNR
23175	PP-SNS
22580	PP-SNW
20218	PP-SNY
19425	PP-SRX
21000	PP-VME
21001	PP-VMF
21002	PP-VMG
21003	PP-VMH
21004	PP-VMI
21005	PP-VMJ
21006	PP-VMK
21007	PP-VML
21008	PP-VMM
21009	PP-VMN
22504	PP-VNF
22505	PP-VNG
23499	PT-TEA
23500	PT-TEB

ST- Sudan

c/n	reg
21169	ST-AFK
21170	ST-AFL
22859	ST-AIB

SU- Egypt

c/n	reg
21191	SU-AYH
21192	SU-AYI
21193	SU-AYJ
19425	SU-AYK
21194	SU-AYK
21195	SU-AYL
21196	SU-AYM
21226	SU-AYN
21227	SU-AYO
20222	SU-AYT
21196	SU-BBW
21193	SU-BBX
22071	SU-BCJ

SX- Greece

c/n	reg
21224	SX-BCA
21225	SX-BCB
21301	SX-BCC
21302	SX-BCD
22300	SX-BCE
22301	SX-BCF
22338	SX-BCG
22339	SX-BCH
22343	SX-BCI
22400	SX-BCK
22401	SX-BCL

TF- Iceland

c/n	reg
22453	TF-VLK
21715	TF-VLM
20458	TF-VLT

TJ- Cameroon

c/n	reg
20590	TJ-CBA
20591	TJ-CBB
21295	TJ-CBD
23386	TJ-CBE

TN- Congo

c/n	reg
21538	TN-AEE

TR- Gabon

c/n	reg
21467	TR-LXL

TS- Tunisia

c/n	reg
22407	TS-IEB
21973	TS-IOC
21974	TS-IOD
22624	TS-IOE
22625	TS-IOF

TZ- Mali

c/n	reg
20544	TZ-ADL

V8- Brunei

c/n	reg
20913	V8-UEB
22138	V8-UEC
21809	V8-UED

VH- Australia

c/n	reg
23653	VH-CZA
23654	VH-CZB
23655	VH-CZC
23656	VH-CZD
23657	VH-CZE
23658	VH-CZF
23659	VH-CZG
23660	VH-CZH
23661	VH-CZI
23662	VH-CZJ
23663	VH-CZK
23664	VH-CZL
22645	VH-CZM
22646	VH-CZN
22647	VH-CZO
22648	VH-CZP
22649	VH-CZQ
22650	VH-CZR
22651	VH-CZS
22652	VH-CZT
22653	VH-CZU
22654	VH-CZV
22655	VH-CZW
22656	VH-CZX
23477	VH-TAF
23478	VH-TAG
23479	VH-TAH
23483	VH-TAI
23484	VH-TAJ
23485	VH-TAK
23486	VH-TAU
23487	VH-TAV
23488	VH-TAW
23489	VH-TAX
23490	VH-TAY
23491	VH-TAZ

VR- Bermuda

c/n	reg
21957	VR-BEG
20194	VR-BEH
21206	VR-BOX

VR- Hong Kong

c/n	reg
22071	VR-HKP

VR- Brunei

c/n	reg
20913	VR-UEB
21138	VR-UEC
21809	VR-UED

VS- Brunei

c/n	reg
20913	VS-UEB
21138	VS-UEC
21809	VS-UED

VT- India

c/n	reg
20480	VT-EAG
20481	VT-EAH
20482	VT-EAI
20483	VT-EAJ
20484	VT-EAK
20485	VT-EAL
20486	VT-EAM
20960	VT-ECP
20961	VT-ECQ
20962	VT-ECR
20963	VT-ECS
21163	VT-EDR
21164	VT-EDS
21496	VT-EFK
21497	VT-EFL
21498	VT-EFM
22280	VT-EGD

22281	VT-EGE
22282	VT-EGF
22283	VT-EGG
22284	VT-EGH
22285	VT-EGI
22286	VT-EGJ
22473	VT-EGM
22860	VT-EHE
22861	VT-EHF
22862	VT-EHG
22863	VT-EHH
23036	VT-EHW
23037	VT-EHX
20943	VT-EKC

YI- Iraq

20892	YI-AGH
20893	YI-AGI
21183	YI-AGJ

YS- El Salvador

21599	YS-08C

YU- Yugoslavia

23329	YU-AND
23330	YU-ANF
23415	YU-ANH

23416	YU-ANI
23714	YU-ANJ
23715	YU-ANK
23716	YU-ANL

YV- Venezuela

19771	YV-405C
19016	YV-406C

Z- Zimbabwe

22408	Z-NAL

ZK- New Zealand

19929	ZK-NAC
19930	ZK-NAD
19931	ZK-NAE
20344	ZK-NAJ
20156	ZK-NAK
20158	ZK-NAL
19758	ZK-NAM
21130	ZK-NAP
21131	ZK-NAQ
21645	ZK-NAR
22088	ZK-NAS
22657	ZK-NAT
23470	ZK-NAT
23471	ZK-NAU

23472	ZK-NAV
23473	ZK-NAW
23474	ZK-NAX
23475	ZK-NAY
22994	ZK-NQC

ZS- South Africa

19707	ZS-EUY
19708	ZS-EUZ
20229	ZS-FKH
19707	ZS-SBL
19708	ZS-SBM
20229	ZS-SBN
20329	ZS-SBO
20330	ZS-SBP
20331	ZS-SBR
22580	ZS-SIA
22581	ZS-SIB
22582	ZS-SIC
22583	ZS-SID
22584	ZS-SIE
22585	ZS-SIF
22586	ZS-SIG
22587	ZS-SIH
22588	ZS-SII
22589	ZS-SIJ
22590	ZS-SIK
22591	ZS-SIL
22828	ZS-SIM

Military operated

Brasil

21165	VC96-2115
21166	VC96-2116

India

21497	K-2371
23036	K-2412
23037	K-2413
21498	K-2370

Indonesia

22777	AI-7301
22778	AI-7302
22779	AI-7303

Mexico

20127	TP-03
19772	TP-04

South Korea

23152	85101

Thailand

23059	22-222

United States

20685	71-1403
20686	71-1404
20687	71-1405
20688	71-1406
20689	72-0282
20690	72-0283
20691	72-0284
20692	72-0285
20693	72-0286
20694	72-0287
20695	72-0288
20696	72-1149
20697	73-1150
20698	73-1151
20699	73-1152
20700	73-1153
20701	73-1154
20702	73-1155
20703	73-1156

Venezuela

21167	0001

BOEING 757

Short/medium-range commercial transport, powered by two wing-mounted Rolls-Royce RB.211 advanced-technology turbofans. The narrow-body 757 made its maiden flight on 19 February 1982 and entered commercial service with Eastern Airlines on 1 January 1983. Current production version is the 757-200 with accommodation for up to 224 passengers and fuel efficient RB211-535C or E4 turbofans. The Pratt & Whitney PW2037 is also available. To date 110 aircraft have been delivered and a further 81 are on order with the production rate currently two and a half aircraft per month.

Dimensions :	Wing span: 124ft 10in (38.05m) Length: 155ft 3in (47.32m) Height: 44ft 6in (13.56m)
Powerplants :	Two Rolls Royce RB.211-535E4 turbofans or two Pratt & Whitney PW2037 turbofans
Performance :	Max cruising speed 502 knots (930km/h) Range: with max payload 3,180nm (5,890km)
Accommodation:	239 passengers in a six abreast layout
Manufacturer :	Boeing - PO Box 3707, Seattle, Washington 98124, USA Telephone: (206) 237-2121 Telex: 32 94 30

BOEING

C/N	Registration	Owner/Operator	Series	First Flight	Delivery	Remarks
22172	G-BIKA	British Airways	236	25/OCT/82	28/MAR/83	
22173	G-BIKB	British Airways	236	23/DEC/82	25/JAN/83	
22174	G-BIKC	British Airways	236	06/JAN/83	31/JAN/83	
22175	G-BIKD	British Airways	236	18/FEB/83	10/MAR/83	
22176	G-BIKF	British Airways	236			Not taken-up
	G-BKRM	Air Europe		16/MAR/83	06/APR/83	
	G-BKRM	British Airways			08/NOV/84	Leased
	G-BKRM	Air Europe			30/APR/85	
	G-BKRM	British Airways			NOV/85	Leased
	G-BKRM	Air Europe			30/APR/85	
22177	G-BIKF	British Airways	236	06/APR/83	28/APR/83	
	G-BIKF	Air Europe			30/APR/83	Leased
	G-BIKF	British Airways			31/OCT/83	
22178	G-BIKG	British Airways	236	12/AUG/83	26/AUG/83	
22179	G-BIKH	British Airways	236	20/SEP/83	18/OCT/83	
22180	G-BIKI	British Airways	236	06/OCT/83	30/NOV/83	
22181	G-BIKJ	British Airways	236	15/DEC/83	09/JAN/84	
22182	G-BIKK	British Airways	236	12/JAN/84	01/FEB/84	
22183	G-BIKL	British Airways	236	13/FEB/84	29/FEB/84	
22184	G-BIKM	British Airways	236	02/MAR/84	21/MAR/84	
22185	G-BIKO	British Airways	236			Not taken-up
	G-BNEP	Air Europe				Reg. not taken-up
	G-BPGW	Air Europe		14/MAR/84	27/MAR/84	
22186	G-BIKN	British Airways	236	04/JAN/85	23/JAN/85	
22187	G-BIKO	British Airways	236	25/JAN/85	14/FEB/84	
22188	G-BIKP	British Airways	236	22/FEB/85	11/MAR/85	
22189	G-BIKR	British Airways	236	13/MAR/85	29/MAR/85	
22190	G-BIKS	British Airways	236	14/MAY/85	31/MAY/85	
22191	N501EA	Eastern Air Lines	225	28/MAR/82	18/AUG/83	
22192	N502EA	Eastern Air Lines	225	29/APR/82	28/SEP/83	
22193	N503EA	Eastern Air Lines	225	04/JUN/83	25/MAY/83	
22194	N504EA	Eastern Air Lines	225	04/FEB/83	28/FEB/83	
22195	N505EA	Eastern Air Lines	225	02/JUL/82	20/MAY/83	
22196	N506EA	Eastern Air Lines	225	29/NOV/82	22/DEC/82	
22197	N507EA	Eastern Air Lines	225	09/DEC/82	28/DEC/82	
22198	N508EA	Eastern Air Lines	225	27/JAN/83	18/FEB/83	
22199	N509EA	Eastern Air Lines	225	30/MAR/83	15/APR/83	
22200	N510EA	Eastern Air Lines	225	03/JUN/83	28/JUN/83	
22201	N511EA	Eastern Air Lines	225	13/JUL/83	28/JUL/83	
22202	N512EA	Eastern Air Lines	225	29/JUL/83	19/AUG/83	
22203	N513EA	Eastern Air Lines	225	25/OCT/83	09/NOV/83	
22204	N514EA	Eastern Air Lines	225	01/NOV/83	14/NOV/83	
22205	N515EA	Eastern Air Lines	225	23/NOV/83	14/DEC/83	
22206	N516EA	Boeing	225	03/FEB/84		Test Aircraft
	N516EA	Eastern Air Lines			26/FEB/85	
22207	N517EA	Eastern Air Lines	225	19/SEP/84	29/OCT/84	
22208	N518EA	Eastern Air Lines	225	27/SEP/84	30/OCT/84	
22209	N519EA	Eastern Air Lines	225	11/OCT/84	21/NOV/84	
22210	N520EA	Eastern Air Lines	225	22/OCT/84	30/NOV/84	
22211	N521EA	Eastern Air Lines	225	29/OCT/85	06/DEC/84	
22212	N757A	Boeing	200	24/FEB/82		Prototype/Test aircraft
22611	N522EA	Eastern Air Lines	225	08/NOV/85	05/DEC/85	
22612	N523EA	Eastern Air Lines	225		NOV/86	Sched.delivery
22688	N524EA	Eastern Air Lines	225		DEC/86	Sched.delivery
22689	N525EA	Eastern Air Lines	225		DEC/86	Sched.delivery
22690	N526EA	Eastern Air Lines	225		NOV/87	Sched.delivery
22691	N527EA	Eastern Air Lines	225		DEC/87	Sched.delivery
22780	G-MONB	Monarch Airlines	2T7	04/MAR/83	22/MAR/83	
22781	G-MONC	Monarch Airlines	2T7	12/APR/83	25/APR/83	
22782	PT-	Transbrasil	2Q4		OCT/83	Cancelled order
22783	PT-	Transbrasil	2Q4		NOV/83	Cancelled order
22784	PT-	Transbrasil	2Q4		JUN/84	Cancelled order
22808	N601DL	Delta Air Lines	232	01/JUN/84	28/FEB/85	
22809	N602DL	Delta Air Lines	232	06/JUL/84	05/NOV/84	
22810	N603DL	Delta Air Lines	232	10/AUG/84	07/NOV/84	
22811	N604DL	Delta Air Lines	232	84	03/DEC/84	
22812	N605DL	Delta Air Lines	232	84	07/DEC/84	
22813	N606DL	Delta Air Lines	232	13/DEC/84	17/JAN/85	
22814	N607DL	Delta Air Lines	232	22/APR/85	14/MAY/85	

C/N	Registration	Owner/Operator	Series	First Flight	Delivery	Remarks
22815	N608DL	Delta Air Lines	232	15/MAY/85	31/MAY/85	
22816	N609DL	Delta Air Lines	232	30/MAY/85	11/JUN/85	
22817	N610DL	Delta Air Lines	232	10/JUN/85	28/JUN/85	
22818	N611DL	Delta Air Lines	232	01/AUG/85	23/AUG/85	
22819	N612DL	Delta Air Lines	232	26/AUG/85	18/OCT/85	
22820	N613DL	Delta Air Lines	232	06/JAN/86	24/JAN/86	
22821	N614DL	Delta Air Lines	232	10/JAN/86	27/JAN/86	
22822	N615DL	Delta Air Lines	232	06/FEB/86	28/FEB/86	
22823	N616DL	Delta Air Lines	232	07/MAR/86	02/APR/86	
22907	N617DL	Delta Air Lines	232	31/MAR/86	21/MAY/86	
22908	N618DL	Delta Air Lines	232	10/APR/86	25/APR/86	
22909	N619DL	Delta Air Lines	232	28/MAY/86	11/JUN/86	
22910	N620DL	Delta Air Lines	232		86	Sched.delivery
22911	N621DL	Delta Air Lines	232		87	Sched.delivery
22912	N622DL	Delta Air Lines	232		87	Sched.delivery
22913	N623DL	Delta Air Lines	232		87	Sched.delivery
22914	N624DL	Delta Air Lines	232		87	Sched.delivery
22915	N625DL	Delta Air Lines	232		87	Sched.delivery
22916	N626DL	Delta Air Lines	232		87	Sched.delivery
22917	N627DL	Delta Air Lines	232		87	Sched.delivery
22918	N628DL	Delta Air Lines	232		87	Sched.delivery
22919	N629DL	Delta Air Lines	232		88	Sched.delivery
22920	N630DL	Delta Air Lines	232		88	Sched.delivery
22960	G-MOND	Monarch Airlines	2T7	29/APR/83	16/MAY/83	
22976	N	Air Florida	2T4		SEP/83	Cancelled order
22977	N	Air Florida	2T4		SEP/83	Cancelled order
22978	N	Air Florida	2T4		OCT/83	Cancelled order
23118	D-AMUR	LTS	2G5		25/MAY/84	
23119	D-AMUS	LTS	2G5	16/JAN/85	11/FEB/85	
23125	9V-SGK	Singapore Airlines	212	28/SEP/84	12/NOV/84	
23126	9V-SGL	Singapore Airlines	212	09/NOV/84	26/NOV/84	
23127	9V-SGM	Singapore Airlines	212		11/DEC/84	
23128	9V-SGN	Singapore Airlines	212		12/DEC/84	
23190	N501US	Northwest Orient	251	08/FEB/85	28/FEB/85	
23191	N502US	Northwest Orient	251	26/FEB/85	11/MAR/85	
23192	N503US	Northwest Orient	251	05/APR/85	22/APR/85	
23193	N504US	Northwest Orient	251	11/APR/85	25/APR/85	
23194	N505US	Northwest Orient	251	02/MAY/85	17/MAY/85	
23195	N506US	Northwest Orient	251	14/JUN/85	08/JUL/85	
23196	N507US	Northwest Orient	251	27/JUN/85	22/JUL/85	
23197	N508US	Northwest Orient	251	16/JUL/85	23/AUG/85	
23198	N509US	Northwest Orient	251	25/JUL/85	04/OCT/85	
23199	N511US	Northwest Orient	251	15/AUG/85	22/OCT/85	
23200	N512US	Northwest Orient	251	04/DEC/85	18/DEC/85	
23201	N513US	Northwest Orient	251	11/DEC/85	11/FEB/86	
23202	N514US	Northwest Orient	251	23/JAN/86	19/FEB/86	
23203	N515US	Northwest Orient	251	14/FEB/86	01/MAY/86	
23204	N516US	Northwest Orient	251	20/JUN/86	08/JUL/86	
23205	N517US	Northwest Orient	251	15/JUL/86	01/AUG/86	
23206	N518US	Northwest Orient	251	11/AUG/86	22/AUG/86	
23207	N519US	Northwest Orient	251		OCT/86	Sched.delivery
23208	N520US	Northwest Orient	251		NOV/86	Sched.delivery
23209	N521US	Northwest Orient	251		DEC/86	Sched.delivery
23227	G-CJIG	Air Europe	236			Reg. not taken-up
	G-BNHG	Air Europe				Reg. not taken-up
	G-BLVH	Air Europe		12/MAR/85	26/MAR/85	
23293	G-MONE	Monarch Airlines	2T7	01/MAR/85	13/MAR/85	
23321	N601RC	Republic Airlines	2S7	11/DEC/85	19/DEC/85	
23322	N602RC	Republic Airlines	2S7	14/NOV/85	06/DEC/85	
23323	N603RC	Republic Airlines	2S7	09/DEC/85	27/DEC/85	
23398	G-BIKT	British Airways	236	14/OCT/85	01/NOV/85	
23399	G-BIKU	British Airways	236	23/OCT/85	07/NOV/85	
23400	G-BIKV	British Airways	236	20/NOV/85	09/DEC/85	
23452	V8-RBA	Royal Brunei Airlines	2M8	08/APR/86	06/MAY/86	
23453	V8-RBB	Royal Brunei Airlines	2M8	22/MAY/86	13/JUN/86	
23454	V8-RBC	Royal Brunei Airlines	2M8	11/JUN/86	29/JUL/86	
23492	G-BIKW	British Airways	236	19/FEB/86	07/MAR/86	
23493	G-BIKX	British Airways	236	26/FEB/86	14/MAR/86	
23532	G-BIKZ	British Airways	236	01/MAR/86	15/MAR/86	
23533	G-BIKY	British Airways	236	14/MAR/86	28/MAR/86	
23566	N604RC	Republic Airlines	2S7	17/APR/86	19/MAY/86	
23567	N605RC	Republic Airlines	2S7	02/MAY/86	19/MAY/86	
23568	N606RC	Republic Airlines	2S7	14/MAY/86	28/MAY/86	
23612	N	Delta Air Lines	232		88	Sched.delivery
23613	N	Delta Air Lines	232		88	Sched.delivery
23614	N	Delta Air Lines	232		88	Sched.delivery
23615	N	Delta Air Lines	232		88	Sched.delivery
23616	N522US	Northwest Orient	251		87	Sched.delivery
23617	N523US	Northwest Orient	251		87	Sched.delivery
23618	N524US	Northwest Orient	251		88	Sched.delivery
23619	N525US	Northwest Orient	251		88	Sched.delivery
23620	N526US	Northwest Orient	251		88	Sched.delivery
23651	D-AMUT	LTS	2G5		DEC/86	Sched.delivery
23686	N32831	Boeing	2B6	24/JUN/86		
	CN-RMT	Royal Air Maroc			15/JUL/86	
23687	CN-RMZ	Royal Air Maroc	2B6	28/JUL/86	07/AUG/86	
23710	G-BMRA	British Airways	236		MAR/87	Sched.delivery
23723	N401UP	United Parcel Service	24APF		SEP/87	Sched.delivery
23724	N402UP	United Parcel Service	24APF			
23725	N403UP	United Parcel Service	24APF			
23726	N404UP	United Parcel Service	24APF			
23727	N405UP	United Parcel Service	24APF			
23728	N406UP	United Parcel Service	24APF			
23729	N407UP	United Parcel Service	24APF			
23730	N408UP	United Parcel Service	24APF			
23731	N409UP	United Parcel Service	24APF			
23732	N410UP	United Parcel Service	24APF			
23760	N	Delta Air Lines	232		88	Sched.delivery
23761	N	Delta Air Lines	232		88	Sched.delivery
23762	N	Delta Air Lines	232		89	Sched.delivery
23763	N	Delta Air Lines	232		89	Sched.delivery
23767	N	International Lease Finance	28A		APR/87	Sched.delivery
	G-	Air 2000			APR/87	Sched.lease

BOEING 757

C/N	Registration	Owner/Operator	Series	First Flight	Delivery	Remarks

ADDITIONAL ORDERS

C/N	Registration	Owner/Operator	Series	First Flight	Delivery	Remarks
	N	Delta Air Lines	232		89	Sched.delivery
	N	Delta Air Lines	232		89	Sched.delivery
	N	Delta Air Lines	232		89	Sched.delivery
	N	Delta Air Lines	232		89	Sched.delivery
	N	Delta Air Lines	232		89	Sched.delivery
	N	Delta Air Lines	232		89	Sched.delivery
	N	Delta Air Lines	232		89	Sched.delivery
	N	Delta Air Lines	232		90	Sched.delivery
	N	Delta Air Lines	232		90	Sched.delivery
	N	Delta Air Lines	232		90	Sched.delivery
	N	Delta Air Lines	232		90	Sched.delivery
	N	Delta Air Lines	232		90	Sched.delivery
	N	Delta Air Lines	232		90	Sched.delivery
	N	Delta Air Lines	232		90	Sched.delivery
	N	Delta Air Lines	232		91	Sched.delivery
	N	Delta Air Lines	232		91	Sched.delivery
	N	Delta Air Lines	232		91	Sched.delivery
	N	Delta Air Lines	232		91	Sched.delivery
	N	Delta Air Lines	232		91	Sched.delivery
	N	Delta Air Lines	232		91	Sched.delivery
	N	Delta Air Lines	232		91	Sched.delivery
	N	Northwest Orient	251		88	Sched.delivery
	N	Northwest Orient	251		88	Sched.delivery
	N	Northwest Orient	251		88	Sched.delivery
	N	Northwest Orient	251		89	Sched.delivery
	N	Northwest Orient	251		89	Sched.delivery
	9N-	Royal Nepal	200		SEP/87	Sched.delivery
	9N-	Royal Nepal	200 COM		SEP/88	Sched.delivery
	N	United Parcel Service	24APF			
	N	United Parcel Service	24APF			
	N	United Parcel Service	24APF			
	N	United Parcel Service	24APF			
	N	United Parcel Service	24APF			
	N	United Parcel Service	24APF			
	N	United Parcel Service	24APF			
	N	United Parcel Service	24APF			
	N	United Parcel Service	24APF			
	N	United Parcel Service	24APF			

Boeing 757 cross-reference index

9V- Singapore

C/N	Reg
23125	9V-SGK
23126	9V-SGL
23127	9V-SGM
23128	9V-SGN

CN- Morocco

C/N	Reg
23686	CN-RMT
23687	CN-RMZ

D- West Germany

C/N	Reg
23118	D-AMUR
23119	D-AMUS
23651	D-AMUT

G- United Kingdom

C/N	Reg
22172	G-BIKA
22173	G-BIKB
22174	G-BIKC
22175	G-BIKD
22176	G-BIKF
22177	G-BIKF
22178	G-BIKG
22179	G-BIKH
22180	G-BIKI
22181	G-BIKJ
22182	G-BIKK
22183	G-BIKL
22184	G-BIKM
22186	G-BIKN
22185	G-BIKO
22187	G-BIKO
22188	G-BIKP
22189	G-BIKR
22190	G-BIKS
23398	G-BIKT
23399	G-BIKU
23400	G-BIKV
23492	G-BIKW
23493	G-BIKX
23533	G-BIKY
23532	G-BIKZ
22176	G-BKRM
23227	G-BLVH
23710	G-BMRA
22185	G-BNEP
23227	G-BNHG
22185	G-BPGW
23227	G-CJIG
22780	G-MONB
22781	G-MONC
22960	G-MOND
23293	G-MONE

N United States

C/N	Reg
23686	N32831
23723	N401UP
23724	N402UP
23725	N403UP
23726	N404UP
23727	N405UP
23728	N406UP
23729	N407UP
23730	N408UP
23731	N409UP
23732	N410UP
22191	N501EA
23190	N501US
22192	N502EA
23191	N502US
22193	N503EA
23192	N503US
22194	N504EA
23193	N504US
22195	N505EA
23194	N505US
22196	N506EA
23195	N506US
22197	N507EA
23196	N507US
22198	N508EA
23197	N508US
22199	N509EA
23198	N509US
22200	N510EA
22201	N511EA
23199	N511US
22202	N512EA
23200	N512US
22203	N513EA
23201	N513US
22204	N514EA
23202	N514US
22205	N515EA
23203	N515US
22206	N516EA
23204	N516US
22207	N517EA
23205	N517US
22208	N518EA
23206	N518US
22209	N519EA
23207	N519US
22210	N520EA
23208	N520US
22211	N521EA
23209	N521US
22611	N522EA
23616	N522US
22612	N523EA
23617	N523US
22688	N524EA
23618	N524US
22689	N525EA
23619	N525US
22690	N526EA
23620	N526US
22691	N527EA
22808	N601DL
23321	N601RC
22809	N602DL
23322	N602RC
22810	N603DL
23323	N603RC
22811	N604DL
23566	N604RC
22812	N605DL
23567	N605RC
22813	N606DL
23568	N606RC
22814	N607DL
22815	N608DL
22816	N609DL
22817	N610DL
22818	N611DL
22819	N612DL
22820	N613DL
22821	N614DL
22822	N615DL
22823	N616DL
22907	N617DL
22908	N618DL
22909	N619DL
22910	N620DL
22911	N621DL
22912	N622DL
22913	N623DL
22914	N624DL
22915	N625DL
22916	N626DL
22917	N627DL
22918	N628DL
22919	N629DL
22920	N630DL
22212	N757A

V8- Brunei

C/N	Reg
23452	V8-RBA
23453	V8-RBB
23454	V8-RBC

FOKKER F.28 FELLOWSHIP

Short/medium range jet transport, powered by two rear-mounted Rolls-Royce Spey turbofans.
Designated to complement the F.27, the F.28 Fellowship first flew on 9 May 1967 and entered service on 24 February 1969.
Initial production versions were the MK-1000 and 2000 with seating for 65 and 79 passengers respectively, and these were
superseded by the MK.3000 with more powerful engines, and a stretched developemnt MK.4000 for up to 85 passengers. A
MK.6000 featured an increase in wing span and other aerodynamic improvements. The current model is the series -4000 and
to date, 239 aircraft have been delivered and a further two are on order, with the production line due to close shortly.

Dimensions :	Wing span: 77ft 4in (23.58m) Length: 89ft 11in (24.4m) Height: 27ft 9in (8.47m) (1000) Wing span: 77ft 4in (23.58m) Length: 97ft 2in (29.6m) Height: 27ft 9in (8.47m) (2000) Wing span: 82ft 3in (25.07m) Length: 89ft 11in (24.4m) Height: 27ft 9in (8.47m) (3000) Wing span: 82ft 3in (25.07m) Length: 97ft 2in (29.6m) Height: 27ft 9in (8.47m) (4000)
Powerplant :	Two Rolls Royce Spey 555-15 turbofans (1000/2000), two Rolls Royce Spey 555-15P turbofans (3000/4000), two Rolls Royce Spey 555-15H turbofans (5000/6000)
Performance :	Max cruising speed 458 knots (849km/h) Range: with max payload 941nm (1,538km) (1000) Range: with max payload 470nm (870km) (2000) Range: with max payload 970nm (1,797km) (3000) Range: with max payload 890nm (1,650km) (6000)
Accommodation:	65 passengers in a five abreast layout (1000/3000/5000), 79 passenger in a five abreast layout (2000/6000), 85 passengers in a five abreast layout (4000)
Manufacturer :	Fokker - PO Box 1065, 1000 BB Amsterdam, The Netherlands Telephone: (020) 544 9111 Telex: 11526 NL

C/N	Registration	Owner/Operator	Series	First Flight	Delivery	Remarks
11001	PH-JHG	Fokker	1000	09/MAY/67		1st Prototype
	PH-JHG	Fokker	2000		28/APR/71	Converted
	PH-JHG	Fokker	6000		28/SEP/73	Converted
	PH-JHG	Fokker	4000		11/OCT/85	Converted
						Fokker 100 Avionics testbed
11002	PH-WEV	Fokker	1000	03/AUG/67		WFU 02/APR/75
11003	PH-MOL	Fokker	1000	20/OCT/67		
	PH-MOL	Itavia			17/APR/69	Leased
	PH-MOL	Fokker			18/NOV/69	
	LN-SUM	Braathens Safe			19/DEC/69	Leased
	PH-MOL	Fokker			22/APR/70	
	LN-SUM	Braathens Safe			26/JUN/70	Leased
	PH-MOL	Fokker			11/AUG/70	
	PH-MOL	Martinair			15/OCT/70	Leased
	PH-MOL	Fokker			19/NOV/70	
	LN-SUM	Braathens Safe			25/FEB/71	Leased
	PH-MOL	Fokker			17/MAR/71	
	PH-MOL	LTU			17/MAR/71	Leased
	PH-MOL	Fokker			31/MAY/71	
	PH-MOL	Alisarda			01/JUN/71	Leased
	PH-MOL	Fokker			01/OCT/71	
	PH-MOL	Ghana Airways			01/NOV/71	Leased
	PH-MOL	Fokker			16/NOV/74	
	PH-MOL	Nigeria Airways			13/FEB/75	Leased
	PH-MOL	Fokker			08/MAY/75	
	PH-MOL	Air Gabon			30/JUN/75	Leased
	PH-MOL	Fokker			30/DEC/75	
	PH-MOL	Martinair			07/JAN/76	Leased
	PH-MOL	Fokker			01/FEB/77	
	PH-MOL	Nigeria Airways				Not taken-up
	PH-MOL	Air Anglia			07/AUG/78	Leased
	PH-MOL	Fokker			30/JUL/79	
	EP-PBF	Pars Air			22/AUG/79	Leased
	PH-MOL	Fokker			25/DEC/80	
	PH-MOL	Air Alsace			25/APR/81	Leased
	PH-MOL	Fokker			82	
	PH-MOL	Lina Congo			11/JUN/82	Leased
	PH-MOL	Fokker			02/SEP/82	
	PH-MOL	TAT			27/SEP/82	Leased
	PH-MOL	Fokker				
	PH-MOL	Air UK			24/NOV/84	Leased
	PH-MOL	Fokker			03/NOV/85	
	F-GMOL	TAT			13/NOV/85	
11004	PH-ZAA	Fokker	1000	21/MAY/68		
	D-ABAQ	LTU			24/FEB/69	Damaged 26/FEB/69
	PH-ZAA	Fokker			26/FEB/69	
	D-ABAQ	LTU			19/MAR/69	
	D-ABAQ	Itavia			23/APR/73	
	I-TIDU	Itavia			01/JUL/73	WFU 12/DEC/80
	F-GECK	TAT			DEC/83	
11005		Static Test Frame				
11006	PH-ZAB	Fokker	1000	19/MAR/69		
	D-ABAX	LTU			03/APR/69	
	D-ABAX	Itavia			23/APR/73	
	I-TIDB	Itavia			01/JUL/73	WFU 12/DEC/80
	I-TIDB	Uni-Fly			84	
	I-TIDB	TAT			30/MAR/85	Leased
	I-TIDB	Uni-Fly			02/MAY/85	
11007		Test Air Frame				
11008	PH-ZAC	Fokker	1000	05/AUG/69		
	PH-MAT	Martinair			01/OCT/69	
	PH-MAT	Braathens Safe			16/MAR/73	Leased
	PH-MAT	Martinair			20/MAR/73	
	PH-MAT	Linjeflyg			11/MAR/74	Leased
	PH-MAT	Martinair			11/MAY/74	
	PH-MAT	Air France			03/JUN/74	Leased
	PH-MAT	Martinair			13/JUN/74	
	PH-MAT	Linjeflyg			07/MAR/75	Leased

FOKKER F-28 FELLOWSHIP

C/N	Registration	Owner/Operator	Series	First Flight	Delivery	Remarks
	PH-MAT	Martinair			26/APR/75	
	PH-MAT	Linjeflyg			11/MAR/76	Leased
	PH-MAT	Martinair			17/AUG/76	
	PH-MAT	Linjeflyg			01/NOV/76	Leased
	PH-MAT	Martinair			02/FEB/77	
	PH-MAT	TAT			04/NOV/79	Leased
	PH-MAT	Air Alsace			25/FEB/80	Leased
	PH-MAT	Martinair			28/MAR/80	
	VH-FKF	MMA			01/OCT/80	
	VH-FKF	Airline of Western Australia			01/JUL/81	
11009	PH-ZAD	Fokker	1000	16/JAN/69		
	LN-SUC	Braathens Safe			03/MAR/69	
11010	PH-ZAE	Fokker	1000	06/MAR/69		
	LN-SUX	Braathens Safe			27/MAR/69	
11011	PH-ZAF	Fokker	1000	14/APR/69		
	LN-SUY	Braathens Safe			29/APR/69	W/O 23/DEC/72, Asdolfjern, Oslo
11012	PH-ZAG	Fokker	1000	19/MAY/69		
	LN-SUN	Braathens Safe			17/JUN/69	
11013	PH-ZAH	Fokker	1000	30/JUN/69		
		Braathens Safe				Not taken up.
	VH-MMJ	MMA			14/AUG/69	Leased.
	PH-EXA	Fokker			17/JUN/70	
	LN-SUO	Braathens Safe			31/JUL/70	
11014	PH-ZAI	Fokker	1000	07/OCT/69		
	I-TIDA	Itavia			05/NOV/69	W/O 09/APR/75, Bergano, Italy
11015	PH-ZAK	Fokker	1000	05/NOV/69		
	I-TIDE	Itavia			28/FEB/70	W/O 01/JAN/74, Turin Ap. Italy
11016	PH-ZAL	Fokker	1000VIP	19/AUG/69		
	N28IFH	Fairchild			13/SEP/69	
	N27W	Eastex Corp.			06/APR/73	
	N27W	Time Inc.			DEC/83	
	N930TL	Time Inc.			APR/84	
11017	PH-ZAM	Fokker	1000	12/JAN/70		
	EC-BVA	Iberia			23/APR/70	
	EC-BVA	Fokker			18/DEC/74	
	PH-ZAM	Itavia			23/MAY/75	Leased
	PH-ZAM	Fokker			03/FEB/76	
	XY-ADV	Burma Airways Corp.			23/JUL/76	
	PH-ZAM	Fokker			07/JUL/86	
11018	PH-ZAN	Fokker	1000	16/DEC/69		
	N282FH	Fairchild			07/MAR/70	
	PH-EXW	Fokker			01/AUG/74	
	PH-EXW	Fokker	1000C		04/JUL/75	Converted
	TC-54	LADE			23/JUL/75	
11019	PH-ZAO	Fokker	1000	13/FEB/70		
	EC-BVB	Iberia			22/MAY/70	
	EC-BVB	Fokker			19/DEC/74	
	PH-ZAO	Fokker			21/MAY/75	
	PH-ZAO	Itavia			13/JUN/75	Leased
	PH-ZAO	Fokker			15/NOV/75	
	XY-ADU	Burma Airways Corp.			01/APR/76	
11020	PH-ZAP	Fokker	1000	17/MAR/70		
	N283FH	Fairchild			06/JUL/70	
	PH-EXX	Fokker			01/APR/74	
	PH-EXX	Fokker	1000C		29/APR/75	Converted.
	TC-53	LADE			07/MAY/75	
11021	PH-ZAS	Fokker	1000	29/APR/70		
	VH-FKA	Ansett-MMA			04/JUN/70	
	VH-FKA	Airline of Western Australia			01/JUL/81	
11991	PH-ZAR	Fokker	1000	08/APR/70		
		Fairchild				Not Taken-up.
	I-TIDI	Itavia			28/APR/70	WFU 12/DEC/80
	I-TIDI	Uni-Fly			83	
	C-GTEO	Norcanair			DEC/85	
11022	PH-ZAT	Fokker	1000	10/JUN/70		
	VH-FKB	Ansett-MMA			08/JUL/70	
	VH-FKB	Airline of Western Australia			01/JUL/81	
	VH-FKB	Ansett Airlines of NSW			JUN/84	Leased
11992	PH-EXA	Fokker	1000VIP	29/JUN/70		
		Fairchild				Not taken-up.
	PH-EXF	Fokker			21/DEC/70	
	FAC-001	Colombian Air Force			18/JAN/71	
11023	PH-EXA	Fokker	1000	28/JUL/70		
	PH-ZAV	Fokker			AUG/70	
	EC-BVC	Iberia			13/AUG/70	W/O 28/DEC/72, Bilbao, Spain
11024	PH-EXC	Fokker	1000	13/AUG/70		
	N284FH	Fairchild			24/OCT/70	
	PH-EXZ	Fokker			01/OCT/74	
	PH-EXZ	Fokker	1000C		24/SEP/75	
	TC-55	LADE			06/OCT/75	
11993	PH-EXE	Fokker	1000	09/SEP/70		
		Fairchild				Not taken-up
	PH-ZAU	Nigeria Airways			07/DEC/70	Leased
	PH-ZAU	Fokker			31/MAY/72	
	5N-ANA	Nigeria Airways			16/AUG/72	W/O 01/MAR/78, Kano
11025	PH-EXF	Fokker	1000	30/SEP/70		
	VH-FKC	Ansett-MMA			17/OCT/70	
	VH-FKC	Airline of Western Australia			01/JUL/81	
11026	PH-EXA	Fokker	1000	26/OCT/70		
	VH-FKD	Ansett Airlines of NSW			07/NOV/70	
	VH-FKD	Ansett-MMA			13/APR/71	
	VH-FKD	Airline of Western Australia			01/JUL/81	
	VH-FKD	Air New South Wales			MAR/83	Leased
	VH-FKD	Airline of Western Australia			APR/85	
11994	PH-EXB	Fokker	1000	05/NOV/70		
						Not taken-up
	I-VAFE	Turavia				Leased
	PH-FPI	Martinair			28/MAR/71	
	PH-FPT	Fokker			11/APR/71	
	PH-FPT	Linair			10/AUG/71	Leased
	PH-FPT	Fokker			23/SEP/71	
	PH-FPT	Iran Air			28/SEP/71	Leased
	PH-FPT	Fokker			21/OCT/71	
	PH-FPT	Nigeria Airways			31/JAN/72	Leased
	PH-FPT	Nigeria Airways			01/MAR/72	W/O 19/SEP/72, Port Harcourt

C/N	Registration	Owner/Operator	Series	First Flight	Delivery	Remarks
11027	PH-ZBB	Fokker	1000	08/FEB/71		
	D-AHLA	Aviation			25/FEB/71	
	PH-ZBG	Fokker			12/DEC/73	
	PH-ZBG	Itavia			10/MAY/75	Leased
	PH-ZBG	Fokker			01/NOV/75	
	PH-ZBG	Nigeria Airways				Not taken-up
	EP-PAS	Parsair			07/MAR/77	Leased
	PH-ZBG	Fokker			01/AUG/77	
	F-GBBX	Air Alsace			29/MAR/78	Leased
	F-GBBX	Air Alsace			20/DEC/80	Purchased
	F-GBBX	TAT/Air France			AUG/82	
11028	PH-ZBC	Fokker	1000VIP	08/DEC/70		
		Fairchild				Not taken-up
	T-01	Argentine Government			28/DEC/70	
	T-02	Argentine Government			01/MAR/75	
	T-01	Argentine Government			01/AUG/77	
11029	PH-ZBD	Fokker	1000	28/JAN/71		
	D-ABAN	LTU			22/FEB/71	
	D-ABAN	Itavia			03/JUL/74	Leased
	PK-PJU	Pelita			20/DEC/74	
11030	D-ABAM	LTU	1000	23/FEB/71	16/MAR/71	
	PK-PJS	Pelita			01/AUG/74	
11031	D-AHLB	Aviation	1000	11/MAR/71	01/APR/71	
	D-AHLB	Braathens Safe			15/JAN/73	Leased
	D-AHLB	Aviation			29/APR/73	
	PH-ZBH	Fokker			12/DEC/73	
	PH-ZBH	TAT/Air France			01/JUN/74	Leased
	F-BUTE	TAT/Air France			01/JAN/75	Purchased
	F-BUTE	Air Alsace			24/OCT/77	Leased
	F-BUTE	TAT/Air France			01/APR/78	
	VH-FKG	MMA			27/MAR/81	
	VH-FKG	Airline of Western Australia			17/JUL/81	
11032	PH-EXB	Fokker	1000	05/MAY/71		
	I-VAGA	Turavia				Not taken-up.
	D-AHLD	Aviation				Not taken-up
	PH-ZAV	Fokker			09/JUL/71	
	PH-ZAV	Ghana Airways			05/AUG/72	Leased
	PH-ZAV	Fokker			05/OCT/72	
	LN-SUM	Braathens Safe			29/DEC/72	Leased
	PH-ZAV	Fokker			14/JAN/73	
	OB-R-390	SATCO			19/APR/73	Leased
	OB-R-1030	Aero Peru			22/MAY/73	Leased
	OB-R-1030	Fokker			09/JUN/73	
	TC-JAZ	THY			19/JUN/73	Leased
	PH-ZAV	Fokker			09/AUG/73	
	PH-ZAV	Ghana Airways			11/AUG/73	Leased
	PH-ZAV	Fokker			05/SEP/73	
	PK-GVM	Garuda			11/DEC/74	
	PH-EXW	Fokker			30/JUN/83	
	N282N	Piedmont Airlines			27/APR/84	
11033	N285FH	Fokker	1000	04/JUN/71		
	N285FH	Fairchild			15/JUL/71	
	CF-TAV	Transair			11/OCT/72	
	P2-ANE	Air Niugini			06/JUN/79	
	P2-ANE	MMA			17/AUG/80	Leased
	P2-ANE	Air Niugini			01/OCT/80	
11034	PH-ZBI	Fokker	1000	08/JUN/71		
	D-AHLC	Aviation			06/JUL/71	
	PH-ZBI	Fokker			13/DEC/73	
	PH-ZBI	Nigeria Airways			11/JAN/74	Leased
	PH-ZBI	Fokker			01/JUN/74	
	PH-ZBI	Nigeria Airways			19/OCT/74	Leased
	PH-ZBI	Fokker			01/FEB/75	
	PH-ZBI	TAT/Air France			21/MAR/75	Leased
	PH-ZBI	TAT/Air France			01/AUG/75	Purchased
	F-BUTI	TAT/Air France			20/AUG/75	
	F-BUTI	Itavia			05/APR/78	Leased
	F-BUTI	TAT/Air France			01/NOV/78	
	F-BUTI	Air Alpes			01/APR/79	Leased
	F-BUTI	TAT/Air France			08/NOV/80	
11035	PH-EXF	Fokker	1000	01/JUL/71		
	OB-R-231	Aerocoop				Not taken-up
	PK-GJZ	Garuda			19/AUG/71	
	PK-GVA	Garuda			01/JUL/74	
	PK-GVA	Garuda			29/AUG/83	
	N283N	Piedmont Airlines			30/MAY/84	
11036	PK-GJY	Fokker	1000	31/AUG/71		
	OB-R-232	Aerocoop				Not taken-up
	PK-GJY	Garuda			27/OCT/71	
	PK-GVB	Garuda			01/JUL/74	
	PK-GVB	Fokker			28/JUL/83	
	N284N	Piedmont Airlines			26/JUN/84	
11037	PH-EXE	Fokker	1000	17/AUG/71		
	I-TIDO	Itavia				Not taken-up
	PH-ZBF	Fokker				
	PK-GJR	Garuda			25/SEP/73	
	PK-GVI	Garuda			01/JUL/74	
	PH-EZA	Fokker			31/MAY/83	
	N273N	Piedmont Airlines			18/JUN/85	
11038	N286FH	Fokker	1000	12/OCT/71		
	N286FH	Fairchild			23/FEB/72	
	PH-EXM	Fokker			73	
	CF-TAY	Transair			12/APR/73	
	P2-ANF	Air Niugini			23/FEB/79	
11039	PK-GJX	Fokker	1000	28/OCT/71		
	OB-R-233	Aerocoop				Not taken-up
	PK-GJX	Garuda			29/NOV/71	
	PK-GVC	Garuda			01/JUL/74	W/O 24/SEP/75, nr. Palembang.
11040	VH-FKE	Ansett-MMA	1000	07/SEP/71	21/SEP/71	
	VH-FKE	Airline of Western Australia			01/JUL/81	
11041	PH-EXF	Fokker	1000	28/SEP/71		
	C2-RN1	Air Nauru			18/JAN/72	
	P2-ANU	Air Niugini			01/NOV/77	
11042	PK-PJX	Pertamina/Pelita	1000	27/OCT/71	27/NOV/71	
	PK-PJT	Pertamina/Pelita			JAN/72	

FOKKER F-28 FELLOWSHIP

C/N	Registration	Owner/Operator	Series	First Flight	Delivery	Remarks
	PK-PJT	Indonesian Government			DEC/83	
11043	PH-EXA	Fokker	1000	20/DEC/71		
	N287FH	Fairchild			30/DEC/71	
	N287FH	Fokker			01/DEC/74	
	PH-EXM	Fokker			28/MAY/75	
	PK-GVN	Garuda			10/JUN/75	
	PK-GVN	Fokker			30/OCT/84	
	N291N	Piedmont Airlines			25/MAR/85	
11044	N288FH	Fairchild	1000	29/DEC/71	09/JAN/72	
	N288FH	Fokker			01/DEC/74	
	PH-EXR	Fokker			17/AUG/75	
	PK-GVO	Garuda			05/SEP/75	
	PK-GVO	Fokker			31/OCT/83	
	N286N	Piedmont Airlines			23/JUL/84	
11045	PH-PBX	Netherlands Government	1000VIP	12/JAN/72	03/FEB/72	
11046	D-AGAB	Germanair	1000	03/FEB/72	10/MAR/72	
	LV-LRG	Aerolineas Argentinas			24/MAR/76	
11047	N289FH	Fairchild	1000	22/FEB/72	01/DEC/72	
	N289FH	Fokker			01/DEC/74	
	PH-EXI	Fokker			27/APR/77	
	VH-ATD	Australian DOT/ATG			23/MAY/77	
11048	PH-EXF	Fokker	1000	08/MAR/72		
	N280FH	Fairchild			05/MAY/72	
	PH-ZBM	Fokker			01/JUL/74	
	TG-CAO	Aviateca			05/AUG/74	Leased
	PH-ZBM	Fokker			10/AUG/75	
	LV-LZN	Aerolineas Argentinas			29/NOV/76	Leased
	LV-LZN	Fokker			31/MAR/77	
	T-02	Argentine President Flight	1000VIP		12/DEC/77	
11049	PH-EXD	Fokker	1000VIP	22/MAR/72		
		Fairchild				Not taken-up
	PH-EXG	Fokker			01/JAN/73	
	5N-AGN	Nigerian Government			16/FEB/73	
11050	D-AGAC	Germanair	1000	11/APR/72	25/MAY/72	
	D-AGAC	Itavia			14/APR/76	Leased
	D-AGAC	Germanair			07/NOV/77	
	F-GBBS	TAT			29/DEC/77	
	F-GBBS	Air Alpes			08/NOV/80	Leased
	F-GBBS	TAT			SEP/81	
11051	D-AGAD	Germanair	1000	25/APR/72	09/MAY/72	
	D-AGAD	Itavia			11/FEB/76	Leased
	D-AGAD	Germanair			07/NOV/77	
	F-GBBR	TAT			01/APR/78	Leased
11052	PH-ZAW	Fokker	1000	15/MAY/72		
	D-AGAE	Germanair			29/MAY/72	
	D-AGAE	Itavia			15/APR/76	Leased
	D-AGAE	Germanair			13/NOV/76	
	EP-PBA	Parsair			26/JUL/77	Leased
	D-AGAE	Germanair			28/JUL/79	
	F-GBBT	TAT			29/JUL/79	
11053	PH-EXF	Fokker	2000	02/JUN/72		
	PH-ZAX	Fokker			18/AUG/72	
	PH-ZAX	Nigeria Airways			19/OCT/72	Leased
	5N-ANB	Nigeria Airways			06/JAN/73	Purchased
	F-GDUS	TAT			JUL/85	
11054	PK-GJW	Garuda	1000	22/JUN/72	01/AUG/72	
	PK-GVD	Garuda			01/JUL/74	
	PK-GVD	Fokker			30/AUG/84	
	N288N	Piedmont Airlines			30/JAN/85	
11055	PK-GJV	Garuda	1000	19/JUL/72	25/AUG/72	
	PK-GVE	Garuda			01/JUL/74	W/O 11/JUL/79, Medon, Sumatra
11056	PH-EXF	Fokker	1000	14/AUG/72		
		Ansett				Not taken-up
	PH-EXH	Fokker			07/APR/74	
	C2-RN2	Air Nauru			18/JUN/74	
	P2-ANW	Air Niugini			01/NOV/77	
	VH-FKF	MMA			18/APR/80	Not taken-up
	P2-ANW	Air Niugini			18/APR/80	
11057	PH-ZBA	Fokker	1000	05/SEP/72		
	TC-JAO	THY			13/JAN/73	W/O 26/JAN/74, Izmir, Turkey
11058	PH-ZBB	Fokker	1000	27/SEP/72		
	TC-JAP	THY			22/MAR/73	W/O 30/JAN/75, Yesilkoy, Turkey
11059	PH-ZBD	Fokker	1000	08/DEC/72		
	OB-R-397	SATCO			15/MAR/73	
	OB-R-1020	Aero Peru			01/OCT/73	
11060	PH-ZBC	Fokker	1000	06/NOV/72		
	TC-JAR	THY			23/MAR/73	
11061	PK-GJU	Garuda	1000	17/OCT/72	15/NOV/72	
	PK-GVF	Garuda			01/JUL/74	
	PK-GVF	Fokker			FEB/83	
	N280N	Piedmont Airlines			02/MAR/84	
11062	PH-ZBE	Fokker	2000	29/DEC/72		
	9G-ABZ	Ghana Airways			31/JUL/74	
11063	PH-EXE	Fokker	1000	19/JAN/73		
	PK-GJT	Garuda			01/MAR/73	
	PK-GVG	Garuda			01/JUL/74	
	PH-EZE	Fokker			FEB/83	
	N274N	Piedmont Airlines			26/JUN/85	
11064	PH-EXD	Fokker	1000	06/FEB/73		
	PK-GJS	Garuda			20/FEB/73	
	PK-GVH	Garuda			01/JUL/74	
	PK-GVH	Fokker			31/JAN/83	
	N289N	Piedmont Airlines			23/JUL/85	
11065	PH-EXN	Fokker	1000	18/MAY/73		
	OB-R-398	SATCO			31/MAY/73	
	OB-R-1018	Aero Peru			01/OCT/73	
11066	PH-EXO	Fokker	1000	06/JUN/73		
	OB-R-399	SATCO			02/JUL/73	
	OB-R-1019	Aero Peru			01/OCT/73	
11067	PH-EXL	Fokker	1000	12/APR/73		
	SE-DGA	Linjeflyg			18/MAY/73	
11068	PH-EXI	Fokker	1000	02/MAR/73		
	SE-DGB	Linjeflyg			25/APR/73	
11069	PH-EXK	Fokker	1000	18/MAR/73		
	SE-DGC	Linjeflyg			04/MAY/73	

C/N	Registration	Owner/Operator	Series	First Flight	Delivery	Remarks
11070	PH-EXP	Fokker	1000	22/JUN/73		
	TC-JAS	THY			10/JUL/73	
11071	PH-EXR	Fokker	1000	20/JUL/73		
	TC-JAT	THY			06/AUG/73	W/O 23/DEC/79, nr. Ankara
11072	PH-EXS	Fokker	1000	17/AUG/73		
	TN-ACP	Congo Government	1000VIP		25/APR/75	
	TN-ACP	Congo Government	1000		30/APR/82	Converted
	TN-ACP	LINA Congo			27/AUG/82	
11073	PH-EXT	Fokker	1000VIP	10/OCT/73		
	PK-PJV	Pertamina/Pelita			10/NOV/73	
11074	PH-EXG	Fokker	1000C	19/DEC/73		
	PH-EXZ	Fokker		19/DEC/74		Proto. freight door
	TC-52	LADE			30/JAN/73	
11075	PH-EXV	Fokker	1000	25/OCT/73		
	PK-GJQ	Garuda			09/NOV/73	
	PK-GVJ	Garuda			01/JUL/74	
	PH-EZM	Fokker			MAY/83	
	N281N	Piedmont Airlines			30/MAR/84	
11076	PH-EXY	Fokker	1000	26/NOV/74		
	TC-51	LADE			13/JAN/75	
	TC-51	LADE	1000C		03/JUN/75	Converted
11077	PH-EXU	Fokker	2000	08/NOV/73		
	9G-ACA	Ghana Airways			31/MAY/74	W/O 11/MAR/81, Accra Ap., Ghana
11078	PH-EXZ	Fokker	1000	17/JAN/74		
	PK-GJP	Garuda			01/FEB/74	
	PK-GVK	Garuda			01/JUL/74	W/O 20/MAR/82
11079	PH-EXB	Fokker	1000	25/APR/74		
	PH-ZBK	Fokker				
	5V-TAB	Togo Government	1000VIP		24/APR/75	
	5V-MAB	Togo Government			01/JUL/75	
11080	PH-EXC	Fokker	2000	14/JUN/74		
		Linjeflyg				Not taken-up
	TR-LST	Air Gabon			17/JUL/74	
11081	PH-EXD	Fokker	2000	01/JUL/74		
		Linjeflyg				Not taken-up
	TR-LSU	Air Gabon			22/JUL/74	
11082	PH-EXN	Fokker	1000	07/AUG/74		Stored at Woensdrecht
	VH-ATE	Australian DOT/ATG			13/DEC/76	
11083	PH-EXQ	Fokker	1000	26/AUG/74		
	LV-LOC	Aerolineas Argentinas			13/FEB/75	
11084	PH-EXP	Fokker	1000	11/SEP/74		
	VH-ATG	Australian DOT/ATG			28/FEB/77	
11085	PH-EXT	Fokker	1000	18/OCT/74		
	LV-LOA	Aerolineas Argentinas			13/JAN/75	
	HK-3126	ACES			APR/84	Leased
	LV-LOA	Aerolineas Argentinas			OCT/84	
11086	PH-EXU	Fokker	1000	13/NOV/74		
	LV-LOB	Aerolineas Argentinas			13/JAN/75	W/O 15/NOV/75, Concordia
11087	PH-EXV	Fokker	1000	08/NOV/74		
	PK-GVL	Garuda			20/NOV/74	
	PK-GVL	Fokker			29/SEP/83	
	N287N	Piedmont Airlines			28/AUG/84	
11088	PH-EXI	Fokker	1000VIP	25/FEB/75		
	FM2101	Royal Malaysian Air Force			02/MAY/75	Call sign 9M-EBS
	M28-01	Royal Malaysian Air Force			JAN/84	
11089	PH-EXL	Fokker	1000VIP	21/MAR/75		
	FM2102	Royal Malaysian Air Force			02/MAY/75	Call sign 9M-EBT
	M28-02	Royal Malaysian Air Force			JAN/84	
11090	PH-EXH	Fokker	2000	10/FEB/75		
	5N-ANF	Nigeria Airways			23/MAR/75	W/O 29/NOV/83, Enugu, Nigeria
11091	PH-EXT	Fokker	2000	19/JUN/75		
	5N-ANH	Nigeria Airways			04/JUL/75	
	F-GDUT	TAT			JUL/85	
11092	PH-SIX	Fokker	6000	01/JUL/75		
		Parsair				Not taken-up
	PH-SIX	Linjeflyg			30/JUL/76	Leased
	PH-SIX	Fokker			23/DEC/76	
	PH-SIX	NLM			20/APR/78	Leased
	PH-SIX	Fokker			05/FEB/79	
	PH-SIX	NLM			03/APR/79	Leased
	PH-SIX	Fokker			09/APR/79	
	PH-SIX	Libyan Arab Airlines			27/APR/79	Leased
	PH-SIX	Fokker			12/SEP/79	
	EP-PBG	Pars Air			26/JUL/80	Leased
	PH-SIX	Fokker			16/FEB/81	
	PH-SIX	Linjeflyg			26/NOV/81	Leased
	PH-SIX	Fokker			DEC/82	
	PH-SIX	Fokker	4000		NOV/83	Converted
	5T-CLF	Air Mauritanie			19/DEC/83	
11093	PH-ZBL	Fokker	6000	17/SEP/75		
		Parsair				Not taken-up
	PH-ZBL	Linjeflyg			13/AUG/76	Leased
	PH-ZBL	Fokker			09/MAR/77	
	EP-PBB	Parsair			30/JUN/77	Leased
	PH-ZBL	Fokker			22/JUL/80	Stored
	EP-PBB	Parsair			20/FEB/81	Leased
	EP-PBB	Iranian Asseman Airlines			01/APR/81	Leased
	PH-ZBL	Fokker			11/SEP/81	
	PH-ZBL	NLM			02/DEC/81	Leased
	PH-ZBL	Fokker	4000		01/JUL/82	Converted
	5T-CLG	Air Mauritanie			18/NOV/83	
11094	PH-EXY	Fokker	1000	15/JUL/75		
	PK-GVP	Garuda			05/AUG/75	W/O 06/MAR/79, Mt. Sambas
11095	PH-EXQ	Fokker	1000	13/AUG/75		
	PK-PJW	Pelita/Pertamina				Not taken-up
	PK-GVT	Garuda			07/FEB/76	
	PK-GVT	Fokker			AUG/84	
	N272N	Piedmont Airlines			23/APR/85	
11096	PH-EXH	Fokker	1000	18/SEP/75		
	PK-GVQ	Garuda			10/OCT/75	
	PK-GVQ	Fokker			MAR/84	
	N296N	Piedmont Airlines			25/OCT/84	
11097	PH-EXS	Fokker	1000VIP	07/OCT/75		
	PH-ZBN	Fokker			15/OCT/75	
	TU-VAA	Ivory Coast Government			16/OCT/75	

C/N	Registration	Owner/Operator	Series	First Flight	Delivery	Remarks
	TU-TIM	Air Ivoire			12/MAY/79	
	PH-ZBN	Fokker			23/AUG/84	
	N801PH	Horizon Air			21/NOV/84	
11098	PH-EXI	Fokker	1000	04/NOV/75		
	PK-GVR	Garuda			18/NOV/75	
	PK-GVR	Fokker			APR/84	
	N297N	Piedmont Airlines			21/NOV/84	
11099	PH-EXL	Fokker	1000C	11/DEC/75		
	TU-VAB	Ivory Coast Government			26/MAY/76	
	TU-TIN	Air Ivoire				
11100	PH-EXY	Fokker	1000VIP	13/NOV/75		
	FAP 390	Peruvian Air Force			30/MAR/76	
11101	PH-EXG	Fokker	1000	21/OCT/75		
	PK-GVS	Garuda			13/FEB/76	
	PK-GVS	Fokker			29/FEB/84	
	N294N	Piedmont Airlines			26/SEP/84	
11102	PH-EXZ	Fokker	1000C	25/FEB/76		
	TR-LTS	Air Gabon			26/MAY/76	
11103	PH-EXH	Fokker	1000	20/APR/76		
	PK-GVU	Garuda			11/MAY/76	
	PK-GVU	Fokker			23/JUL/84	
	N298N	Piedmont Airlines			19/DEC/84	
11104	PH-EXU	Fokker	1000VIP	01/APR/76		
	TR-LTR	Gabon Government			11/MAY/76	Op. by Air Gabon
	TR-LTR	Air Gabon			JAN/83	
11105	PH-EXV	Fokker	1000	25/MAY/76		
	PK-GVV	Garuda			11/JUN/76	
	PK-GVV	Fokker			28/SEP/84	
	N271N	Piedmont Airlines			04/MAR/85	
11106	PH-EXD	Fokker	1000	21/JUN/76		
	PK-GVW	Garuda			12/JUL/76	
	PK-GVW	Fokker			20/MAR/85	
	N290N	Piedmont Airlines			27/AUG/85	
11107	PH-EXE	Fokker	1000	05/AUG/76		
	PK-GVX	Garuda			15/SEP/76	
	PK-GVX	Fokker			APR/85	
	N293N	Piedmont Airlines			24/SEP/85	
11108	PH-EXF	Fokker	2000	07/JUL/76		
	5N-ANI	Nigeria Airways			03/AUG/76	
	F-GDUU	TAT			JUL/85	
11109	PH-EXG	Fokker	2000	29/AUG/76		
	5N-ANJ	Nigeria Airways			05/OCT/76	
	F-GDUV	TAT			JUL/85	
11110	PH-EXL	Fokker	2000	28/SEP/76		
	PH-ZBO	Fokker			02/NOV/76	
	5N-ANK	Nigeria Airways			04/NOV/76	
	F-GDUX	TAT			JUL/85	
	F-GDUX	Aviona Leasing			DEC/85	
11111	PH-EHZ	Fokker	4000	20/OCT/76		
	SE-DGD	Linjeflyg			14/DEC/76	
11112	PH-EXK	Fokker	4000	12/NOV/76		
	SE-DGE	Linjeflyg			14/DEC/76	
11113	PH-EXR	Fokker	3000	23/DEC/76		Proto Mk 3000
	PK-GFR	Garuda			27/JUL/77	
11114	PH-EXU	Fokker	4000	14/MAR/77		
	XY-ADW	Burma Airways Corp.			30/JUN/77	
11115	PH-EXM	Fokker	4000	24/NOV/76		
	SE-DGF	Linjeflyg			17/DEC/76	
11116	PH-EXV	Fokker	4000	13/JAN/77		
	SE-DGG	Linjeflyg			01/MAR/77	
11117	PH-EXW	Fokker	3000	01/MAR/77		
	PK-GFQ	Garuda			08/JUL/77	
11118	PH-EXN	Fokker	4000	13/JUL/77		
	TU-VAH	Ivory Coast Government			03/DEC/77	
	TU-TIJ	Air Ivoire			02/APR/79	
11119	PH-EXX	Fokker	3000	26/APR/77		
	PK-GFS	Garuda			08/SEP/77	
11120	PH-EXY	Fokker	4000	01/FEB/77		
	SE-DGH	Linjeflyg			25/FEB/77	
11121	PH-EXO	Fokker	4000	19/AUG/77		
	TU-VAN	Ivory Coast Government			28/MAR/78	
	TU-TIK	Air Ivoire			02/APR/79	
11122	PH-EXP	Fokker	4000	05/APR/77		
	SE-DGI	Linjeflyg			22/APR/77	
11123	PH-EXZ	Fokker	4000	31/MAY/77		
	SE-DGK	Linjeflyg			24/JUL/77	
11124	PH-EXY	Fokker	4000VIP	77		Not taken-up
	TU-VAZ	Ivory Coast Government				
	TU-VAJ	Ivory Coast Government			19/APR/78	
11125	PH-EXP	Fokker	3000VIP	20/SEP/77		
	PH-ZBP	Fokker			11/SEP/78	
	G-530	Ghana Air Force			20/SEP/78	
11126	PH-EXV	Fokker	4000	05/AUG/77		
	SE-DGL	Linjeflyg			30/AUG/77	
11127	PH-EXT	Fokker	4000	12/DEC/77		
		Parsair				Not taken-up
	PH-BBV	NLM			01/MAR/78	Leased
	PH-BBV	Fokker			13/DEC/78	
	PH-BBV	Air Anglia			09/MAR/79	Leased
	PH-BBV	Fokker			15/OCT/79	
	PH-BBV	NLM			02/NOV/79	Leased
	PH-BBV	Fokker			09/NOV/79	
	LV-MZD	Aerolineas Argentinas			06/DEC/79	Leased
	LV-MZD	Aerolineas Argentinas			17/APR/80	Purchased
11128	PH-EXR	Fokker	4000	04/NOV/77		
	SE-DGM	Linjeflyg			25/NOV/77	
11129	PH-EXS	Fokker	3000	06/MAR/78		
	PK-GFT	Garuda			31/MAR/78	
11130	PH-EXU	Fokker	4000	02/JAN/78		
	SE-DGN	Linjeflyg				Not taken-up
	PH-JPV	Fokker			09/FEB/78	
	SE-DGN	Linjeflyg			14/APR/78	
11131	PH-EXW	Fokker	3000	05/APR/80		
	PK-GFU	Garuda			22/APR/78	
11132	PH-EXX	Fokker	3000	02/MAY/80		

C/N	Registration	Owner/Operator	Series	First Flight	Delivery	Remarks
	PK-GFV	Garuda			30/MAY/78	W/O 02/JUN/83, Telukbetung
11133	PH-EXO	Fokker	4000	30/JAN/79		
	PH-ZBU	Fokker			11/SEP/79	
	G-WWJC	Air Anglia			12/OCT/79	
	G-WWJC	Air UK			16/JAN/80	
	G-WWJC	Air Alsace/Air France			01/APR/80	Leased
	F-GDFC	Air Alsace/Air France			01/MAY/81	Leased
	F-GDFC	Air France			82	Leased
	F-GDFC	TAT			AUG/82	Leased
	F-GDFC	TAT			APR/86	Purchased
11134	PH-EXZ	Fokker	3000	09/JUN/78		
	PK-GFW	Garuda			02/JUL/78	
11135	PH-EXR	Fokker	4000	12/OCT/78		
	PH-ZBT	Fokker			17/MAY/79	
	G-JCWW	Air Anglia			21/MAY/79	
	G-JCWW	Air UK			16/JAN/80	
	G-JCWW	Air Alsace/Air France			23/AUG/80	Leased
	F-GDFD	Air Alsace/Air France			01/MAY/81	Leased
	F-GDFD	TAT			AUG/82	Leased
	F-GDFD	TAT			APR/86	Purchased
11136	PH-EXN	Fokker	3000	30/JUN/78		
	PH-ZBR	Fokker				
	3D-ALN	Royal Swazi			20/JUL/78	
11137	PH-EXS	Fokker	3000VIP	07/NOV/78		
	PH-ZBS	Fokker			28/NOV/78	
	5H-CCM	Tanzanian Government			28/NOV/78	
11138	PH-EXT	Fokker	4000	13/NOV/78		
	PH-CHB	NLM			11/DEC/78	
11139	PH-EXU	Fokker	4000	05/DEC/78		
	PH-CHD	NLM			09/JAN/79	
11140	PH-EXN	Fokker	4000	28/DEC/78		
	PH-CHF	NLM			07/MAR/79	
11141	PH-EXP	Fokker	4000	22/FEB/79		
	PH-CHI	NLM			23/MAR/79	W/O 06/NOV/81, Moerdijk
11142	PH-EXY	Fokker	4000	19/FEB/79		
	5N-ANU	Nigeria Airways			21/JUL/79	
	F-GDUY	TAT			26/SEP/85	
11143	PH-EXZ	Fokker	3000	07/MAR/79		
	OY-BRM	Cimber Air			10/APR/79	
	OY-BRM	TAT			01/MAY/79	Leased
	OY-BRM	Cimber Air			18/AUG/79	
	OY-BRM	Saudia			28/JUN/80	Leased
11144	PH-EXS	Fokker	4000	06/APR/79		
	5N-ANV	Nigeria Airways			21/JUL/79	
	F-GDUZ	TAT			JUL/85	
	HB-AAS	Zimex Aviation			86	Op. for Sirte Oil Co.
11145	PH-EXV	Fokker	3000C	08/MAR/79		
	5-T-20	Argentine Navy			05/APR/79	
11146	PH-EXN	Fokker	4000VIP	09/AUG/79		
	PK-PJY	Pelita/Pertamina			21/MAR/80	
11147	PH-EXW	Fokker	3000VIP	08/MAY/79		
	5-T-10	Argentine Navy			06/JUN/79	
11148	PH-EXT	Fokker	4000	13/SEP/79		
	PK-PJW	Pelita/Pertamina			31/JAN/80	
11149	PH-EXP	Fokker	4000	16/OCT/79		
	N106UR	Empire Airlines			02/AUG/80	
	N106UR	Piedmont Airlines			15/JAN/86	
11150	PH-EXX	Fokker	3000C	18/JUN/79		
	5-T-21	Argentine Navy			01/AUG/79	
11151	PH-EXU	Fokker	3000	12/JUL/79		
	OY-BRN	Cimber Air			14/AUG/79	
	OY-BRN	TAT			18/AUG/79	
	OY-BRN	Cimber Air			31/AUG/79	
	OY-BRN	Saudia			28/JUN/80	Leased
11152	PH-EXR	Fokker	4000	21/DEC/79		
	N504	Altair			07/AUG/80	WFU 82, stored Philadelphia
	N504	Dolphin Airways			83	Not taken-up
	N504	Empire Airlines			DEC/83	
	N504	Piedmont Airlines			15/JAN/86	
11153	PH-EXV	Fokker	3000VIP	05/DEC/79		
	PH-ZBV	Fokker			28/AUG/80	
	RP-1177	Philippine Government			30/AUG/80	
11154	PH-EXW	Fokker	4000	28/MAR/80		
	PK-GKA	Garuda			26/APR/80	
11155	PH-EXX	Fokker	4000	17/APR/80		
	PK-GKB	Garuda			28/MAY/80	
11156	PH-EXY	Fokker	4000	22/FEB/80		
	N505	Altair			07/AUG/80	WFU 82, stored Philadelphia
	N505	Dolphin Airways			83	Not taken-up
	N505	Empire Airlines			JUL/84	
	N505	Piedmont Airlines			15/JAN/86	
11157	PH-EXZ	Fokker	4000	22/MAY/80		
	PH-ZBW	Fokker			28/AUG/80	
	PK-GKC	Garuda			19/SEP/80	
11158	PH-EXN	Fokker	4000	13/JUN/80		
	PK-GKD	Garuda			24/JUL/80	
11159	PH-EXT	Fokker	4000	10/OCT/80		
	PH-ZBX	Fokker			07/NOV/80	
	N107UR	Empire Airlines			17/NOV/80	
	N107UR	Piedmont Airlines			15/JAN/86	
11160	PH-EXO	Fokker	4000	09/AUG/80		
	PK-GKE	Garuda			09/SEP/80	
11161	PH-EXS	Fokker	4000	04/SEP/80		
	N509	Altair			08/OCT/80	WFU 82, stored Philadelphia
	N509	Dolphin Airways			83	Not taken-up
	N509	Empire Airlines			DEC/83	
	N509	Piedmont Airlines			15/JAN/86	
11162	PH-EXU	Fokker	3000	03/JUL/80		
	N	Sun Pacific				Cancelled order
	CP-	Lloyd Aereo Boliviano			SEP/81	Not taken-up, stored Woensdrecht
	PH-EXY	Fokker			APR/82	
	PH-EZL	Fokker	3000C			Converted

FOKKER F-28 FELLOWSHIP

C/N	Registration	Owner/Operator	Series	First Flight	Delivery	Remarks
11163	FAC-1141	SATENA			08/FEB/85	
	PH-EXW	Fokker	3000	03/DEC/80		
	N	Sun Pacific				Cancelled order
	PH-ZBJ	Fokker			14/JAN/81	
	XT-FZP	Air Volta			82	Cancelled order
	N163PM	Pilgrim Airlines			23/JAN/84	
	N163PM	Business Express			86	
11164	PH-EXR	Fokker	4000	05/JAN/81		
	PH-ZCA	Fokker			28/APR/81	
	EP-PAT	Iran Asseman Airlines			06/MAY/81	
11165	PH-EXV	Fokker	3000	27/JAN/81		
	N	Sun Pacific				Cancelled order
	CP-	Lloyd Aereo Boliviano			NOV/81	Cancelled order, stored Woensdrecht
	PH-EXS	Fokker			APR/84	
	PH-ZCG	Fokker			15/MAY/84	
	FAC-1140	SATENA			19/MAY/84	
11166	PH-EXY	Fokker	4000	18/FEB/81		W/O 28/MAR/85, Florencia
	PH-ZCB	Fokker				
	EP-PAU	Iran Asseman Airlines			06/JUN/81	
11167	PH-EXO	Fokker	4000	12/MAR/81		
	PH-ZBZ	Fokker			28/APR/81	
	N510	Altair			29/APR/81	WFU 82, stored Philadelphia
	N510	Fokker			FEB/84	Stored Philadelphia
	N510	Empire Airlines			JUL/84	
	N510	Piedmont Airlines			15/JAN/86	
11168	PH-EXP	Fokker	4000		MAY/81	
	PH-ZCC	Fokker		21/MAY/81	20/MAY/81	
	N512	Altair			22/MAY/81	WFU 82
	N512	Empire Airlines			JUN/83	
	N512	Piedmont Airlines			15/JAN/86	
11169	PH-EXT	Fokker	4000		MAY/81	
	PH-ZBY	Fokker		11/MAY/81	11/MAY/81	
	N513	Altair			20/JUN/81	WFU 82, stored Philadelphia
	N513	Dolphin Airways			83	Not taken-up
	N513	Empire Airlines			JUN/83	
	N513	Piedmont Airlines			15/JAN/86	
11170	PH-EXU	Fokker	4000	27/MAY/81		
	PK-GKF	Garuda			29/JUN/81	
11171	PH-EXR	Fokker	4000	24/JUN/81		
	PK-GKG	Garuda			28/JUL/81	
11172	PH-EXX	Fokker	4000	30/JUL/81		
	S2-ACH	Bangladesh Biman			26/SEP/81	
11173	PH-EXN	Fokker	4000	17/AUG/81		
	VH-EWA	East West Airlines				Not taken-up
	N1346U	Empire Airlines				
	N108UR	Empire Airlines			31/OCT/81	Reg. Not taken-up
	N108UR	Piedmont Airlines			15/JAN/86	
11174	PH-EXO	Fokker	4000	05/NOV/81		
	PK-GKH	Garuda			02/DEC/81	
11175	PH-EXT	Fokker	4000	27/NOV/81		
	N521	Altair			81	Cancelled order
	PK-GKL	Garuda			29/APR/83	
11176	PH-EXU	Fokker	4000	28/DEC/81		
	N522	Altair			JAN/82	Cancelled order
	PH-CHN	Fokker			14/JUL/82	
	PH-CHN	NLM	4000		15/JUL/82	
11177	PH-EXR	Fokker	4000	28/JAN/82		
	N523	Altair			FEB/82	Cancelled order
	PH-ZCD	Fokker			05/AUG/82	Demonstrator
	PK-GKM	Garuda			01/JUL/83	
11178	PH-EXW	Fokker	4000	24/APR/82		
	PK-PJM	Pertamina/Pelita			16/OCT/81	
11179	PH-EXX	Fokker	4000	15/FEB/82		
	PH-LEX	Fokker			14/APR/82	
	PH-LEX	Air Alsace/Air France			27/APR/82	Leased
	F-GDSK	TAT			SEP/82	Leased
	PH-LEX	TAT			24/APR/85	
11180	PH-EXZ	Fokker	4000	16/OCT/81		
	S2-ACI	Bangladesh Biman			29/NOV/81	
	S2-ACJ	Bangladesh Biman			29/NOV/81	
11181	PH-EXS	Fokker	4000	11/MAR/82		
	VH-EWB	East West Airlines				Not taken-up
	N109UR	Empire Airlines			06/APR/82	
	N109UR	Piedmont Airlines			15/JAN/86	
11182	PH-EXN	Fokker	4000	31/MAR/82		
	TN-	Lina Congo			82	Not taken-up
	N110UR	Empire Airlines			24/APR/82	
	N110UR	Piedmont Airlines			15/JAN/86	
11183	PH-EXZ	Fokker	4000	14/APR/82		
	PK-	Pertamina/Pelita			82	Not taken-up
	VH-FKI	Airline of Western Australia			16/JUL/82	
11184	PH-EXO	Fokker	4000	18/MAY/82		
	N524	Altair			82	Cancelled order
	PH-ZCE	Fokker			25/NOV/82	
	TY-BBN	Air Benin	4000VIP		27/NOV/82	
	TY-BBN	T.A.B. Benin				
11185	PH-EXP	Fokker	4000	14/JUN/82		
	N111UR	Empire Airlines			82	Cancelled order
	XT-FZP	Air Volta			27/JAN/83	
	XT-FZP	Air Bourkina				
11186	PH-EXS	Fokker	4000	02/JUL/82		
	VH-FKJ	Airline of Western Australia			09/DEC/82	
11187	PH-EXW	Fokker	4000	28/JUL/82		
	9G-ADA	Ghana Airways			21/AUG/82	
11188	PH-EXN	Fokker	4000	03/SEP/82		
	9G-	Ghana Airways			82	Not taken-up
	PK-GKI	Garuda			01/FEB/83	
11189	PH-EXX	Fokker	4000	27/OCT/82		
	PK-GKJ	Garuda			04/MAR/83	
11190	PH-EXU	Fokker	4000	22/OCT/82		
	SE-DGO	Linjeflyg			26/NOV/82	
11191	PH-EXZ	Fokker	4000	01/DEC/82		
	SE-DGP	Linjeflyg			17/DEC/82	

C/N	Registration	Owner/Operator	Series	First Flight	Delivery	Remarks
11192	N112UR	Empire Airlines	4000		83	Cancelled order
	PH-EXW	Fokker				
	PK-PJK	Pelita			28/APR/83	
11193	PH-EXR	Fokker	4000	07/JAN/83		
	PK-GKK	Garuda			MAR/83	
11194	N113UR	Empire Airlines	4000	07/FEB/83	83	Cancelled order
	PH-EXZ	Fokker				
	5A-DLW	Libyan Arab Airlines			15/FEB/84	
11195	PH-EXO	Fokker	4000			
	VH-EWA	East West Airlines			30/APR/83	
11196	PH-EXU	Fokker	4000			
	PK-GKN	Garuda			29/SEP/83	
11197	N114UR	Empire Airlines	4000		83	Cancelled order
	PH-EXS	Fokker				
	5A-DLU	Libyan Arab Airlines			31/NOV/83	
11198	PH-EXP	Fokker	4000			
	PK-GKO	Garuda			01/JUL/83	
11199	PH-EXN	Fokker	4000			
	PK-GKP	Garuda			28/JUL/83	
11200	N115UR	Empire Airlines	4000		83	Cancelled order
	PH-EXV	Fokker				
	5A-DLV	Libyan Arab Airlines			05/NOV/83	
11201	PH-EXO	Fokker	4000			
	PK-GKQ	Garuda			30/AUG/83	
11202	PH-EXT	Fokker	4000			
	PK-GKR	Garuda			31/OCT/83	
11203	PH-EXP	Fokker	4000			
	HL7265	Korean Air			30/JUN/84	
11204	PH-EXR	Fokker	4000			
	SE-DGR	Linjeflyg			13/AUG/84	
11205	VH-EWB	East West Airlines	4000		23/NOV/83	
11206	PH-EXU	Fokker	4000			
	PK-GKS	Garuda			02/FEB/84	
11207	PH-EXX	Fokker	4000			
	VH-EWC	East West Airlines			21/SEP/84	
11208	PH-EXT	Fokker	4000			
	VH-EWD	East West Airlines			13/NOV/84	
11209	PH-EXF	Fokker	4000		29/FEB/84	
	PK-GKT	Garuda				
11210	PH-EXO	Fokker	4000		29/MAR/84	
	PK-GKU	Garuda				
11211	PH-EXU	Fokker	4000		17/APR/84	
	PK-GKV	Garuda				
11212	PH-EXZ	Fokker	4000			
	VH-LAR	Lloyd Aviation			12/JUN/85	
11213	PH-EZA	Fokker	4000		28/MAY/84	
	PK-GKW	Garuda				
11214	PH-EZB	Fokker	4000		29/JUN/84	
	PK-GKX	Garuda				
11215	PH-EZC	Fokker	4000		31/JUL/84	
	PK-GKY	Garuda				
11216	PH-EZD	Fokker	4000		07/SEP/84	
	PK-GKZ	Garuda				
11217	PH-EZZ	Fokker	4000		29/SEP/84	
	PK-GQA	Garuda				
11218	PH-EZP	Fokker	4000		12/NOV/84	
	PK-GQB	Garuda				
11219	PH-EZR	Fokker	4000		12/JUN/85	
	HL7270	Korean Air				
11220	PH-EZS	Fokker	4000		14/JAN/85	
	PH-ZCH	Fokker				
	Z-	Air Zimbabwe			85	Cancelled Order
	HC-BMD/	TAME			19/DEC/85	
	FAE-220					
11221	PH-EZT	Fokker	4000			
	N281MP	Mid Pacific Air			04/JUL/85	
11222	PH-EZU	Fokker	4000			
	N117UR	Empire Airlines			03/MAR/85	
	N117UR	Piedmont Airlines			15/JAN/86	
11223	PH-EZV	Fokker	4000			
	N282MP	Mid Pacific Air			04/JUL/85	
11224	PH-EZW	Fokker	4000			
	N118UR	Empire Airlines			30/APR/85	
	N118UR	Piedmont Airlines			15/JAN/86	
11225	7Q-	Air Malawi	4000		SEP/86	Sched.delivery
11226	PH-EZB	Fokker	4000			
	N119UR	Empire Airlines			23/SEP/85	
	N119UR	Piedmont Airlines			15/JAN/86	
11227	PH-EZC	Fokker	4000			
	N204P	Piedmont Airlines			18/DEC/85	
11228	PH-EZO	Fokker	4000			
	N205P	Piedmont Airlines			24/DEC/85	
11229	PH-EZP	Fokker	4000			
	N206P	Piedmont Airlines			27/FEB/86	
11230	PH-EZZ	Fokker	4000			
	N207P	Piedmont Airlines			28/APR/86	
11231	PH-EZD	Fokker	4000			
	N120UR	Empire Airlines			09/DEC/85	
	N120UR	Piedmont Airlines			15/JAN/86	
11232	PH-EZG	Fokker	4000			
	XY-AGA	Burma Airways			26/MAR/86	
11233	PH-EZI	Fokker	4000			
	N208P	Piedmont Airlines			27/MAY/86	
11234	PH-EZJ	Fokker	4000			
	N209P	Piedmont Airlines			09/JUL/86	
11235	PH-	Fokker	4000			
	N210P	Piedmont Airlines			AUG/86	Sched.delivery
11236	PH-EZA	Fokker	4000			
	SE-DGS	Linjeflyg			04/APR/86	
11237	PH-EZE	Fokker	4000			
	N121UR	Empire Airlines			21/MAY/86	
	N121UR	Piedmont Airlines			21/MAY/86	
11238	N122UR	Empire Airlines	4000		15/JUL/86	
	N122UR	Piedmont Airlines			15/JUL/86	
11239	PH-EZL	Fokker	4000			

FOKKER F-28 FELLOWSHIP

C/N	Registration	Owner/Operator	Series	First Flight	Delivery	Remarks
11240	SE-DGT	Linjeflyg				
	PH-	Fokker	4000		SEP/86	Sched.delivery
	N211P	Piedmont Airlines			SEP/86	Sched.delivery
11241	PH-	Fokker	4000			
	SE-	Linjeflyg			JUN/87	Sched.delivery

Fokker F.28 cross-reference index

3D- Swaziland
11136 3D-ALN

5A- Libya
11197 5A-DLU
11200 5A-DLV
11194 5A-DLW

5H- Tanzania
11137 5H-CCM

5N- Nigeria
11049 5N-AGN
11993 5N-ANA
11053 5N-ANB
11090 5N-ANF
11091 5N-ANH
11108 5N-ANI
11109 5N-ANJ
11110 5N-ANK
11142 5N-ANU
11144 5N-ANV

5T- Mauritania
11092 5T-CLF
11093 5T-CLG

5V- Togo
11079 5V-MAB
11079 5V-TAB

9G- Ghana
11062 9G-ABZ
11077 9G-ACA
11187 9G-ADA

C- Canada
11991 C-GTEO

C2- Nauru
11041 C2-RN1
11056 C2-RN2

CF- Canada
11033 CF-TAV
11038 CF-TAY

D- West Germany
11030 D-ABAM
11029 D-ABAN
11004 D-ABAQ
11004 D-ABAQ
11006 D-ABAX
11046 D-AGAB
11050 D-AGAC
11051 D-AGAD
11052 D-AGAE
11027 D-AHLA
11031 D-AHLB
11034 D-AHLC
11032 D-AHLD

EC- Spain
11017 EC-BVA
11019 EC-BVB
11023 EC-BVC

EP- Iran
11027 EP-PAS
11164 EP-PAT
11166 EP-PAU
11052 EP-PBA
11093 EP-PBB
11003 EP-PBF
11092 EP-PBG

F- France
11031 F-BUTE
11034 F-BUTI
11051 F-GBBR
11050 F-GBBS
11052 F-GBBT
11027 F-GBBX
11133 F-GDFC
11135 F-GDFD
11179 F-GDSK
11053 F-GDUS
11091 F-GDUT
11108 F-GDUU
11109 F-GDUV
11110 F-GDUX
11142 F-GDUY
11144 F-GDUZ
11004 F-GECK
11003 F-GMOL

G- United Kingdom
11135 G-JCWW
11133 G-WWJC

HB- Switzerland
11144 HB-AAS

HC- Ecuador
11220 HC-BMD

HK- Colombia
11085 HK-3126

HL South Korea
11203 HL7265
11219 HL7270

I- Italy
11014 I-TIDA
11006 I-TIDB
11015 I-TIDE
11991 I-TIDI
11037 I-TIDO
11004 I-TIDU
11994 I-VAFE
11032 I-VAGA

LN- Norway
11009 LN-SUC
11003 LN-SUM
11032 LN-SUM
11012 LN-SUN
11013 LN-SUO
11010 LN-SUX
11011 LN-SUY

LV- Argentina
11085 LV-LOA
11085 LV-LOA
11086 LV-LOB
11083 LV-LOC
11046 LV-LRG
11048 LV-LZN
11127 LV-MZD

N United States
11149 N106UR
11159 N107UR
11173 N108UR
11181 N109UR
11182 N110UR
11185 N111UR
11192 N112UR
11194 N113UR
11197 N114UR
11200 N115UR
11222 N117UR
11224 N118UR
11226 N119UR
11231 N120UR
11237 N121UR
11238 N122UR
11173 N1346U
11163 N163PM
11227 N204P
11228 N205P
11229 N206P
11230 N207P
11233 N208P
11234 N209P
11235 N210P
11240 N211P
11105 N271N
11095 N272N
11037 N273N
11063 N274N
11016 N27W
11048 N280FH
11061 N280N
11221 N281MP
11075 N281N
11018 N282FH
11223 N282MP
11032 N282N
11020 N283FH
11035 N283N
11024 N284FH
11036 N284N
11033 N285FH
11038 N286FH
11044 N286N
11043 N287FH
11044 N288FH
11054 N288N
11047 N289FH
11047 N289FH
11064 N289N
11016 N28IFH
11106 N290N
11043 N291N
11107 N293N
11101 N294N
11096 N296N
11098 N297N
11103 N298N
11152 N504
11156 N505
11161 N509
11167 N510
11168 N512
11169 N513
11175 N521
11176 N522
11177 N523
11184 N524
11097 N801PH
11016 N930TL

OB- Peru
11065 OB-R-1018
11066 OB-R-1019
11059 OB-R-1020
11032 OB-R-1030
11035 OB-R-231
11036 OB-R-232
11039 OB-R-233
11032 OB-R-390
11059 OB-R-397
11065 OB-R-398
11066 OB-R-399

OY- Denmark
11143 OY-BRM
11151 OY-BRN

P2- Papua New Guinea
11033 P2-ANE
11038 P2-ANF
11041 P2-ANU
11056 P2-ANW

PH- Netherlands
11127 PH-BBV
11138 PH-CHB
11139 PH-CHD
11140 PH-CHF
11141 PH-CHI
11176 PH-CHN
11111 PH-EHZ
11013 PH-EXA
11992 PH-EXA
11023 PH-EXA
11026 PH-EXA
11043 PH-EXA
11994 PH-EXB
11032 PH-EXB
11079 PH-EXB
11024 PH-EXC
11080 PH-EXC
11049 PH-EXD
11064 PH-EXD
11081 PH-EXD
11106 PH-EXD
11993 PH-EXE
11037 PH-EXE
11063 PH-EXE
11107 PH-EXE
11992 PH-EXF
11025 PH-EXF
11035 PH-EXF
11041 PH-EXF
11048 PH-EXF
11053 PH-EXF
11056 PH-EXF
11108 PH-EXF
11209 PH-EXF
11049 PH-EXG
11074 PH-EXG
11101 PH-EXG
11109 PH-EXG
11056 PH-EXH
11090 PH-EXH
11096 PH-EXH
11103 PH-EXH
11047 PH-EXI
11068 PH-EXI
11088 PH-EXI
11098 PH-EXI
11069 PH-EXK
11112 PH-EXK
11067 PH-EXL
11089 PH-EXL
11099 PH-EXL
11110 PH-EXL
11038 PH-EXM
11043 PH-EXM
11115 PH-EXM
11065 PH-EXN
11082 PH-EXN
11118 PH-EXN
11136 PH-EXN
11140 PH-EXN
11146 PH-EXN
11158 PH-EXN
11173 PH-EXN
11182 PH-EXN
11188 PH-EXN
11199 PH-EXN
11066 PH-EXO
11121 PH-EXO
11133 PH-EXO
11160 PH-EXO
11167 PH-EXO
11174 PH-EXO
11184 PH-EXO
11195 PH-EXO
11201 PH-EXO
11210 PH-EXO
11070 PH-EXP
11084 PH-EXP
11122 PH-EXP
11125 PH-EXP
11141 PH-EXP
11149 PH-EXP
11168 PH-EXP
11185 PH-EXP
11198 PH-EXP
11203 PH-EXP
11083 PH-EXQ
11095 PH-EXQ
11044 PH-EXR
11071 PH-EXR
11113 PH-EXR
11128 PH-EXR
11135 PH-EXR
11152 PH-EXR
11164 PH-EXR
11171 PH-EXR
11177 PH-EXR
11193 PH-EXR
11204 PH-EXR
11073 PH-EXS
11097 PH-EXS
11129 PH-EXS
11137 PH-EXS
11144 PH-EXS
11161 PH-EXS
11165 PH-EXS
11181 PH-EXS
11186 PH-EXS
11197 PH-EXS
11073 PH-EXT
11085 PH-EXT
11091 PH-EXT
11127 PH-EXT
11138 PH-EXT
11148 PH-EXT
11159 PH-EXT
11169 PH-EXT
11175 PH-EXT
11202 PH-EXT
11208 PH-EXT
11077 PH-EXU
11086 PH-EXU
11104 PH-EXU
11114 PH-EXU
11130 PH-EXU
11139 PH-EXU
11151 PH-EXU
11162 PH-EXU
11170 PH-EXU
11176 PH-EXU
11190 PH-EXU
11196 PH-EXU
11206 PH-EXU
11211 PH-EXU
11075 PH-EXV
11087 PH-EXV
11105 PH-EXV
11116 PH-EXV
11126 PH-EXV
11145 PH-EXV
11153 PH-EXV
11165 PH-EXV
11200 PH-EXV
11018 PH-EXW
11032 PH-EXW
11117 PH-EXW
11147 PH-EXW
11154 PH-EXW
11163 PH-EXW
11178 PH-EXW
11187 PH-EXW
11192 PH-EXW
11131 PH-EXX
11020 PH-EXX
11119 PH-EXX
11132 PH-EXX
11150 PH-EXX
11155 PH-EXX
11172 PH-EXX
11179 PH-EXX
11189 PH-EXX
11207 PH-EXY
11076 PH-EXY
11094 PH-EXY
11100 PH-EXY
11120 PH-EXY
11124 PH-EXY
11142 PH-EXY
11156 PH-EXY
11162 PH-EXY
11166 PH-EXY
11024 PH-EXZ
11074 PH-EXZ
11078 PH-EXZ
11102 PH-EXZ
11123 PH-EXZ
11134 PH-EXZ
11143 PH-EXZ
11157 PH-EXZ
11180 PH-EXZ
11183 PH-EXZ
11191 PH-EXZ
11194 PH-EXZ
11212 PH-EXZ
11037 PH-EZA
11213 PH-EZA
11236 PH-EZA
11214 PH-EZB
11226 PH-EZB
11215 PH-EZC
11227 PH-EZC
11216 PH-EZD
11231 PH-EZD
11237 PH-EZE
11063 PH-EZE
11232 PH-EZG
11233 PH-EZI
11234 PH-EZJ
11162 PH-EZL
11239 PH-EZL

11075	PH-EZM	11137	PH-ZBS	11036	PK-GVB
11228	PH-EZO	11135	PH-ZBT	11054	PK-GVD
11218	PH-EZP	11133	PH-ZBU	11055	PK-GVE
11229	PH-EZP	11153	PH-ZBV	11061	PK-GVF
11219	PH-EZR	11157	PH-ZBW	11063	PK-GVG
11220	PH-EZS	11159	PH-ZBX	11064	PK-GVH
11221	PH-EZT	11169	PH-ZBY	11037	PK-GVI
11222	PH-EZU	11167	PH-ZBZ	11075	PK-GVJ
11223	PH-EZV	11164	PH-ZCA	11078	PK-GVK
11224	PH-EZW	11166	PH-ZCB	11087	PK-GVL
11217	PH-EZZ	11168	PH-ZCC	11032	PK-GVM
11230	PH-EZZ	11177	PH-ZCD	11043	PK-GVN
11994	PH-FPI	11184	PH-ZCE	11044	PK-GVO
11994	PH-FPT	11165	PH-ZCG	11094	PK-GVP
11001	PH-JHG	11220	PH-ZCH	11096	PK-GVQ
11130	PH-JPV			11098	PK-GVR
11179	PH-LEX	**PK- Indonesia**		11101	PK-GVS
11008	PH-MAT			11095	PK-GVT
11003	PH-MOL	11117	PK-GFQ	11103	PK-GVU
11045	PH-PBX	11113	PK-GFR	11105	PK-GVV
11092	PH-SIX	11119	PK-GFS	11106	PK-GVW
11002	PH-WEV	11129	PK-GFT	11107	PK-GVX
11004	PH-ZAA	11131	PK-GFU	11192	PK-PJK
11005	PH-ZAB	11132	PK-GFV	11178	PK-PJM
11006	PH-ZAC	11134	PK-GFW	11030	PK-PJS
11009	PH-ZAD	11078	PK-GJP	11042	PK-PJT
11010	PH-ZAE	11075	PK-GJQ	11029	PK-PJU
11011	PH-ZAF	11037	PK-GJR	11073	PK-PJV
11012	PH-ZAG	11064	PK-GJS	11095	PK-PJW
11013	PH-ZAH	11063	PK-GJT	11148	PK-PJW
11014	PH-ZAI	11061	PK-GJU	11042	PK-PJX
11015	PH-ZAK	11055	PK-GJV	11146	PK-PJY
11016	PH-ZAL	11054	PK-GJW		
11017	PH-ZAM	11039	PK-GJX	**RP- Philippines**	
11018	PH-ZAN	11036	PK-GJY		
11019	PH-ZAO	11035	PK-GJZ	11153	RP-1177
11020	PH-ZAP	11154	PK-GKA		
11991	PH-ZAR	11155	PK-GKB	**S2- Bangladesh**	
11021	PH-ZAS	11157	PK-GKC		
11022	PH-ZAT	11158	PK-GKD	11172	S2-ACH
11993	PH-ZAU	11160	PK-GKE	11180	S2-ACI
11023	PH-ZAV	11170	PK-GKF	11180	S2-ACJ
11032	PH-ZAV	11171	PK-GKG		
11052	PH-ZAW	11174	PK-GKH		
11053	PH-ZAX	11188	PK-GKI	**SE- Sweden**	
11057	PH-ZBA	11189	PK-GKJ		
11027	PH-ZBB	11193	PK-GKK	11067	SE-DGA
11058	PH-ZBB	11175	PK-GKL	11068	SE-DGB
11028	PH-ZBC	11177	PK-GKM	11069	SE-DGC
11060	PH-ZBC	11196	PK-GKN	11111	SE-DGD
11029	PH-ZBD	11198	PK-GKO	11112	SE-DGE
11059	PH-ZBD	11199	PK-GKP	11115	SE-DGF
11062	PH-ZBE	11201	PK-GKQ	11116	SE-DGG
11037	PH-ZBF	11202	PK-GKR	11120	SE-DGH
11027	PH-ZBG	11206	PK-GKS	11122	SE-DGI
11031	PH-ZBH	11209	PK-GKT	11123	SE-DGK
11034	PH-ZBI	11210	PK-GKU	11126	SE-DGL
11163	PH-ZBJ	11211	PK-GKV	11128	SE-DGM
11079	PH-ZBK	11213	PK-GKW	11130	SE-DGN
11093	PH-ZBL	11214	PK-GKX	11130	SE-DGN
11048	PH-ZBM	11215	PK-GKY	11190	SE-DGO
11097	PH-ZBN	11216	PK-GKZ	11191	SE-DGP
11110	PH-ZBO	11217	PK-GQA	11204	SE-DGR
11125	PH-ZBP	11218	PK-GQB	11236	SE-DGS
11136	PH-ZBR	11035	PK-GVA	11239	SE-DGT

TC- Turkey

11057	TC-JAO
11058	TC-JAP
11060	TC-JAR
11070	TC-JAS
11071	TC-JAT
11032	TC-JAZ

TG- Guatemala

11048	TG-CAO

TN- Congo

11072	TN-ACP

TR- Gabon

11080	TR-LST
11081	TR-LSU
11104	TR-LTR
11102	TR-LTS

TU- Ivory Coast

11118	TU-TIJ
11121	TU-TIK
11097	TU-TIM
11099	TU-TIN
11097	TU-VAA
11099	TU-VAB
11118	TU-VAH
11124	TU-VAJ
11121	TU-VAN
11124	TU-VAZ

TY- Benin

11184	TY-BBN

VH- Australia

11047	VH-ATD
11082	VH-ATE
11084	VH-ATG
11173	VH-EWA
11195	VH-EWA
11181	VH-EWB
11205	VH-EWB
11207	VH-EWC
11208	VH-EWD
11021	VH-FKA
11022	VH-FKB
11025	VH-FKC
11026	VH-FKD
11040	VH-FKE
11008	VH-FKF
11056	VH-FKF
11031	VH-FKG
11183	VH-FKI
11186	VH-FKJ
11212	VH-LAR
11013	VH-MMJ

XT- Bourkina Faso

11163	XT-FZP
11185	XT-FZP

XY- Burma

11019	XY-ADU
11017	XY-ADV
11114	XY-ADW
11232	XY-AGA

Military operated

Argentina

11147	5-T-10
11145	5-T-20
11150	5-T-21
11028	T-01
11028	T-02
11048	T-02
11076	TC-51
11074	TC-52
11020	TC-53
11018	TC-54
11024	TC-55

Colombia

11992	FAC-001
11165	FAC-1140
11162	FAC-1141

Ecuador

11220	FAE-220

Ghana

11125	G-530

Malaysia

11088	FM2101
11089	FM2102
11088	M28-01
11089	M28-02

Peru

11100	FAP 390

FOKKER F.100

Short-range twin-engined jet airliner, powered by rear-mounted Rolls-Royce Tay turbofans. The F.100 is closely modelled on the F.28 Fellowship and will have increased seating for 100-110 passengers. First flight occurred in March 1986 with deliveries to Swissair due to begin in 1987. To date 45 aircraft have been ordered.

Dimensions :	Wing span: 92ft 1in (28.08m) Length: 116ft 7in (35.31) Height: 27ft 10in (8.60m)
Powerplant :	Two Rolls Royce Tay 620-15 turbofans
Performance :	Max cruising speed 432 knots (800km/h) Range: with max payload 1,088nm (2,015km)
Accommodation:	107 passengers in a five abreast layout
Manufacturer :	Fokker - PO Box 1065, 1000 BB Amsterdam, The Netherlands Telephone: (020) 544 9111 Telex: 11526 NL

C/N	Registration	Owner/Operator	Series	First Flight	Delivery	Remarks
11242	PH-	Fokker	100		87	Test Aircraft
11243	PH-	Fokker	100		87	Test Aircraft.
11244	HB-IVA	Swissair	100		NOV/87	Sched.delivery
11250	HB-IVB	Swissair	100		DEC/87	Sched.delivery
11251	HB-IVC	Swissair	100		DEC/87	Sched.delivery
11252	HB-IVD	Swissair	100		JAN/88	Sched.delivery
11253	HB-IVE	Swissair	100		JAN/88	Sched.delivery
11254	HB-IVF	Swissair	100		JAN/88	Sched.delivery
11255	HB-IVG	Swissair	100		FEB/88	Sched.delivery
11256	HB-IVH	Swissair	100		FEB/88	Sched.delivery
11268	PH-KLC	KLM	100		APR/88	Sched.delivery
11269	PH-KLD	KLM	100		APR/88	Sched.delivery
11270	PH-KLE	KLM	100		MAY/88	Sched.delivery
11271	PH-KLG	KLM	100		MAY/88	Sched.delivery
11272	PH-KLH	KLM	100		JUN/88	Sched.delivery
11273	PH-KLI	KLM	100		JUN/88	Sched.delivery
11274	PH-KLK	KLM	100		JUL/88	Sched.delivery
11275	PH-KLL	KLM	100		JUL/88	Sched.delivery
11276	PH-KLN	KLM	100		AUG/88	Sched.delivery
11277	PH-KLO	KLM	100		AUG/88	Sched.delivery

ADDITIONAL ORDERS

C/N	Registration	Owner/Operator	Series	First Flight	Delivery	Remarks
	N	US Air	100		88	Sched.delivery
	N	US Air	100		88	Sched.delivery
	N	US Air	100		89	Sched.delivery
	N	US Air	100		89	Sched.delivery
	N	US Air	100		89	Sched.delivery
	N	US Air	100		89	Sched.delivery
	N	US Air	100		89	Sched.delivery
	N	US Air	100		89	Sched.delivery
	N	US Air	100		89	Sched.delivery
	N	US Air	100		89	Sched.delivery
	N	US Air	100		89	Sched.delivery
	N	US Air	100		89	Sched.delivery
	N	US Air	100		89	Sched.delivery
	N	US Air	100		90	Sched.delivery
	N	US Air	100		90	Sched.delivery
	N	US Air	100		90	Sched.delivery
	N	US Air	100		90	Sched.delivery
	N	US Air	100		90	Sched.delivery
	N	US Air	100		90	Sched.delivery

Fokker 100 cross-reference index

MCDONNELL DOUGLAS DC-9

Short/medium-range jet transport with two rear-mounted P & W JT8D turbofans.
The DC-9 family was produced in a whole range of different versions. It first flew on 25 February 1965, and the 90-seat Series 10 entered service with Delta Airlines on 8 December 1965. Two years later came the Series 30 with various improvements and a fuselage lengthened to accommodate up to 119 passengers, and two more were produced to meet a SAS requirement, the Series 20 which was basically a combination of the earlier Series 10 and 30, and the short-range, high capacity Series 40 for 132 passengers. A further stretch resulted in the series 50 which can seat up to 139 passengers. All versions were also available in mixed passenger/cargo and all-cargo configurations, and several derivatives were also produced. A total of 976 aircraft were delivered before production was completed in September 1982.

Dimensions :	Wing span: 89ft 5in (27.25m) Length: 104ft 5in (31.82m) Height: 27ft 6in (8.38m) (10) Wing span: 93ft 5in (28.5m) Length: 104ft 5in (31.82m) Height: 27ft 6in (8.38m) (20) Wing span: 93ft fin (28.5m) Length: 119ft 4in (36.37m) Height: 27ft 6in (8.38m) (30) Wing span: 93ft 5in (28.5m) Length: 125ft 7in (38.3m) Height: 28ft 0in (8.53m) (40) Wing span: 93ft 5in (28.47m) Length: 132ft 0in (40.30m) Height: 28ft 0in (8.53m) (50)
Powerplant :	Two Pratt & Whitney JT8D-1, JT8D-5, JT8D-7 turbofans (10), two Pratt & Whitney JT8D-9 or JT8D-11 turbofans (20/30), two Pratt & Whitney JT8D-15 or JT8D-17 turbofans (40/50)
Performance :	Max cruising speed 488 knots (903km/h) (10/40) Range: with max payload 570nm (1,055km) (10) Max cruising speed 496 knots (918km/h) (30) Range: with max payload 956nm (1,770km) (30) Max cruising speed 499 knots (925km/h) (40) Range: with max payload 713nm (1,320km) (40)
Accommodation:	90 passengers (10/20), 115 passengers (30), 125 passengers (40), 139 passengers (50)
Manufacturer :	McDonnell Douglas - 3855 Lakewood Boulevard, Long Beach, California 90846, USA Telephone: (213) 593-5511

MCDONNELL DOUGLAS

C/N	Registration	Owner/Operator	Series	First Flight	Delivery	Remarks
45695	N9DC	Douglas	14	25/FEB/65		Prototype
	N1301T	Texas International			30/SEP/66	Leased
	N1301T	Continental Airlines			31/OCT/82	
	N1301T	Sunworld International			13/MAY/83	
45696	N3301L	Delta Airlines	14		19/JUL/66	
	N3301L	Southern Airways			24/SEP/73	
	EC-CGY	Spantax			23/FEB/74	
	N3301L	Best Airlines			06/NOV/83	
	N3301L	Skybus			JUN/85	Leased
45697	N3302L	Delta Airlines	14		09/JUN/66	
	N3302L	Southern Airways			26/JUL/73	
	N3302L	Republic			01/JUL/79	
	N3302L	McDonnell Douglas			29/MAY/81	WFU 29/MAY/81
45698	N3303L	Delta Airlines	14		04/DEC/65	
	N3303L	Southern Airways			20/FEB/73	
	N3303L	Republic			01/JUL/79	
	EC-DIR	Spantax			13/JAN/80	
	N931EA	Emerald Air			03/FEB/84	
45699	N3304L	Delta Airlines	14		18/SEP/65	
	N3304L	Southern Airways			28/MAR/73	
	EC-CGZ	Spantax			23/FEB/74	
	EC-CGZ	Aeroandina			81	Leased
	EC-CGZ				APR/81	
	N932EA	Emerald Air			11/FEB/84	
45700	N3305L	Delta Airlines	14		26/NOV/65	W/O 30/MAY/72, Fort Worth, Tx
45701	N3306L	Delta Airlines	14		30/NOV/65	
	N3306L	Southern Airways			29/MAY/73	
	N3306L	Republic			01/JUL/79	
	N3306L	Northwest Orient			01/AUG/86	
45702	N3307L	Delta Airlines	14		11/JAN/66	
	N3307L	Southern Airways			29/FEB/73	
	I-SARJ	Alisarda			11/JAN/74	
	N15NP	Northwest Pipeline Corp			12/MAY/81	
	N99YA	Omar Yehia			16/DEC/82	Leased
	N5NP	Northwest Pipeline Corp			23/FEB/83	
	HB-IAA	Omar Yehia			APR/83	
	HB-IEF	Aeroleasing			OCT/85	
45703	N3308L	Delta Airlines	14		16/MAR/66	
	N3308L	Southern Airways			19/APR/73	
	YV-C-AVB	Avensa			04/JAN/75	Leased
	N3308L	Southern Airways			04/MAY/75	
	N3308L	Republic			01/JUL/79	
	N3308L	Northwest Orient			01/AUG/86	
45704	N3309L	Delta Airlines	14		28/APR/66	
	N3309L	Southern Airways			16/MAY/73	
	N3309L	Republic			01/JUL/79	
	N3309L	Northwest Orient			01/AUG/86	
45705	N3310L	Delta Airlines	14		24/SEP/66	
	N3310L	Southern Airways			17/AUG/73	
	N3310L	Republic			01/JUL/79	
	N3310L	Northwest Orient			01/AUG/86	
45706	N3311L	Delta Airlines	14		27/OCT/66	
	N3311L	Southern Airways			24/OCT/73	
	I-SARV	Alisarda			12/APR/74	
	N5NE	Northwest Pipeline Corp			29/APR/81	
	N13FE	Funk Exploration			01/MAY/84	
45707	N3312L	Delta Airlines	14		23/NOV/66	
	N3312L	Southern Airways			12/JUL/73	
	N3312L	Republic			01/JUL/79	
	N3312L	Northwest Orient			01/AUG/86	
45708	N3313L	Delta Airlines	14		30/DEC/66	
	N3313L	Southern Airways			30/AUG/73	
	N3313L	Republic			01/JUL/79	
	N3313L	Northwest Orient			01/AUG/86	
45709	N3314L	Delta Airlines	14		06/JAN/67	
	N3314L	Southern Airways			15/JUN/73	
	N3314L	Republic			01/JUL/79	
	N3314L	Northwest Orient			01/AUG/86	

MCDONNELL DOUGLAS DC-9

C/N	Registration	Owner/Operator	Series	First Flight	Delivery	Remarks
45710	N3315L	Delta Airlines	32		09/APR/67	
	YV-66C	Avensa			04/JUN/66	
	N900ML	Avensa Leasing			27/DEC/84	
	N900ML	Midway Airlines			27/DEC/84	Leased
45711	N9684Z	Douglas	14			
	CF-TLB	Air Canada			12/APR/66	
	N13699	Douglas			15/NOV/68	
	N13699	Hawaiian Airlines			06/JUN/69	Leased
	N13699	Douglas			15/OCT/69	
	N13699	Southern Airways			18/FEB/70	
	OH-LYC	Finnair			11/MAR/71	
	OH-LYC	British Midland Airways			28/FEB/83	Leased
	OH-LYC	Finnair			04/SEP/83	
	N85AS	All Star Airlines			12/NOV/83	Leased
	N85AS	McDonnell Douglas			85	
	N500ME	Midwest Express			NOV/85	
45712	CF-TLC	Air Canada	14		06/JAN/66	
	N1792U	Douglas			17/SEP/68	
	N1792U	Texas International			28/SEP/68	Leased
	N1792U	Southern Airways			22/DEC/69	
	OH-LYB	Finnair			13/FEB/71	
	OH-LYB	British Midland Airways			SEP/77	Leased
	OH-LYB	Finnair			30/DEC/79	
	G-BMAH	British Midland Airways			24/JUN/83	Leased
45713	CF-TLD	Air Canada	14		09/FEB/66	
	N13614	Douglas			24/SEP/68	
	N13614	Southern Airways			18/OCT/68	
	N13614	Douglas			06/DEC/70	
	OH-LYA	Finnair			24/JAN/71	
	G-BMAI	British Midland			01/SEP/83	Leased
45714	N1051T	Trans World Airlines	14		25/MAR/66	
	N1051T	Texas International			01/DEC/74	Leased
	N1051T	Trans World Airlines			31/OCT/75	
	N651TX	Texas International			03/MAY/77	
	N651TX	Continental Airlines			31/OCT/82	
45715	N1052T	Trans World Airlines	14		05/FEB/66	
	N1052T	Texas International			30/APR/74	Leased
	N1052T	Trans World Airlines			NOV/75	
	N652TX	Texas International			NOV/77	
	N652TX	Continental Airlines			31/OCT/82	
45716	N1053T	Trans World Airlines	14		19/FEB/66	
	N1053T	Texas International			15/SEP/74	Leased
	N1053T	Trans World Airlines			30/NOV/75	
	N653TX	Texas International			16/SEP/77	
	N653TX	Continental Airlines			31/OCT/82	
45717	N901H	Hawaiian Airlines	15		12/MAR/66	
	I-TIGE	Itavia			08/DEC/71	WFU 15/DEC/80 to 01/AUG/83
	N927AX	Airborne Express	15LWF		01/AUG/83	
45718	PH-DNA	KLM	15		25/MAR/66	
	PH-DNA	Itavia			15/MAR/75	Leased
	I-TIGU	Itavia			21/MAY/77	Purchased, WFU 15/DEC/80 to 01/AUG/83
	N928AX	Airborne Express			01/AUG/83	
	N300ME	Midwest Express			MAR/84	
45719	PH-DNB	KLM	15		03/APR/66	
	PH-DNB	Cyprus Airways			NOV/75	Leased
	PH-DNB	KLM			DEC/75	
	G-BMAG	British Midland Airways			02/FEB/83	
45720	PH-DNC	KLM	15		02/MAY/66	
45721	PH-DND	KLM	15		17/AUG/66	
	PJ-DNC	ALM			01/OCT/70	
	N48200	Douglas			25/JUN/75	
	N48200	Cyprus Airways			20/AUG/75	Leased
	N48200	Douglas			OCT/76	
	XA-GOJ	Aeromexico			01/NOV/76	Leased
	N908DC	Douglas			DEC/82	
	HK-2864	Aeropesca			29/OCT/82	Leased
	HK-2864	Intercontinental Aviation			83	
45722	PH-DNE	KLM	15		10/OCT/66	
	PJ-DNA	ALM			01/NOV/68	
	N54648	Douglas			11/FEB/75	
	N54648	Cyprus Airways			14/AUG/75	Leased
	N54648	Douglas			01/NOV/76	
	XA-GOK	Aeromexico			01/NOV/76	Leased
	N2896W	Douglas			29/MAR/82	
	HK-2865	Aeropesca			05/NOV/82	Leased
	HK-2865	Intercontinental Aviation			83	
45723	PH-DNF	KLM	15		16/NOV/66	
	PJ-DNB	ALM			01/NOV/68	
	N48075	Douglas			05/MAR/75	
	YV-65C	Avensa			01/JUL/75	Leased
	N48075	Douglas			12/OCT/77	
	N48075	Southern Airways			12/JAN/78	
	N48075	British Midland Airways			17/FEB/78	Leased
	N48075	Southern Airways			14/JUN/78	
	N48075	Republic			01/JUL/79	
	N48075	Northwest Orient			01/AUG/86	
45724	N902H	Hawaiian Airlines	15		29/MAR/66	
	N902H	Douglas			07/JAN/72	
	I-TIGI	Itavia			27/FEB/72	W/O 27/JUN/80, Tyrrhenian Sea, Italy.
45725	CF-TLE	Air Canada	14		24/FEB/66	
	N15335	Douglas			25/SEP/68	
	N15335	Texas International			14/OCT/68	Leased
	N15335	Southern Airways			19/NOV/69	
	OH-LYD	Finnair			06/APR/71	
	OH-LYD	British Midland Airways			27/FEB/83	Leased
	OH-LYD	Finnair			26/JUN/83	
	N25AS	All Star Airlines			03/OCT/84	
	N25AS	McDonnell Douglas			85	
	N600ME	Midwest Express			OCT/85	
45726	CF-TLF	Air Canada	14		24/JUN/66	
	N5726	Texas International			23/NOV/68	
	N626TX	Continental Airlines			31/OCT/82	

AIR FRANCE
F-GEGE
GE

ISTANBUL
HAVAYOLLARI
AIRLINES
TC-ARI
Super Caravelle

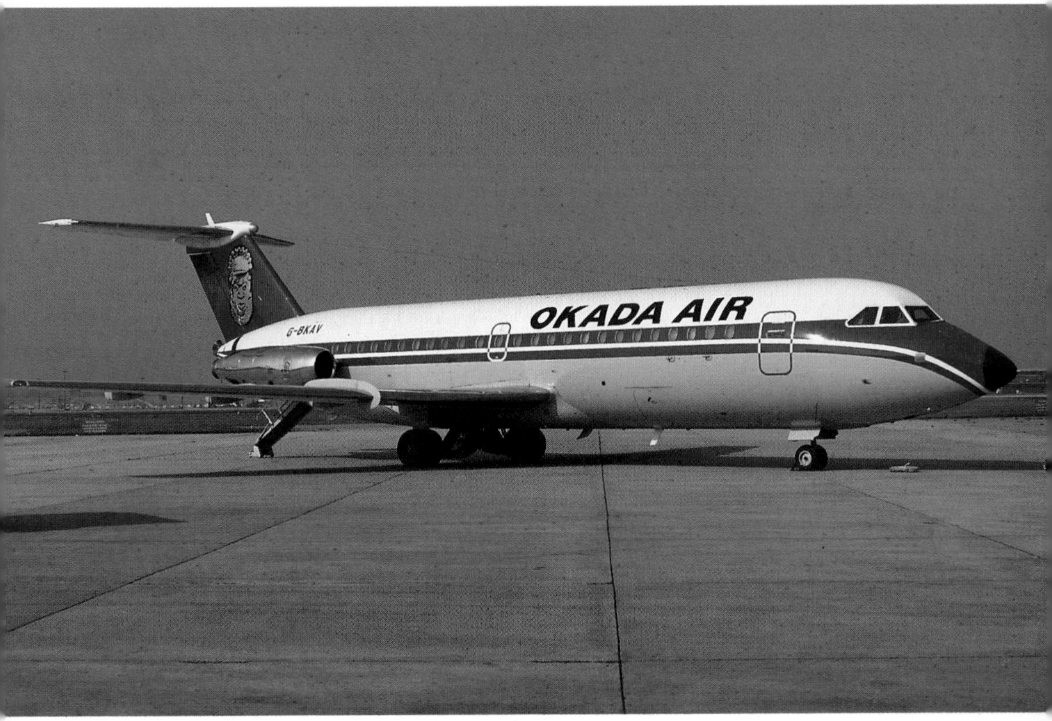
OKADA AIR
G-BKAV

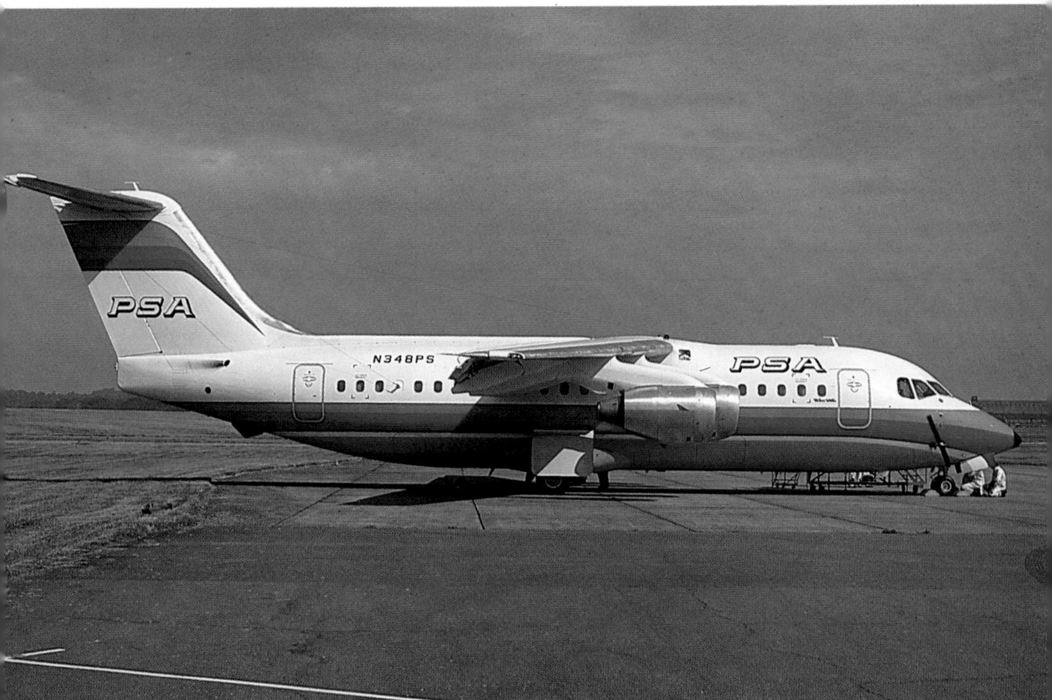
PSA
N348PS
PSA

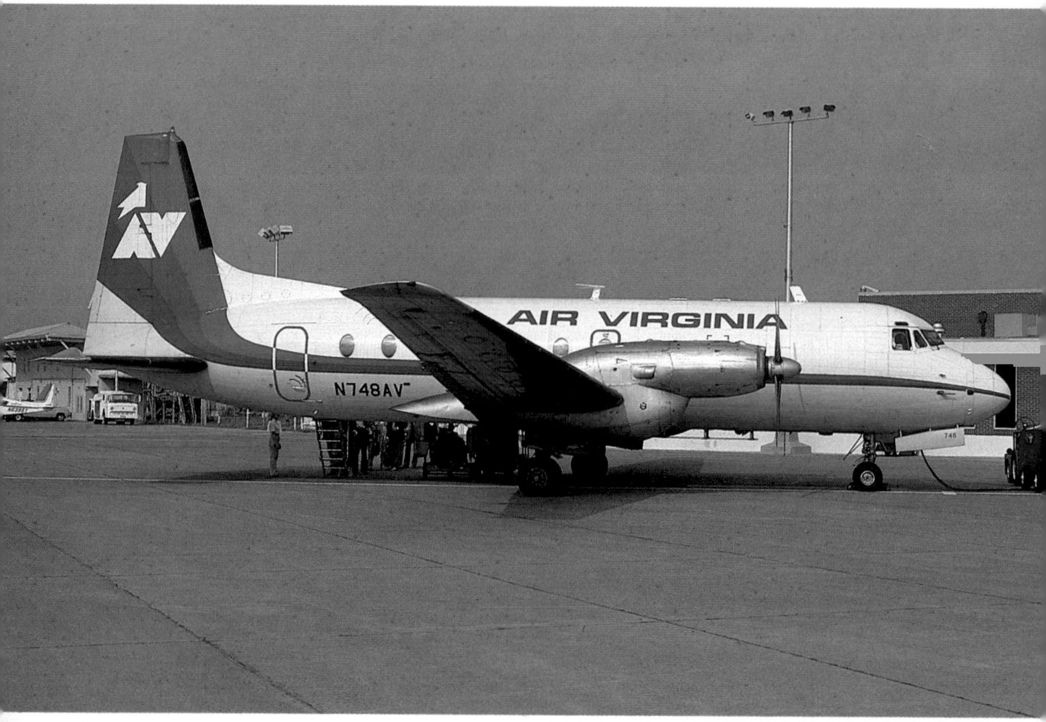
AIR VIRGINIA
N748AV

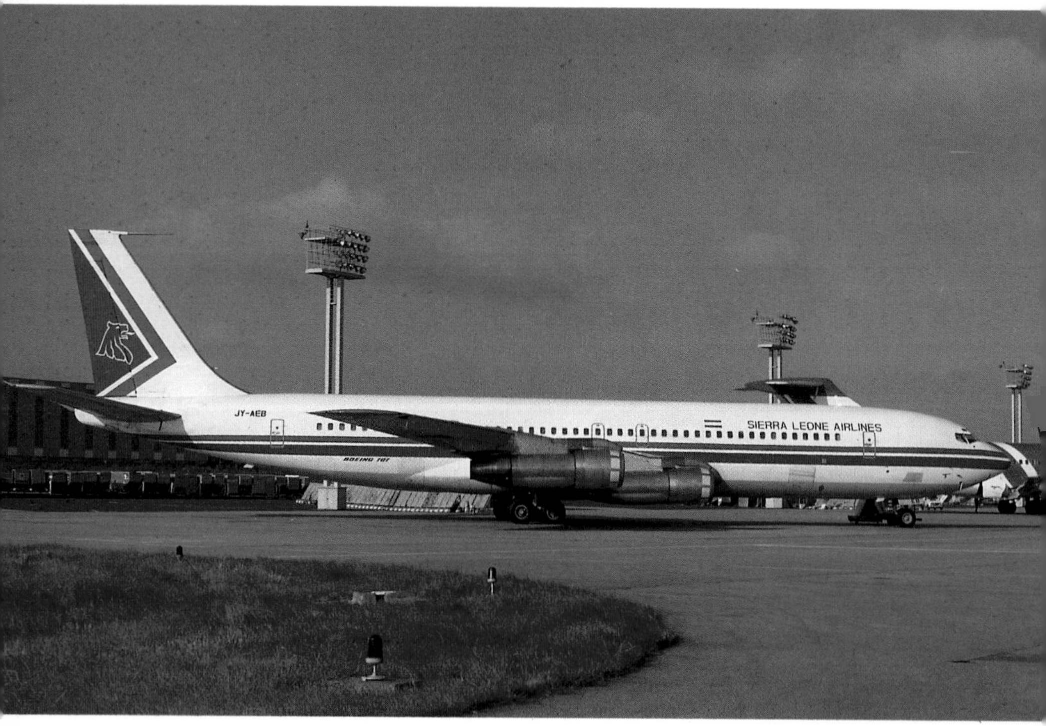
SIERRA LEONE AIRLINES
JY-AEB

AVENSA
AVENSA
YV-87C
AVENSA
BOEING 727
87C

CONTINENTAL West
N17306

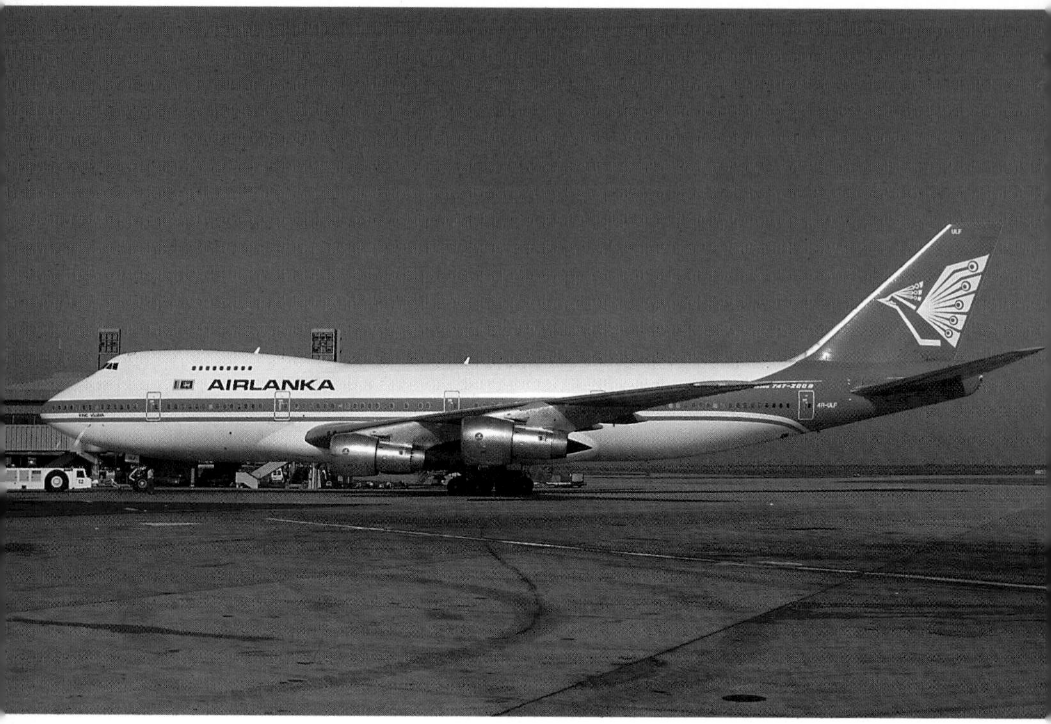
AIRLANKA
747-200B
4R-ULF
ULF

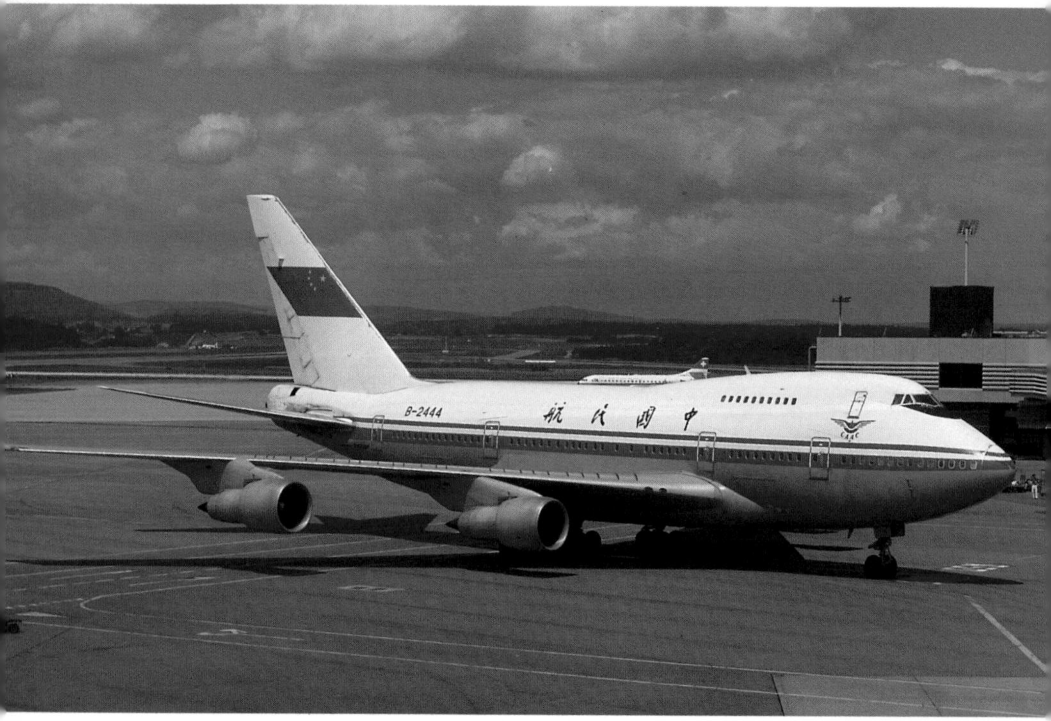
B-2444
航民國中
CAAC

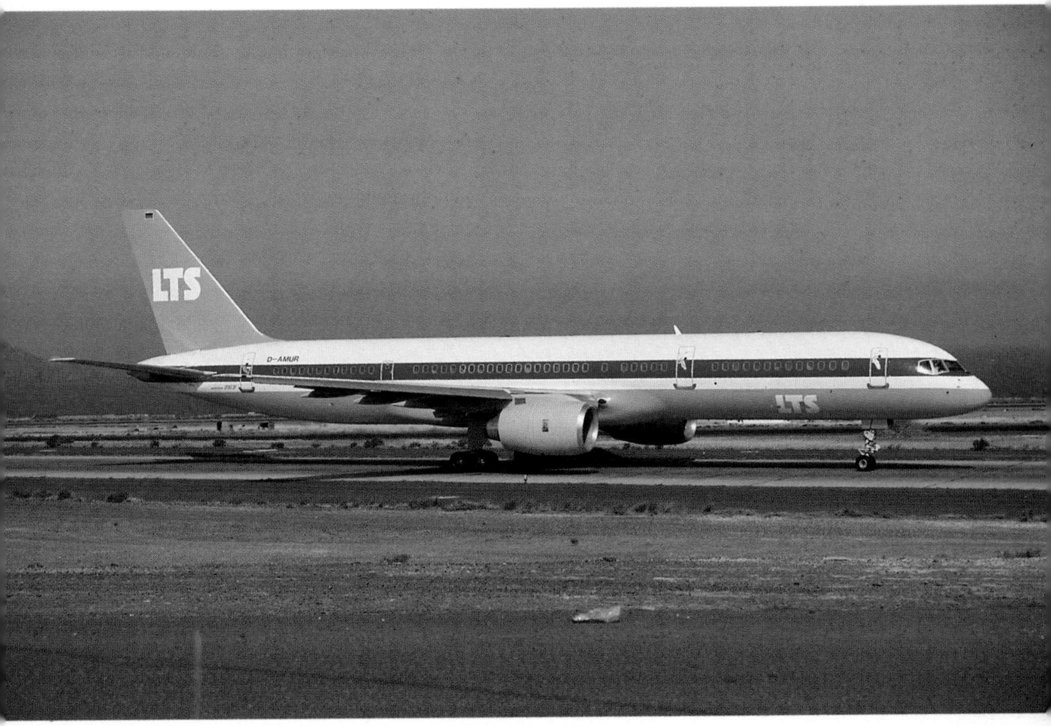
LTS
D-AMUR
LTS

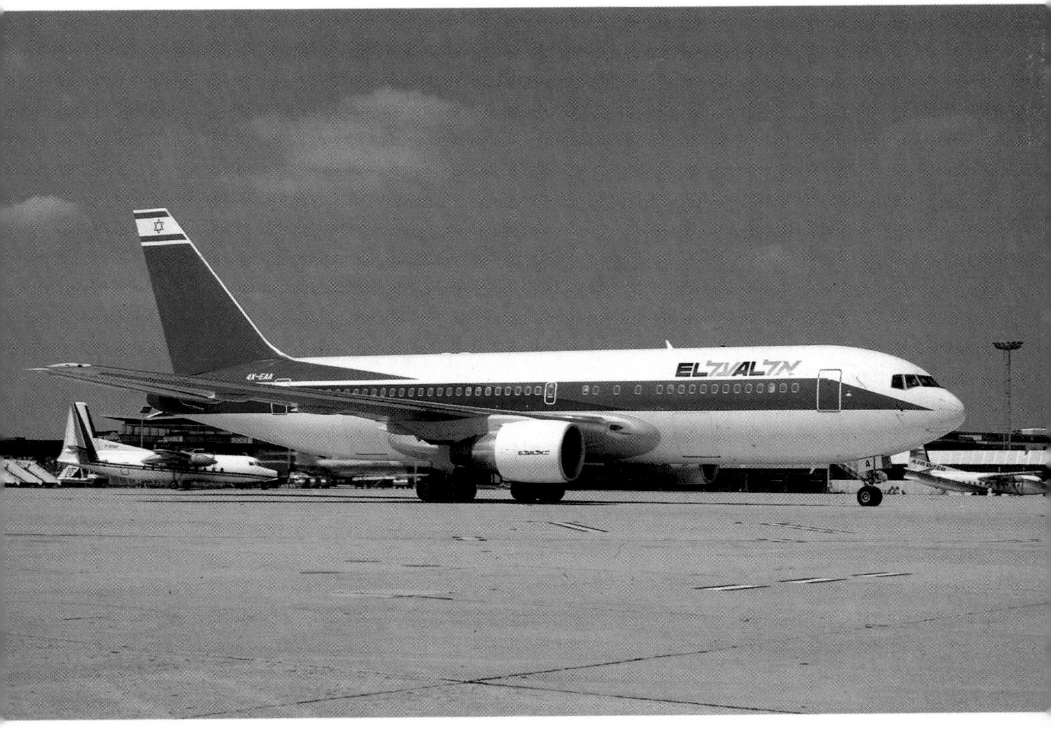
EL AL
4X-EAA

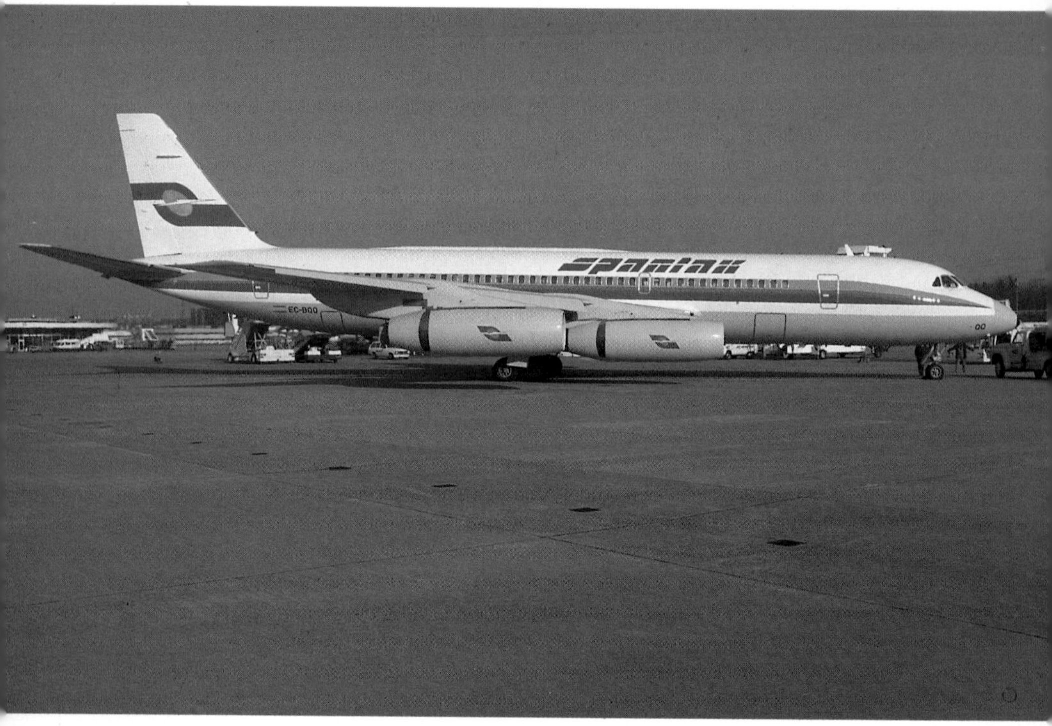
EC-BQQ

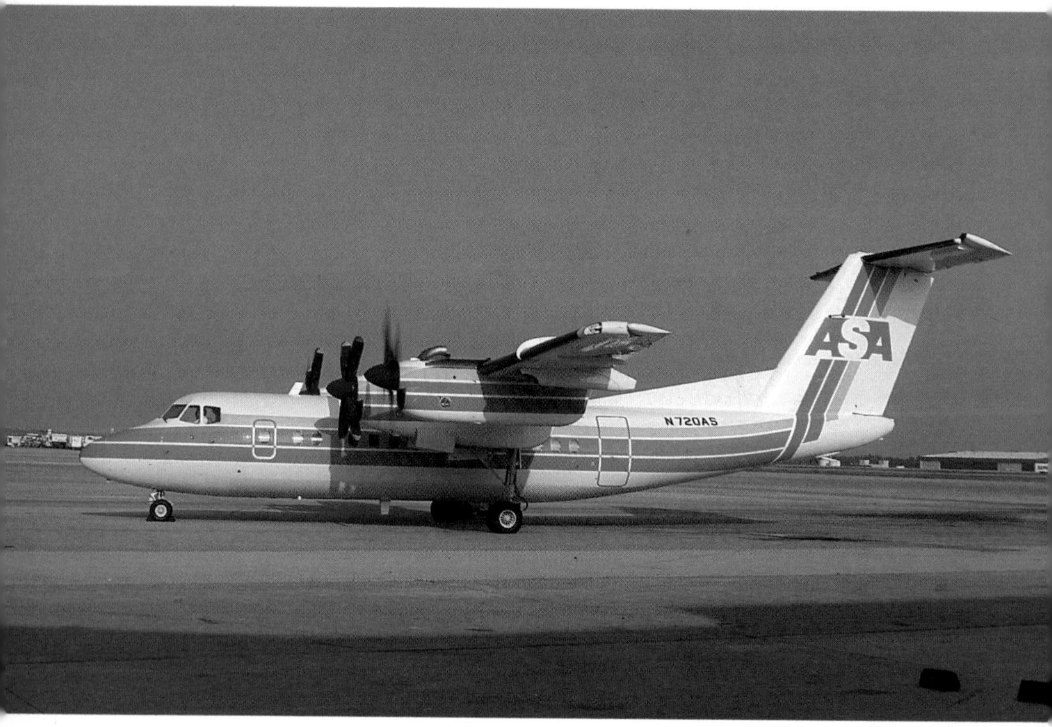
ASA
N720AS

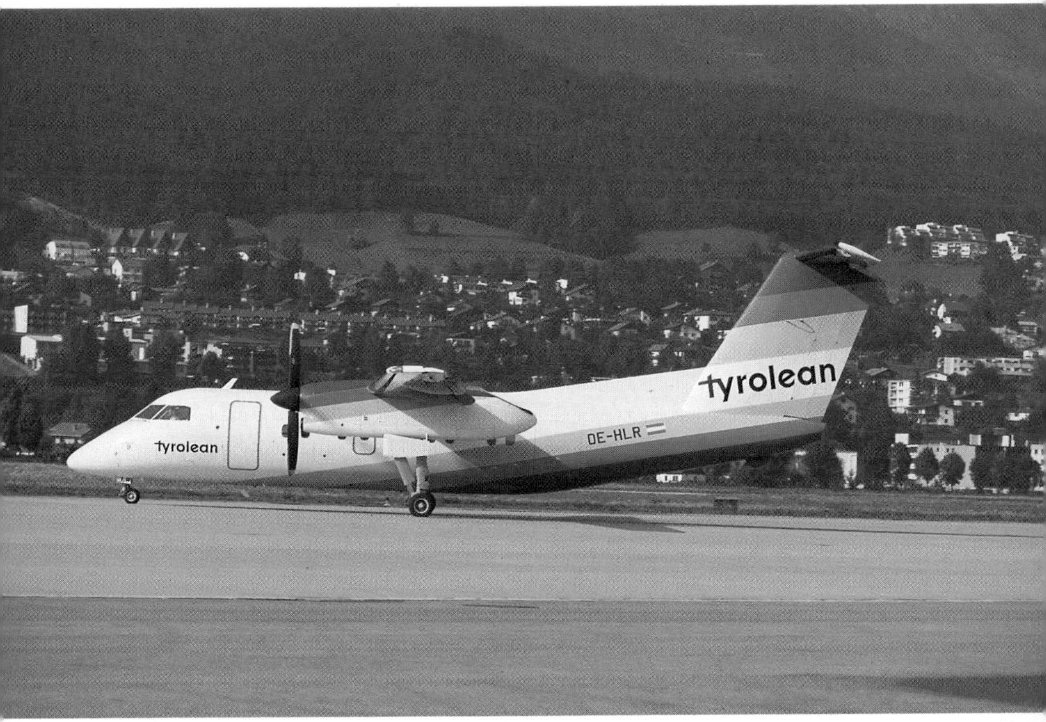
tyrolean
tyrolean
OE-HLR

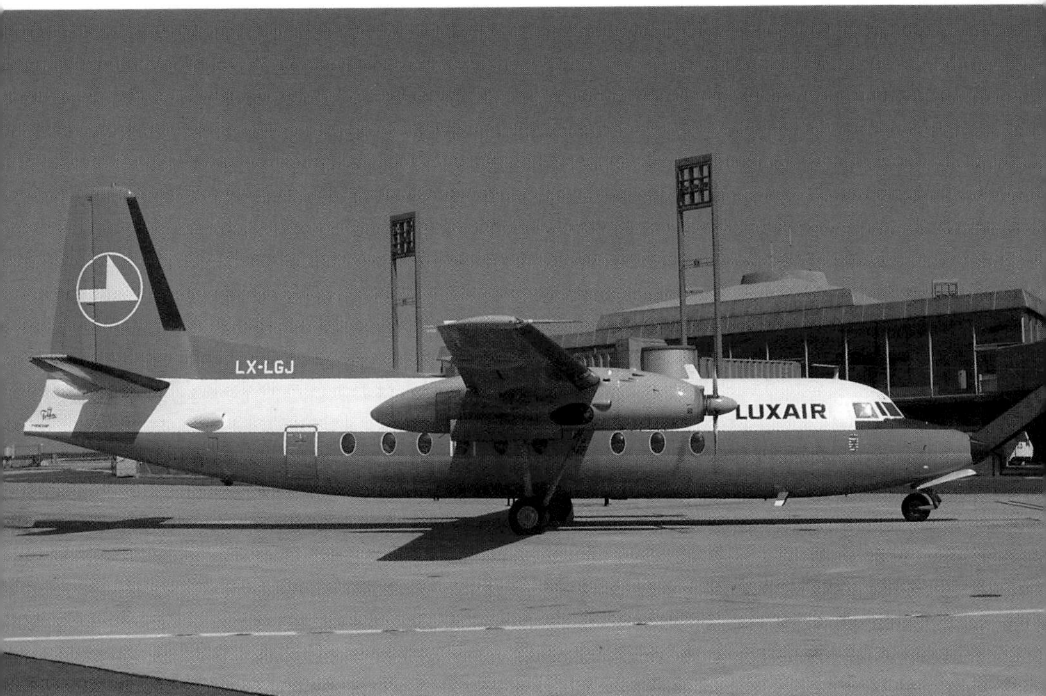
LX-LGJ
LUXAIR

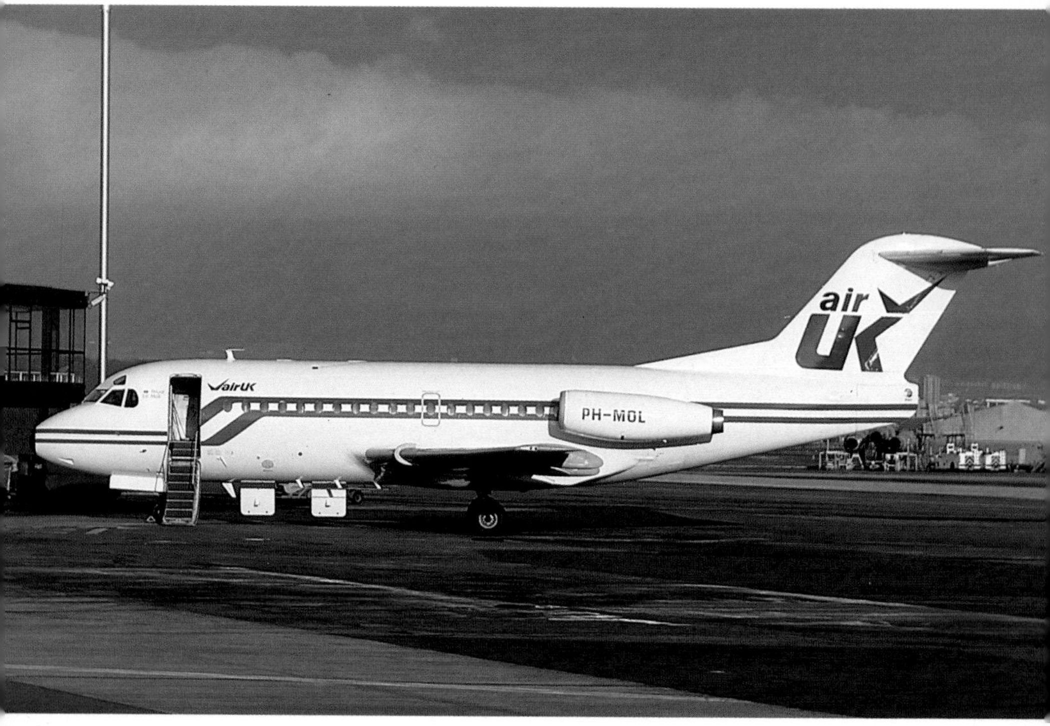
air
UK
airUK
PH-MOL

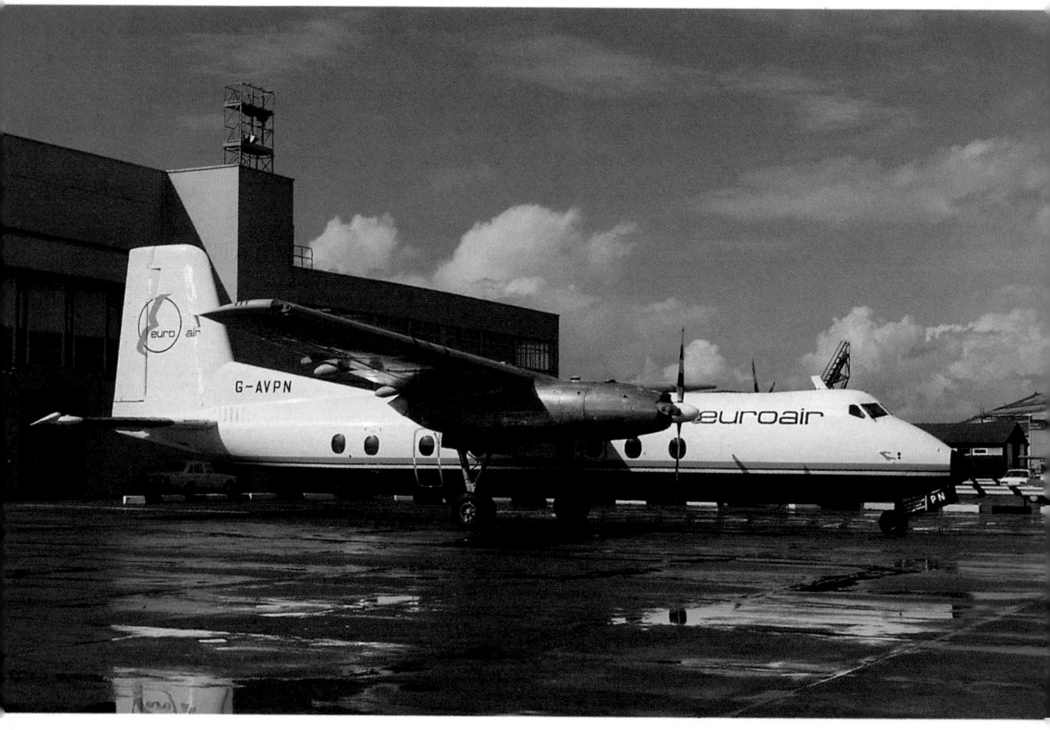
euro air
G-AVPN
euroair

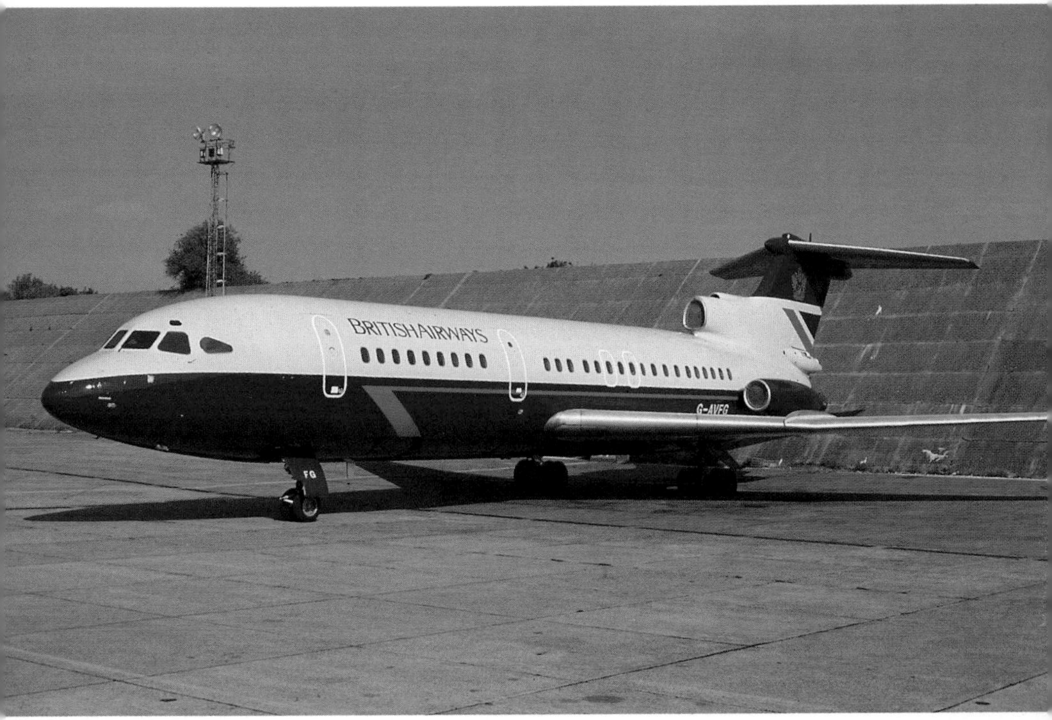
BRITISHAIRWAYS
G-AVFG
FG

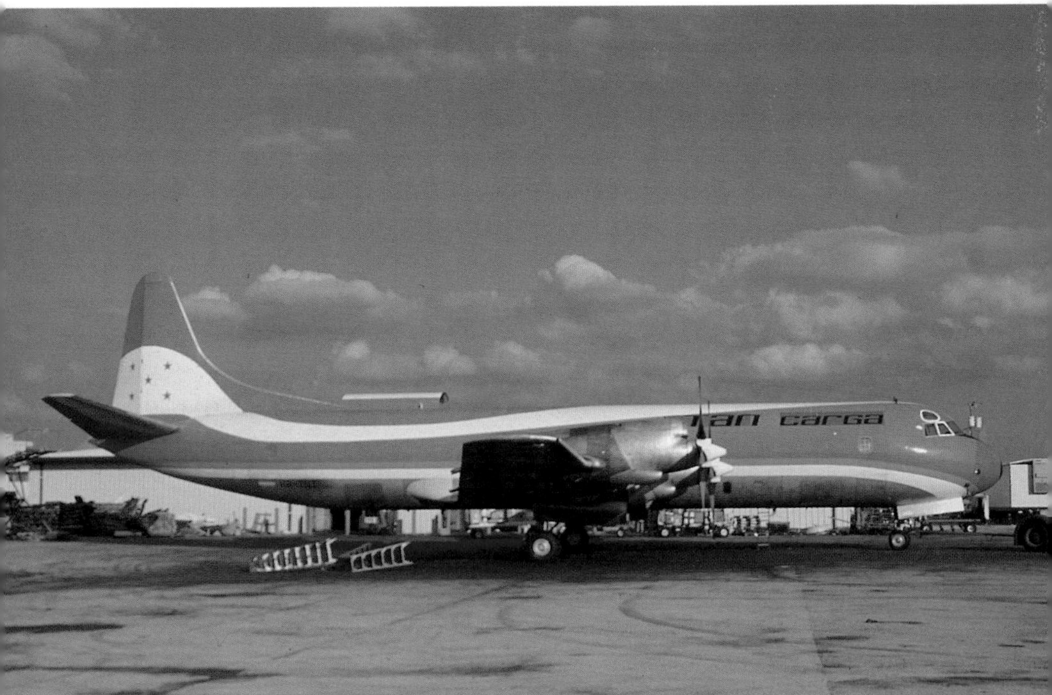
carga

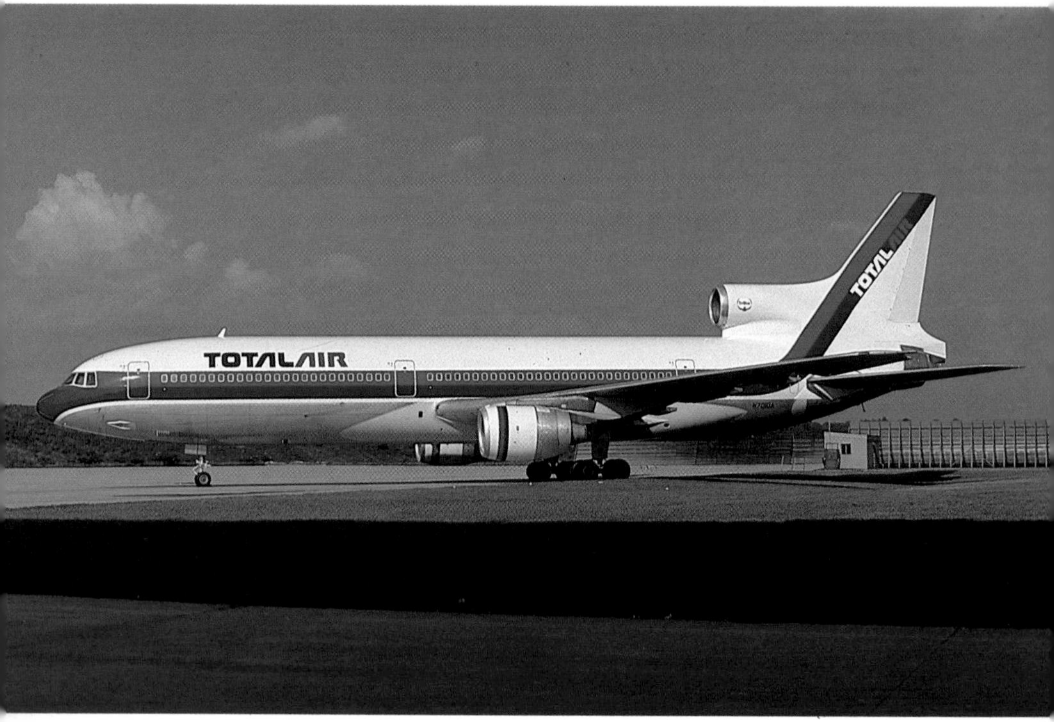
TOTALAIR
TOTAL AIR

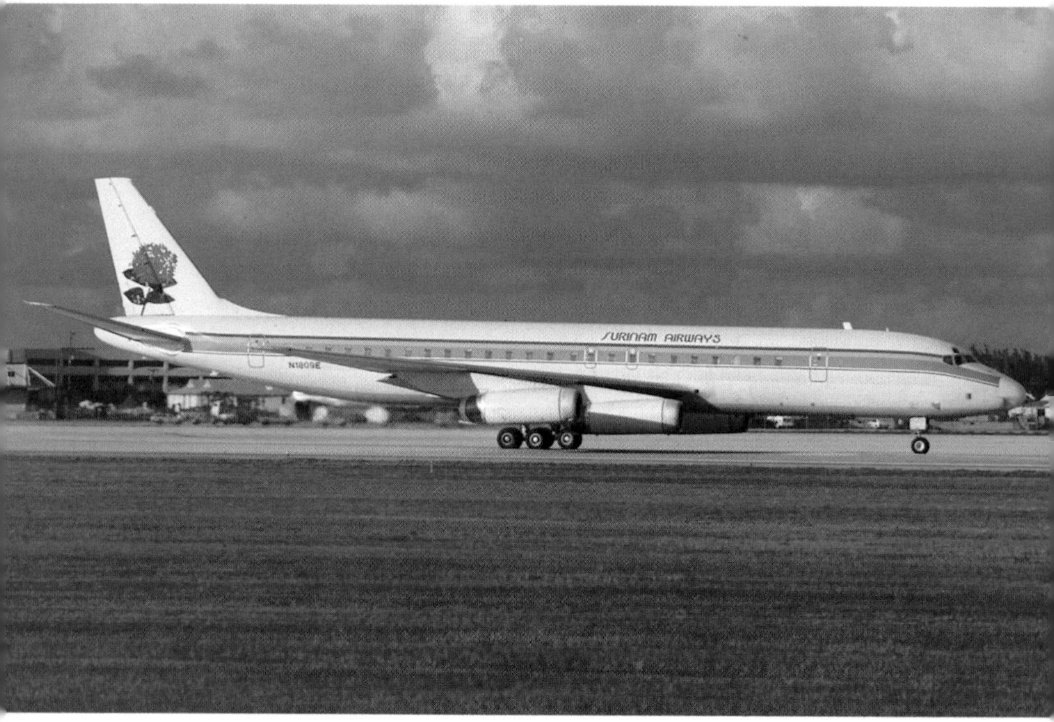
SURINAM AIRWAYS
N1809E

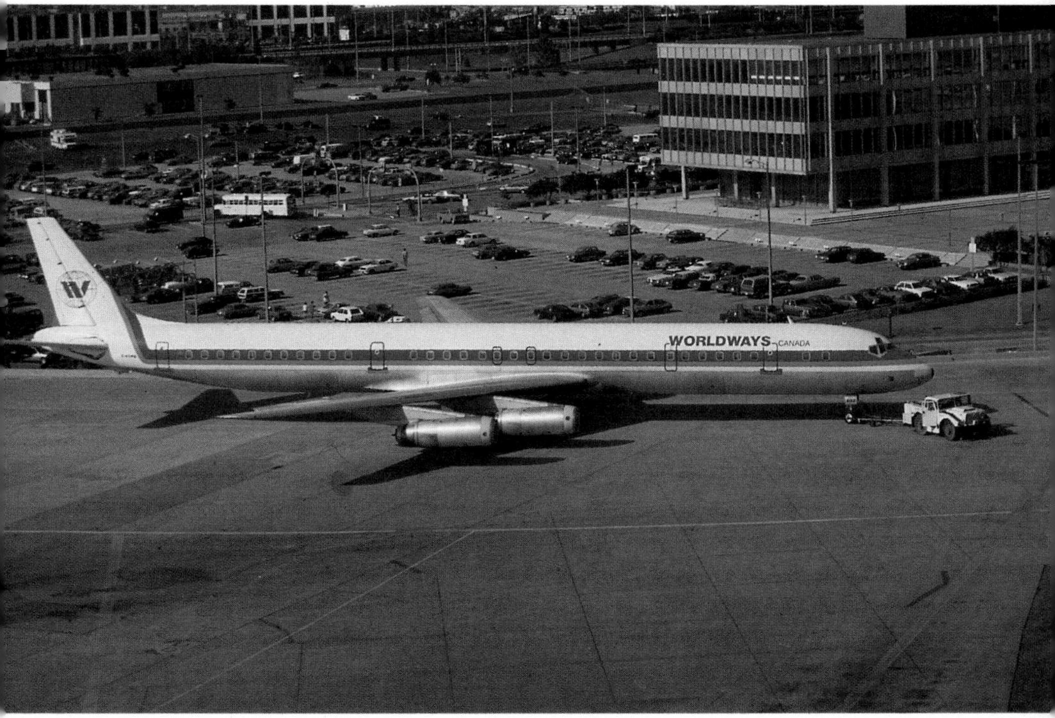
WORLDWAYS CANADA

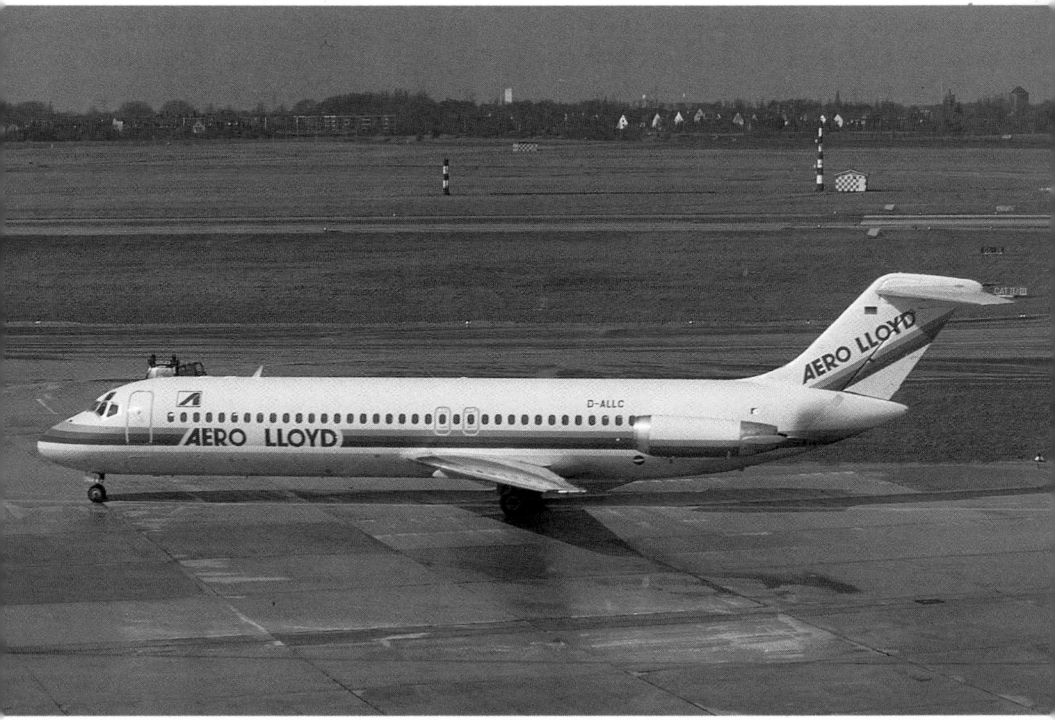
AERO LLOYD
D-ALLC
AERO LLOYD

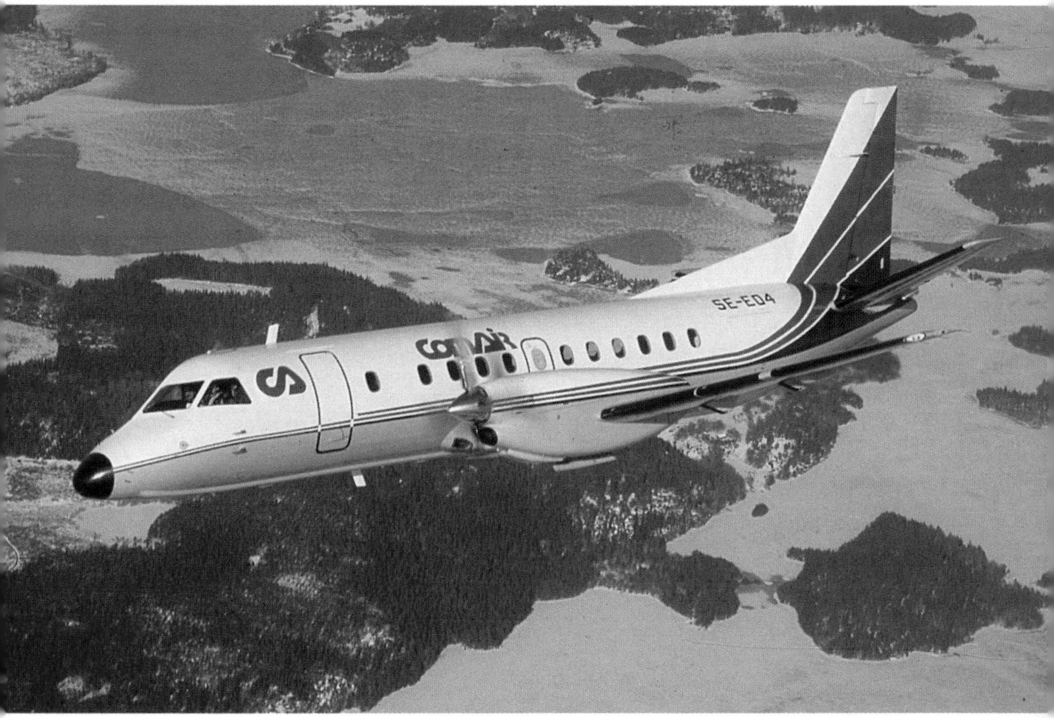
SE-ED4

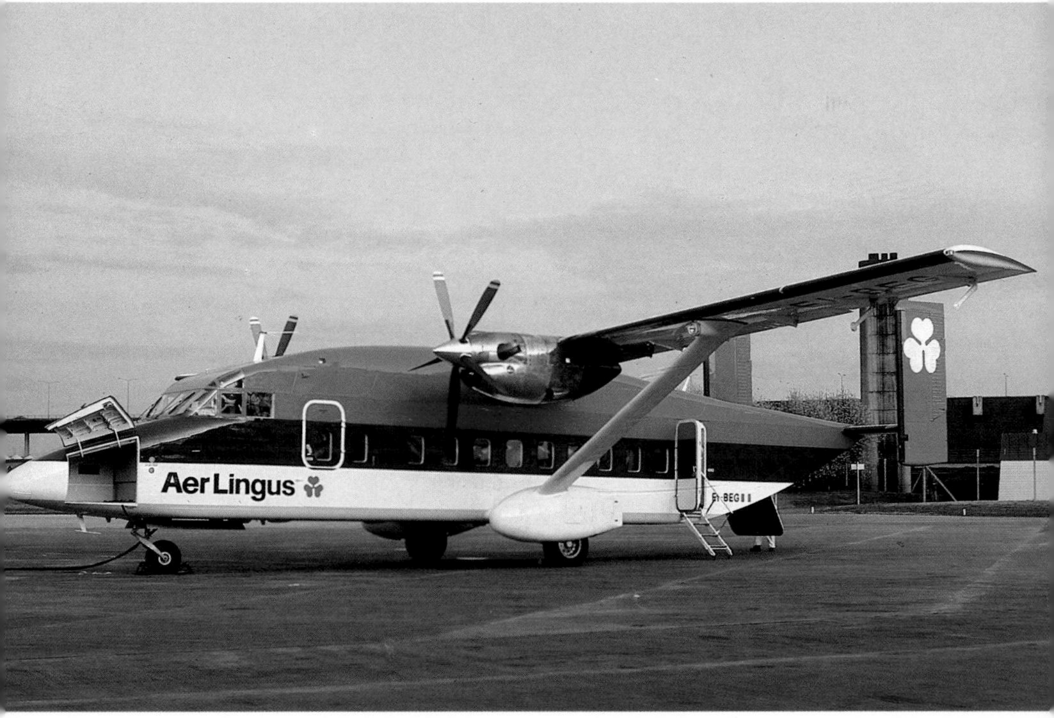
Aer Lingus

C/N	Registration	Owner/Operator	Series	First Flight	Delivery	Remarks
45727	CF-TLG	Air Canada	14		31/JUL/66	
	N5728	Douglas			68	
	N628TX	Texas International			18/NOV/68	
	N628TX	Continental Airlines			21/OCT/82	
	N400ME	Midwest Express			16/APR/84	
45728	N945L	Bonanza Airlines	14		19/DEC/65	
	N945L	Hughes Airwest			18/APR/68	
	N945L	Douglas			28/MAY/69	
	I-TIGA	Itavia			12/OCT/71	WFU 15/DEC/80 to 01/AUG/83
	N925AX	Airborne Express	14LWF		01/AUG/83	
45729	N946L	Bonanza Airlines	14		17/JAN/66	
	N946L	Douglas			14/MAY/69	
	N946L	Southern Airways			27/FEB/70	Leased
	OH-LYE	Finnair			24/JUL/71	
	N930RC	Republic			DEC/85	
	N930RC	Northwest Orient			01/AUG/86	
45730	N947L	Bonanza Airlines	14		01/JUL/66	
	N947L	Hughes Airwest			18/APR/68	
	N947L	Douglas			04/JUN/69	
	N947L	Southern Airways			28/FEB/70	
	OH-LYG	Finnair			05/OCT/71	
	OH-LYG	Touraine Air Transport			24/FEB/82	Leased
	OH-LYG	Finnair			83	
	G-BMAI	British Midland Airways			16/SEP/83	
	N903EA	Emerald Air			25/NOV/82	
45731	HB-IFA	Swissair	15		20/JUL/66	
	N8500	Douglas			17/SEP/68	
	N8500	Dominicana			16/DEC/68	Leased
	N8500	Douglas			22/OCT/70	
	N60FM	Forbes Magazines			17/OCT/73	
	N901B	Westinghouse Electronics			12/NOV/76	
	N2H	Harrahs Club			JUN/85	
45732	HB-IFB	Swissair	15		15/AUG/66	
	HB-IFB	Douglas			75	
	N119	FAA			16/AUG/68	
	N29	FAA				
45733	N8916E	Eastern Air Lines	31	01/AUG/66	20/OCT/67	
45734	N8917E	Eastern Air Lines	31	27/MAR/67		
45735	N1054T	Trans World Airlines	14		26/AUG/66	
	N1054T	Texas International			03/SEP/74	Leased
	N1054T	Trans World Airlines			15/DEC/75	
	N654TX	Texas International			29/SEP/77	
	N654TX	Continental Airlines			31/OCT/82	
45736	N1055T	Trans World Airlines	14		26/AUG/66	
	N655TX	Texas International			21/OCT/77	
	N655TX	Continental Airlines			31/OCT/82	
45737	N1056T	Trans World Airlines	14		12/SEP/66	
	N1056T	Douglas			79	
	N1056T	Midway Airlines			27/SEP/79	
45738	N1057T	Trans World Airlines	15		11/OCT/66	
	G-BMAB	British Midland Airways			06/FEB/80	
45739	N1058T	Trans World Airlines	15		28/OCT/66	
	G-BMAC	British Midland Airways			JAN/80	
	N29259	Best Airlines			06/MAR/82	Leased
	G-BMAC	British Midland Airways			23/DEC/82	
45740	N1059T	Trans World Airlines	15		16/NOV/66	
	N310MJ	Southwest Petroleum			21/APR/80	
	N310MJ	Golden Nugget			29/MAR/82	
	N711SW	Golden Nugget				
45741	N1060T	Trans World Airlines	15		29/NOV/66	
	N1060T	Midway Airlines			DEC/80	
45742	N8901E	Eastern Airlines	14		26/APR/66	
	N8901E	Delta Airlines			27/APR/70	Leased
	N8901E	Eastern Airlines			23/APR/71	
	N8901E	Texas International			31/MAY/79	
	N8901E	Continental Airlines			NOV/82	
45743	N8902E	Eastern Airlines	14		13/MAY/66	
	N8902E	Delta Airlines			14/MAY/70	Leased
	N8902E	Eastern Airlines			26/APR/71	
	N8902E	Texas International			02/MAY/72	
	N8902E	Continental Airlines			31/OCT/82	
45744	N8903E	Eastern Airlines	14		19/MAY/66	
	N8903E	Douglas			19/MAY/70	
	N8903E	Southern Airways			24/OCT/70	
	N8903E	Republic			01/JUL/79	
	N8903E	Northwest Orient			01/AUG/86	
45745	N8904E	Eastern Airlines	14		31/MAY/66	
	N8904E	Douglas			26/MAY/70	
	N8904E	Southern Airways			26/FEB/71	
	N8904E	Republic			01/JUL/79	
	N8904E	Northwest Orient			01/AUG/86	
45746	N8905E	Eastern Airlines	14		01/JUL/66	
	N8905E	Douglas			01/JUL/70	
	N8905E	Southern Airways			02/DEC/70	
	N8905E	Republic			01/JUL/79	
	N8905E	Northwest Orient			01/AUG/86	
45747	N8906E	Eastern Airlines	14		19/JUL/66	
	N8906E	Douglas			29/AUG/70	
	N8906E	Southern Airways			12/FEB/71	
	N8906E	Republic			01/JUL/79	
	N8906E	Northwest Orient			01/AUG/86	
45748	N8907E	Eastern Airlines	14		29/AUG/66	
	N8907E	Douglas			31/AUG/70	
	N8907E	Southern Airways			19/JAN/71	
	N8907E	Republic			01/JUL/79	
	N8907E	Northwest Orient			01/AUG/86	
45749	N8908E	Eastern Airlines	14		11/SEP/66	
	N8908E	Republic			10/SEP/79	
	N8908E	Northwest Orient			01/AUG/86	
45770	N8909E	Eastern Airlines	14		07/NOV/66	
	N8909E	Republic			09/NOV/79	
	N8909E	Northwest Orient			01/AUG/86	
45771	N8910E	Eastern Airlines	14		27/OCT/66	W/O 09/FEB/79, Dade Collier, Fl.
45772	N970Z	Ozark Airlines	15		25/MAY/66	
45773	N971Z	Ozark Airlines	15		10/JUL/66	

MCDONNELL DOUGLAS DC-9

C/N	Registration	Owner/Operator	Series	First Flight	Delivery	Remarks
45774	TC-JAB	Türk Hava Yollari	32		09/JUL/68	
45775	N1061T	Trans World Airlines	15		12/DEC/66	
	N1061T	Tracinda Investment Corp.			07/AUG/79	
	N241TC	Tracinda Investment Corp.			MAY/80	
	N9KR	Kenny Rogers			24/JAN/84	
	N9KR	Syntek Corp.			APR/86	
45776	N1062T	Trans World Airlines	15		22/DEC/66	
	N1062T	Midway Airlines			27/MAY/80	
45777	N1063T	Trans World Airlines	15		19/JAN/67	W/O 09/MAR/67, Nr.Urbana, Oh.
45778	N1064T	Trans World Airlines	15		02/FEB/67	
	I-	Itavia				Not taken-up
	N1064T	Midway Airlines			22/OCT/80	
45779	N1065T	Trans World Airlines	15		13/MAR/67	
	I-	Itavia				Not taken-up
	N1065T	Midway Airlines			24/OCT/80	
45780	N1066T	Trans World Airlines	15		31/MAR/67	
	N1066T	Douglas			79	
	N1066T	Midway Airlines			04/OCT/79	
45781	N1067T	Trans World Airlines	15		11/APR/67	
	N1067T	Douglas			79	
	N1067T	Midway Airlines			11/OCT/79	
45782	N1068T	Trans World Airlines	15		30/MAY/67	
	N1068T	Great American Airways			15/AUG/79	
45783	N1069T	Trans World Airlines	15		01/JUL/67	
	N1069T	Midway Airlines			16/AUG/80	
45784	N1070T	Trans World Airlines	15		19/AUG/67	
	N1070T	Douglas			10/JAN/80	
	N1070T	Sunstream			18/DEC/80	
	N1070T	Douglas			18/MAR/81	
	N1070T	Midway Airlines			02/JUN/81	
45785	HB-IFC	Swissair	15		30/NOV/66	
	N1790U	Douglas			21/AUG/68	
	N1790U	Texas International			68	Leased
	N1790U	Douglas			SEP/68	
	N1790U	Hawaiian Airlines			07/JUN/69	
	N1790U	Douglas			15/NOV/69	
	XA-SOJ	Aeromexico			28/AUG/70	
45786	HB-IFD	Swissair	15		11/MAR/67	
	N1791U	Douglas			30/AUG/68	
	HP-505	Air Panama			08/JUL/69	Leased
	N1791U	Douglas			22/NOV/72	
	N968E	Ozark Airlines			07/DEC/72	
	N968E	Texas International			28/MAR/74	
	N968E	Continental Airlines			31/OCT/82	
45787	HB-IFE	Swissair	15		26/JUN/67	
	N1793U	Douglas			08/SEP/68	
	D-AMOR	Germanair			28/APR/69	Leased
	N1793U	Douglas			27/AUG/69	
	HL7205	Korean Airlines			01/JUN/70	
	N9348	Hughes Airwest			14/DEC/72	
	N9348	Republic			01/JUL/79	
	N9348	Northwest Orient			01/AUG/86	
45788	HB-IFF	Swissair	32		21/OCT/67	
	N3505T	Texas International			10/NOV/76	
	N3505T	Continental Airlines			31/OCT/82	
	N3505T	New York Air			FEB/85	
45789	HB-IFG	Swissair	32		23/DEC/67	
	N543TX	New York Air			13/AUG/81	
	N543NY	New York Air			82	
45790	HB-IFH	Swissair	32		28/FEB/68	
	N540TX	Texas International			JUL/81	
	N540TX	Continental Airlines			31/OCT/82	
45791	HB-IFI	Swissair	32		27/JUL/68	
	N532TX	Texas International			16/NOV/80	
	N532TX	Continental Airlines			31/OCT/82	
45792	HB-IFK	Swissair	32		12/SEP/68	
	EC-DQP	Spantax			21/APR/82	Leased
	HB-IFK	Swissair			02/MAY/83	
	N539TX	New York Air			16/MAY/83	
	N539NY	New York Air				
45793	HB-IFL	Swissair	32		28/SEP/68	
	N541TX	New York Air			20/NOV/81	
	N541NY	New York Air			82	
45794	N9101	West Coast Airways	14		16/SEP/66	W/O 01/OCT/66, Portland, Or.
45795	N9102	West Coast Airways	14		04/NOV/66	
	N9102	Hughes Airwest			18/APR/68	
	N9102	Southern Airways			01/DEC/74	Leased
	N9102	Hughes Airwest			30/AUG/76	
	N9102	Texas International			16/SEP/76	
	N9102	Continental Airlines			31/OCT/82	
	N9102	Sunworld International			01/NOV/83	
45796	N9103	West Coast Airways	14		15/DEC/66	
	N9103	Hughes Airwest			18/APR/68	
	N9103	Texas International			08/NOV/75	W/O 17/MAR/80, Baton Rouge, Louisiana
45797	N8953U	Northeast Airlines	15		29/DEC/66	
	N8953U	Douglas			JUN/67	
	N8953U	Delta Airlines			13/JUL/67	
	N8860	Richard M. Scaife			29/OCT/71	
45798	N490SA	Standard Airways	15		03/NOV/66	
	N490SA	Ozark Airlines			01/OCT/68	
45799	N491SA	Standard Airways	15		30/NOV/66	
	N491SA	Ozark Airlines			01/OCT/68	
45825	N8911E	Eastern Airlines	14		24/NOV/66	
	N8911E	Republic			26/NOV/79	
	N8911E	Northwest Orient			01/AUG/86	
45826	N8901	Continental Airlines	15F		07/MAR/67	
	CF-TON	Air Canada			11/APR/72	
	N29AF	Air Florida			10/JUN/77	
	N29AF	Cayman Airways			JAN/78	Leased
	N29AF	Air Florida			30/APR/78	
	N29AF	Ross Aviation			15/AUG/79	
	N29AF	U.S. Dept. of Energy			NOV/83	
45827	HL7201	Korean Airlines	32		19/JUL/66	
	N9347	Hughes Airwest			02/FEB/73	

C/N	Registration	Owner/Operator	Series	First Flight	Delivery	Remarks
	N9347	Republic			01/JUL/79	
	N9347	Northwest Orient			01/AUG/86	
45828	N8918	Continental Airlines	15F		19/JAN/68	
	N9359	Hughes Airwest			17/MAR/75	
	N9359	Republic			01/JUL/79	
	N566PC	Orion Air			14/JUN/84	Op. for Purolator Courier
45829	N8912E	Eastern Air Lines	14		30/NOV/66	
	N8912E	Republic			18/DEC/80	
	N8912E	Northwest Orient			01/AUG/86	
45830	N8913E	Eastern Air Lines	14		23/DEC/66	
	N8913E	Republic			21/DEC/79	
	N8913E	Northwest Orient			01/AUG/86	
45831	N8914E	Eastern Air Lines	14		29/DEC/66	
	N8914E	Republic			21/DEC/79	
	N8914E	Northwest Orient			01/AUG/86	
45832	N8915E	Eastern Air Lines	14		08/FEB/67	
	N8915E	Republic			04/JAN/80	
	N8915E	Northwest Orient			01/AUG/86	
45833	N8918E	Eastern Air Lines	31		27/JAN/67	
45834	N8919E	Eastern Air Lines	31		22/FEB/67	
45835	N8920E	Eastern Air Lines	31		20/MAR/67	
45836	N8921E	Eastern Air Lines	31		22/MAR/67	
45837	N8922E	Eastern Air Lines	31		13/APR/67	
45838	N8923E	Eastern Air Lines	31		18/APR/67	
45839	N8924E	Eastern Air Lines	31		30/MAY/67	
45840	N8925E	Eastern Air Lines	31		28/MAY/67	
45841	N972Z	Ozark Airlines	15		24/AUG/66	
	OH-LYK	Finnair			31/OCT/74	
	N2892Q	Best Airlines			08/SEP/82	
	OH-LYK	Finnair			AUG/83	
	N2892QQ	Best Airlines				
	N2892Q	Skybus			JUN/86	Leased
45842	N8961	Douglas	14			
	N8961	Continental Airlines			04/MAR/66	Leased
	N8961	Douglas			04/JAN/68	
	N8961	Air California			06/MAR/68	Leased
	N8961	Texas International			01/MAY/69	
	N8961	Continental Airlines			31/OCT/82	
	N8961	Sunworld International			26/MAY/83	
45843	N8962	Douglas	14			
	N8962	Continental Airlines			01/MAY/66	Leased
	N8962	Douglas			07/JAN/68	
	N8962	Air California			06/MAR/68	Leased
	N8962	Texas International			MAY/69	
	N8962	Continental Airlines			31/OCT/82	
	N8962	Royale Airlines			27/JAN/84	Leased
	N8962	Continental Airlines			14/DEC/84	
45844	N8963	Douglas	14			
	N8963	Continental Airlines			02/JUN/66	Leased
	N949L	Bonanza Airlines			31/OCT/67	
	N949L	Hughes Airwest			15/JUL/68	
	N949L	Texas International			16/MAY/72	
	N949L	Continental Airlines			31/OCT/82	
45845	CF-TLH	Air Canada	32			
45846	CF-TKL	Air Canada	32		12/MAY/67	
		Columbia Air			03/MAR/82	Not taken-up
	C-FTKL	Air Canada			21/MAY/82	
	N901AK	Altair			MAY/82	WFU 82, stored Philadelphia
	N901AK	Air Canada			83	
	N705PS	Pacific Southwest Airlines			15/JUN/83	
45847	HB-IFM	Swissair	32		17/OCT/68	
	N531TX	Texas International			01/OCT/80	
	N531TX	Continental Airlines			31/OCT/82	
45863	N8926E	Eastern Air Lines	31		21/JUN/67	
45864	N8927E	Eastern Air Lines	31		01/JUL/67	
45865	N8928E	Eastern Air Lines	31		27/JUL/67	
45866	N8929E	Eastern Air Lines	31		29/JUL/67	
45867	N8952E	Eastern Air Lines	31		28/MAR/68	
45868	N8953E	Eastern Air Lines	31		11/APR/68	
	N930VJ	Allegheny			05/JUN/78	
	N930VJ	US Air			28/OCT/79	
45869	N8960E	Eastern Air Lines	31		25/JUN/68	
45870	N8961E	Eastern Air Lines	31		22/JUN/68	W/O 18/MAY/72, Fort Lauderdale
45871	N8962E	Eastern Air Lines	31		19/JUL/68	
45872	N8963E	Eastern Air Lines	31		26/JUL/68	
45873	N8964E	Eastern Air Lines	31		02/AUG/68	
45874	N8965E	Eastern Air Lines	31		01/AUG/68	
45875	N8968E	Eastern Air Lines	31		24/AUG/68	
45876	N8969E	Eastern Air Lines	31		28/AUG/68	
47000	HZ-AEA	Saudi Arabian Airlines	15		08/FEB/67	
	YV-C-ANP	LAV			16/JUN/72	
	YV-03C	LAV				
	YV-03C	Fuerza Aerea Venezolana			JUN/77	Leased
	YV-O3C	LAV				
	0003	Fuerza Aerea Venezolana			01/DEC/80	Leased
	YV-03C	LAV			MAR/85	
47001	HZ-AEB	Saudi Arabian Airlines	15		30/MAR/67	
	N969Z	Ozark Airlines			03/JUL/72	
	YV-18C	LAV			08/AUG/75	Leased
	N969Z	Ozark Airlines			15/OCT/76	
	N969Z	Southern Airways			10/SEP/77	
	N969Z	Ozark Airlines			01/JUN/78	
47002	HZ-AEC	Saudi Arabian Airlines	15		29/APR/67	
	YV-C-ANV	LAV			21/JUL/72	
	YV-02C	LAV				
	I-TIGB	Itavia			09/MAY/77	WFU DEC/80
	N926AX	Airborne Express			28/JUL/83	
47003	VH-CZA	Ansett Airlines	31		17/MAR/67	
	162390	U.S.Navy			27/JUL/82	
47004	VH-CZB	Ansett Airlines	31		11/APR/67	
	162391	U.S.Navy			20/SEP/82	
47005	VH-CZC	Ansett Airlines	31		24/AUG/67	
	N937ML	Midway Airlines			16/AUG/82	
47006	N891PS	Pacific Southwest Airlines	32		23/MAR/67	
	YV-C-LEV	LAV			28/JAN/70	

MCDONNELL DOUGLAS DC-9

C/N	Registration	Owner/Operator	Series	First Flight	Delivery	Remarks
	YV-300C	LAV				
	YV-51C	LAV			79	
	YV-51C	F.B. Ayer			29/JAN/79	
	XA-IOV	Aeromexico			08/MAR/79	Leased
47007	VH-TJJ	Trans Australia Airlines	31		18/MAR/67	WFU FEB/82
	VH-TJJ	Australian Aircraft Sales			82	
	VH-TJJ	Trans Australia Airlines			AUG/82	Leased
	VH-TJJ	Australian Airlines			04/AUG/86	Leased
47008	VH-TJK	Trans Australia Airlines	31		14/APR/67	
	VH-TJK	Australian Aircraft Sales			82	
	VH-TJK	Trans Australia Airlines			AUG/82	
	N908AX	Airborne Express	31LWF		08/JAN/83	
47009	VH-TJL	Trans Australia Airlines	31		20/AUG/67	
	VH-TJL	Australian Airlines			04/AUG/86	
47010	N8902	Continental Airlines	15F		11/APR/67	
	CF-TOO	Air Canada			18/APR/72	
	N50AF	Air Florida			10/JUN/77	
	N50AF	Cayman Airways			21/MAY/78	Leased
	N50AF	Air Florida			29/JUN/78	
	N50AF	International Air Lease			27/NOV/81	
	N50AF	Emerald Air			27/NOV/81	Leased
47011	N8903	Continental Airlines	15F		25/APR/67	
	CF-TOP	Air Canada			09/MAY/72	
	N60AF	Air Florida			23/JUN/77	
	N79SL	Ross Aviation			27/NOV/79	
	N79SL	US Dept. of Energy			NOV/83	
47012	N8904	Continental Airlines	15F		23/MAY/67	
	CF-TOQ	Air Canada			28/JUL/72	
	N75AF	Air Florida			28/JAN/78	
	N75AF	Emerald Airlines			02/OCT/81	
	N75AF	Air National			15/SEP/83	
	N562PC	Orion Air			15/FEB/84	Op. for Purolator Courier
47013	N8905	Continental Airlines	15F		26/JUN/67	
	CF-TOR	Air Canada			22/SEP/72	WFU OCT/80
	N73AF	Air Florida			25/FEB/81	
	N73AF	Emerald Airlines			30/NOV/81	
	N73AF	Air Florida			APR/82	
	N73AF	All Star Airlines			27/SEP/82	
	N557AS	All Star Airlines			85	
	N557AS	McDonnell Douglas			85	
	N557AS	CIS Corp.			DEC/85	
	N557AS	Hawaiian Airlines			DEC/85	Leased
47014	N8906	Continental Airlines	15F		23/JUL/67	
	CF-TOS	Air Canada			04/DEC/72	
	N70AF	Air Florida			02/SEP/77	
	N70AF	Emerald Airlines			13/NOV/81	Leased
	N70AF	Air Florida			29/APR/82	
	N70AF	Air National			23/SEP/82	Leased
	N561PC	Orion Air			15/FEB/84	Op. for Purolator Courier
47015	N8907	Continental Airlines	15RC		29/AUG/67	
	CF-TOT	Air Canada			24/APR/73	WFU OCT/80
	N72AF	Air Florida			10/DEC/80	Leased
	N72AF	Air Florida			81	Purchased
	N72AF	Emerald Airlines			12/NOV/81	
	N72AF	Puralator Courier			JAN/82	Leased
	N72AF	Emerald Air			82	
47016	N8909	Continental Airlines	15RC		04/OCT/67	
	N9349	Hughes Airwest			16/APR/73	
	N9349	Republic			01/JUL/79	
	N9349	Northwest Orient			01/AUG/86	
47017	N8911	Continental Airlines	15RC		28/OCT/67	
	N9352	Hughes Airwest			17/FEB/75	
	N9352	Republic			01/JUL/79	
	N9352	Connie Kalitta			MAR/86	Leased
47018	N8913	Continental Arlines	15RC		22/NOV/67	
	N9354	Hughes Airwest			17/FEB/75	
	N9354	Republic			01/JUL/79	
	N9354	Northwest Orient			01/AUG/86	
47019	CF-TLJ	Air Canada	32		21/MAY/67	
47020	CF-TLK	Air Canada	32		30/MAY/67	
	C-FTLK	Columbia Air			03/MAR/82	Not taken-up
	C-FTLK	Air Canada			21/MAY/82	Stored Montreal
	N902AK	Altair			MAY/82	WFU 82, stored Philadelphia
	N902AK	Air Canada			APR/83	
	N706PS	Pacific Southwest Airlines			15/JUN/83	
47021	CF-TLL	Air Canada	32		07/JUL/67	
47022	CF-TLM	Air Canada	32		27/JUL/67	
47023	CF-TLN	Air Canada	32		30/AUG/67	
	N715CL	Columbia Air			03/MAR/82	Not taken-up
	C-FTLN	Air Canada			14/JUN/82	Stored Toronto
	N905AK	Altair			30/JUN/82	Reg. Not taken-up
	N904AK	Altair			30/JUN/82	Not taken-up
	N904AK	Air Canada			30/JUN/82	
	N707PS	Pacific Southwest Airlines			15/JUN/83	
47024	CF-TLO	Air Canada	32		31/AUG/67	WFU OCT/80
47025	N3316L	Delta Airlines	32		02/MAY/67	
	YV-67C	Avensa			19/JUN/76	W/O 11/MAR/83, Barquisimeto
47026	N3317L	Delta Airlines	32		14/JUN/67	
	N946VJ	Allegheny Airlines			02/SEP/76	
	N946VJ	US Air			28/OCT/79	
47027	N3318L	Delta Airlines	32		10/JUL/67	
	N995Z	Ozark Airlines			03/FEB/77	
47028	N3319L	Delta Airlines	32		02/AUG/67	
	N996Z	Ozark Airlines			13/JUL/77	
47029	N3320L	Delta Airlines	32		01/SEP/67	
	N997Z	Ozark Airlines			28/JUL/77	
47030	N3321L	Delta Airlines	32		03/OCT/67	
	N998Z	Ozark Airlines			15/JUN/77	
47031	N3322L	Delta Airlines	32		01/NOV/67	
	YV-68C	Avensa			01/NOV/76	
	N3322L	Republic			13/OCT/81	
	N3322L	Northwest Orient			01/AUG/86	
47032	N3323L	Delta Airlines	32		01/DEC/67	W/O 27/NOV/73, Chattanooga, Tn.
47033	N973Z	Ozark Airlines	15		31/JUL/67	
	N973Z	New York Yankees			80	Leased

C/N	Registration	Owner/Operator	Series	First Flight	Delivery	Remarks
	N973Z	Ozark Airlines			80	•
47034	N974Z	Ozark Airlines	15		01/SEP/67	
	N974Z	West Coast Airlines			12/APR/68	Leased
	N974Z	Hughes Airwest			15/JUL/68	Leased
	N974Z	Ozark Airlines			16/OCT/68	W/O 27/DEC/68, Sioux City, Iowa
47035	N975Z	Ozark Airlines	15		10/OCT/67	
47036	N8973E	Eastern Air Lines	31		13/SEP/68	
47037	EC-BIG	Iberia	32		30/JUN/67	
47038	I-DIKA	Alitalia	32		08/AUG/67	
	N901DC	McDonnell Douglas			31/JAN/83	
	N901DC	Alitalia			31/JAN/83	Leased
47039	I-DIKE	Alitalia	32		01/SEP/67	
	N902DC	McDonnell Douglas			31/JAN/83	
	N902DC	Alitalia			31/JAN/83	Leased
47040	N931F	Overseas National Airways	32CF		06/OCT/67	
	N931F	Evergreen International			29/OCT/76	
	N904AX	Airborne Express			15/AUG/81	
47041	N932F	Overseas National Airways	32CF		07/NOV/67	
	CF-TMN	Air Canada			23/MAY/73	
	N59T	Southern Airways			20/OCT/77	
	N59T	Republic			01/JUL/79	
	163036	U.S. Navy			13/SEP/84	
47042	N89S	Southern Airways	31		29/APR/69	
	N89S	Republic			01/JUL/79	
	N89S	Northwest Orient			01/AUG/86	
47043	N1302T	Texas International	14		02/FEB/67	
	N1302T	Continental Airlines			31/OCT/82	
	N1302T	Sunworld International			25/JAN/84	
47044	N1303T	Texas International	15MC		28/SEP/67	
	OH-LYH	Finnair			15/MAY/72	
47045	N1304T	Texas International	15MC		09/NOV/67	
	OH-LYI	Finnair			15/MAY/72	
	N558HA	Polaris Leasing			FEB/86	
	N558HA	Hawaiian Air			FEB/86	Leased
47046	I-DIKI	Alitalia	32		25/SEP/67	
	N903DC	McDonnell Douglas			31/JAN/83	
	N903DC	Alitalia			31/JAN/83	Leased
47047	I-DIKO	Alitalia	32		31/OCT/67	
	N904DC	McDonnell Douglas			31/JAN/83	
	N904DC	Alitalia			31/JAN/83	Leased
47048	N8964	Douglas	15			
	N8964	Continental Airlines			03/JUL/66	Leased
	N8964	Douglas			JAN/67	
	TC-JAA	Turk Hava Yollari			07/AUG/67	Leased
	N8964	Douglas			21/MAR/73	
	XA-DEV	Aeromexico			01/MAY/73	Leased
	YV-C-AVC	Avensa			22/APR/75	
	YV-52C	Avensa				
	N65358	Douglas			17/JUN/76	
	N65358	British Midland Airways			26/AUG/76	Leased
	G-BFIH	British Midland Airways			APR/78	
	G-BMAA	British Midland Airways			01/APR/80	
47049	N6140A	Douglas	14			
	N6140A	Allegheny Airlines			29/JUL/66	Leased
	N948L	Bonanza Airlines			29/JUN/67	
	N948L	Hughes Airwest			15/JUL/68	
	N948L	Republic			01/OCT/80	
	N948L	Northwest Orient			01/AUG/86	
47050	N970VJ	Allegheny Airlines	31		02/JUN/67	
	N970VJ	US Air			28/OCT/79	
47051	N971VJ	Allegheny Airlines	31		26/JUN/67	
	N971VJ	US Air			28/OCT/79	
47052	N972VJ	Allegheny Airlines	31		28/JUL/67	
	N972VJ	US Air			28/OCT/79	
47053	N970NE	Northeast Airlines	31		05/MAY/67	
	N970NE	Delta Airlines			01/AUG/72	
	N940VJ	Allegheny Airlines			31/MAY/74	
	N940VJ	US Air			28/OCT/79	
47054	N971NE	Northeast Airlines	31		08/MAY/67	
	N971NE	Delta Airlines			01/AUG/72	
	N971NE	Allegheny Airlines			02/JUL/74	
	N941VJ	US Air			28/OCT/79	
47055	N1305T	Texas International	15MC		22/NOV/67	
	N1305T	Air National			31/JUL/82	
	N563PC	Purolator Courier			24/MAR/84	Op. by Orion Air
47056	YV-C-AVM	Avensa	14		28/FEB/67	W/O 22/DEC/74, Nr. Maturin
47057	N972NE	Northeast Airlines	31		14/JUN/67	
	N972NE	Delta Airlines			01/AUG/72	
	N942VJ	Allegheny Airlines			02/AUG/74	
	N942VJ	US Air			28/OCT/79	
47058	N973NE	Northeast Airlies	31		16/JUN/67	
	N973NE	Delta Airlines			01/AUG/72	
	N943VJ	Allegheny Airlines			15/AUG/74	
	N943VJ	US Air			28/OCT/79	
47059	XA-SOA	Aeromexico	15		30/MAY/67	
47060	YV-C-AVR	Avensa	14		10/MAY/67	
	YV-57C	Avensa				
	N38641	Emerald Air			JUN/83	
47061	N1306T	Texas International	15MC		22/DEC/67	
	N1306T	Coleman Air Transport			31/OCT/79	
	N1306T	Nelson Steel & Wire Co.			80	
	N1306T	Sunstream Aircraft Inc.			15/APR/80	
	N1306T	Douglas			18/DEC/80	
	N1306T	Sunstream Aircraft Inc.			15/OCT/81	Leased
	XA-BCS	Aero California			01/JUN/82	
47062	N1307T	Texas International	15F		26/JAN/68	
	N1307T	Continental Airlines			31/OCT/82	
	N564PC	Purolator Courier			26/MAR/84	Op. by Orion Air
47063	N91S	Southern Airways	15		11/MAY/67	
	N91S	Bonanza Airlines			28/FEB/68	Leased
	N91S	Southern Airways			28/FEB/69	
	N91S	Republic Airlines			01/JUL/79	
	N91S	Northwest Orient			01/AUG/86	
47064	N92S	Southern Airways	15		09/JUN/67	
	N92S	Republic Airlines			01/JUL/79	

MCDONNELL DOUGLAS DC-9

C/N	Registration	Owner/Operator	Series	First Flight	Delivery	Remarks
	N92S	Northwest Orient			01/AUG/86	
47065	VH-CZD	Ansett Airlines	31		08/MAR/68	
	VH-CZD	Air Vanuatu			MAY/82	Leased
	VH-CZD	Ansett Airlines			82	
	162392	U.S.Navy			17/SEP/82	
47066	N974NE	Northeast Airlines	31		14/AUG/67	
	N974NE	Delta Airlines			01/AUG/72	
	N945VJ	Allegheny Airlines			05/SEP/74	
	N945VJ	US Air			01/JUL/79	
47067	N951N	North Central	31		27/JUL/67	
	N951N	Texas International			31/MAR/77	
	N951N	New York Air			10/FEB/81	
47068	CF-TLP	Air Canada	32		31/AUG/67	
	N915CL	Columbia Air			DEC/81	Not delivered
	N904AK	Altair			16/JUL/82	WFU 82 to 25/MAY/83
	N708PS	Pacific Southwest Airlines			25/MAY/83	
47069	CF-TLQ	Air Canada	32		30/SEP/67	
47070	CF-TLR	Air Canada	32		30/SEP/67	
	N906AK	Altair			82	
	C-FTLR	Air Canada			82	
47071	CF-TLS	Air Canada	32		02/NOV/67	
47072	VH-TJM	Trans Australia Airlines	31	29/FEB/68	08/MAR/68	
	N906AX	Airborne Express	31LWF		03/APR/82	
47073	N952N	North Central	31		01/SEP/67	
	N952N	Republic			01/JUL/79	
	N952N	Northwest Orient			01/AUG/86	
47074	N8974E	Eastern Air Lines	31		14/SEP/68	
47075	N975NE	Northeast Airlines	31		25/SEP/67	
	N975NE	Delta Airlines			01/AUG/72	W/O 31/JUL/73, Logan Intl, Bo.
47076	EC-BIH	Iberia	32		19/JUL/67	
47077	EC-BII	Iberia	32		14/AUG/67	W/O 05/MAR/73, Nantes, France
47078	N93S	Southern Airways	15		28/JUL/67	
	N93S	Republic Airlines			01/JUL/79	
	N93S	Northwest Orient			01/AUG/86	
47079	EC-BIJ	Iberia	32		15/SEP/67	
	EC-BIJ	Aviaco			82	Leased
	EC-BIJ	Iberia			82	
47080	EC-BIK	Iberia	32		14/SEP/67	
	EC-BIK	Aviaco			12/MAY/82	
47081	N9104	West Coast Airlines	14		23/AUG/67	
	N9104	Hughes Airwest			15/NOV/68	
	N9104	Texas International			08/NOV/75	W/O 16/NOV/76, Stapleton Ap. Denver
47082	N976NE	Northeast Airlines	31		19/OCT/67	
	N976NE	Delta Airlines			01/AUG/72	
	N993Z	Ozark Airlines			02/MAY/75	
47083	N953N	North Central	31		05/OCT/67	
	N953N	Republic			01/JUL/79	
	N953N	Northwest Orient			01/AUG/86	
47084	EC-BIL	Iberia	32		11/OCT/67	
47085	XA-SOY	Aeromexico	15		19/JUL/67	
47086	N8915	Continental Airlines	15RC		16/DEC/67	
	N9356	Hughes Airwest			26/APR/74	
	N9356	Republic			01/JUL/79	
	N568PC	Purolator Courier			14/SEP/84	Op. by Orion Air
47087	N8917	Continental Airlines	15RC		09/OCT/68	
	N9358	Hughes Airwest			24/MAY/74	
	XC-BCM	Banco de Mexico			30/SEP/77	
	XC-BCO	Aeromexico			77	Leased
	XC-BCO	Banco de Mexico			77	
47088	EC-BIM	Iberia	32		28/OCT/67	
	EC-BIM	Aviaco			85	Sched.delivery
47089	EC-BIN	Iberia	32		06/NOV/67	
	EC-BIN	Aviaco			85	Sched.delivery
47090	EC-BIO	Iberia	32		07/NOV/67	
	EC-BIO	Aviaco			85	Sched.delivery
47091	EC-BIP	Iberia	32		05/DEC/67	
	EC-BIP	Aviaco			15/MAY/80	Leased
47092	EC-BIQ	Iberia	32		20/DEC/67	
	EC-BIQ	Aviaco			22/JUL/80	Leased
47093	EC-BIR	Iberia	32		12/JAN/68	
47094	HB-IFN	Swissair	32		13/SEP/67	
	SE-DBZ	SAS			13/SEP/67	Leased
	HB-IFN	Swissair			29/AUG/68	
	N545TX	New York Air			13/JUL/81	
	N545NY	New York Air			82	
47095	N977NE	Northeast Airlines	31		03/NOV/67	
	N977NE	Delta Airlines			01/AUG/72	
	N992Z	Ozark Airlines			03/APR/75	
47096	N978NE	Northeast Airlines	31		04/NOV/67	
	N978NE	Delta Airlines			01/AUG/72	
	N991Z	Ozark Airlines			06/FEB/75	
47097	N979NE	Northeast Airlines	31		06/NOV/67	
	N979NE	Delta Airlines			01/AUG/72	
	N994Z	Ozark Airlines			06/JUN/75	
	N994Z	Aviation Sales			20/DEC/83	Stored 20/DEC/83 to JUN/85
	N994Z	Republic			JUN/85	
	N994Z	Northwest Orient			01/AUG/86	
47098	N938PR	Overseas National Airways	31		01/JUN/67	
	N938PR	Caribair			02/DEC/67	Leased
	N938PR	Overseas National Airways			24/MAR/68	
	N938PR	Caribair			14/OCT/68	Purchased
	N8988E	Eastern Air Lines			15/MAY/73	
47099	N973VJ	Allegheny Airlines	31		14/NOV/67	
	N973VJ	US Air			28/OCT/79	
47100	XA-SOC	Aeromexico	15		25/AUG/67	W/O 20/JUN/73, Nr. Puerta Vallarta
47101	I-DIKU	Alitalia	32		24/NOV/67	
	N905DC	McDonnell Douglas			01/FEB/83	
	N905DC	Alitalia			01/FEB/83	Leased
47102	PH-DNG	KLM	32		21/NOV/67	
47103	N3324L	Delta Airlines	32		30/NOV/67	
	YV-70C	Avensa			30/SEP/77	
	N3324L	Republic			15/OCT/81	
	N3324L	Northwest Orient			01/AUG/86	
47104	N3325L	Delta Airlines	32		19/DEC/67	

C/N	Registration	Owner/Operator	Series	First Flight	Delivery	Remarks
	YV-71C	Avensa			02/MAR/78	
	N901ML	Avensa Leasing			06/DEC/84	
	N901ML	Midway Airlines			06/DEC/84	Leased
47105	N3326L	Delta Airlines	32		20/DEC/67	
	YV-72C	Avensa			21/JUN/78	
	N902ML	Avensa Leasing			FEB/85	
	N902ML	Midway Airlines			FEB/85	Leased
47106	N3327L	Delta Airlines	32		13/JAN/68	
	YV-73C	Avensa			19/DEC/78	
	XA-JEC	F.B. Ayer			03/JUL/80	
	XA-JEC	Aeromexico			03/JUL/80	Leased
47107	N3328L	Delta Airlines	32		12/JAN/68	
	N921L	Ozark Airlines			20/DEC/78	
47108	N3329L	Delta Airlines	32		01/FEB/68	
	N922L	Ozark Airlines			06/MAR/79	
47109	N3330L	Delta Airlines	32		06/FEB/68	
	N923L	Ozark Airlines			05/JUN/79	
47110	HB-IFO	Swissair	32		08/OCT/67	
	OY-KGU	SAS			08/OCT/67	Leased
	HB-IFO	Swissair			09/AUG/68	
	N534TX	Texas International			03/APR/81	
	N534TX	Continental Airlines			31/OCT/82	
47111	HB-IFP	Swissair	32		07/NOV/67	
	LN-RLS	SAS			08/NOV/67	Leased
	HB-IFP	Swissair			20/AUG/68	
	N535TX	Texas International			06/JUN/81	
	N535TX	Continental Airlines			31/OCT/82	
	N535TX	New York Air			MAR/86	
47112	HB-IFR	Swissair	32		05/DEC/67	
	SE-DBY	SAS			05/DEC/67	Leased
	HB-IFR	Swissair			29/MAY/68	
	N537TX	Texas International			03/SEP/81	
	N537TX	Continental Airlines			31/OCT/82	
	N537TX	New York Air			MAR/86	
47113	HB-IFS	Swissair	32		30/DEC/67	
	OY-KGW	SAS			20/DEC/67	Leased
	HB-IFS	Swissair			07/SEP/68	
	N536TX	New York Air			20/JUN/81	
	N536TX	Texas International			21/JUN/82	
	N536TX	Continental Airlines			31/OCT/82	
	N536TX	New York Air			29/SEP/83	
47114	N8960U	Douglas	41			
	SE-DBX	SAS			23/MAY/68	
47115	N8961U	Douglas	41			
	OY-KGA	SAS			28/FEB/68	
	HB-IDW	Swissair			01/OCT/74	Leased
	OY-KGA	SAS			03/OCT/75	
47116	LN-RTO	SAS	41		14/MAY/68	
	LN-RLK	SAS				
	HB-IDV	Swissair			12/DEC/74	Leased
	LN-RLK	SAS			22/AUG/75	
47117	SE-DBW	SAS	41		28/MAY/68	
	HB-IDX	Swissair			30/OCT/74	Leased
	SE-DBW	SAS			10/OCT/75	
47118	I-DIKB	Alitalia	32		22/NOV/67	W/O 07/JAN/80, Fiumicino Ap.
47119	N8975E	Eastern Air Lines	31		19/SEP/68	
47120	N939PR	Caribair	31		13/DEC/67	
	N8990E	Eastern Air Lines			15/MAY/73	
47121	N967PR	Caribair	31		23/MAR/68	
	N8989E	Eastern Air Lines			15/MAR/73	
47122	XA-SOD	Aeromexico	15		20/DEC/67	
47123	XA-SOE	Aeromexico	15		09/FEB/68	
47124	XA-SOF	Aeromexico	15		08/FEB/68	W/O 02/SEP/76, Leon, Mexico
47125	XA-SOG	Aeromexico	15		09/OCT/68	
47126	XA-SOH	Aeromexico	15		08/NOV/68	
47127	XA-SOI	Aeromexico	15		27/NOV/68	
47128	I-DIKC	Alitalia	32		11/DEC/67	
	N516MD	Douglas			14/DEC/83	
	N516MD	Alitalia			01/MAY/84	Leased
	N516MD	Aermediterranea			17/DEC/83	Sub-leased
	N516MD	Alitalia			16/DEC/83	Leased
47129	I-DIKD	Alitalia	32		25/DEC/67	
	N906DC	McDonnell Douglas			01/FEB/83	
	N906DC	Alitalia			01/FEB/83	Leased
47130	N974VJ	Allegheny Airlines	31		08/DEC/67	
	N974VJ	US Air			28/OCT/79	
47131	PH-DNH	KLM	32		17/DEC/67	
47132	PH-DNI	KLM	32		03/JAN/68	
47133	PH-DNK	KLM	32		15/JAN/68	
47134	N980NE	Northeast Airlines	31		15/DEC/67	
	N980NE	Delta Airlines			01/AUG/72	
	N988Z	Ozark Airlines			01/APR/74	
47135	N981NE	Northeast Airlines	31		15/JAN/68	
	N981NE	Delta Airlines			01/AUG/72	
	N989Z	Ozark Airlines			01/MAY/74	
47136	N982NE	Northeast Airlines	31		24/JAN/68	
	N982NE	Delta Airlines			01/AUG/72	
	N990Z	Ozark Airlines			03/JUN/74	
47137	N983NE	Northeast Airlines	31		23/FEB/68	
	N983NE	Delta Airlines			01/AUG/72	
	N987Z	Ozark Airlines			01/MAR/74	
47138	N9105	West Coast Airways	31			Not taken-up
	N9330	Bonanza Airlines			27/MAY/68	
	N9330	Hughes Airwest			27/MAY/68	
	N9330	Republic			01/JUL/79	
	N9330	Northwest Orient			01/AUG/86	
47139	N8930E	Eastern Air Lines	31		04/OCT/67	
	N915RW	Hughes Airwest			01/JUN/78	
	N915RW	Republic			01/JUL/79	
	N915RW	Northwest Orient			01/AUG/86	
47140	N8931E	Eastern Air Lines	31		07/DEC/67	
47141	N8932E	Eastern Air Lines	31		23/DEC/67	
47142	N8933E	Eastern Air Lines	31		30/DEC/67	
47143	N8934E	Eastern Air Lines	31		17/JAN/68	
47144	N8935E	Eastern Air Lines	31		15/JAN/68	
	N916RW	Hughes Airwest			26/AUG/77	

C/N	Registration	Owner/Operator	Series	First Flight	Delivery	Remarks
	N916RW	Republic			01/JUL/79	
	N916RW	Northwest Orient			01/AUG/86	
47145	N8936E	Eastern Airlines	31		30/JAN/68	
	N917RW	Hughes Airwest			20/JUL/77	
	N917RW	Republic			01/JUL/79	
	N917RW	Northwest Orient			01/AUG/86	
47146	N975VJ	Allegheny Airlines	31		28/DEC/68	
	N975VJ	US Air			28/OCT/79	
47147	N933F	Overseas National Airways	32CF		14/DEC/67	
	N933F	Evergreen International			29/OCT/76	
	N905AX	Airborne Express			15/JUL/81	
47148	N934F	Overseas National Airways	32CF		25/JAN/68	
	N934F	Hawaiian Airlines			13/JUN/72	Leased
	N934F	Itavia			07/JAN/79	Leased
	N934F	Hawaiian Airlines			22/NOV/80	
	N934F	American International			15/OCT/81	Leased
	N934F	Hawaiian Airlines			01/SEP/84	
	N909AX	Airborne Express			DEC/84	
47149	N903H	Hawaiian Airlines	31		22/NOV/67	
	N911RW	Hughes Airwest			13/MAY/76	
	N911RW	Ghana Airways			01/MAR/76	Leased
	N911RW	Hughes Airwest			23/MAY/76	
	N911RW	Republic			01/JUL/79	
	N911RW	Northwest Orient			01/AUG/86	
47150	N905H	Hawaiian Airlines	31		05/APR/68	
	N912RW	Hughes Airwest			01/MAR/76	
	N912RW	Republic			01/JUL/79	
	N912RW	Northwest Orient			01/AUG/86	
47151	N228Z	Trancinda Investment Corp.	15		21/APR/68	
	N228Z	American Capital Aviation			15/SEP/72	
	N112AK	American Capital Aviation			NOV/75	
	VR-CKO	Handlingair				
47152	N8908	Continental Airlines	15F		22/SEP/68	
	CF-TOU	Air Canada			01/MAY/73	
	N73AF	Air Florida			04/JUN/78	Leased
	C-FTOU	Air Canada			09/JUN/78	
	N65AF	Air Florida			31/JAN/79	Leased
	C-FTOU	Air Canada			23/AUG/80	WFU OCT/80
	N66AF	Air Florida			05/FEB/81	
	N66AF	Emerald Airlines			04/NOV/81	
	N66AF	Ross Aviation			15/JUN/84	
47153	N8910	Continental Airlines	15F		18/OCT/67	
	N8910	Southern Airways			24/JUN/72	Leased
	N8910	Continental Airlines			31/AUG/72	
	N9350	Hughes Airwest			07/JUN/73	
	N9350	Republic			01/JUL/79	
	N567PC	Purolator Courier			14/SEP/84	Op. by Orion Air
47154	N8912	Continental Airlines	15F		28/NOV/67	
	N9353	Hughes Airwest			29/NOV/73	
	XC-BDM	Banco de Mexico			15/JUL/77	
	N9353	Republic			01/JUL/79	
	N9353	Connie Kalitta			JUL/84	
47155	N8914	Continental Airlines	15F		12/DEC/67	
	N9355	Hughes Airwest			26/MAR/74	
	N9355	Republic			01/JUL/79	
	N9355	Northwest Orient			01/AUG/86	
47156	N8916	Continental Airlines	15RC		29/DEC/67	
	N9357	Hughes Airwest			02/MAY/74	
	N9357	Southern Airways			08/MAY/78	
	N9357	Republic			01/JUL/79	
	N9357	Northwest Orient			01/AUG/86	
47157	N8959E	Eastern Air Lines	31		08/JUN/68	
47158	N8937E	Eastern Air Lines	31		31/OCT/68	
	N918RW	Hughes Airwest			14/OCT/77	
	N918RW	Republic			01/JUL/79	
	N918RW	Northwest Orient			01/AUG/86	
47159	N954N	North Central	31		02/JAN/68	W/O 20/DEC/72, Chicago O'Hare Ap., Ill.
47160	N955N	North Central	31		16/JAN/68	
	N955N	Republic			01/JUL/79	
	N955N	Northwest Orient			01/AUG/86	
47161	N8938E	Eastern Air Lines	31		02/FEB/68	
47162	N8939E	Eastern Air Lines	31		17/FEB/68	
	N919RW	Hughes Airwest			15/SEP/77	
	N919RW	Republic			01/JUL/79	
	N919RW	Northwest Orient			01/AUG/86	
47163	N8940E	Eastern Air Lines	31		15/FEB/68	
	N920RW	Hughes Airwest			17/MAY/77	
	N920RW	Republic			01/JUL/79	
	N920RW	Northwest Orient			01/AUG/86	
47164	N8941E	Eastern Air Lines	31		19/FEB/68	
	N921RW	Hughes Airwest			10/JUN/78	
	N921RW	Republic			01/JUL/79	
	N921RW	Northwest Orient			01/AUG/86	
47165	N8942E	Eastern Air Lines	31		22/FEB/68	
47166	N8943E	Eastern Air Lines	31		25/FEB/68	
47167	N8944E	Eastern Air Lines	31		27/FEB/68	
47168	PH-DNS	KLM	32		14/DEC/68	
47169	PH-DNT	KLM	32		16/DEC/68	
47170	PH-DNV	KLM	32		19/DEC/68	
47171	N906H	Hawaiian Airlines	31		28/MAR/69	
	N913RW	Hughes Airwest			10/JAN/76	
	N913RW	Republic			01/JUL/79	
	N913RW	Northwest Orient			01/AUG/86	
47172	N3331L	Delta Airlines	32		29/FEB/68	
	N3331L	Ozark Airlines			11/DEC/79	
	YU-AJX	Inex Adria			21/APR/80	Leased
	N3331L	Ozark Airlines			15/NOV/80	
	YU-AJX	Inex Adria			15/APR/81	Leased
	N926L	Ozark Airlines			19/OCT/81	
47173	N3332L	Delta Airlines	32		18/MAR/68	
	N931L	Ozark Airlines			19/MAY/81	
47174	N3333L	Delta Airlines	32		07/APR/68	
	N3333L	Ozark Airlines			10/JUN/80	
	N929L	Ozark Airlines			MAY/81	

C/N	Registration	Owner/Operator	Series	First Flight	Delivery	Remarks
47175	N3334L	Delta Airlines	32		28/APR/68	
	PJ-SNE	ALM			05/JUL/80	
	PJ-SNE	Viasa			03/AUG/81	Leased
	PJ-SNE	ALM			03/JAN/82	
	N3991C	American International			03/JUN/83	
	N3991C	Grenada Partnership			01/OCT/84	
	N3991C	Marfreless			JUL/85	
	N3991C	Republic			JUL/85	Leased
	N3991C	Northwest Orient			01/AUG/86	Leased
47176	N3335L	Delta Airlines	32		25/MAY/68	
47177	N3336L	Delta Airlines	32		21/JUN/68	
	N3336L	Air One			82	Not taken-up
	N3336L	Delta Airlines			82	
47178	OY-KGB	SAS	41		10/JUN/68	
47179	LN-RTF	SAS	41		29/JUN/68	
	LN-RLC	SAS				
47180	SE-DBU	SAS	41		27/JUL/68	
47181	N8945E	Eastern Air Lines	31		29/FEB/68	
47182	N8946E	Eastern Air Lines	31		08/MAR/68	
	N922RW	Hughes Airwest			19/OCT/78	
	N922RW	Republic			01/JUL/79	
	N922RW	Northwest Orient			01/AUG/86	
47183	N8947E	Eastern Air Lines	31		14/MAR/68	
	N923RW	Hughes Airwest			11/SEP/78	
	N923RW	Republic			01/JUL/79	
	N923RW	Northwest Orient			01/AUG/86	
47184	N8948E	Eastern Air Lines	31		22/MAR/68	
47185	N8949E	Eastern Air Lines	31		16/MAR/68	
	N924RW	Hughes Airwest			19/APR/78	
	N924RW	Republic			01/JUL/79	
	N924RW	Northwest Orient			01/AUG/86	
47186	N8950E	Eastern Air Lines	31		20/MAR/68	
47187	N8951E	Eastern Air Lines	31		26/MAR/68	
47188	N8954E	Eastern Air Lines	31		11/APR/68	
	N931VJ	Allegheny Airlines			02/AUG/78	
	N931VJ	US Air			28/OCT/79	
47189	N8955E	Eastern Air Lines	31		04/MAY/68	
	N932VJ	Allegheny Airlines			25/AUG/78	
	N932VJ	US Air			28/OCT/79	
47190	PH-DNL	KLM	32		24/JAN/68	
47191	PH-DNM	KLM	33RC		30/APR/68	
	PH-DNM	United Aviation Services			30/DEC/85	
	PH-DNM	KLM			30/DEC/85	Leased
47192	N8963U	Douglas	33RC			
	PH-DNN	KLM			17/APR/68	
	PH-DNN	United Aviation Services			30/DEC/85	
	PH-DNN	KLM			30/DEC/85	Leased
47193	PH-DNO	KLM	33RC		21/MAY/68	
47194	PH-DNP	KLM	33RC		12/JUN/68	
47195	CF-TLT	Air Canada	32		22/MAR/68	
47196	CF-TLU	Air Canada	32		07/APR/68	W/O 02/JUN/83, Cincinnati, Ohio
47197	CF-TLV	Air Canada	32		07/APR/68	W/O 26/JUN/78, Toronto Intl.
47198	CF-TLW	Air Canada	32		30/APR/68	
47199	CF-TLX	Air Canada	32		31/MAY/68	
47200	CF-TLY	Air Canada	32		11/JUL/68	W/O 02/JUN/82, Montreal Intl. Ap
47201	PH-DNW	KLM	32		22/FEB/69	
47202	VH-CZE	Ansett Airlines	31		02/NOV/68	
	VH-CZE	Air Vanuatu			81	Leased
	VH-CZE	Ansett Airlines			81	
	N931ML	Midway Airlines			15/OCT/81	
	N931ML	American International			11/JUN/82	Leased
	N931ML	Midway Airlines			01/MAR/83	
47203	VH-TJN	Trans Australia Airlines	31		31/OCT/68	
	N907AX	Airborne Express	31LWF		19/JUN/83	
47204	N94S	Southern Airways	15		09/FEB/68	
	N94S	Republic			01/JUL/79	
	N94S	Northwest Orient			01/AUG/86	
47205	N95S	Southern Airways	15		09/FEB/68	
	N95S	Republic			01/JUL/79	
	N95S	Northwest Orient			01/AUG/86	
47206	N96S	Southern Airways	15		17/JUN/68	
	N96S	Republic			01/JUL/79	
	N96S	Northwest Orient			01/AUG/86	
47207	N984VJ	Allegheny Airlines	31		17/APR/68	
	N984VJ	US Air			28/OCT/79	
47208	N985VJ	Allegheny Airlines	31		10/MAY/68	
	N985VJ	US Air			28/OCT/79	
47209	N986VJ	Allegheny Airlines	31		14/JUN/68	
	N986VJ	US Air			28/OCT/79	
47210	N987VJ	Allegheny Airlines	31		12/JUL/68	
	N987VJ	US Air			28/OCT/79	
47211	N988VJ	Allegheny Airlines	31		09/AUG/68	W/O 09/SEP/69, Shelbyville, In.
47212	N989VJ	Allegheny Airlines	31		29/AUG/68	
	N989VJ	US Air			28/OCT/79	
47213	TC-JAC	Turk Hava Yollari	32		13/AUG/68	W/O 21/JAN/72, Adana Ap.
47214	N8956E	Eastern Air Lines	31		10/MAY/68	
47215	N8957E	Eastern Air Lines	31		23/MAY/68	
47216	N8958E	Eastern Air Lines	31		25/MAY/68	
	N933VJ	Allegheny Airlines			30/JUN/78	
	N933VJ	US Air			28/OCT/79	
47217	N8966E	Eastern Air Lines	31		16/AUG/68	
47218	D-ACEB	Sudflug	32		21/MAY/68	
	HB-IFX	Swissair			20/OCT/68	
	N53BTX	Texas International			FEB/82	
	N538TX	Continental Airlines			31/OCT/82	
47219	D-ACEC	Sudflug	32		13/JUN/68	
	HB-IFY	Swissair			22/OCT/68	
	N544TX	Texas International			OCT/81	
	N544TX	New York Air			MAR/86	
47220	I-DIKF	Alitalia	32F		03/MAY/68	
	N935F	Evergreen International			03/NOV/81	
47221	I-DIKG	Alitalia	32F		09/MAY/68	
	N938F	Overseas National Airways			10/FEB/72	
	N938F	Evergreen International			29/OCT/76	
	163037	U.S. Navy			01/AUG/84	

MCDONNELL DOUGLAS DC-9

C/N	Registration	Owner/Operator	Series	First Flight	Delivery	Remarks
47222	I-DIKJ	Alitalia	32		03/MAY/68	
	N43265	McDonnell Douglas			01/FEB/83	
	N43265	Alitalia			01/FEB/83	Leased
47223	I-DIKL	Alitalia	32		30/APR/68	
	N2786T	McDonnell Douglas			01/FEB/83	
	N2786T	Alitalia			01/FEB/83	Leased
47224	I-DIKM	Alitalia	32		25/MAY/68	
	I-DIKM	ATI			04/NOV/81	
47225	I-DIKN	Alitalia	32		27/MAY/68	
	I-DIKN	ATI			28/MAR/82	
	N515MD	Douglas			14/DEC/83	
	N515MD	ATI			17/DEC/83	Leased
47226	I-DIKP	Alitalia	32		28/JUN/68	
	I-DIKP	ATI			01/APR/80	
47227	I-DIKQ	Alitalia	32		29/JUN/68	W/O 23/DEC/78, nr.Palermo, Italy
47228	I-DIKR	Alitalia	32		09/AUG/68	
	I-DIKR	ATI			10/DEC/81	
47229	I-DIKS	Alitalia	32		08/AUG/68	
	I-DIKS	Aermediterranea			15/JUN/82	
	I-DIKS	ATI			APR/85	
47230	I-DIKT	Alitalia	32		18/OCT/68	
	I-DIKT	Aermediterranea			07/AUG/82	
	I-DIKT	ATI			APR/85	
47231	I-DIKV	Alitalia	32		19/OCT/68	
47232	I-DIKY	Alitalia	32		18/DEC/68	
	I-DIKY	JAT			15/APR/69	Leased
	I-DIKY	Alitalia			25/MAY/70	
	I-DIKY	ATI			31/MAR/79	
47233	I-DIBC	Alitalia	32		19/DEC/68	
47234	I-DIBD	Alitalia	32		04/JAN/69	
47235	I-DIBJ	Alitalia	32		09/JAN/69	
47236	I-DIBQ	Alitalia	32		04/FEB/69	
47237	I-DIBO	Alitalia	32		06/FEB/69	
	I-DIBO	Aermediterranea			08/JUN/81	
	I-DIBO	ATI			APR/85	
47238	I-DIZA	Alitalia	32		14/MAR/69	
47239	I-DIZE	Alitalia	32			Not taken-up
	YU-AHJ	Inex Adria			25/APR/69	
	YU-AHJ	Adria Airways			APR/86	
47240	N8919	Continental Airlines	15RC		20/JUL/68	
	N9351	Hughes Airwest			15/OCT/73	
	N9351	Republic			01/JUL/79	
	N565PC	Purolator Courier			07/JUN/84	Op. by Orion Air
47241	67-22583	United States Air Force	C9A		13/SEP/68	
47242	67-22584	United States Air Force	C9A		08/AUG/68	
47243	YV-C-AVD	Avensa	32		27/FEB/69	
	YV-C-AVD	Viasa			MAR/69	Leased
						W/O 16/MAR/69, Maracaibo
47244	N90S	Southern Airways	31		23/MAY/69	
	N90S	Republic			01/JUL/79	
	N90S	Northwest Orient			01/AUG/86	
47245	N97S	Southern Airways	31		20/JUN/69	W/O 14/NOV/70, Huntingdon
47246	N950L	Bonanza Airlines	31			Not taken-up
	N9333	Hughes Airwest			24/JUN/68	
	N9333	Toa Domestic Airlines			11/SEP/73	Leased
	N9333	Hughes Airwest			28/FEB/75	
	N9333	Republic			01/JUL/79	
	N9333	Northwest Orient			01/AUG/86	
47247	N9334	Hughes Airwest	31		17/JUL/68	
	N9334	Toa Domestic Airlines			11/DEC/73	Leased
	N9334	Hughes Airwest			21/NOV/74	
	N9334	Republic			01/JUL/79	
	N9334	Northwest Orient			01/AUG/86	
47248	N976Z	Ozark Airlines	31		26/FEB/68	
47249	N977Z	Ozark Airlines	31		19/APR/68	
47250	N978Z	Ozark Airlines	31		10/MAY/68	
47251	N982PS	Pacific Southwest Airlines	31		24/JAN/68	
	N982PS	Ozark Airlines			14/JUL/69	
47252	N956N	North Central	31		15/APR/68	
	N956N	Republic			01/JUL/79	
	N956N	Northwest Orient			01/AUG/86	
47253	N957N	North Central	31		19/APR/68	
	N957N	Republic			01/JUL/79	
	N957N	Northwest Orient			01/AUG/86	
47254	N958N	North Central	31		30/APR/68	
	N958N	Republic			01/JUL/79	
	N958N	Northwest Orient			01/AUG/86	
47255	N959N	North Central	31		13/MAY/68	
	N959N	Republic			01/JUL/79	
	N959N	Northwest Orient			01/AUG/86	
47256	N960N	North Central	31		17/JUN/68	
	N960N	Republic			01/JUL/79	
	N960N	Northwest Orient			01/AUG/86	
47257	N1262L	Delta Airlines	32		04/OCT/68	
47258	N1263L	Delta Airlines	32		10/OCT/68	
47259	N1264L	Delta Airlines	32		15/NOV/68	
47260	N1265L	Delta Airlines	32		21/NOV/68	
47261	N1266L	Delta Airlines	32		19/NOV/68	
47262	N1267L	Delta Airlines	32		23/NOV/68	
47263	N9106	West Coast Airways	31			Not taken-up
	N9331	Bonanza Airlines			04/JUN/68	
	N9331	Hughes Airwest			04/JUN/68	
	N9331	Republic			OCT/80	
	N9331	Northwest Orient			01/AUG/86	
47264	N9107	West Coast Airways	31			Not taken-up
	N9332	Bonanza Airlines			20/JUN/68	
	N9332	Hughes Airwest			20/JUN/68	
	N9332	Republic			OCT/80	
	N9332	Northwest Orient			01/AUG/86	
47265	CF-TLZ	Air Canada	32		10/JUL/68	
47266	CF-TMA	Air Canada	32		27/JUL/68	
47267	N8967E	Eastern Air Lines	31		17/AUG/68	W/O 27/JAN/73, Akron-Canton Ap.
47268	N8970E	Eastern Air Lines	31		04/SEP/68	
47269	N8971E	Eastern Air Lines	31		06/SEP/68	
47270	N8972E	Eastern Air Lines	31		11/SEP/68	
47271	N8976E	Eastern Air Lines	31		09/OCT/68	

C/N	Registration	Owner/Operator	Series	First Flight	Delivery	Remarks
47272	N8977E	Eastern Air Lines	31		09/OCT/68	
47273	N3337L	Delta Airlines	32		25/JUL/68	
47274	N3338L	Delta Airlines	32		27/JUL/68	
47275	N3339L	Delta Airlines	32		22/AUG/68	
47276	N3340L	Delta Airlines	32		14/SEP/68	
47277	N5341L	Delta Airlines	32		25/SEP/68	
47278	N5342L	Delta Airlines	32		26/SEP/68	
47279	PH-DNR	KLM	33RC		05/JUL/68	
47280	N1334U	Southern Airways	31		29/JUN/71	
	N1334U	Republic			01/JUL/79	
	N1334U	Northwest Orient			01/AUG/86	
47281	HB-IFT	Swissair	32		20/DEC/68	
	N533TX	Texas International			13/JAN/81	
	N533TX	Continental Airlines			31/OCT/82	
47282	HB-IFU	Swissair	32		31/JAN/69	
47283	I-DIKW	Alitalia	32		24/OCT/68	
	N2786S	McDonnell Douglas			01/FEB/83	
	N2786S	Alitalia			01/FEB/83	Leased
47284	N1268L	Delta Airlines	32		26/NOV/68	
47285	N1269L	Delta Airlines	32		07/DEC/68	
47286	OY-KGC	SAS	41		17/AUG/68	
47287	LN-RTG	SAS	41		24/AUG/68	
	LN-RLJ	SAS				
47288	SE-DBT	SAS	41		28/AUG/68	
47289	CF-TMB	Air Canada	32		29/JUL/68	
47290	CF-TMC	Air Canada	32		28/AUG/68	
47291	PH-MAN	Martinair	32F		21/JUL/68	
	N94454	Chase Manhattan Bank			15/NOV/73	Leased
	N94454	Hawaiian Airlines			15/NOV/73	Leased
	N94454	Itavia			21/OCT/78	Sub-Leased
	N94454	Hawaiian Airlines			15/JUL/81	WFU 81, Oakland
	N94454	American International			15/SEP/81	Leased
	N94454	Hawaiian Airlines			01/SEP/84	
	N933AX	Airborne Express			DEC/84	
47292	CF-TMD	Air Canada	32		28/SEP/68	
47293	CF-TME	Air Canada	32		26/SEP/69	
47294	CF-TMP	Air Canada	32		04/NOV/68	
47295	67-22585	United States Air Force	C9A		21/AUG/68	
47296	67-22586	United States Air Force	C9A		24/SEP/68	W/O 16/SEP/71,Scott AFb,III.
47297	68-8932	United States Air Force	C9A		14/OCT/68	
47298	68-8933	United States Air Force	C9A		27/NOV/68	
47299	68-8934	United States Air Force	C9A		18/DEC/68	
47300	68-8935	United States Air Force	C9A		06/FEB/69	
47301	N8965U	Douglas	21			
	LN-RLL	SAS			22/MAR/69	
47302	OY-KGD	SAS	21		11/DEC/68	
	OY-KGD	Touraine Air Transport			11/SEP/81	Leased
	OY-KGD	SAS			23/OCT/82	
47303	SE-DBS	SAS	21		06/JAN/69	
47304	N1794U	Douglas	21			
	LN-RLM	SAS			30/JAN/69	W/O 30/JAN/73, Oslo Ap.
47305	OY-KGE	SAS	21		22/JAN/69	
	OY-KGE	Touraine Air Transport			07/OCT/81	Leased
	OY-KGE	SAS			23/OCT/82	
47306	SE-DBR	SAS	21		27/FEB/69	
47307	LN-RLO	SAS	21		06/MAR/69	
47308	OY-KGF	SAS	21		31/MAR/69	
	OY-KGF	Itavia			18/JUL/80	Leased
	OY-KGF	SAS			OCT/80	
47309	YV-C-AAA	LAV	14		23/OCT/68	
	YV-01C	LAV			76	
	YV-69C	LAV			77	
	YV-69C	Avensa			15/OCT/76	
	N100ME	K.C. Aviation			19/JAN/83	
	N100ME	Midwest Express			01/MAR/84	
47310	N991VJ	Allegheny Airlines	31		05/FEB/69	
	N991VJ	US Air			28/OCT/79	
47311	I-DIKZ	Alitalia	32		21/OCT/68	
47312	EC-BIS	Iberia	32		24/FEB/68	
47313	EC-BIT	Iberia	32		08/MAR/68	
47314	EC-BIU	Iberia	32		28/MAR/68	
47315	N1308T	Texas International	31		10/JAN/69	
	N1308T	Allegheny Airlines			MAY/76	Leased
	N1308T	Texas International				
	N1308T	New York Air			01/DEC/80	
47316	N1309T	Texas International	31		23/JAN/69	
	N1309T	New York Air			08/DEC/80	
47317	N1261L	Delta Airlines	32		09/OCT/68	
47318	N1270L	Delta Airlines	32		14/DEC/68	
47319	N1271L	Delta Airlines	32		06/FEB/69	
47320	N1272L	Delta Airlines	32		19/FEB/69	
47321	N1273L	Delta Airlines	32		28/FEB/69	
47322	N1274L	Delta Airlines	32		26/FEB/69	
	N1274L	Ozark Airlines			10/JUL/79	Leased
	N1274L	Delta Airlines			79	
47323	N1275L	Delta Airlines	32		03/APR/69	
	N1275L	F.B.Ayer			30/NOV/79	
	N1275L	Delta Airlines			79	Leased
47324	N1276L	Delta Airlines	32		16/APR/69	
	N924L	Ozark Airlines			10/JUL/79	
47325	VH-CZF	Ansett Airlines	31		10/JUL/69	
	VH-CZF	Ansett/Air Vanuatu			05/SEP/81	
	VH-CZF	Ansett Airlines			MAY/82	
	162393	US Navy			18/SEP/82	
47326	VH-TJO	Trans Australia Airlines	31		11/JUL/69	
	VH-TJO	Australian Airlines			04/AUG/86	
47327	N8978E	Eastern Air Lines	31		15/OCT/68	
47328	N8979E	Eastern Air Lines	31		17/OCT/68	
47329	N8980E	Eastern Air Lines	31		09/NOV/68	
47330	N8981E	Eastern Air Lines	31		09/NOV/68	
47331	N8982E	Eastern Air Lines	31		15/NOV/68	
47332	N993VJ	Allegheny Airlines	31		27/FEB/69	
	N993VJ	US Air			28/OCT/79	
47333	N994VJ	Allegheny Airlines	31		11/APR/69	W/O 23/JUN/76, Philadelphia, PA
47334	N995VJ	Allegheny Airlines	31		12/MAY/69	
	N995VJ	US Air			28/OCT/79	

MCDONNELL DOUGLAS DC-9

C/N	Registration	Owner/Operator	Series	First Flight	Delivery	Remarks
47335	N996VJ	Allegheny Airlines	31		14/MAY/69	
	N996VJ	US Air			28/OCT/79	
47336	N997VJ	General Electric Credit Corp	31		27/MAY/69	
	N997VJ	Allegheny Airlines	31		27/MAY/69	Leased
	N997VJ	US Air			28/OCT/79	Leased
47337	N9335	Hughes Airwest	31		27/NOV/69	
	N9335	Allegheny Airlines			05/MAR/73	Leased
	N9335	Hughes Airwest			29/NOV/74	
	N9335	Republic			01/JUL/79	
	N9335	Northwest Orient			01/AUG/86	
47338	N9336	Hughes Airwest	31		26/NOV/68	
	N9336	Republic			01/AUG/80	
	N9336	Northwest Orient			01/AUG/86	
47339	I-DIBN	Alitalia	32		11/JAN/69	
47340	CF-TMG	Air Canada	32		07/NOV/68	
47341	CF-TMH	Air Canada	32		07/NOV/68	
47342	CF-TMI	Air Canada	32		27/NOV/68	
47343	N979Z	Ozark Airlines	31		25/FEB/69	
47344	N980Z	Ozark Airlines	31		27/MAR/69	
47345	N981Z	Ozark Airlines	31		21/APR/69	
	N981Z	Allegheny Airlines			18/FEB/74	Leased
	N981Z	Ozark Airlines			14/FEB/76	
47346	N9337	Hughes Airwest	31		06/MAR/69	
	N9337	Republic			01/OCT/80	
	N9337	Northwest Orient			01/AUG/86	
47347	N9338	Hughes Airwest	31		10/APR/69	
	N9338	Republic			01/OCT/80	
	N9338	Northwest Orient			01/AUG/86	
47348	CF-TMJ	Air Canada	32		18/DEC/68	
47349	CF-TMK	Air Canada	32		07/DEC/68	
47350	CF-TML	Air Canada	32		29/DEC/68	
47351	CF-TMM	Air Canada	32			Not taken-up
	6Y-JGA	Air Jamaica			07/MAR/69	
	N958VJ	US Air			19/NOV/80	
47352	CF-TMN	Air Canada	32			Not taken-up
	6Y-JGB	Air Jamaica			07/MAR/69	
	N959VJ	US Air			19/NOV/80	
47353	CF-TMO	Air Canada	32		26/MAR/69	
47354	CF-TMP	Air Canada	32		17/APR/69	
47355	I-DIBK	Alitalia	32F		12/FEB/69	
	N932F	Evergreen International			12/DEC/80	
47356	N1277L	Delta Airlines	32		18/APR/69	
	N1277L	F.B. Ayer			30/NOV/79	
	XA-JEC	Aeromexico			30/NOV/79	Leased
47357	N1278L	Delta Airlines	32		08/MAY/69	
	N925L	Ozark Airlines			24/JUL/79	
47358	N1279L	Delta Airlines	32		08/MAY/69	
	N1279L	Ozark Airlines			24/JUL/79	Leased
	N1279L	Delta Airlines			79	
47359	N1280L	Delta Airlines	32		23/MAY/69	
47360	SE-DBP	SAS	21		12/APR/69	
47361	SE-DBO	SAS	21		01/MAY/69	
47362	N907H	Hawaiian Airlines	31		09/MAY/69	
	N914RW	Hughes Airwest			06/SEP/75	
	N914RW	Ghana Airways			01/MAR/76	Leased
	N914RW	Hughes Airwest			20/JUL/76	
	N914RW	Republic			01/JUL/79	
	N914RW	Northwest Orient			01/AUG/86	
47363	PH-MAO	Martinair	33F		09/FEB/69	
	N502MD	Douglas			28/APR/83	
	N502MD	Muse Air			31/JUL/83	
	N930AX	Airborne Express			29/MAR/84	
47364	EC-BPF	Iberia	32		17/APR/69	
47365	EC-BPG	Iberia	32		07/SEP/79	
47366	68-10958	United States Air Force	C9A		30/SEP/69	
47367	68-10959	United States Air Force	C9A		07/NOV/69	
47368	EC-BPH	Iberia	32		07/JUN/69	
47369	N1798U	Hawaiian Airlines	31		31/OCT/69	
	N1798U	Itavia			11/FEB/74	Leased
	N1798U	Hawaiian Airlines			20/JUL/76	
	N1798U	Southern Airways			20/JUL/76	
	N1798U	Republic			01/JUL/79	
	N1798U	Northwest Orient			01/AUG/86	
47370	N1799U	Hawaiian Airlines	31		30/SEP/71	
	N1799U	Allegheny Airlines			30/OCT/72	Leased
	N1799U	Hawaiian Airlines			30/JUN/73	
	N1799U	Southern Airways			13/NOV/75	
	N1799U	Republic			01/JUL/79	
	N1799U	Northwest Orient			01/AUG/86	
47371	N978VJ	General Electric Credit Corp	31		12/JUN/69	
	N978VJ	Allegheny Airlines			12/JUN/69	Leased
	N978VJ	US Air			28/OCT/79	Leased
47372	N979VJ	General Electric Credit Corp	31		01/JUL/69	
	N979VJ	Allegheny Airlines			01/JUL/69	Leased
	N979VJ	US Air			28/OCT/79	Leased
47373	N964VJ	Allegheny Airlines	31		09/SEP/69	
	N964VJ	US Air			28/OCT/79	
47374	N965VJ	Allegheny Airlines	31		09/SEP/69	
	N965VJ	US Air			28/OCT/79	
47375	N967VJ	Allegheny Airlines	31		16/SEP/69	
	N967VJ	US Air			28/OCT/79	
47376	N394PA	Purdue Airlines	32		22/JUL/69	
	N9346	Hughes Airwest			14/JUL/71	
	N9346	Republic			01/JUL/79	
	N9346	Northwest Orient			01/AUG/86	
47377	N1281L	Delta Airlines	32		27/MAY/69	
47378	N1282L	Delta Airlines	32		02/JUL/69	
47379	N1283L	Delta Airlines	32		10/JUL/69	
47380	N1284L	Delta Airlines	32		08/AUG/69	
	N1284L	Airborne Express	32LWF		12/DEC/80	
	N900AX	Airborne Express			81	
47381	N1285L	Delta Airlines	32		03/SEP/69	
	N901AX	Airborne Express	32LWF		10/FEB/81	
47382	N9339	Hughes Airwest	31		11/APR/69	
	N9339	Purdue Airlines			23/APR/69	Leased
	N9339	Hughes Airwest			12/APR/71	
	N9339	Republic			01/JUL/79	

C/N	Registration	Owner/Operator	Series	First Flight	Delivery	Remarks
	N9339	Northwest Orient			01/AUG/86	
47383	HB-IFV	Swissair	32		03/OCT/69	
47384	HB-IFW	Swissair	33F		23/OCT/69	
	N931AX	Airborne Express			06/MAY/84	
47385	PK-GJE	Garuda	32		15/OCT/69	
	PK-GNA	Garuda				
47386	PK-GJF	Garuda	32		15/NOV/69	
	PK-GNB	Garuda				
47389	N9340	Hughes Airwest	31		25/APR/69	
	N9340	Republic			01/OCT/80	
	N9340	Northwest Orient			01/AUG/86	
47390	N9341	Hughes Airwest	31		13/MAY/69	
	N9341	Republic			01/OCT/80	
	N9341	Northwest Orient			01/AUG/86	
47391	N9342	Hughes Airwest	31		13/MAY/69	
	N9342	Allegheny Airlines			18/NOV/71	Leased
	N9342	Hughes Airwest			28/JUN/72	
	N9342	Republic			01/JUL/79	
	N9342	Northwest Orient			01/AUG/86	
47392	N393PA	Purdue Airlines	33RC		03/FEB/69	
	YU-AJB	Inex Adria			18/MAY/71	
	N928AX	Airborne Express			JUN/85	
47393	N1335U	Southern Airways	31		29/JUN/71	W/O 04/APR/77, New Hope, Ga.
47394	N950PB	Hugh Heffner/Playboy Clubs	32		24/FEB/69	
	N950PB	Purdue Airlines			20/FEB/70	
	N950PB	Ozark Airlines			11/OCT/72	Leased
	N950PB	Hugh Heffner/Playboy Clubs			02/APR/76	
	N950PB	Omni Aircraft Sales			31/MAR/76	
	YV-19C	LAV			09/APR/76	
	XA-JEB	F. B. Ayer			15/JAN/80	
	XA-JEB	Aeromexico			15/JAN/80	Leased
47395	OY-KGG	SAS	41		23/NOV/69	
	HS-TGM	Thai International			29/JAN/70	Leased
	OY-KGG	SAS			01/OCT/71	
	HB-IDY	Swissair			21/NOV/74	Leased
	OY-KGG	SAS			26/SEP/75	
47396	LN-RLR	SAS	41		21/DEC/69	
	HS-TGN	Thai International			27/JAN/70	Leased
	LN-RLD	SAS			01/APR/72	
47397	TC-JAK	Turk Hava Yollari	32		18/AUG/71	
47399	N8983E	Eastern Air Lines	31		24/JAN/69	
47400	N8984E	Eastern Air Lines	31		30/JAN/69	W/O 11/SEP/74, Charlotte, NC.
47401	N8985E	Eastern Air Lines	31		21/MAR/69	
47402	N8986E	Eastern Air Lines	31		08/MAY/69	
47403	N8987E	Eastern Air Lines	31		11/JUL/69	
47404	N1332U	Hawaiian Airlines	31		05/NOV/71	
	N1332U	Allegheny Airlines			05/NOV/71	Leased
	N1332U	Hawaiian Airlines			02/JUN/73	
	N1332U	Allegheny Airlines			16/OCT/73	Leased
	N1332U	Hawaiian Airlines			14/JUN/74	
	N1332U	Southern Airways			14/SEP/75	
	N1332U	Republic			01/JUL/79	
	N1332U	Northwest Orient			01/AUG/86	
47405	N961N	North Central	31		09/MAY/69	
	N961N	Republic			01/JUL/79	
	N961N	Northwest Orient			01/AUG/86	
47406	N962N	North Central	31		23/MAY/69	
	N962N	Republic			01/JUL/79	
	N962N	Northwest Orient			01/AUG/86	
47407	N915U	Universal Airlines	33F		07/MAR/69	Not taken-up
	N935F	Overseas National Airways				Leased
	N935F	ALM			70	W/O 02/MAY/70, St.Croix, USVI
47408		Universal Airlines	33F			Not taken-up
	N936F	Overseas National Airways			14/MAR/69	
	YU-AJP	Inex Adria			30/MAY/75	
	N936F	Evergreen International			77	Leased
	YU-AJP	Inex Adria			79	
	VH-IPF	Ipec Aviation			31/AUG/82	
47409	N937F	Overseas National Airways	33F		22/MAY/69	
	N937F	Ozark Airlines			15/NOV/76	
47410	PH-MAR	Martinair	33F		19/APR/69	
	N909DC	Douglas			15/NOV/82	
	162753	U.S. Navy			29/JUN/83	
47411	N983Z	Ozark Airlines	31		08/DEC/69	
47412	N984Z	Ozark Airlines	31		11/DEC/69	
47413	SE-DBN	SAS	33F		31/JUL/69	
47414	LN-RLW	SAS	33F		03/OCT/69	
47415	N963N	North Central	31		15/SEP/69	
	N963N	Republic			01/JUL/79	
	N963N	Northwest Orient			01/AUG/86	
47416	N964N	North Central	31		31/JUL/70	
	N964N	Republic			01/JUL/79	
	N964N	Northwest Orient			01/AUG/86	
47417	N965N	North Central	31		31/JUL/70	
	N965N	Republic			01/JUL/79	
	N965N	Northwest Orient			01/AUG/86	
47418	VH-TJP	Trans Australia Airlines	31		08/FEB/70	
	VH-TJP	Australian Airlines			04/AUG/86	
47419	VH-TJQ	Trans Australia Airlines	31		17/AUG/70	
	VH-TJQ	Australian Airlines			04/AUG/86	
47420	N966VJ	Allegheny Airlines	31		05/DEC/69	
	N966VJ	US Air			28/OCT/79	
47421	N969VJ	Allegheny Airlines	31		30/MAR/70	
	N969VJ	US Air			28/OCT/79	
47422	CF-TMQ	Air Canada	32		28/FEB/70	
47423	CF-TMR	Air Canada	32		09/APR/70	
	N556NY	New York Air			15/JAN/81	
47424	CF-TMS	Air Canada	32		08/APR/70	
	N557NY	New York Air			03/FEB/81	
47425	YU-AHL	JAT	32		08/MAY/70	
47426	N1286L	Delta Airlines	32		19/FEB/70	
	N902AX	Airborne Express			23/DEC/80	
47427	N1287L	Delta Airlines	32		25/FEB/70	
	N903AX	Airborne Express			09/MAR/81	
47428	EC-BYK	Iberia	33RC		08/AUG/72	
47429	N968VJ	Allegheny Airlines	31		16/JUN/69	

MCDONNELL DOUGLAS DC-9

C/N	Registration	Owner/Operator	Series	First Flight	Delivery	Remarks
	N968VJ	US Air			28/OCT/79	
47430	5H-MOI	East African Airways	32		09/DEC/79	
	5Y-BBH	Kenya Airways			15/JAN/77	
	HB-IKB	Airfinco			08/AUG/77	Leased
	HB-IKB	Alisarda			08/AUG/77	Sub-leased
	I-SARW	Alisarda			19/MAY/81	Sub-leased
	N503MD	McDonnell Douglas			DEC/83	
	G-BMAK	British Midland Airways			17/MAR/84	
47431	I-ATIA	ATI	32		24/JUL/69	
	N506MD	McDonnell Douglas			21/SEP/85	
47432	I-DIZI	Alitalia	32		28/AUG/69	
	I-DIZI	ATI			20/MAY/80	
47433	I-DIZU	Alitalia	32		15/AUG/69	
	I-DIZU	ATI			10/MAY/80	
47434	I-DIZB	Alitalia	32		26/SEP/69	
	I-DIZB	ATI			30/JUN/70	Leased
47435	I-DIZC	Alitalia	32		15/OCT/69	
	I-DIZC	ATI			28/MAY/70	Leased
47436	I-DIZF	Alitalia	32			Not Taken-up
	I-ATIE	ATI			08/OCT/69	
47437	I-DIZG	Alitalia	32			Not taken-up
	I-ATIO	ATI			27/OCT/69	
47438	I-DIZL	Alitalia	32			Not taken-up
	I-ATIU	ATI			07/NOV/69	
47439	N9343	Hughes Airwest	31		04/JUN/69	
	N9343	Republic			01/OCT/80	
	N9343	Northwest Orient			01/AUG/86	
47440	N9344	Hughes Airwest	31		04/JUN/69	
	N9344	Republic			01/OCT/80	
	N9344	Northwest Orient			01/AUG/86	
47441	N9345	Hughes Airwest	31		04/JUN/69	W/O 06/JUN/71, Azusa, Cal.
47442	N1797U	Douglas	32			
	TC-JAG	Turk Hava Yollari			24/AUG/70	
47443	N1795U	Douglas	32			
	N1288L	Delta Airlines			10/APR/70	
47444	N1289L	Delta Airlines	32		09/APR/70	
47445	N1290L	Delta Airlines	32		06/MAY/70	
47446	EC-BQT	Iberia	32		24/DEC/69	
	EC-BQT	Aviaco			82	Leased
	EC-BQT	Iberia			82	
47447	EC-BQU	Iberia	32		08/JAN/70	
	EC-BQU	Aviaco			82	Leased
	EC-BQU	Iberia			82	
47448	68-10960	United States Air Force	C9A		01/DEC/69	
47449	68-10961	United States Air Force	C9A		31/DEC/69	
47450	N1796U	Douglas	32			
	D-ADIT	Atlantis			23/FEB/70	
	N941N	North Central			05/JAN/73	
	N941N	Republic			01/JUL/79	
	N941N	Northwest Orient			01/AUG/86	
47451	N1795U	Douglas	32			
	TC-JAF	Turk Hava Yollari			07/AUG/70	
47452	EC-BYI	Iberia	32		10/MAY/72	
47453	EC-BQV	Iberia	32		09/JAN/70	
47454	EC-BQX	Iberia	32		24/JAN/70	
47455	EC-BQY	Iberia	32		18/MAR/70	
47456	EC-BQZ	Iberia	32		26/MAR/70	
47457	D-ADIU	Atlantis	32		01/APR/71	
	YU-AJO	Inex Adria			13/MAR/73	W/O 30/OCT/75, Sadlec, Czech.
47458	OE-LDF	Austrian Airlines	32		02/DEC/71	
	EC-DSV	Spantax			01/APR/83	Leased
	OE-LDF	Austrian Airlines			05/FEB/84	
47459	D-ADIS	Atlantis	32		15/JAN/70	
	N942N	North Central			02/JAN/73	
	N942N	Republic			01/JUL/79	
	N942N	Northwest Orient			01/AUG/86	
47460	YU-AHV	JAT	32		14/MAY/71	
47461	EC-BYJ	Iberia	32		09/JUN/72	
47462	PH-DNY	KLM	33RC		17/JAN/70	
	PH-DNY	United Aviation Services			30/DEC/85	
	PH-DNY	KLM			30/DEC/85	Leased
47463	PK-GJH	Garuda	32		05/JAN/72	
	PK-GND	Garuda				W/O 13/JAN/80, Banjarmasin, Indonesia
47464	SE-DAN	SAS	41		03/SEP/70	
47465	HB-IDN	Balair	33CF		17/APR/70	
	N7465B	Douglas			07/NOV/76	
	N7465B	Hawaiian Airlines			29/APR/77	
	N7465B	Itavia			30/APR/77	Leased
	N7465B	Hawaiian Airlines			15/JUL/81	WFU 81, stored Oakland
	N7465B	American International			16/NOV/81	Leased
	N7465B	Hawaiian Airlines			01/SEP/84	
	N932AX	Airborne Express			DEC/84	
47466	N1291L	Delta Airlines	32		14/APR/71	
47467	71-874	United States Air Force	C9A		17/DEC/71	
47468	5Y-ALR	East African Airways	32		19/FEB/71	
	5Y-ALR	Kenya Airways			JAN/77	
	5Y-ALR	Air Tanzania			15/JAN/77	Leased
	5Y-ALR	Kenya Airways			OCT/77	
	HB-IKC	Airfinco			13/OCT/77	Leased
	HB-IKC	Alisarda			13/OCT/77	Sub-leased
	I-SARZ	Alisarda			83	Sub-leased
	G-BMAM	British Midland Airways			12/JAN/84	
47469	YU-AHM	JAT	32		13/MAY/70	
	N927RC	Corsair			DEC/85	
	N927RC	Republic			DEC/85	Leased
	N927RC	Northwest Orient			01/AUG/86	Leased
47470	YU-AHN	JAT	32		15/MAY/70	
47471	71-875	United States Air Force	C9A		10/FEB/72	
47472	YU-AHO	JAT	32		08/JUN/70	
47473	YU-AHP	JAT	32		18/JUN/70	
	N926RC	Corsair			NOV/85	
	N926RC	Republic			NOV/85	Leased
	N926RC	Northwest Orient			01/AUG/86	Leased
47474	I-ATIX	ATI	32		04/DEC/70	
	N507MD	McDonnell Douglas			23/OCT/85	
47475	71-876	United States Air Force	C9A		03/MAR/72	

C/N	Registration	Owner/Operator	Series	First Flight	Delivery	Remarks
47476	PH-DNZ	KLM	33RC		06/FEB/70	
	N2679T	Douglas			13/DEC/81	
	YV-139C	Viasa			27/JAN/82	Leased
	YV-139C	Douglas			12/FEB/83	
	162754	U.S. Navy			27/JUN/83	
47477	I-ATIK	ATI	32		26/FEB/71	
	N508MD	McDonnell Douglas			18/JAN/86	
47478	5X-UVY	East African Airways	32		24/FEB/71	
	5Y-BBR	Kenya Airways			15/MAR/77	
47479	HB-IFZ	Swissair	32		18/SEP/70	
	HB-IFZ	Balair			01/APR/79	
	HB-IFZ	Swissair			05/NOV/79	Leased
	HB-IFZ	Balair			27/FEB/80	
47480	HB-IDO	Swissair	32		08/OCT/70	
47481	PK-GJG	Garuda	32		04/FEB/71	
	PK-GNC	Garuda				
47482	YU-AHT	JAT	32		02/FEB/71	W/O 26/JAN/72, Nr. Ceska Kamenice, Czechoslovakia
47484	OE-LDG	Austrian Airlines	32		20/DEC/71	
47485	CF-TMX	Air Canada	32		07/JUL/72	
47486	N1293L	Delta Airlines	32		11/JUN/71	
47487	N1310T	Texas International	31		19/NOV/69	
	N1310T	Allegheny Airlines			03/SEP/74	Leased
	N1310T	Texas International			21/NOV/75	
	N1310T	New York Air			18/FEB/81	
47488	TC-JAD	Turk Hava Yollari	32		27/AUG/69	
47489	TC-JAE	Turk Hava Yollari	32		27/AUG/69	
	TC-JAE	Kibris Turk Hava Yollari			FEB/79	Leased
	TC-JAE	Turk Hava Yollari			80	
47490	N1311T	Texas International	31		17/DEC/69	
	N1311T	New York Air			05/JUN/81	
47491	N985Z	Ozark Airlines	31		25/JUN/70	
47492	SE-DAK	SAS	41		09/JAN/70	
47493	OY-KGH	SAS	41		16/JAN/70	
47494	OY-KGI	SAS	41		15/SEP/70	
47495	71-877	United States Air Force	C9A		31/MAR/72	
47496	EC-BYM	Iberia	33RC		19/SEP/72	
47497	LN-RLB	SAS	41		01/OCT/70	
47498	SE-DAL	SAS	41		25/JAN/70	
47499	SE-DAM	SAS	41		18/FEB/70	
47500	HI-177	Dominicana	32		16/DEC/69	W/O 15/FEB/70, Punta Caucedo Ap.
47501	VH-CZG	Ansett Airlines	31		13/FEB/70	
	N936ML	Midway Airlines			01/MAY/82	
47502	I-DIZE	Alitalia	32		20/FEB/70	
	I-DIZE	ATI			31/MAY/79	
47503	YU-AHR	Inex Adria	32		27/APR/70	W/O 19/MAR/72, Nr. Aden
47504	EC-BYE	Iberia	32		04/FEB/72	
47505	N960VJ	Allegheny Airlines	32		11/JUN/71	
	N960VJ	US Air			28/OCT/79	
47506	N961VJ	Allegheny Airlines	31		18/NOV/70	
	N961VJ	US Air			28/OCT/79	
47507	N962VJ	Allegheny Airlines	31		22/NOV/70	
	N962VJ	US Air			28/OCT/79	
47508	N963VJ	Allegheny Airlines	31		14/JUN/71	
	N963VJ	US Air			28/OCT/79	
47509	SE-DAO	SAS	41		02/DEC/71	
47510	OY-KGK	SAS	41		09/DEC/71	
47511	LN-RLU	SAS	41		01/DEC/72	
47512	SE-DAP	SAS	41		05/DEC/72	
47513	LN-RLX	SAS	41		15/DEC/72	
47514	PH-MAX	Martinair	32		24/FEB/71	
	PH-MAX	Iran Air			JAN/76	Leased
	PH-MAX	Martinair			02/FEB/76	
	PH-MAX	British Midland Airways			08/JAN/79	Leased
	PH-MAX	Martinair			12/JAN/79	
	PH-MAX	ALM			07/DEC/79	Leased
	PH-MAX	Martinair				
	PH-MAX	Nigeria Airways			12/APR/81	Leased
	PH-MAX	Martinair			APR/81	
	PH-MAX	Douglas			18/DEC/81	
	PH-MAX	KLM			18/DEC/81	
47516	N1294L	Delta Airlines	32		24/JUN/71	
47517	N908H	Hawaiian Airlines	31		28/APR/70	
	N908H	Southern Airways			13/APR/76	
	N908H	Republic			01/JUL/79	
	N908H	Northwest Orient			01/AUG/86	
47518	I-DIZO	Alitalia	32		16/FEB/71	
	I-DIZO	ATI			29/SEP/80	
47519	I-DIZF	Alitalia	32		18/FEB/71	
	I-DIZF	Aermediterranea			31/JUN/81	
	I-DIZF	ATI			APR/85	
47520	OE-LDC	Austrian Airlines	32		10/AUG/71	
	OE-LDC	Air Malta			01/NOV/79	Leased
	OE-LDC	Austrian Airlines			01/APR/80	
	N523TX	New York Air			15/OCT/81	
	N523TX	Texas International			01/AUG/82	
	N523NY	New York Air			12/SEP/82	
47521	OE-LDA	Austrian Airlines	32		10/JUN/71	
	N521TX	Texas International			13/DEC/80	
	N521TX	Continental Airlines			31/OCT/82	
47522	N1336U	Douglas	32			
	EC-BYD	Iberia			11/JUN/71	
47523	HB-IDP	Swissair	32		19/NOV/70	
47524	OE-LDB	Austrian Airlines	32		09/JUL/71	
	N522TX	Texas International			21/AUG/81	
	N522TX	Continental Airlines			31/OCT/82	
47525	N1295L	Delta Airlines	32		08/JUL/71	
47526	VH-CZH	Ansett Airlines	31		28/AUG/70	
	N934ML	Midway Airlines			28/FEB/82	
47527	VH-CZI	Ansett Airlines	31		17/FEB/71	
	N930ML	Midway Airlines			10/SEP/81	
47528	VH-TJR	Trans Australia Airlines	31		05/FEB/71	
	VH-TJR	Australian Airlines			04/AUG/86	
47529	N1292L	Delta Airlines	32		12/MAY/71	
47530	YU-AHW	Inex Adria	33RC		22/APR/71	

MCDONNELL DOUGLAS DC-9

C/N	Registration	Owner/Operator	Series	First Flight	Delivery	Remarks
	YU-AHW	Adria Airways			APR/86	
47531	OE-LDE	Austrian Airlines	32		09/SEP/71	
	EC-DQQ	Spantax			28/APR/82	Leased
	OE-LDE	Austrian Airlines			03/APR/83	
	N525TX	Texas International			14/APR/82	
	N525TX	Continental Airlines			31/OCT/82	
	N525NY	New York Air			APR/83	
47532	YU-AHU	JAT	32		07/MAY/71	
47533	I-ATIW	ATI	32		02/DEC/71	
47534	TC-JAL	Turk Hava Yollari	32		09/NOV/71	
47535	HB-IDR	Swissair	32		03/DEC/70	
	N542TX	Texas International			30/SEP/81	
	N542TX	Continental Airlines			31/OCT/82	
47536	71-878	United States Air Force	C9A		05/MAY/72	
47537	71-879	United States Air Force	C9A		24/MAY/72	
47538	71-880	United States Air Force	C9A		30/JUN/72	
47539	OE-LDD	Austrian Airlines	32		26/AUG/71	
	N524TX	Texas International			26/FEB/82	
	N524TX	Continental Airlines			31/OCT/82	
	N524TX	New York Air			20/APR/84	
47540	71-881	United States Air Force	C9A		27/JUL/72	
47541	71-882	United States Air Force	C9A		18/AUG/72	
47542	EC-BYF	Iberia	32		21/FEB/72	
47543	EC-BYG	Iberia	32		29/FEB/72	
47544	I-ATIJ	ATI	32		18/OCT/72	
47545	EC-BYL	Iberia	33RC		29/AUG/72	
47546	CF-TMT	Air Canada	32		21/MAR/72	
47547	VH-CZJ	Ansett Airlines	31		29/MAR/71	
	N932ML	Midway Airlines			12/NOV/81	
47548	VH-CZK	Ansett Airlines	31		19/JUL/71	
	N933ML	Midway Airlines			24/NOV/81	
	N933ML	American International			02/MAR/82	Leased
	N933ML	Midway Airlines			15/DEC/82	
47549	VH-CZL	Ansett Airlines	31		17/NOV/71	
	N935ML	Midway Airlines			21/MAR/82	
47550	VH-TJS	Trans Australia Airlines	31		01/APR/71	
	VH-TJS	Australian Airlines			04/AUG/86	
47551	VH-TJT	Trans Australia Airlines	31		27/JUL/72	
	VH-TJT	Australian Airlines			04/AUG/86	
47552	VH-TJU	Trans Australia Airlines	31		14/OCT/71	
	VH-TJU	Australian Airlines			04/AUG/86	
47553	I-ATIH	ATI	32		09/DEC/71	
	I-ATIH	Aermediterranea			06/MAY/82	
	I-ATIH	ATI			83	
	I-ATIH	Aermediterranea			83	
	I-ATIH	ATI			APR/85	
47554	CF-TMU	Air Canada	32		20/APR/72	
47555	OE-LDH	Austrian Airlines	32		17/JUL/72	
47556	EC-BYH	Iberia	32		10/APR/72	
	EC-BYH	Aviaco			17/MAY/79	
47557	CF-TMV	Air Canada	32		17/MAY/72	
47559	OE-LDI	Austrian Airlines	32		30/AUG/72	
47560	CF-TMW	Air Canada	32		14/JUN/72	
47561	PK-GJI	Garuda	32		21/SEP/72	
	PK-GNE	Garuda				W/O 13/JUN/84, Kemoyoran, Jakarta
47562	N1345U	Douglas	32			
	YU-AJH	JAT			12/FEB/73	
47563	N1346U	Douglas	32			
	YU-AJI	JAT			28/FEB/73	
47564	N950VJ	Allegheny Airlines	31		06/FEB/73	
	N950VJ	US Air			28/OCT/79	
47565	EC-BYN	Iberia	33RC		07/OCT/72	
47566	N949N	North Central	31		10/APR/72	
	N949N	Republic			01/JUL/79	
	N949N	Northwest Orient			01/AUG/86	
47567	N1347U	Douglas	32			
	YU-AJJ	JAT			19/MAR/73	
47568	YU-AJK	JAT	32		06/APR/73	
47569	PK-GJJ	Garuda	32		16/JAN/73	
	PK-GNF	Garuda				
47570	N1343U	Douglas	32			
	YU-AJF	Pan Adria			16/MAY/73	
	YU-AJF	Inex Adria			01/APR/74	Leased
	YU-AJF	Adria Airways			APR/86	
47571	YU-AJL	JAT	32		21/MAY/73	
47572	N940N	North Central	31		25/OCT/73	
	N940N	Republic			01/JUL/79	
	N940N	Northwest Orient			01/AUG/86	
47573	N967N	North Central	31		15/MAY/73	
	N967N	Republic			01/JUL/79	
	N967N	Republic	32		OCT/80	Converted
	N967N	Northwest Orient			01/AUG/86	
47574	N952VJ	Allegheny Airlines	31		17/APR/73	
	N952VJ	US Air			28/OCT/79	
47575	I-ATIY	ATI	32		13/DEC/72	
47576	N951VJ	Allegheny Airlines	31		22/JAN/73	
	N951VJ	US Air			28/OCT/79	
47577	159113	US Navy	C9B		08/MAY/73	
47578	159119	US Navy	C9B		17/AUG/73	
47579	YU-AJN	Inex Adria	32		10/MAY/73	
	YU-AJN	JAT			15/APR/74	Leased
						W/O 23/NOV/74, Surcin Ap, Belgrade
47580	159116	US Navy	C9B		14/SEP/73	
47581	159117	US Navy	C9B		08/MAY/73	
47582	YU-AJM	JAT	32		31/JUL/73	
47583	N953VJ	Allegheny Airlines	31		20/JUN/73	
	N953VJ	US Air			28/OCT/79	
47584	159114	US Navy	C9B		13/JUN/73	
47585	159118	US Navy	C9B		03/JUL/73	
47586	159120	US Navy	C9B		30/OCT/73	
47587	159115	US Navy	C9B		26/JUL/73	
47588	N54630	Douglas	31			
	N956VJ	Allegheny Airlines			07/FEB/74	
	N956VJ	US Air			28/OCT/79	

C/N	Registration	Owner/Operator	Series	First Flight	Delivery	Remarks
47589	N986Z	Ozark Airlines	31		04/DEC/73	
47590	N954VJ	Allegheny Airlines	31		24/AUG/73	
	N954VJ	US Air			28/OCT/79	
47591	I-ATIQ	ATI	32		28/SEP/73	
	I-ATIQ	Aermediterranea			20/DEC/81	
	I-ATIQ	ATI			APR/85	
47592	CF-TMY	Air Canada	32		19/DEC/73	
47593	N955VJ	Allegheny Airlines	31		25/SEP/73	
	N955VJ	US Air			28/OCT/79	
47594	XA-DEJ	Aeromexico	32		11/FEB/74	
47595	MM62012	Italian Air Force	32		19/JAN/74	
47596	SE-DAR	SAS	41		14/JAN/74	
47597	N54631	Douglas	41			
	OY-KGL	SAS			27/FEB/74	
47598	C-FTMZ	Air Canada	32		20/FEB/74	
47599	LN-RLA	SAS	41		29/JAN/74	
47600	N54635	Douglas	32			
	MM62013	Italian Air Force			18/MAR/74	
47601	PK-GJK	Garuda	32		23/JAN/74	
	PK-GNG	Garuda				
47602	XA-DEK	Aeromexico	32		19/FEB/74	
47603	JA8423	Toa Domestic Airlines	41		18/MAR/74	
	OH-LNA	Finnair			29/MAR/81	
	OH-LNA	Touraine Air Transport			24/OCT/82	Leased
	OH-LNA	Finnair			01/SEP/83	
	N935L	Ozark Airlines			25/NOV/83	
47604	JA8424	Toa Domestic Airlines	41		25/MAR/74	
	OH-LNB	Finnair			10/JUN/81	
47605	JA8425	Toa Domestic Airlines	41		10/APR/74	
	OH-LNE	Finnair			15/FEB/82	
47606	JA8426	Toa Domestic Airlines	41		07/MAY/74	
	OH-LND	Finnair			12/JAN/82	
47607	XA-DEL	Aeromexico	32		21/MAR/74	
47608	JA8427	Toa Domestic Airlines	41		13/JUN/74	
47609	XA-DEM	Aeromexico	32		05/APR/74	
47610	SE-DAS	SAS	41		18/APR/74	
47611	C-FTMM	Air Canada	32		25/APR/74	
47612	JA8428	Toa Domestic Airlines	41		11/JUL/74	
47613	JA8429	Toa Domestic Airlines	41		06/OCT/81	
	OH-LNC	Finnair			MAY/82	Leased
	EC-DQT	Aviaco			01/NOV/83	
	OH-LNC	Finnair				
47614	JA8430	Toa Domestic Airlines	41		17/OCT/74	
	OH-LNF	Finnair			12/JAN/83	
47615	JA8432	Toa Domestic Airlines	41		08/NOV/74	
	JA8432	Kogin Lease			29/MAR/82	Leased
	JA8432	Toa Domestic Airlines			29/MAR/82	
47616	JA8433	Toa Domestic Airlines	41		20/DEC/74	
	JA8433	Kogin Lease			29/MAR/82	
	JA8433	Toa Domestic Airlines			29/MAR/82	Leased
47617	JA8434	Toa Domestic Airlines	41		14/FEB/75	
	N933L	Ozark Airlines			26/NOV/82	
47618	N54645	Douglas	41			
	JA8435	Toa Domestic Airlines			25/FEB/75	
	N934L	Ozark Airlines			02/FEB/83	
47619	JA8436	Toa Domestic Airlines	41		20/MAR/75	
47620	JA8437	Toa Domestic Airlines	41		28/JUL/75	
47621	XA-DEN	Aeromexico	32		21/MAY/74	W/O 27/JUL/81, Chihuahua
47622	XA-DEO	Aeromexico	32		15/JAN/75	W/O 08/NOV/81, nr. Zihuatenejo
47623	LN-RLS	SAS	41		14/MAY/74	
47624	OY-KGM	SAS	41		18/JUN/74	
47625	SE-DAT	SAS	41		17/JUL/74	
47626	LN-RLT	SAS	41		24/JUL/74	
47627	SE-DAU	SAS	41		05/AUG/74	
47628	OY-KGN	SAS	41		07/AUG/74	
47629	SE-DAW	SAS	41		05/SEP/74	
47630	LN-RLN	SAS	41		12/SEP/74	
47631	SE-DAX	SAS	41		28/AUG/74	
47632	OY-KGO	SAS	41		04/OCT/74	
47633	SE-DBM	SAS	41		04/NOV/74	
47634	LN-RLZ	SAS	41		18/DEC/74	
47635	PK-GNH	Garuda	32		14/NOV/74	
47636	PK-GNI	Garuda	32		19/DEC/74	W/O 30/DEC/84, Ngurah Rai Ap.
47637	EC-CGN	Aviaco	32		04/JUN/74	
47638	N3504T	Texas International	31		10/JUN/74	
	N3504T	New York Air			29/DEC/80	
47639	6Y-JIJ	Air Jamaica	32		28/JUN/74	
	PJ-SND	ALM			28/JUN/77	Leased
	6Y-JIJ	Air Jamaica			05/NOV/78	
	PJ-SND	ALM			28/APR/80	Leased
	6Y-JIJ	Air Jamaica			06/JUL/80	
	6Y-JIJ	Guinness Peat			15/NOV/82	
	6Y-JIJ	Air Jamaica			15/NOV/82	Leased
	6Y-JIJ	Guinness Peat			MAY/83	
	EC-DTI	Spantax			12/JUN/83	Leased
	EC-DTI	Guinness Peat			83	
	N4549V	American International			01/NOV/83	
	N4549V	Grenada Partnership			25/OCT/84	
	N4549V	US Navy			DEC/84	
47640	EC-CGO	Aviaco	32		02/JUL/74	
47641	I-ATJA	ATI	32		19/SEP/74	
47642	EC-CGP	Aviaco	32		11/OCT/74	
47643	EC-CGQ	Aviaco	32		18/OCT/74	
47644	EC-CGR	Aviaco	32		27/FEB/75	
47645	EC-CGS	Aviaco	32		20/MAR/75	W/O 07/DEC/83, Madrid Ap.
47646	OY-KGP	SAS	41		22/NOV/74	
47647	N943N	North Central	31		13/MAY/75	
	N943N	Republic			01/JUL/79	
	N943N	Northwest Orient			01/AUG/86	
47648	PJ-SNA	ALM	32		16/JAN/75	
47649	N54638	Douglas	32			
	YU-AJR	Inex Adria			28/FEB/75	W/O 10/SEP/76, Nr. Zagreb
47650	XA-DEI	Aeromexico	32		29/MAY/75	
47651	OE-LDK	Austrian Airlines	51		25/AUG/75	
	N675MC	Polaris Leasing			DEC/85	
	N675MC	Muse Air			DEC/85	Leased

C/N	Registration	Owner/Operator	Series	First Flight	Delivery	Remarks
	N675MC	Transtar Airlines			17/FEB/86	Leased
47652	OE-LDL	Austrian Airlines	51		12/DEC/75	
	N676MC	Polaris Leasing			DEC/85	
	N676MC	Transtar Airlines			DEC/85	Leased
47653	I-ATJB	ATI	32		09/JAN/75	
	I-ATJB	Aermediterranea			26/NOV/81	
	I-ATJB	ATI			APR/85	
47654	N54641	Douglas	51	17/DEC/74		Prototype -51
	HB-ISK	Swissair			19/NOV/75	
	HB-ISK	Crown Arcot Corp.			30/AUG/85	
	HB-ISK	Swissair			30/AUG/85	Leased
47655	N54642	Douglas	51			
	HB-ISL	Swissair			12/SEP/75	
	HB-ISL	Crown Arcot Corp.			30/AUG/85	
	HB-ISL	Swissair			30/AUG/85	Leased
47656	HB-ISM	Swissair	51		15/AUG/75	
	HB-ISM	Crown Arcot Corp.			30/AUG/85	
	HB-ISM	Swissair			30/AUG/85	Leased
47657	HB-ISN	Swissair	51		11/SEP/75	
	HB-ISN	Crown Arcot Corp.			30/AUG/85	
	HB-ISN	Swissair			30/AUG/85	Leased
47658	HB-ISO	Swissair	51		30/SEP/75	
	HB-ISO	Crown Arcot Corp.			30/AUG/85	
	HB-ISO	Swissair			30/AUG/85	Leased
47659	HB-ISP	Swissair	51		12/FEB/76	
	N670MC	Muse Air			03/OCT/83	
	N670MC	Transtar Airlines			17/FEB/86	
47660	HB-ISR	Swissair	51		27/FEB/76	
	N671MC	Muse Air			13/OCT/83	
	N671MC	Transtar Airlines			17/FEB/86	
47661	HB-ISS	Swissair	51		10/MAR/76	
	N672MC	Muse Air			06/FEB/84	
	N672MC	Transtar Airlines			17/FEB/86	
47662	HB-IST	Swissair	51		04/FEB/77	
	N679HA	Integrity Aircraft			10/MAR/86	
	N679HA	Hawaiian Airlines			10/MAR/86	Leased
47663	HB-ISU	Swissair	51		16/FEB/77	
	N689HA	Integrity Aircraft			12/APR/86	
	N689HA	Hawaiian Airlines			12/APR/86	Leased
47664	N945N	North Central	31		20/MAY/75	
	N945N	Republic			01/JUL/79	
	N945N	Republic	32		80	Converted
	N945N	Northwest Orient			01/AUG/86	
47665	N923VJ	Allegheny Airlines	51		16/DEC/75	
	N404EA	Eastern Air Lines			01/AUG/78	
47666	PJ-SNB	GATX Leasing	32		11/APR/75	
	PJ-SNB	ALM			11/APR/75	Leased
47667	I-ATJC	ATI	32		19/FEB/75	W/O 13/SEP/79, Cagliari, Sardinia
47668	73-1681	United States Air Force	VC9C		21/FEB/75	
47669	PJ-SNC	ALM	32		13/JUN/75	
47670	73-1682	United States Air Force	VC9C		11/MAR/75	
47671	73-1683	United States Air Force	VC9C		02/MAY/75	
47672	PK-GNJ	Garuda	32		26/JUN/75	
	D-ALLC	Aero Lloyd			15/MAR/82	
47673	PK-GNK	Garuda	32		07/JUL/75	
	D-ALLA	Aero Lloyd			09/MAR/82	
47674	TC-JBK	Turk Hava Yollari	32		22/OCT/75	
47675	EC-CLD	Aviaco	32		25/JUL/75	
47676	N609HA	Hawaiian Airlines	51		10/SEP/75	
	N609HA	Itavia			14/JUN/76	Leased
	N609HA	Hawaiian Airlines			11/JUN/77	
	N609HA	Eastern Air Lines			17/OCT/80	
	N418EA	Eastern Air Lines			04/NOV/80	
47677	N619HA	Hawaiian Airlines	51		07/OCT/75	
	N419EA	Eastern Air Lines			15/JUN/81	
47678	EC-CLE	Aviaco	32		27/SEP/75	
47679	N629HA	Hawaiian Airlines	51		20/NOV/75	
	N629HA	Ghana Airways			20/OCT/77	Leased
	N629HA	Hawaiian Airlines			28/APR/78	
	N421EA	Eastern Air Lines			19/SEP/81	
47680	PK-GNL	Garuda	32		22/JUL/75	
	D-ALLB	Aero Lloyd			15/MAR/82	
47681	160048	US Navy	C9B		18/AUG/75	
47682	N920VJ	Allegheny Airlines	51		28/OCT/75	
	N401EA	Eastern Air Lines			16/NOV/78	
47683	N921VJ	Allegheny Airlines	51		05/NOV/75	
	N402EA	Eastern Air Lines			28/OCT/78	
47684	160046	US Marines	C9B		22/AUG/75	
47685	N922VJ	Allegheny Airlines	51		21/NOV/75	
	N403EA	Eastern Air Lines			01/JUN/78	
47686	N925VJ	Allegheny Airlines	51		27/FEB/76	
	N406EA	Eastern Air Lines			01/AUG/78	Leased
47687	160047	US Marines	C9B		07/NOV/75	
47688	N924VJ	Allegheny Airlines	5i		27/FEB/76	
	N405EA	Eastern Air Lines			07/JUL/78	Leased
47689	N639HA	Hawaiian Airlines	51		19/DEC/75	
	N420EA	Eastern Air Lines			12/SEP/81	
	N420EA	GATX Leasing			DEC/81	
	N420EA	Eastern Air Lines			DEC/81	Leased
47690	KAF-321	Kuwait Air Force	32		30/OCT/76	
47691	KAF-320	Kuwait Air Force	32		15/OCT/76	
47692	N926VJ	Allegheny Airlines	51		12/MAR/76	
	N407EA	Eastern Air Lines			01/SEP/78	
47693	N927VJ	Allegheny Airlines	51		12/MAR/76	
	N408EA	Eastern Air Lines			02/OCT/78	
47694	OH-LYN	Finnair	51		24/JAN/76	
	OH-LYN	Austrian Airlines			23/JUN/84	Leased
	OH-LYN	Finnair			22/JUL/84	
47695	OH-LYO	Finnair	51		01/FEB/76	
47696	OH-LYP	Finnair	51		21/FEB/76	
	N9MD	Toa Domestic Airlines			06/JUN/77	Leased
	OH-LYP	Finnair			30/OCT/78	
47697	N8709Q	Douglas	51			
	YU-AJT	Inex Adria			12/MAY/76	

C/n	Registration	Owner/Operator	Series	First Flight	Delivery	Remarks
	YU-AJT	SAS			06/OCT/84	Leased
	YU-AJT	Inex Adria			30/APR/85	
	YU-AJT	Adria Airways			APR/86	
47698	160049	US Navy	C9B		19/DEC/75	
47699	160050	US Navy	C9B		26/FEB/76	
47700	160051	US Navy	C9B		18/MAR/76	
47701	PK-GNM	Garuda	32		26/MAY/76	
47702	N19B	Douglas	34CF			
	EC-CTR	Aviaco			01/MAY/76	
47703	YV-22C	LAV	51		16/OCT/76	
47704	EC-CTS	Aviaco	34CF		19/OCT/76	
47705	YV-20C	LAV	51		23/NOV/76	
47706	EC-CTT	Aviaco	34CF		21/MAY/76	
47707	EC-CTU	Aviaco	34CF		13/JUL/76	
47708	N760NC	North Central	51		06/APR/76	
	N760NC	Republic			01/JUL/79	
	N760NC	Northwest Orient			01/AUG/86	
47709	N761NC	North Central	51		12/APR/76	
	N761NC	Republic			01/JUL/79	
	N761NC	Northwest Orient			01/AUG/86	
47710	N762NC	North Central	51		23/APR/76	
	N762NC	Toa Domestic Airlines			20/SEP/76	Leased
	N762NC	North Central				
	N762NC	Republic			15/JUL/79	
	N762NC	Northwest Orient			01/AUG/86	
47711	HB-IDT	Balair	34		03/NOV/76	
	N936L	Ozark Airlines			JAN/85	
47712	N649HA	Hawaiian Airlines	51		06/APR/76	
	N649HA	F.B.Ayer			15/DEC/79	
	YV-35C	LAV			15/DEC/79	
47713	N659HA	Hawaiian Airlines	51		03/MAY/76	
	HB-IKH	Airfinco			19/MAY/81	
	HB-IKH	Alisarda			19/MAY/81	Leased
	I-SMEA	Alisarda			MAR/84	Purchased
47714	N669HA	Hawaiian Airlines	51		08/JUN/76	
	HB-IKF	Airfinco			24/FEB/81	
	HB-IKF	Alisarda			24/FEB/81	Leased
	I-SMEI	Alisarda			FEB/84	Purchased
47715	N679HA	Hawaiian Airlines	51		16/JUN/76	
	HB-IKG	Airfinco			06/APR/81	
	HB-IKG	Alisarda			06/APR/81	Leased
	I-SMEU	Alisarda			APR/84	Purchased
47716	N763NC	North Central	51		16/SEP/76	
	N763NC	Toa Domestic Airlines			16/SEP/76	Leased
	N763NC	North Central			14/APR/78	
	N763NC	Republic			01/JUL/79	
	N763NC	Northwest Orient			01/AUG/86	
47717	N764NC	North Central	51		21/DEC/76	
	N764NC	Republic			01/JUL/79	
	N764NC	Northwest Orient			01/AUG/86	
47718	N765NC	North Central	51		24/NOV/76	
	N765NC	Republic			01/JUL/79	
	N765NC	Northwest Orient			01/AUG/86	
47719	YV-21C	LAV	51		12/NOV/76	
47720	YV-23C	LAV	32		18/NOV/76	
47721	YV-25C	LAV	32		10/DEC/76	
47722	PK-GNN	Garuda	32		04/AUG/76	
47723	TC-JBL	Turk Hava Yollari	32		30/SEP/76	
47724	N767NC	North Central	51		05/APR/77	
	N767NC	Republic			01/JUL/79	
	N767NC	Northwest Orient			01/AUG/86	
47725	OY-KGR	SAS	41		29/JUL/76	
47726	OE-LDM	Austrian Airlines	51		18/DEC/76	
	N673MC	Muse Air			20/MAR/84	
	N673MC	Transtar Airlines			17/FEB/86	
47727	YV-24C	LAV	32		17/DEC/76	
47728	N991EA	Eastern Air Lines	51		13/JUL/77	
	N409EA	Eastern Air Lines			78	
47729	N768NC	North Central	51		27/MAY/77	
	N768NC	Republic			01/JUL/79	
	N768NC	Northwest Orient			01/AUG/86	
47730	PK-GNO	Garuda	32		15/AUG/76	
47731	N992EA	Eastern Air Lines	51			
	N410EA	Eastern Air Lines			78	
47732	N993EA	Eastern Air Lines	51		31/AUG/77	
	N411EA	Eastern Air Lines			78	
47733	N994EA	Eastern Air Lines	51		22/SEP/77	
	N412EA	Eastern Air Lines			78	
47734	N920L	Ozark Airlines	32		23/NOV/77	
	YU-AJX	Inex Adria			APR/80	Leased
	N920L	Ozark Airlines				
47735	OE-LDN	Austrian Airlines	51		03/DEC/77	
	N674MC	Muse Air			26/MAR/84	
	N674MC	Transtar Airlines			17/FEB/86	
47736	OH-LYR	Finnair	51		16/SEP/76	
47737	OH-LYS	Finnair	51		24/JUL/76	
	9Y-TFF	BWIA			24/JUL/76	Leased
	OH-LYS	Finnair			24/JUL/77	
47738	OH-LYT	Finnair	51		04/OCT/76	
	OH-LYT	Alisarda			01/APR/84	Leased
	OH-LYT	Finnair			01/NOV/84	
47739	N766NC	North Central	51		25/MAR/77	
	N766NC	Republic			01/JUL/79	
	N766NC	Northwest Orient			01/AUG/86	
47740	PK-GNP	Garuda	32		01/NOV/76	
47741	PK-GNQ	Garuda	32		16/DEC/76	
47742	9Y-TFG	BWIA	51		21/JUN/77	
47743	9Y-TFH	BWIA	51		29/JUL/77	
47744	PK-GNR	Garuda	32		06/JAN/77	
47745	N995EA	Eastern Air Lines	51		05/OCT/77	
	N413EA	Eastern Air Lines			78	
47746	N996EA	Eastern Air Lines	51		21/OCT/77	
	N414EA	Eastern Air Lines			78	
47747	SE-DDP	SAS	41		24/NOV/76	
47748	LN-RLH	SAS	41		01/NOV/77	
47749	N997EA	Eastern Air Lines	51		03/NOV/77	

MCDONNELL DOUGLAS DC-9

C/N	Registration	Owner/Operator	Series	First Flight	Delivery	Remarks
	N415EA	Eastern Air Lines			78	
47750	SE-DDR	SAS	41		16/DEC/77	
47751	N998EA	Eastern Air Lines	51		14/NOV/77	
	N416EA	Eastern Air Lines			78	
47752	9Y-TFI	BWIA	34CF		13/JAN/78	
47753	N999EA	Eastern Air Lines	51		21/NOV/77	
	N417EA	Eastern Air Lines			78	
47754	YU-AJU	Inex Adria	51		19/MAY/77	
	YU-AJU	SAS			15/SEP/83	Leased
	YU-AJU	Inex Adria			01/APR/84	
	YU-AJU	SAS			15/OCT/84	Leased
	YU-AJU	Inex Adria			31/MAY/85	
	YU-AJU	Adria Airways			APR/86	
47755	9G-ACM	Ghana Airways	51		13/JUL/78	
47756	OE-LDO	Austrian Airlines	51	20/JAN/78	31/JAN/78	
	N677MC	Polaris Leasing			DEC/85	
	N677MC	Muse Air			DEC/85	Leased
	N677MC	Transtar Airlines			14/FEB/86	
47757	N769NC	North Central	51		10/MAY/78	
	N769NC	Republic			01/JUL/79	
	N769NC	Northwest Orient			01/AUG/86	
47758	N770NC	North Central	51		28/JUL/78	
	N770NC	Republic			01/JUL/79	
	N770NC	Northwest Orient			01/AUG/86	
47759	JA8439	Toa Domestic Airlines	41		16/DEC/77	
47760	JA8440	Toa Domestic Airlines	41		08/FEB/78	
47761	N8710Q	Douglas				
	JA8441	Toa Domestic Airlines	41		06/MAR/78	
47762	JA8442	Toa Domestic Airlines	41		21/APR/78	
47763	N699HA	Hawaiian Airlines	51		11/JUL/78	
47764	N709HA	Hawaiian Airlines	51		15/AUG/78	
	N709HA	North Central			15/AUG/78	Leased
	N709HA	Hawaiian Airlines			15/JUN/79	
47765	N3506T	Texas International	32		14/MAR/79	
	N3506T	Continental Airlines			31/OCT/82	
47766	OY-KGS	SAS	41		14/OCT/78	
47767	JA8448	Toa Domestic Airlines	41		20/SEP/78	
47768	JA8449	Toa Domestic Airlines	41		07/OCT/78	
47769	N771NC	North Central	51		11/AUG/78	
	N771NC	Republic			01/JUL/79	
	N771NC	Northwest Orient			01/AUG/86	
47770	YV-32C	LAV	51		22/NOV/78	
47771	OH-LYU	Finnair	51		09/SEP/78	
47772	N8713Q	Finnair	51		07/DEC/78	
	N8713Q	Austral			07/DEC/78	Leased
	OH-LYV	Finnair			03/APR/80	
47773	N8714Q	Finnair	51		14/DEC/78	
	N8714Q	Austral			14/DEC/78	Leased
	OH-LYW	Finnair			28/NOV/80	
47774	N772NC	North Central	51		01/SEP/78	
	N772NC	Republic			01/JUL/79	
	N772NC	Northwest Orient			01/AUG/86	
47775	N773NC	North Central	51		26/OCT/78	
	N773NC	Republic			01/JUL/79	
	N773NC	Northwest Orient			01/AUG/86	
47776	N774NC	North Central	51		14/NOV/78	
	N774NC	Republic			01/JUL/79	
	N774NC	Northwest Orient			01/AUG/86	
47777	SE-DDS	SAS	41		30/JAN/79	
47778	LN-RLP	SAS	41		07/FEB/79	
47779	N1002L	Douglas	41			
	SE-DDT	SAS			07/MAR/79	
47780	JA8450	Toa Domestic Airlines	41		09/JAN/79	
47781	JA8451	Toa Domestic Airlines	41		31/JAN/79	
47782	YV-33C	LAV	51		21/DEC/78	
47783	HB-ISV	Swissair	51		07/MAR/79	
47784	HB-ISW	Swissair	51		02/MAY/79	
47785	N775NC	North Central	51		20/APR/79	
	N775NC	GATX Leasing			15/JUL/79	
	N775NC	Republic			15/JUL/79	Leased
	N775NC	Northwest Orient			01/AUG/86	Leased
47786	N776NC	North Central	51		27/APR/79	
	N776NC	GATX Leasing			15/JUL/79	
	N776NC	Republic			15/JUL/79	Leased
	N776NC	Northwest Orient			01/AUG/86	Leased
47787	N777NC	North Central	51		22/JUN/79	
	N777NC	GATX Leasing			15/JUL/79	
	N777NC	Republic			15/JUL/79	Leased
	N777NC	Northwest Orient			01/AUG/86	Leased
47788	N3507T	Texas International	32		14/MAR/79	
	N3507T	Continental Airlines			31/OCT/82	
47789	PK-GNS	Garuda	32		11/MAY/79	
47790	PK-GNT	Garuda	32		16/MAY/79	
47791	PK-GNU	Garuda	32		25/MAY/79	
47792	PK-GNV	Garuda	32		13/JUN/79	
47793	PK-GNW	Garuda	32		20/JUN/79	
47794	PK-GNX	Garuda	32		28/JUL/79	
47795	PK-GNY	Garuda	32		06/AUG/79	
47796	9Y-TGC	BWIA	51		18/APR/79	
47797	N3508T	Texas International	32		03/JUL/79	
	N3508T	Continental Airlines			31/OCT/82	
47798	N3509T	Texas International	32		12/JUL/79	
	N3509T	Continental Airlines			31/OCT/82	
47799	N3510T	Texas International	32		21/AUG/79	
	N3510T	Continental Airlines			31/OCT/82	
48100	N778NC	GATX Leasing	51		02/NOV/79	
	N778NC	Republic			02/NOV/79	Leased
	N778NC	Northwest Orient			01/AUG/86	Leased
48101	N779NC	GATX Leasing	51		07/DEC/79	
	N779NC	Republic			07/DEC/79	Leased
	N779NC	Northwest Orient			01/AUG/86	Leased
48102	N780NC	GATX Leasing	51		14/DEC/79	
	N780NC	Republic			14/DEC/79	Leased
	N780NC	Northwest Orient			01/AUG/86	Leased
48103	EC-DGB	Aviaco	34		31/OCT/79	
48104	EC-DGC	Aviaco	34		19/NOV/79	

C/N	Registration	Owner/Operator	Series	First Flight	Delivery	Remarks
48105	EC-DGD	Aviaco	34		30/NOV/79	
48106	EC-DGE	Aviaco	34		27/DEC/79	
48107	N782NC	GATX Leasing	51		24/JAN/80	
	N782NC	Republic			24/JAN/80	Leased
	N782NC	Northwest Orient			01/AUG/86	Leased
48108	N783NC	GATX Leasing	51		30/JAN/80	
	N783NC	Republic			30/JAN/80	Leased
	N783NC	Northwest Orient			01/AUG/86	Leased
48109	N784NC	GATX Leasing	51		20/FEB/80	
	N784NC	Republic			20/FEB/80	Leased
	N784NC	Northwest Orient			01/AUG/86	Leased
48110	N785NC	Republic	51		01/APR/80	
	N785NC	Northwest Orient			01/AUG/86	
48111	N3512T	Texas International	32		09/OCT/79	
	N3512T	Continental Airlines			31/OCT/82	
48112	N3513T	Texas International	32		02/NOV/79	
	N3513T	Continental Airlines			31/OCT/82	
48113	N3514T	Texas International	32		06/DEC/79	
	N3514T	Continental Airlines			31/OCT/82	
48114	N934VJ	US Air	31		28/AUG/79	
48115	N935VJ	US Air	31		11/SEP/79	
48116	N936VJ	US Air	31		19/SEP/79	
48117	N937VJ	US Air	31		28/SEP/79	
48118	N929VJ	US Air	31		03/MAR/80	
48119	N938VJ	US Air	31		12/MAR/80	
48120	N939VJ	US Air	31		25/APR/80	
48121	N781NC	GATX Leasing	51		28/DEC/79	
	N781NC	Republic			28/DEC/79	Leased
	N781NC	Northwest Orient			01/AUG/86	Leased
48122	9Y-TGP	BWIA	51		27/JAN/80	
48123	N927L	Ozark Airlines	34		28/DEC/79	
48124	N928L	Ozark Airlines	34		10/JUN/80	
48125	XA-AMA	Aeromexico	32		04/APR/80	
48126	XA-AMB	Aeromexico	32		30/APR/80	
48127	XA-AMC	Aeromexico	32		25/JUL/80	
48128	XA-AMD	Aeromexico	32		20/AUG/80	
48129	XA-AME	Aeromexico	32		11/NOV/80	
48130	XA-AMF	Aeromexico	32		05/DEC/80	
48131	N928VJ	US Air	31		20/FEB/80	
48132	PH-DOA	KLM	32		10/JUN/80	
48133	PH-DOB	KLM	32		21/JUL/80	
48134	OH-LYX	Finnair	51		25/JAN/81	
48135	OH-LYY	Finnair	51		24/MAR/81	
48136	OH-LYZ	Finnair	51		23/APR/81	
48137	161266	U.S.Navy	C9B		17/MAR/81	
48138	N918VJ	US Air	31		14/OCT/81	
48139	N919VJ	US Air	31		21/OCT/81	
48140	N920VJ	US Air	31		17/NOV/81	
48141	N921VJ	US Air	31		01/DEC/81	
48142	N922VJ	US Air	31		08/DEC/81	
48143	N923VJ	US Air	31		14/DEC/81	
48144	N924VJ	US Air	31		18/DEC/81	
48145	N925VJ	US Air	31		22/DEC/81	
48146	N926VJ	US Air	31		14/JAN/82	
48147	N976VJ	US Air	31		08/FEB/82	
48148	N786NC	GATX Leasing	51		31/DEC/80	
	N786NC	Republic			31/DEC/80	Leased
	N786NC	Northwest Orient			01/AUG/86	Leased
48149	N787NC	Republic	51		17/APR/81	
	N787NC	Northwest Orient			01/AUG/86	
48150	XA-AMG	Aeromexico	32			Reg.not taken-up
	N1003P	Aeromexico			08/OCT/81	
48151	XA-AMH	Aeromexico	32		NOV/81	Reg.not taken-up
	N1003U	Aeromexico			24/NOV/81	
48154	N927VJ	US Air	31		25/JAN/82	
48155	N977VJ	US Air	31		16/FEB/82	
48156	N980VJ	US Air	31		11/MAR/82	
48157	N981VJ	US Air	31		18/MAR/82	
48158	N982VJ	US Air	31		25/MAR/82	
48159	N983VJ	US Air	31		06/APR/82	
48165	161529	U.S. Navy	C9B		30/SEP/82	
48166	161530	U.S. Navy	C9B		28/OCT/82	

5H- Tanzania

47430	5H-MOI

5X- Uganda

47478	5X-UVY

5Y- Kenya

47468	5Y-ALR
47430	5Y-BBH
47478	5Y-BBR

6Y- Jamaica

47351	6Y-JGA
47352	6Y-JGB
47639	6Y-JIJ

9G- Ghana

47755	9G-ACM

9Y- Trinidad & Tobago

47737	9Y-TFF
47742	9Y-TFG
47743	9Y-TFH
47752	9Y-TFI
47796	9Y-TGC
48122	9Y-TGP

C/CF- Canada

45846	C-FTKL
47020	C-FTLK
47023	C-FTLN
47070	C-FTLR
47611	C-FTMM
47598	C-FTMZ
47152	C-FTOU
45846	CF-TKL
45711	CF-TLB
45712	CF-TLC
45713	CF-TLD
45725	CF-TLE
45726	CF-TLF
45727	CF-TLG
45845	CF-TLH
47019	CF-TLJ
47020	CF-TLK
47021	CF-TLL
47022	CF-TLM
47023	CF-TLN
47024	CF-TLO
47068	CF-TLP
47069	CF-TLQ
47070	CF-TLR
47071	CF-TLS
47195	CF-TLT
47196	CF-TLU
47197	CF-TLV
47198	CF-TLW
47199	CF-TLX
47200	CF-TLY
47265	CF-TLZ
47266	CF-TMA
47289	CF-TMB
47290	CF-TMC
47292	CF-TMD
47293	CF-TME
47294	CF-TMF
47340	CF-TMG
47341	CF-TMH
47342	CF-TMI
47348	CF-TMJ
47349	CF-TMK
47350	CF-TML
47351	CF-TMM
47041	CF-TMN
47352	CF-TMN
47353	CF-TMO
47354	CF-TMP
47422	CF-TMQ
47423	CF-TMR
47424	CF-TMS
47546	CF-TMT
47554	CF-TMU
47557	CF-TMV
47560	CF-TMW
47485	CF-TMX
47592	CF-TMY
45826	CF-TON
47010	CF-TOO
47011	CF-TOP
47012	CF-TOQ
47013	CF-TOR
47014	CF-TOS
47015	CF-TOT
47152	CF-TOU

D- West Germany

47218	D-ACEB
47219	D-ACEC
47459	D-ADIS
47450	D-ADIT
47457	D-ADIU
47673	D-ALLA
47680	D-ALLB
47672	D-ALLC
47787	D-AMOR

EC- Spain

47037	EC-BIG
47076	EC-BIH
47077	EC-BII
47079	EC-BIJ
47080	EC-BIK
47084	EC-BIL
47088	EC-BIM
47089	EC-BIN
47090	EC-BIO
47091	EC-BIP
47092	EC-BIQ
47093	EC-BIR
47312	EC-BIS
47313	EC-BIT
47314	EC-BIU
47364	EC-BPF
47365	EC-BPG
47368	EC-BPH
47446	EC-BQT
47447	EC-BQU
47453	EC-BQV
47454	EC-BQX
47455	EC-BQZ
47456	EC-BYD
47504	EC-BYE
47542	EC-BYF
47543	EC-BYG
47556	EC-BYH
47452	EC-BYI
47461	EC-BYJ
47428	EC-BYK
47545	EC-BYL
47496	EC-BYM
47565	EC-BYN
47637	EC-CGN
47640	EC-CGO
47642	EC-CGP
47643	EC-CGQ
47644	EC-CGR
47645	EC-CGS
45696	EC-CGY
45699	EC-CGZ
47675	EC-CLD
47678	EC-CLE
47702	EC-CTR
47704	EC-CTS
47706	EC-CTT
47707	EC-CTU
48103	EC-DGB
48104	EC-DGC
48105	EC-DGD
48106	EC-DGE
45698	EC-DIR
45792	EC-DQP
47531	EC-DQQ
47613	EC-DQT
47458	EC-DSV
47639	EC-DTI

G- United Kingdom

47048	G-BFIH
47048	G-BMAA
45738	G-BMAB
45739	G-BMAC
45719	G-BMAG
45712	G-BMAH
45713	G-BMAI
45730	G-BMAJ
47430	G-BMAK
47468	G-BMAL

HB- Switzerland

45702	HB-IAA
47465	HB-IDN
47480	HB-IDO
47523	HB-IDP
47535	HB-IDR
47711	HB-IDT
47116	HB-IDV
47115	HB-IDW
47117	HB-IDX
47395	HB-IDY
45702	HB-IEF
45731	HB-IFA
45732	HB-IFB
45785	HB-IFC
45786	HB-IFD
45787	HB-IFE
45788	HB-IFF
45789	HB-IFG
45790	HB-IFH
45791	HB-IFI
45792	HB-IFK
47793	HB-IFL
45847	HB-IFM
47094	HB-IFN
47110	HB-IFO
47111	HB-IFP
47112	HB-IFR
47113	HB-IFS
47281	HB-IFT
47282	HB-IFU
47383	HB-IFV
47384	HB-IFW
47218	HB-IFX
47219	HB-IFY
47479	HB-IFZ
47430	HB-IKB
47468	HB-IKC
47714	HB-IKF
47715	HB-IKG
47713	HB-IKH
47654	HB-ISK
47655	HB-ISL
47656	HB-ISM
47657	HB-ISN
47658	HB-ISO
47659	HB-ISP
47660	HB-ISR
47661	HB-ISS
47662	HB-IST
47663	HB-ISU
47783	HB-ISV
47784	HB-ISW

HI- Dominican Republic

47500	HI-177

HK- Colombia

45721	HK-2864
45722	HK-2865

HL South Korea

45827	HL7201
45787	HL7205

HP- Panama

45786	HP-505

HS- Thailand

47395	HS-TGM
47396	HS-TGN

HZ- Saudi Arabia

47000	HZ-AEA
47001	HZ-AEB
47002	HZ-AEC

I- Italy

47431	I-ATIA
47436	I-ATIE
47553	I-ATIH
47544	I-ATIJ
47477	I-ATIK
47591	I-ATIO
47437	I-ATIQ
47438	I-ATIU
47533	I-ATIW
47474	I-ATIX
47575	I-ATIY
47641	I-ATJA
47653	I-ATJB
47667	I-ATJC
47233	I-DIBC
47234	I-DIBD
47235	I-DIBJ
47355	I-DIBK
47339	I-DIBN
47237	I-DIBO
47236	I-DIBQ
47038	I-DIKA
47118	I-DIKB
47128	I-DIKC
47129	I-DIKD
47039	I-DIKE
47220	I-DIKF
47221	I-DIKG
47046	I-DIKI
47222	I-DIKJ
47223	I-DIKL
47224	I-DIKM
47225	I-DIKN
47047	I-DIKO
47226	I-DIKP
47227	I-DIKQ
47228	I-DIKR
47229	I-DIKS
47230	I-DIKT
47101	I-DIKU
47231	I-DIKV
47283	I-DIKW
47232	I-DIKY
47311	I-DIKZ
47238	I-DIZA
47434	I-DIZB
47435	I-DIZC
47502	I-DIZE
47239	I-DIZE
47436	I-DIZF
47519	I-DIZF
47437	I-DIZG
47432	I-DIZI
47438	I-DIZL
47518	I-DIZO
47433	I-DIZU
45702	I-SARJ
45706	I-SARV
47430	I-SARW
47468	I-SARZ
47713	I-SMEA
47714	I-SMEI
47715	I-SMEU
45728	I-TIGA
47002	I-TIGB
45717	I-TIGE
45724	I-TIGI
45718	I-TIGU

JA Japan

47603	JA8423
47604	JA8424
47605	JA8425
47606	JA8426
47608	JA8427
47612	JA8428
47613	JA8429
47614	JA8430
47615	JA8432
47616	JA8433
47617	JA8434
47618	JA8435
47619	JA8436
47620	JA8437
47759	JA8439
47760	JA8440
47761	JA8441
47762	JA8442
47767	JA8448
47768	JA8449
47780	JA8450
47781	JA8451

LN- Norway

47599	LN-RLA
47497	LN-RLB
47179	LN-RLC
47748	LN-RLH
47287	LN-RLJ
47116	LN-RLK
47301	LN-RLL
47304	LN-RLM
47630	LN-RLN
47307	LN-RLO
47778	LN-RLP
47396	LN-RLR
47623	LN-RLS
47111	LN-RLS
47626	LN-RLT
47511	LN-RLU
47414	LN-RLW
47513	LN-RLX
47634	LN-RLZ
47179	LN-RTF
47287	LN-RTG
47116	LN-RTO

N United States

47779	N1002L
48150	N1003P
48151	N1003U
47309	N100ME
45714	N1051T
45715	N1052T
45716	N1053T
45735	N1054T
45736	N1055T
45737	N1056T
45738	N1057T
45739	N1058T
45740	N1059T
45741	N1060T
45775	N1061T
45776	N1062T
45777	N1063T
45778	N1064T
45779	N1065T
45780	N1066T
45781	N1067T
45782	N1068T
45783	N1069T
45784	N1070T
47151	N112AK
45732	N119
47317	N1261L
47257	N1262L
47258	N1263L
47259	N1264L
47260	N1265L
47261	N1266L
47262	N1267L
47284	N1268L
47285	N1269L
47318	N1270L
47319	N1271L
47320	N1272L
47321	N1273L
47322	N1274L
47323	N1275L
47324	N1276L
47356	N1277L
47357	N1278L
47358	N1279L
47359	N1280L
47377	N1281L
47378	N1282L
47379	N1283L
47380	N1284L
47381	N1285L
47426	N1286L
47427	N1287L
47443	N1288L
47444	N1289L
47445	N1290L
47466	N1291L
47529	N1292L
47486	N1293L
47516	N1294L
47525	N1295L
46595	N1301T
47043	N1302T
47044	N1303T
47045	N1304T
47055	N1305T
47061	N1306T
47062	N1307T
47315	N1308T
47316	N1309T
47487	N1310T
47490	N1311T
47404	N1332U
47280	N1334U
47393	N1335U
47522	N1336U
47570	N1343U
47562	N1345U
47563	N1346U
47567	N1347U
45713	N13614
45711	N13699
45706	N13FE
45725	N15335
45702	N15NP
45785	N1790U
45786	N1791U
45712	N1792U
45787	N1793U
47304	N1794U
47443	N1795U
47451	N1795U
47450	N1796U
47442	N1797U
47369	N1798U
47370	N1799U
47702	N19B
47151	N228Z
45775	N241TC
45725	N25AS
47476	N2679T
47283	N2786S
47223	N2786T
45841	N2892Q
45722	N2896W
45732	N29
45739	N29259
45826	N29AF
45731	N2H
45718	N300ME
45740	N310MJ
45696	N3301L
45697	N3302L
45698	N3303L
45699	N3304L
45700	N3305L
45701	N3306L
45702	N3307L
45703	N3308L
45704	N3309L
45705	N3310L
45706	N3311L
45707	N3312L
45708	N3313L
45709	N3314L
45710	N3315L
47025	N3316L
47026	N3317L
47027	N3318L
47028	N3319L
47029	N3320L
47030	N3321L
47031	N3322L
47032	N3323L

c/n	reg	c/n	reg	c/n	reg	c/n	reg	c/n	reg
47103	N3324L	47424	N557NY	47014	N8906	47121	N8989E	45698	N931EA
47104	N3325L	47045	N558HA	47547	N8906E	47120	N8990E	47040	N931F
47105	N3326L	47014	N561PC	47015	N8907	47042	N895	47173	N931L
47106	N3327L	47012	N562PC	45748	N8907E	47380	N900AX	47202	N931ML
47107	N3328L	47055	N563PC	47152	N8908	45710	N900AL	47188	N931VJ
47108	N3329L	47062	N564PC	45749	N8908E	45846	N901AK	47465	N932AX
47109	N3330L	47240	N565PC	47016	N8909	47381	N901AX	45699	N932EA
47172	N3331L	45828	N566PC	45770	N8909E	45731	N901B	47041	N932F
47172	N3331L	47153	N567PC	47153	N8910	47038	N901DC	47355	N932F
47173	N3332L	47086	N568PC	45771	N8910E	45717	N901H	47506	N961VJ
47174	N3333L	45726	N5726	47017	N8911	47104	N901ML	47406	N962N
47175	N3334L	45727	N5728	45825	N8911E	47020	N902AK	47507	N962VJ
47176	N3335L	47041	N59T	47154	N8912	47426	N902AX	47415	N963N
47177	N3336L	45706	N5NE	45829	N8912E	47039	N902DC	47508	N963VJ
47273	N3337L	45702	N5NP	47018	N8913	45724	N902H	47416	N964N
47274	N3338L	45725	N600ME	45830	N8913E	47105	N902ML	47373	N964VJ
47275	N3339L	47676	N609HA	47155	N8914	47427	N903AX	47417	N965N
47276	N3340L	47011	N60AF	45831	N8914E	47046	N903DC	47374	N965VJ
47638	N3504T	45731	N60FM	47086	N8915	45730	N903EA	47420	N966VJ
45788	N3505T	47049	N6140A	45832	N8915E	47149	N903H	47573	N967N
47765	N3506T	47677	N619HA	47156	N8916	47023	N904AK	47121	N967PR
47788	N3507T	45726	N626TX	45733	N8916E	47068	N904AX	47375	N967VJ
47797	N3507T	45727	N628TX	47087	N8917	47040	N904AX	45711	N9684Z
47798	N3509T	47679	N629HA	47734	N8917E	47047	N904DC	45786	N968E
47799	N3510T	47689	N639HA	45828	N8918	47023	N905AK	47429	N968VJ
48111	N3512T	47712	N649HA	45833	N8918E	47147	N905AX	47429	N968VJ
48112	N3513T	45714	N651TX	47240	N8919	47101	N905DC	47421	N969VJ
48113	N3514T	45715	N652TX	45834	N8919E	47150	N905H	47001	N969Z
47060	N38641	47048	N6535S	47006	N891PS	47070	N906AK	47206	N96S
47392	N393PA	45716	N653TX	45835	N8920E	47072	N906AX	47053	N970NE
47376	N394PA	45735	N654TX	45836	N8921E	47129	N906DC	47050	N970VJ
47175	N3991C	45736	N655TX	45837	N8922E	47171	N906H	45772	N970Z
45727	N400ME	47713	N659HA	45838	N8923E	47203	N907AX	47054	N971NE
47682	N401EA	47152	N65AF	45839	N8924E	47362	N907H	47051	N971VJ
47683	N402EA	47714	N669HA	45840	N8925E	47008	N908AX	45773	N971Z
47685	N403EA	47152	N66AF	45863	N8926E	45721	N908DC	47057	N972NE
47665	N404EA	47659	N670MC	45864	N8927E	47517	N908H	47052	N972VJ
47688	N405EA	47660	N671MC	45865	N8928E	47148	N909AX	45841	N972Z
47686	N406EA	47661	N672MC	45866	N8929E	47410	N909DC	47058	N973NE
47692	N407EA	47726	N673MC	47139	N8930E	47244	N90S	47099	N973VJ
47693	N408EA	47735	N674MC	47140	N8931E	47794	N9101	47033	N973Z
47728	N409EA	47651	N675MC	47141	N8932E	45795	N9102	47066	N974NE
47731	N410EA	47652	N676MC	47142	N8933E	45796	N9103	47130	N974VJ
47732	N411EA	47756	N677MC	47143	N8934E	47081	N9104	47034	N974Z
47733	N412EA	47662	N679HA	47144	N8935E	47138	N9105	47075	N975NE
47745	N413EA	47715	N679HA	47145	N8936E	47263	N9106	47146	N975VJ
47746	N414EA	47663	N689HA	47158	N8937E	47264	N9107	47035	N975Z
47749	N415EA	47763	N699HA	47161	N8938E	47149	N911RW	47082	N976NE
47751	N416EA	45846	N705PS	47162	N8939E	47150	N912RW	48147	N976VJ
47753	N417EA	47020	N706PS	47163	N8940E	47171	N913RW	47248	N976Z
47676	N418EA	47023	N707PS	47164	N8941E	47362	N914RW	47095	N977NE
47677	N419EA	47068	N708PS	47165	N8942E	47068	N915CL	48155	N977VJ
47689	N420EA	47764	N709HA	47166	N8943E	47139	N915RW	47249	N977Z
47679	N421EA	47014	N70AF	47167	N8944E	47407	N915U	47096	N978NE
47222	N43265	45740	N711SW	47181	N8945E	47144	N916RW	47371	N978VJ
45549	N4549V	47023	N715CL	47182	N8946E	47145	N917RW	47250	N978Z
45723	N48075	47015	N72AF	47183	N8947E	47158	N918RW	47097	N979NE
45721	N48200	47013	N73AF	47184	N8948E	48138	N918VJ	47372	N979VJ
45798	N490SA	47152	N73AF	47185	N8949E	47162	N919RW	47343	N979Z
45799	N491SA	47465	N7465B	47186	N8950E	48139	N919VJ	47245	N97S
45711	N500ME	47012	N75AF	47187	N8951E	47063	N91S	47134	N980NE
47363	N502MD	47708	N760NC	45867	N8952E	47734	N920L	48156	N980VJ
47430	N503MD	47709	N761NC	45868	N8953E	47163	N920RW	47344	N980Z
47431	N506MD	47710	N762NC	45797	N8953U	47682	N920VJ	47135	N981NE
47474	N507MD	47716	N763NC	47188	N8954E	48140	N920VJ	48157	N981VJ
47477	N508MD	47717	N764NC	47189	N8955E	47107	N921L	47345	N981Z
47010	N50AF	47718	N765NC	47214	N8956E	47164	N921RW	47136	N982NE
47225	N515MD	47739	N766NC	47215	N8957E	47683	N921VJ	47251	N982PS
47128	N516MD	47724	N767NC	47216	N8958E	48141	N921VJ	48158	N982VJ
47521	N521TX	47729	N768NC	47157	N8959E	47108	N921L	47137	N983NE
47524	N522TX	47757	N769NC	45869	N8960E	47182	N922RW	48159	N983VJ
47520	N523NY	47758	N770NC	47114	N8960U	47685	N922VJ	47411	N983Z
47520	N523TX	47769	N771NC	45842	N8961	48142	N922VJ	47207	N984VJ
47539	N524TX	47774	N772NC	45870	N8961E	47109	N923L	47412	N984Z
47531	N525NY	47775	N773NC	47115	N8961U	47183	N923RW	47208	N985VJ
47531	N525TX	47776	N774NC	45843	N8962	47665	N923VJ	47491	N985Z
45847	N531TX	47785	N775NC	45871	N8962E	48143	N923VJ	47209	N986VJ
45791	N532TX	47786	N776NC	45844	N8963	47324	N924L	47589	N986Z
47281	N533TX	47787	N777NC	45872	N8963E	47185	N924RW	47210	N987VJ
47277	N5341L	48100	N778NC	47192	N8963U	47688	N924VJ	47137	N987Z
47278	N5342L	48101	N779NC	47048	N8964	48144	N924VJ	47211	N988VJ
47110	N534TX	48102	N780NC	45873	N8964E	45728	N925AX	47134	N988Z
47111	N535TX	48121	N781NC	45874	N8965E	47357	N925L	47212	N989VJ
47113	N536TX	48107	N782NC	47301	N8965U	47686	N925VJ	47135	N989Z
47112	N537TX	48108	N783NC	47217	N8966E	48145	N925VJ	47136	N990Z
47218	N538TX	48109	N784NC	47267	N8967E	47002	N926AX	47728	N991EA
45792	N539NY	48110	N785NC	45875	N8968E	47172	N926L	47310	N991VJ
45792	N539TX	48148	N786NC	45876	N8969E	47473	N926RC	47096	N991Z
45790	N540TX	48149	N787NC	47268	N8970E	47692	N926VJ	47731	N992EA
45793	N541NY	47011	N79SL	47269	N8971E	48146	N926VJ	47095	N992Z
45793	N541TX	45731	N8500	47270	N8972E	45717	N927AX	47732	N993EA
47535	N542TX	45711	N85AS	47036	N8973E	48123	N927L	47332	N993VJ
45789	N543NY	47697	N8709Q	47074	N8974E	47469	N927RC	47082	N993Z
45789	N543TX	47761	N8710Q	47119	N8975E	47693	N927VJ	47733	N994EA
47219	N544TX	47772	N8713Q	47271	N8976E	48154	N927VJ	47333	N994VJ
47094	N545NY	47773	N8714Q	47272	N8977E	45718	N928AX	47097	N994Z
47094	N545TX	45797	N8860	47327	N8978E	47392	N928AX	47745	N995EA
47588	N54630	45826	N8901	47328	N8979E	48124	N928L	47334	N995VJ
47597	N54631	45742	N8901E	47329	N8980E	48131	N928VJ	47027	N995Z
47600	N54635	47010	N8902	47330	N8981E	47174	N929L	47746	N996EA
47649	N54638	45743	N8902E	47331	N8982E	48118	N929VJ	47335	N996VJ
47654	N54641	47011	N8903	47400	N8984E	47064	N92S	47028	N996Z
47655	N54642	45744	N8903E	47401	N8985E	47363	N930AX	47749	N997EA
47618	N54645	47012	N8904	47402	N8986E	47527	N930ML	47336	N997VJ
45722	N54648	45745	N8904E	47403	N8987E	45729	N930RC	47029	N997Z
47423	N556NY	47013	N8905	47098	N8988E	45868	N930VJ	47751	N998EA
47013	N557AS	45746	N8905E			47384	N931AX	47030	N998R

McDonnell Douglas DC-9 cross-reference index

47753	N999EA
45702	N99YA
45695	N9DC
45775	N9KR
47696	N9MD

OE- Austria

47521	OE-LDA
47524	OE-LDB
47520	OE-LDC
47539	OE-LDD
47531	OE-LDE
47458	OE-LDF
47458	OE-LDF
47484	OE-LDG
47555	OE-LDH
47559	OE-LDI
47651	OE-LDK
47652	OE-LDL
47726	OE-LDM
47735	OE-LDN
47756	OE-LDO

OH- Finland

47603	OH-LNA
47604	OH-LNB
47613	OH-LNC
47606	OH-LND
47605	OH-LNE
47614	OH-LNF
47713	OH-LYA
47712	OH-LYB
45711	OH-LYC
45725	OH-LYD
45729	OH-LYE
45730	OH-LYG
47044	OH-LYH
47045	OH-LYI
45841	OH-LYK
47694	OH-LYN
47695	OH-LYO
47696	OH-LYP
47736	OH-LYR
47737	OH-LYS
47738	OH-LYT
47771	OH-LYU
47772	OH-LYV
47773	OH-LYW
48134	OH-LYX
48135	OH-LYY
48136	OH-LYZ

OY- Denmark

47715	OY-KGA
47178	OY-KGB
47286	OY-KGC
47302	OY-KGD
47305	OY-KGE
47308	OY-KGF
47395	OY-KGG
47493	OY-KGH
47494	OY-KGI
47510	OY-KGK
47597	OY-KGL
47624	OY-KGM
47628	OY-KGN
47632	OY-KGO
47646	OY-KGP
47725	OY-KGR
47766	OY-KGS
47110	OY-KGU
47113	OY-KGW

PH- Netherlands

45718	PH-DNA
45719	PH-DNB
45720	PH-DNC
45721	PH-DND
45722	PH-DNE
45723	PH-DNF
47102	PH-DNG
47131	PH-DNH
47132	PH-DNI
47133	PH-DNK
47190	PH-DNL
47191	PH-DNM
47192	PH-DNN
47193	PH-DNO
47194	PH-DNP
47279	PH-DNR
47168	PH-DNS
47169	PH-DNT
47170	PH-DNV
47201	PH-DNW
47462	PH-DNY
47476	PH-DNZ
48132	PH-DOA
48133	PH-DOB
47291	PH-MAN
47363	PH-MAO
47410	PH-MAR
47514	PH-MAX

PJ- Netherlands Antilles

45722	PJ-DNA
45723	PJ-DNB
45721	PJ-DNC
47648	PJ-SNA
47666	PJ-SNB
47669	PJ-SNC
47639	PJ-SND
47175	PJ-SNE

PK- Indonesia

47385	PK-GJE
47386	PK-GJF
47481	PK-GJG
47463	PK-GJH
47561	PK-GJI
47569	PK-GJJ
47601	PK-GJK
47385	PK-GNA
47386	PK-GNB
47481	PK-GNC
47463	PK-GND
47561	PK-GNE
47569	PK-GNF
47601	PK-GNG
47635	PK-GNH
47636	PK-GNI
47672	PK-GNJ
47673	PK-GNK
47680	PK-GNL
47701	PK-GNM
47722	PK-GNN
47730	PK-GNO
47740	PK-GNP
47741	PK-GNQ
47744	PK-GNR
47789	PK-GNS
47790	PK-GNT
47791	PK-GNU
47792	PK-GNV
47793	PK-GNW
47794	PK-GNX
47795	PK-GNY

SE- Sweden

47492	SE-DAK
47498	SE-DAL
47499	SE-DAM
47464	SE-DAN
47509	SE-DAO
47512	SE-DAP
47596	SE-DAR
47610	SE-DAS
47625	SE-DAT
47627	SE-DAU
47629	SE-DAW
47631	SE-DAX
47633	SE-DBM
47413	SE-DBN
47361	SE-DBO
47360	SE-DBP
47306	SE-DBR
47303	SE-DBS
47288	SE-DBT
47180	SE-DBU
47117	SE-DBW
47114	SE-DBX
47112	SE-DBY
47094	SE-DBZ
47747	SE-DDP
47750	SE-DDR
47777	SE-DDS
47779	SE-DDT

TC- Turkey

47048	TC-JAA
45774	TC-JAB
47213	TC-JAC
47488	TC-JAD
47489	TC-JAE
47451	TC-JAF
47442	TC-JAG
47397	TC-JAK
47534	TC-JAL
47674	TC-JBK
47723	TC-JBL

VH- Australia

47003	VH-CZA
47004	VH-CZB
47005	VH-CZC
47065	VH-CZD
47202	VH-CZE
47325	VH-CZF
47501	VH-CZG
47526	VH-CZH
47527	VH-CZI
47547	VH-CZJ
47548	VH-CZK
47549	VH-CZL
47408	VH-IPF
47007	VH-TJJ
47008	VH-TJK
47009	VH-TJL
47072	VH-TJM
47203	VH-TJN
47326	VH-TJO
47418	VH-TJP
47419	VH-TJQ
47528	VH-TJR
47550	VH-TJS
47551	VH-TJT
47552	VH-TJU

VR- Cayman Islands

47151	VR-CKO

XA/XC- Mexico

48125	XA-AMA
48126	XA-AMB
48127	XA-AMC
48128	XA-AMD
48129	XA-AME
48130	XA-AMF
48150	XA-AMG
48151	XA-AMH
47061	XA-BCS
47650	XA-DEI
47594	XA-DEJ
47602	XA-DEK
47607	XA-DEL
47609	XA-DEM
47621	XA-DEN
47622	XA-DEO
47048	XA-DEV
45721	XA-GOJ
45722	XA-GOK
47006	XA-IOV
47394	XA-JEB
47356	XA-JEC
47106	XA-JEC
47059	XA-SOA
47100	XA-SOC
47122	XA-SOD
47123	XA-SOE
47124	XA-SOF
47125	XA-SOG
47126	XA-SOH
47127	XA-SOI
45785	XA-SOJ
47085	XA-SOY
47087	XC-BCM
47087	XC-BCO
47154	XC-BDM

YU- Yugoslavia

47239	YU-AHJ
47425	YU-AHL
47469	YU-AHM
47470	YU-AHN
47472	YU-AHO
47473	YU-AHP
47503	YU-AHR
47482	YU-AHT
47532	YU-AHU
47460	YU-AHV
47530	YU-AHW
47392	YU-AJB
47298	YU-AJF
47562	YU-AJH
47563	YU-AJI
47567	YU-AJJ
47568	YU-AJK
47571	YU-AJL
47582	YU-AJM
47579	YU-AJN
47457	YU-AJO
47408	YU-AJP
47649	YU-AJR
47697	YU-AJT
47754	YU-AJU
47734	YU-AJX
47172	YU-AJX

YV- Venezuela

47309	YV-01C
47002	YV-02C
47000	YV-03C
47476	YV-139C
47001	YV-18C
47394	YV-19C
47705	YV-20C
47719	YV-21C
47703	YV-22C
47720	YV-23C
47727	YV-24C
47721	YV-25C
47006	YV-300C
47770	YV-32C
47782	YV-33C
47712	YV-35C
47006	YV-51C
47048	YV-52C
47060	YV-57C
45723	YV-65C
47510	YV-66C
47025	YV-67C
47031	YV-68C
47309	YV-69C
47103	YV-70C
47104	YV-71C
47105	YV-72C
47106	YV-73C
47309	YV-C-AAA
47000	YV-C-ANP
47002	YV-C-ANV
45703	YV-C-AVB
47048	YV-C-AVC
47243	YV-C-AVD
47056	YV-C-AVM
47060	YV-C-AVR
47006	YV-C-LEV

Military Operated

Italy

47595	MM62012
47600	MM62013

Kuwait

47691	KAF-320
47690	KAF-321

United States

47577	159113
47584	159114
47587	159115
47580	159116
47581	159117
47585	159118
47578	159119
47586	159120
47684	160046
47687	160047
47681	160048
47698	160049
47699	160050
47700	160051
48137	161266
48165	161529
48166	161530
47003	162390
47004	162391
47065	162392
47325	162393
47410	162753
47476	162754
47041	163036
47221	163037
47241	67-22583
47242	67-22584
47295	67-22585
47296	67-22586
47366	68-10958
47367	68-10959
47448	68-10960
47449	68-10961
47297	68-8932
47298	68-8933
47299	68-8934
47300	68-8935
47467	71-874
47471	71-875
47475	71-876
47495	71-877
47536	71-878
47537	71-879
47538	71-880
47540	71-881
47541	71-882
47668	73-1681
47670	73-1682
47671	73-1683

Venezuela

47000	0003

MCDONNELL DOUGLAS MD-80

The MD-80 series evolved as a development of the DC9-50 with quieter and more fuel-effecient engines, as well as greater capacity, and were originally designated DC-9-81 and 82. The MD-81 features yet another fuselage stretch for up to 172 passengers, and is powered by the advanced-technology Pratt & Whitney JT8D-200 series of turbofans. The MD-82 differs in having higher thrust engines for operation in 'hot and high' environments. A longer-range MD-83 is also available. To date, 317 aircraft have been delivered and a further 439 are on order with current production rate around six aircraft per month.

Dimensions :	Wing span: 107ft 10in (32.87m) Length: 147ft 11in (45.06m) Height: 29ft 7in (9.04m)
	Powerplant : Two Pratt & Whitney JT8D-209 turbofans (MD-81), two Pratt & Whitney JT8D-217 turbofans (MD-82), two Pratt & Whitney JT8D-219 turbofans (MD-83)
Performance :	Max cruising speed 454 knots (840km/h) Range: with max payload 1,385nm (2,565km) (MD-81)
	Range: with max payload 1,860nm (3,445km) (MD-82)
	Range: with max payload 2,369nm (4,387km) (MD-83)
Accommodation:	172 passengers in a five abreast layout
Manufacturer :	McDonnell Douglas - 3855 Lakewood Boulevard, Long Beach, California 90846, USA
	Telephone: (213) 593-5511

C/N	Registration	Owner/Operator	Series	First Flight	Delivery	Remarks
48000	N980DC	McDonnell Douglas	81	18/OCT/79		Prototype
	HB-INA	Swissair				Not taken-up
	N980DC	McDonnell Douglas				
48001	N1002G	McDonnell Douglas	81			W/O 19/JUN/80, Yuma, Az.
	HB-INB	Swissair				Not taken-up
48002	HB-INC	Swissair	81		14/SEP/80	
48003	HB-IND	Swissair	81		27/OCT/80	
48004	HB-INE	Swissair	81		23/NOV/80	
	HB-INE	Air Afrique			11/OCT/82	Leased
	HB-INE	Swissair			10/JUL/83	
48005	HB-INF	Swissair	81		27/JAN/81	
48006	HB-ING	Swissair	81		05/APR/81	
48007	HB-INH	Swissair	81		09/MAY/81	
48008	HB-INI	Swissair	81		02/JUL/81	
48009	HB-INK	Swissair	81		20/JUN/81	
48010	HB-INL	Swissair	81		24/JUL/81	
48011	HB-INM	Swissair	81		05/AUG/81	
48012	HB-INN	Swissair	81		29/AUG/81	
48013	HB-INO	Swissair	81		03/SEP/81	
48014	HB-INP	Swissair	81		29/OCT/81	
48015	N1002W	McDonnell Douglas	81			
	OE-LDP	Austrian Airlines			16/MAY/81	
48016	OE-LDR	Austrian Airlines	81		03/OCT/80	
48017	OE-LDS	Austrian Airlines	81		16/JAN/81	
48018	OE-LDT	Austrian Airlines	81		25/JUL/81	
48019	OE-LDU	Austrian Airlines	81		05/SEP/81	
48020	OE-LDV	Austrian Airlines	81		12/FEB/82	
48021	OE-LDX	Austrian Airlines	81		28/FEB/83	
48022	N1004W	McDonnell Douglas	81			
	OE-LDY	Austrian Airlines			FEB/83	Not taken-up
	PH-MCD	Martinair	82		29/MAR/83	
	PH-MCD	Austrian Airlines			22/MAR/84	Leased
	PH-MCD	Martinair			31/MAY/84	
	PH-MCD	Alisarda			01/JUN/84	Leased
	PH-MCD	Martinair			84	
	OE-LYM	Austrian Airlines			01/NOV/84	Leased
	PH-MCD	Martinair			03/NOV/85	
	PH-MCD	Frontier Airlines			15/NOV/85	Leased
	PH-MCD	Martinair			31/OCT/87	Sched.return
48024	N10022	McDonnell Douglas	81			
	N10022	Austral			08/JAN/81	Leased
48025	N10027	McDonnell Douglas	81			
	N10027	Austral			08/JAN/81	Leased
48026	N10028	McDonnell Douglas	81			
	N10028	Muse Air			29/JUN/81	Leased
	N10028	McDonnell Douglas			JUN/82	
	N10028	Jet America Airlines			09/DEC/82	Leased
	N10028	McDonnell Douglas			16/MAR/83	
	N10028	Midway Airlines			10/SEP/83	Leased
	N10028	McDonnell Douglas			85	
	N922PS	Pacific Southwest Airlines			18/MAY/85	Leased
48027	N475AC	GATX Leasing	81		15/MAY/81	
	N475AC	Air Cal			15/MAY/81	Leased
	N475AC	Frontier			28/FEB/86	Leased
48028	N476AC	GATX Leasing	81		08/JUN/81	
	N476AC	Air Cal			08/JUN/81	Leased
	N476AC	McDonnell Douglas			08/JUL/85	
	N950PS	Pacific Southwest Airlines			03/JUL/85	Leased
48029	JA8458	Toa Domestic Airlines	81		30/JAN/81	
48030	JA8459	Toa Domestic Airlines	81		05/MAR/81	
48031	JA8460	Toa Domestic Airlines	81		17/APR/81	
48032	JA8461	Toa Domestic Airlines	81		05/JUN/81	
48033	JA8462	Toa Domestic Airlines	81		29/JUL/81	
48034	N924PS	Pacific Southwest Airlines	81		17/NOV/80	
48035	N925PS	Pacific Southwest Airlines	81		31/MAR/81	
48036	N926PS	Pacific Southwest Airlines	81		09/MAR/81	
48037	N927PS	Pacific Southwest Airlines	81		08/JAN/81	

MCDONNELL DOUGLAS MD-80

C/N	Registration	Owner/Operator	Series	First Flight	Delivery	Remarks
48038	N930PS	Pacific Southwest Airlines	81		10/SEP/81	
48039	N931PS	Pacific Southwest Airlines	81		10/SEP/81	
48040	N932PS	Pacific Southwest Airlines	81		10/SEP/81	
48041	N933PS	Pacific Southwest Airlines	81		28/SEP/81	
48042	N934PS	Pacific Southwest Airlines	81		28/SEP/81	
48043	N935PS	Pacific Southwest Airlines	81		08/OCT/81	
48044	N749HA	Hawaiian Air	81			Reg.not taken-up
	N809HA	Hawaiian Air			24/APR/81	Leased
	N809HA	Frontier			15/FEB/86	Leased
48045	N759HA	Hawaiian Air	81			Reg.not taken-up
	N819HA	Hawaiian Air	81		04/MAY/81	
	N819HA	Pacific Southwest Airlines			01/JUN/85	Leased
	N819HA	Hawaiian Air			10/SEP/85	
	N819HA	Frontier			03/MAR/86	Leased
48046	YU-AJZ	Inex Adria	81		10/JUN/81	
48047	YU-ANA	Inex Adria	82		11/AUG/81	W/O 01/DEC/81, nr. Campo dell'Oro Ap., Corsica
48048	YU-ANB	Inex Adria	82		19/SEP/81	
	PH-MBY	Martinair			01/NOV/81	Leased
	YU-ANB	Inex Adria			28/FEB/83	
48049	N10029	McDonnell Douglas	81			
	N10029	Muse Air			02/JUL/81	Leased
	N10029	McDonnell Douglas			21/DEC/82	
	N10029	Midway Airlines			17/SEP/83	
	N10029	McDonnell Douglas			21/MAY/85	
	N923PS	Pacific Southwest Airlines			21/MAY/85	Leased
48050	N1003G	McDonnell Douglas	81			
	N1003G	Austral			08/AUG/81	
48051	N769HA	Hawaiian Air	81			Reg.not taken-up
	N829HA	Hawaiian Air			10/JUN/81	
	N920PS	Pacific Southwest Airlines			26/MAY/85	Leased
	N829HA	Hawaiian Air			15/SEP/85	
	N829HA	Frontier	82		15/OCT/86	Sched.lease
48052	N928PS	Pacific Southwest Airlines	81		15/MAY/81	
48053	N929PS	Pacific Southwest Airlines	81		10/JUL/81	
48054	N301RC	McDonnell Douglas	82		05/AUG/81	
	N301RC	Republic Airlines			05/AUG/81	Leased
	N301RC	Northwest Orient			01/AUG/86	
48055	N302RC	Republic Airlines	82		05/SEP/81	
	N302RC	Northwest Orient			01/AUG/86	
48056	N304RC	Republic Airlines	82		82	
	N10034	Muse Air			07/MAY/82	
	N930MC	Muse Air			82	
	N930MC	Transtar			17/FEB/86	
48057	N305RC	Republic Airlines	82		82	
	N10035	Muse Air			07/MAY/82	
	N931MC	Muse Air			82	
	N931MC	Transtar			17/FEB/86	
48058	N779HA	Hawaiian Air	81			Reg.not taken-up
	N839HA	Hawaiian Air			20/JUL/81	
	N839HA	Frontier			15/NOV/86	Sched.lease
48059	OE-LDW	Austrian Airlines	81		20/FEB/82	
48062	N477AC	Air Cal	82		15/OCT/81	
	N477AC	Frontier			19/DEC/85	Leased
48063	N478AC	Air Cal	82		21/OCT/81	
	N478AC	Frontier			25/FEB/86	Leased
48066	N479AC	Air Cal	82		09/NOV/81	
	N479AC	International Lease Finance			85	
	N479AC	New York Air			01/MAR/85	Leased
	N813NY	New York Air			AUG/85	
48067	XA-AMI	Aeromexico	82			Reg.not taken-up
	N1003X	Aeromexico			14/DEC/81	
48068	XA-AMJ	Aeromexico	82			Reg.not taken-up
	N1003Y	Aeromexico			22/DEC/81	
48069	XA-AMK	Aeromexico	82			Reg.not taken-up
	N1003Z	Aeromexico			27/DEC/81	
48070	JA8468	Toa Domestic Airlines	81		09/NOV/81	
48071	JA8469	Toa Domestic Airlines	81		18/DEC/81	
48072	JA8470	Toa Domestic Airlines	81		25/FEB/82	
48073	N789HA	Hawaiian Air	81			Reg.not taken-up
	N849HA	Hawaiian Air			25/NOV/81	
	N849HA	American International			15/APR/83	Leased
	N849HA	Hawaiian Air			01/SEP/84	
	N849HA	Frontier			01/OCT/85	Leased
48074	N859HA	Hawaiian Air	81		11/DEC/81	
	N859HA	American International			09/JUN/83	Leased
	N859HA	Hawaiian Air			01/SEP/84	
	N859HA	Frontier			07/JAN/86	Leased
48079	N779JA	GATX Leasing	82		13/NOV/81	
	N779JA	Jet America Airlines			13/NOV/81	Leased
48080	N778JA	McDonnell Douglas	82		13/NOV/81	
	N778JA	Jet America Airlines			13/NOV/81	Leased
48081	YV-	LAV	82			Cancelled order
48082	YV-	LAV	82			Cancelled order
48083	XA-AML	Aeromexico	82			Reg.not taken-up
	N10033	Aeromexico			26/FEB/82	
48084	YV-	Viasa	82		82	Re-allocated
48085	YV-	Viasa	82		82	Re-allocated
48086	N307RC	Republic Airlines	82		21/DEC/81	
	N307RC	Northwest Orient			01/AUG/86	
48087	N19B	Douglas	82			
	YU-ANC	Inex Adria			02/APR/82	
48088	N309RC	Republic Airlines	82		02/DEC/82	
	N309RC	Northwest Orient			01/AUG/86	
48089	N311RC	Republic Airlines	82		02/DEC/82	
48090	N1004F	McDonnell Douglas	82			
	N312RC	Republic Airlines			08/DEC/82	
	N312RC	Northwest Orient			01/AUG/86	
48091	N313RC	Republic Airlines	82		26/APR/83	
	N313RC	Northwest Orient			01/AUG/86	
48092	N936PS	Pacific Southwest Airlines	81		17/DEC/81	
48093	N937PS	Pacific Southwest Airlines	81		22/MAR/82	
48094	N938PS	Pacific Southwest Airlines	81		07/APR/82	
48095	N940PS	Pacific Southwest Airlines	82		23/APR/82	
48096	N941PS	Pacific Southwest Airlines	82		20/MAY/82	

C/N	Registration	Owner/Operator	Series	First Flight	Delivery	Remarks
48097	N942PS	Pacific Southwest Airlines	82		20/MAY/82	
48098	N943PS	Pacific Southwest Airlines	82		27/MAY/82	
48099	N939PS	Pacific Southwest Airlines	82		17/JUN/82	
49100	HB-INA	Swissair	81		09/DEC/81	
49101	HB-INB	Swissair	81		18/MAR/82	
	HB-INB	Balair			01/APR/82	Leased
49102	N9805F	Frontier	82		24/NOV/82	
	N9805F	United Airlines			FEB/85	
	N9805F	Frontier			FEB/85	Leased
49103	N782JA	Jet America Airlines	82		82	
	N1005A	McDonnell Douglas			83	
	N782JA	New York Air			83	Leased
49103	N1005A	Viasa	82		07/JAN/83	
	YV-158C	Viasa			83	
	N782JA	Jet America Airlines			30/MAY/84	
49104	N1105B	Viasa	82		07/JAN/83	
	YV-159C	Viasa			83	
	N783JA	Jet America Airlines			30/MAY/84	
49110	N1004L	McDonnell Douglas	82			
	N1004L	Republic Airlines			26/AUG/83	
	N1004L	Jet America Airlines			26/AUG/83	
	N314RC	Republic Airlines			JAN/85	
	N314RC	Northwest Orient			01/AUG/86	
49111	N1004F	McDonnell Douglas	82			
	N316RC	Republic Airlines				Not taken-up
	N781JA	Jet America Airlines			09/DEC/83	
49112	N480AC	Air Cal	82		28/MAY/82	
	N480AC	International Lease Finance			85	
	N480AC	New York Air			03/MAY/85	Leased
	N814NY	New York Air			AUG/85	
49113	N481AC	Air Cal	82		22/JUN/82	
	N481AC	International Lease Finance			85	
	N481AC	New York Air			03/MAY/85	Leased
	N815NY	New York Air			AUG/85	
49114	N9804F	Frontier	82		03/DEC/82	
	N9804F	United Airlines			FEB/85	
	N9804F	Frontier			FEB/85	Leased
49115	OE-LDY	Austrian Airlines	81		05/MAY/84	
49116	N9801F	Frontier	81		22/APR/82	
	N9801F	United Airlines			11/APR/85	WFU 11/APR/85 to 09/JUL/85
	N9801F	Air Cal			09/JUL/85	Leased
	N9801F	United Airlines			03/SEP/85	
	N9801F	Frontier			03/SEP/85	Leased
49117	N9802F	Frontier	82		04/MAY/82	
	N9802F	United Airlines			02/APR/85	WFU 02/APR/85 to 24/JUN/85
	N9802F	BWIA			24/JUN/85	Leased
	N9802F	United Airlines			06/MAR/86	
	N9802F	Frontier			06/MAR/86	Leased
49118	N9803F	Frontier	82		13/MAY/82	
	N9803F	United Airlines			FEB/85	
	N9803F	Frontier			FEB/85	Leased
49119	N869HA	Hawaiian Air	82			Not taken-up
	N944PS	Pacific Southwest Airlines			15/JUL/82	
49120	N932MC	Muse Air	81		28/SEP/82	
	N932MC	Transtar			17/FEB/86	
49121	N933MC	Muse Air	81		28/SEP/82	
	N933MC	Transtar			17/FEB/86	
49122	N934MC	Muse Air	81		14/DEC/82	
	N934MC	Transtar			17/FEB/86	
49123	PJ-SEF	ALM	82		14/OCT/82	
49124	PJ-SEG	ALM	82		04/OCT/82	
49125	N935MC	Muse Air	81		29/NOV/82	
	N935MC	Transtar			17/FEB/86	
49126	N780JA	Jet America Airlines	82		11/MAR/83	Leased
	N780JA	McDonnell Douglas			26/AUG/83	
	N780JA	New York Air			22/SEP/83	Leased
	N780JA	McDonnell Douglas			12/NOV/84	
	N790JA	International Lease Finance			07/DEC/84	
	N780JA	Jet America Airlines			07/DEC/84	Leased
49127	N483AC	Air Cal	82			
	N483AC	McDonnell Douglas				
	N801NY	New York Air			02/SEP/83	Leased
49138	N945PS	Pacific Southwest Airlines	82		18/APR/83	
49139	N946PS	Pacific Southwest Airlines	82		12/MAY/83	
49140	N1004S	McDonnell Douglas	82			
	B-2101	CAAC			12/DEC/83	
49141	N10046	McDonnell Douglas	82			
	B-2102	CAAC			12/DEC/83	
49142	N947PS	McDonnell Douglas	82		17/OCT/83	
	N947PS	Pacific Southwest Airlines			17/OCT/83	Leased
49143	N948PS	Pacific Southwest Airlines	82		30/NOV/83	
49144	PH-MBZ	Martinair	82		18/FEB/83	
49145	N203AA	American Airlines	82		12/MAY/83	
49149	XA-AMO	Aeromexico	82			Cancelled order
	N505MD	McDonnell Douglas				
	PP-CJM	Cruzeiro			08/DEC/82	Leased
	N505MD	McDonnell Douglas			13/MAR/83	
	N505MD	Aeromexico			28/DEC/83	
49150	XA-AMP	Aeromexico	82			Cancelled order
	OH-LMN	Finnair			11/MAR/83	
49151	XA-	Aeromexico	82			Cancelled order
	OH-LMO	Finnair			25/MAR/83	
49152	XA-	Aeromexico	82			Cancelled order
	OH-LMP	Finnair			29/APR/83	
49153	N902TW	Trans World Airlines	82		27/APR/83	
49154	N903TW	Trans World Airlines	82		12/MAY/83	
49155	N205AA	American Airlines	82		06/JUN/83	
49156	N904TW	Trans World Airlines	82		24/MAY/83	
49157	N905TW	Trans World Airlines	82		27/MAY/83	
49158	N207AA	American Airlines	82		07/JUN/83	
49159	N208AA	American Airlines	82		27/JUN/83	
49160	N906TW	Trans World Airlines	82		23/JUN/83	
49161	N210AA	American Airlines	82		28/JUN/83	
49162	N214AA	American Airlines	82		29/JUL/83	
49163	N215AA	American Airlines	82		01/AUG/83	

MCDONNELL DOUGLAS MD-80

C/N	Registration	Owner/Operator	Series	First Flight	Delivery	Remarks
49164	OE-LDZ	Austrian Airlines	81		15/FEB/85	
49165	N901TW	Trans World Airlines	82		02/SEP/83	
49166	N901TW	Trans World Airlines	82		18/APR/83	
49167	N216AA	American Airlines	82		10/MAY/83	
49168	N218AA	American Airlines	82		04/MAY/83	
49169	N908TW	Trans World Airlines	82		22/SEP/83	
49170	N909TW	Trans World Airlines	82		13/OCT/83	
49171	N219AA	American Airlines	82		02/AUG/83	
49172	N221AA	American Airlines	82		17/AUG/83	
49173	N223AA	American Airlines	82		02/SEP/83	
49174	N224AA	American Airlines	82		27/AUG/83	
49175	N225AA	American Airlines	82		08/SEP/83	
49176	N226AA	American Airlines	82		26/OCT/83	
49177	N227AA	American Airlines	82		28/OCT/83	
49178	N228AA	American Airlines	82		01/NOV/83	
49179	N232AA	American Airlines	82		03/NOV/83	
49180	N233AA	American Airlines	82		30/NOV/83	
49181	N234AA	American Airlines	82		06/DEC/84	
49182	N911TW	Trans World Airlines	82		10/DEC/83	
49183	N912TW	Trans World Airlines	82		18/DEC/83	
49184	N913TW	Trans World Airlines	82		23/MAR/84	
49185	N914TW	Trans World Airlines	82		13/APR/84	
49186	N915TW	Trans World Airlines	82		19/APR/84	
49187	N916TW	Trans World Airlines	82		25/APR/84	
49188	XA-AMO	Aeromexico	82		17/DEC/84	
49189	XA-AMP	Aeromexico	82		20/DEC/84	
49190	XA-AMQ	Aeromexico	82		19/FEB/85	
49191	XA-AMR	Aeromexico	82			
49192	I-DAWA	Alitalia	82		20/DEC/83	
49193	N13627	McDonnell Douglas				
	I-DAWE	Alitalia			20/DEC/83	
49194	I-DAWI	Alitalia	82		24/FEB/84	
49195	I-DAWO	Alitalia	82		11/MAY/84	
49196	I-DAWU	Alitalia	82		20/MAY/84	
49197	I-DAWB	Alitalia	82		27/MAY/84	
49198	I-DAWC	Alitalia	82		26/JUN/84	
49199	I-DAWD	Alitalia	82		30/JUN/84	
49200	I-DAWF	Alitalia	82		24/JUL/84	
49201	I-DAWG	Alitalia	82		30/JUL/84	
49202	I-DAWH	Alitalia	82		30/NOV/84	
49203	I-DAWJ	ATI	82		18/DEC/84	
	I-DAWJ	Alitalia			03/JUL/85	
49204	I-DAWL	Alitalia	82		19/FEB/85	
49205	I-DAWM	Alitalia	82		27/FEB/85	
49206	I-DAWP	Alitalia	82		15/MAR/85	
49207	I-DAWQ	Alitalia	82		20/MAR/85	
49208	I-DAWR	Alitalia	82		25/MAR/85	
49209	I-DAWS	Alitalia	82		02/APR/85	
49210	I-DAWT	ATI	82		08/APR/85	
49211	I-DAWV	ATI	82		24/MAY/85	
49212	I-DAWW	ATI	82		04/NOV/85	
49213	I-DAWY	ATI	82		18/DEC/85	
49214	I-DAWZ	ATI	82		18/DEC/85	
49215	I-DAVA	ATI	82		18/FEB/86	
49216	I-DAVB	ATI	82		MAR/86	
49217	I-DAVC	ATI	82		APR/86	
49218	I-DAVD	ATI	82		MAY/86	
49219	I-DAVF	ATI	82		OCT/86	Sched.delivery
49220	I-DAVG	ATI	82		NOV/86	Sched.delivery
49221	I-DAVH	ATI	82		DEC/86	Sched.delivery
49222	N802NY	Continental Airlines	82		25/JUN/84	
49229	N803NY	Continental Airlines	82		21/JUN/84	
49230	N950U	American Airlines	82		19/JUN/84	Leased
	N950U	Ozark Airlines			01/DEC/84	
49231	N930AS	Alaska Airlines	83		29/MAR/85	
49232	N931AS	Alaska Airlines	83		20/FEB/85	
49233	N932AS	Alaska Airlines	83		14/JUN/85	
49234	N933AS	Alaska Airlines	83		28/JUN/85	
49235	N934AS	Alaska Airlines	83		16/NOV/85	
49236	N935AS	Alaska Airlines	83		10/DEC/85	
49237	N949PS	Pacific Southwest Airlines	82		30/JUN/84	
49238	N	Pacific Southwest Airlines	82			Cancelled order
49239	N	Pacific Southwest Airlines	82			Cancelled order
49240	N	Pacific Southwest Airlines	82			Cancelled order
49241	N	Pacific Southwest Airlines	82			Cancelled order
49242	N	Pacific Southwest Airlines	82			Cancelled order
49245	N951U	American Airlines	82		26/JUN/84	Leased
	N951U	Ozark Airlines			01/DEC/84	
49246	N804NY	Continental Airlines	82		06/AUG/84	
49247	HB-IKK	Alisarda	82		20/SEP/84	WFU 20/SEP/84 to 14/DEC/84
	HB-IKK	National Airlines			14/DEC/84	
	HB-IKK	Alisarda			12/MAY/85	
49248	HB-IKL	Alisarda	82		27/SEP/84	WFU 27/SEP/84 to 29/MAR/85
	HB-IKL	Northeastern Airlines			DEC/85	
	HB-IKL	Alisarda			06/MAR/86	
49249	N805NY	New York Air	82		14/AUG/84	
49250	N812NY	Continental Airlines	82		04/APR/85	
49251	N236AA	American Airlines	82		06/SEP/84	
49252	N19B	McDonnell Douglas	83	17/DEC/84		Prototype series -83
	OH-LMS	Finnair			19/OCT/85	
49253	N237AA	American Airlines	82		14/SEP/84	
49254	N241AA	American Airlines	82		11/SEP/84	
49255	N242AA	American Airlines	82		17/SEP/84	
49256	N244AA	American Airlines	82		21/SEP/84	
49257	N245AA	American Airlines	82		02/OCT/84	
49258	N246AA	American Airlines	82		09/OCT/84	
49259	N248AA	American Airlines	82		15/OCT/84	
49260	N806NY	New York Air	82		22/AUG/84	
49261	N807NY	Continental Airlines	82		05/SEP/84	
49262	N808NY	Continental Airlines	82		15/NOV/84	
49263	N809NY	Continental Airlines	82		15/NOV/84	
49264	N810NY	New York Air	82		20/DEC/84	
	N810NY	Continental Airlines			28/APR/85	
49265	N811NY	Continental Airlines	82		29/MAR/85	
49266	N952U	Ozark Airlines	82		27/NOV/85	
49267	N953U	Ozark Airlines	82		04/DEC/85	

C/N	Registration	Owner/Operator	Series	First Flight	Delivery	Remarks
49269	N249AA	American Airlines	82		26/OCT/84	
49270	N251AA	American Airlines	82		31/OCT/84	
49271	N274AA	American Airlines	82		07/NOV/84	
49272	N275AA	American Airlines	82		13/NOV/84	
49273	N276AA	American Airlines	82		20/NOV/84	
49277	HB-INR	Balair	82		01/FEB/85	
49278	OE-LMA	Austrian Airlines	81		27/FEB/85	
49279	OE-LMB	Austrian Airlines	81		20/OCT/85	
49280	JA8496	Toa Domestic Airlines	81		09/APR/85	
49281	JA8497	Toa Domestic Airlines	81		20/MAY/85	
49282	JA8498	Toa Domestic Airlines	81		JUN/86	
49283	JA8499	Toa Domestic Airlines	81		SEP/86	Sched.delivery
49284	OH-LMR	Finnair	82		26/JUN/85	
49286	N253AA	American Airlines	82		04/JAN/85	
49287	N255AA	American Airlines	82		15/JAN/85	
49288	N258AA	American Airlines	82		08/MAR/85	
49289	N259AA	American Airlines	82		08/APR/85	
49290	N262AA	American Airlines	82		19/APR/85	
49291	N266AA	American Airlines	82		02/JUL/85	
49292	N269AA	American Airlines	82		10/JUL/85	
49293	N271AA	American Airlines	82		16/JUL/85	
49294	N278AA	American Airlines	82		17/JUL/85	
49295	N279AA	American Airlines	82		25/JUL/85	
49296	N283AA	American Airlines	82		29/JUL/85	
49297	N285AA	American Airlines	82		03/AUG/85	
49298	N286AA	American Airlines	82		06/AUG/85	
49299	N287AA	American Airlines	82		13/AUG/85	
49300	N288AA	American Airlines	82		16/AUG/85	
49301	N289AA	American Airlines	82		22/AUG/85	
49302	N290AA	American Airlines	82		27/AUG/85	
49303	N291AA	American Airlines	82		03/SEP/85	
49304	N292AA	American Airlines	82		06/SEP/85	
49305	N293AA	American Airlines	82		23/SEP/85	
49306	N294AA	American Airlines	82		25/SEP/85	
49307	N295AA	American Airlines	82		02/OCT/85	
49308	N296AA	American Airlines	82		07/OCT/85	
49309	N297AA	American Airlines	82		JAN/86	
49310	N298AA	American Airlines	82		JAN/86	
49311	N400AA	American Airlines	82		JAN/86	
49312	N70401	American Airlines	82		JAN/86	
49313	N402A	American Airlines	82		28/FEB/86	
49314	N403A	American Airlines	82		24/FEB/86	
49315	N70404	American Airlines	82		MAR/86	
49316	N405A	American Airlines	82		MAR/86	
49317	N406A	American Airlines	82		MAR/86	
49318	N407AA	American Airlines	82		APR/86	
49319	N408AA	American Airlines	82		APR/86	
49320	N409AA	American Airlines	82		APR/86	
49321	N410AA	American Airlines	82		MAY/86	
49322	N411AA	American Airlines	82		JUN/86	
49323	N412AA	American Airlines	82		JUN/86	
49324	N413AA	American Airlines	82		86	Sched.delivery
49325	N33414	American Airlines	82		86	Sched.delivery
49326	N415AA	American Airlines	82		86	Sched.delivery
49327	N416AA	American Airlines	82		86	Sched.delivery
49328	N417AA	American Airlines	82		86	Sched.delivery
49329	N418AA	American Airlines	82		86	Sched.delivery
49331	N419AA	American Airlines	82		86	Sched.delivery
49332	N420AA	American Airlines	82		86	Sched.delivery
49333	N77421	American Airlines	82		86	Sched.delivery
49334	N422AA	American Airlines	82		86	Sched.delivery
49335	N423AA	American Airlines	82		86	Sched.delivery
49336	N424AA	American Airlines	82		86	Sched.delivery
49337	N	American Airlines	82		87	Sched.delivery
49338	N	American Airlines	82		87	Sched.delivery
49339	N	American Airlines	82		87	Sched.delivery
49340	N	American Airlines	82		87	Sched.delivery
49341	N	American Airlines	82		87	Sched.delivery
49342	N	American Airlines	82		87	Sched.delivery
49343	N	American Airlines	82		87	Sched.delivery
49344	N	American Airlines	82		87	Sched.delivery
49345	N	American Airlines	82		87	Sched.delivery
49346	N	American Airlines	82		87	Sched.delivery
49347	N	American Airlines	82		87	Sched.delivery
49348	N	American Airlines	82		87	Sched.delivery
49349	N	American Airlines	82		87	Sched.delivery
49350	N	American Airlines	82		87	Sched.delivery
49351	N	American Airlines	82		87	Sched.delivery
49352	N	American Airlines	82		87	Sched.delivery
49353	N	American Airlines	82		87	Sched.delivery
49355	B-2103	CAAC	82		07/OCT/85	
49356	HB-INS	Swissair	82		26/JAN/86	
49357	HB-INT	Swissair	82		14/FEB/86	
49358	HB-INU	Swissair	81		SEP/86	Sched.delivery
49359	HB-INV	Swissair	81		MAR/87	Sched.delivery
49363	N936AS	Alaska Airlines	83		MAY/86	
49364	N937AS	Alaska Airlines	83		MAY/86	
49365	N938AS	Alaska Airlines	83		JUN/86	
49366	N917TW	Trans World Airlines	82		23/APR/85	
49367	N918TW	Trans World Airlines	82		25/APR/85	
49368	N919TW	Trans World Airlines	82		02/MAY/85	
49369	N920TW	Trans World Airlines	82		08/MAY/85	
49370	N816NY	Continental Airlines	82		25/JUN/85	
49371	N817NY	Continental Airlines	82		28/JUN/85	
49372	OE-LMC	Austrian Airlines	81		28/FEB/86	
49373	N1004Y	McDonnell Douglas	82			
	N	Muse Air				Cancelled order
	HL7272	Korean Air			10/AUG/85	
49374	N1005Y	McDonnell Douglas	82			
	N	Muse Air				Cancelled order
	HL7273	Korean Air			21/AUG/85	
49379	YU-ANG	Inex Adria	82		08/OCT/85	
49380	OY-KGT	SAS	81		10/OCT/85	
49381	OY-KGZ	SAS	81		19/OCT/85	
49382	LN-RLE	SAS	81		26/OCT/85	
49383	LN-RLF	SAS	82		16/NOV/85	

MCDONNELL DOUGLAS MD-80

C/N	Registration	Owner/Operator	Series	First Flight	Delivery	Remarks
49384	SE-DFS	SAS	82		02/DEC/85	
49385	SE-DFT	SAS	82		20/DEC/85	
49386	N	Jet America Airlines	82		86	Sched.delivery
49387	N	Jet America Airlines	82		86	Sched.delivery
49390	9Y-THN	Irish Aerospace	83		25/APR/86	
	9Y-THN	BWIA			25/APR/86	Leased
49391	EI-BTA	Irish Aerospace	83		APR/86	
	N9806F	Frontier				Reg. not taken-up
	EI-BTA	Frontier			APR/86	Leased
49392	EI-BTB	Irish Aerospace	83		MAY/86	
	N9807F	Frontier				Reg. not taken-up
	EI-BTB	Frontier			MAY/86	Leased
49393	EI-BTC	Irish Aerospace	83		JUN/86	Sched.delivery
	N9808F	Frontier			MAY/86	Reg. not taken-up
	EI-BTC	Frontier			JUN/86	Leased
49394	EI-BTD	Irish Aerospace	83		JUN/86	
	N9809F	Frontier			JUN/86	Reg. not taken-up
	EI-BTD	Frontier			JUN/86	Leased
49395		Irish Aerospace	83		21/JUL/86	
	YV-	Aeropostal			21/JUL/86	Purchased
49396	EI-	Irish Aerospace	83		FEB/87	Sched.delivery
49397	EI-	Irish Aerospace	83		FEB/87	Sched.delivery
49398	EI-	Irish Aerospace	83		MAR/87	Sched.delivery
49399	EI-	Irish Aerospace	83		MAR/87	Sched.delivery
49400	EI-	Irish Aerospace	83		MAR/87	Sched.delivery
49401	EI-	Irish Aerospace	83		APR/87	Sched.delivery
49402	D-ALLD	Aero Lloyd	83		25/MAR/86	
49403	OH-	Finnair	87			
49404	OH-	Finnair	87		SEP/87	Sched.delivery
49405	OH-	Finnair	87			
49406	OH-	Finnair	87			
49407	OH-	Finnair	87			
49408	OH-	Finnair	87			
49409	OH-	Finnair	87			
49410	OH-	Finnair	87		91	Sched.delivery
49411	OE-	Austrian Airlines	87		JUN/87	Sched.delivery
49412	OE-	Austrian Airlines	87			
49413	OE-	Austrian Airlines	87			
49414	OE-	Austrian Airlines	87		90	Sched.delivery
49416	HL7275	Korean Air	82		MAY/86	
49417	HL7276	Korean Air	82		JUN/86	
49420	OY-KGY	SAS	81		17/FEB/86	
49421	SE-DFU	SAS	82		21/MAR/86	
49422	SE-DFW	SAS	81		25/MAR/86	
49423	LN-RLG	SAS	82		17/JUN/86	
49424	SE-DFX	SAS	82		19/JUN/86	
49425	B-2104	CAAC	82		28/NOV/85	
49428	B-2105	CAAC	82		26/DEC/85	
49429	N951PS	Pacific Southwest Airlines	82		APR/86	
49436	OY-KHC	SAS	81		SEP/86	Sched.delivery
49437	LN-RLR	SAS	82		FEB/87	Sched.delivery
49438	SE-DFY	SAS	81		MAR/87	Sched.delivery
49439	N	Ozark Airlines	82		86	Sched.delivery
49441	N	Ozark Airlines	82		86	Sched.delivery
49443	N952PS	Pacific Southwest Airlines	82		86	Sched.delivery

ADDITIONAL ORDERS

C/N	Registration	Owner/Operator	Series	First Flight	Delivery	Remarks
	YV-	Aeropostal	83		APR/87	Sched.delivery
	EI-	Irish Aerospace	83		88	Sched.delivery
	EI-	Irish Aerospace	83		88	Sched.delivery
	EI-	Irish Aerospace	83		88	Sched.delivery
	EI-	Irish Aerospace	83		88	Sched.delivery
	EI-	Irish Aerospace	83		88	Sched.delivery
	EI-	Irish Aerospace	83		88	Sched.delivery
	HB-	Balair	82		87	Sched.delivery
	HB-	Swissair	81		JAN/88	Sched.delivery
	HB-	Swissair	81		FEB/88	Sched.delivery
	HB-	Swissair	81		MAR/88	Sched.delivery
		SAS	81		MAY/87	Sched.delivery
		SAS	82		MAY/87	Sched.delivery
		SAS	83		Autumn/87	Sched.delivery
		SAS	83		Autumn/87	Sched.delivery
	HL	Korean Air Lines	82		87	Sched.delivery
	HL	Korean Air Lines	82		87	Sched.delivery
	N	Jet America Airlines	82		JUN/87	Sched.delivery
	N	Jet America Airlines	82		JUN/87	Sched.delivery
	9Y-	BWIA	83		OCT/86	Sched.delivery
	9Y-	BWIA	83		OCT/86	Sched.delivery
	D-ALLE	Aero Lloyd	83		MAR/87	Sched.delivery
	N	Frontier	82		08/DEC/86	Sched.delivery
	N	Frontier	82		01/DEC/86	Sched.delivery
	N	Pacific Southwest	82		JUL/87	Sched.delivery
	N	Pacific Southwest	82		JUL/87	Sched.delivery
	VH-	Trans Pacific	83		87	Sched.delivery
	VH-	Trans Pacific	83		87	Sched.delivery
	VH-	Trans Pacific	83		87	Sched.delivery
	VH-	Trans Pacific	83		87	Sched.delivery
	VH-	Trans Pacific	83		87	Sched.delivery
	VH-	Trans Pacific	83		87	Sched.delivery
	B-	CAAC	82			Assembled in China
	B-	CAAC	82			Assembled in China
	B-	CAAC	82			Assembled in China
	B-	CAAC	82			Assembled in China
	B-	CAAC	82			Assembled in China
	B-	CAAC	82			Assembled in China
	B-	CAAC	82			Assembled in China
	B-	CAAC	82			Assembled in China
	B-	CAAC	82			Assembled in China
	B-	CAAC	82			Assembled in China
	B-	CAAC	82			Assembled in China
	B-	CAAC	82			Assembled in China
	B-	CAAC	82			Assembled in China
	B-	CAAC	82			Assembled in China

C/N	Registration	Owner/Operator	Series	First Flight	Delivery	Remarks
	B-	CAAC	82			Assembled in China
	B-	CAAC	82			Assembled in China
	B-	CAAC	82			Assembled in China
	B-	CAAC	82			Assembled in China
	B-	CAAC	82			Assembled in China
	B-	CAAC	82			Assembled in China
	B-	CAAC	82			Assembled in China
	B-	CAAC	82			Assembled in China
	B-	CAAC	82			Assembled in China
	B-	CAAC	82		91	Assembled in China
	JA	Toa Domestic Airlines	81		APR/87	Sched.delivery
	JA	Toa Domestic Airlines	81			
	JA	Toa Domestic Airlines	81		MAY/88	Sched.delivery
	JA	Toa Domestic Airlines	87		APR/88	Sched.delivery
	JA	Toa Domestic Airlines	87			
	JA	Toa Domestic Airlines	87			
	JA	Toa Domestic Airlines	87		MAY/90	Sched.delivery
	N	Delta Airlines	88		Spring/87	Sched.delivery
	N	Delta Airlines	88		87	Sched.delivery
	N	Delta Airlines	88		87	Sched.delivery
	N	Delta Airlines	88		87	Sched.delivery
	N	Delta Airlines	88		87	Sched.delivery
	N	Delta Airlines	88		87	Sched.delivery
	N	Delta Airlines	88		87	Sched.delivery
	N	Delta Airlines	88		87	Sched.delivery
	N	Delta Airlines	88		87	Sched.delivery
	N	Delta Airlines	88		87	Sched.delivery
	N	Delta Airlines	88		88	Sched.delivery
	N	Delta Airlines	88			
	N	Delta Airlines	88			
	N	Delta Airlines	88			
	N	Delta Airlines	88			
	N	Delta Airlines	88			
	N	Delta Airlines	88			
	N	Delta Airlines	88			
	N	Delta Airlines	88			
	N	Delta Airlines	88			
	N	Delta Airlines	88			
	N	Delta Airlines	88			
	N	Delta Airlines	88			
	N	Delta Airlines	88			
	N	Delta Airlines	88			
	N	Delta Airlines	88			
	N	Delta Airlines	88			
	N	Delta Airlines	88		92	Sched.delivery
	N	Texas Air Corp.	82			
	N	Texas Air Corp.	82			
	N	Texas Air Corp.	82			
	N	Texas Air Corp.	82			
	N	Texas Air Corp.	82			
	N	Texas Air Corp.	82			
	N	Texas Air Corp.	82			
	N	Texas Air Corp.	82			
	N	Texas Air Corp.	82			
	N	Texas Air Corp.	82			
	N	Texas Air Corp.	82			
	N	Texas Air Corp.	82			
	N	Texas Air Corp.	82			
	N	Texas Air Corp.	82			
	N	Texas Air Corp.	82			
	N	Texas Air Corp.	82			
		SAS	87		JUN/88	Sched.delivery
		SAS	87			
		SAS	87			
		SAS	87			
		SAS	87			
		SAS	87			
		SAS	87			
		SAS	87			
		SAS	87		91	Sched.delivery
		SAS	81/82		88	Sched.delivery
		SAS	81/82			
		SAS	81/82			
		SAS	81/82			
	EI-	Guinness Peat Aviation	83		88	Sched.delivery
	EI-	Guinness Peat Aviation	83			
	EI-	Guinness Peat Aviation	83			
	EI-	Guinness Peat Aviation	83			
	EI-	Guinness Peat Aviation	83			
	EI-	Guinness Peat Aviation	83			
	EI-	Guinness Peat Aviation	83			
	EI-	Guinness Peat Aviation	83			
	EI-	Guinness Peat Aviation	83			
	EI-	Guinness Peat Aviation	83			
	EI-	Guinness Peat Aviation	83			
	EI-	Guinness Peat Aviation	83			
	EI-	Guinness Peat Aviation	83			
	EI-	Guinness Peat Aviation	83			
	EI-	Guinness Peat Aviation	83		89	Sched.delivery

McDonnell Douglas MD-80 cross-reference index

9Y- Trinidad & Tobago
49390	9Y-THN

B- China
49140	B-2101
49141	B-2102
49355	B-2103
49425	B-2104
49428	B-2105

D- West Germany
49402	D-ALLD

EI- Eire
49391	EI-BTA
49392	EI-BTB
49393	EI-BTC
49394	EI-BTD

HB- Switzerland
49247	HB-IKK
49248	HB-IKL
48000	HB-INA
49100	HB-INA
48001	HB-INB
49101	HB-INB
48002	HB-INC
48003	HB-IND
48004	HB-INE
48005	HB-INF
48006	HB-ING
48007	HB-INH
48008	HB-INI
48009	HB-INK
48010	HB-INL
48011	HB-INM
48012	HB-INN
48013	HB-INO
48014	HB-INP
49277	HB-INR
49356	HB-INS
49357	HB-INT
49358	HB-INU
49359	HB-INV

HL South Korea
49373	HL7272
49374	HL7273
49416	HL7275
49417	HL7276

I- Italy
49215	I-DAVA
49216	I-DAVB
49217	I-DAVC
49218	I-DAVD
49219	I-DAVF
49220	I-DAVG
49221	I-DAVH
49192	I-DAWA
49197	I-DAWB
49198	I-DAWC
49199	I-DAWD
49193	I-DAWE
49200	I-DAWF
49201	I-DAWG
49202	I-DAWH
49194	I-DAWI
49203	I-DAWJ
49204	I-DAWL
49205	I-DAWM
49195	I-DAWO
49206	I-DAWP
49207	I-DAWQ
49208	I-DAWR
49209	I-DAWS
49210	I-DAWT
49196	I-DAWU
49211	I-DAWV
49212	I-DAWW
49213	I-DAWY
49214	I-DAWZ

JA Japan
48029	JA8458
48030	JA8459
48031	JA8460
48032	JA8461
48033	JA8462
48070	JA8468
48071	JA8469
48072	JA8470
49280	JA8496
49281	JA8497
49282	JA8498
49283	JA8499

LN- Norway
49382	LN-RLE
49383	LN-RLF
49423	LN-RLG
49437	LN-RLR

N United States
48024	N10022
48025	N10027
48026	N10028
48049	N10029
48001	N1002G
48015	N1002W
48083	N10033
48056	N10034
48057	N10035
48050	N1003G
48067	N1003X
48068	N1003Y
48069	N1003Z
49141	N10046
48090	N1004F
49111	N1004F
49110	N1004L
49140	N1004N
48022	N1004W
49373	N1004Y
49103	N1005A
49374	N1005Y
49104	N1105B
49193	N13627
48087	N19B
49252	N19B
49145	N203AA
49155	N205AA
49158	N207AA
49159	N208AA
49161	N210AA
49162	N214AA
49163	N215AA
49167	N216AA
49168	N218AA
49171	N219AA
49172	N221AA
49173	N223AA
49174	N224AA
49175	N225AA
49176	N226AA
49177	N227AA
49178	N228AA
49179	N232AA
49180	N233AA
49181	N234AA
49251	N236AA
49253	N237AA
49254	N241AA
49255	N242AA
49256	N244AA
49257	N245AA
49258	N246AA
49259	N248AA
49269	N249AA
49270	N251AA
49286	N253AA
49287	N255AA
49288	N258AA
49289	N259AA
49290	N262AA
49291	N266AA
49292	N269AA
49293	N271AA
49271	N274AA
49272	N275AA
49273	N276AA
49294	N278AA
49295	N279AA
49296	N283AA
49297	N285AA
49298	N286AA
49299	N287AA
49300	N288AA
49301	N289AA
49302	N290AA
49303	N291AA
49304	N292AA
49305	N293AA
49306	N294AA
49307	N295AA
49308	N296AA
49309	N297AA
49310	N298AA
48054	N301RC
48055	N302RC
48056	N304RC
48057	N305RC
48086	N307RC
48086	N307RC
48088	N309RC
48089	N311RC
48090	N312RC
48091	N313RC
49110	N314RC
49111	N316RC
49325	N33414
49311	N400AA
49313	N402A
49314	N403A
49316	N405A
49317	N406A
49318	N407AA
49319	N408AA
49320	N409AA
49321	N410AA
49322	N411AA
49323	N412AA
49324	N413AA
49326	N415AA
49327	N416AA
49328	N417AA
49329	N418AA
49331	N419AA
49332	N420AA
49334	N422AA
49335	N423AA
49336	N424AA
48027	N475AC
48028	N476AC
48062	N477AC
48063	N478AC
48066	N479AC
48112	N480AC
49113	N481AC
49127	N483AC
49149	N505MD
49312	N70401
49315	N70404
48044	N749HA
48045	N759HA
48051	N769HA
49333	N77421
48080	N778JA
48058	N779HA
48079	N779JA
49126	N780JA
49126	N780JA
49111	N781JA
49103	N782JA
49103	N782JA
49104	N783JA
48073	N789HA
49127	N801NY
49222	N802NY
49229	N803NY
49246	N804NY
49249	N805NY
49260	N806NY
49261	N807NY
49262	N808NY
48044	N809NY
49263	N809NY
49264	N810NY
49265	N811NY
49250	N812NY
48066	N813NY
49112	N814NY
49113	N815NY
49370	N816NY
49371	N817NY
49045	N819HA
48051	N829HA
49058	N839HA
48073	N849HA
49074	N859HA
49119	N869HA
49166	N901TW
49153	N902TW
49154	N903TW
49156	N904TW
49157	N905TW
49160	N906TW
49165	N907TW
49169	N908TW
49170	N909TW
49182	N911TW
49183	N912TW
49184	N913TW
49185	N914TW
49186	N915TW
49187	N916TW
49366	N917TW
49367	N918TW
49368	N919TW
49051	N920PS
49369	N920TW
49026	N922PS
49049	N923PS
48034	N924PS
48035	N925PS
48036	N926PS
48037	N927PS
48052	N928PS
48053	N929PS
49231	N930AS
48056	N930MC
48038	N930PS
49232	N931AS
48057	N931MC
49039	N931PS
49233	N932AS
48120	N932MC
48040	N932PS
49234	N933AS
49121	N933MC
48041	N933PS
49235	N934AS
48122	N934MC
48042	N934PS
49236	N935AS
49125	N935MC
48043	N935PS
49363	N936AS
48092	N936PS
49364	N937AS
48093	N937PS
49365	N938AS
48094	N938PS
49099	N939PS
48095	N940PS
49096	N941PS
48097	N942PS
48098	N943PS
49119	N944PS
49138	N945PS
49139	N946PS
49142	N947PS
49143	N948PS
49237	N949PS
48028	N950PS
49230	N950U
49429	N951PS
49245	N951U
49443	N952PS
49266	N952U
49267	N953U
49116	N9801F
49117	N9802F
49118	N9803F
49114	N9804F
49102	N9805F
49391	N9806F
49392	N9807F
49393	N9808F
49394	N9809F
48000	N980DC

OE- Austria
48015	OE-LDP
48016	OE-LDR
48017	OE-LDS
48018	OE-LDT
48019	OE-LDU
48020	OE-LDV
48059	OE-LDW
48021	OE-LDX
48022	OE-LDY
49115	OE-LDY
49164	OE-LDZ
49278	OE-LMA
49279	OE-LMB
49372	OE-LMC
48022	OE-LYM

OH- Finland
49150	OH-LMN
49151	OH-LMO
49152	OH-LMP
49284	OH-LMR
49252	OH-LMS

OY- Denmark
49380	OY-KGT
49420	OY-KGY
49381	OY-KGZ
49436	OY-KHC

PH- Netherlands
48048	PH-MBY
49144	PH-MBZ
48022	PH-MCD

PJ- Netherlands Antilles
49123	PJ-SEF
49124	PJ-SEG

PP- Brasil
49149	PP-CJM

SE- Sweden
49384	SE-DFS
49385	SE-DFT
49421	SE-DFU
49422	SE-DFW
49424	SE-DFX
49438	SE-DFY

XA- Mexico
48067	XA-AMI
48068	XA-AMJ
48069	XA-AMK
48083	XA-AML
49149	XA-AMO
48188	XA-AMO
49150	XA-AMP
48189	XA-AMP
49190	XA-AMQ
49191	XA-AMR

YU- Yugoslavia
48046	YU-AJZ
48047	YU-ANA
48048	YU-ANB
48048	YU-ANB
48087	YU-ANC
49379	YU-ANG

YV- Venezuela
49103	YV-158C
49104	YV-159C

AEROSPATIALE/AERITALIA ATR 42

Short-range, high wing commuter airliner, manufactured jointly by Aerospatiale (France) and Aeritalia (Italy). The ATR42 ('Avion de Transport Regional') made its maiden flight on 16 August 1984, with initial deliveries, to Air Littoral and Cimber Air, taking place in December of the following year. The aircraft is currently available in two models, the ATR42-200 and ATR42-300, with the latter offering higher gross, maximum landing and zero fuel weights. To date, 20 aircraft have been delivered and over 60 are on order, with the production rate currently three aircraft per month, due to rise to four per month during 1987.

Dimensions :	Wing span 80 ft 6 in (24.57m) Length: 74 ft 5 in (22.7m) Height: 24 ft 9 in (7.59m).
Powerplant :	Two Pratt & Whitney PW120 Turboprops.
	Performance : Max cruising speed 275 knots (509 km/h) Range: with max payload 1,307 nm (2,420 km).
Accommodation:	46 passenger in a four abreast layout.
Manufacturer :	Aerospatiale - 37 Boulevard de Montmorency, F-75781, Paris Cedex 16, France
	Telephone: (33) 1 524 438 Telex: 620059 F AISPA
	: Aeritalia - Piazzale Via Tecchio 51, A-80125 Napoli, Italy
	Telephone: (081) 619522 Telex: 710370 AERIT I

C/N	Registration	Owner/Operator	Series	First Flight	Delivery	Remarks
1001	F-WEGA	Aerospatiale/Aeritalia	200	16/AUG/84		Prototype
	F-GDXL	Brit Air			86	
1002	F-WEGB	Aerospatiale/Aeritalia	200	31/OCT/84		Development aircraft
	F-GFJP	Brit Air			MAR/86	
1003	F-WEGC	Aerospatiale/Aeritalia	300	30/APR/85		
	PH-HWJ	Holland Aero Lines			03/JAN/86	Leased
	F-WEGE	Aerospatiale/Aeritalia			05/MAR/86	
	F-GEGE	Air Littoral			27/MAR/86	
1004	F-WEGD	Aerospatiale/Aeritalia	300	21/NOV/85		
	F-GEGD	Air Littoral			02/DEC/85	
	F-GEGD	Air France			30/MAR/86	Leased
1005	F-WWEA	Aerospatiale/Aeritalia	300	12/DEC/85		
	OY-CIA	Cimber Air			20/DEC/85	
1006	F-WWEB	Aerospatiale/Aeritalia	300	05/FEB/86		
	OH-LTA	Finnair			13/MAR/86	
1007	F-WWEC	Aerospatiale/Aeritalia	300	30/JAN/86		
	OY-CIB	Cimber Air			12/FEB/86	
1008	F-WWED	Aerospatiale/Aeritalia	300	21/FEB/86		
	PH-ATR	Holland Aero Lines			04/MAR/86	
1009	F-WWEE	Aerospatiale/Aeritalia	300	16/JAN/86		
	N140DD	Command Airways			27/JAN/86	
1010	F-WDXL	Aerospatiale/Aeritalia	300	18/MAR/86		
	F-GDXL	Brit Air			25/MAR/86	
1012	F-WWED	Aerospatiale/Aeritalia	300	14/APR/86		
	N420MQ	Simmons Airlines			29/APR/86	
1012A	F-WWEC	Aerospatiale/Aeritalia	200	04/APR/86		
	VH-AQC	Air Queensland			18/APR/86	
1014	F-WWEB	Aerospatiale/Aeritalia	300	20/MAY/86		
	N421MQ	Simmons Airlines			19/JUN/86	
1015	F-WWEA	Aerospatiale/Aeritalia	300	24/APR/86		
	N141DD	Command Airways			06/MAY/86	
1016	F-WWEE	Aerospatiale/Aeritalia	300	03/JUL/86		
1018	F-ODGM	Aerospatiale/Aeritalia	300	06/JUN/86		
	F-ODGM	Air Caledonie			12/JUN/86	
1019	F-WWEF	Aerospatiale/Aeritalia	200	06/MAY/86		
	VH-AQD	Air Queensland			16/MAY/86	
1020	F-WWEG	Aerospatiale/Aeritalia	300	23/JUN/86		
	I-ATRB	ATI			10/JUL/86	
1021	F-WWEH	Aerospatiale/Aeritalia	300	10/JUL/86		
	I-ATRC	ATI			24/JUL/86	
1022	F-WWEI	Aerospatiale/Aeritalia	300	26/JUN/86		
	OH-LTB	Finnair			10/JUL/86	
1024	F-WWEC	Aerospatiale/Aeritalia	300			
	OY-CIC	Cimber Air			SEP/86	Sched.delivery
1025	F-WWED	Aerospatiale/Aeritalia	200	21/JUL/86		
	VH-AQE	Air Queensland			AUG/86	Sched.delivery
1026	F-	Aerospatiale/Aeritalia	300			
	CS-	SATA			AUG/86	Sched.delivery
1027	F-	Aerospatiale/Aeritalia	300			
	PH-ITH	Holland Aero Lines			SEP/86	Sched.delivery
1028	F-	Aerospatiale/Aeritalia	300			
	N	Simmons Airlines			SEP/86	Sched.delivery
1029	F-	Aerospatiale/Aeritalia	300			
	F-	Reunion Air Service			OCT/86	Sched.delivery
1030	F-	Aerospatiale/Aeritalia	300			
	N	Simmons Airlines			OCT/86	Sched.delivery
1031	F-	Aerospatiale/Aeritalia	300			
	3B-	Air Mauritius			OCT/86	Sched.delivery
1032	F-	Aerospatiale/Aeritalia	300			
	I-	ATI			NOV/86	Sched.delivery
1033	F-	Aerospatiale/Aeritalia	300			
	OH-LTC	Finnair			NOV/86	Sched.delivery
1034	F-	Aerospatiale/Aeritalia	300			
	I-	ATI			NOV/86	Sched.delivery
1042	F-	Aerospatiale/Aeritalia	300			
	I-	ATI			NOV/86	Sched.delivery

C/N	Registration	Owner/Operator	Series	First Flight	Delivery	Remarks

ADDITIONAL ORDERS

C/N	Registration	Owner/Operator	Series	First Flight	Delivery	Remarks
	TR-	Gabon Government	300F		JUN/87	Sched.delivery
	N	Executive Air Charter	300		20/SEP/86	Sched.delivery
	N	Executive Air Charter	300		OCT/86	Sched.delivery
	N	Executive Air Charter	300		FEB/87	Sched.delivery
	N	Executive Air Charter	300		OCT/87	Sched.delivery
	PH-	Holland Aero Lines	300		DEC/86	Sched.delivery
	OH-LTD	Finnair	300			
	OH-LTE	Finnair	300			
	N	Command Airways	300		86	Sched.delivery
	N	Command Airways	300			
	N	Command Airways	300			
	F-	Air Polynesie	300		86	Sched.delivery
	F-	Air Polynesie	300		87	Sched.delivery
	D-	Nuernberger Flugdienst	300		SEP/86	Sched.delivery
	D-	Nuernberger Flugdienst	300		MAR/87	Sched.delivery
	D-	RFG Regionalflug	300		AUG/87	Sched.delivery
	D-	RFG Regionalflug	300		JAN/88	Sched.delivery
	I-	ATI	300		87	Sched.delivery
	I-	ATI	300			
	I-	ATI	300			
	I-	ATI	300			
	I-	ATI	300		Summer/88	Sched.delivery
	N	Air Guam	300		86	Sched.delivery
	N	Ransome Airlines	300		86	Sched.delivery
	N	Ransome Airlines	300		86	Sched.delivery
	N	Ransome Airlines	300			Sched.delivery
	N	Ransome Airlines	300			Sched.delivery
	N	Ransome Airlines	300			Sched.delivery
	N	Ransome Airlines	300		87	Sched.delivery
	F-	Air Caledonie	300		OCT/86	Sched.delivery
	I-	Aligiulia	300		86	Sched.delivery
	I-	Aligiulia	300		JAN/87	Sched.delivery
	I-	Unifly	300		87	Sched.delivery
	I-	Unifly	300			
	I-	Unifly	300			
	F-O	Air Guadeloupe	300		Summer/86	Sched.delivery
	F-O	Air Guadeloupe	300		Summer/86	Sched.delivery
	F-O	Air St. Pierre	300		MAR/87	Sched.delivery
	N	Pioneer Airlines	300		Summer/86	Sched.delivery
	N	Pioneer Airlines	300		86	Sched.delivery
	N	Pioneer Airlines	300		86	Sched.delivery
	N	Pioneer Airlines	300		87	Sched.delivery
	N	Pioneer Airlines	300		87	Sched.delivery
	VH-	Air Queensland	200			
	DQ-	Air Pacific	300		88	Sched.delivery
	DQ-	Air Pacific	300		88	Sched.delivery
	N	Simmons Airlines	300		APR/87	Sched.delivery
	N	Simmons Airlines	300		MAY/87	Sched.delivery

Aerospatiale/Aeritalia ATR-42 cross-reference index

F- France

1001	F-GDXL
1010	F-GDXL
1004	F-GEGD
1003	F-GEGE
1002	F-GFJP
1018	F-ODGM
1010	F-WDXL
1001	F-WEGA
1002	F-WEGB
1003	F-WEGC
1004	F-WEGD

1003	F-WEGE
1005	F-WWEA
1015	F-WWEA
1006	F-WWEB
1014	F-WWEB
1007	F-WWEC
1012A	F-WWEC
1024	F-WWEC
1008	F-WWED
1012	F-WWED
1025	F-WWED
1009	F-WWEE
1016	F-WWEE

1019	F-WWEF
1020	F-WWEG
1021	F-WWEH
1022	F-WWEI

I- Italy

1020	I-ATRB
1021	I-ATRC

N United States

1009	N140DD
1015	N141DD

1012	N420MQ
1014	N421MQ

OH- Finland

1006	OH-LTA
1022	OH-LTB
1033	OH-LTC

OY- Denmark

1005	OY-CIA
1007	OY-CIB

1024	OY-CIC

PH- The Netherlands

1008	PH-ATR
1003	PH-HWJ
1027	PH-ITH

VH- Australia

1012A	VH-AQC
1019	VH-AQD
1025	VH-AQE

AEROSPATIALE/AERITALIA ATR 72

A new stretched version of the ATR 42 which is expected to enter service with launch customer, Finnair, in 1989. Although fundamentally similar to its predecessor, the ATR 72 will feature additional fuselage sections forward and aft of the wing assembly, plus an extended wingspan.

Dimensions :

Powerplant :   Two Pratt & Whitney PW124-2 Turboprops

Performance :
Accommodation: Between 64 and 72 passengers in a four-abreast layout.
Manufacturer :   Aerospatiale - 37 Boulevard de Montmorency, F-75781, Paris Cedex 16, France
                    Telephone: (33) 1 524 438 Telex: 620059 F AISPA
                    : Aeritalia - Piazzale Via Tecchio 51, A-80125 Napoli, Italy
                    Telephone: (081) 619522 Telex: 710370 AERIT I

C/N	Registration	Owner/Operator	Series	First Flight	Delivery	Remarks
ANNOUNCED ORDERS						
	OH-	Finnair	ATR72		89	Sched.delivery
	OH-	Finnair	ATR72		89	Sched.delivery
	OH-	Finnair	ATR72		89	Sched.delivery
	OH-	Finnair	ATR72		89	Sched.delivery
	OH-	Finnair	ATR72		89	Sched.delivery
	N	Simmons Airlines	ATR72			Total undisclosed

BRITISH AEROSPACE JETSTREAM 31

Light turboprops transport up to 19 passengers, developed from earlier Handley Page Jetstream 1. The Jetstream 31 is available in three prime versions: 18/19-seat commuters, 8/10-seat corporate and 12-seat Executive Shuttle. A quick change (QC) fit is also available, and the Jetstream 31EZ for patrol work is under development. The first production aircraft made its maiden flight on March 18th 1982. To date, more than 100 aircraft have been delivered and over 30 are on order.

Dimensions :	Wing span: 52 ft 0in (15.85m) Length: 47 ft 2 in (14.36m) Height: 17 ft 6 in (5.32m)
Powerplant :	Two Garrett TPE-331-10 Turboprops
Performance :	Max cruising speed 263 knots (486km/h) Range: with max payload 820nm (1,519km)
Accommodation:	18 passengers in a two-abreast layout
Manufacturer :	British Aerospace - Civil Aircraft Division, Prestwick Airport, Ayrshire, KA9 2RW, Scotland Telephone: (0292) 79888 Telex: 77432 G

C/N	Registration	Owner/Operator	Series	First Flight	Delivery	Remarks
601	G-TALL	British Aerospace	31	18/MAR/82		Demonstrator
	G-WMCC	Birmingham Executive			03/OCT/83	
602	G-31-39	British Aerospace	31	26/MAY/82		
	N92MA	Mall Airways			SEP/82	Not taken-up
	G-JBAE	British Aerospace			SEP/82	
	N331J	British Aerospace Inc.			26/SEP/82	
	N331J	Atlantis Airlines			84	Leased
	N331J	British Aerospace Inc.			84	
603	G-31-42	British Aerospace	31	08/JUL/82		
	G-CONE	British Aerospace			82	
	D-CONE	Contactair			17/DEC/82	
	D-CONE	DLT			MAY/84	Leased
	D-CONE	Contactair			87	Sched.return
604	G-BKHI	Peregrine Airways	31	04/OCT/82	30/DEC/82	
	G-BKHI	Air Commuter			83	Leased
	G-BKHI	Peregrine Airways				
	G-BKHI	British Aerospace			86	
605	G-31-45	British Aerospace	31	30/OCT/82		
	N331JS	British Aerospace Inc.			18/DEC/82	Demonstrator
606	G-31-46	British Aerospace	31	24/NOV/82		
	G-BKKY	Peregrine Airways			23/MAY/83	
	G-BKKY	British Aerospace			86	
607	G-31-47	British Aerospace	31	21/DEC/82		
	G-OBEA	Birmingham Executive			10/MAY/83	
608	G-31-48	British Aerospace	31	18/JAN/83		
	G-JSBA	British Aerospace			MAY/83	Corporate demonstrator
	G-JSBA	Netherlines			DEC/84	Leased
	G-JSBA	British Aerospace			01/MAR/85	
	N331BJ	British Aerospace Inc.			10/MAY/85	
609	G-31-49	British Aerospace	31	01/FEB/83		
	G-CBEA	Birmingham Executive			03/JUN/83	
610	G-31-50	British Aerospace	31	25/FEB/83		
	D-CONI	Contactair			30/JUL/83	
611	G-11-611	British Aerospace	31	15/MAR/83		
	N155AA	Atlantis Airlines			29/JUL/83	
	N988AX	Eastern Atlantis Express			85	
612	G-11-612	British Aerospace	31	01/APR/83		
	G-BKTN	McAlpine Aviation			09/JUN/83	
613	G-11-613	British Aerospace	31	04/MAY/83		
	N331BG	British Aerospace Inc.			21/JUN/83	
	N331BA	British Aerospace Inc.			83	
614	G-11-614	British Aerospace	31	30/MAY/83		
	G-BWWW	Distillers Corp.			29/JUL/83	
615	G-11-615	British Aerospace	31	25/JUL/83		
	G-BKVU	McAlpine Aviation			25/AUG/83	Not taken-up
	G-31-615	British Aerospace				
	N822JS	Jetstream International			16/FEB/84	
616	G-11-616	British Aerospace	31	08/AUG/83		
	G-BKUY	McAlpine Aviation			09/SEP/83	
617	N156AA	Atlantis Airlines	31	25/AUG/83	24/NOV/83	
	N989AX	Eastern Atlantis Express			85	
618	G-31-618	British Aerospace	31	14/SEP/83		
	N820JS	Jetstream International			12/DEC/83	
619	G-31-619	British Aerospace	31	26/SEP/83		
	N821JS	Jetstream International			18/DEC/83	
620	G-31-620	British Aerospace	31	21/OCT/83		
	VH-JSW	Skywest Airlines			10/FEB/84	
621	G-31-621	British Aerospace	31	03/NOV/83		
	G-BLCY	McAlpine Aviation				Reg. Not taken-up
	G-BLDO	McAlpine Aviation			23/JAN/84	
622	G-31-622	British Aerospace	31	16/DEC/83		
	G-BLCB	British Aerospace	31		28/DEC/83	For tests
	VH-HSW	Skywest Airlines			05/APR/84	
623	G-31-623	British Aerospace	31	21/NOV/83		
	N823JS	Jetstream International			15/MAR/84	
	N823JS	Eastern Metro Express			01/APR/84	Leased
624	G-31-624	British Aerospace	31	30/NOV/83		
	N400MX	Eastern Metro Express			30/APR/84	

C/N	Registration	Owner/Operator	Series	First Flight	Delivery	Remarks
625	G-31-625	British Aerospace	31	15/DEC/83		
	N404MX	Eastern Metro Express				
626	G-31-626	British Aerospace	31	28/DEC/83		
	D-CONU	Contactair			JUL/84	
	D-CONU	DLT			NOV/84	Leased
627	G-31-627	British Aerospace	31			
	N824JS	Jetstream International			13/APR/84	
628	G-31-628	British Aerospace	31			
	N401MX	Eastern Metro Express			JUN/84	
629	G-31-629	British Aerospace	31			
	VH-OSW	Skywest Airlines			JUL/84	
630	G-31-630	British Aerospace	31			
	N402MX	Eastern Metro Express				
631	G-31-631	British Aerospace	31			
	N406MX	Eastern Metro Express				
632	G-31-632	British Aerospace	31			
	N403MX	Eastern Metro Express				
633	G-31-633	British Aerospace	31			
	N825JS	Jetstream International				
634	G-31-634	British Aerospace	31			
	G-BLEX	McAlpine Aviation			JUN/84	
	G-BLKP	British Aerospace				
	G-BLKP	Netherlines			01/MAR/85	Leased
	G-BLKP	British Aerospace			01/FEB/86	
635	G-31-635	British Aerospace	31			
	N405MX	Eastern Metro Express				
636	G-31-636	British Aerospace	31			
	N407MX	Eastern Metro Express				
638	G-31-638	British Aerospace	31			
	N408MX	Eastern Metro Express				
639	G-31-639	British Aerospace	31			
	N409MX	Eastern Metro Express				
640	G-31-640	British Aerospace	31			
	N410MX	Eastern Metro Express			27/OCT/84	
641	G-31-641	British Aerospace	31		20/DEC/84	
	SE-IPD	Swedair				
642	G-31-642	British Aerospace	31	03/SEP/84	19/DEC/84	
	N402AE	Metro/American Eagle				
643	G-31-643	British Aerospace	31	03/OCT/84	20/DEC/84	
	N157AA	Atlantis Airlines			85	
	N990AX	Eastern Atlantis Express				
644	G-31-644	British Aerospace	31	30/OCT/84	24/JAN/85	
	N403AE	Metro/American Eagle				
645	G-31-645	British Aerospace	31	13/NOV/84	15/MAR/85	
	PH-KJA	Netherlines				
646	G-31-646	British Aerospace	31	13/NOV/84	01/MAR/85	
	N404AE	Metro/American Eagle				
647	G-31-647	British Aerospace	T.3	19/NOV/84	11/APR/85	
	ZE438	Royal Navy				
648	G-31-648	British Aerospace	31		23/MAR/85	
	PH-KJB	Netherlines				
649	G-31-649	British Aerospace	31		20/APR/85	
	PH-KJC	Netherlines				
650	G-31-650	British Aerospace	31			
	N405AE	Metro/American Eagle				
651	G-31-651	British Aerospace	31	09/JAN/85	06/APR/85	
	N406AE	Metro/American Eagle				
652	G-31-652	British Aerospace	31	23/JAN/85	28/APR/85	
	N300PX	Republic Express				
653	G-31-653	British Aerospace	31	30/JAN/85	09/MAY/85	
	N407AE	Metro/American Eagle				
654	G-31-654	British Aerospace	31	11/FEB/85	17/MAY/85	
	N301PX	Republic Express				
655	G-31-655	British Aerospace	31	21/FEB/85	10/JUN/85	
	PH-KJD	Netherlines				
656	G-31-656	British Aerospace	T.3	04/MAR/85	11/APR/86	
	ZE439	Royal Navy				
657	G-31-657	British Aerospace	31	11/MAR/85	07/JUN/85	
	N991AX	Eastern Atlantis Express				
658	G-31-658	British Aerospace	31	21/MAR/85	14/JUN/85	
	N992AX	Eastern Atlantis Express				
659	G-31-659	British Aerospace	T.3	21/MAY/85	07/JUL/86	
	ZE440	Royal Navy				
660	G-31-660	British Aerospace	31	14/APR/85	85	
	N411MX	Eastern Metro Express				
661	G-31-661	British Aerospace	31	15/APR/85	14/JUL/85	
	N302PX	Republic Express				
662	G-31-662	British Aerospace	31	08/MAY/85	20/JUL/85	
	N303PX	Republic Express				
663	G-31-663	British Aerospace	31	26/MAY/85		
	N304PX	Republic Express				
664	G-31-664	British Aerospace	31	28/MAY/85	85	
	N408AE	Metro/American Eagle				
665	G-31-665	British Aerospace	31	04/JUN/85	30/AUG/85	
	VH-ESW	Skywest Airlines				
666	G-31-666	British Aerospace	31	14/JUN/85	21/AUG/85	
	N305PX	Republic Express				
667	G-31-667	British Aerospace	T.3	21/JUN/85	SEP/86	Sched.delivery
		Royal Navy				
668	G-31-668	British Aerospace	31		27/SEP/85	
	N410AE	Metro/American Eagle				
669	G-31-669	British Aerospace	31		17/OCT/85	
	N409AE	Metro/American Eagle				
670	G-31-670	British Aerospace	31		10/OCT/85	
	N306PX	Republic Express				
671	G-31-671	British Aerospace	31	22/AUG/85	15/OCT/85	
	N411AE	Metro/American Eagle				
672	G-31-672	British Aerospace	31	23/AUG/85	18/DEC/85	
	N310PX	Republic Express				
673	G-31-673	British Aerospace	31	03/SEP/85	09/NOV/85	
	N307PX	Republic Express				
674	G-31-674	British Aerospace	31	11/SEP/85	14/NOV/85	
	N308PX	Republic Express				
675	G-31-675	British Aerospace	31	17/SEP/85		
	N161PC	CC Air/Piedmont Commuter			DEC/85	

BRITISH AEROSPACE JETSTREAM 31

C/N	Registration	Owner/Operator	Series	First Flight	Delivery	Remarks
676	G-31-676	British Aerospace	31	26/SEP/85		
	N309PX	Republic Express			04/DEC/85	
677	G-31-677	British Aerospace	31	04/OCT/85		
	N162PC	CC Air/Piedmont Commuter			DEC/85	
678	G-31-678	British Aerospace	31			
	N163PC	CC Air/Piedmont Commuter			20/DEC/85	
679	G-31-679	British Aerospace	31			
	N311PX	Republic Express			27/DEC/85	
680	G-31-680	British Aerospace	31			
	N312PX	Republic Express			27/DEC/85	
681	G-31-681	British Aerospace	31			
	N313PX	Republic Express			22/JAN/86	
682	G-31-682	British Aerospace	31			
	N164PC	CC Air/Piedmont Commuter			18/FEB/86	
683	G-31-683	British Aerospace	31			
	N165PC	CC Air/Piedmont Commuter			08/FEB/86	
684	G-31-684	British Aerospace	31			
	N314PX	Republic Express			16/FEB/86	
685	G-31-685	British Aerospace	31			
	N315PX	Republic Express			25/FEB/86	
686	G-31-686	British Aerospace	31			
	PH-KJF	Netherlines			14/MAR/86	
687	G-31-687	British Aerospace	31			
	N316PX	Republic Express			13/MAR/86	
688	G-31-688	British Aerospace	31			
	N317PX	Republic Express			21/MAR/86	
689	G-31-689	British Aerospace	31			
	N318PX	Republic Express			23/MAR/86	
690	G-31-690	British Aerospace	31	22/JAN/86		
	PH-KJG	Netherlines			11/APR/86	
691	G-31-691	British Aerospace	31	28/JAN/86		
	N319PX	Republic Express			11/APR/86	
692	G-31-692	British Aerospace	31	04/FEB/86		
	N166PC	CC Air/Piedmont Commuter			22/APR/86	
693	G-31-693	British Aerospace	31	11/FEB/86		
	N331BK	British Aerospace Inc.			12/MAY/86	
694	G-31-694	British Aerospace	31	18/FEB/86		
	N168PC	CC Air/Piedmont Commuter			09/MAY/86	
695	G-31-695	British Aerospace	31	25/FEB/86		
	N169PC	CC Air/Piedmont Commuter			09/MAY/86	
696	G-31-696	British Aerospace	31	05/MAR/86		
	G-BMNR	British Aerospace			MAY/86	
697	G-31-697	British Aerospace	31	11/MAR/86		
	N331BL	British Aerospace Inc.			23/MAY/86	
698	G-31-698	British Aerospace	31	18/MAR/86		
	G-BMTV	British Aerospace			MAY/86	
	N330PX	Republic Express			17/JUN/86	
699	G-31-699	British Aerospace	31	25/MAR/86		
	N414MX	Eastern Metro Express			24/JUN/86	
700	G-31-700	British Aerospace	31	08/APR/86		
	N331PX	Republic Express			02/JUL/86	
701	G-31-701	British Aerospace	31	21/APR/86		
	D-	Contactair			JUL/86	Sched.delivery
702	G-31-702	British Aerospace	31	23/APR/86		
	N332PX	Republic Express			09/JUL/86	
703	G-31-703	British Aerospace	31	29/APR/86		
	VH-TQJ	Australian Airlines			AUG/86	
704	G-31-704	British Aerospace	31	08/MAY/86		
	N333PX	Republic Express			24/JUL/86	
705	G-31-705	British Aerospace	31	15/MAY/86		
	VH-TQK	Australian Airlines			AUG/86	
706	G-31-706	British Aerospace	31	21/MAY/86		
	N334PX	Republic Express			86	
707	G-31-707	British Aerospace	31	06/JUN/86		
	VH-TQL	Australian Airlines			SEP/86	Sched.delivery
708	G-31-708	British Aerospace	31	03/JUN/86		
	N331BN	British Aerospace Inc.			JUL/86	
709	G-31-709	British Aerospace	31	17/JUN/86		
	G-BMNS	British Aerospace			JUL/86	Demonstrator
710	G-31-710	British Aerospace	31	23/JUN/86		
711	G-31-711	British Aerospace	31	25/JUN/86		
712	G-31-712	British Aerospace	31	08/JUL/86		
713	G-31-713	British Aerospace	31	25/JUL/86		
714	G-31-714	British Aerospace	31			
715	G-31-715	British Aerospace	31			
716	G-31-716	British Aerospace	31			
	G-BRGL	Berlin Regional U.K.			AUG/86	Sched.delivery

ADDITIONAL ORDERS

	G-BRWK	Berlin Regional U.K.	31		OCT/86	Sched.delivery
	LN-	Air-X AB/Aros Flyg	31		86	Sched.delivery
	VH-	Skywest	31		86	Sched.delivery
	N	Eastern Atlantis Express	31			
	N	Eastern Atlantis Express	31			
	N	Eastern Atlantis Express	31			
	N	Republic Express	31			
	N	Republic Express	31			
	N	Republic Express	31			
	N	CC Air/Piedmont Commuter	31		86	Sched.delivery
	N	CC Air/Piedmont Commuter	31		86	Sched.delivery
	N	CC Air/Piedmont Commuter	31		87	Sched.delivery
	N	CC Air/Piedmont Commuter	31			
	N	CC Air/Piedmont Commuter	31			
	N	CC Air/Piedmont Commuter	31			
	N	CC Air/Piedmont Commuter	31			
	N	Metro/American Eagle	31		86	Sched.delivery
	N	Metro/American Eagle	31			
	N	Metro/American Eagle	31			
	N	Metro/American Eagle	31			
	N	Metro/American Eagle	31			
	N	Jetstream International	31		86	Sched.delivery
	N	Jetstream International	31		86	Sched.delivery
	N	Jetstream International	31		86	Sched.delivery
	N	Jetstream International	31		86	Sched.delivery

C/N	Registration	Owner/Operator	Series	First Flight	Delivery	Remarks
	N	Jetstream International	31		86	Sched.delivery
	N	Jetstream International	31		86	Sched.delivery
	N	Jetstream International	31		86	Sched.delivery

British Aerospace Jetstream 31
cross-reference index

D- West Germany

603	D-CONE
610	D-CONI
626	D-CONU

G- United Kingdom

611	G-11-611
612	G-11-612
613	G-11-613
614	G-11-614
615	G-11-615
616	G-11-616
602	G-31-39
603	G-31-42
605	G-31-45
606	G-31-46
607	G-31-47
608	G-31-48
609	G-31-49
610	G-31-50
615	G-31-615
618	G-31-618
619	G-31-619
620	G-31-620
621	G-31-621
622	G-31-622
623	G-31-623
624	G-31-624
625	G-31-625
626	G-31-626
627	G-31-627
628	G-31-628
629	G-31-629
630	G-31-630
631	G-31-631
632	G-31-632
633	G-31-633
634	G-31-634
635	G-31-635
636	G-31-636
638	G-31-638
639	G-31-639
640	G-31-640
641	G-31-641
642	G-31-642
643	G-31-643
644	G-31-644
645	G-31-645
646	G-31-646
647	G-31-647
648	G-31-648
649	G-31-649
650	G-31-650
651	G-31-651
652	G-31-652
653	G-31-653
654	G-31-654
655	G-31-655
656	G-31-656
657	G-31-657
658	G-31-658
659	G-31-659
660	G-31-660
661	G-31-661
662	G-31-662
663	G-31-663
664	G-31-664
665	G-31-665
666	G-31-666
667	G-31-667
668	G-31-668
669	G-31-669
670	G-31-670
671	G-31-671
672	G-31-672
673	G-31-673
674	G-31-674
675	G-31-675
676	G-31-676
677	G-31-677
678	G-31-678
679	G-31-679
680	G-31-680
681	G-31-681
682	G-31-682
683	G-31-683
684	G-31-684
685	G-31-685
686	G-31-686
687	G-31-687
688	G-31-688
689	G-31-689
690	G-31-690
691	G-31-691
692	G-31-692
693	G-31-693
694	G-31-694
695	G-31-695
696	G-31-696
697	G-31-697
698	G-31-698
699	G-31-699
700	G-31-700
701	G-31-701
702	G-31-702
703	G-31-703
704	G-31-704
705	G-31-705
706	G-31-706
707	G-31-707
708	G-31-708
709	G-31-709
710	G-31-710
711	G-31-711
712	G-31-712
604	G-BKHI
606	G-BKKY
612	G-BKTN
616	G-BKUY
615	G-BKVU
622	G-BLCB
621	G-BLCY
621	G-BLDO
634	G-BLEX
634	G-BLKP
696	G-BMNR
709	G-BMNS
698	G-BMTV
716	G-BRGL
614	G-BWWW
609	G-CBEA
603	G-CONE
602	G-JBAE
608	G-JSBA
607	G-OBEA
601	G-TALL
601	G-WMCC

N United States

611	N155AA
617	N156AA
643	N157AA
675	N161PC
677	N162PC
678	N163PC
682	N164PC
683	N165PC
692	N166PC
694	N168PC
695	N169PC
652	N300PX
654	N301PX
661	N302PX
662	N303PX
663	N304PX
666	N305PX
670	N306PX
673	N307PX
674	N308PX
676	N309PX
672	N310PX
679	N311PX
680	N312PX
681	N313PX
684	N314PX
685	N315PX
687	N316PX
688	N317PX
689	N318PX
691	N319PX
698	N330PX
613	N331BA
613	N331BG
608	N331BJ
693	N331BK
697	N331BL
602	N331J
605	N331JS
700	N331PX
702	N332PX
704	N333PX
706	N334PX
624	N400MX
628	N401MX
642	N402AE
630	N402MX
644	N403AE
632	N403MX
646	N404AE
625	N404MX
650	N405AE
635	N405MX
651	N406AE
631	N406MX
653	N407AE
636	N407MX
664	N408AE
638	N408MX
669	N409AE
639	N409MX
668	N410AE
640	N410MX
671	N411AE
660	N411MX
699	N414MX
618	N820JS
619	N821JS
615	N822JS
623	N823JS
627	N824JS
633	N825JS
602	N92MA
611	N988AX
617	N989AX
643	N990AX
657	N991AX
658	N992AX

PH- Netherlands

645	PH-KJA
648	PH-KJB
649	PH-KJC
655	PH-KJD
686	PH-KJF
690	PH-KJG

SE- Sweden

641	SE-IPD

VH- Australia

665	VH-ESW
622	VH-HSW
620	VH-JSW
629	VH-OSW
703	VH-TQJ
705	VH-TQK
707	VH-TQL

Military operated

United Kingdom

647	ZE438
656	ZE439
659	ZE440

BRITISH AEROSPACE 748

Short-range, twin-turboprop 44-52 seat transprot, powered by Rolls-Royce Dart engines. The 748 started life as an Avro project and made its first flight on 24 June 1960. The first production Series 1 with accommodation for 48 passengers and Dart 514 engines, was followed by the Series 2 and 2A with more powerful engines. In 1979, the 748-2A was replaced with the series 2B with improved 'hot and high' Dart 536-2s, and the latest version, the Super 748, incorporates a number of significant new development including engine hush kits. Some 262 aircraft have been delivered but the production line is now being wound-down in favour of the new BAe ATP.

Dimensions :	Wing span: 98ft 6in (30.02m) Length: 67ft 0in (20.42m) Height: 24ft 10in (7.57m) (Srs. 1/2)
	Wing span: 102ft 6in (31.23m) Length: 67ft 0in (20.42m) Height: 24ft 10in (7.57m) (Super)
Powerplant :	Two Rolls Royce Dart 514 turboprops (Srs.1), two Rolls Royce Dart 531 turboprops (Srs.2A/2C)
	two Rolls Royce Dart 532-2L (Srs.2S), two Rolls Royce Dart 552-2 turboprops (Super)
Performance :	Max cruising speed 230 knots (426km/h) (Srs.1) Range: with max payload 90nm (167km) (Srs.1)
	Max cruising speed 241 knots (448km/h) (Srs.2) Range: with max payload 460nm (852km) (Srs.2)
	Max cruising speed 243 knots (452km/h) (Super) Range: with max payload 1,264nm (2,341km) (Super)
Accommodation:	48 passengers in a 4 abreast layout
Manufacturer :	British Aerospace - Civil Aircraft Division, Woodford, Stockport, Cheshire, England
	Telephone: (061) 439 5050 Telex: 6675454 G

C/N	Registration	Owner/Operator	Series	First Flight	Delivery	Remarks
1534	G-APZV	Hawker Siddeley	100	24/JUN/60		To C/N 1548
1535	G-ARAY	Hawker Siddeley	200	10/APR/61		
	YV-C-AMC	LAV			FEB/65	Leased
	G-ARAY	Hawker Siddeley				
	PP-VJQ	Varig			DEC/65	Leased
	G-ARAY	Hawker Siddeley				
	VP-LIO	LIAT			APR/66	Leased
	G-ARAY	Hawker Siddeley				
	PI-C784	Philippine Airlines			FEB/67	Leased
	G-ARAY	Hawker Siddeley				
	OY-DFV	Falckair/Maerskair			04/AUG/67	
	G-ARAY	Dan-Air			03/MAY/71	
1536	G-ARMV	Skyways Coach Air	101	31/AUG/61	03/SEP/61	W/O 11/JUL/65,Lympne
1537	G-ARMW	Skyways Coach Air	101	08/MAY/62	02/APR/62	
	G-ARMW	BKS			05/JUN/62	
	G-ARMW	Hawker Siddeley			NOV/62	Leased
	VP-LII	LIAT			JAN/65	Leased
	G-ARMW	Hawker Siddeley				
	G-ARMW	BKS			NOV/67	Leased
	G-ARMW	Dan-Air			06/APR/72	
	VP-LVO	Air BVI			85	Leased
1538	G-ARMX	Skyways Coach Air	101	19/OCT/62	02/APR/63	
	G-ARMX	BKS			MAR/66	Leased
	G-ARMX	Dan-Air			06/APR/72	
	VP-LVN	Air BVI			22/NOV/83	Leased
	VP-LVN	Air BVI			01/JAN/84	
1539	LV-PIZ	Aerolineas Argentinas	105	09/DEC/61	18/JAN/62	
	LV-HGW	Aerolineas Argentinas				
1540	LV-PJA	Aerolineas Argentinas	105	23/FEB/62	24/FEB/62	W/O 04/FEB/70,Corrientes
	LV-HHA	Aerolineas Argentinas				
	LV-HHA	Yacimientos Petroliferos Fiscales			28/MAR/73	
1541	LV-PRJ	Aerolineas Argentinas	105	02/APR/62	24/APR/62	W/O 14/APR/76,Neuquen
	LV-HHC	Aerolineas Argentinas				
	G-BEKC	Dan-Air			SEP/76	
1542	LV-PUC	Aerolineas Argentinas	105	22/APR/62	07/MAY/62	
	LV-HHD	Aerolineas Argentinas				
	LV-HHD	Yacimientos Petroliferos Fiscales			19/MAR/73	
	G-BEKF	Dan-Air			SEP/76	
1543	LV-PUF	Aerolineas Argentinas	105	21/MAY/62	05/JUN/62	W/O 31/JUL/79,Sumburgh
	LV-HHE	Aerolineas Argentinas				
	LV-HHE	Yacimientos Petroliferos Fiscales			18/APR/75	
	G-BEJD	Dan-Air			SEP/76	
1544	LV-PUM	Aerolineas Argentinas	105	20/JUN/62	30/JUN/62	
	LV-HHF	Aerolineas Argentinas				
	G-BEKD	Dan-Air			SEP/76	
	EC-DTP	Air Condal			01/JUL/83	
	EC-DTP	Dan-Air			21/JAN/86	
	EI-BSF	Ryan Air			21/JAN/86	
1545	LV-PUP	Aerolineas Argentinas	105	29/JUN/62	20/JUL/62	
	LV-HHG	Aerolineas Argentinas				
	LV-HHG	Yacimientos Petroliferos Fiscales			12/APR/73	
	G-BEKE	Dan-Air			SEP/76	
1546	LV-PVH	Aerolineas Argentinas	105	14/JUL/62	10/AUG/62	
	LV-HHH	Aerolineas Argentinas				
1547	LV-PVF	Aerolineas Argentinas	105	20/JUL/62	20/AUG/62	W/O 19/DEC/70, Samiento
	LV-HHI	Aerolineas Argentinas				W/O 27/NOV/69, Santa Rosa Ap.
1548	G-ARRV	Hawker Siddeley		21/DEC/63		Proto.Andover
						WFU 03/APR/79, derelict Benson
1549	G-ARRW	BKS	106	10/APR/63	23/APR/63	
	G-ARRW	Skyways Coach Air			13/MAR/67	
	G-ARRW	BKS			68	Leased
	G-ARRW	Dan-Air			06/APR/72	
	EI-BSE	Ryan Air			01/PAR/86	
1550	C91-2500	Brasilian Air Force	204	27/AUG/62	17/NOV/62	

C/N	Registration	Owner/Operator	Series	First Flight	Delivery	Remarks
1551	C91-2501	Brasilian Air Force	204	16/JAN/63	26/FEB/63	
1552	C91-2502	Brasilian Air Force	204	22/FEB/63	20/MAR/63	
1553	C91-2503	Brasilian Air Force	204	19/MAR/63	18/APR/63	
1554	C91-2504	Brasilian Air Force	204	07/JUN/63	04/JUL/63	
1555	C91-2505	Brasilian Air Force	204	30/AUG/63	28/SEP/63	
1556	LV-PXD	Aerolineas Argentinas	105	19/JUL/63	31/AUG/63	
	LV-IDV	Aerolineas Argentinas				
	LV-IDV	Yacimientos Petroliferous				
		Fiscales			75	
	G-BEJE	Dan-Air			SEP/76	
1557	LV-PXH	Aerolineas Argentinas	105	06/SEP/63	15/NOV/63	
	LV-IEE	Aerolineas Argentinas				
	G-BEKG	Dan-Air			SEP/76	
	VR-CBH	Cayman Airways			24/FEB/82	
	G-VAJK	Venture Airways			29/FEB/84	
	G-VAJK	Euroair			13/JUN/85	
	G-VAJK	Tunisavia			JUL/85	Leased
	G-VAJK	Euroair			DEC/85	
1558	LV-PXP	Aerolineas Argentinas	105	24/OCT/63	15/NOV/63	
	LV-IEV	Aerolineas Argentinas				W/O 15/JUL/69, Bahia Blanca Ap.
1559	G-ASJT	Smiths Aviation Division	107	11/OCT/63	20/OCT/63	
	XW750	Royal Aircraft Establishment			13/JAN/70	
1560	G-ASPL	BKS	108	31/MAR/64	14/APR/64	
	G-ASPL	Skyways Coach Air			18/MAR/67	
	G-ASPL	Dan-Air			06/APR/72	W/O 26/JUN/81, nr. Nailstone
1561	XS789	RAF/Queens Flight	206	15/MAY/64	07/AUG/64	Andover CC2
1562	XS790	RAF/Queens Flight	206	26/JUN/64	10/JUL/64	Andover CC2
1563	XS791	Royal Air Force	206	17/NOV/64	21/DEC/64	Andover CC2
1564	XS792	Royal Air Force	206	14/JAN/65	08/FEB/65	Andover CC2
1565	XS793	RAF/Queens Flight	206	11/MAR/65	12/MAR/65	Andover CC2
1566	XS794	Royal Air Force	206	06/MAY/65	09/SEP/65	Andover CC2
1567	HS-THA	Thai Airways	207	14/AUG/64	27/AUG/64	
	PK-OBW	Airfast			81	
1568	HS-THB	Thai Airways	207	27/SEP/64	07/OCT/64	W/O 27/APR/80, Don Muang Ap. Bangkok
1569	HS-THC	Thai Airways	207	12/NOV/64	19/NOV/64	
	60-203	Royal Thai Air Force			83	
1570	HS-TAF	Royal Thai Air Force	208	23/DEC/64	31/DEC/64	
	11-111	Royal Thai Air Force				
1571	4R-ACJ	Air Ceylon	212	09/OCT/64	22/OCT/64	W/O 07/SEP/78, Rat Malana
1572	XS594	Royal Air Force			02/DEC/64	Andover C1
1573	XS595	Royal Air Force			25/JAN/66	Andover C1
1574	XS596	Royal Air Force			01/JUN/66	Andover C1
1575	XS597	Royal Air Force			01/APR/66	Andover C1
1576	G-ATAM	BKS	214	09/FEB/65	17/FEB/65	
	XA-SEI	Aerotaxi-Aerosafari			13/JUN/66	Leased
	G-ATAM	Hawker Siddeley			12/JUL/67	
	PI-C1020	Philippine Airlines			FEB/68	Leased
	G-ATAM	Hawker Siddeley				
	9G-ABV	Ghana Airways			APR/69	Leased
	G-ATAM	Hawker Siddeley				
	OY-DFS	Maersk Air			JAN/70	Leased
	G-ATAM	Hawker Siddeley			FEB/70	
	9J-ABL	Zambia Airways			MAR/70	Leased
	G-ATAM	Hawker Siddeley				
	ZS-HSA	South African Airways			SEP/70	Leased
	G-ATAM	Hawker Siddeley			FEB/71	
	TR-LQY	Trans Gabon			03/OCT/72	
	C-GMAA	Austin Airways			29/MAY/76	
1577	YV-C-AME	LAV	215	26/APR/65	15/MAY/65	
	YV-04C	LAV			75	
	C-GDUI	Austin Airways			DEC/80	
	C-GDUI	Regionair			DEC/82	
	C-GDUI	Quebecair			MAR/84	
1578	YV-C-AMI	LAV	215	07/MAY/65	02/MAY/65	
	6201	Venezuelan Air Force			SEP/77	
	YV-05C	LAV			MAY/80	
	C-GDUL	Austin Airways			DEC/80	
	C-GDUL	Regionair			DEC/82	
	C-GDUL	Quebecair			MAR/84	
1579	YV-C-AMO	LAV	215	06/JUL/65	30/JUL/65	
	YV-06C	LAV				
	TR-0203	Venezuelan Navy			23/JUL/77	
	C-GFFU	Austin Airways			10/AUG/81	
1580	YV-C-AMY	LAV	215	26/OCT/65	17/NOV/65	W/O 28/AUG/68
1581	YV-C-AMF	LAV	215	23/DEC/65	04/FEB/66	
	YV-07C	LAV				
	VP-LAX	LIAT			77	Leased
	YV-07C	LAV				
	C-GDUN	Austin Airways			DEC/80	
	C-GDUN	Regionair			81	
	C-GDUN	Quebecair			MAR/84	
	C-GDUN	Bradley Air Services			84	
1582	YV-C-AMC	LAV	215	08/MAY/66	24/MAY/66	
	YV-08C	LAV				
	C-GDOV	Austin Airways			05/DEC/80	
	C-GDOV	Northern Wings			26/JAN/81	
	C-GDOV	Regionair			MAY/81	
	C-GDOV	Quebecair			MAR/84	
	C-GDOV	Bradley Air Services			84	
1583	VP-LIK	LIAT	217	09/MAY/66	21/MAY/66	
	V2-LIK	LIAT			82	
1584	VP-LIP	LIAT	217	04/AUG/66	16/AUG/66	
	V2-LIP	LIAT			82	
	RP-C				FEB/86	
1585	G-ATEH	Channel Airways	222	07/SEP/65	08/OCT/65	
	HP-416	COPA-Panama			OCT/65	Leased
	G-ATEH	Channel Airways				
	VP-LIW	LIAT			21/JUN/68	
	PK-OBV	Airfast			28/FEB/81	
1586	G-ATEI	Channel Airways	222	01/NOV/65	21/FEB/66	
	VP-LIN	LIAT			DEC/65	Leased
	CF-TAX	Transair			MAY/69	Leased
	G-ATEI	Channel Airways				
	G-ATEI	Rousseau Aviation			MAY/70	Leased

C/N	Registration	Owner/Operator	Series	First Flight	Delivery	Remarks
	G-ATEI	Channel Airways				
	PI-C1029	Philippine Airlines			16/OCT/70	
	RP-C1029	Philippine Airlines				W/O 10/MAY/75, Manila
1587	G-ATEJ	Channel Airways	222	20/JAN/66	21/FEB/66	
	CF-MAL	Midwest			14/DEC/67	
	CF-MAL	Transair				
	TG-MAL	Aviateca			FEB/75	Leased
	C-GGZY	Transair				
	4R-ACR	Air Ceylon			04/MAY/75	
	CR-831	Sri-Lankan Air Force			01/SEP/79	
1588	G-ATEK	Channel Airways	222	10/FEB/66	28/MAR/66	
	VP-LIV	LIAT			16/MAY/68	
	V2-LIV	LIAT			82	
	RP-C	Philippine Airlines			31/AUG/85	
1589	OE-LHS	Austrian Airlines	226	22/APR/66	30/APR/66	
	G-AXVG	Skyways Coach Air			15/NOV/69	
	G-AXVG	Dan-Air			05/OCT/71	
	RP-C1031	Philippine Airlines			17/OCT/84	Leased
1590	OE-LHT	Austrian Airlines	226	23/MAY/66	31/MAY/66	
	PI-C1028	Philippine Airlines			03/SEP/70	W/O 03/FEB/75, Manila
1591	0111	Venezuelan MoD	223	02/JUL/66	01/AUG/66	VIP
1592	G-ATMI	Autair	225	16/MAR/66	30/MAR/66	
	VP-LIU	LIAT			NOV/67	Leased
	G-ATMI	Skyways			MAY/68	Leased
	VP-LIU	LIAT			NOV/69	Leased
	G-ATMI	SATA			MAY/70	Leased
	VP-LIU	LIAT			DEC/70	Leased
	G-ATMI	British Air Ferries			APR/71	Leased
	VP-LIU	LIAT			16/DEC/71	
	G-ATMI	Dan-Air			10/MAY/76	
	G-ATMI	Air BVI			15/DEC/81	Leased
	G-ATMI	Dan Air			14/APR/82	
1593	G-ATMJ	Autair	225	06/APR/66	20/APR/66	
	6Y-JFJ	Jamaica Air Services			JAN/68	Leased
	G-ATMJ	SATA			APR/69	Leased
	G-ATMJ	British Air Ferries			NOV/70	Leased
	VP-LAJ	LIAT			NOV/71	Leased
	VP-LAJ	Rousseau Aviation			APR/72	Sub-leased
	VP-LAJ	LIAT			JUL/72	Leased
	G-ATMJ	CAA Flying Unit			20/OCT/72	
	G-ATMJ	Dan-Air			21/JUL/78	
	G-ATMJ	British Airways			01/MAR/82	Leased
1594	HP-432	COPA-Panama	227	17/JUL/66	29/JUL/66	
	C-GEPI	Eastern Provincial Airways			15/MAY/78	
	C-GEPI	Air Maritime				
1595	A10-595	Royal Australian Air Force	229	18/JAN/67	17/MAR/67	VIP
1596	A10-596	Royal Australian Air Force	229	10/MAR/67	27/APR/67	VIP
1597	T-01	Argentine Air Force	221	09/DEC/66	20/DEC/66	VIP
	T-02	Argentine Air Force			JAN/71	VIP
	T-03	Argentine Air Force			JUL/75	VIP
	C-GQWO	Austin Airways			01/OCT/78	
1598	G-11	Hawker Siddeley	230	31/AUG/66		
	XA-SEV	Aeromaya			10/NOV/66	
	XA-SEV	SAESA			SEP/69	W/O 06/JAN/72, Chetumal
1599	G-11	Hawker Siddeley	230	23/SEP/66		
	XA-SEY	Aeromaya			02/JAN/67	
	XA-SEY	SAESA			SEP/69	
	XA-SEY	Aero Caribe			JAN/77	
	C-GAPC	Northern Wings			19/AUG/79	
	C-GAPC	Regionair			MAY/81	
	C-GAPC	Quebecair			MAR/84	
1600	AF-601	Zambian Air Force	231	23/MAY/67	21/JUN/67	W/O 26/AUG/69
1601	G-AVZD	Hawker Siddeley	228	21/FEB/68		
	A10-601	Royal Australian Air Force			07/JUN/68	
1602	A10-602	Royal Australian Air Force	228	01/AUG/68	03/OCT/68	
1603	A10-603	Royal Australian Air Force	228	13/SEP/68	30/OCT/68	
1604	A10-604	Royal Australian Air Force	228	07/NOV/68	15/DEC/68	
1605	A10-605	Royal Australian Air Force	228	19/DEC/68	28/FEB/69	
1606	A10-606	Royal Australian Air Force	228	24/FEB/69	15/MAY/69	
1607	A10-607	Royal Australian Air Force	228	28/MAR/69	27/JUN/69	
1608	A10-608	Royal Australian Air Force	228	02/JUN/69	29/JUL/69	
1609	VP-BCJ	Bahamas Airways	232	12/DEC/66	22/DEC/66	
	PI-C1027	Philippine Airlines			JUL/70	W/O 28/NOV/72, Bisling
1610	VP-BCK	Bahamas Airways	232	20/FEB/67	03/MAR/67	
	PK-RHQ	Mandala Airlines			23/JUN/71	
	PK-RHS	Mandala Airlines			74	W/O 18/OCT/77, Manila
1611	VP-BCL	Bahamas Airways	232	07/MAR/67	13/APR/67	
	CF-INE	Inexco Oil				
	A2-ABA	Air Botswana			22/MAR/74	Leased
	CF-INE	Inexco Oil				
	C-FINE	Eastern Provincial Airways			01/FEB/75	
	C-FINE	Air Maritime				
1612	VP-BCM	Bahamas Airways	232	05/APR/67	23/APR/67	
	A2-ABB	Air Botswana			01/OCT/74	
	A2-ABB	Zambia Airways			05/JAN/76	Leased
	A2-ABB	Air Botswana				
	G-AZSU	Dan-Air			29/MAR/76	
	G-AZSU	British Airways			13/MAR/80	Leased
	G-AZSU	Dan Air			13/FEB/85	
1613	VQ-FAL	Fiji Airways	233	16/AUG/67	11/SEP/67	
	DQ-FAL	Air Pacific			APR/71	
	G-BEBA	Dan-Air			29/JUN/76	
	RP-C1032	Philippine Airlines			31/DEC/84	Leased
1614	CC-CEC	Lan-Chile	234	12/JUN/67	13/SEP/67	
	PK-IHA	Bouraq			23/FEB/78	
1615	CC-CED	Lan-Chile	234	21/JUL/67	18/AUG/67	
	PK-IHB	Bouraq			21/SEP/78	
	PK-IHS	Bouraq				
1616	CC-CEE	Lan-Chile	234	19/SEP/67	05/OCT/67	
	PK-IHC	Bouraq			16/MAR/78	
1617	CC-CEF	Lan-Chile	234	27/NOV/67	15/DEC/67	
	C-GQTH	Austin Airways			MAY/79	
	OY-MBH	Maersk Air			80	Leased
	C-GQTH	Austin Airways			04/APR/81	
	C-GQTH	Ilford Riverton Airways				

C/N	Registration	Owner/Operator	Series	First Flight	Delivery	Remarks
1618	CC-CEG	Lan-Chile	234	27/MAR/68	02/MAY/68	
	C-GQSV	Austin Airways			JUN/79	
	OY-MBY	Maersk Air			21/AUG/80	Leased
	C-GQSV	Austin Airways			18/JUL/81	
1619	CC-CEH	Lan-Chile	234	08/JUL/68	20/NOV/68	
	C-GQTG	Austin Airways			MAY/79	
	C-GQTG	Air Maritime				
1620	CC-CEI	Lan-Chile	234	18/OCT/68	22/JAN/69	
	PK-IHE	Bouraq			16/MAR/78	
1621	CC-CEJ	Lan-Chile	234	12/DEC/68	18/JUN/69	
	C-GOUT	Austin Airways			MAY/79	
	OY-APT	Maersk Air			07/JUN/80	Leased
	C-GOUT	Austin Airways			JUN/81	
	C-GOUT	Air Inuit			84	
1622	CC-CEK	Lan-Chile	234	14/MAY/68	07/AUG/68	
	PK-IHF	Bouraq			16/MAR/68	
1623	G-AVXI	CAA Flying Unit	238	13/FEB/69	15/JUL/69	
1624	G-AVXJ	CAA Flying Unit	238	04/JUN/69	04/SEP/69	
1625	PP-VDN	Varig	235	12/OCT/67	04/NOV/67	W/O 17/JUN/75, Pedro Afonso
1626	PP-VDO	Varig	235	12/DEC/67	03/JAN/68	
	PK-IHI	Bouraq			13/DEC/76	W/O
1627	PP-VDP	Varig	235	09/JAN/68	25/JAN/68	
	PK-IHG	Bouraq			05/DEC/76	
1628	PP-VDQ	Varig	235	26/JAN/68	17/FEB/68	W/O 14/DEC/69, Umberlandia
1629	PP-VDR	Varig	235	07/MAR/68	11/APR/68	
	PK-IHH	Bouraq			05/JAN/77	
1630	PP-VDS	Varig	235	18/APR/68	16/MAY/68	
	PK-IHJ	Bouraq			08/JAN/77	
1631	PP-VDT	Varig	235	02/MAY/68	26/JUN/68	
	LN-FOM	Fred Olsen Air Transport			29/OCT/75	
1632	PP-VDU	Varig	235	13/JUN/68	18/JUL/68	W/O 04/FEB/72, Porto Alegre
1633	PP-VDV	Varig	235	19/JUL/68	21/AUG/68	
	PK-IHK	Bouraq			05/DEC/76	W/O 09/FEB/77, Ujung Pandang
1634	PP-VDX	Varig	235	14/AUG/68	15/SEP/68	
	PK-IHM	Bouraq			05/DEC/76	
1635	G-AVRR	Hawker Siddeley	239	05/SEP/67		Proto. Series 2A
	G-AVRR	SATA			FEB/69	Leased
	G-AVRR	Skyways			APR/69	Leased
	CF-YQD	Transair			MAY/69	Leased
	G-AVRR	Olympic Airways			JUN/69	Leased
	ZS-IGI	Air Cape			DEC/69	Leased
	ZS-IGI	National Airways Corp.			DEC/69	Leased
	ZS-IGI	Suidwes Lugdiens			DEC/69	Leased
	9J-ABM	Zambia Airways			MAR/70	Leased
	ZS-HSI	South African Airways			MAY/70	Leased
	G-AVRR	Merpati Nusantara			JAN/71	Leased
	TR-LQJ	Trans Gabon			OCT/71	Leased
	TR-LQJ	Trans Gabon			03/OCT/71	Purchased
	TR-LQJ	Air Gabon				
	C-GEPH	Eastern Provincial Airlines			07/MAR/76	W/O 29/DEC/81
1636	PI-C1014	Philippine Airlines	209	12/SEP/67	30/SEP/67	
	RP-C1014	Philippine Airlines				W/O 11/JUL/82
1637	PI-C1015	Philippine Airlines	209	17/OCT/67	02/NOV/67	
	RP-C1015	Philippine Airlines				
1638	PI-C1016	Philippine Airlines	209	25/OCT/67	21/NOV/67	
	RP-C1016	Philippine Airlines				
	PK-OBQ	Airfast			MAY/80	
1639	PI-C1017	Philippine Airlines	209	16/NOV/67	13/FEB/67	
	RP-C1017	Philippine Airlines				
1640	PI-C1018	Philippine Airlines	209	21/DEC/67	16/JAN/68	
	RP-C1018	Philippine Airlines				
	C-GJVN	Bradley Air Services			FEB/80	
1641	PI-C1019	Philippine Airlines	209	13/FEB/68	13/MAR/68	
	RP-C1019	Philippine Airlines				
	RP-C1019	Philippine CAA			NOV/78	
1642	PI-C1021	Philippine Airlines	209	24/MAY/68	18/JUL/68	
	RP-C1021	Philippine Airlines				
	RP-C1021	Philippine CAA			NOV/78	
	RP-C1021	Philippine Airlines				
1643	PI-C1022	Philippine Airlines	209	24/JUN/68	04/AUG/68	W/O 21/APR/73, Pantabangan
1644	HS-THD	Thai Airways	243	18/SEP/68	05/OCT/68	
	60-204	Royal Thai Air Force			24/DEC/83	
1645	HS-THE	Thai Airways	243	29/OCT/68	07/NOV/68	WFU 82, Bangkok
	60-205	Royal Thai Air Force			24/DEC/83	
1646	HS-THF	Thai Airways	243	13/NOV/68	29/NOV/68	
	60-206	Royal Thai Air Force			24/DEC/83	
1647	ZK-CWJ	Mount Cook Airlines	242	05/SEP/68	26/SEP/68	
1648	TC-71	Argentine Air Force	240			Cancelled NOV/67
1649	TC-72	Argentine Air Force	240			Cancelled NOV/67
1650	TC-73	Argentine Air Force	240			Cancelled NOV/67
1651	TC-74	Argentine Air Force	240			Cancelled NOV/67
1652	TC-75	Argentine Air Force	240			Cancelled NOV/67
1653	TC-76	Argentine Air Force	240			Cancelled NOV/67
1654	TC-77	Argentine Air Force	240			Cancelled NOV/67
1655	TC-78	Argentine Air Force	240			Cancelled NOV/67
1656	D-AFSD	BFS	244	12/SEP/69	19/DEC/69	
	N57910	N.A. Kalt			DEC/84	
		Unnanounced operator			85	
1657	HK-1408	Avianca	245	16/AUG/68	07/SEP/68	
						W/O 05/JUL/73, Bucaramanga
1658	HK-1409	Avianca	245	04/OCT/68	25/OCT/68	
	G-BFLL	Dan-Air			FEB/78	
	G-BFLL	British Airways			82	Leased
	G-BFLL	Dan-Air			30/JAN/85	
1659	PI-C1023	Philippine Airlines	209	29/JAN/69	08/MAR/69	
	RP-C1023	Philippine Airlines				
1660	PI-C1024	Philippine Airlines	209	19/FEB/69	26/MAR/69	
	RP-C1024	Philippine Airlines				
1661	VQ-FBH	Fiji Airways	233	27/NOV/68	08/DEC/68	
	DQ-FBH	Air Pacific			APR/71	
	ZK-MCJ	Mount Cook Airlines			06/OCT/79	
1662	HP-484	COPA-Panama	227	22/APR/69	10/MAY/69	
	G-BCDZ	Hawker Siddeley			20/MAY/74	Coastguarder proto.
	G-BCDZ	DLT			JAN/81	Leased
	G-BCDZ	British Aerospace			AUG/81	

C/N	Registration	Owner/Operator	Series	First Flight	Delivery	Remarks
	G-BCDZ	British Airways			JAN/82	Leased
	G-BCDZ	British Aerospace			DEC/82	Demonstrator
	G-BCDZ	Air Sinai			83	Lease not taken-up
	G-BCDZ	British Aerospace			83	
	G-BCDZ	SATA			83	Leased
	G-11-3	British Aerospace			SEP/84	
	C-GSBF	Calm Air			27/SEP/84	
1663	PI-C1025	Philippine Airlines	209	14/MAY/69	28/MAY/69	
	CF-TAZ	Transair			MAY/69	Leased
	RP-C1025	Philippine Airlines			NOV/69	
	G-BHCJ	Dan Air			30/OCT/79	
	G-BHCJ	SATA			01/JUN/81	Leased
	G-BHCJ	Dan Air			16/SEP/81	
	RP-C1030	Philippine Airlines			24/OCT/84	Leased
1664	PI-C1026	Philippine Airlines	209	09/JUN/69	25/JUN/69	
	CF-TAG	Transair			JUN/69	Leased
	RP-C1026	Philippine Airlines			NOV/69	
1665	VQ-FBK	Fiji Airways	233	22/AUG/69	06/OCT/69	
	DQ-FBK	Air Pacific			APR/71	
	C-GYMX	Bradley Air Services			26/NOV/80	
1666	7Q-YKA	Air Malawi	256	13/NOV/69	06/DEC/69	
1667	7Q-YKB	Air Malawi	256	09/DEC/69	10/JAN/70	
1668	CF-MAK	Transair	257	17/JUN/69	17/JUL/69	
	CF-MAK	Gateway Aviation			APR/72	
	C-FMAK	Calm Air			DEC/79	W/O 19/MAR/82, Manitoba
1669	CF-AMO	AMOCO	258	30/JUL/69	21/AUG/69	
1670	9Y-TDH	BWIA	217	12/SEP/69		Not taken-up
	VP-LAA	LIAT			08/OCT/69	
	V2-LAA	LIAT			82	
	RP-C				MAR/86	
1671	G-AXVZ	Hawker Siddeley	253	16/DEC/68		
	9N-AAU	Royal Nepal Airlines			21/JAN/70	
1672	9N-AAV	Royal Nepal Airlines	253	07/JAN/70	03/MAR/70	
1673	XA-SAB	SAESA	259	02/FEB/70	27/FEB/70	W/O 28/JUL/73, Acapulco
1674	XA-SAC	SAESA	259	11/FEB/70	16/MAR/70	
	C-GSXS	Austin Airways			14/NOV/77	
1675	XA-SAF	SAESA	259	02/MAR/70	25/MAR/70	
	C-GPAA	Austin Airways			03/DEC/76	W/O 17/JUL/79, Moosonee
1676	9J-ABJ	Zambia Airways	263	24/MAR/70	17/APR/70	
	6V-AET	Air Senegal			25/MAR/80	
1677	9J-ABK	Zambia Airways	263	02/JUL/70	20/JUL/70	
1678	G-11-2	Hawker Siddeley	264	07/MAY/70		
	G-AYDH	Hawker Siddeley				
	F-BSRA	Rouseau Aviation			15/MAY/70	
	F-BSRA	Reunion Air Services			AUG/77	
1679	G-11-1	Hawker Siddeley	269	24/APR/70		
	G-AYFL	Hawker Siddeley				
	CF-CSE	Chevron Oil			29/SEP/70	
1680	G-11-4	Hawker Siddeley	263			
	9J-ABW	Zambia Airways			02/SEP/70	
1681	G-11-3	Hawker Siddeley	264	21/MAY/70		
	G-AYIR	Hawker Siddeley				
	F-BSRU	Rousseau Aviation			27/OCT/70	
	F-BSRU	SATA			14/OCT/71	Leased
	F-BSRU	Rousseau Aviation				
	CS-TAF	SATA				
	A2-ABC	Air Botswana			23/DEC/75	
	ZS-LHN	United Air			82	
	7P-LAI	Lesotho Airways			DEC/83	Leased
	ZS-LHN	United Air			MAR/84	
	ZS-LHN	Protea Airways			84	
1682	FAE 682/					
	HC-AUD	Ecuadorean Air Force/TAME	246	02/SEP/70	03/OCT/70	
1683	FAE 683/					
	HC-AUE	Ecuadorean Air Force/TAME	246	18/SEP/70	23/OCT/70	W/O 20/JAN/76, Andes Mts.
1684	FAE 001/					
	HC-AUK	Ecuadorean Air Force	267	09/OCT/70	21/NOV/70	VIP
1685	9G-ABW	Ghana Airways	254	20/NOV/70	10/DEC/70	W/O 22/JAN/71, Kotoko Ap.
1686	9G-ABX	Ghana Airways	254	07/DEC/70	01/JAN/71	
	C-GEPB	Eastern Provincial Airways			03/MAY/81	
	C-GEPB	Air Maritime				
1687	G-11-5	Hawker Siddeley	270	17/JUL/70		
	G-AYIM	Hawker Siddeley				
	G-AYIM	SATA			21/OCT/71	Leased
	CS-TAG	SATA			30/APR/72	Purchased
1688	AF-602	Zambian Air Force	265	23/DEC/70	17/FEB/71	VIP
1689	ZK-DES	Mount Cook Airlines	242	04/JUN/71	02/JUL/71	
	ZK-DES	SATA			08/JUL/82	Leased
	ZK-DES	Mount Cook Airlines			82	
1690	ZS-SBU	South Africa Airways	272	19/JAN/71	17/FEB/71	
	C-GGNZ	Austin Airways			14/NOV/83	
1691	ZS-SBW	South African Airways	272	12/JAN/71	29/JAN/71	
	A2-ZFT	Botswana Airways			JAN/71	Leased
	ZS-SBW	South African Airways			15/MAY/71	
	C-GGOB	Austin Airways			05/DEC/83	
1692	ZS-SBV	South African Airways	272	29/JAN/71	17/FEB/71	
	C-GGOO	Austin Airways			19/NOV/83	
1693	HS-THG	Thai Airways	243	11/NOV/70	09/DEC/70	W/O 21/JUN/80, Chiang Rai, Thailand
1694	AMDB-110	Royal Brunei Regiment	273	04/NOV/70	20/JAN/71	
	VR-UEH	Royal Brunei Airlines			82	
	VS-UEH	Royal Brunei Airlines			01/JAN/84	
	V8-UEH	Royal Brunei Airlines			20/FEB/84	
	ZK-MCP	Mount Cook Airlines			30/APR/84	
1695	G-11-10	Hawker Siddeley	274	05/APR/71		
	G-AZAE	Hawker Siddeley				
	PK-MHM	Merpati Nusantara			16/JUN/71	
1696	PK-MHR	Merpati Nusantara	274	24/JUN/71	15/DEC/71	
1697	G-11-9	Hawker Siddeley		07/MAY/71		
	G-AYYG	Hawker Siddeley				
	G-AYYG	Howard Hughes			19/OCT/73	
	ZK-MCF	Mount Cook Airlines			28/SEP/76	
	G-AYYG	Dan-Air			16/JUN/78	Leased
	ZK-MCF	Mount Cook Airlines			13/OCT/78	
	G-AYYG	Dan-Air			29/APR/79	Leased

C/N	Registration	Owner/Operator	Series	First Flight	Delivery	Remarks
	ZK-MCF	Mount Cook Airlinesc			OCT/79	
	G-AYYG	Dan-Air			31/MAR/80	
	ZK-MCF	Mount Cook Airlines			82	
	C-GRCU	Calm Air			23/JUN/82	Leased
	ZK-MCF	Mount Cook Airlines			21/AUG/83	
1698	G-AZJH	Hawker Siddeley	275	31/DEC/71		
	9N-RAC	Royal Nepal Government			23/JAN/75	
	RAN-20	Royal Nepal Air Force			11/APR/80	
1699	G-11-6	Hawker Siddeley	276	04/MAR/71		
	CF-AGI	Air Gaspe			01/APR/71	
	CF-AGI	Northern Wings			01/MAY/75	
	CF-AGI	Air Gaspe				
	C-FAGI	Regionair			82	
	C-FAGI	Quebecair			MAR/84	
1700	G-11-7	Hawker Siddeley	216	17/MAR/71		
	G-AYVR	Hawker Siddeley				
	PK-IHD	Bouraq			03/JAN/73	W/O 23/JAN/76, Palu Ap.
1701	G-11-8	Hawker Siddeley	266	15/APR/71		
	G-AYYH	Hawker Siddeley				
	5W-FAN	Polynesian Airlines			11/JAN/72	
	5W-FAN	Dan Air			01/OCT/80	
	5W-FAN	Polynesian Airlines			01/OCT/80	Leased
	G-BIUV	Dan Air			APR/81	
1702	G-11-1	Hawker Siddeley	260	18/JUL/71		
	FAC 1101	SATENA			02/MAR/72	W/O 22/AUG/79
1703	G-11-2	Hawker Siddeley	260	25/AUG/71		
	FAC 1102	SATENA			03/MAR/72	W/O 25/FEB/85, Bogota
1704	G-11-3	Hawker Siddeley	260	14/SEP/71		
	FAC 1103	SATENA			16/MAR/72	W/O 09/JAN/74, Florencia
1705	G-11-4	Hawker Siddeley	260	08/OCT/71		
	FAC 1104	SATENA			09/FEB/72	W/O 07/AUG/73
1706	G-11-5	Hawker Siddeley	263	20/OCT/71		
	A2-ZGF	Air Botswana			09/FEB/72	Leased
	A2-ZGF	Hawker Siddeley				
	9J-ADM	Zambia Airways			JUN/72	
1707	G-11-6	Hawker Siddeley	243	09/NOV/71		
	HS-THH	Thai Airways			21/JAN/72	
1708	HS-THI	Thai Airways	243	23/DEC/71	07/FEB/72	
1709	N15-709	Royal Australian Navy	268	11/JAN/73	29/MAY/73	
1710	N15-710	Royal Australian Navy	268	16/MAR/73	03/AUG/73	
1711	D-AFSE	BFS	244	16/JUL/73	02/NOV/73	
	TF-GMB	(Icelandic Broker)			AUG/85	
	C-	Inter City Air			OCT/85	
1712	G-11-7	Hawker Siddeley	242	19/JAN/72		
	ZK-MCA	Mount Cook Airlines			14/SEP/72	
	ZK-MCA	SATA			11/APR/80	Leased
	ZK-MCA	Mount Cook Airlines			OCT/80	
1713	G-11-8	Hawker Siddeley	280	02/MAR/72		
	G-BBGY	Hawker Siddeley				
	1713	Republic of Korea Air Force			12/APR/74	
1714	G-11-10	Hawker Siddeley	266	16/MAR/72		
	5W-FAO	Polynesian Airlines			17/NOV/72	
	G-BMFT	Euroair			85	
1715	HS-TAF	Thai Royal flight	208	20/DEC/72	26/JAN/73	
	99-999	Royal Thai Air Force			73	
1716	G-11-3	Hawker Siddeley		23/OCT/72		
	G-BAFY	Hawker Siddeley				
	N748LL	Air Illinois			10/OCT/73	W/O 12/OCT/83, nr. Pinckneyville
1717	G-11-9	Hawker Siddeley	264	16/MAR/73		
	G-BASZ	Hawker Siddeley				
	F-BUTR	Rouseau Aviation			28/JUN/74	
	ZS-JAY	Air Cape			17/NOV/74	
1718	G-11-1	Hawker Siddeley	280	10/JUL/72		
	G-BABJ	Hawker Siddeley				
	1718	Republic of Korea Air Force			09/JUL/74	
1719	G-11-2	Hawker Siddeley	278	29/SEP/72		
	G-BBLN	Hawker Siddeley				
	CR-CAV	TACV			19/OCT/73	
	D4-CAV	TACV			NOV/84	
1720	G-11-4	Hawker Siddeley	278	24/NOV/72		
	G-BBPT	Hawker Siddeley				
	CR-CAW	TACV			29/NOV/73	
	D4-CAW	TACV			NOV/84	
1721	CS-TAH	SATA	270	19/APR/73	05/JUN/73	
1722	G-BBTA	Hawker Siddeley	216	06/DEC/73		
	PK-IHR	Bouraq			14/DEC/73	
	C-GTLD	Bradley Air Services			26/DEC/78	
1723	D-AFSF	BFS	244	12/SEP/75	20/NOV/75	
1724	D-AFSG	BFS	244	05/SEP/75	31/OCT/75	
1725	D-AFSH	BFS	244	29/NOV/75	15/DEC/75	
1726	D-AFSI	BFS	244	06/DEC/75	22/DEC/75	
1727	D-AFSJ	BFS	244	23/JAN/76	08/APR/76	
1728	5H-STZ	Tanzanian Government	282	21/MAR/74	29/APR/74	
1729	C91-2506	Brasilian Air Force	281	05/NOV/74	24/JAN/75	
1730	C91-2507	Brasilian Air Force	281	24/JAN/75	27/MAR/75	
1731	C91-2508	Brasilian Air Force	281	13/MAR/75	16/MAY/75	
1732	C91-2509	Brasilian Air Force	281	12/MAY/75	20/JUN/75	
1733	C91-2510	Brasilian Air Force	281	14/AUG/75	31/OCT/75	
1734	C91-2511	Brasilian Air Force	281	21/NOV/75	18/DEC/75	
1735	G-BCDM	Hawker Siddeley	216	02/APR/74		
	PK-KHL	Bouraq			26/JUL/74	
1736	G-BCOE	British Airways	287	17/JUN/75	10/JUL/75	
	G-BCOE	British Airways	2B		85	onverted
1737	G-BCOF	British Airways	287	14/AUG/75	03/SEP/75	
	G-BCOF	British Airways	2B		FEB/85	overted.
1738	FAE 738/		285	22/OCT/75	21/NOV/75	
	HC-BAZ	Ecuadorean Air Force/TAME				
1739	FAE 739	Ecuadorean Air Force	285	12/FEB/76	10/APR/76	
1740	5H-WDL	Williamson Diamonds	286	19/MAR/76	23/APR/76	
1741	CS-01	Royal Belgian Air Force	288	27/MAY/76	24/JUN/76	
1742	CS-02	Royal Belgian Air Force	288	06/JUL/76	31/JUL/76	
1743	CS-03	Royal Belgian Air Force	288	11/AUG/76	01/OCT/76	
1744	YV-45C	LAV	283	31/AUG/76	26/NOV/76	W/O 03/MAR/78, Caracas
1745	YV-46C	LAV	283	24/SEP/76	25/NOV/76	
	C-GDOP	Austin Airways			05/DEC/80	

BRITISH AEROSPACE 748

C/N	Registration	Owner/Operator	Series	First Flight	Delivery	Remarks
	C-GDOP	Eastern Provincial Airways			16/APR/82	
	C-GDOP	Air Maritime				
1746	G-BDVH	Hawker Siddeley	301	11/NOV/76		Demonstrator
	C6-BEA	Bahamasair			09/JAN/79	Leased
	G-BDVH	British Aerospace			13/AUG/79	Demonstrator
1747	8R-GEU	Guyana Airways	309	26/JAN/77	08/MAR/77	
1748	8R-GEV	Guyana Airways	309	11/MAY/77	22/JUN/77	
1749	TJ-XAF	Cameroon Air Force	310	27/APR/77	30/SEP/77	
	TJ-AAN	Cameroon Air Force			81	
	TJ-CCD	Cameroon Airlines			22/FEB/82	
1750	TJ-XAH	Cameroon Air Force	310	01/AUG/77	30/SEP/77	
	TJ-AAO	Cameroon Air Force			81	
	TJ-CCE	Cameroon Airlines			22/FEB/82	
1751	G-BETZ	Hawker Siddeley	314	29/SEP/77		
	JW9008	Tanzanian Air Force			15/NOV/77	
1752	G-BETY	Hawker Siddeley	314	07/NOV/77		
	JW9009	Tanzanian Air Force			20/JAN/78	
1753	G-BETX	Hawker Siddeley	314	12/DEC/77		
	JW9010	Tanzanian Air Force			27/JAN/78	
1754	XT-MAL	Upper Volta Government	320	22/JUN/77	02/SEP/77	
	XT-MAL	Bourkina Faso Government				
1755	EL-AIH	Air Liberia	329	30/JAN/78	24/FEB/78	W/O 16/APR/83, Khartoum
1756	G-11-8	Hawker Siddeley	334	07/DEC/77		
	9Y-TFS	TTAS			23/DEC/77	
1757	9Y-TFT	TTAS	334	16/JAN/78	04/FEB/78	
	VP-LCG	LIAT			80	
	V2-LCG	LIAT			MAY/82	
	9Y-TFT	TTAS			83	
1758	9Y-TFX	TTAS	334	26/MAY/78	05/JUL/78	
1759	9Y-TGD	TTAS	334		19/DEC/78	
1760	G-11-9	Hawker Siddeley	333	27/APR/78		
	J5-GAT	Linhas Aereas Guinee-Bissau		01/DEC/78		
1761	G-11-10	Hawker Siddeley	344	22/SEP/78		
	C6-BEB	Bahamasair			14/FEB/79	
	G-BFVR	Hawker Siddeley		26/JUN/78		
1762	VP-LAZ	LIAT	343	23/NOV/78	07/DEC/78	
	V2-LAZ	LIAT			APR/82	
	C-GCUK	Air Inuit			MAR/85	
1763	C6-BEC	Bahamasair	348	15/JUN/79		Reg.not taken-up
	C6-BED	Bahamasair			06/JUL/79	
1764	C6-BED	Bahamasair	344	25/JUL/79		Reg.not taken-up
	C6-BEE	Bahamasair			24/AUG/79	
1765	C6-BEE	Bahamasair	344	19/OCT/79		Reg.not taken-up
	C6-BEF	Bahamasair			08/NOV/79	
1766	G-BGMN	British Aerospace	347	05/JUN/79		
	9Y-TGH	TTAS			16/JUL/79	
	G-DGMN	Euroair			APR/86	
	G-DGMN	British Airways			APR/86	Leased
1767	G-BGMO	British Aerospace	347	29/AUG/79		
	9Y-TGI	TTAS			22/NOV/79	
	G-BGMO	Euroair			APR/86	
	G-BGMO	British Airways			APR/86	Leased
1768	G-BGJV	British Aerospace	357	22/JUN/79		Demonstrator
	G-BGJV	DLT			FEB/81	Leased
	G-BGJV	British Aerospace			MAR/81	
	G-BGJV	Air Virginia			06/AUG/81	Leased
	G-BGJV	British Aerospace			20/SEP/81	
	MI-GJV	Airline of the Marshall Islands			05/JUL/82	Leased
	G-BGJV	British Aerospace			FEB/83	Demonstrator
	G-BGJV	Air Sinai				Lease not taken-up
	G-BGJV	British Aerospace			83	
	G-BGJV	British Airways			10/JAN/85	
1769	G-11-11	British Aerospace	353	04/APR/79		
	6V-AEO	Air Senegal			12/JUL/79	
	6V-AEO	Tunisavia				Leased
	6V-AEO	Air Senegal			83	
1770	G-BGPR	British Aerospace	351	29/JUN/79		
	ZS-XGE	Transkei Airways			30/JUL/79	
1771	9N-ABR	Royal Nepal Airlines	352	18/OCT/79	12/NOV/79	
1772	5R-MJA	Air Madagascar	312	03/DEC/79	04/JAN/80	
1773	5R-MJB	Air Madagascar	312	29/OCT/80	28/NOV/80	
1774	G-11-12	British Aerospace	2B	26/MAY/80		
	G-BKLD	British Aerospace				
	PK-IHO	Bouraq			13/MAY/83	
1775	G-11-13	British Aerospace	2A	06/JUN/80		
	XT-MAN	Upper Volta Air Force			05/AUG/81	
1776	G-11-14	Hawker Siddeley	2B	20/JUN/80		
	FAC-1108	Satena			01/AUG/81	
1777	CS-TAO	SATA	372	02/MAY/80	23/MAY/80	
1778	G-11-20	Hawker Siddeley	2B	12/AUG/81		
	5U-BAS	Air Niger			22/JAN/82	
1779	G-11-19	British Aerospace	2B	02/DEC/81		
	5U-BAR	Air Niger			21/DEC/81	
1780	G-11-16	Hawker Siddeley	2B	27/MAR/81		
	5R-MTI	Air Madagascar			16/APR/81	
1781	G-11-15	British Aerospace	2B	21/DEC/80		
	G-BIRF	British Aerospace				
	N117CA	Cascade Airways			29/DEC/81	
1782	G-BICK	British Aerospace	2A	12/DEC/80		
	N748AV	Air Virginia			18/SEP/81	
	N748AV	Business Jet Aviation				Stored
1783	N749LL	Air Illinois	2B	14/DEC/80	20/DEC/80	
	N748BA	British Aerospace Inc.			FEB/83	
	N748BA	Air Virginia			83	Leased
	C-GRXE	Eastern Provincial Airways			MAR/85	
	C-GRXE	British Aerospace			21/APR/85	
	G-11-10	British Aerospace			03/JUL/85	
	G-BMJU	British Aerospace			JUL/85	
	ZS-LMO	Bop Air			86	
1784	D-AHSA	DLT	2B	13/MAR/81	23/MAR/81	
1785	G-11-17	Hawker Siddeley	2B	16/APR/81		
	D-AHSB	DLT			24/APR/81	
1786	G-11-18	British Aerospace	2B	06/JUL/81		
	D-AHSC	DLT			17/AUG/81	
1787	G-11-22	British Aerospace	2B	02/JUN/82		

C/N	Registration	Owner/Operator	Series	First Flight	Delivery	Remarks
	G-BKLE	British Aerospace				
	PK-IHP	Bouraq			05/MAY/83	
1788	G-BKLF	British Aerospace	2B			
	PK-IHW	Bouraq			28/APR/83	
1789	G-BJGI	Hawker Siddeley	2B	20/SEP/81		
	N118CA	Cascade Airways			29/DEC/81	
1790	G-BJTL	British Aerospace	2B			
	N749AV	Air Virginia			29/MAY/82	
	G-11-6	British Aerospace			21/JAN/85	
1791	G-BKAL	British Aerospace	2B			
	N119CA	Cascade Airways				Not taken-up
	D-AHSD	DLT			08/NOV/83	
1792	G-BJTM	British Aerospace	2B	02/MAY/84		
	N750AV	Air Virginia				Not taken-up
	D-AHSE	DLT			15/MAY/84	
1793	G-11-23	British Aerospace	2B	08/APR/83		
	G-BKLG	British Aerospace				
	PK-IHT	Bouraq			27/APR/83	
1794	G-11-24	British Aerospace	2B			
	G-BKLH	British Aerospace				
	PK-IHM	Bouraq				Registration not taken-up
	PK-IHN	Bouraq			26/APR/83	
1795	G-BKLI	British Aerospace	2B	18/APR/83		
	PK-IHV	Bouraq			29/APR/83	
1796	G-BKIG	British Aerospace	2B			
	MI8203	Airline of Marshall Islands			18/DEC/82	
1797	D-AHSF	DLT	2B		28/SEP/84	
1798	G-HDBA	British Airways	2B	05/NOV/84	13/DEC/84	
1799	G-HDBB	British Airways	2B	15/NOV/84	14/DEC/84	
1800	G-BLGJ	British Aerospace	2B	30/JUL/84		'Super 748' demonstrator
	V2-LCQ	LIAT			18/DEC/84	
1801	G-11-4	British Aerospace	2B	13/DEC/84		
	V2-LCR	LIAT			21/DEC/84	
1802	G-11-5	British Aerospace	2B			
	G-BLYL	British Aerospace			26/APR/85	
	V2-LCS	LIAT			07/MAY/85	
1803	G-11-09	British Aerospace	2B			
	V2-LCT	LIAT			29/JUN/85	
1804	TJ-CCF	Cameroon Airlines	2B		29/OCT/85	
1805	TJ-CCG	Cameroon Airlines	2B		NOV/85	

4R- Sri Lanka

1571	4R-ACJ
1587	4R-ACR

5H- Tanzania

1728	5H-STZ
1740	5H-WDL

5R- Malagasy Republic

1772	5R-MJA
1773	5R-MJB
1780	5R-MTI

5U- Niger

1779	5U-BAR
1778	5U-BAS

5W- Western Samoa

1701	5W-FAN
1714	5W-FAO

6V- Senegal

1769	6V-AEO
1676	6V-AET

6Y- Jamaica

1593	6Y-JFJ

7P- Lesotho

1681	7P-LAI

7Q- Malawi

1666	7Q-YKA
1667	7Q-YKB

8R- Guyana

1747	8R-GEU
1748	8R-GEV

9G- Ghana

1576	9G-ABV
1685	9G-ABW
1686	9G-ABX

9J- Zambia

1676	9J-ABJ
1677	9J-ABK
1576	9J-ABL
1635	9J-ABM
1680	9J-ABW
1706	9J-ADM

9N- Nepal

1671	9N-AAU
1672	9N-AAV
1771	9N-ABR
1698	9N-RAC

9Y- Trinidad & Tobago

1670	9Y-TDH
1756	9Y-TFS
1757	9Y-TFT
1757	9Y-TFT
1758	9Y-TFX
1759	9Y-TGD
1766	9Y-TGH
1767	9Y-TGI

A2- Botswana

1611	A2-ABA
1612	A2-ABB
1681	A2-ABC
1691	A2-ZFT
1706	A2-ZGF

C- Canada

1699	C-FAGI
1611	C-FINE
1668	C-FMAK
1599	C-GAPC
1762	C-GCUK
1745	C-GDOP
1582	C-GDOV
1577	C-GDUI
1578	C-GDUL
1581	C-GDUN
1686	C-GEPB
1635	C-GEPH
1594	C-GEPI
1579	C-GFFU
1690	C-GGNZ
1691	C-GGOB
1692	C-GGOO
1587	C-GGZY
1640	C-GJVN
1576	C-GMAA
1621	C-GOUT
1675	C-GPAA
1618	C-GQSV
1619	C-GQTG
1617	C-GQTH
1597	C-GQWO
1697	C-GRCU
1783	C-GRXE
1662	C-GSBF
1674	C-GSXS
1722	C-GTLD
1665	C-GYMX

C6- Bahamas

1746	C6-BEA
1761	C6-BEB
1763	C6-BEC
1763	C6-BED
1764	C6-BED
1764	C6-BEE
1765	C6-BEE
1765	C6-BEF

CC- Chile

1614	CC-CEC
1615	CC-CED
1616	CC-CEE
1617	CC-CEF
1618	CC-CEG
1619	CC-CEH
1620	CC-CEI
1621	CC-CEJ
1622	CC-CEK

CF- Canada

1699	CF-AGI
1669	CF-AMO
1679	CF-CSE
1611	CF-INE
1668	CF-MAK
1587	CF-MAL
1664	CF-TAG
1586	CF-TAX
1663	CF-TAZ
1635	CF-YQD

CR- Cape Verde

1719	CR-CAV
1720	CR-CAW

CS- Portugal

1681	CS-TAF
1687	CS-TAG
1721	CS-TAH
1777	CS-TAO

D- West Germany

1656	D-AFSD
1711	D-AFSE
1723	D-AFSF
1724	D-AFSG
1725	D-AFSH
1726	D-AFSI
1727	D-AFSJ
1784	D-AHSA
1785	D-AHSB
1786	D-AHSC
1791	D-AHSD
1792	D-AHSE
1797	D-AHSF

D4- Cape Verde

1719	D4-CAV
1720	D4-CAW

DQ- Fiji

1613	DQ-FAL
1661	DQ-FBH
1665	DQ-FBK

EC- Spain

1544	EC-DTP

EI- Eire

1549	EI-BSE
1544	EI-BSF

EL- Liberia

1755	EL-AIH

F- France

1678	F-BSRA
1681	F-BSRU
1717	F-BUTR

G- United Kingdom

1598	G-11
1599	G-11
1803	G-11-09
1679	G-11-1
1702	G-11-1
1718	G-11-1
1695	G-11-10
1714	G-11-10
1761	G-11-10
1783	G-11-10
1769	G-11-11
1774	G-11-12
1775	G-11-13
1776	G-11-14
1781	G-11-15
1780	G-11-16
1785	G-11-17
1786	G-11-18
1779	G-11-19
1678	G-11-2
1703	G-11-2
1719	G-11-2
1778	G-11-20
1787	G-11-22
1793	G-11-23
1794	G-11-24
1662	G-11-3
1681	G-11-3
1704	G-11-3
1716	G-11-3
1680	G-11-4
1705	G-11-4
1720	G-11-4
1801	G-11-4
1687	G-11-5
1706	G-11-5
1802	G-11-5
1699	G-11-6
1707	G-11-6
1790	G-11-6
1700	G-11-7
1712	G-11-7
1701	G-11-8
1713	G-11-8
1756	G-11-8
1697	G-11-9
1717	G-11-9
1760	G-11-9
1534	G-APZV
1535	G-ARAY
1536	G-ARMV
1537	G-ARMW
1538	G-ARMX
1548	G-ARRV
1549	G-ARRW
1559	G-ASJT
1560	G-ASPL
1576	G-ATAM
1585	G-ATEH
1586	G-ATEI
1587	G-ATEJ
1588	G-ATEK
1592	G-ATMI
1593	G-ATMJ
1635	G-AVRR
1623	G-AVXI
1624	G-AVXJ
1601	G-AVZD
1589	G-AXVG
1671	G-AXVZ
1678	G-AYDH
1679	G-AYFL
1687	G-AYIM
1681	G-AYIR
1700	G-AYVR
1697	G-AYYG
1701	G-AYYH
1695	G-AZAE
1698	G-AZJH
1612	G-AZSU
1718	G-BABJ
1716	G-BAFY
1717	G-BASZ
1713	G-BBGY
1719	G-BBLN
1720	G-BBPT
1722	G-BBTA
1735	G-BCDM
1662	G-BCDZ
1736	G-BCOE
1737	G-BCOF
1746	G-BDVH
1613	G-BEBA
1543	G-BEJD
1556	G-BEJE
1541	G-BEKC
1544	G-BEKD
1545	G-BEKE
1542	G-BEKF
1557	G-BEKG
1753	G-BETX
1752	G-BETY
1751	G-BETZ
1658	G-BFLL
1760	G-BFVR
1768	G-BGJV
1766	G-BGMN
1767	G-BGMO
1770	G-BGPR
1663	G-BHCJ
1782	G-BICK
1781	G-BIRF
1701	G-BIUV
1789	G-BJGI
1790	G-BJTL
1792	G-BJTM
1791	G-BKAL
1796	G-BKIG
1774	G-BKLD
1787	G-BKLE
1788	G-BKLF
1793	G-BKLG
1794	G-BKLH
1795	G-BKLI
1800	G-BLGJ
1802	G-BLYL
1714	G-BMFT
1783	G-BMJU
1766	G-DGMN
1798	G-HDBA
1799	G-HDBB
1557	G-VAJK

HC- Ecuador

1682	HC-AUD
1683	HC-AUE
1684	HC-AUK
1738	HC-BAZ

HK- Colombia

1657	HK-1408
1658	HK-1409

HP- Panama

1585	HP-416
1594	HP-432
1662	HP-484

HS- Thailand

1570	HS-TAF
1715	HS-TAF
1567	HS-THA
1568	HS-THB
1569	HS-THC
1644	HS-THD
1645	HS-THE
1646	HS-THF
1693	HS-THG
1707	HS-THH
1708	HS-THI

J5- Guinea-Bissau

1760	J5-GAT

LN- Norway

1631	LN-FOM

LV- Argentina

1539	LV-HGW
1540	LV-HHA
1541	LV-HHC
1542	LV-HHD
1543	LV-HHE
1544	LV-HHF
1545	LV-HHG
1546	LV-HHH
1547	LV-HHI
1556	LV-IDV
1557	LV-IEE
1558	LV-IEV
1539	LV-PIZ
1540	LV-PJA
1541	LV-PRJ
1542	LV-PUC
1543	LV-PUF
1544	LV-PUM
1545	LV-PUP
1547	LV-PVF
1546	LV-PVH
1556	LV-PXD
1557	LV-PXH
1558	LV-PXP

MI Marshall Islands

1768	MI-GJV
1796	MI8203

N United States

1781	N117CA
1789	N118CA
1791	N119CA
1656	N57910
1782	N748AV
1783	N748BA
1716	N748LL
1790	N749AV
1783	N749LL
1792	N750AV

OE- Austria

1589	OE-LHS
1590	OE-LHT

OY- Denmark

1621	OY-APT
1576	OY-DFS
1535	OY-DFV
1617	OY-MBH
1618	OY-MBY

PI- Philippines

1636	PI-C1014
1637	PI-C1015
1638	PI-C1016
1639	PI-C1017
1640	PI-C1018
1641	PI-C1019
1576	PI-C1020
1642	PI-C1021
1643	PI-C1022
1659	PI-C1023
1660	PI-C1024
1663	PI-C1025
1664	PI-C1026
1609	PI-C1027
1590	PI-C1028
1586	PI-C1029
1535	PI-C784

PK- Indonesia

1614	PK-IHA
1615	PK-IHB
1616	PK-IHC
1700	PK-IHD
1620	PK-IHE
1622	PK-IHF
1627	PK-IHG
1629	PK-IHH
1626	PK-IHI
1630	PK-IHJ
1633	PK-IHK
1634	PK-IHM
1794	PK-IHM
1794	PK-IHN
1774	PK-IHO
1787	PK-IHP
1722	PK-IHR
1615	PK-IHS
1793	PK-IHT
1795	PK-IHV
1788	PK-IHW
1735	PK-KHL
1695	PK-MHM
1696	PK-MHR
1638	PK-OBQ
1585	PK-OBV
1567	PK-OBW
1610	PK-RHQ
1610	PK-RHS

PP- Brasil

1625	PP-VDN
1626	PP-VDO
1627	PP-VDP
1628	PP-VDQ
1629	PP-VDR
1630	PP-VDS
1631	PP-VDT
1632	PP-VDU
1633	PP-VDV
1634	PP-VDX
1535	PP-VJQ

RP- Philippines

1636	RP-C1014
1637	RP-C1015
1638	RP-C1016
1639	RP-C1017
1640	RP-C1018
1641	RP-C1019
1642	RP-C1021
1659	RP-C1023
1660	RP-C1024
1663	RP-C1025
1664	RP-C1026
1586	RP-C1029

BRITISH AEROSPACE ATP

Advanced twin-turboprop airliner with seating for 64 passengers. The ATP will be powered by the new fuel-efficient Pratt & Whitney PW124 engines and is due to make its maiden flight on 6 August 1986. Projected in-service date is September 1987. Orders have been placed by LIAT of Antigua and the British Midland Group for operation with Manx Airlines and Loganair. To date announced firm orders total 5 aircraft.

Dimensions :	Wing span: 100ft 6in (30.63m) Length: 85ft 4in (26.01m) Height: 23ft 5in (7.14m)
Powerplant :	Two PWAC PW124/125 turboprops
Performance :	Max cruising speed 266 knots (492km/h) Range: with max payload 851nm (1,576km)
Accommodation:	64 passengers in a four abreast layout
Manufacturer :	British Aerospace - Civil Aircraft Division, Woodford, Stockport, Cheshire, England Telephone: (061) 439 5050 Telex: 6675454 G

C/N	Registration	Owner/Operator	Series	First Flight	Delivery	Remarks
2001	G-MATP	British Aerospace	ATP	06/AUG/86		Prototype

ANNOUNCED ORDERS

	V2-	LIAT	ATP		Early/88	Sched.delivery
	V2-	LIAT	ATP			Sched.delivery
	G-	Manx Airlines	ATP		AUG/87	Sched.delivery
	G-	British Midland Airways	ATP		SEP/87	Sched.delivery
	G-	British Midland Airways	ATP		MAR/88	Sched.delivery

CASA/NURTANIO CN-235

Short-range commuter aircraft, powered by two General Electric CT7-7 turboprops.
The CN-235 is a true joint venture and made its maiden flight on 11 November 1983. Deliveries are planned to commence in 1987. Accommodation is for a maximum of 44 passengers. To date orders total 114 aircraft.

Dimensions :	Wing span: 94ft 6in (28.81m) Length: 70ft 0in (21.35m) Height: 26ft 9in (8.18m)
Powerplant :	Two General Electric CT7-7A turboprops
Performance :	Max cruising speed 241 knots (446km/h) Range: with max payload 954nm (1,766km)
Accommodation:	44 passengers in a four abreast layout
Manufacturer :	CASA - Rey Francisco 4, Madrid 8, Spain Telephone: 247 2500 Telex: 27418 NURTANIO - Menara Patra Building, 8th floor, Jalan M.H. Thamrin 8, Jakarta, Indonesia Telephone: 353776 Telex: 44331 APT JKT

casa Nurtanio

C/N	Registration	Owner/Operator	Series	First Flight	Delivery	Remarks
P1	ECT-100	CASA	235	11/NOV/83		Prototype
P2	PK-XNC	Nurtanio	235	30/DEC/83		Prototype
P3	ECT-135	CASA	235			

ANNOUNCED ORDERS

		Royal Saudi Air Force	235		Spring/87	Sched.delivery
		Royal Saudi Air Force	235			
		Royal Saudi Air Force	235			
		Royal Saudi Air Force	235			
	EC-	Aviaco	235			
	EC-	Aviaco	235			
	EC-	Aviaco	235			
	EC-	Aviaco	235			
	EC-	Aviaco	235			
	EC-	Aviaco	235			
	EC-	Aviaco	235			
	EC-	Aviaco	235			
	EC-	Aviaco	235			
	EC-	Aviaco	235			
	EC-	Aviaco	235			
	EC-	Aviaco	235			
	EC-	Aviaco	235			
	EC-	Aviaco	235			
	EC-	Aviaco	235			
	EC-	Aviaco	235			
	EC-	Aviaco	235			
	EC-	Aviaco	235			
	EC-	Aviaco	235			
	PK-	Deraya Air Taxi	235			
	PK-	Deraya Air Taxi	235			
	PK-	Deraya Air Taxi	235			
	PK-	Deraya Air Taxi	235			
	PK-	Deraya Air Taxi	235			
	PK-	Deraya Air Taxi	235			
	PK-	Deraya Air Taxi	235			
	PK-	Deraya Air Taxi	235			
	PK-	Deraya Air Taxi	235			
	A-	Indonesian Air Force	235			
	A-	Indonesian Air Force	235			
	A-	Indonesian Air Force	235			
	A-	Indonesian Air Force	235			
	A-	Indonesian Air Force	235			
	A-	Indonesian Air Force	235			
	A-	Indonesian Air Force	235			
	A-	Indonesian Air Force	235			
	A-	Indonesian Air Force	235			
	A-	Indonesian Air Force	235			
	A-	Indonesian Air Force	235			
	A-	Indonesian Air Force	235			
	A-	Indonesian Air Force	235			
	A-	Indonesian Air Force	235			
	A-	Indonesian Air Force	235			
	A-	Indonesian Air Force	235			
	A-	Indonesian Air Force	235			
	A-	Indonesian Air Force	235			
	A-	Indonesian Air Force	235			
	A-	Indonesian Air Force	235			
	A-	Indonesian Air Force	235			

CASA-NURTANIO CN-235

C/N	Registration	Owner/Operator	Series	First Flight	Delivery	Remarks
	A-	Indonesian Air Force	235			
	A-	Indonesian Air Force	235			
	A-	Indonesian Air Force	235			
	A-	Indonesian Air Force	235			
	A-	Indonesian Air Force	235			
	A-	Indonesian Air Force	235			
	PK-	Merpati Nusantara	235			
	PK-	Merpati Nusantara	235			
	PK-	Merpati Nusantara	235			
	PK-	Merpati Nusantara	235			
	PK-	Merpati Nusantara	235			
	PK-	Merpati Nusantara	235			
	PK-	Merpati Nusantara	235			
	PK-	Merpati Nusantara	235			
	PK-	Merpati Nusantara	235			
	PK-	Merpati Nusantara	235			
	PK-	Merpati Nusantara	235			
	PK-	Merpati Nusantara	235			
	PK-	Merpati Nusantara	235			
	PK-	Merpati Nusantara	235			
	PK-	Merpati Nusantara	235			
	PK-	Pelita Air Services	235			
	PK-	Pelita Air Services	235			
	PK-	Pelita Air Services	235			
	PK-	Pelita Air Services	235			
	PK-	Pelita Air Services	235			
	PK-	Pelita Air Services	235			
	PK-	Pelita Air Services	235			
	PK-	Pelita Air Services	235			
		Royal Jordanian Air Force	235			
		Royal Jordanian Air Force	235			
	PK-	Pelita Air Services	235			
	PK-	Pelita Air Services	235			
		Indonesian Navy	235			
		Indonesian Navy	235			
		Indonesian Navy	235			
		Indonesian Navy	235			
		Indonesian Navy	235			
		Indonesian Navy	235			
		Indonesian Navy	235			
		Indonesian Navy	235			
		Indonesian Navy	235			
		Indonesian Navy	235			
		Indonesian Navy	235			
		Indonesian Navy	235			
		Indonesian Navy	235			
		Indonesian Navy	235			
		Indonesian Navy	235			
	HP-	Metachem	235			

DE HAVILLAND CANADA DHC-7

High-wing short/medium range STOL transport, powered by four PWAC PT6A-50 turboprops.
The quiet dash 7, which made its maiden flight on 27 March 1975, can accommodate up to 50 passengers. An all-cargo version, designated DHC-7-101, serves with the Canadian Armed Forces. The first operator was Rocky Mountain Airways which put the DHC-7 into service in February 1978. To date, some 110 aircraft have been delivered.

Dimensions :	Wing span: 92ft 11in (28.35m) Length: 80ft 7in (24.58m) Height: 26ft 2in (7.98m)
Powerplant :	Four Pratt & Whitney PWAC PT6A-50 turboprops
Performance :	Max cruising speed 230 knots (427km/h) Range: with max payload 420nm (778km)
Accommodation:	50 passengers in a four abreast layout
Manufacturer :	De Havilland Canada - Downsview, Ontario, M3K 1Y5, Canada Telephone: (416) 633 7310 Telex: 0622128

de HAVILLAND

C/N	Registration	Owner/Operator	Series	First Flight	Delivery	Remarks
01	C-GBNX	De Havilland Canada	102	27/MAR/75	27/MAR/75	Demonstrator
02	C-GNCA	De Havilland Canada	102	26/JUN/75	26/JUN/75	
03	C-GQIW	De Havilland Canada	102	30/MAY/77	30/MAY/77	
	EC-DCB	Spantax			31/MAY/78	
	C-GFEL	De Havilland Canada			03/MAY/81	
	C-GFEL	Air BC/CP Commuter			17/JUL/83	
04	C-GQYX	De Havilland Canada	102	31/OCT/77	31/OCT/77	
	N27RM	Rocky Mountain Airways			21/NOV/77	
	N27RM	Golden Gate Airlines			17/JUN/80	WFU 28/AUG/81
	N27RM	Great American Assurance			FEB/82	
	N27RM	Rocky Mountain Airways			83	
05	C-GNPU	De Havilland	102	31/APR/78	31/APR/78	
	N9058P	Air Pacific			02/MAY/79	
	N9058P	Golden Gate Airlines			80	Leased
	N9058P	Rocky Mountain Airways			11/MAY/82	
	N9058P	Air West Airlines			JUL/85	Leased
	N9058P	Rocky Mountain Airways			20/AUG/85	
06	N37RM	Rocky Mountain	102		15/DEC/78	
	C-GSEV	Air Atlantic/CP Commuter			28/FEB/86	Leased
07	C-GXVF	Wardair	103		08/JUN/78	
	N27AP	Air Pacific			12/NOV/79	
	N27AP	Golden Gate Airlines			01/MAR/80	WFU 28/AUG/81
	N27AP	De Havilland Canada			81	
	N27AP	Emirates Air Service			15/MAR/82	Leased
	N27AP	De Havilland Canada			83	
	N27AP	Era Helicopters			JUN/83	
	N27AP	Jet Alaska			JAN/86	
	C-GWTG	Air Atlantic/CP Commuter			29/MAY/86	Leased
08	132001	Canadian Armed Forces	CC-132	31/MAY/79	24/AUG/79	
09	A6-ALM	Emirates Air Service	103	31/JUL/79	31/JUL/78	
10	C-GRQB	De Havilland	103	26/JAN/79		
	OY-CBT	Greenlandair			16/FEB/79	
11	C-GXVG	Wardair	103	07/JUN/79	07/JUN/79	
	N791S	Air Wisconsin			19/JAN/80	
	N791S	Air West Airlines			OCT/84	
	N210AW	Air West Airlines			01/DEC/84	WFU 16/AUG/85, stored Love Field Dallas, Tx.
12	132002	Canadian Armed Forces	CC-132	13/JUL/79	21/SEP/79	
	C-GILE	De Havilland Canada	102		28/AUG/85	Converted
	C-GILE	Air Atlantic/CP Commuter			27/FEB/86	Leased
13	N890S	Air Wisconsin	102	07/JUL/79	24/JUL/79	
	N890S	Hawaiian Airlines			13/DEC/84	
14	N170RA	Ransome Airlines	102	22/AUG/79	11/SEP/79	
15	C-GXVH	Wardair	103	11/OCT/79		Not taken-up
	70-ACK	Alyemda			02/NOV/79	W/O 09/MAY/82, Aden
16	N171RA	Ransome Airlines	102	18/OCT/79	30/NOV/79	
17	N47RM	Rocky Mountain Airways	102	23/OCT/79	21/DEC/79	
18	C-GBOZ	De Havilland	102	04/DEC/79		
	N895S	Air Wisconsin			17/DEC/79	
	N701AC	Southern Jersey Airways			21/APR/85	
	N701AC	Aviation Enterprises			01/APR/86	
	N701AC	Southern Jersey Airways			01/APR/86	Leased
19	N4860J	Air Oregon	102	12/JAN/80		Not taken-up
	N4860J	Golden Gate Airways			14/FEB/80	WFU 28/AUG/81
	N4860J	American International			82	
	N4860J	Atlantic Southeast			APR/84	Leased
20	OY-CBU	Greenlandair	103	29/JAN/80	29/FEB/80	
21	N701GW	Golden West	102	03/MAR/80	28/MAR/80	WFU 29/MAR/83, stored Las Vegas
	N701GW	De Havilland Canada			24/DEC/83	
	C-GXPO	Air BC/CP Commuter			24/MAY/84	
22	OE-HLS	Tyrolean Airways	102	06/MAR/80	23/MAR/80	
	OE-LLS	Tyrolean Airways			86	Proposed Re-reg.
23	70-ACL	Alyemda	103	25/MAR/80	09/APR/80	
24	HR-AND	ANHSA	102	16/APR/80	30/APR/80	
	N234SL	Aviation Enterprises			83	
	TC-JCJ	Turk Hava Yollari			16/MAY/83	
	TC-JCJ	De Havilland Canada			20/JUN/86	

De Havilland Canada DHC-7

C/N	Registration	Owner/Operator	Series	First Flight	Delivery	Remarks
	OY-	Maersk Air			86	
25	N900HA	Henson Airlines	102	24/APR/80	15/MAY/80	
26	C-GTAD	Time Air	102	15/MAY/80	29/MAY/80	
27	N172RA	Ransome Airlines	102	10/JUN/80	26/JUN/80	
28	N721S	Air Wisconsin	102	18/JUL/80	15/AUG/80	
	LN-WFN	Wideroe			07/OCT/85	
29	N705ZW	Air Wisconsin	102	22/AUG/80	09/SEP/80	
	LN-WFO	Wideroe			28/FEB/86	
30	C-GTAJ	Time Air	102	12/SEP/80	26/SEP/80	
31	70-ACM	Alyemda	103	06/OCT/80	31/OCT/80	
32	4W-ACK	Yemen Airways	102	27/OCT/80	12/NOV/80	
33	N8504A	Golden Gate Airlines	102	06/NOV/80	21/NOV/80	WFU 28/AUG/81
	N8504A	De Havilland Canada			81	
	TC-JCG	Turk Hava Yollari			28/MAR/83	
	TC-JCG	De Havilland Canada			20/JUN/86	
	OY-	Maersk Air			86	
34	N700PR	Prinair	102			Cancelled order
	N703GG	Golden Gate Airlines		18/NOV/80	19/DEC/80	WFU 28/AUG/81
	N703GG	Great American Insurance			10/MAY/82	
	N703GG	Atlanta Express			10/MAY/82	
	N703GG	Air National			30/JAN/83	
	LN-WFK	Wideroe			15/APR/83	WFU 15/APR/83 to JUL/83
35	4W-ACL	Yemen Airways	102	01/DEC/80	16/DEC/80	
36	N702GW	Golden West	102	09/DEC/80	23/DEC/80	WFU 29/MAR/83
	N702GW	De Havilland Canada			21/JAN/84	
	C-GJPI	Air BC/CP Commuter			21/JAN/84	
37	N703GW	Golden West	102	17/JAN/81	27/JAN/81	WFU 22/APR/83
	N703GW	Rocky Mountain Airways			83	
	N67RM	Rocky Mountain Airways			MAY/84	
38	N173RA	Ransome Airlines	102		26/FEB/81	
39	N724GW	Golden West	102	17/FEB/81	17/FEB/81	WFU 22/APR/83
	N724GW	De Havilland Canada			83	
	N724GW	Rocky Mountain Airways			83	
	N87RM	Rocky Mountain Airways			MAY/84	
40	C-GELN	De Havilland Canada	102			
	N919HA	Hawaiian Airlines			08/APR/81	
41	LN-WFE	Wideroe	102		08/MAR/81	
42	N901HA	Henson Airlines	102		25/MAR/81	
43	N705GW	Golden West	102		09/APR/81	WFU 22/APR/83
	N705GW	Ransome Airlines			83	
	N705GW	Hawaiian Airlines			APR/84	Leased
44	N702GG	Golden Gate Airlines	102		21/APR/81	WFU 28/AUG/81
	N702GG	De Havilland Canada			81	
	TC-JCH	Turk Hava Yollari			10/APR/83	
	TC-JCH	De Havilland Canada			20/JUN/86	
45	OY-MMZ	Maersk Air	102		23/APR/81	Not taken-up
	OY-MBC	Maersk Air			23/APR/81	
46	LN-WFI	Wideroe	102		04/MAY/81	
47	N701GG	Golden Gate Airlines	102		07/MAY/81	WFU 28/AUG/81
	N701GG	Great American Assurance			10/MAY/82	
	N701GG	Atlanta Express			10/MAY/82	
	N701GG	Atlantic Southeast Airlines			01/MAY/83	
48	N705GG	Golden Gate Airlines	102		13/MAY/81	WFU 28/AUG/81
	N705GG	Great American Assurance			10/MAY/82	
	N705GG	Atlanta Express			10/MAY/82	
	N705GG	American International			APR/83	
	N705GG	Atlantic Southeast Airlines			01/MAY/84	Leased
49	N706ZW	Air Wisconsin	102		14/MAY/81	
	LN-WFP	Wideroe			14/JAN/86	
50	OE-HLT	Tyrolean Airways	102		17/MAY/81	
	OE-LLT	Tyrolean Airways			01/APR/86	
51	N929HA	Hawaiian Airlines	102		28/MAY/81	
52	N902HA	Henson Airlines	102		05/JUN/81	
53	N174RA	Ransome Airlines	102		17/JUN/81	
54	C-GFCO	De Havilland Canada	111	12/JUN/81		
	G-BRYC	Brymon Airways			04/AUG/81	
55	OY-MMY	Maersk Air	102		16/JUL/81	Not taken-up
	OY-MBD	Maersk Air			16/JUL/81	
56	N175RA	Ransome Airlines	102		28/JUL/81	
57	C-GTAZ	Time Air	100		09/SEP/81	
58	C-GFJS	De Havilland Canada	102			
	N2704J	Golden Gate			AUG/81	Cancelled order
	C-GFYI	De Havilland Canada			AUG/81	
	N42RA	Rio Airways			02/SEP/81	
	N42RA	General Electric Credit			31/DEC/85	WFU JAN/86, stored Love Field, Dallas, Tx.
59	C-GFBW	De Havilland Canada	102	01/SEP/81		
	N707ZW	Air Wisconsin			11/SEP/81	
60	C-GEWQ	De Havilland Canada	102	01/SEP/81		
	4X-AHA	Arkia			29/SEP/81	
61	N708ZW	Air Wisconsin	102		01/OCT/81	
62	G-BRYA	Brymon Airways	111		13/OCT/81	
63	C-GEWQ	De Havilland Canada	103	17/OCT/81		
	P2-ANN	Air Niugini			06/NOV/81	
64	C-GFCF	De Havilland Canada	102	23/OCT/81		
	4X-AHB	Arkia			30/OCT/81	
	C-GGXS	City Express			06/AUG/84	
65	C-GFBW	de Havilland Canada	102	03/SEP/81		
	N706GW	Golden West			81	Not taken-up
	N2655P	Resorts International			29/JAN/82	Op. by Southern Jersey Airways
66	C-GRLA	De Havilland Canada	111	12/DEC/81		
	G-BRYB	Brymon Airways			31/DEC/81	
67	N939HA	Hawaiian Airlines	102		09/DEC/81	
68	C-GFBW	De Havilland Canada	102	11/DEC/81		
	ARV-0203	Venezuela Navy			21/JUL/82	
69	C-GFBW	De Havilland Canada	102			
	N709ZW	Air Wisconsin			10/DEC/81	
70	C-GEWQ	De Havilland Canada	102			
	N710ZW	Air Wisconsin			17/DEC/81	
71	C-GFNN	De Havilland Canada	102	12/OCT/81		
	N	Golden West			81	Not taken-up
	N2655W	De Havilland Canada			14/APR/82	Stored
	N53RA	Rio Airways			13/OCT/82	
	N53RA	General Electric Credit			31/DEC/85	WFU JAN/86, stored Love Field, Dallas, Tx.

C/N	Registration	Owner/Operator	Series	First Flight	Delivery	Remarks
	N53RA	Ransome Airlines			86	
72	C-GEWQ	De Havilland Canada	103	12/OCT/81		
	P2-ANO	Air Niugini			02/FEB/82	
73	N720AS	Atlantic Southeast Airlines	102		25/FEB/82	
74	C-GEWQ	De Havilland Canada	102	27/FEB/82		
	N903HA	Henson Airlines			22/MAY/82	
	C-GHRV	De Havilland Canada			06/MAR/85	
	C-GHRV	City Express			06/MAR/85	
75	C-GFCF	De Havilland Canada	103	04/JAN/82		
	ET-	Ethiopian Airlines				Cancelled order
	PK-PSZ	Pelita			26/FEB/82	Op. for Mobil Oil
76	C-GFOD	De Havilland Canada	102	04/JAN/82		
	N176RA	Ransome Airlines			08/APR/82	
77	C-GFCF	De Havilland Canada	102	17/JAN/82		
	C-GFQL	De Havilland Canada			11/APR/82	
	OY-MBE	Maersk Air			26/APR/82	
78	C-GFRP	De Havilland Canada	102	13/MAR/82		
	N60RA	Rio Airways			10/NOV/82	
	N60RA	General Electric Credit			31/DEC/85	WFU JAN/86, stored Love Field, Dallas, Tx.
79	C-GFOM	De Havilland Canada	102	23/APR/82		
	N949HA	Hawaiian Airlines			28/MAY/82	
80	C-GFYI	De Havilland Canada	102	27/APR/82		
	N904HA	Henson Airlines			03/MAY/82	
	C-GHSL	Air BC/CP Commuter			31/JUN/85	Leased
81	C-GFOD	De Havilland Canada	103	22/APR/82		
	P2-ANP	Air Niugini			05/MAY/82	
82	C-GFUM	De Havilland Canada	102	29/APR/82		
	4X-AHC	Arkia			12/MAY/82	
83	C-GFQL	De Havilland Canada	102	03/MAY/82		
	N721AS	Atlantic Southeast Airlines			19/MAY/82	
84	C-GEWQ	De Havilland Canada	102			
	LN-WFL	Wideroe			08/APR/83	
85	C-GFOD	De Havilland Canada	102			
	N177RA	Ransome Airlines			22/JUL/82	
86	C-GFUM	De Havilland Canada	103	18/JUN/82		
	PK-PSY	Pelita			07/JUL/82	Op. for Mobil Oil
87	C-GFBW	De Havilland Canada	102			
	C-GBZR	De Havilland Canada			83	
	HK-3111	Intercor Colombia			13/NOV/83	
88	C-GFOD	De Havilland Canada	102			
	C-GESG	De Havilland Canada			83	
	HK-3112	Intercor Colombia			13/NOV/83	
89	C-GFQL	De Havilland Canada	102			
	N62RA	Rio Airways			FEB/83	
	N62RA	General Electric Credit			31/DEC/85	WFU JAN/86, stored Love Field, Dallas, Tx.
90	C-GFRP	De Havilland Canada	102			
	YU-AIE	Inex Adria			20/JAN/84	
91	C-GFUM	De Havilland Canada	102			
	LN-WFG	Wideroe			15/MAR/83	
92	C-GFCF	De Havilland Canada	102			
	YU-AIF	Inex Adria			20/JAN/84	
93	C-GFYI	De Havilland Canada	102			
	SU-CBA	Petroleum Air Services			17/FEB/84	
94	C-GFYI	De Havilland Canada	103			
	PK-PSX	Pelita			30/NOV/83	
95	C-GFQL	De Havilland Canada	102			
	N905HA	Henson Airlines			09/MAR/83	
	C-GGUZ	De Havilland Canada			30/MAR/84	
	N5382W	Ross Aviation			23/JUL/84	Op. for Allegheny Commuter
96	C-GEWQ	De Havilland Canada	102			
	SU-CBB	Petroleum Air Services			21/FEB/84	
97	C-GFQL	De Havilland Canada	102			
	SU-CBC	Petroleum Air Services			21/FEB/84	
98	C-GEWQ	De Havilland Canada	102			
	SU-CBD	Petroleum Air Services			05/JUN/84	
99	C-GFBW	De Havilland Canada	102			
	SU-CBE	Petroleum Air Services			11/JUL/84	
100	C-GFCF	De Havilland Canada	103			
	PK-PSW	Pelita			27/JUN/84	
101	C-GFQL	De Havilland Canada	102			
	ZK-NEW	Newmans Air			14/DEC/84	
102	C-GCFR	De Havilland Canada	102R			
	C-GCFR	Canadian Dept. of Environmen			29/MAY/86	Op. by Bradley Air Service
103	ZK-NEX	Newmans Air			25/JAN/85	
104	C-GFUM	De Havilland Canada	103			
	N53993	Ross Aviation			23/APR/85	
105	C-GFOD	De Havilland Canada	103			
	PK-PSV	Pelita			27/JUL/84	
106	C-GFYI	De Havilland Canada	102			
	N54026	Ross Aviation			31/MAY/85	Op. for U.S. Dept. of Energy
107	C-GEWQ	De Havilland Canada	102			
	3X-GCJ	Air Guinea			30/JUL/85	
108	C-GFBW	De Havilland Canada	102			
	B-	Shenzhen Airline (CAAC)	102		86	Sched.delivery
109	N722AS	Atlantic Southeast Airlines	102			
110	B-	Shenzhen Airline (CAAC)	102		86	Sched.delivery
111	N723AS	Atlantic Southeast Airlines	102			
112	B-	Shenzhen Airline (CAAC)	102		86	Sched.delivery

De Havilland Canada DHC-7
cross-reference index

3X- Guinea

107	3X-GCJ

4W- North Yemen

32	4W-ACK
35	4W-ACL

4X- Israel

60	4X-AHA
64	4X-AHB
82	4X-AHC

70- South Yemen

15	70-ACK
23	70-ACL
31	70-ACM

A6- United Arab Emirates

09	A6-ALM

C- Canada

01	C-GBNX
18	C-GBOZ
87	C-GBZR
102	C-GCFR
40	C-GELN
88	C-GESG
60	C-GEWQ
63	C-GEWQ
70	C-GEWQ
72	C-GEWQ
74	C-GEWQ
84	C-GEWQ
96	C-GEWQ
98	C-GEWQ
107	C-GEWQ
59	C-GFBW
65	C-GFBW
68	C-GFBW
69	C-GFBW
87	C-GFBW
99	C-GFBW
108	C-GFBW
64	C-GFCF
75	C-GFCF
77	C-GFCF
92	C-GFCF
100	C-GFCF
54	C-GFCO
03	C-GFEL
58	C-GFJS
71	C-GFNN
76	C-GFOD
81	C-GFOD
85	C-GFOD
88	C-GFOD
105	C-GFOD
79	C-GFOM
77	C-GFQL
83	C-GFQL
89	C-GFQL
97	C-GFQL
101	C-GFQL
95	C-GFQL
78	C-GFRP
90	C-GFRP
82	C-GFUM
86	C-GFUM
91	C-GFUM
104	C-GFUM
58	C-GFYI
80	C-GFYI
93	C-GFYI
94	C-GFYI
106	C-GFYI
95	C-GGUZ
64	C-GGXS
74	C-GHRV
80	C-GHSL
12	C-GILE
36	C-GJPI
02	C-GNCA
05	C-GNPU
03	C-GQIW
04	C-GQYX
66	C-GRLA
10	C-GRQB
06	C-GSEV
26	C-GTAD
30	C-GTAJ
57	C-GTAZ
07	C-GWTG
21	C-GXPO
07	C-GXVF
11	C-GXVG
15	C-GXVH

EC- Spain

03	EC-DCB

G- United Kingdom

62	G-BRYA
66	G-BRYB
54	G-BRYC

HK- Colombia

87	HK-3111
88	HK-3112

HR- Honduras

24	HR-AND

LN- Norway

41	LN-WFE
91	LN-WFG
46	LN-WFI
34	LN-WFK
84	LN-WFL
28	LN-WFN
29	LN-WFO
49	LN-WFP

N United States

14	N170RA
16	N171RA
27	N172RA
38	N173RA
53	N174RA
56	N175RA
76	N176RA
85	N177RA
11	N210AW
24	N234SL
65	N2655P
71	N2655W
58	N2704J
07	N27AP
04	N27RM
06	N37RM
58	N42RA
17	N47RM
19	N4860J
95	N5382W
104	N53993
71	N53RA
106	N54026
78	N60RA
89	N62RA
37	N67RM
34	N700PR
18	N701AC
47	N701GG
21	N701GW
44	N702GG
36	N702GW
34	N703GG
37	N703GW
48	N705GG
43	N705GW

29	N705ZW
65	N706GW
49	N706ZW
59	N707ZW
61	N708ZW
69	N709ZW
70	N710ZW
73	N720AS
83	N721AS
28	N721S
109	N722AS
111	N723AS
39	N724GW
11	N791S
33	N8504A
39	N87RM
13	N890S
18	N895S
25	N900HA
42	N901HA
52	N902HA
74	N903HA
80	N904HA
05	N9058P
95	N905HA
40	N919HA
51	N929HA
67	N939HA
79	N949HA

OE- Austria

22	OE-HLS
50	OE-HLT
22	OE-LLS
50	OE-LLT

OY- Denmark

10	OY-CBT
20	OY-CBU
45	OY-MBC
55	OY-MBD
77	OY-MBE
55	OY-MMY
45	OY-MMZ

P2- Papua New Guinea

63	P2-ANN
72	P2-ANO
81	P2-ANP

PK- Indonesia

105	PK-PSV
100	PK-PSW
94	PK-PSX

86	PK-PSY
75	PK-PSZ

SU- Egypt

93	SU-CBA
96	SU-CBB
97	SU-CBC
98	SU-CBD
99	SU-CBE

TC- Turkey

33	TC-JCG
44	TC-JCH
24	TC-JCJ

YU- Yugoslavia

90	YU-AIE
92	YU-AIF

ZK- New Zealand

101	ZK-NEW
103	ZK-NEX

Military operated

Canada

08	132001
12	132002

Venezuela

68	ARV-0203

DE HAVILLAND CANADA DHC-8

High-wing, short-range STOL commuter transport for up to 36 passengers, powered PWAC PW120 turboprops. The DHC-8-100, basically a smaller brother to the DHC-7, made its first flight on 20 June 1983, and entered service with the Canadaian operator, NorOntair 19 December 1984. A stretched series 300 version has recently been launched with a capacity for up to 56 passengers and deliveries of this version are due to commence in early 1988. To date, more than 40 aircraft have been delivered and over 90 further aircraft are on order.

Dimensions :	Wing span: 85ft 0in (25.91m) Length: 73ft 0in (22.25m) Height: 25ft 0in (7.62m) (100)
	Wing span: 90ft 0in (27.4m) Length: 84ft 4in (25.68m) Height: 25ft 0in (7.62m) (300)
Powerplant :	Two Pratt & Whitney PWAC PW120 turboprops (100), two Pratt & Whitney PWAC PW123 turboprops (300)
Performance :	Max cruising speed 265 knots (554km/h) (100) Range: with max payload 550nm (1,019km) (100)
Accommodation:	39 passengers in a four abreast layout (100), 56 passengers in a four abreast layout (300)
Manufacturer :	De Havilland Canada - Downsview, Ontario, M3K 1Y5, Canada
	Telephone: (416) 633 7310 Telex: 0622128

de HAVILLAND

C/N	Registration	Owner/Operator	Series	First Flight	Delivery	Remarks
01	C-GDNK	De Havilland Canada	100	20/JUN/83		Prototype
02	C-GGMP	De Havilland Canada	100	26/OCT/83		
03	C-GGOM	De Havilland Canada	101	22/DEC/83		
	C-GGOM	Air BC			17/DEC/85	
04	C-GGPJ	De Havilland Canada	101		03/APR/84	Demonstrator
05	C-GGTO	De Havilland Canada	101		14/JUN/84	
	C-GGTO	City Express			05/SEP/85	
06	C-GJCB	De Havilland Canada	101		16/AUG/84	
	C-GJCB	Norontair			12/DEC/84	
07	C-GEOA	De Havilland Canada	101		15/NOV/84	
	N800MX	Eastern Metro Express			20/DEC/84	
08	C-GERL	De Havilland Canada	101		08/FEB/85	
	C-GHXY	De Havilland Canada			26/MAR/85	
	N801MX	Eastern Metro Express			25/APR/85	
09	C-GHRI	De Havilland Canada	101		08/FEB/85	
	N906HA	Henson/Piedmont Commuter			03/APR/85	
10	C-GERL	De Havilland Canada	101		18/APR/85	
	C-GIAU	De Havilland Canada			25/APR/85	
	OE-HLR	Tyrolean			29/APR/85	
	C-GIQQ	De Havilland Canada			08/NOV/85	Leased
	C-GIQQ	Air BC			08/DEC/85	Sub-leased
	C-GIQQ	De Havilland Canada			04/JAN/86	Leased
	C-GIQQ	City Express			16/JAN/86	Sub-leased
	C-GIQQ	De Havilland Canada			20/FEB/86	Leased
	OE-HLR	Tyrolean			27/MAR/86	
	OE-LLR	Tyrolean			01/APR/86	
11	C-GESR	De Havilland Canada	101		10/MAY/85	
	N907HA	Henson/Piedmont Commuter			22/MAY/85	
12	C-GPYD	De Havilland Canada	101		16/JUL/85	
	C-GPYD	Norontair			25/NOV/85	
13	C-GETI	De Havilland Canada	101		28/JUN/85	
	N802MX	Eastern Metro Express			10/JUL/85	
14	C-GCTX	De Havilland Canada	101		17/JUL/85	
	C-GCTX	City Express			05/SEP/85	
15	C-GEVP	De Havilland Canada	101		17/JUL/85	
	C-GIBQ	De Havilland Canada			30/AUG/85	
	N908HA	Henson/Piedmont Commuter			30/AUG/85	
16	C-GEOA	De Havilland Canada	101		18/SEP/85	
	N803MX	Eastern Metro Express			26/SEP/85	
17	C-GFSJ	De Havilland Canada	101		23/SEP/85	
	C-GFSJ	Alberta Government			18/NOV/85	
18	C-GESR	De Havilland Canada	101		30/OCT/85	
	N909HA	Henson/Piedmont Commuter			08/NOV/85	
19	C-GLOT	De Havilland Canada	101		20/NOV/85	
	N804MX	Eastern Metro Express			27/NOV/85	
20	C-GCFJ	De Havilland Canada	101		28/NOV/85	
	C-GCFJ	Canadian Dept. of Transport			12/MAY/86	
21	C-GIQK	De Havilland Canada	101		10/DEC/85	
	V2-LCV	LIAT			19/DEC/85	
22	C-GEVP	De Havilland Canada	101		16/DEC/85	
	N910HA	Henson/Piedmont Commuter			23/DEC/85	
23	C-GEOA	De Havilland Canada	101		23/DEC/85	
	N811PH	Horizon Air			30/DEC/85	
24	C-GMOK	De Havilland Canada	101		30/DEC/85	
	C-GMOK	Innotech Aviation/Mobil Oil			17/JAN/86	
25	C-GABF	De Havilland Canada	101		15/JAN/86	
	C-GABF	Air BC			05/MAR/86	
26	C-GESR	De Havilland Canada	101		31/JAN/86	
	N812PH	Horizon Air			13/FEB/86	
27	C-FCTE	De Havilland Canada	101		11/FEB/86	
	C-FCTE	City Express			27/MAR/86	
28	C-GCFK	De Havilland Canada	101		14/FEB/86	
	C-GCFK	Canadian Dept. of Transport			20/JUN/86	
29	C-GLOT	De Havilland Canada	101		27/FEB/86	
	V2-LCW	LIAT			18/MAR/86	
30	C-GEOA	De Havilland Canada	101		13/MAR/86	
	N444T	Fairways Corporation			25/MAR/86	
31	C-GESR	De Havilland Canada	101		20/MAR/86	

De Havilland Canada DHC-8

C/N	Registration	Owner/Operator	Series	First Flight	Delivery	Remarks
	V2-LCX	LIAT			03/APR/86	
32	C-GETI	De Havilland Canada	101		26/MAR/86	
	N813PH	Horizon Air			10/APR/86	
33	C-GEVP	De Havilland Canada	101		04/APR/86	
	N805MX	Eastern Metro Express			18/APR/86	
34	C-GEOA	De Havilland Canada	101		16/APR/86	
	N911HA	Henson/Piedmont Commuter			26/APR/86	
35	C-GESR	De Havilland Canada	101		22/APR/86	
	V2-LCY	LIAT			30/APR/86	
36	C-GEVP	De Havilland Canada	101		05/MAY/86	
	N806MX	Eastern Metro Express			15/MAY/86	
37	C-GLOT	De Havilland Canada	101		25/MAY/86	
	N801AP	LTV Corp./Sierra Research			05/MAY/86	
38	142001	Canadian Armed Forces	CC142		APR/86	
39	C-FCTA	De Havilland Canada	101		09/JUN/86	
	C-FCTA	Air Nova			26/JUN/86	
40	C-GEOA	De Havilland Canada	101		20/MAY/86	
	N912HA	Henson/Piedmont Commuter			05/JUN/86	
41	C-GESR	De Havilland Canada	101		05/JUN/86	
	N807MX	Eastern Metro Express			18/JUN/86	
42	C-GANF	De Havilland Canada	101		20/JUN/86	
	C-GANF	Air Nova			08/JUL/86	
43	C-GETI	De Havilland Canada	101		28/JUN/86	
	N814PH	Horizon Air			08/JUL/86	
44	C-FABN	De Havilland Canada	101		22/JUL/86	
	C-FABN	Air BC			86	Sched.delivery
45	C-GEVP	De Havilland Canada	101		09/JUL/86	
	N802AP	LTV Corp./Sierra Research			15/JUL/86	
46	142002	Canadian Armed Forces	CC142		86	Sched.delivery
47	C-GAAC	Air Atlantic	101		SEP/86	
48	V2-LCZ	LIAT	101		86	Sched.delivery
49	C-	Air BC	101		86	Sched.delivery
50	N	Horizon Airlines	101		86	Sched.delivery

ADDITIONAL ORDERS

C/N	Registration	Owner/Operator	Series	First Flight	Delivery	Remarks
	N	Henson/Piedmont Commuter	101		SEP/86	Sched.delivery
	N	Henson/Piedmont Commuter	101		JAN/87	Sched.delivery
	N	Henson/Piedmont Commuter	101		87	Sched.delivery
	N	Henson/Piedmont Commuter	101		87	Sched.delivery
	N	Henson/Piedmont Commuter	101		87	Sched.delivery
	N	Henson/Piedmont Commuter	101		87	Sched.delivery
	N	Henson/Piedmont Commuter	101		87	Sched.delivery
	D-	Contactair	101		OCT/86	Sched.delivery
	D-	Contactair	101		SEP/87	Sched.delivery
	N	Horizon Air	101		86	Sched.delivery
	N	Horizon Air	101		86	Sched.delivery
	N	Horizon Air	101		86	Sched.delivery
	N	Horizon Air	101		86	Sched.delivery
	N	America West Airlines	101		JAN/87	Sched.delivery
	N	America West Airlines	101		MAR/87	Sched.delivery
	N	America West Airlines	101		MAR/87	Sched.delivery
	C-	City Express	101			
	C-	City Express	101			
	C-	City Express	101		86	Sched.delivery
	VH-	Air New South Wales	101			
	C-	Government of Alberta	101			
		Canadian Armed Forces	101			
		Canadian Armed Forces	101			
		Canadian Armed Forces	101			
		Canadian Armed Forces	101		MAR/88	Sched.delivery
	ZK-	Newmans Airways	101		86	Sched.delivery
	ZK-	Newmans Airways	101		86	Sched.delivery
	ZK-	Newmans Airways	101			
	C-	Home Oil	101			
	N	Southern Jersey Airways	101			
	N	Southern Jersey Airways	101			
	N	Southern Jersey Airways	101			
	N	Southern Jersey Airways	101			
	ZS-	Magnum Airlines	101			
	ZS-	Magnum Airlines	101			
	P2-	Talair	101		OCT/87	Sched.delivery
	C-	Air Ontario	101		87	Sched.delivery
	C-	Air Ontario	101		87	Sched.delivery
	C-	Air Ontario	101		87	Sched.delivery
	C-	Air Ontario	101		87	Sched.delivery
	C-	Air Ontario	101		87	Sched.delivery
	C-	Air Ontario	101		87	Sched.delivery
	C-	Air Ontario	101		87	Sched.delivery
	C-	Air Ontario	101		87	Sched.delivery
	C-	Air Ontario	101		87	Sched.delivery
	C-	Air Ontario	101		87	Sched.delivery
	C-	Air Ontario	101		87	Sched.delivery
	C-	Air Ontario	101		87	Sched.delivery
	C-	Air Ontario	101		87	Sched.delivery
	C-	Air Ontario	101		87	Sched.delivery
	C-	Air Ontario	300		88	Sched.delivery
	C-	Air Ontario	300		8	Sched.delivery
	C-	Air Ontario	300		8	Sched.delivery
	C-	Air Ontario	300		8	Sched.delivery
	C-	Air Ontario	300		89	Sched.delivery
	C-	Austin Airways	101		MAR/87	Sched.delivery
	C-	Austin Airways	101		87	Sched.delivery
	C-	Austin Airways	101		87	Sched.delivery
	C-	Austin Airways	101		87	Sched.delivery
	C-	Austin Airways	101		87	Sched.delivery
	C-	Austin Airways	300		88	Sched.delivery
	C-	Austin Airways	300		88	Sched.delivery
	C-	Austin Airways	300		88	Sched.delivery
	C-	Time Air	101		JAN/87	Sched.delivery
	C-	Time Air	101		87	Sched.delivery
	C-	Time Air	101		87	Sched.delivery
	C-	Time Air	101		87	Sched.delivery
	C-	Time Air	300		88	Sched.delivery

C/N	Registration	Owner/Operator	Series	First Flight	Delivery	Remarks

ADDITIONAL ORDERS

	C-	Time Air	300		88	Sched.delivery
	C-	Time Air	300		88	Sched.delivery
	C-	Time Air	300		88	Sched.delivery
	C-	Time Air	300		88	Sched.delivery
	C-	Time Air	300		88	Sched.delivery
	C-	National Defence Dept.	101		86	Sched.delivery
	C-	National Defence Dept.	101		86	Sched.delivery
	C-	National Defence Dept.	101		86	Sched.delivery
	C-	National Defence Dept.	101		86	Sched.delivery
	C-	National Defence Dept.	101		86	Sched.delivery
	C-	National Defence Dept.	101		86	Sched.delivery

De Havilland Canada DHC-8
cross-reference index

C- Canada

44	C-FABN
39	C-FCTA
27	C-FCTE
47	C-GAAC
25	C-GABF
42	C-GANF
20	C-GCFJ
28	C-GCFK
14	C-GCTX
01	C-GDNK
07	C-GEOA
16	C-GEOA
23	C-GEOA
30	C-GEOA
34	C-GEOA
40	C-GEOA
08	C-GERL
10	C-GERL

11	C-GESR
18	C-GESR
26	C-GESR
31	C-GESR
35	C-GESR
41	C-GESR
13	C-GETI
32	C-GETI
43	C-GETI
15	C-GEVP
22	C-GEVP
33	C-GEVP
36	C-GEVP
45	C-GEVP
17	C-GFSJ
02	C-GGMP
03	C-GGOM
04	C-GGPJ
05	C-GGTO
09	C-GHRI

08	C-GHXY
10	C-GIAU
15	C-GIBQ
21	C-GIQK
10	C-GIQQ
06	C-GJCB
19	C-GLOT
29	C-GLOT
37	C-GLOT
24	C-GMOK
12	C-GPYD

N United States

30	N444T
07	N800MX
37	N801AP
08	N801MX
45	N802AP
13	N802MX

16	N803MX
19	N804MX
33	N805MX
36	N806MX
41	N807MX
23	N811PH
26	N812PH
32	N813PH
43	N814PH
09	N906HA
11	N907HA
15	N908HA
18	N909HA
22	N910HA
34	N911HA
40	N912HA

OE- Austria

10	OE-HLR

10	OE-LLR

V2- Antigua

21	V2-LCV
29	V2-LCW
31	V2-LCX
35	V2-LCY
48	V2-LCZ

Military operated

Canada

38	142001
46	142002

DORNIER DO 228

High-wing, twin-engined STOL commuter aircraft, powered by two Garrett AiResearch TPE331-5 turboprops. The DO 228 made its maiden flight on 28 March 1983. The initial version was designated DO 228-100 and has accommodation 15 passengers. A slightly longer model 200 for up to 19 passengers followed soon after. Improved higher-weight versions of both types, designated 101 and 201 respectively are now all available. Up to 150 aircraft are due to be produced by HAL for the India third-level, Vayudoot. To date, more than 80 aircraft of all models have been delivered and over 25 are on order.

Dimensions : Wing span: 55ft 8in (16.97m) Length: 54ft 4in (16.55m) Height: 15ft 8in (4.89m) (200)
Powerplant : Two Garret AiResearch TPE331-5 turboprops
Performance : Max cruising speed 231 knots (424km/h) Range: with max payload 672nm (1,245km)
Accommodation: 15 passengers in a two abreast layout (100), 19 passengers in a two abreast layout (200)
Manufacturer : Dornier - PO Box 2160, D-8000 Munich 66, West Germany

C/N	Registration	Owner/Operator	Series	First Flight	Delivery	Remarks
4358	D-IFNS	Dornier	100	28/MAR/81		Prototype. W/O 26/MAR/82 nr. Oberpfaffeholen Ap.
4359	D-ICDO	Dornier	200			Prototype
7001	LN-HPG	Norving	100	21/JAN/82	04/APR/82	
	D-ICOG	Dornier			10/APR/82	
8002	D-IDCO	Dornier	200	16/OCT/82	82	
	9M-AXB	Malaysia Air Charter			11/NOV/82	Leased
	D-IDCO	Dornier			83	
	D-IDCO	Air Hudik			20/AUG/83	Leased
	D-IDCO	Dornier			OCT/83	
	9M-AXB	Malaysia Air Charter			20/JUN/84	
7003	D-IDNI	Dornier	100	07/JUL/82		
	LN-HPA	Norving			15/MAR/83	
7004	D-ICGO	Dornier	100	11/NOV/82		
	LN-HPE	Norving			27/AUG/82	
7005	LN-HPB	Norving	100	30/AUG/82	26/OCT/82	Leased
	D-IDOM	Dornier			82	
	D-IDOM	Northern Air Charter			15/DEC/82	
	D-IDOM	Dornier			83	
	D-IDOM	Holiday Express			OCT/84	
	D-IDOM	Netherlines			10/NOV/85	Leased
	D-IDOM	Holiday Express			01/MAR/86	
8006	D-IBOO	Dornier	200	21/DEC/82		
	A5-RGB	Druk Air			05/JAN/83	
8007	D-IDID	Dornier	200	08/AUG/83		
	JA8835	Japan Air Commuter			15/SEP/83	
8008	D-IHIC	Dornier	200	13/JAN/83		
	B-12208	Formosa Airlines			29/JAN/83	
8009	D-IDON	Dornier	200	28/APR/83	83	
	SX-BHB	Olympic Aviation			24/JAN/84	
	9M-	Malaysia Air Charter			85	Not taken-up
	D-IDON	Dornier	201			
	PH-SDO	Schreiner Airways			24/DEC/85	Leased
8010	D-IHDO	Dornier	200	11/MAY/83	83	
	SX-BHA	Olympic Aviation			SEP/83	Leased
	D-IHDO	Dornier			DEC/83	
	9M-DMF	Malaysia Air Charter			16/DEC/83	
	9M-AXF	Malaysia Air Charter			86	
7011	D-ICIP	Dornier	100	30/MAY/83		
	5N-AQV	Jambo Airlines			1?/JUN/83	
8012	D-IDMC	Dornier	200	18/AUG/83		
	5N-AQO	Jambo Airlines			10/AUG/83	
8013	D-IDMI	Dornier	200	21/APR/83		
	5N-AOH	Genz Nigeria			30/AUG/83	
	5N-ARP	Genz Nigeria			83	
7014	D-IAWI	Alfred Wegener Institute	100	24/JUN/83	16/DEC/83	
	D-CAWI	Alfred Wegener Institute	101		85	Converted
7015	D-IDOC	Dornier	100	31/AUG/83		
	5N-AQW	Jambo Airlines			20/DEC/83	
	5N-AOR	Okada Air				
8016	D-IBLH	Dornier	200	21/SEP/83		
	SE-IKY	Air Hudik			19/OCT/83	
8017	D-IBLI	Dornier	200	23/SEP/83		
	A5-RGC	Druk Air			02/OCT/83	
7018	D-IBLB	Dornier	100	07/OCT/83		
	D-IBLB	Genz Nigeria			09/APR/84	
8019	D-IBLJ	Dornier	200	28/OCT/83		
	JA8836	Japan Air Commuter			07/NOV/83	
7020	D-IBLC	Dornier	100	22/NOV/83		
	A40-CP	Oman Police Air Wing			07/JAN/84	
8021	D-IBLK	Dornier	200	25/NOV/83		
	9M-AXD	Malaysia Air Charter			16/DEC/83	
7022	D-IBLD	Dornier	100	09/DEC/83		
	LN-HPG	Norving			30/DEC/83	
7023	D-IBLE	Dornier	100	23/DEC/83		
	5N-AQX	Jambo Airlines			20/DEC/83	
7024	D-IBLF	Dornier	100	23/JAN/84		

C/N	Registration	Owner/Operator	Series	First Flight	Delivery	Remarks
	LN-NVB	Norving			28/FEB/84	
8025	D-IBLL	Dornier	200	07/APR/84		
	N228RP	Precision Airlines			10/OCT/84	
8026	D-IBLM	Dornier	200	08/MAY/84		
	N232RP	Precision Airlines			10/OCT/84	
7027	D-IBLG	Dornier	100	09/APR/84		
	5N-ARK	Technical Industrial Group			11/SEP/84	
7028	D-IBLN	Dornier	100	16/MAR/84		
	A40-CQ	Oman Police Air Wing			07/MAY/84	
7029	D-IASS	Delta Air	100	13/APR/84	27/APR/84	Leased
	D-IASS	Dornier			SEP/84	
	D-IASS	RFG			SEP/84	Leased
	D-IASS	Dornier			DEC/84	
	MI8604	Airline of Marshall Islands	101		85	
8030	D-IDBB	Dornier	200	06/MAY/84		
	SX-BHC	Olympic Aviation			30/MAY/84	
8031	D-IDBC	Dornier	200	03/MAY/84		
	NAF-028	Nigerian Air Force			02/APR/85	
7032	D-IBLP	Dornier	100	18/MAY/84		
	VT-EIX	ONGC			01/APR/85	
8033	D-IDBD	Dornier	200	25/JUN/84		
	NAF-029	Nigerian Air Force			02/APR/85	
8034	D-IDBE	Dornier	200	19/JUN/84		
	SX-BHD	Olympic Aviation			12/JUL/84	
8035	D-IASX	Delta Air	200	08/AUG/84	18/SEP/84	
7036	D-IBLQ	Dornier	100	10/AUG/84		
	A2-ACF	Air Botswana			84	
	D-IBLQ	Dornier			NOV/84	
	A2-ABA	Air Botswana			04/NOV/84	
8037	D-IDBG	Dornier	200	21/SEP/84		
	VT-EIO	Vayudoot			14/DEC/84	
8038	D-IDBH	Dornier	200	05/NOV/84		
	VT-EIP	Vayudoot			15/NOV/84	
7039	D-IGVN	Dornier	100	28/SEP/84		
	D-IGVN	BGR			16/OCT/84	Leased W/O 24/FEB/85 West Sahara Desert
8040	D-IDBI	Dornier	200	28/SEP/84		
	N233RP	Precision Airlines			20/DEC/84	
8041	D-IDBJ	Dornier	200	08/NOV/84		
	N234RP	Precision Airlines			16/NOV/84	
8042	D-IDBK	Dornier	200	20/DEC/84		
	VT-EIQ	Vayudoot			19/FEB/85	
7043	D-IBLS	Dornier	100	07/SEP/84		
	NAF-027	Nigerian Air Force			31/JAN/85	
8044	D-IDBL	Dornier	201	06/DEC/84		
	D-COKI	SAGECO			08/JAN/85	
	HZ-SSS1	SAGECO			08/JAN/85	
	HZ-SG1	SAGECO			86	
8045	D-IDBM	Dornier	201	13/FEB/85		
	60-	Somali Airlines				Not taken-up
	D-COKO	SAGECO			04/APR/85	
	HZ-SG2	SAGECO			04/APR/85	
8046	D-IDBN	Dornier	201	11/JAN/85		
	LN-NVC	Norving			28/JAN/85	
8047	D-IDBO	Dornier	201	27/NOV/84		
	5N-ARF	Genz Nigeria			30/JUL/85	
8048	D-IDBP	Dornier	201	04/FEB/85		
	N235RP	Precision Airlines			01/MAR/85	
8049	N236RP	Precision Airlines	201	11/MAR/85	27/MAR/85	
8050	D-IDBR	Dornier	201	27/APR/85		
	SX-BHE	Olympic Aviation			10/MAY/85	
7051	D-CALM	DFVLR	101	28/JUN/85	20/AUG/85	
8052	VT-EJF	Vayudoot	201	11/APR/85	09/OCT/85	
8054	VT-EJO	Vayudoot	201	24/MAY/85	30/OCT/85	
8055	VT-EJN	Indian Air Force	201		15/FEB/85	Assembled by HAL
8056	D-CAMI	Dornier	201	04/MAR/85		
	D-CAMI	Lesotho Airways			26/JUN/86	
8057	SX-BHF	Olympic Aviation	201	08/MAY/85	15/MAY/85	
8058	D-IERA	Dornier	200	19/APR/85		
	VH-NSC	National Safety Council			05/SEP/85	
7059	D-CIRI	Dornier	101	14/MAR/86		
	CG759	Indian Coast Guard			16/JUL/86	
8060	VT-EJN	Vayudoot	201	31/JAN/86	31/MAR/86	Assembled by HAL
8061	SX-BHG	Olympic Aviation	201	28/JUN/85	12/JUL/85	
7062	CG752	Indian Coast Guard	101	13/MAY/86	16/JUL/86	
8063	D-CAOS	Dornier	201	01/JUL/85		
	G-BMMR	Suckling Airways			22/APR/86	
8064	VT-EJT	Vayudoot	201	21/FEB/86	31/MAR/86	Assembled by HAL
8065	D-CBOL	Dornier	201	18/JUL/85		Demonstrator
8066	D-CECK	Dornier	201	29/APR/85		
	D-IAHG	Sunshine Aviation			16/JUL/86	
8067	VT-EJU	Vayudoot	201	05/MAR/86	31/MAR/86	Assembled by HAL
8068	9878	Dornier	201	29/NOV/85		
	9878	West Germany Navy			31/JAN/86	Leased
8069	D-CHOF	Nuernberger Flugdienst	201	21/AUG/86	18/DEC/85	
8070	D-CLIC	Dornier	201	04/SEP/85		
	LN-NVG	Norving			30/JAN/86	
8071	N71FB	Fischer Brothers Aviation	201	20/SEP/86	08/MAY/86	
8072	VT-EJV	Vayudoot	201	13/MAR/86	31/MAR/86	Assembled by HAL
7073	D-CICE	Alfred Wegener Institute	101	29/OCT/85	29/NOV/85	
8074	5U-MBI	Niger Air Force	201	24/SEP/85	10/MAR/86	
8075	VT-EJW	Vayudoot	201	20/MAR/86	31/MAR/86	Assembled by HAL
8076	D-CEPT	Dornier	201			
		Indian Government				
8077	G-BMND	Harvest Air	201	28/NOV/86	28/MAY/86	
8078	D-CFAN	Dornier	201	04/DEC/85		
	MI-B605	Airline of Marshall Islands			03/JUN/86	
8079	D-CLEC	Dornier	201	17/DEC/85		
	SX-BHH	Olympic Aviation			30/APR/86	
8080	SX-BHI	Olympic Aviation	201	07/JAN/86	28/MAY/86	
8081	VT-	Indian Air Force	201		20/MAY/85	Assembled by HAL
8082	VT-	Indian Air Force	201		20/MAY/85	Assembled by HAL
7083	D-	DFVLR	101			
8084	D-CLAB	Dornier	201			
	G-	Harvest Air				

DORNIER DO-228

C/N	Registration	Owner/Operator	Series	First Flight	Delivery	Remarks
8086	VT-	Civil Aviation Department	201			
8087	N87FB	Fischer Brothers Aviation	201	23/APR/86	17/MAY/86	
8088	N88FB	Fischer Brothers Aviation	201	24/APR/86	28/MAY/86	
8089	VT-	Indian Air Force	201		30/AUG/85	Assembled by HAL
8090	VT-	Indian Air Force	201		30/AUG/85	Assembled by HAL
8092	7Q-	Malawi Air Wing	201	21/MAY/86		
8093	D-CEMA	Dornier	201			
8115	7Q-	Malawi Air Wing	201			

ADDITIONAL ORDERS

	Registration	Owner/Operator	Series	First Flight	Delivery	Remarks
	D-IDLS	XIXCA Mexico	100			
	D-	Delta Air	200			
	9Q-	Sominki Mine Company	100		Autumn/86	Sched.delivery
	D-	Holiday Express	201			
	5U-	Niger Government	201		Apring/86	Sched.delivery
	7Q-	Malawi Air Wing	201			
	7Q-	Malawi Air Wing	201			
	7Q-	Malawi Air Wing	201			
	SX-	Olympic Aviation	201		86	Sched.delivery
	SX-	Olympic Aviation	201		86	Sched.delivery
	A2-	Air Botswana	101		86	Sched.delivery
	PH-	Schreiner Airways	201		86	Sched.delivery
	LN-NVH	Norving	201		86	Sched.delivery
	HB-	Sunshine Aviation	201			
	HB-	Sunshine Aviation	201			
	CP-	Linea Aerea Imperial Bolivia	201			
	CP-	(Unannounced)	201			
	N	Fischer Brothers	201			
	N	Southern Jersey Airways	201			
	N	Southern Jersey Airways	201			
	G-	Malinair	201		OCT/86	Sched.delivery
	G-	Malinair	201			
	G-	Malinair	201			
	G-	Malinair	201			
	G-	Malinair	201			
	G-	Malinair	201		88	Sched.delivery

Dornier 228 Cross-Reference Index

5N- Nigeria

C/N	Registration
8013	5N-AOH
7015	5N-AOR
8012	5N-AQO
7011	5N-AQV
7015	5N-AQW
7023	5N-AQX
8047	5N-ARF
7027	5N-ARK
8013	5N-ARP

5U- Niger

8074	5U-MBI

9M- Malaysia

8002	9M-AXB
8021	9M-AXD
8010	9M-AXF
8010	9M-DMF

A2- Botswana

7036	A2-ABA
7036	A2-ACF

A40- Oman

7020	A40-CP
7028	A40-CQ

A5- Bhutan

8006	A5-RGB
8017	A5-RGC

B- Taiwan

8008	B-12208

D- West Germany

7051	D-CALM
8056	D-CAMI
8063	D-CAOS
7014	D-CAWI
8065	D-CBOL
8066	D-CECK
8093	D-CEMA
8076	D-CEPT
8078	D-CFAN
8069	D-CHOF
7073	D-CICE
7059	D-CIRI
8084	D-CLAB
8079	D-CLEC
8070	D-CLIC
8044	D-COKI
8045	D-COKO
8066	D-IAHG
7029	D-IASS
8035	D-IASX
7014	D-IAWI
7018	D-IBLB
7020	D-IBLC
7022	D-IBLD
7023	D-IBLE
7024	D-IBLF
7027	D-IBLG
8016	D-IBLH
8017	D-IBLI
8019	D-IBLJ
8021	D-IBLK
8025	D-IBLL
8026	D-IBLM
7028	D-IBLN
7032	D-IBLP
7036	D-IBLQ
7036	D-IBLQ
7043	D-IBLS
8006	D-IBOO
4359	D-ICDO
7004	D-ICGO
7011	D-ICIP
7001	D-ICOG
8030	D-IDBB
8031	D-IDBC
8033	D-IDBD
8034	D-IDBE
8037	D-IDBG
8038	D-IDBH
8040	D-IDBI
8041	D-IDBJ
8042	D-IDBK
8044	D-IDBL
8045	D-IDBM
8046	D-IDBN
8047	D-IDBO
8048	D-IDBP
8050	D-IDBR
8002	D-IDCO
8007	D-IDID
8012	D-IDMC
8013	D-IDMI
7003	D-IDNI
7015	D-IDOC
7005	D-IDOM
8009	D-IDON
8058	D-IERA
4358	D-IFNS
7039	D-IGVN
8010	D-IHDO
8008	D-IHIC

G- United Kingdom

8063	G-BMMR
8077	G-BMND

HZ- Saudi Arabia

8044	HZ-SG1
8045	HZ-SG2
8044	HZ-SSS1

JA Japan

8007	JA8835
8019	JA8836

LN- Norway

7003	LN-HPA
7005	LN-HPB
7004	LN-HPE
7022	LN-HPG
7001	LN-HPG
7024	LN-NVB
8046	LN-NVC
8070	LN-NVG

MI Marshall Islands

8078	MI8605
7029	MI8604

N United States

8025	N228RP
8026	N232RP
8040	N233RP
8041	N234RP
8048	N235RP
8049	N236RP
8071	N71FB
8087	N87FB
8088	N88FB

PH- Netherlands

8009	PH-SDO

SE- Sweden

8016	SE-IKY

SX- Greece

8010	SX-BHA
8009	SX-BHB
8030	SX-BHC
8034	SX-BHD
8050	SX-BHE
8057	SX-BHF
8061	SX-BHG
8079	SX-BHH
8080	SX-BHI

VH- Australia

8058	VH-NSC

VT- India

8037	VT-EIO
8038	VT-EIP
8042	VT-EIQ
7032	VT-EIX
8052	VT-EJF
8055	VT-EJN
8060	VT-EJN
8054	VT-EJO
8064	VT-EJT
8067	VT-EJU
8072	VT-EJV
8075	VT-EJW

Military Operated

India

7062	CG752
7059	CG759

Nigeria

7043	NAF-027
8031	NAF-028
8033	NAF-029

West Germany

8068	9878

EMBRAER EMB-120 BRASILIA

Short/medium commuter airline, powered by two Pratt & Whitney PW115 turboprops. The EMB-120 Brasilia made its maiden flight on 27 July 1983, and the first aircraft was delivered to Atlantic Southeast Airlines of the USA in September 1985. To date, more than 12 aircraft have been delivered and a further 66 are on order.

Dimensions :	Wing span: 64ft 11in (19.78m) Length: 65ft 7in (20.0m) Height: 20ft 10in (6.35m)
Powerplant :	Two PWAC PW115 turboprops
Performance :	Max cruising speed 294 knots (545km/h) Range: with max payload 1,760nm (3,263km)
Accommodation:	30 passengers in a three abreast layout
Manufacturer :	Embraer - CP 343, 1200 Sao Jose dos Campos, Brazil Telephone: (123) 227070 Telex: 1133589 EBAE BR

EMBRAER

C/N	Registration	Owner/Operator	Series	First Flight	Delivery	Remarks
001	PT-ZBA	Embraer	120	27/JUL/83		Prototype
002		Embraer	120			Structural test airframe
003	PT-ZBB	Embraer	120	21/DEC/83		
	PT-ZBB	Brasilian Air Force			86	Leased
004	PT-ZBC	Embraer	120	09/MAY/84		
	PT-SIH	DLT			16/JAN/86	Leased
005		Embraer	120			Structural test airframe
006	PT-ZAS	Embraer	120			First production model
	PT-SIA	Embraer				
	N210AS	Atlantic Southeast Airlines			21/AUG/85	
007	PT-SIB	Embraer	120			
	N211AS	Atlantic Southeast Airlines			21/SEP/85	
008	PT-SIC	Embraer	120			
	N212AS	Atlantic Southeast Airlines			25/OCT/85	
009	PT-SID	Embraer	120			
	N214AS	Atlantic Southeast Airlines			28/NOV/85	
010	PT-SIE	Embraer	120			
	N215AS	Atlantic Southeast Airlines			21/DEC/85	
011	PT-SIF	Embraer	120			
	N217AS	Atlantic Southeast Airlines			28/DEC/85	
012	PT-SIG	Embraer	120			
	N120AM	Air Midwest/American Eagle			20/MAR/86	
013	PT-SII	Embraer	120			
	N122AM	Air Midwest/American Eagle			10/MAY/86	
014	PT-SIJ	Embraer	120			
	PT-SIJ	DLT			15/APR/86	Leased
015	PT-SIK	Embraer	120			
	N218AS	Atlantic Southeast Airlines			19/JUN/86	
016	PT-SIL	Embraer	120			
	N124AM	Air Midwest/American Eagle			23/JUL/86	

ADDITIONAL ORDERS

	LN-	Norsk Flytjeneste	120		JUL/86	Sched.delivery
	PT-SIT	Embraer	120			
	LN-	Norsk Flytjeneste			SEP/86	Sched.delivery
	D-	DLT	120		86	Sched.delivery
	D-	DLT	120			
	D-	DLT	120			
	D-	DLT	120			
	D-	DLT	120			
	G-	Euroair	120			
	G-	Euroair	120			
	N	United Technologies	120		86	Sched.delivery
	ZS-	Bop Air	120		Early/87	Sched.delivery
	ZS-	Bop Air	120		Early/87	Sched.delivery
	FAB-	Brasilian Air Force	120		86	Sched.delivery
	FAB-	Brasilian Air Force	120		86	Sched.delivery
	FAB-	Brasilian Air Force	120		86	Sched.delivery
	FAB-	Brasilian Air Force	120		86	Sched.delivery
	N	Westair Commuter	120		AUG/86	Sched.delivery
	N	Westair Commuter	120		OCT/86	Sched.delivery
	N	Westair Commuter	120			Sched.delivery
	N	Westair Commuter	120			Sched.delivery
	N	Westair Commuter	120			Sched.delivery
	N	Westair Commuter	120			Sched.delivery
	N	Westair Commuter	120			Sched.delivery
	N	Westair Commuter	120			Sched.delivery
	N	Westair Commuter	120		MAY/88	Sched.delivery
	PH-	Holland Aero Lines	120		FEB/87	Sched.delivery
	PH-	Holland Aero Lines	120		MAR/87	Sched.delivery
	PH-	Holland Aero Lines	120		APR/87	Sched.delivery
	PH-	Holland Aero Lines	120		MAY/87	Sched.delivery
	VH-	Lloyd Aviation	120			
	VH-	Lloyd Aviation	120			
	VH-	Opal Air	120			
	VH-	Opal Air	120			

EMBRAER EMB-120 BRASILIA

C/N	Registration	Owner/Operator	Series	First Flight	Delivery	Remarks
	P2-	Talair	120			
	N	Skywest Airlines	120		SEP/86	Sched.delivery
	N	Skywest Airlines	120		86	Sched.delivery
	N	Skywest Airlines	120		86	Sched.delivery
	N	Skywest Airlines	120		MAR/87	Sched.delivery
	N	Skywest Airlines	120		87	Sched.delivery
	N	Skywest Airlines	120		SEP/87	Sched.delivery
	N	Atlantic Southeast Airlines	120			
	N	Atlantic Southeast Airlines	120			
	N	Atlantic Southeast Airlines	120		SEP/86	
	N	Atlantic Southeast Airlines	120		MAR/87	Sched.delivery
	N	Atlantic Southeast Airlines	120			
	N	Atlantic Southeast Airlines	120			
	N	Atlantic Southeast Airlines	120			
	N	Atlantic Southeast Airlines	120			
	N	Atlantic Southeast Airlines	120			
	N	Atlantic Southeast Airlines	120			
	N	Atlantic Southeast Airlines	120			
	N	Atlantic Southeast Airlines	120			
	N	Atlantic Southeast Airlines	120			
	N	Atlantic Southeast Airlines	120			
	N	Atlantic Southeast Airlines	120			
	N	Atlantic Southeast Airlines	120			
	N	Atlantic Southeast Airlines	120			
	N	Atlantic Southeast Airlines	120			
	N	Atlantic Southeast Airlines	120			
	N	Atlantic Southeast Airlines	120			
	N	Atlantic Southeast Airlines	120			
	N	Atlantic Southeast Airlines	120			
	N	Atlantic Southeast Airlines	120		DEC/88	Sched.delivery

Embraer EMB-120 Brasilia
cross-reference index

FOKKER F.27 FRIENDSHIP

Medium-range, high-wing transport for up to 60 passengers, powered by two Rolls-Royce Dart turboprops. The most successful turboprop airliner to date, the F.27 Friendship first flew as long ago as 24 November 1955, and the last batch is being delivered. Versions produced comprise the MK 100 and 200 for up to 52 passengers; MK 300 and 400 Combi; MK 500 with a lengthened fuselage seating up to 60 passengers; MK 600 with a large cargo door, and a MK 700 which is a modified MK 600 with different powerplants. Military models include the Mk. 400M and the 500M, and a maritime patrol aircraft. A total of over 590 production aircraft were built and production was completed in 1986.

Dimensions :	Wing span: 95ft 1in (29.0m) Length: 77ft 3in (23.56m) Height: 27ft 11in (8.27m) (100/400/600) Wing span: 95ft 1in (29.0m) Length: 82ft 2in (25.06m) Height: 28ft 6in (8.71m) (500)
Powerplant :	Two Rolls Royce Dart 511, 511-7E or 514-7 turboprops (100), two Rolls Royce Dart 528 or 528-7E turboprops (200/300/400/500/600), two Rolls Royce Dart 552-7R turboprops (500)
Performance :	Max cruising speed 231 knots (428km/h) (100) Range: with max payload 674nm (1,250km) (100) Max cruising speed 262 knots (486km/h) (200) Range: with max payload 1,117nm (2,070km) (200) Max cruising speed 259 knots (480km/h) (500) Range: with max payload 1,017nm (1,883km) (500)
Accommodation:	52 passengers in a four abreast layout (100/200/500), mixed passenger/cargo loads (300/400/600)
Manufacturer :	Fokker - PO Box 1065, 1000 BB Amsterdam, The Netherlands Telephone: (020) 544 9111 Telex: 11526 NL

C/N	Registration	Owner/Operator	Series	First Flight	Delivery	Remarks
10101	PH-NIV	Fokker	100	24/NOV/55		WFU 08/JUN/61, Scrapped 12/OCT/61
10102	PH-NVF	Fokker	100	29/JAN/57		Second prototype
	PH-NVF	LTU			14/FEB/61	Leased
	PH-NVF	Fokker			18/OCT/61	
	PH-NVF	Luxair			09/MAY/53	Leased
	D-BAKI	LTU			10/MAY/63	
	D-BAKI	IFG			01/JAN/69	
	D-BAKI	WDL			10/JUL/74	
	D-BAKI	DLT			01/APR/80	Leased
	D-BAKI	WDL			84	
	D-BAKI	Crossair			84	Leased
	D-BAKI	WDL			84	
	D-BAKI	DLT			84	Leased
	D-BAKI	WDL			14/JAN/86	
10103		Non-flying prototype				Static test aircraft
10104		Non-flying prototype				Fatigue test aircraft
10105	PH-FAA	Fokker	100	23/MAY/58		
	EI-AKA	Aer Lingus			19/NOV/58	
	PH-FSF	Fokker			08/JUN/66	
	ZK-NAH	National Airways Corp.			19/JUN/66	
	ZK-NAH	Air New Zealand			01/APR/78	
	ZK-NAH	Australian Aircraft Sales			01/SEP/81	
	VH-NLS	Australian Aircraft Sales			14/NOV/83	Stored Melbourne
	VH-NLS	Great Aircruise			JAN/86	
10106	PH-FAB	Fokker	100	16/JUN/58		
	EI-AKB	Aer Lingus			19/NOV/58	
	PI-C-530	Philippine Airlines			17/JAN/66	
	PI-C-530	MMA			66	Leased
	PI-C-530	Philippine Airlines				
	PH-FSH	Fokker			20/MAR/67	
	JY-ADD	Alia			24/SEP/67	Leased
	PH-FSH	Fokker			26/SEP/67	
	EC-BNJ	Spantax			03/NOV/67	
	EC-BNJ	Aviaco			01/APR/72	Leased
	EC-BNJ	Aviaco			01/APR/76	Purchased
	D-BOBY	Air Classics			20/AUG/81	
	D-BOBY	WDL			17/NOV/81	Leased
	D-BOBY	Air Classics			FEB/82	
	G-IOMA	British Midland Airways			20/SEP/82	
	G-IOMA	Manx Airlines			25/SEP/82	Leased
	G-IOMA	British Midland Airways			27/SEP/83	
	G-IOMA	Loganair			21/NOV/83	Leased
	G-IOMA	British Midland Airways			28/MAY/86	WFU 28/MAY/86, Norwich
	G-IOMA	Shorts			86	
10107	PH-FAC	Fokker	100	23/AUG/58		
	EI-AKC	Aer Lingus			11/DEC/58	
	EI-AKC	Fokker			18/MAR/66	
	PH-SAP	Schreiner Airways			09/MAY/66	Leased
	PH-SAP	Fokker			30/SEP/66	
	PH-SAP	Spantax			28/OCT/66	Leased
	PH-SAP	Fokker			03/SEP/67	
	EC-BFV	Spantax			15/NOV/67	
	EC-BFV	Aviaco			01/APR/72	Leased
	EC-BFV	Aviaco			01/APR/76	Purchased
	N144PM	Pilgrim Airlines			21/APR/82	
	N144PM	Business Express			86	
10108	PH-FAD	Fokker	100	30/OCT/58		
	LN-SUN	Braathens Safe			20/DEC/58	
	PH-FAD	Fokker			24/AUG/67	
	EC-BPJ	Spantax			01/OCT/68	
	EC-BPJ	Aviaco			01/APR/72	Leased
	EC-BPJ	Aviaco			01/APR/76	Purchased
	N148PM	Pilgrim Airlines			17/JUL/82	W/O 13/JAN/84, New York-JFK
	N148PM	Business Express			86	
10109	PH-FAE	Fokker	100	24/DEC/58		
	EI-AKD	Aer Lingus			23/JAN/59	
	PH-YFF	Fokker			23/FEB/66	

FOKKER F-27 FRIENDSHIP

C/N	Registration	Owner/Operator	Series	First Flight	Delivery	Remarks
	D-BAKA	LTU			14/APR/66	
	D-BAKA	IFG			01/JAN/69	Leased
	D-BAKA	LTU			69	
	PH-YFF	Fokker			08/APR/69	
	EC-BRN	Spantax			09/JUN/69	
	EC-BRN	Aviaco			01/APR/72	Leased
	EC-BRN	Aviaco			01/APR/76	Purchased
	N143PM	Pilgrim Airlines			15/JAN/82	
	N143PM	Business Express			86	
10110	PH-FAF	Fokker	100	14/JAN/59		
	EI-AKE	Aer Lingus			04/FEB/59	
	PH-FSE	Fokker			07/JUN/66	
	ZK-NAF	National Airways Corp.			28/JUN/66	
	ZK-NAF	Air New Zealand			01/APR/78	
	ZK-NAF	Australian Aircraft Sales			01/MAY/81	
	TS-LVA	Tunisavia			19/AUG/83	
		South Yemen Air Force			AUG/83	
10111	PH-FAG	Fokker	100	16/JAN/59		
	VH-TFA	TAA			13/JUN/59	
	VH-TFA	TAA New Guinea			09/DEC/70	
	VH-TFA	Air Nuigini			01/NOV/73	
	P2-TFA	Air Niugini			01/JUN/74	
	P2-ANA	Air Niugini			10/NOV/75	
	P2-ANA	Aviateca			25/MAY/78	
	TG-AIA	Aviateca			08/SEP/78	WFU AUG/79
	1094	Guatemalan Air Force			01/JUL/83	
0112	PH-FAH	Fokker	100	26/FEB/59		
	VH-TFB	TAA			06/APR/59	W/O 10/JUN/60 Mackay, Aus.
10113	PH-FAI	Fokker	100	13/MAY/59		
	VH-TFC	TAA			18/JUN/59	
	VH-TFC	Australian Aircraft Sales			15/AUG/77	
	F-BYAP	Uni Air			17/NOV/77	
	F-BYAP	Air Inter			01/JUL/79	Leased
	F-BYAP	Uni Air			28/JUL/79	
	F-BYAP	Air Inter			20/NOV/79	Leased
	F-BYAP	Uni Air			20/NOV/80	
	F-BYAP	Air Alsace			01/APR/81	Leased
	F-BYAP	Uni Air			01/JAN/82	
	F-BYAP	Brit Air			MAR/83	Leased
	F-BYAP	Uni Air			83	
10114	PH-FAK	Fokker	100	09/APR/59		
	VH-TFD	TAA			05/MAY/59	
	VH-TFD	MacRobertson Miller Airlines			01/SEP/62	Leased
	VH-TFD	TAA			27/OCT/62	
	VH-TFD	Australian Aircraft Sales			17/OCT/80	
	N1036P	Australian Aircraft Sales			14/NOV/80	
	N141PM	Pilgrim Airlines			02/MAR/81	
	N141PM	Business Express			86	
10115	PH-FAM	Fokker	100VIP	08/JUL/59		
	59-0259	Philippine Air Force			02/SEP/59	
	59-0259	Philippine Air Force	200VIP		01/JAN/66	Converted
10116	PH-FAL	Fokker	100	07/MAR/59		
	LN-SUO	Braathens Safe			22/APR/59	
	PH-FAL	Fokker			01/JUL/68	
	EC-BPK	Spantax			11/NOV/68	
	EC-BPK	Aviaco			01/APR/72	Leased
	EC-BPK	Aviaco			01/APR/76	Purchased
	EC-BPK	Pilgrim Airlines			05/JAN/82	
	EC-BPK	Aviaco			05/JAN/82	Leased
	N145PM	Pilgrim Airlines			26/JAN/84	
	N145PM	Business Express			86	
10117						Not built
10118	PH-FAN	Fokker	100	09/APR/59		
	EI-AKF	Aer Lingus			06/MAY/59	
	PH-FSA	Fokker			04/JAN/66	
	ZK-NAA	National Airways Corp.			20/JAN/66	
	ZK-NAA	Air New Zealand			01/APR/78	
	ZK-NAA	Australian Aircraft Sales			01/JUN/81	
	TS-LVB	Tunisavia			19/AUG/83	
	YN-BZF	Aeronica				W/O 20/APR/85 nr. Greenland on delivery
10119	PH-FAO	Fokker	100	20/APR/59		
	EI-AKG	Aer Lingus			12/MAY/59	
	PH-FSB	Fokker			04/JAN/66	
	ZK-NAB	National Airways Corp.			15/MAR/66	
	ZK-NAB	Air New Zealand			01/APR/78	
	ZK-NAB	Australian Aircraft Sales			01/FEB/81	
	TS-LVC	Tunisavia			19/AUG/83	
	8Q-PNA	Maldives Intl. Airways			20/MAY/84	
10120	PH-FAP	Fokker	100	21/MAY/59		
	VH-TFE	TAA			06/JUN/59	
	VH-TFE	Australian DCA			25/MAR/66	Leased
	VH-TFE	Australian DCA			05/MAY/71	Purchased
	VH-TFE	Australian Dept. of Transpor			07/JUN/74	
	VH-TFE	Air Anglia			25/JUL/78	
	G-SPUD	Air Anglia			31/JAN/79	
	G-SPUD	Air UK			16/JAN/80	
	G-SPUD	Nile Valley Aviation			20/AUG/81	Leased
	G-SPUD	Air UK			SEP/82	
	G-OMAN	Manx Airlines			20/SEP/82	Leased
	G-OMAN	Air UK			05/MAR/84	
	G-BLFJ	Air UK			MAR/84	
10121	PH-FAR	Fokker	100	08/JUN/59		
	VH-TFF	TAA			24/JUN/59	
	VH-TFF	East West Airlines			18/MAR/75	Leased
	VH-TFF	TAA			01/DEC/75	
	VH-TFFU	Australian Aircraft Sales			17/OCT/80	
	N1036U	Evergreen International			01/MAR/81	
	F-GAOT	TAT			01/MAY/81	
	F-GAOT	Uni Air			01/OCT/81	
10122	PH-FAS	Fokker	100	22/JUN/59		
	VH-TFG	TAA			13/JUL/59	
	VH-TFG	Australian Aircraft Sales			06/APR/79	
	N300AS	Evergreen International			02/MAY/79	
	N142PM	Pilgrim Airlines			16/AUG/79	

C/N	Registration	Owner/Operator	Series	First Flight	Delivery	Remarks
	N142PM	Business Express			86	
10123	PH-FAT	Fokker	100	16/AUG/60		
		Aviaco				Not taken-up
	TC-TEZ	THY			27/OCT/60	W/O 17/FEB/70 Samsun, Turkey
10124	PH-FAU	Fokker	100	16/SEP/60		
		Aviaco				Not taken-up
	TC-TON	THY			27/OCT/60	
	TC-TON	Fokker			19/JUL/73	
	N47SB	International Air			11/NOV/75	
	5001	Burmese Air Force			18/MAY/76	
10125	PH-FAV	Fokker	100	05/OCT/60		
		Aviaco				Not taken-up
	TC-TOY	THY			27/OCT/60	
	TC-TOY	Fokker			20/AUG/73	
	PH-FAV	Fokker			15/NOV/74	
	HB-AAP	Transvalair				Not taken-up
	N48SB	International Air			23/APR/75	
	D2-FPH	OTAL-CTA			29/OCT/75	
	D2-FPH	TAAG-Angola			01/MAR/79	WFU
	D2-TFK	TAAG-Angola			15/SEP/80	WFU
10126	PH-FAW	Fokker	100VIP	28/AUG/59		
		FIAT				Not taken-up
	EP-MRP	Iranian Govt.			12/SEP/59	
	EP-MRP	Iranian Govt.	200VIP		17/JAN/61	Convtd. W/O 10/OCT/62 nr. Karai Dam, Iran
10127	PH-FAX	Fokker	100	16/JUL/59		
	VH-TFH	TAA				Not taken-up
	VH-EWA	East West Airlines			29/JUL/59	
	VH-EWA	Australian Aircraft Sales			14/NOV/77	
	F-BYAO	Uni Air			15/NOV/77	
	F-BYAO	Air Senegal			11/NOV/78	Leased
	F-BYAO	Uni Air			13/MAY/79	
	F-BYAO	Transair	700		JUN/85	Converted
10128		Not Built				
10129		Not Built				
10130		Not Built				
10131	PH-FAY	Fokker	100	22/AUG/59		
	VH-CAV	Australian DCA			19/SEP/59	
	VH-CAV	Air Anglia			20/JAN/79	
	G-STAN	Air Anglia			02/JUL/79	
	G-STAN	Air UK			01/JAN/80	
	G-STAN	Air UK	200		JAN/81	Converted
10132	PH-FAZ	Fokker	100	11/SEP/59		
	VH-CAT	Australian DCA			28/SEP/59	
	VH-CAT	CSIRO			01/JUL/78	
10133	PH-FBA	Fokker	200	20/SEP/59		
	VH-FNA	Ansett-ANA			05/OCT/59	
	VH-FNA	MMA			07/SEP/67	Leased
	VH-FNA	Ansett-ANA			APR/68	
	VH-FNA	MMA			31/DEC/68	Leased
	VH-FNA	Ansett-ANA			11/MAR/69	
	VH-FNA	MMA			27/APR/69	Leased
	VH-FNA	Ansett Airlines			28/SEP/69	
	VH-FNA	Ansett Airlines of PNG			13/JUL/70	
	P2-ANJ	Air Niugini			01/NOV/72	Leased
	PT-LCX	Rio Sul			01/JUL/76	Purchased
10134	PH-FBB	Fokker	200	24/SEP/59	29/MAR/82	
	VH-TFI	TAA			05/OCT/59	
	VH-TFI	TAA New Guinea			22/FEB/67	
	VH-TFI	Air Niugini			01/NOV/73	
	P2-TFI	Air Niugini			01/JUN/74	
	P2-ANB	Air Niugini			30/DEC/75	
	VH-TFI	Connair			APR/79	Not taken-up
	P2-ANZ	Air Niugini			15/JUN/79	WFU 15/JUN/79
	N1036S	Aircraft Sales			31/MAY/80	
	N1036S	British Midland Airways			23/APR/82	Leased
	G-BMAR	British Midland Airways			APR/82	Reg. Not taken-up
	N1036S	British Midland Airways			APR/82	WFU NOV/82, East Midlands
	N1036S	Air North			26/NOV/83	
	N1036S	Brockway Air			01/MAY/84	
	PT-LGH	Rio Sul			JAN/85	
10135	PH-FBC	Fokker	200	07/OCT/59		
	VH-TFJ	TAA			21/OCT/59	
	VH-TFJ	TAA New Guinea Division			MAR/67	
	VH-TFJ	Air Niugini			01/NOV/73	
	P2-TFJ	Air Niugini			06/MAY/74	
	P2-ANC	Air Niugini			01/NOV/75	
	VH-TFJ	Connair			APR/79	Not taken-up
	P2-ANC	Air Niugini				
	G-BLML	Air UK			JUL/84	
10136	PH-FBD	Fokker	200	15/OCT/59		
	VH-FNB	Ansett-ANA			30/OCT/59	
	VH-FNB	Ansett Airlines of NSW			NOV/59	
	VH-FNB	Ansett-ANA			MAY/62	
	VH-FNB	Ansett Airlines of Australia			01/JAN/69	
	VH-FNB	Ansett of South Australia			26/FEB/71	
	VH-FNB	Ansett Airlines of Australia			28/MAR/71	
	VH-FNB	Ansett of South Australia			03/OCT/71	
	VH-FNB	Ansett Airlines			03/JUL/76	
	PK-MFP	Merpati Nusantara			28/AUG/77	
10137	PH-FBE	Fokker	200VIP	19/DEC/59		
	D-BATU	Helmut Horten			30/DEC/66	
	PH-FSD	Fokker			18/FEB/66	
	PH-FSD	ATI			25/APR/66	Leased
	PH-FSD	KLA			25/APR/66	Sub-Leased
	PH-FSD	Fokker			01/MAY/67	
		Faroe Airways				Not taken-up
	PH-FSD	Air Inter			07/JUN/67	Leased
	PH-FSD	Fokker			14/NOV/68	
	F-BRHL	Euralair			22/NOV/68	
	F-BRHL	Europe Air Charter			08/JUN/72	
	F-BRHL	Air Littoral			16/DEC/72	
	TN-ACR	Lina Congo			07/MAR/75	
	D-BAKU	WDL			15/JAN/83	WFU 01/OCT/83, Essen

FOKKER F-27 FRIENDSHIP

C/N	Registration	Owner/Operator	Series	First Flight	Delivery	Remarks
	D-BAKU	DLT			DEC/83	Leased
	D-BAKU	WDL			84	
	D-BAKU	Crossair			JUN/84	Leased
	D-BAKU	WDL			OCT/84	
	D-BAKU	DLT			01/APR/85	Leased
10138	PH-FBF	Fokker	200	04/NOV/59		
	VH-TFK	TAA			30/NOV/59	
	VH-TFK	Associated Airlines			01/JUL/60	
	VH-TFK	TAA			09/DEC/60	
	VH-TFK	TAA New Guinea			12/OCT/69	
	VH-TFK	Air Niugini			01/OCT/73	
	P2-TFK	Air Niugini			01/JUN/74	
	P2-AND	Air Niugini			11/NOV/75	
	VH-TFK	Connair			15/JUN/79	
	VH-TFK	East West Airlines			24/FEB/80	
	VH-TFK	Wards Air Freight			01/APR/80	Leased
	VH-TFK	East West Airlines			24/DEC/80	
	VH-TFK	Wards Air Frieght			20/JAN/81	Leased
	VH-TFK	East West Airlines			01/NOV/81	
	VH-TFK	Fokker			17/FEB/84	
	PH-FBF	Fokker			09/APR/85	
	CP-2013	Lloyd Aereo Boliviano			21/JUN/85	
10139	PH-FBG	Fokker	200	16/NOV/59		
	VH-TFL	TAA				Not taken-up
	VH-MMS	MMA			07/DEC/59	
	VH-MMS	Ansett Airlines of Australia			08/JUN/72	
	VH-MMS	Ansett Airlines of NSW			26/MAY/79	
	VH-MMS	Ansett Airlines of Australia			01/MAR/80	
10140	PH-IOK	Fokker	100	12/DEC/59		
	PH-IOK	Iranian Oil			11/JAN/60	
	EP-IOK	OSCO			01/NOV/73	Operated by Iran Air.
10141	PH-IOP	Fokker	100	30/DEC/59		
	PH-IOP	Iranian Oil			22/JAN/60	
	PH-IOP	Fokker			22/NOV/63	
	PH-IOP	Fokker	200			Converted
	HB-AAI	Balair			02/APR/64	W/O 13/SEP/64 Malaga, Spain
10142	PH-PBF	Fokker	100VIP	18/MAR/60		
	PH-PBF	Dutch Govt. Royal Flight			13/MAY/60	
	PH-PBF	Fokker			22/FEB/72	
	PK-KFR	Bouraq			17/MAR/73	
	PK-KFR	Bali International			21/MAY/74	W/O 04/NOV/76 Sjamsuddin a/p, Borneo
10143	PH-FBH	Fokker	200	29/DEC/59		
	VH-FNC	Ansett Airlines of NSW			04/FEB/60	
	PK-MFR	Merpati Nusantara			25/JUL/77	
10144	PH-FBI	Fokker	200	06/JAN/60		
	VH-FND	Ansett Airlines of NSW			12/FEB/60	
	ZS-JVA	Comair			14/NOV/76	
	ZS-JVA	Royal Swazi			81	Leased
	ZS-JVA	Comair			82	
10145	PH-FBK	Fokker	200	20/JAN/60		
	VH-FNE	Ansett-OAL			25/FEB/60	
	VH-FNE	Ansett Airlines of NSW			NOV/66	
	VH-FNE	MMA			12/MAR/69	Leased
	VH-FNE	Ansett Airlines of NSW			01/SEP/69	W/O 25/MAR/71 Essendon Ap.
10146	PH-FBL	Fokker	200	26/JAN/60		
	VH-FNF	Ansett-ANA			10/MAR/60	
	VH-MMO	MMA			16/JUN/64	
	VH-MMO	Ansett Airlines of Australia			01/JUN/69	
	VH-MMO	Airlines of North Australia			01/JUL/81	
	VH-MMO	Air New South Wales			07/MAR/83	
	VH-MMO	Ansett			26/JAN/84	
	VH-MMO	Air Queensland			JUL/84	Leased
	VH-MMO	Ansett Airlines of Australia			OCT/84	
10147	PH-FBM	Fokker	100	10/FEB/60		
	PI-C501	Philippine Airlines			23/FEB/60	W/O 28/FEB/67 Mactan, Phillipines
10148	PH-FBN	Fokker	100	19/FEB/60		
	PI-C502	Philippine Airlines			09/MAR/60	
	10148	Philippine Air Force			26/NOV/71	
	10148	Philippine Air Force	200	13/DEC/78	18/JAN/79	Converted
10149	PH-FBO	Fokker	100	15/JUN/60		
	C-2	Royal Netherlands Air Force			06/JUL/60	
	C-2	United Nations Organisation			11/JUN/67	Leased
	C-2	Royal Netherlands Air Force			21/AUG/67	
10150	PH-FBP	Fokker	100	28/JUN/60		
	C-3	Royal Netherlands Air Force			06/AUG/60	
10151	PH-IOS	Fokker	300	02/MAY/60		
	PH-FRA	KLM			11/MAY/60	Not taken-up
	PH-IOS	Iranian Oil			11/MAY/60	Leased
	PH-IOS	Iranian Oil			01/JUL/62	Purchased
	EP-IOS	OSCO			01/NOV/73	Operated by Iran Air
10152	PH-FBR	Fokker	100VIP	14/JUL/60		
	C-1	Royal Netherlands Air Force			23/AUG/60	
10153	PH-IOT	Fokker	300	23/MAY/60		
	PH-FRB	KLM			31/MAY/60	Not taken-up
	PH-IOT	Iranian Oil			31/MAY/60	
	PH-IOT	Iranian Oil			01/JUL/62	Purchased
	EP-IOT	OSCO			01/NOV/73	Operated by Iran Air
10154	PH-FBS	Fokker	300M	17/AUG/60		
	C-4	Royal Netherlands Air Force			06/OCT/60	
	C-4	United Nations Organisation			21/AUG/67	Leased
	C-4	Royal Netherlands Air Force			21/NOV/67	
10155	PH-FBT	Fokker	300M		26/AUG/60	
	C-5	Royal Netherlands Air Force			30/SEP/60	
10156	PH-FBU	Fokker	300M	19/SEP/60		
	C-6	Royal Netherlands Air Force			07/DEC/60	
10157	PH-FBV	Fokker	300M	30/SEP/60		
	C-7	Royal Netherlands Air Force			29/DEC/60	
	C-7	United Nations Organisation			24/OCT/72	Leased
	C-7	Royal Netherlands Air Force			24/JAN/73	
10158	PH-FBW	Fokker	300M	06/OCT/60		
	C-8	Royal Netherlands Air Force			28/DEC/60	
	PH-FSC	Fokker			06/APR/62	Leased
	C-8	Royal Netherlands Air Force			20/JUL/62	

C/N	Registration	Owner/Operator	Series	First Flight	Delivery	Remarks
10159	PH-FBX	Fokker	300M	19/OCT/60	19/DEC/60	
	C-9	Royal Netherlands Air Force			04/JAN/61	
	PH-KFA	NLM			31/AUG/66	Leased
	C-9	Royal Netherlands Air Force			01/MAR/72	
10160	PH-FBY	Fokker	300M	04/NOV/60		
	C-10	Royal Netherlands Air Force			17/JAN/61	
10161	PH-FBZ	Fokker	300M	22/NOV/60		
	C-11	Royal Netherlands Air Force			02/FEB/61	
	C-11	Royal Netherlands Air Force	300			Converted
	PH-FKB	NLM			01/AUG/66	Leased
	C-11	Royal Netherlands Air Force			05/APR/72	
10162	PH-FCA	Fokker	300M	07/MAR/61		
	C-12	Royal Netherlands Air Force			28/APR/61	
10163	PH-FCB	Fokker	200	09/DEC/60		
	AP-ALM	PIA			03/JAN/61	W/O 06/AUG/70 Islamabad, Pakistan
10164	PH-FCC	Fokker	200	12/DEC/60		
	AP-ALN	PIA			19/JAN/61	
10165	PH-FCD	Fokker	200	10/JAN/61		
	AP-ALO	PIA			06/FEB/61	W/O 25/JUN/64 Dacca A/P
10166	PH-FCE	Fokker	100	07/NOV/60		
	ZK-BXA	National Airways Corp.			26/NOV/60	
	ZK-BXA	Air New Zealand			01/APR/78	
	PK-MFS	Merpati Nusantara			19/APR/78	
	ZK-BXA	Air New Zealand			19/DEC/78	
	ZK-BXA	Lloyds			JAN/79	
	9V-BLP	Singapore General Aviation			JAN/79	
	PK-OBP	AirFast			25/JUN/80	
10167	PH-FCF	Fokker	100	18/JAN/61		
	ZK-BXB	National Airways Corp.			09/FEB/61	
	ZK-BXB	Air New Zealand			01/APR/78	
	NZ2781	RNZAF			25/FEB/80	
10168	PH-FCG	Fokker	100	03/FEB/61		
	ZK-BXC	National Airways Corp.			24/FEB/61	
	ZK-BXC	Air New Zealand			01/APR/78	
	NZ2782	RNZAF			10/OCT/80	
10169	PH-FCH	Fokker	100	14/FEB/61		
	ZK-BXD	National Airways Corp.			03/MAR/61	
	ZK-BXD	Air New Zealand			01/APR/78	
	NZ2783	RNZAF			27/JUN/80	
10170	PH-FCI	Fokker	100	28/FEB/61		
	VH-FNG	Ansett Airlines of NSW			17/MAR/61	
	VH-FNG	Ansett Airlines of Australia			DEC/70	
	VH-FNG	Ansett Airlines of PNG			01/FEB/71	
	VH-FNG	Air Niugini			01/NOV/73	Leased
	P2-ANK	Air Niugini			01/JUL/76	Purchased
	PT-LCY	Rio Sul			25/APR/82	
10171	PH-FCK	Fokker	100	03/MAR/61		
	VT-DMA	Indian Airlines			05/APR/61	W/O 02/FEB/71 Lahore, India
10172	PH-FCL	Fokker	100	15/MAR/61		
	VT-DMB	Indian Airlines			07/APR/61	
10173	PH-FCM	Fokker	100	23/MAR/61		
	VT-DMC	Indian Airlines			24/APR/61	
	CG-710	Indian Coast Guard			MAY/83	
10174	PH-FCN	Fokker	100	06/APR/61		
	VT-DMD	Indian Airlines			28/APR/61	W/O 24/JUL/76 Bhubaneshwar
10175	PH-FCO	Fokker	100	26/APR/61		
	VT-DME	Indian Airlines			04/MAY/61	W/O 11/AUG/72 Palam, India
10176	PH-FCP	Fokker	100	09/MAY/61		
	LN-SUG	Braathens Safe			18/MAY/61	
	LN-SUG	Luxair			09/OCT/66	Leased
	LN-SUG	Braathens Safe			19/MAY/67	
	PH-FCP	Fokker			19/MAY/69	
	PH-FCP	Fokker	700		23/DEC/69	Converted
	VH-TFH	TAA			30/DEC/69	Leased
	PH-FCP	Fokker			01/JUN/71	
	D-BEKU	LTU			15/MAR/72	
	D-BEKU	IFG			01/JUN/72	
	TF-FIP	Icelandair			06/MAY/74	
	TF-FLP	Icelandair			21/SEP/79	
	TF-FLP	Aircraft Sales			15/FEB/80	
	N146PM	Pilgrim Airlines			19/FEB/80	
	N146PM	Icelandair			22/JAN/81	Leased
	N146PM	Pilgrim Airlines			01/DEC/81	
	N146PM	Business Express			86	
10177	PH-FCR	Fokker	200	23/MAY/61		
	JA8601	All Nippon			30/MAY/61	
	PK-PFW	Pelita/Pertamina			15/NOV/72	
	PK-PFW	Pelita/Pertamina	600		01/JUL/75	Converted
	PH-FCR	Fokker			22/OCT/79	
	PT-LAF	TAM			18/JAN/80	
10178	PH-FCS	Fokker	200	01/JUN/61		
	JA8602	All Nippon			14/JUN/61	
	PK-PFX	Pelita/Pertamina			04/DEC/72	
	PK-PFX	Pelita/Pertamina	600		01/JAN/75	Converted
	PH-FCS	Fokker			15/APR/80	
	PT-LAH	TAM			05/JUL/80	
10179	PH-FCT	Fokker	200	16/JUN/61		
	JA8603	All Nippon			21/JUN/61	
	P2-MNE	Air Niugini			25/JAN/75	
	P2-ANE	Air Niugini			01/NOV/75	
	TG-AEA	Aviateca			18/APR/78	
		Guatemalan Air Force			01/JAN/83	
10180	PH-FCU	Fokker	200	23/JUN/61		
	VN-FNH	Ansett Airlines of NSW			11/JUL/61	W/O 17/MAR/65, Launceston
10181	PH-FCV	Fokker	200	06/JUL/61		
	VH-FNI	Ansett-ANA			14/JUL/61	
	VH-FNI	Ansett of South Australia			15/APR/68	
	VH-FNI	Ansett Airlines of Australia			01/OCT/77	
	ZS-KVI	Comair			29/JAN/81	
10182	PH-FCW	Fokker	100	11/JUL/61		
	TC-TAY	THY			30/AUG/61	W/O 23/SEP/61 Ankara, Turkey
10183	PH-FCX	Fokker	100	25/JUL/61		
	TC-TEK	THY			30/AUG/61	
	TC-TEK	Fokker			01/JAN/74	

FOKKER F-27 FRIENDSHIP

C/N	Registration	Owner/Operator	Series	First Flight	Delivery	Remarks
	PH-FCX	Fokker	100MAR		28/FEB/76	Maritime prototype
						WFU 08/JAN/85
		KLM Apprentice Training			FEB/85	Used for apprentice training
10184	PH-FCY	Fokker	100	22/AUG/61		
	ZK-BXE	National Airways Corp.			30/AUG/61	
	ZK-BXE	Air New Zealand			01/APR/78	
	ZK-BXE	Australian Aircraft Sales			01/JUN/81	
	ZK-BXE	Air New Zealand			31/OCT/83	
10185	PH-FCZ	Fokker	100	04/SEP/61		
	ZK-BXF	National Airways Corp.			12/SEP/61	
	ZK-BXF	Air New Zealand			01/APR/78	
	ZK-BXF	Australian Aircraft Sales			OCT/81	
	ZK-BXF	Air New Zealand			DEC/83	
10186	PH-FDA	Fokker	300	18/SEP/61		
	D-BAKU	LTU			16/NOV/61	
	PH-FSG	Fokker			01/DEC/66	
	PH-FSG	Luxair			20/JAN/67	Leased
	PH-FSG	Fokker			01/OCT/67	
	D-BAKU	LTU			24/NOV/67	
	D-BAKU	Sabena			17/APR/68	Leased
	D-BAKU	LTU			26/MAY/69	
	PH-FSG	Fokker			27/MAY/69	
	VH-MMB	MMA			04/AUG/70	
	VH-MMB	Fokker			14/MAR/71	
	VH-MMB	East West Airlines			16/MAR/71	
	VH-MMB	Ansett Airlines of NSW			75	Leased
	VH-MMB	East West Airlines			75	
	LN-NPH	Air Executive			26/JUL/78	
	LN-NPH	Busy Bee			01/SEP/80	
10187	PH-FDB	Fokker	400	06/OCT/61		
	AP-ALW	PIA			19/OCT/61	
10188	PH-FDC	Fokker	200	20/OCT/61		
	AP-ALX	PIA			06/NOV/61	W/O 13/DEC/71 nr. Iranian
						Border
10189	PH-FDD	Fokker	100	03/NOV/61		
	ZK-BXG	National Airways Corp.			17/NOV/61	
	ZK-BXG	Air New Zealand			01/APR/78	
	ZK-BXG	Australian Aircraft Sales			OCT/81	
	ZK-BXG	Air New Zealand			OCT/81	
10190	PH-FDE	Fokker	100	20/NOV/61		
	ZK-BXH	National Airways Corp.			30/NOV/61	
	VH-EWH	East West Airlines			14/SEP/63	Leased
	ZK-BXH	National Airways Corp.			16/JAN/65	
	ZK-BXH	Air New Zealand			01/APR/78	
	ZK-BXH	Australian Aircraft Sales			OCT/81	
	ZK-BXH	Air New Zealand			OCT/81	
10191	PH-FDF	Fokker	100	08/DEC/61		
	PI-C503	Philippine Airlines			14/DEC/61	W/O 12/OCT/62 Manila
10192	PH-FDG	Fokker	200	02/JAN/62		
	ST-AAA	Sudan Airways			23/JAN/62	
10193	PH-FDH	Fokker	200	25/JAN/62		
	ST-AAR	Sudan Airways			02/FEB/62	
10194	PH-FDI	Fokker	200	13/FEB/62		
	ST-AAS	Sudan Airways			20/FEB/62	W/O 05/OCT/82, Nr. Khartoum
10195	PH-FDK	Fokker	200	06/FEB/62		
	JA8605	All Nippon			20/FEB/62	
	PK-PFR	Pelita/Pertamina			31/AUG/71	
	PK-PFR	Pelita/Pertamina	600		01/APR/77	Converted
	PH-FDK	Fokker			28/OCT/85	
	PT-ODM	Rio Sul			31/OCT/85	
10196	PH-FDL	Fokker	200	20/FEB/62		
	JA8606	All Nippon			01/MAR/62	
	PK-PFS	Pelita/Pertamina			01/OCT/71	
	PK-PFS	Pelita/Pertamina	600		01/APR/77	
	PK-PFS	Seulawah Air Services			04/APR/77	Leased
	PK-PFS	Pelita/Pertamina			08/MAR/78	
	F-GBDK	TAT			15/AUG/79	
	G-BHMY	Air UK			14/MAR/80	
10197	PH-FDM	Fokker	200	08/MAR/62		
	JA8607	All Nippon			16/MAR/62	
	PK-PFT	Pelita/Pertamina			01/NOV/71	
	PK-PFT	Pelita/Pertamina	600		01/AUG/76	Converted
	PH-FDM	Fokker			05/FEB/80	
	PT-LAG	TAM			15/APR/80	
10198	PH-LIP	Fokker	100VIP	27/MAR/62		
	PH-LIP	Philips			07/APR/62	
	PH-LIP	Philips	100			Converted
	PH-LIP	NLM			10/FEB/75	Leased
	PH-LIP	Philips			01/MAR/75	
	PH-LIP	WDL			15/APR/75	
	D-BAKA	WDL			28/JUN/75	
	D-BAKA	DLT			FEB/81	Leased
	D-BAKA	WDL			81	
	D-BAKA	Crossair			OCT/84	Leased
	D-BAKA	WDL			DEC/84	
	D-BAKA	DLT			JAN/86	Leased
10199	PH-FDN	Fokker	100	10/APR/62		
	LN-SUW	Braathens Safe			18/APR/62	
	PH-FDN	Fokker			09/MAY/69	
	560	Uruguayan Air Force			10/FEB/70	
	T-560	Uruguayan Air Force				
	CX-BHV	PLUNA			01/APR/75	Leased
	T-560/					
	CX-BHV	TAMU			01/JAN/77	
10200	PH-FDR	Fokker	100	03/MAY/62		
	LV-PTO	Austral				Not taken-up
	D-BAKE	LTU			30/AUG/62	
	PH-FDO	Fokker			01/12/64	
	PH-FDO	Fokker	200			Convtd.
	HB-AAU	Balair			30/MAR/65	
	PH-KFC	NLM			01/APR/72	
	OY-	Cimber Air				Not taken-up
	PH-KFC	Aviona Leasing			06/MAY/81	
	A2-ADG	Air Botswana			05/SEP/81	
10201	PH-FDP	Fokker	100	15/MAY/62		

C/N	Registration	Owner/Operator	Series	First Flight	Delivery	Remarks
	LV-PTP	Austral				Not taken-up
	PH-FDP	Fokker	200			Convtd.
	JA8615	All Nippon			27/FEB/63	
	PH-OGA	Limburg Airlines			10/JUN/73	
	G-BCDN	Air Anglia			07/MAY/74	
	G-BCDN	Air UK			16/JAN/80	
10202	PH-FDR	Fokker	100	28/MAY/62		
	LV-PTQ	Austral				Not taken-up
	LN-SUA	Braathens Safe			13/JUL/62	
	PH-FDR	Fokker			01/JUL/69	
	PH-FDR	Spantax			04/JUL/69	Leased
	PH-FDR	Fokker			16/AUG/69	
	561	Uruguayan Air Force			11/MAR/70	
	T-561	Uruguayan Air Force				
	T-561/					
	CX/BHW	PLUNA			01/APR/75	Leased
	T-561/					
	CX-BHW	TAMU			01/FEB/77	
10203	PH-FDS	Fokker	200	07/JUN/62		
	LV-PTR	Austral	100			Not taken-up
	JA8608	Fujita Airlines	200		28/JUN/62	
	JA8608	All Nippon			01/NOV/63	
	PK-PFU	Pelita/Pertamina			01/DEC/71	
	F-GBRX	TAT			07/JUL/79	
	F-GBRX	Uni Air			DEC/79	
	F-GBRX	Air Comores			04/JAN/80	Leased
	D6-CAI	Air Comores			01/DEC/81	Purchased
10204	PH-FDT	Fokker	200	21/JUN/62		
	CR-AIA	DETA			06/JUL/62	
	C9-AIA	DETA			01/JAN/75	
	C9-AIA	Air Tanzania			21/MAY/77	Leased
	C9-AIA	DETA			31/DEC/77	
	C9-AIA	LAM			14/MAY/80	
	N379SL	Manufacturers Hanover			07/NOV/81	
	PT-LCF	Votec			08/MAR/82	
10205	PH-FDU	Fokker	200	05/JUL/62		
	CR-AIB	DETA			20/JUL/62	
	C9-AIB	DETA				W/O 27/MAR/70 Gaco Coutinho A/P
10206	PH-FDV	Fokker	200	20/JUL/62		
	CR-AIC	DETA			06/AUG/62	
	C9-AIC	DETA			01/JAN/75	
	C9-AIC	LAM			14/MAY/80	
	N379SF	Manufacturers Hanover			07/NOV/81	
	PT-LCG	Votec			MAR/82	
10207	PH-FDW	Fokker	200	31/JUL/62		
	CR-LEO	DETA			23/AUG/62	
	D2-LEO	TAAG Angola			01/NOV/73	
	D2-TEO	TAAG Angola			11/NOV/75	
	PH-FDW	Fokker			24/OCT/80	
	AP-BBF	PIA			28/AUG/81	
10208	PH-FDX	Fokker	200	29/AUG/62		
	CR-LEP	DTA			19/SEP/62	
	CR-LEP	TAAG Angola			01/NOV/73	
	9Q-CEB	Zaire Aero Service			SEP/76	WFU 79, scrapped AUG/82, N'dola Airport
10209	PH-FDY	Fokker	100	07/SEP/62		W/O 01/JUL/70, Dumaquette A/P, Philippines
	PI-C504	Philippine Airlines			25/SEP/62	
10210	PH-FDZ	Fokker	100	26/SEP/62		
	PI-C506	Philippine Airlines			09/OCT/62	
	10210	Philippine Air Force			30/OCT/71	
	10210	Philippine Air Force	200		05/MAY/79	Converted
10211	PH-FEA	Fokker	200	10/OCT/62		
	VP-KSA	East African Airways			23/OCT/62	
	5Y-AAB	East African Airways			01/JAN/64	
	5Y-AAB	Kenya Airways			31/JAN/77	
10212	PH-FEB	Fokker	200	23/OCT/62		
	VP-KSB	East African Airways			06/NOV/62	
	5Y-AAC	East African Airways			01/JAN/64	
	5Y-AAC	Air Tanzania			31/JAN/77	
	5H-AAC	Air Tanzania			01/MAR/78	
	5H-MRH	Air Tanzania			20/OCT/78	
	G-BMAW	British Midland Airways			81	Not taken-up
	G-BMAW	British Midland Airways			06/SEP/83	
10213	PH-FEC	Fokker	200	08/NOV/62		
	VP-KSC	East African Airways			16/NOV/62	
	5H-AAI	East African Airways			01/JAN/64	
	5H-AAI	Kenya Airways			31/JAN/77	
	5Y-BBS	Kenya Airways			01/OCT/77	
10214	PH-FED	Fokker	100	29/NOV/62		W/O 21/APR/69 Khulna, India
	VT-DOJ	Indian Airlines			14/DEC/62	
10215	PH-FEE	Fokker	100	10/DEC/62		
	VT-DOK	Indian Airlines			28/DEC/62	
10216	PH-FEF	Fokker	200	24/DEC/62		
	5N-AAV	Nigeria Airways			17/JAN/63	W/O 07/OCT/67, nr. Lagos.
10217	PH-FEG	Fokker	200	16/JAN/63		
	5N-AAW	Nigeria Airways			05/FEB/63	W/O 25/APR/77, Sokato
10218	PH-FEH	Fokker	200	28/JAN/63		
	5N-AAX	Nigeria Airways			12/FEB/63	W/O 04/APR/71, Jos Ap.
10219	PH-FEI	Fokker	100	06/FEB/63		
	VT-DOL	Indian Airlines			22/FEB/63	
10220	PH-FEK	Fokker	100	20/FEB/63		
	VT-DOM	Indian Airlines			08/MAR/63	
10221	PH-FEL	Fokker	100	06/MAR/63		
	VT-DON	Indian Airlines			25/MAR/63	
	CG-711	Indian Coast Guard			MAY/83	
10222	PH-FEM	Fokker	200	05/MAR/63		
	5N-AAY	Nigeria Airways			24/APR/63	
	5N-AAY	Ghana Airways			01/AUG/67	Leased
	5N-AAY	Nigeria Airways			01/AUG/71	
	5N-AAY	Avioleasing			28/JUL/80	
	5N-AAY	Fokker			04/AUG/80	
	PK-GRA	Garuda			16/JAN/81	
	PK-MFA	Merpati Nusantara			28/FEB/81	

FOKKER F-27 FRIENDSHIP

C/N	Registration	Owner/Operator	Series	First Flight	Delivery	Remarks
10223	PH-FEN	Fokker	200	05/APR/63		
	5N-AAZ	Nigerian Airways			01/MAY/63	
	5N-AAZ	Avioleasing			04/AUG/80	
	5N-AAZ	Fokker			28/JUL/80	
	PK-GRC	Garuda			27/MAR/81	
	PK-MFC	Merpati Nusantara			04/APR/81	
10224	PH-FEO	Fokker	100	10/APR/63		
	LX-LGA	Luxair			07/MAY/63	
10225	PH-FEP	Fokker	200	19/APR/63		
	9M-AMI	Malayan Airways			06/MAY/63	
	9V-BAP	Malaysian Singapore Airlines			01/JAN/67	
	PH-FEP	Fokker			17/OCT/71	
	G-BAUR	Air Anglia			09/APR/73	
	G-BAUR	Air UK			16/JAN/80	
	G-BAUR	British Midland Airways			03/MAR/82	Leased
	G-BAUR	Air UK			08/JAN/84	
	G-BAUR	British Midland Airways			FEB/84	
	G-BAUR	Air UK			SEP/84	
10226	PH-FER	Fokker	200	10/MAY/63		
	9M-AMJ	Malayan Airways			24/MAY/63	
	9M-AMJ	Malaysian Singapore Airlines			01/JAN/67	
	9M-AMJ	Fokker			23/MAY/72	
	PK-JFK	Sempati			25/MAY/72	
	PK-JFK	Royal Air Cambodge			04/JUL/72	Leased
	PK-JFK	Sempati			12/OCT/72	
10227	PH-FES	Fokker	200	22/MAY/63		
	JA8616	All Nippon			31/MAY/63	
	F-OCSH	Air Polynesie			31/MAR/72	
	F-BVTA	TAT	200		01/MAR/74	
	F-BVTA	Somali Airlines			01/NOV/75	Leased
	F-BVTA	TAT			27/FEB/76	
	F-BVTA	Somali Airlines			17/MAY/76	Leased
	F-BVTA	TAT			04/SEP/77	
	F-BVTA	Danish Aero Lease			21/DEC/80	
	G-BMAS	British Midland Airways			28/OCT/81	Leased
	G-BMAS	Danish Aero Lease			12/MAY/83	
	OY-BST	Danish Aero Lease			29/NOV/83	
	ZS-LMZ	Comair			09/DEC/83	
10228	PH-FET	All Nippon	200	06/JUN/63		
	JA8617	Fokker			19/JUN/63	
	F-BUFU	TAT	200		18/MAY/73	
	F-BUFU	TAF			29/MAY/73	Leased
	F-BUFU	TAT			01/JUL/75	
	F-BUFU	Air Senegal			27/MAR/77	Leased
	F-BUFU	TAT			18/JUL/77	
	6V-AEG	Air Senegal			21/JUL/77	
	6V-AEG	Air Alsace			MAR/80	
	F-GCMA	Air Alsace			01/APR/80	
	G-NRSY	Jersey European Airways			30/NOV/83	WFU 30/NOV/83, stored Norwich
	N267MA	Mesaba Airlines			MAY/84	
10229	PH-FEU	Fokker	200	21/JUN/63		
	JA8618	All Nippon			04/JUL/63	
	F-BUTA	TAT			31/JUL/73	
	F-OGIF	Air Guadeloupe			12/MAR/78	
	F-BSIF	TAT			17/FEB/80	
	G-BHMW	Air UK			10/SEP/80	
	G-BHMW	British Midland Airways			19/DEC/82	Leased
	G-BHMW	Air UK			01/OCT/83	
10230	PH-FEV	Fokker	200	05/JUL/63		
	JA8619	All Nippon			25/JUL/63	
	F-OCSI	Air Polynesie			24/MAY/72	
	F-BVTE	TAT	200		01/MAR/74	
	F-BVTE	Somali Airlines			01/SEP/75	Leased
	F-BVTE	TAT			21/MAY/76	
	AP-BAO	PIA			01/JUN/79	
	F-BVTE	TAT			01/JUN/79	Leased
	AP-BAO	PIA			01/AUG/79	
10231	PH-FEW	Fokker	200	19/JUL/63		
	9M-AML	Malayan Airways			08/AUG/63	
	9V-BAQ	Malaysian Singapore Airlines			01/JAN/67	
	9V-BAQ	Fokker			07/JUN/72	
	PK-KFG	Bouraq/Nusantara			10/JUN/72	
	PK-KFG	Bali International			21/MAY/74	
	G-BLGW	Air Anglia			21/APR/78	
	G-BLGW	Air UK			16/JAN/80	
	G-BLGW	British Midland Airways			01/APR/82	Leased
	G-BLGW	Air UK			APR/83	
	G-BLGW	Busy Bee			MAR/84	Leased
10232	PH-FEX	Fokker	200	15/AUG/63		
	9M-AMM	Malayan Airways			29/AUG/63	
	9M-AMM	Malaysian Singapore Airlines			01/JAN/67	
	PH-FEX	Fokker			04/MAY/71	
	S2-ABK	Bangladesh Biman			25/APR/73	
	G-BDVS	Air Anglia			24/MAR/76	
	G-BDVS	British Island Airways			12/MAR/79	Leased
	G-BDVS	Air Anglia			16/MAR/79	
	G-BDVS	Air UK			16/JAN/80	
	G-BDVS	British Midland Airways			01/JAN/80	Leased
	G-BDVS	Air UK			14/JAN/80	
10233	PH-FEY	Fokker	200	03/SEP/63		
	9M-AMN	Malayan Airways			12/SEP/63	
	9V-BAR	Malaysian Singapore Airlines			01/JAN/67	
	PH-EXD	Fokker			17/SEP/72	
	PH-FEY	Fokker			27/MAR/73	
	S2-ABL	Bangladesh Biman			11/MAY/73	
	G-BDVT	Air Anglia			19/APR/76	
	G-BDVT	British Midland Airways			05/OCT/79	Leased
	G-BDVT	Air Anglia			26/OCT/79	
	G-BDVT	Air UK			16/JAN/80	
	G-BDVT	British Midland Airways			83	Leased
	G-BDVT	Air UK			MAY/86	
	G-BDVT	Icelandair			MAY/86	Leased
10234	PH-FEZ	Fokker	200	12/SEP/63		
	JA8621	Fujita Airlines				Not taken-up
	JA8621	All Nippon Airways			02/OCT/63	

C/N	Registration	Owner/Operator	Series	First Flight	Delivery	Remarks
	PH-OGB	Limburg Airlines			11/AUG/73	
	G-BCDO	Air Anglia			31/MAY/74	
	G-BCDO	Air UK			14/JAN/80	
	G-BCDO	British Midland Airways			14/JAN/80	Leased
	G-BCDO	Air UK			28/JAN/80	
	G-BCDO	British Midland Airways			20/APR/83	Leased
	G-BCDO	Air UK			10/MAY/83	
10235	PH-FFA	Fokker	200	01/OCT/63		
	XY-ADK	Union of Burma Airways			10/OCT/63	
	XY-ADK	Burma Airways Corp.			01/MAY/72	W/O 25/MAR/78, Mingaladon Ap.
10236	PH-FFB	Fokker	200	14/OCT/63		
	XY-ADL	Union of Burma Airways			29/OCT/63	W/O 25/JUN/66, Moulmein, Burma
10237	PH-FFC	Fokker	200	02/NOV/63		
	XY-ADM	Union of Burma Airways			18/NOV/63	
	XY-ADM	Burma Airways Corp.			01/MAY/72	W/O 30/APR/74, Bassein, Burma
10238	PH-FFD	Fokker	200	14/NOV/63		
	ST-AAY	Sudan Airways			02/DEC/63	W/O 06/DEC/71, Southern Sudan
10239	PH-FFE	Fokker	200	25/NOV/63		
	HL5201	Korean Airlines			20/DEC/63	
	TF-FLS	Icelandair			12/JAN/80	
	OH-LKA	Finnair			25/APR/80	
10240	PH-FFF	Fokker	200	13/DEC/63		
	HL5202	Korean Airlines			03/JAN/64	
	TF-FLT	Icelandair			12/JAN/80	
	OH-LKB	Finnair			03/APR/80	
	TF-FLP	Icelandair			MAY/86	
10241	PH-FFG	Fokker	200	24/DEC/63		
	VP-KTK	East African Airways			16/JAN/64	
	5X-AAP	East African Airways			16/JAN/64	
	5X-AAP	Air Tanzania			31/JAN/77	
	5H-AAP	Air Tanzania			01/MAR/78	
	5H-MRO	Air Tanzania			20/OCT/78	
	G-BMAU	British Midland Airways			81	Not taken-up
	G-BMAU	British Midland Airways			05/OCT/83	
10242	PH-FFH	Fokker	200	07/JAN/64		
	JA8622	All Nippon			19/FEB/64	
	F-BUFA	TAT			16/FEB/73	
	F-BUFA	Air Senegal			03/DEC/76	Leased
	F-BUFA	TAT			29/MAR/77	WFU 80
	F-BUFA	Danish Aero Lease			22/APR/80	
	TZ-BAB	Esso Oil (Mali)			APR/80	Not taken-up
	F-BUFA	Danish Aero Lease			22/APR/80	
	9M-MCZ	Malaysian Airline System			07/MAY/80	Leased
	9M-MCZ	Danish Aero Lease			26/JUN/81	
	PK-JFN	Sempati Air Transport			01/JUL/81	Leased
10243	PH-FFI	Fokker	200	24/JAN/64		
	JA8623	All Nippon			26/FEB/64	
	F-BUFE	TAT			09/MAR/73	
	AP-BAL	PIA			26/JAN/79	
10244	PH-FFK	Fokker	200	20/JAN/64		
	JA8624	All Nippon	200		06/MAR/64	
	PK-PFV	Pelita/Pertamina			17/OCT/72	
	F-GBRV	TAT			08/JUN/79	
	G-BHMZ	Air UK			31/JUL/80	
10245	PH-FFL	Fokker	100	19/FEB/64		
	LN-SUE	Braathens Safe			06/MAR/64	
	LN-SUE	Fokker			27/JUN/69	
	LN-SUE	Braathens Safe			27/JUN/69	Leased
	LN-SUE	Braathens Safe			31/JUL/70	Purchased
	LN-SUE	Air Executive			25/OCT/75	
	LN-SUE	Busy Bee			01/SEP/80	
10246	PH-FFM	Fokker	100	04/MAR/64		
	PI-C507	Philippine Airlines			23/MAR/64	
	10246	Philippine Air Force			28/JUL/71	
	10246	Philippine Air Force	200VIP		18/JUN/81	Converted
10247	PH-FFN	Fokker	100	13/MAR/64		
	PI-C508	Philippine Airlines			07/APR/64	
	I-SARK	Alisarda			19/MAY/71	
	F-BVTO	TAT			02/DEC/74	
	F-OGIM	Air Martinique			16/MAR/78	
	F-BSIF	Air Alpes			18/MAR/80	
	F-BSIF	TAT			31/MAY/80	Leased
	F-BSIF	Air Alpes			31/JUL/80	
	F-BIUK	Uni Air			07/AUG/80	
10248	PH-FFO	Fokker	100	25/MAR/64		
		Braathens Safe				Not taken-up
	PH-SAF	Schreiner Airways			12/APR/64	Leased
	LN-SUL	Braathens Safe			12/APR/65	
	LN-SUL	Air Executive			15/FEB/77	
	LN-SUL	Busy Bee			01/SEP/80	
10249	PH-FFP	Fokker	200	09/APR/64		
		Alitalia				Not taken-up
		ATI			06/MAY/64	
	I-ATIM	ATI			16/JUN/67	Leased
	I-ATIM	KLA			01/SEP/69	Leased
	I-ATIM	Libyan Arab Airlines			19/DEC/69	
	I-ATIM	ATI			16/MAR/74	
	I-ATIM	NLM			13/MAY/74	
	PH-KFG	NLM				
10250	PH-FFR	Fokker	200	23/JUL/64		
		SATT				Not taken-up
	AP-ATO	PIA			13/AUG/64	W/O 17/DEC/78, Karachi Ap.
10251	PH-FFS	Fokker	200	08/MAY/64		
		Alitalia				Not taken-up
	I-ATIP	ATI			25/MAY/64	W/O 16/APR/72, nr. Fresinone, Italy
10252	PH-FFT	Fokker	200	21/MAY/64		
	JA8630	All Nippon Airways			03/JUN/64	
	VH-FNV	Ansett of South Australia			27/OCT/71	
	VH-FNV	Ansett Airlines of Australia			01/OCT/77	
	VH-FNV	Air Queensland			04/JAN/82	Leased
10253	PH-FFU	Fokker	200	04/JUN/64		
	JA8631	All Nippon Airways			17/JUN/64	
	VH-TFW	Trans Australia Airlines			12/MAY/72	
	PT-LDJ	Rio Sul			16/SEP/82	
10254	PH-FFV	Fokker	200	18/JUN/64		

FOKKER F-27 FRIENDSHIP

C/N	Registration	Owner/Operator	Series	First Flight	Delivery	Remarks
	JA8632	All Nippon Airways			01/JUL/64	
	VH-FNW	Ansett of South Australia			10/NOV/71	
	VH-FNW	Ansett Airlines of Australia			AUG/75	
	VH-FNW	Air Queensland			04/JAN/82	Leased
10255	PH-FFW	Fokker	200	03/JUL/64		
	JA8633	All Nippon Airways			15/JUL/64	
	TF-FIN	Icelandair			07/JUL/72	
	TF-FLN	Icelandair			21/SEP/79	
	TF-FLN	Libyan Arab Airlines			08/JAN/81	Leased
	TF-FLN	Icelandair			23/FEB/81	
	TF-FLN	Libyan Arab Airlines			DEC/81	Leased
	TF-FLN	Icelandair			14/JAN/82	
10256	PH-FFX	Fokker	200	16/JUL/64		
		Alitalia				Not taken-up
	I-ATIS	ATI			22/JUL/64	
	I-ATIS	KLA			15/JUN/66	Leased
	I-ATIS	Libyan Arab Airlines			01/SEP/69	Leased
	I-ATIS	ATI			19/DEC/69	
	PH-KFH	NLM			15/NOV/74	
	PH-KFH	British Midland Airways			25/OCT/81	Leased
	G-BMAE	British Midland Airways			01/NOV/82	Purchased
	G-BMAE	Loganair			MAY/86	Leased
10257	PH-FFY	Fokker	100	14/AUG/64		
	PI-C509	Philippine Airlines			27/AUG/64	
	I-SARQ	Alisarda			27/FEB/69	
	D-BOBY	Special Air Transport			13/MAR/78	
	D-BOBY	Lauda Air			15/FEB/79	
	OE-HLA	Lauda Air			25/APR/79	
	OE-HLA	Egyptair			12/DEC/81	Leased
	OE-HLA	Air Sinai			01/AUG/82	Leased
	OE-HLA	Lauda Air			14/APR/83	
	OE-HLA	Nile Delta Airlines			20/APR/83	
	OE-HLA	Lauda Air			NOV/83	
	OE-HLA	WDL			11/OCT/84	
	OE-HLA	Crossair			29/OCT/84	Leased
	OE-HLA	WDL			DEC/85	
	D-BAKE	WDL			86	
10258	PH-FFZ	Fokker	100	07/SEP/64		
	PI-C512	Philippine Airlines			28/SEP/64	
	VH-MMU	MacRobertson Miller Airlines			15/JAN/66	Leased
	PI-C512	Philippine Airlines			14/NOV/68	
	I-SARO	Alisarda			27/FEB/69	
	F-BVTU	TAT			19/DEC/74	
	F-OGJA	Air Martinique			17/JUN/79	Leased
	F-GCPA	TAT			17/APR/80	
	F-GCPA	Air Alsace			24/JUN/80	
	F-GCPA	Lauda Air			MAY/82	Leased
	F-GCPA	Air Alsace			AUG/82	
	F-GCPA	TAT			15/AUG/82	
	LN-NPC	Busy Bee			22/APR/83	
10259	PH-FGA	Fokker	200	10/SEP/64		
	JA8634	All Nippon			18/SEP/64	
	F-BUFO	TAT			11/APR/73	
	F-BUFO	Air France			24/APR/73	Leased
	F-BUFO	TAT			MAR/76	
	F-BUFO	Air Rouergue			10/APR/76	Leased
	F-BUFO	TAT			25/FEB/77	
	G-BHMX	Air UK			17/JUL/80	
10260	PH-FGB	Fokker	200	25/SEP/64		
	JA8635	All Nippon			20/OCT/64	
	TF-SYR	Icelandic Coastguard			13/MAY/72	
	ST-	Kenana Sugar Corp.				Not taken-up
	TF-FLS	Icelandair			08/DEC/80	
	TF-FLS	Libyan Arab Airlines			06/FEB/81	Leased
	TF-FLS	Icelandair			01/JUN/82	
	OH-LKC	Finnair			30/JUN/82	
10261	PH-FGC	Fokker	200	08/OCT/64		
	JA8636	All Nippon			03/NOV/64	
	JA8636	Air Niugini			29/NOV/74	
	P2-BNF	Air Niugini			01/JAN/75	
	P2-ANF	Air Niugini			01/NOV/75	
	TG-AOA	Aviateca			06/APR/78	
		Guatemalan Air Force			01/JAN/83	
		Guatemalan Air Force	600		SEP/84	Converted
10262	PH-FGD	Fokker	200	26/OCT/64		
	JA8637	All Nippon			17/NOV/64	
	ZK-DCG	New Zealand DCA			28/FEB/72	
	ZK-DCG	Air New Zealand			01/DEC/79	
	ZK-DCG	New Zealand DCA			06/MAY/80	Leased
	ZK-DCG	Mount Cook Airlines			18/SEP/81	Leased
	ZK-DCG	New Zealand DCA			NOV/81	
	AP-BBG	PIA			18/JAN/82	
	10262	Pakistan Navy			18/JAN/82	Leased
	PN-62	Pakistan Navy	200MAR		SEP/85	Converted
10263	PH-FGE	Fokker	200	09/NOV/64		
	JA8638	All Nippon			01/DEC/64	
	TF-FIM	Icelandair			24/MAY/72	
	TF-FLM	Icelandair			15/SEP/79	
	TF-FLM	Libyan Arab Airlines			14/DEC/80	Leased
	TF-FLM	Icelandair			DEC/81	
10264	PH-FGF	Fokker	200	25/NOV/64		
	VH-FNJ	Ansett Airlines of NSW			01/DEC/64	
	VH-FNJ	Ansett Airlines of Australia			01/FEB/71	
	VH-FNJ	Ansett of South Australia			30/JUN/76	Leased
	VH-FNJ	Ansett Airlines of Australia			24/JUL/77	
	ZS-KVJ	Comair			26/NOV/80	
10265	PH-FGG	Fokker	100	14/DEC/64		
	PI-C514	Philippine Airlines			11/JAN/65	
	10265	Philippine Air Force			13/NOV/71	WFU, stored Manila
10266	PH-FGH	Fokker	100	24/DEC/64		
	VH-EWG	East West Airlines			05/JAN/65	
	LN-NPI	Air Executive			21/OCT/78	
	LN-NPI	Busy Bee			01/SEP/80	
10267	PH-FGI	Fokker	100	02/FEB/65		
	PI-C516	Philippine Airlines			09/FEB/65	

C/N	Registration	Owner/Operator	Series	First Flight	Delivery	Remarks
	10267	Philippine Air Force			11/AUG/71	
	10267	Philippine Air Force	200	09/MAR/79	05/MAR/79	Converted
10268	PH-FGK	Fokker	400	25/JAN/65		
	D-BARI	Condor			02/FEB/65	
	PH-ARI	Fokker			05/JUN/68	
	PH-ARI	Air Congo			07/JUN/68	Leased
	PH-ARI	Fokker			06/AUG/69	
	F-BRQL	Euralair			15/OCT/69	
	HB-AAZ	Balair			26/JUN/73	Op. by United Nations
10269	PH-FGL	Fokker	100	17/FEB/65		
	LX-LGB	Luxair			26/FEB/65	
10270	PH-FGM	Fokker	400	23/FEB/65		
	D-BARO	Condor			05/MAR/65	
	PH-ARO	Fokker			08/JUN/68	
	PH-ARO	Air Congo			22/AUG/68	Leased
	PH-ARO	Fokker			08/MAY/69	
	PH-ARO	ATI			25/JUL/69	Leased
	PH-ARO	Fokker			27/NOV/69	
	PH-ARO	Linair			30/DEC/69	Leased
	PH-ARO	Fokker			30/MAR/70	
	PH-ARO	Lina Congo			02/APR/70	Leased
	PH-ARO	Fokker			02/JUN/70	
	PH-ARO	Linair			04/JUN/70	Leased
	PH-ARO	Fokker			11/NOV/76	
	PH-ARO	Air Anglia			13/NOV/76	Leased
	G-BFDS	Air Anglia			25/OCT/77	
	G-BFDS	BIAS			26/OCT/77	
	G-BFDS	Air Anglia			26/OCT/77	
	PH-ARO	BIAS			30/NOV/78	Leased
	PH-ARO	NLM			01/DEC/78	Leased
	PH-ARO	Danish Aero Lease			23/DEC/80	
	PK-JFM	Sempati			20/FEB/81	Leased
	PK-JFM	Danish Aero Lease			03/NOV/83	
	TG-ACA	Guatemalan Air Force			JAN/85	
	1467	Guatemalan Air Force			MAR/85	
10271	PH-FGN	Fokker	200	22/MAR/65	02/APR/65	
	PH-SAB	Schreiner Airways			04/JAN/66	W/O 02/FEB/66, Kashmir
	PH-SAB	Indian Airlines	200	26/MAR/65		
10272	PH-FGO	Fokker			05/APR/65	
	PH-SAD	Schreiner Airways			01/DEC/67	
	PH-SAD	KLM			19/SEP/68	Leased
	PH-SAD	Fokker			21/SEP/68	Sub-leased
	PH-SAD	Euralair			02/NOV/68	
	PH-SAD	Fokker			04/NOV/68	
	PH-SAD	KLM			01/JAN/72	
10273	PH-FGP	Fokker	400M	24/APR/65		
	833	Sudan Air Force			07/MAY/65	
	ST-ADX	Sudan Airways	400		15/AUG/70	W/O 11/MAY/72, El Obeid, Sudan
10274	PH-FGR	Fokker	100	26/APR/65		
	TF-FIJ	Icelandair			04/MAY/65	
	TF-FIJ	Icelandair			18/SEP/79	
	OH-KFA	Kar Air			17/MAR/80	
	FF-2	Finnish Air Force			15/JUN/80	Leased
10275	PH-FGS	Fokker	400	20/MAY/65		
	N10625	Oasis Oil			25/MAY/65	
	5A-DBE	Oasis Oil			16/APR/74	
	5A-DBE	Libyan Arab Airlines			29/NOV/76	W/O 28/NOV/81, Chad
10276	PH-FGT	Fokker	200	03/JUN/65		
	HB-AAV	Balair			11/JUN/65	
	PH-KFD	NLM			07/MAR/72	
10277	PH-FGU	Fokker	400M	21/JUN/65		
	844	Sudan Air Force			28/JUN/65	
	ST-ADY	Sudan Airways	400		15/AUG/70	W/O 16/AUG/86, nr. Malaktal, Southern Sudan
10278	PH-FGV	Fokker	200	30/JUN/65		
	AP-ATU	PIA			08/JUL/65	
10279	PH-FGW	Fokker	200	09/JUL/65		
	AP-ATT	PIA			23/JUL/65	W/O 08/OCT/65, Azad-Kashmir bdr.
10280	PH-FGX	Fokker	200	23/JUL/65		
	VH-FNK	Ansett Airlines			09/AUG/65	
	VH-FNK	Ansett Airlines of PNG			01/SEP/69	Leased
	VH-FNK	Air Niugini			01/NOV/73	Leased
	P2-ANL	Air Niugini			01/JUL/76	Purchased
	LX-LGJ	Luxair			23/JUN/84	
10281	PH-FGY	Fokker	200	10/SEP/66		
	AP-ATW	DGCA of Pakistan			29/SEP/65	
	J-752	Pakistan Air Force			76	
10282	PH-FGZ	Fokker	400M	03/SEP/65		
	888	Sudan Air Force			20/SEP/65	
	ST-ADW	Sudan Airways	400		15/AUG/70	W/O 06/JUN/77, El Fasher, Sudan
10283	PH-FIA	Fokker	400M	04/OCT/65	11/OCT/65	
	899	Sudan Air Force				W/O 10/NOV/69, Sudan border
10284	PH-FIB	Fokker	200	27/SEP/65	11/OCT/65	
	VH-TFL	Trans Australia Airlines			70	
	VH-TFL	Trans Australia of NG			13/JUL/73	
	VH-TFL	Trans Australia Airlines			03/DEC/81	
	VH-TFL	East West Airlines			OCT/84	
	VH-TFL	Fokker			08/NOV/85	
	PH-FIB	Fokker			14/NOV/85	
	N268MA	Mesaba Airlines				
10285	PH-FIC	Fokker	100	13/OCT/65	26/OCT/65	W/O 06/JUL/67, Bacolod Philippines
	PI-C527	Philippine Airlines				
10286	PH-FID	Fokker	100	02/NOV/65	09/NOV/65	
	ZK-BXI	National Airways Corp.			01/APR/78	
	ZK-BXI	Air New Zealand				
10287	PH-FIE	Fokker	100	06/NOV/65	12/NOV/65	
	VH-EWJ	East West Airlines			09/JUL/81	
	LN-NPM	Busy Bee				
10288	PH-FIF	Fokker	200	24/NOV/65	03/DEC/65	
	I-ATIG	ATI			06/APR/73	
	AP-AXB	PIA				
10289	PH-FIG	Fokker	200	10/DEC/65	15/DEC/65	
	I-ATIB	ATI				

FOKKER F-27 FRIENDSHIP

C/N	Registration	Owner/Operator	Series	First Flight	Delivery	Remarks
	I-ATIB	KLA			01/NOV/68	Leased
	I-ATIB	ATI			MAR/70	
	LN-DAF	Air Services Ibis				Not taken-up
	LN-DAF	Air Anglia			17/APR/75	
	G-BDDH	Air Anglia			01/MAY/75	
	G-BDDH	Air UK			16/JAN/80	
	G-BDDH	British Midland			01/APR/82	Leased
	G-BDDH	Air UK			15/FEB/84	
10290	PH-FIH	Fokker	200	27/DEC/65		
	9N-AAR	Royal Nepal Airlines			20/JAN/66	W/O 25/JAN/70, nr. Delhi
10291	PH-FII	Fokker	200	10/DEC/65		
	VH-FNL	Ansett Airlines			16/DEC/65	
	VH-FNL	MacRobertson Miller Airlines			22/JUN/66	Leased
	VH-FNL	Ansett Airlines			06/JUN/66	
	P2-ANI	Air Niugini			15/JAN/76	
	PT-LCZ	Rio Sul			05/FEB/82	W/O AUG/84, Rio De Janeiro
10292	PH-FIK	Fokker	200	10/JAN/66		
	VH-FNM	Ansett Airlines			14/JAN/66	
	VH-FNM	Ansett Airlines of PNG			67	Leased
	VH-FNM	Ansett Airlines of Australia			01/NOV/73	
	VH-FNM	Bush Pilots Airways			25/OCT/80	Leased
	VH-FNM	Air Queensland			04/JAN/82	Leased
10293	PH-FIL	Fokker	200	25/JAN/66		
	9M-AOJ	Malayan Airways			28/JAN/68	
	9M-AOJ	Malaysian Singapore Airlines			01/JAN/67	
	PH-FIL	Fokker			24/MAY/72	
	PH-FIL	Air Anglia			26/MAY/72	Leased
	G-BAKL	Air Anglia			31/OCT/72	Purchased
	G-BAKL	Air UK			16/JAN/80	
	G-BAKL	British Midland Airways			30/OCT/82	Leased
	G-BAKL	Air UK			19/DEC/82	
10294	PH-FIN	Fokker	400	09/FEB/66		
	N710A	Aramco			15/FEB/66	
	PH-SFA	Schreiner Airways			02/MAY/86	
10295	PH-FIO	Fokker	400	25/FEB/66		
	N714A	Aramco			03/MAR/66	
	PH-SFB	Schreiner Airways			01/AUG/86	
10296	PH-FIP	Fokker	100	09/MAR/66		
	PI-C528	Philippine Airlines			28/MAR/66	
	10296	Philippine Air Force			20/NOV/71	
	10296	Philippine Air Force	200VIP		06/DEC/79	Converted
10297	PH-FIR	Fokker	200	25/MAR/66		
	VH-FNN	Queensland Airlines			31/MAR/66	
	VH-FNN	Ansett Airlines			28/NOV/66	
	VH-FNN	Ansett Airlines of PNG			01/JUL/68	
	P2-ANM	Air Niugini			01/NOV/73	Leased
	LX-LGK	Luxair			01/JUL/76	Purchased
					23/JUN/84	
10298	PH-FIS	Fokker	100	05/APR/66		
	LN-SUF	Braathens Safe				Not taken-up
	PH-SAN	Schreiner Airways			14/APR/66	Leased
	LN-SUF	Braathens Safe			28/SEP/66	
	LN-SUF	Air Executive			03/APR/76	
	LN-SUF	Busy Bee			18/JUL/80	
10299	PH-FIT	Fokker	400	16/MAY/66		
	PK-PFA	Pelita/Pertamina			15/JUN/66	
	PK-MFT	Merpati Nusantara			JAN/86	
10300	PH-FIU	Fokker	100	24/MAY/66		
	TF-FIK	Icelandair			27/MAY/66	
	TF-FLK	Icelandair			18/SEP/79	
	TF-FLK	Kar Air			17/MAR/80	
	OH-KLC	Kar Air			17/MAR/80	
	FF-1	Finnish Air Force			15/JUN/80	Leased
10301	PH-FIV	Fokker	200	27/APR/66		
	I-ATIR	ATI			29/APR/66	W/O 30/OCT/72, nr. Bari, Italy
10302	PH-FIW	Fokker	200	20/JUN/66		
	VT-DUT	Indian Airlines			01/JUL/66	
	9N-AAS	Royal Nepal Airlines			16/DEC/67	Leased
	VT-DUT	Indian Airlines			18/JAN/68	
	9N-AAW	Royal Nepal Airlines			11/FEB/70	Leased
	VT-DUT	Indian Airlines			11/MAR/70	
	S2-ABF	Bangladesh Biman			03/MAR/72	
	G-BMAP	British Midland Airways			20/NOV/82	
	G-BMAP	Loganair			21/MAY/86	Damaged 27/MAY/86, WFU Manchester
10303	PH-FIX	Fokker	200	14/JUL/66		
	VH-MMR	MacRobertson Miller Airlines			19/JUL/66	
	VH-MMR	Ansett Airlines of NSW			01/JUN/69	
	VH-MMR	Ansett Airlines of Australia			01/OCT/77	
	VH-MMR	Ansett of South Australia			01/OCT/77	
	VH-MMR	Airlines of South Australia			01/JUL/81	
	VH-MMR	Ansett Airlines of Australia			APR/86	
10304	PH-FIY	Fokker	600	02/AUG/66		
	VH-FNO	Ansett of South Australia			05/AUG/66	
	VH-FNO	Ansett Airlines of Australia			17/APR/68	
	VH-FNO	MacRobertson Miller Airlines			14/MAR/76	
	VH-FNO	Ansett Airlines of Australia			04/SEP/76	
	VH-FNO	MacRobertson Miller Airlines			17/MAY/78	Leased
	VH-FNO	Ansett Airlines of Australia			26/DEC/80	
	VH-FNO	Airlines of North Australia			OCT/81	
	VH-FNO	Ansett Airlines of Australia			MAY/86	
10305	PH-FIZ	Fokker	200	17/AUG/66		
	VH-FNP	Ansett Airlines of NSW			23/AUG/66	
	VH-FNP	Ansett of South Australia			23/JUL/77	
	VH-FNP	Airlines of South Australia			01/JUL/81	
	VH-FNP	Ansett Airlines of Australia			MAY/86	
10306	PH-FKA	Fokker	400	25/AUG/66		
	PK-PFB	Pelita/Pertamina			29/DEC/66	W/O 27/APR/67, Malaybalay
10307	PH-FKB	Fokker	200	12/SEP/66		
	AP-AUR	PIA			24/SEP/66	
	AP-AUR	Libyan Arab Airlines			01/JUL/72	Leased
	AP-AUR	PIA			01/MAY/76	
10308	PH-FKC	Fokker	200	26/SEP/66		

C/N	Registration	Owner/Operator	Series	First Flight	Delivery	Remarks
	VT-DVF	Indian Airlines			10/OCT/66	
	9N-AAT	Royal Nepal Airlines			28/SEP/69	Leased
	VT-DVF	Indian Airlines			24/OCT/69	
	S2-ABG	Bangladesh Biman			07/MAR/72	W/O 18/NOV/79, Savar Bazar, Bangladesh
10309	PH-FKD	Fokker	200	11/OCT/66		
	VT-DVG	Indian Airlines			19/OCT/66	W/O 07/JUN/70, Agartala, India
10310	PH-FKE	Fokker	100	17/OCT/66		
	PI-C531	Philippine Airlines			08/DEC/66	
	10310	Philippine Air Force			28/JUL/71	
	10310	Philippine Air Force	200		23/JAN/79	Converted
10311	PH-FKF	Fokker	100	27/OCT/66		
	PI-C532	Philippine Airlines			12/JAN/67	W/O 09/MAY/70, Lligan Ap.
10312	PH-FKG	Fokker	400	08/NOV/66		
	XY-ADN	Union of Burma Airways			05/DEC/66	
	XY-ADN	Burma Airways Corp.			01/MAY/72	W/O JUN/81, Sandoway
10313	PH-FKH	Fokker	400	23/NOV/66		
	XY-ADO	Union of Burma Airways			15/DEC/66	
	XY-ADO	Burma Airways Corp.			01/MAY/72	W/O 19/AUG/80, Moulmein Ap. Burma.
10314	PH-FKI	Fokker	600	02/DEC/66		
	AP-AUS	PIA			16/DEC/66	W/O 08/DEC/72, Nr. Jalkot, Pakistan
10315	PH-FKK	Fokker	600	03/DEC/66		
	VH-FNQ	Ansett Airlines of Australia			16/DEC/66	
10316	PH-FKL	Fokker	600	28/DEC/66		
	G-AVDN	Gulf Aviation			06/JAN/67	
	G-AVDN	Gulf Air			01/JAN/74	
	A40-FN	Gulf Air			01/OCT/75	
	A40-FN	Oman Aviation Services			01/JUN/81	
	HL5262	Korean Air Lines			10/JUL/82	Leased
	A40-FN	Oman Aviation Services			10/JUL/85	
10317	PH-FKM	Fokker	600	09/JAN/67		
	VH-FNR	Ansett MAL			17/JAN/67	
	VH-FNR	Ansett-ANA			30/JAN/67	
	VH-FNR	Ansett Airlines of Australia			01/JUN/69	
	VH-FNR	Airlines of South Australia			13/JUL/82	
10318	PH-FKN	Fokker	600	19/JAN/67		
	VH-FNS	Ansett MAL			26/JAN/67	
	VH-FNS	Ansett ANA			08/FEB/67	
	VH-FNS	Ansett Airlines of Australia			01/JUN/69	
	P2-ANS	Air Niugini			27/JUL/77	
	G-BLMM	Air UK			JUL/84	
	OY-CCK	Alkair			23/OCT/85	
10319	PH-FKO	Fokker	100	09/FEB/67		
	VH-EWK	East West Airlines			17/FEB/67	
	VH-EWK	Wards Air Freight			04/MAR/80	Leased
	VH-EWK	East West Airlines			01/APR/80	
	VH-EWK	Fokker			03/DEC/83	
	PH-FKO	Fokker			27/MAR/84	
	LN-NPD	Busy Bee			06/APR/84	
10320	PH-FKP	Fokker	200	26/JAN/67		
	I-ATID	ATI			30/JAN/67	
	F-SEBF	Cen.Nat.Et.Tel.			16/MAR/74	
10321	PH-FKR	Fokker	200	20/FEB/67		
	I-ATIF	ATI			22/FEB/67	
	LN-RNX	SAS			MAY/86	
10322	PH-FKS	Fokker	600	03/MAR/67		
	VH-FNT	Ansett ANA			09/MAR/67	
	VH-FNT	Ansett Airlines of Australia			01/JUN/69	
10323	PH-FKT	Fokker	600	15/MAR/67		
	HB-AAW	Balair			23/MAR/67	
	G-AZFD	Gulf Aviation			01/OCT/71	
	G-AZFD	Gulf Air			01/JAN/74	
	A40-FD	Gulf Air			01/OCT/75	
	A40-FD	Oman Aviation Services			01/JUN/81	
	PH-FKT	Fokker			17/APR/83	
	PH-FKT	XP Express Parcel Systems			14/MAY/83	Leased
	PH-FKT	XP Express Parcel Systems			27/DEC/85	Purchased
10324	PH-FKU	Fokker	200	22/MAR/67		
	I-ATIL	ATI			28/MAR/67	
	OO-PSF	Cie Europeene des Recherches			03/JAN/77	
	F-GCMR	Aig Alsace			06/JUN/80	
	G-JRSY	Jersey European Airways			AUG/83	
	N266MA	Mesaba Airlines			MAR/84	
10325	PH-FKV	Fokker	600	06/APR/67		
	PH-SAR	Schreiner Airways			18/APR/67	
	PH-SAR	KLM			01/DEC/67	
	G-AWFU	Gulf Aviation			03/APR/68	
	G-AWFU	Gulf Air			01/JAN/74	
	A40-FU	Gulf Air			01/OCT/75	
	A40-FU	Malaysian Airline System			21/JUL/79	Leased
	A40-FU	Oman Aviation Services			22/OCT/81	
	PH-SAR	Fokker			05/APR/83	
	PH-SAR	Air Sinai			22/APR/83	Leased
	PH-SAR	Fokker			12/DEC/83	
	XY-AEK	Burma Airways			31/MAY/84	
10326	PH-FKW	Fokker	200	19/APR/67		
	CR-LIJ	DTA			25/APR/67	
	CR-LIJ	TAAG Angola			01/JAN/73	
	D2-LIJ	TAAG Angola			11/NOV/75	
	D2-TIJ	TAAG Angola			01/SEP/76	
	PH-FKW	Fokker			24/OCT/80	
	PT-LAI	TAM			21/SEP/81	
10327	PH-FKX	Fokker	100	27/APR/67		
	PI-C534	Philippine Airlines			24/JUL/67	
	10327	Philippine Air Force			06/SEP/71	
	10327	Philippine Air Force	200		05/DEC/80	Converted
10328	PH-FKY	Fokker	100	10/MAY/67		
	PI-C536	Philippine Airlines			04/SEP/67	
	10328	Philippine Air Force			01/OCT/71	
	10328	Philippine Air Force	200VIP		01/DEC/77	Converted W/O 14/SEP/78, Nr. Manila Ap.
10329	PH-FKZ	Fokker	600	26/MAY/67		
	VH-TFM	Trans Australia Airlines			13/JUN/67	

FOKKER F-27 FRIENDSHIP

C/N	Registration	Owner/Operator	Series	First Flight	Delivery	Remarks
	VH-TFM	Trans Australia of NG			JUL/70	
	VH-TFM	Trans Australia Airlines			73	WFU 17/JUL/82, stored Brisbane
	SE-IRF	SAS			DEC/84	
10330	PH-FLA	Fokker	200	02/JUN/67		
	AP-AUV	PIA			14/JUN/67	W/O 30/DEC/70, Shamshernagar, Pakistan
10331	PH-FLB	Fokker	200	14/JUN/67		
	AP-AUW	PIA			27/JUN/67	W/O 28/MAY/73, Risalewala, Pakistan
10332	PH-FLC	Fokker	600	22/JUN/67		
	EC-BMS	Iberia			29/SEP/67	
	EC-BMS	Transeuropa			20/APR/81	
	EC-BMS	Aviaco			01/MAR/82	
10333	PH-FLD	Fokker	600	25/SEP/67		
	F-BOOC	Air France			13/OCT/67	Leased
	F-BOOC	Air France			01/MAR/68	Purchased
	PH-FLD	Fokker			03/APR/69	
	PH-FLD	Euralair			17/JUN/69	Leased
	PH-FLD	Fokker			17/OCT/69	
	A2-ZEW	Air Botswana			24/OCT/69	Leased
	A2-ZEW	Fokker			15/JAN/71	
	A2-ZEW	Air Botswana			24/JAN/74	
	A2-ZEW	Indian Airlines			02/JUN/71	
	VT-EBJ	Indian Airlines			01/JUL/71	
	VT-EBJ	Vayudoot			21/JAN/81	Leased
	VT-EBJ	Indian Airlines			SEP/81	
	VT-EBJ	Indian Navy			SEP/81	Leased
	VT-EBJ	Indian Airlines			82	
	VT-EBJ	Vayudoot			30/APR/83	Leased
10334	PH-FLE	Fokker	600	04/OCT/67		
	F-BOOD	Air France			24/OCT/67	Leased
	F-BOOD	Air France			01/MAR/68	Purchased
	PH-EXC	Fokker			02/JUL/70	
	VH-FNU	Ansett Airlines of Australia			05/AUG/70	
	VH-FNU	Air Nauru			DEC/71	Leased
	VH-FNU	Ansett Airlines of Australia			72	
	VH-FNU	Air Pacific			APR/84	Leased
	VH-FNU	Ansett Airlines of Australia			SEP/84	
	VH-FNU	Air Queensland			OCT/84	Leased
	VH-FNU	Ansett Airlines of Australia			AUG/85	
10335	PH-FLF	Fokker	600	24/JUL/67		
	AP-AUX	PIA			16/AUG/67	
	AP-AUX	Libyan Arab Airlines			01/JUL/72	Leased
	AP-AUX	PIA			01/MAY/76	
10336	PH-FLG	Fokker	400	10/AUG/67		
	VT-DWT	Indian Airlines			28/AUG/67	W/O Assam, India
10337	PH-FLH	Fokker	400	22/AUG/67		
	VT-DWU	Indian Airlines			06/SEP/67	
	VT-DWU	Vayudoot			21/JAN/81	Leased
	VT-DWU	Indian Airlines			SEP/81	
	VT-DWU	Vayudoot			JUL/82	Leased
10338	PH-FLI	Fokker	600	06/SEP/67		
	LX-LGD	Luxair			30/SEP/67	
10339	PH-FLK	Fokker	400	18/OCT/67		
		Garuda				Not taken-up
	PK-PFC	Pelita/Pertamina	400		13/NOV/67	W/O 13/OCT/80, Misool Island
10340	PH-FLL	Fokker	400	11/OCT/67		
		Garuda				Not taken-up
	OO-SBP	Sobelair			15/APR/68	
	OO-SBP	BIAS			15/APR/68	Leased
	OO-SBP	Sobelair			25/APR/68	
	OO-SBP	BIAS			01/MAY/73	Leased
	OO-SBP	Fokker			15/JUN/65	
	OO-SBP	Air Alpes			01/OCT/75	Leased
	F-BYAA	Air Alpes			22/DEC/78	
	F-BYAA	Air Alsace			25/FEB/81	
	F-BYAA	TAT			15/AUG/82	
	A2-AEC	Air Botswana			06/AUG/83	
10341	PH-FLM	Fokker	500	15/NOV/67		Proto.Mk 500
		Luxair				Not taken-up
	OY-STO	Sterling			16/MAY/68	
	OY-STO	Fokker			21/JAN/70	Leased
	OY-STO	Sterling			15/FEB/70	
	OY-STO	Gulf Aviation			15/JAN/73	Leased
	OY-STO	Sterling			01/MAY/73	
	VH-EWO	East West Airlines			03/OCT/73	
	PH-EXM	Fokker			17/NOV/83	
	N272FA	Mississippi Valley Airlines			31/MAY/84	
	N272FA	Air Wisconsin			MAY/85	
	PT-	TAM			APR/86	
10342	PH-FLN	Fokker	600	18/OCT/67		
		Faroe Airways				Not taken-up
	OY-DNF	Danish Aero Lease			29/NOV/68	
	OY-DNF	BIAS/Linair			29/NOV/68	Leased
	PH-FLN	BIAS/Linair			01/MAY/74	Leased
	OO-HLN	Danish Aero Lease				
	OO-HLN	Air Alpes			11/MAY/76	Leased
	F-BYAB	Air Alpes			21/DEC/76	
	F-BYAB	Air Alsace			15/APR/81	Purchased
	F-BYAB	Torraine Air Transport			15/AUG/82	
	F-BYAB	Air Jet			FEB/84	
10343	PH-FLO	Fokker	600	24/OCT/67		
	EC-BMT	Iberia			27/NOV/67	
	EC-BMT	Aviaco			01/APR/74	Leased
	EC-BMT	Iberia			15/OCT/74	
	EC-BMT	Transeuropa			08/MAY/81	
	EC-BMT	Aviaco			01/MAR/82	
10344	PH-FLP	Fokker	100	03/NOV/67		
	VH-EWL	East West Airlines			10/NOV/67	W/O 31/MAY/74, nr. Bathurst
10345	PH-FLR	Fokker	600	16/NOV/67		
		Indian Airlines				Not taken-up
	T-80	Argentine Air Force			12/AUG/68	Leased
	T-80	Argentine Air Force			15/SEP/69	Purchased
	T-41	Argentine Air Force			01/FEB/70	
10346	PH-FLS	Fokker	600	27/NOV/67		

C/N	Registration	Owner/Operator	Series	First Flight	Delivery	Remarks
		Indian Airlines				Not taken-up
	T-79	Argentine Air Force			05/AUG/68	Leased
	T-79	Argentine Air Force			15/SEP/69	Purchased
	T-42	Argentine Air Force			01/FEB/70	
10347	PH-FLT	Fokker	600	04/DEC/67		
	EC-BMU	Iberia			15/JAN/68	
	EC-BMU	Transeuropa			81	
	EC-BMU	Aviaco			NOV/81	
10348	PH-FLU	Fokker	600	11/DEC/67		
	EC-BOA	Iberia			23/JAN/68	
	EC-BOA	Transeuropa			30/OCT/79	
	EC-BOA	Aviaco			01/NOV/81	
10349	PH-FLV	Fokker	600	19/DEC/67		
	I-ATIC	ATI			24/JAN/68	
	I-ATIC	Fokker			27/JAN/70	Leased
	I-ATIC	ATI			19/FEB/70	
	SE-ITH	SAS			OCT/85	
10350	PH-FLW	Fokker	600	04/JAN/68		
	I-ATIN	ATI			24/JAN/68	
	SE-ITI	SAS			JAN/86	
10351	PH-FLX	Fokker	600	16/JAN/68		
	HB-AAX	Balair			30/JAN/68	
	PH-KFE	NLM			08/FEB/72	
10352	PH-FLY	Fokker	600	26/JAN/68		
	EC-BOB	Iberia			28/FEB/68	
	EC-BOB	Transeuropa			16/MAY/81	
	EC-BOB	Aviaco			01/MAR/82	
10353	PH-FLZ	Fokker	600	01/FEB/68		
	EC-BOC	Iberia			15/MAR/68	
	EC-BOC	Transeuropa			30/OCT/79	
	EC-BOC	Aviaco			NOV/81	
10354	PH-FMA	Fokker	600	09/FEB/68		
	JY-ADF	Alia			28/FEB/68	Leased
	5N-CLN	Nigerian Airways			22/NOV/68	Leased
	PH-FMA	Fokker			28/FEB/69	
	PH-FMA	Alia			12/APR/69	
	PH-FMA	BIAS			21/MAY/69	Leased
	PH-FMA	Alia			03/AUG/69	
	OO-SCA	Sabena			05/AUG/69	
	AP-AXF	PIA			06/JUL/73	W/O 06/JUN/81, Gilgit Ap.
10355	PH-FMB	Fokker	200	19/FEB/68		
	VH-MMV	MacRobertson Miller Airlines			01/MAR/68	
	VH-MMV	Ansett Airlines of NSW			70	
	VH-MMV	Ansett of South Australia			01/OCT/77	
	VH-MMV	Airlines of South Australia			01/JUL/81	
10356	PH-FMC	Fokker	300	04/MAR/68		
	TF-FIL	Icelandair			05/APR/68	W/O 26/SEP/70, Mygganaes
10357	PH-FMD	Fokker	200	11/MAR/68		
	XY-ADP	Union of Burma Airways			26/MAR/68	
	XY-ADP	Burma Airways Corp.			01/MAY/72	
10358	PH-FME	Fokker	200	20/MAR/68		
	9V-BBF	Malaysian Singapore Airlines			02/APR/68	
	9V-BBF	Fokker			06/NOV/71	
	CR-LMU	DTA			29/NOV/72	
	CR-LMU	TAAG Angola			01/NOV/73	
	VQ-GAC	Pearl Air			NOV/75	Leased
	9Q-CPC	Zaire Aero Services			DEC/75	
10359	PH-FMF	Fokker	200	29/MAR/68		
	9M-AOX	Malaysian Singapore Airlines			11/APR/68	
	9M-AOX	Fokker			02/JUL/71	
	CR-LMV	DTA			29/NOV/72	
	CR-LMV	TAAG Angola			JAN/74	
	9Q-CPI	Zaire Aero Services			SEP/76	
	9Q-CPI	DIPAL			77	Leased, WFU
10360	PH-FMG	Fokker	600	04/APR/68		
	EC-BOD	Iberia			10/MAY/68	W/O 05/JAN/70, Santa Cruz Canary Islands
10361	PH-FMH	Fokker	600	16/APR/68		
	EC-BOE	Iberia			16/MAY/68	
	F-GCJV	Air Alpes			15/MAR/80	
	F-GCJV	Air Jet			03/DEC/80	
10362	PH-FMI	Fokker	600	02/MAY/68		
	PK-CFD	Caltex Pacific			10/MAY/68	
	PK-JFI	Sempati Air Transport			JAN/86	
10363	PH-FMK	Fokker	600	08/MAY/68		
	I-ATIT	ATI			21/MAY/68	W/O 24/MAY/69, Reggio Ap.
10364	PH-FML	Fokker	500	22/MAY/68		
	PJ-FRE	ALM			31/MAY/68	
	9M-APP	Malaysian Singapore Airlines			30/OCT/70	
	9V-BFK	SIA			01/OCT/72	
	ZK-NAO	National Airways Corp.			07/AUG/73	
	ZK-NAO	Air New Zealand			01/APR/78	
10365	PH-FMM	Fokker	500	05/JUN/68		
	PJ-FRM	ALM			14/JUN/68	
	9V-BCN	Malaysian Singapore Airlines			19/AUG/70	
	9V-BCN	SIA			01/OCT/72	
	ZK-NAN	National Airways Corp.			18/JUL/73	
	ZK-NAN	Air New Zealand			01/APR/78	
10366	PH-FMN	Fokker	500	27/JUL/68		
	F-BPNA	Air Inter			03/AUG/68	
10367	PH-FMO	Fokker	500	26/JUL/68		
	F-BPNB	Air Inter			12/OCT/68	
10368	PH-FMP	Fokker	600	26/JUN/68		Not taken-up
	AP-AUY	PIA				Leased
	PH-FMP	NLM			23/SEP/68	
	PH-FMP	Fokker			30/SEP/68	
	N20XY	Occidental Oil Co.			17/APR/69	
	PH-FMP	Fokker			27/JUN/65	
	TC-79	LADE			15/AUG/75	
	T-45	LADE			NOV/76	
10369	PH-FMR	Fokker	500	26/AUG/68		
	F-BPUA	Air France/CEP			05/SEP/68	
10370	PH-FMS	Fokker	500	30/AUG/68		
	F-BPUB	Air France/CEP			26/SEP/68	
10371	PH-FMT	Fokker	500	09/SEP/68		

FOKKER F-27 FRIENDSHIP

C/N	Registration	Owner/Operator	Series	First Flight	Delivery	Remarks
	F-BPNC	Air Inter			24/SEP/68	
10372	PH-FMU	Fokker	500	20/SEP/68		
	F-BPND	Air Inter			25/SEP/68	
10373	PH-FMV	Fokker	500	04/OCT/68		
	F-BPUC	Air France/CEP			11/OCT/68	
10374	PH-FMW	Fokker	500	14/OCT/68		
	F-BPUD	Air France/CEP			21/OCT/68	
10375	PH-FMX	Fokker	500	18/OCT/68		
	F-BPNE	Air Inter			30/OCT/68	
10376	PH-FMY	Fokker	500	23/OCT/68		
	F-BPNF	Air Inter			01/NOV/68	W/O 05/AUG/74, Quimper
10377	PH-FMZ	Fokker	500	31/OCT/68		
	F-BPUE	Air France/CEP			13/NOV/68	
10378	PH-FNA	Fokker	500	14/NOV/68		
	F-BPUF	Air France/CEP			22/NOV/68	
10379	PH-FNB	Fokker	500	27/NOV/68		
	F-BPUG	Air France/CEP			11/DEC/68	
10380	PH-FNC	Fokker	500	09/DEC/68		
	F-BPNG	Air Inter			18/DEC/68	
	F-BPNG	Brit Air			08/DEC/82	
10381	PH-FND	Fokker	500	06/JAN/69		
	F-BPNH	Air Inter			10/JAN/69	
10382	PH-FNE	Fokker	500	14/JAN/69		
	F-BPUH	Air France/CEP			24/JAN/69	
10383	PH-FNF	Fokker	500	28/JAN/69		
	PH-FNF	Air Inter			08/APR/69	Leased
	F-BPNI	Air Inter			01/JUL/69	Purchased
	F-BPNI	Brit Air			25/MAR/83	
10384	PH-FNG	Fokker	500	13/FEB/69		
	PH-FNG	Air Inter			18/MAY/69	Leased
	F-BPNJ	Air Inter			01/JUL/69	Purchased
10385	PH-FNH	Fokker	600	28/NOV/68		
	VH-TQN	Trans Australia Airlines			06/DEC/68	
	VH-TQN	Australian Aircraft Sales			82	
	OY-KAC	SAS			DEC/84	
10386	PH-FNI	Fokker	600	09/DEC/68		
	VH-TQO	Trans Australia Airlines			17/DEC/68	
	VH-TQO	Australian Aircraft Sales			82	
	LN-RNZ	SAS			DEC/84	
10387	PH-FNK	Fokker	600	17/DEC/68		
	VH-TQP	Trans Australia Airlines			24/DEC/68	
	VH-TQP	Australian Aircraft Sales			82	
	SE-IRG	SAS			DEC/84	
10388	PH-FNL	Fokker	600	02/JAN/69		
	VH-TQQ	Trans Australia Airlines			08/JAN/69	W/O 09/JUN/82, Amberly AFB, Brisbane
10389	PH-FNM	Fokker	500	21/FEB/69		
	F-BPUI	Air France/CEP			07/MAR/69	Damaged and repaired as C/N 10528
10528	F-BPUI	Air France/CEP			15/APR/76	
10390	PH-FNN	Fokker	500	14/MAR/69		
	F-BPUJ	Air France/CEP			28/MAR/69	
10391	PH-FNO	Fokker	600	29/JAN/69		
	9Q-CLK	Air Congo			20/FEB/69	
	9Q-CLK	Air Zaire			25/OCT/71	
10392	PH-FNP	Fokker	600	05/FEB/69		
	9Q-CLL	Air Congo			20/FEB/69	
	9Q-CLL	Air Zaire			25/OCT/71	WFU 81, used for spares, derelict N'Djili
10393	PH-FNR	Fokker	600	03/MAR/69		
	9Q-CLM	Air Congo			12/MAR/69	
	9Q-CLM	Air Zaire			25/OCT/71	W/O 09/JAN/75,Boende Ap.
10394	PH-FNS	Fokker	600	26/FEB/69		
	9Q-CLN	Air Congo			17/MAR/69	
	9Q-CLN	Air Zaire			25/OCT/71	
10395	PH-FNT	Fokker	600	05/MAR/69		
	9Q-CLO	Air Congo			01/APR/69	
	9Q-CLO	Air Zaire			25/OCT/71	W/O 03/MAR/76, Angola
10396	PH-FNU	Fokker	600	11/MAR/69		
	OY-DHW	Danish Aero Lease			04/APR/69	
	OY-DHW	BIAS			06/APR/69	Leased
	OY-DHW	Sabena			25/APR/69	Sub-leased
	OY-DHW	Linair			05/MAY/69	Sub-leased
	OY-DHW	Danish Aero Lease			06/APR/71	
	OY-DHW	Maersk Air			04/MAY/71	Leased
	OY-DHW	Danish Aero Lease			09/NOV/71	
	OY-DHW	Linair			08/JAN/72	
	OY-DHW	Danish Aero Lease			14/AUG/72	
	EC-CAU	Aviaco			16/AUG/72	Leased
	EC-CAU	Danish Aero Lease			14/AUG/76	
	PK-JFH	Sempati Air Transport			23/DEC/76	Leased
10397	PH-FNV	Fokker	500	18/APR/69		
	F-BPUK	Air France/CEP			16/MAY/69	
	F-BPUK	Fokker			23/APR/70	Leased
	F-BPUK	Air France/CEP			03/MAY/70	
10398	PH-FNW	Fokker	500	19/JUN/69		
	F-BPUL	Air France/CEP			10/JUL/69	
10399	PH-FNX	Fokker	600	10/APR/69		
	5N-ABA	Nigeria Airways			22/AUG/69	
	5N-ABA	Avioleasing			28/JUL/80	
	PK-GRD	Garuda			06/MAR/81	
	PK-MFD	Merpati Nusantara			10/MAR/81	
10400	PH-FNY	Fokker	600	17/APR/69		
	5N-ABB	Nigeria Airways			29/JUL/69	
	5N-ABB	Avioleasing			28/JUL/80	
	PK-GRE	Garuda			17/DEC/80	
	PK-MFE	Merpati Nusantara			21/DEC/80	
10401	PH-FNZ	Fokker	600	08/MAY/69		
	PH-FNZ	Maersk Air			01/DEC/69	Leased
	PH-FNZ	Fokker			10/DEC/69	
	PH-FNZ	Sobelair			12/DEC/69	Leased
	PH-FNZ	Fokker			06/JAN/70	
	CR-AMD	DETA	600		05/AUG/70	
	C9-AMD	DETA			01/JAN/75	

C/N	Registration	Owner/Operator	Series	First Flight	Delivery	Remarks
	C9-AMD	LAM			14/MAY/80	
	N379BS	Manufacturers Hanover			FEB/83	
	PT-LDT	Votec			10/DEC/83	
10402	PH-FOA	Fokker	600	29/APR/69		
	9Q-CLP	Air Congo			12/MAY/69	
	9Q-CLP	Air Zaire			25/OCT/71	W/O 08/FEB/80, Ndjili Ap.
10403	PH-FOB	Fokker	400M	13/MAY/69		
	TC-71	LADE			09/JUN/69	
10404	PH-FOC	Fokker	400M	23/MAY/69		
	TC-72	LADE			18/JUN/69	W/O 16/MAR/75, Benlo, Argentina
10405	PH-FOD	Fokker	600	29/MAY/69		
	9Q-CLQ	Air Congo			25/SEP/69	
	9Q-CLQ	Air Zaire			25/OCT/71	WFU 81, used for spares, derelict N'Djili
10406	PH-FOE	Fokker	600	23/JUN/69		
	9Q-CLR	Air Congo			25/SEP/69	
	9Q-CLR	Air Zaire			25/OCT/71	W/O 06/JAN/78, Kisangani Ap.
10407	PH-FOF	Fokker	400M	25/JUN/69		
	TC-73	LADE			24/JUL/69	
10408	PH-FOG	Fokker	400M	14/JUL/69		
	TC-74	LADE			31/JUL/69	
10409	PH-FOH	Fokker	600	09/JUL/69		
	PK-GFE	Garuda			14/AUG/69	
	PK-GFE	Fokker			16/FEB/77	
	PH-FOH	Fokker			28/MAR/78	
	TY-ATM	Benin Air Force				Not taken-up
	TY-AAG	Benin Air Force			02/JUN/78	
	TY-BBI	Air Benin			25/NOV/78	
	TY-BBI	Cameroon Airlines			OCT/81	Leased
	TY-BBI	Air Benin			01/MAR/82	
	TY-BBI	Fokker			27/MAY/82	
	F-SEBG	CNET			07/JUN/83	
10410	PH-FOI	Fokker	600	28/JUL/69		
	PK-GFF	Garuda			14/AUG/69	
	PK-JFF	Sempati Air Transport			08/SEP/71	
	PK-JFF	Danish Aero Lease			08/JUN/77	
	PK-JFF	Sempati Air Transport			08/JUN/77	Leased
10411	PH-FOK	Fokker	400M	04/AUG/69		
	TC-75	LADE			15/AUG/69	W/O 10/JUN/70, Andes Mts. Peru
10412	PH-FOL	Fokker	400M	13/AUG/69		
	TC-76	LADE			26/AUG/69	
10413	PH-FOM	Fokker	600	25/AUG/69		
	PK-GFG	Garuda			02/SEP/69	
	PK-GFG	Fokker			01/MAR/77	
	PH-FOM	Fokker			11/SEP/78	Not taken-up
	TY-AAG	Benin Air Force				Not taken-up
	TY-ATM	Benin Air Force				
	TY-ATM	Air Benin			20/OCT/78	
	TY-BBJ	Air Benin			25/OCT/78	
	F-GBGI	Air Alpes			23/APR/79	
	F-GBGI	Air Inter			07/JUN/80	Leased
	PK-JFG	Sempati Air Transport			30/JUL/80	
10414	PH-FON	Fokker	200	04/SEP/69		
	HL5209	Korean Airlines			29/SEP/69	
	TF-FLO	Icelandair			07/FEB/80	
10415	PH-FOO	Fokker	600	11/SEP/69		
	PK-GFH	Garuda			25/SEP/69	
	PK-MFH	Merpati Nusantara			26/JAN/74	
10416	PH-FOP	Fokker	400M	19/SEP/69		
	TC-77	Argentine Air Force			29/SEP/69	W/O 02/DEC/69
10417	PH-FOR	Fokker	500	25/SEP/69		
	HL5210	Korean Airlines			02/OCT/69	
	TF-FLR	Icelandair			07/FEB/80	
10418	PH-FOS	Fokker	400M	06/OCT/69		
	TC-78	Argentine Air Force			17/OCT/69	
10419	PH-FOT	Fokker	600	15/OCT/69		
	I-ATIV	ATI			27/OCT/69	
	LN-RNY	SAS			JUN/85	
10420	PH-FOU	Fokker	600	05/NOV/69		
	I-ATIZ	ATI			11/NOV/69	
	OY-KAD	SAS			JUN/85	
10421	PH-FOV	Fokker	600	28/OCT/69		
	PK-GFI	Garuda			12/NOV/69	
	PK-GFI	Fokker			12/FEB/77	
	PH-EXT	Fokker			19/AUG/77	
	PH-EXE	Fokker			JAN/78	
	EC-DBM	Iberia			17/JAN/78	
	EC-DBM	Aviaco			29/JAN/82	
10422	PH-FOW	Fokker	600	06/NOV/69		
	PK-GFJ	Garuda			14/NOV/69	W/O 08/SEP/69, Branti Ap., Sumatra
10423	PH-FOX	Fokker	600	17/NOV/69		
	PK-GFK	Garuda			21/NOV/69	
	PK-GFK	Fokker			12/FEB/77	
	PH-EXT	Fokker			24/AUG/77	
	PH-FOX	Fokker			14/JAN/78	
	D2-TAE	TAAG Angola			25/FEB/78	
	D2-TFQ	TAAG Angola			15/SEP/80	
10424	PH-FOY	Fokker	600	27/NOV/69		
	PK-GFL	Garuda			10/DEC/69	
	PK-GFL	Fokker			25/FEB/77	
	PH-EXE	Fokker			DEC/77	
	PH-FTG	Fokker			19/JAN/78	
	D2-TAF	TAAG Angola			20/JAN/78	
	D2-TFP	TAAG Angola			15/SEP/80	
10425	PH-FOZ	Fokker	500	20/NOV/69		
	OY-DKR	Maersk Air				Not taken-up
	OY-APA	Maersk Air			09/DEC/69	
	F-BYAF	Air Rouergue			07/FEB/77	
	F-BYAF	Royal Air Inter			10/SEP/77	Leased
	F-BYAF	Air Rouergue			23/OCT/77	
	VH-EWS	East West Airlines			23/FEB/78	
	VH-EWS	Fokker			20/SEP/83	
	PH-FOZ	Fokker			03/APR/86	
	9Q-CBU	Scibe Airlift			SEP/86	Sched.delivery

C/N	Registration	Owner/Operator	Series	First Flight	Delivery	Remarks
10426	PH-FPA	Fokker	500	09/DEC/69		
	OY-DKS	Maersk Air				Not taken-up
	OY-APB	Maersk Air			17/DEC/69	W/O 27/DEC/69, Ronne Ap.Denmark
10427	PH-FPB	Fokker	500	16/DEC/69		
	HL5211	Korean Airlines			06/JAN/70	
10428	PH-FPC	Fokker	500	30/DEC/69		
	HL5212	Korean Airlines			22/JAN/70	W/O 23/JAN/70, Kansong Port, Korea
10429	PH-FPD	Fokker	600	19/JAN/70		
	PK-GFM	Garuda			02/FEB/70	
	PK-GFM	Fokker			01/MAR/77	
	PH-EXD	Fokker			FEB/78	
	EC-DBN	Iberia			28/FEB/78	
	EC-DBN	Aviaco			29/JAN/82	
10430	PH-FPE	Fokker	600	30/JAN/70		
	PK-GFN	Garuda			13/FEB/70	
	PK-RFN	Mandala Airlines			24/OCT/73	
	PK-RFT	Mandala Airlines			01/NOV/73	
	PK-GFN	Garuda			05/FEB/77	
	PK-GFN	Fokker			23/MAY/77	
	PH-FTC	Fokker			28/DEC/77	
	F-BYAR	Air Alpes			06/JAN/78	
	F-BYAR	Air Inter			06/MAY/79	Leased
	F-BYAR	Air Alpes			23/DEC/80	
	F-BYAR	Zimex Aviation			81	
	5A-DJN	United African Airlines			JUN/81	Leased
	5A-DJN	United African Airlines			01/SEP/81	Purchased
	TT-AAK	Jamahiriyan Air Transport			DEC/82	
10431	PH-FPF	Air Tchad	500	09/FEB/70	01/JUN/83	
	OY-DKT	Fokker				
	OY-APC	Maersk Air				Not taken-up
	F-BYAC	Maersk Air			14/FEB/70	
	VH-EWT	Air Rouergue			14/DEC/76	
	VH-EWT	East West Airlines			14/JUL/78	
	N4560Z	Fokker			16/AUG/83	
	N4560Z	Mississippi Valley Airlines			10/JAN/84	
	N4560Z	Air Wisconsin			MAY/85	
10432	PH-FPG	Mesaba Airlines	600	13/MAR/70	25/JAN/86	
	PK-GFO	Fokker				
	CN-CDA	Garuda				Not taken-up
10433	PH-FPH	Royal Air Inter	600	02/APR/70	25/MAR/70	
	CN-CDB	Fokker			24/APR/70	
10434	PH-FPI	Royal Air Inter	500	13/APR/70		
	OY-STN	Fokker			10/JUN/70	
	OY-STN	Sterling			18/JAN/73	
	OY-STN	United Nations			01/JUN/73	Leased
	VH-EWN	Sterling			14/OCT/73	
	VH-EWN	East West Airlines			OCT/83	
	N271FA	Fokker			09/JUN/84	
	N271FA	Mississippi Valley Airlines			85	Leased
10435	PH-FPK	Mesaba Airlines	600	17/APR/70		
	PK-GFO	Fokker			01/MAY/70	
	PK-MFO	Garuda			24/OCT/73	
10436	PH-FPL	Merpati Nusantara	600	28/MAY/70		
	PH-FPL	Fokker			10/JUL/70	
	5A-DBN	Oasis Oil			29/NOV/76	
	5A-DBN	Libyan Arab Airlines			09/SEP/80	Leased
	5A-DBN	Libyan Red Crescent			JUN/85	
10437	PH-FPM	Libyan Arab Airlines	600	15/MAY/70		
	OY-APD	Fokker			04/AUG/70	
10438	PH-FPN	Maersk Air	600	09/JUN/70		W/O 25/JAN/75, Vagar, Faroes
	AP-AWN	Fokker				Not taken-up
	PH-FPN	PIA	600			Converted
	PH-EXB	Fokker			05/MAR/72	
	PH-FPN	Fokker			07/SEP/72	
	S2-ABH	Fokker			23/SEP/72	
10439	PH-FPO	Bangladesh Biman	200	25/JUN/70		
	CR-LLD	Fokker			07/JUL/70	W/O 21/MAY/72,Nr.Lobito, Angola
10440	PH-EXB	DTA	600	15/JUL/70		
	VH-TQR	Fokker			30/JUL/70	
	VH-TQR	Trans Australia Airlines			04/AUG/86	
10441	PH-EXB	Australian Airlines	600	31/JUL/70		
	VH-TQS	Fokker			12/AUG/70	
	VH-TQS	Trans Australia Airlines			04/AUG/86	
10442	PH-EXA	Australian Airlines	600	04/SEP/70		
	PH-FPR	Fokker			19/APR/71	Leased
	PH-FPR	Southwest Aviation			26/APR/71	Leased
	PH-FPR	Air Anglia			30/JUL/71	
	I-VANA	Fokker	600			Not taken-up
	PH-FPR	Turavia			02/AUG/72	Leased
	PH-FPR	Air Anglia			15/SEP/72	Leased
	PH-FPR	Royal Air Inter			31/OCT/72	
	PH-FPR	Fokker			08/DEC/72	Leased
	PH-FPR	Air Anglia	600		23/DEC/72	
	S2-ABP	Fokker			27/NOV/73	
10443	PH-EXD	Bangladesh Biman	600	28/AUG/70		
	OY-APE	Fokker			12/NOV/70	
	OB-R-1072	Maersk Air			08/MAR/74	
	OB-R-1072	Aero Peru			24/MAY/75	Leased
	OY-APE	Fokker			19/JUL/75	
	F-BYAI	Maersk Air			06/MAR/77	
	F-BYAI	Air Rouergue			07/JUN/77	
	A40-FA	Danish Aero Lease			18/JUL/77	
	A40-FA	Gulf Air			08/NOV/81	
	F-WDFT	Danish Aero Lease			03/AUG/82	
	F-GDFT	Air Jet			09/AUG/82	Leased
	OY-BST	Air Jet			29/FEB/84	
	OY-APE	Danish Aero Lease			OCT/84	Leased
10444	PH-EXE	Alkair	200	30/OCT/70		
	ZK-DCA	Fokker			18/MAR/71	
10445	PH-EXF	Civair	200	07/DEC/70		
	ZK-DCB	Fokker			18/MAR/71	
10446	PH-FPW	Civair	600	10/DEC/70		
	TN-ABZ	Fokker			28/DEC/70	
		Lina Congo				

C/N	Registration	Owner/Operator	Series	First Flight	Delivery	Remarks
10447	PH-FPX	Fokker		19/NOV/70		
	F-BSUM	Air France/CEP			27/NOV/70	Damaged 11/AUG/73 and repaired as C/N 10506
10506	F-BSUM	Air France/CEP		12/NOV/74	18/NOV/74	
10448	PH-FPY	Fokker	500	22/DEC/70		
	F-BSUN	Air France/CEP			14/JAN/71	
10449	PH-FPZ	Fokker	500	29/JAN/71		
	F-BSUO	Air France/CEP			11/FEB/71	
10450	TU-VAJ	Ivory Coast Government	600VIP	16/DEC/70	22/DEC/70	
	TU-VAJ	Air Ivoire			25/MAY/77	
	TU-TIA	Air Ivoire			01/DEC/77	
	TU-TIA	Danish Aero Lease			10/JAN/79	
	TU-TIA	Air Ivoire			10/JAN/79	Leased
	TU-TIA	Danish Aero Lease			27/FEB/79	
	PH-FTR	Danish Aero Lease			15/MAY/79	
	PH-FTR	Avio Ligure			28/JUN/79	
	I-ALML	Avio Ligure			11/AUG/79	Leased
	PH-FTR	Danish Aero Lease			01/MAY/80	
	9M-MCY	Malaysian Airline System			22/OCT/80	Leased
	9M-MCY	Danish Aero Lease			01/AUG/82	
	EC-DSH	Aviaco			01/APR/83	Leased
10451	PH-EXA	Fokker	600	18/APR/71		Not taken-up
		Air Bangui	600		26/DEC/71	
	PH-FRB	Fokker	600		28/DEC/71	
	TC-43	LADE				
10452	XY-ADQ	Union of Burma Airways	600	15/FEB/71	26/FEB/71	
	XY-ADQ	Burma Airways Corp.			01/MAY/72	
10453	PH-EXD	Fokker	600	17/FEB/71		
	PH-FPU	Fokker			14/SEP/72	Not taken-up
	AP-AWM	PIA			16/SEP/72	
	S2-ABJ	Bangladesh Biman				W/O 05/AUG/84, Dhaka
10454	PH-EXB	Fokker	600	01/JUN/71		
	TC-44	LADE			28/DEC/71	
10455	PH-FPR	Fokker	500	22/MAR/71		
	9V-BCS	Malaysian Singapore Airlines			31/MAR/71	
	9M-ARI	Malaysian Airline System			01/OCT/72	
	9M-MCA	Malaysian Airline System			01/JAN/76	
10456	PH-FPS	Fokker	500	30/MAR/71		
	9M-APU	Malaysian Singapore Airlines			15/APR/71	
	9M-APU	Malaysian Airline System			01/OCT/72	
	9M-MCB	Malaysian Airline System			01/APR/76	
	ZK-NFC	National Airways Corp.			04/JUL/77	
	ZK-NFC	Air New Zealand			01/APR/78	W/O 17/FEB/79, Auckland
10457	PH-FPP	Fokker	600	27/APR/71		
	CR-LMB	DTA			11/MAY/71	
	CR-LMB	TAAG Angola			01/JAN/73	
	D2-TMB	TAAG Angola			11/NOV/75	
	D2-TFR	TAAG Angola			15/SEP/81	
10458	PH-EXB	Fokker	600	21/APR/71		
	VH-TQT	Trans Australia Airlines			28/APR/71	
	VH-TQT	Australian Airlines			04/AUG/86	
10459	PH-EXD	Fokker	500	14/MAY/71		Not taken-up
		Lina Congo			29/OCT/71	
	OY-APF	Maersk Air			06/MAR/77	
	F-BYAH	Air Rouergue			11/JUL/77	
	VH-EWR	East West Airlines			15/SEP/80	
	VH-EWR	Northern Airlines			11/JAN/81	
	VH-EWR	East West Airlines			21/APR/83	
	PH-RUA	Fokker			22/APR/83	Leased
	PH-RUA	Air Sinai			20/JAN/84	
	PH-RUA	Fokker			OCT/86	Sched.delivery
	9Q-CBI	Scibe Airlift				
10460	9V-BCT	Fokker	500	03/JUN/71		
	9V-BCT	Malaysian Singapore Airlines			11/JUN/71	
	9M-ARJ	Malaysian Airline System			01/OCT/72	
	9M-MCC	Malaysian Airline System			01/JUN/76	
10461	9M-APV	Malaysian Singapore Airlines	500	16/JUN/71	26/JUL/71	
	9M-APV	Malaysian Airline System			01/OCT/72	
	9M-MCD	Malaysian Airline System			01/MAY/76	W/O 26/SEP/72, Jakarta.
10462	PK-GFP	Garuda	600	24/JUN/71	13/JUL/71	W/O 23/NOV/71, Kota Kinabalu Ap.
10463	9V-BCU	Malaysian Singapore Airlines	500	15/JUL/71	28/JUL/71	Malaysia
10464	9M-APW	Malaysian Singapore Airlines	500	30/JUL/71	19/AUG/71	
	9M-APW	Malaysian Airline System			30/OCT/71	
	9M-MCE	Malaysian Airline System			01/JAN/76	
10465	PH-EXD	Fokker	600	16/AUG/71		
	PK-GFQ	Garuda				Not taken-up
		c/n cancelled to c/n 10484				
10466	PH-EXA	Fokker	600	07/SEP/7		
	PK-GFR	Garuda				Not taken-up
		c/n cancelled to c/n 10486				
10467	9V-BCV	Malaysian Singapore Airlines	500	09/SEP/71	22/SEP/71	
	9M-ARK	Malaysian Airline System			01/OCT/72	
	9M-MCF	Malaysian Airline System			01/APR/76	
10468	9M-APX	Malaysian Singapore Airlines	500	24/SEP/71	06/OCT/71	
	9M-APX	Malaysian Airline System			01/OCT/72	
	9M-MCG	Malaysian Airline System			22/MAR/76	
10469	TU-VAK	Ivory Coast Government	400M	20/OCT/71	01/NOV/71	
	F-GBDE	Air Alpes			26/APR/79	
	F-GBDE	Tunisavia			04/MAY/79	Leased
	F-GBDE	Air Alpes			15/MAY/80	
	F-GBDE	Zimex Aviation			AUG/81	
	5A-DFN	United African Airlines			SEP/81	
	5A-DFN	Libyan Arab Airlines			82	Leased
10470	9V-BCW	Malaysian Singapore Airlines	500	26/OCT/71	04/NOV/71	
	9M-ARL	Malaysian Airline System			01/OCT/72	
	9M-MCH	Malaysian Airline System			01/OCT/75	
10471	PH-EXF	Fokker	500	09/NOV/71		
	9M-ARE	Malaysian Airline System	500		06/SEP/72	
	9M-MCI	Malaysian Airline System			01/FEB/76	
10472	PH-EXA	Fokker	500	29/NOV/71		
	PH-EXF	Fokker	500		06/JUN/73	Converted
	9M-ASF	Malaysian Airline System			14/JUN/73	
	9M-MCJ	Malaysian Airline System			01/MAR/76	
10473	NAF-701	Nigerian Air Force	600	18/JAN/72		

FOKKER F-27 FRIENDSHIP

C/N	Registration	Owner/Operator	Series	First Flight	Delivery	Remarks
	NAF-901	Nigerian Air Force			31/JAN/72	
	PH-FRD	Fokker			10/DEC/74	Leased
	NAF-901	Nigerian Air Force			04/JAN/75	
	5N-ANL	Nigeria Airways			25/APR/76	
	NAF-901	Nigerian Air Force			02/JUN/81	
	N4449D	E.A. Koenig			OCT/83	
	C-GSFS	Conair			JAN/86	
10474	5-201	Imperial Iranian Air Force	600V1P	10/JAN/72	01/FEB/72	
	5-8801	Imperial Iranian Air Force			01/SEP/76	
	5-8801	Iranian Air Force			01/FEB/79	
10475	5-202	Imperial Iranian Air Force	600VIP	01/FEB/72	16/FEB/72	
	5-8802	Imperial Iranian Air Force			01/SEP/76	
	5-8802	Iranian Air Force			01/FEB/79	
10476	NAF-702	Nigerian Air Force	600	27/FEB/72		
	NAF-902	Nigerian Air Force			25/MAR/76	
	5N-ANM	Nigeria Airways			16/APR/76	
	NAF-902	Nigerian Air Force			02/JUL/81	
	N4449C	E.A. Koenig			OCT/83	
	XY-	Burma Airways Corp.			AUG/86	
10477	PH-EXB	Fokker	600	23/FEB/72		
	PH-FRB	Fokker			29/OCT/73	
	S2-ABO	Bangladesh Biman			31/OCT/73	
10478	5-203	Imperial Iranian Air Force	400M	15/FEB/72	02/MAR/72	
	5-8803	Imperial Iranian Air Force			01/SEP/76	
	5-8803	Imperial Iranian Air Force			22/MAR/77	Converted to target-tug
	5-8803	Iranian Air Force			01/FEB/79	
10479	5-204	Imperial Iranian Air Force	400M	09/MAR/72	22/MAR/72	
	5-8804	Imperial Iranian Air Force			01/SEP/76	
	5-8804	Iranian Air Force			01/FEB/79	
10480	5-205	Imperial Iranian Air Force	400M	28/MAR/72	10/APR/72	
	5-8805	Imperial Iranian Air Force			01/SEP/76	
	5-8805	Iranian Air Force			01/FEB/79	
10481	5-206	Imperial Iranian Air Force	400M	17/APR/72		
	PH-FPV	Fokker			APR/72	
	5-206	Imperial Iranian Air Force			17/MAY/72	
	5-8806	Imperial Iranian Air Force			01/SEP/76	
	5-8806	Iranian Air Force			01/FEB/79	
10482	5-207	Imperial Iranian Air Force	400M	05/MAY/72	24/MAY/72	
	5-8807	Imperial Iranian Air Force			01/SEP/76	
	5-8807	Imperial Iranian Air Force				Converted to target tug
	5-8807	Iranian Air Force			01/FEB/79	
10483	5-208	Imperial Iranian Air Force	400M	31/MAY/72	07/JUL/72	
	5-8808	Imperial Iranian Air Force			01/SEP/76	
	5-8808	Iranian Air Force			01/FEB/79	
10484	5-209	Imperial Iranian Air Force	400M	12/JUN/72	25/AUG/72	W/O 25/AUG/72, Nr. Chalus
10485	5-210	Imperial Iranian Air Force	400M	12/JUN/72	19/JUL/72	
	5-209	Imperial Iranian Air Force			20/SEP/73	
	5-8809	Imperial Iranian Air Force			01/SEP/76	
	5-8809	Iranian Air Force			01/FEB/79	
10486	5-211	Imperial Iranian Air Force	600VIP	28/AUG/72	01/SEP/72	
	5-210	Imperial Iranian Air Force			20/SEP/73	
	5-8810	Imperial Iranian Air Force			01/SEP/76	
	5-8810	Iranian Air Force			01/FEB/79	
10487	NAF-903	Nigerian Air Force	400M	04/JUL/72	08/AUG/72	
	5N-ANT	Nigeria Airways			06/JUL/77	Leased
	NAF-903	Nigerian Air Force			02/JUL/81	
	S9-TAC	Linhas Aereas de Sao Tome			01/AUG/81	
10488	PH-EXE	Fokker	400M	31/JUL/72		
	NAF-904	Nigerian Air Force			13/FEB/73	
	PH-FRD	Fokker			12/OCT/74	Leased
	NAF-904	Nigerian Air Force			05/JAN/75	W/O 26/MAY/80, Lagos
10489	PH-EXA	Fokker	400M	28/AUG/72		
	PH-FPW	Fokker			07/SEP/72	
	5-212	Imperial Iranian Air Force			20/SEP/72	
	5-211	Imperial Iranian Air Force			20/SEP/73	W/O 30/SEP/74, Saharood
10490	PH-EXC	Fokker	400M	26/SEP/72		
	NAF-905	Nigerian Air Force			22/FEB/73	
10491	PH-EXA	Fokker	400M	20/OCT/72		
	5-213	Imperial Iranian Air Force			10/NOV/72	
	5-212	Imperial Iranian Air Force			20/SEP/73	
	5-8811	Imperial Iranian Air Force			01/SEP/76	
	5-8811	Iranian Air Force			01/FEB/79	
10492	PH-EXF	Fokker	400M	23/NOV/72		
	5-214	Imperial Iranian Air Force			03/JAN/73	
	5-213	Imperial Iranian Air Force			20/SEP/73	
	5-8812	Imperial Iranian Air Force			01/SEP/76	
	5-8812	Iranian Air Force			01/FEB/79	
10493	PH-EXA	Fokker	400M	04/JAN/73		
	NAF-906	Nigerian Air Force			05/MAR/73	
	5N-ANS	Nigeria Airways			19/DEC/76	
	NAF-906	Nigerian Air Force			02/JUL/81	
	N4449E	E.A. Koenig			OCT/83	
	TG-AFA	Guatemalan Air Force			JUN/84	
	1770	Guatemalan Air Force			JAN/86	
10494	PH-EXB	Fokker	400M	28/FEB/73		
		Air Algerie				Not taken-up
	PH-FPX	Algerian Government			12/APR/73	
	7T-WAI	Algerian Government			19/APR/73	
	7T-VRU	Air Algerie			04/JAN/82	Leased
	7T-VRU	Inter Air Services			APR/84	
	7T-VRU	Air Algerie			NOV/84	
10495	PH-FPZ	Fokker	400M	16/APR/73		
		Air Algerie				Not taken-up
	PH-FPZ	Algerian Government			09/JUN/73	
	7T-WAK	Algerian Government			13/JUN/73	
	7T-VRL	Air Algerie			04/JAN/82	Leased
	7T-VRL	Inter Air Services			APR/84	
	7T-VRL	Air Algerie			NOV/84	
10496	PH-FRA	Fokker	400M	21/JUN/73		
		Air Algerie				Not taken-up
	PH-FRA	Algerian Government			27/JUL/73	
	7T-WAL	Algerian Government			02/AUG/73	
	7T-VRM	Algerian Government			01/NOV/77	
	7T-VRM	Air Algerie			04/JAN/82	Leased

C/N	Registration	Owner/Operator	Series	First Flight	Delivery	Remarks
	7T-VRM	Inter Air Services			APR/84	
	7T-VRM	Air Algerie			NOV/84	
10497	PH-EXW	Fokker	400M	20/SEP/73		
	5-214	Imperial Iranian Air Force			17/OCT/73	
	5-8813	Imperial Iranian Air Force			01/SEP/76	
	5-8813	Iranian Air Force			01/FEB/79	
10498	PH-EXX	Fokker	600VIP	07/NOV/73		
	5-215	Imperial Iranian Air Force			21/NOV/73	
	EP-IAJ	Iran Air			14/JUL/74	Leased
	5-8814	Imperial Iranian Air Force			05/JUN/77	
	5-8814	Iranian Air Force			01/FEB/79	
10499	PH-EXA	Fokker	400M	25/JAN/74		
	5-216	Imperial Iranian Air Force			08/MAR/74	Camera Version
	5-216	National Geographic Organ.			17/MAR/74	leased
	5-216	Imperial Iranian Air Force			23/AUG/76	
	5-8815	Imperial Iranian Air Force			01/SEP/76	
	5-8815	Iranian Air Force			01/FEB/79	
10500	PH-EXE	Fokker	400M	22/MAR/74		
	5-217	Imperial Iranian Air Force			08/MAY/74	Camera Version
	5-217	National Geographic Organ.			10/MAY/74	Leased
	5-217	Imperial Iranian Air Force			01/SEP/76	
	5-8816	Imperial Iranian Air Force			01/SEP/76	
	5-8816	Iranian Air Force			01/FEB/79	
10501	PH-EXF	Fokker	600	14/MAY/74		
		Imperial Iranian Air Force				Not taken-up
	XY-ADS	Burma Airways Corp.			27/MAY/74	W/O 12/OCT/85, Putao
10502	PH-EXI	Fokker	400M	02/JUL/74		
	5-218	Imperial Iranian Air Force			11/SEP/74	
	5-8817	Imperial Iranian Air Force			01/SEP/76	
	5-8817	Iranian Air Force			01/FEB/79	
10503	PH-EXK	Fokker	500C	06/AUG/74		
	N703A	Aramco			28/AUG/74	
10504	PH-EXL	Fokker	600	21/AUG/74		
	5-219	Imperial Iranian Air Force			11/SEP/74	
	EP-IAK	Iran Air			05/OCT/74	Leased
	5-8818	Imperial Iranian Air Force			04/JUN/77	
	5-8818	Iranian Air Force			01/FEB/79	
10505	PH-EXM	Fokker	600VIP	20/JAN/75		
	PH-FRF	Fokker			06/FEB/75	
	G-520/A	Ghana Air Force			07/FEB/75	
10506	F-BSUM	Fokker			SEP/73	
	F-BSUM	Air France			NOV/74	Delivered as repaired c/n 10447
10507	PH-EXR	Fokker	400M	24/DEC/74		
	PH-FRE	Fokker			10/MAR/75	
	G-521/B	Ghana Air Force			08/APR/75	
	PH-FRE	Fokker			22/MAY/75	Leased
	G-521/B	Ghana Air Force			12/JUN/75	
	PH-FRE	Fokker			18/NOV/81	Leased
	G-521/B	Ghana Air Force			29/JAN/82	
10508	PH-EXA	Fokker	600	24/FEB/75		
	OB-R-1042	Aero Peru			07/MAY/75	
	N61AN	Air North			APR/84	
	N61AN	Brockway Air			SEP/84	
10509	PH-EXB	Fokker	400M	25/MAR/75		Not taken-up
	5-2601	Imperial Iranian Navy				
	5-2604	Imperial Iranian Navy			09/APR/75	
	5-2604	Iranian Navy			01/FEB/79	
10510	PH-EXC	Fokker	400M	16/APR/75		
	5-2602	Imperial Iranian Navy			28/MAY/75	
	5-2602	Iranian Navy			01/FEB/79	
10511	PH-EXD	Fokker	600VIP	09/MAY/75		
	5-2603	Imperial Iranian Navy			16/JUL/75	
	5-2603	Iranian Navy			01/FEB/79	
10512	PH-EXE	Fokker	600	26/MAY/75		
	5-2604	Imperial Iranian Navy				Not taken-up
	PH-FRG	Fokker			25/JUL/75	
	5-2601	Imperial Iranian Navy			04/SEP/75	
	5-2601	Iranian Navy			01/FEB/79	
10513	PH-EXG	Fokker	600	13/JUN/75		
	5A-DBO	Libyan Arab Airlines			01/JUL/75	
10514	PH-EXF	Fokker	600	14/JUL/75		
	OB-R-1082	Aero Peru			23/JUL/75	
	N60AN	Air North			14/JAN/84	
	N60AN	Brockway Air			SEP/84	
10515	PH-EXK	Fokker	600	07/JUL/75		
	5A-DBP	Libyan Arab Airlines			30/JUL/75	
10516	PH-EXU	Fokker	400	06/AUG/75		
	5A-DBQ	Libyan Arab Airlines			28/AUG/75	
10517	PH-EXV	Fokker	400	05/SEP/75		
	5A-DBR	Libyan Arab Airlines			29/OCT/75	W/O AUG/81, Chad
10518	PH-EXW	Fokker	400M	26/SEP/75		
	G-522/C	Ghana Air Force			15/OCT/75	
	PH-FRH	Fokker			15/OCT/75	Leased
	G-522/C	Ghana Air Force			04/DEC/75	
10519	PH-EXA	Fokker	600	09/OCT/75		
	5A-DBS	Libyan Arab Airlines			03/DEC/75	
10520	PH-EXX	Fokker	400M	12/NOV/75		
	PH-FRI	Fokker			17/NOV/75	
	G-523/D	Ghana Air Force			04/DEC/75	
10521	PH-EXB	Fokker	600	11/NOV/75		
	5A-DBT	Libyan Arab Airlines			13/DEC/75	
10522	PH-EXC	Fokker	500F	02/DEC/75		
	VH-FCA	Ansett Airlines of NSW			10/DEC/75	
	VH-FCA	Air New South Wales			01/JUN/81	
10523	PH-EXE	Fokker	600	04/DEC/75		
	XY-ADT	Burma Airways Corp.			02/JAN/76	
10524	PH-EXD	Fokker	500F	08/JAN/76		
	VH-FCB	Ansett Airlines of NSW			23/JAN/76	
	VH-FCB	Air New South Wales			01/JUN/81	
	VH-FCB	Setair			05/JAN/83	Leased
	VH-FCB	Air New South Wales			26/MAR/83	
	VH-FCB	Ansett Air Freight			28/APR/83	
	VH-FCB	Air New South Wales			26/JAN/84	
	VH-FCB	Ansett Airlines of Australia				
10525	PH-EXF	Fokker	500C	10/FEB/76		

FOKKER F-27 FRIENDSHIP

C/N	Registration	Owner/Operator	Series	First Flight	Delivery	Remarks
	N702A	Aramco			21/FEB/76	
10526	PH-EXR	Fokker	400	02/MAR/76		
	PH-FRC	Fokker			17/MAR/76	
	7T-WAO	Algerian Government			18/MAR/76	
	7T-WAO	Air Algerie			04/JAN/82	Leased
	7T-VRQ	Inter Air Services			APR/84	
	7T-VRQ	Air Algerie			NOV/84	
10527	PH-EXS	Fokker	600	24/MAR/76		
	PH-FRD	Fokker			14/APR/76	
	7T-VRN	Algerian Govt.			14/APR/76	
	7T-VRN	Inter Air Services			DEC/83	
	7T-VRN	Air Algerie			NOV/84	
10528	F-BPUI	Fokker			75	
	F-BPUI	Air France/CEP			APR/76	Delivered as repaired c/n 10389
10529	PH-EXT	Fokker	400M	17/MAY/76		
	PH-FRK	Fokker			02/JUN/76	
	7T-WAM	Algerian Government			16/JUN/76	
10530	PH-EXK	Fokker	500C	04/MAY/76		
	N737A	Aramco			20/MAY/76	
10531	PH-EXM	Fokker	500C	17/JUN/76		
	N739A	Aramco			01/JUL/76	
10532	PH-EXO	Fokker	500F	01/JUN/76		
	VH-FCC	Ansett Airlines of NSW			18/JUN/76	
	VH-FCC	Air New South Wales			01/JUN/81	
10533	PH-EXS	Fokker	500F	18/JUN/76		
	VH-FCD	Ansett Airlines of NSW			28/JUN/76	
	VH-FCD	Ansett Airlines of Australia			27/MAY/79	
	VH-FCD	Ansett Airlines of NSW			01/MAR/80	
	VH-FCD	Air New South Wales			01/JUN/81	
10534	PH-EXW	Fokker	500F	26/JUL/76		
	VH-EWP	East West Airlines			09/SEP/76	
10535	PH-EXX	Fokker	600	23/SEP/76		
	G-524/E	Ghana Air Force			16/NOV/76	
10536	PH-EXA	Fokker	400M	18/JUL/76		
	PH-FRL	Fokker			03/SEP/76	
	T-2701	Indonesian Air Force			03/SEP/76	
10537	PH-EXB	Fokker	400M	12/AUG/76		
	PH-FRM	Fokker			07/SEP/76	
	T-2702	Indonesian Air Force			10/SEP/76	
10538	PH-EXC	Fokker	400M	31/AUG/76		
	PH-FRN	Fokker			22/SEP/76	
	T-2703	Indonesian Air Force			23/SEP/76	
	PK-VTE	Penas			80	
	T-2703	Indonesian Air Force				
10539	PH-EXY	Fokker	500F	15/SEP/76		
	VH-EWQ	East West Airlines			02/OCT/76	
	VH-EWQ	Fokker			NOV/84	
	PH-JBO	Fokker			31/JAN/85	
10540	PH-EXD	Fokker	400M	30/SEP/76		
	PH-FRO	Fokker			13/OCT/76	
	T-2704	Indonesian Air Force			16/OCT/76	
10541	PH-EXE	Fokker	400M	12/OCT/76		
	PH-FRP	Fokker			25/OCT/76	
	T-2705	Indonesan Air Force			27/OCT/76	
10542	PH-EXF	Fokker	400M	25/OCT/76		
	PH-FRR	Fokker			05/NOV/76	
	T-2706	Indonesian Air Force			09/NOV/76	
10543	PH-EXS	Fokker	400M	29/NOV/76		
	PH-FRU	Fokker			07/DEC/76	
	7T-WAQ	Algerian Govt.			07/DEC/76	
	7T-WAQ	Inter Air Services			JUN/83	
	7T-VRV	Air Algerie			NOV/84	
10544	PH-EXB	Fokker	400M	08/NOV/76		
	PH-FRS	Fokker			23/NOV/76	
	T-2707	Indonesian Air Force			25/NOV/76	
10545	PH-EXC	Fokker	200	07/DEC/76		
	TF-SYN	Icelandic Coastguard			14/JAN/77	
10546	PH-EXH	Fokker	400M	02/DEC/76		
	PH-FRT	Fokker			04/FEB/77	
	T-2708	Indonesian Air Force			05/FEB/77	
10547	PH-EXG	Fokker	400M	27/DEC/76		
	7T-WAS	Air Algerie				Not taken-up
	PH-FRV	Fokker			01/MAR/77	
	7T-WAS	Algerian Government			05/MAR/77	
	7T-VRJ	Algerian Government			03/APR/79	
	7T-VRJ	Air Algerie			03/JUL/79	
	7T-VRJ	Inter Air Services			JAN/84	
	7T-VRJ	Air Algerie			NOV/84	
10548	PH-EXD	Fokker	400MAR	16/JUN/77		
	AE-560	Peruvian Navy			17/SEP/77	
10549	PH-EXE	Fokker	400MAR	14/JUN/77		
	AE-561	Peruvian Navy				Not taken-up
	PH-MPA	Fokker			08/NOV/77	
	AE-561	Peruvian Navy			25/FEB/78	W/O APR/86, Pacific Ocean
10550	PH-EXF	Fokker	500C	21/JAN/77		
	N743A	Aramco			23/FEB/77	
10551	PH-EXA	Fokker	500	01/MAR/77		
	ZK-NFA	National Airways Corp.			30/MAR/77	
	ZK-NFA	Air New Zealand			01/APR/78	
10552	PH-EXB	Fokker	500	25/MAR/77		
	ZK-NFB	National Airways Corp.			22/APR/77	
	ZK-NFB	Air New Zealand			01/APR/78	
10553	PH-EXO	Fokker	400M	11/MAR/77		
	PH-FRW	Fokker			29/APR/77	
	7T-WAT	Algerian Government			03/MAY/77	
	7T-VRK	Algerian Government			03/APR/79	
	7T-VRK	Air Algerie			03/APR/80	Leased
	7T-VRK	Inter Air Services			JUN/83	
	7T-VRK	Air Algerie			NOV/83	
10554	PH-EXK	Fokker	600	12/APR/77		
	PH-FRZ	Fokker			09/MAY/77	
	EP-ANA	National Iron and Copper Ind			10/MAY/77	
10555	PH-EXT	Fokker	400M	29/APR/77		
	PH-FRX	Fokker			09/JUN/77	
	7T-WAU	Algerian Government			14/JUN/77	

C/N	Registration	Owner/Operator	Series	First Flight	Delivery	Remarks
	7T-WAU	Inter Air Services			JUN/83	
	7T-WAU	Air Algerie			NOV/84	
10556	PH-EXS	Fokker	400M	17/MAY/77		
	PH-FRY	Fokker			29/JUN/77	
	7T-WAV	Algerian Government			04/JUL/77	
10557	PH-EXC	Fokker	600	27/MAY/77		
	PH-FTA	Fokker			15/JUN/77	
	6O-SAY	Somali Airlines			16/JUN/77	W/O 20/JUL/81, Balad
10558	PH-EXH	Fokker	500	17/JUN/77		
	VH-FCE	Ansett Airlines of NSW			01/JUL/77	
	VH-FCE	Air New South Wales			01/JUN/81	
10559	PH-EXG	Fokker	600	15/JUL/77		
	PH-FTB	Fokker			02/AUG/77	
	6O-SAZ	Somali Airlines			03/AUG/77	
10560	PH-EXL	Fokker	500	09/AUG/77		
		Aramco				Not taken-up
	VH-FCF	Ansett Airlines of NSW			30/AUG/77	
	VH-FCF	Air New South Wales			01/JUN/81	
10561	PH-EXI	Fokker	400M	01/AUG/77		
		Ansett Airlines of Australia				Not taken-up
		Algerian Government				Not taken-up
	PH-FTT	Fokker			06/DEC/79	
	D2-EFA	Angolan Air Force			18/JAN/80	
	T-101	Angolan Air Force			31/JAN/80	
	D2-TFS	TAAG			JAN/84	
10562	PH-EXK	Fokker	600	07/SEP/77		
		Air Algerie				Not taken-up
	PH-EXK	Fokker				
	PH-YEM	Fokker			05/APR/78	
	PH-YEM	Libyan Arab Airlines			11/APR/79	Leased
	PH-YEM	Fokker			25/NOV/79	
	PH-YEM	Uganda Airlines			04/DEC/79	Leased
	PH-YEM	Fokker			24/JAN/80	
	PH-YEM	Fokker	600			Converted
	OE-ILB	Lauda Air			03/MAR/80	
	OE-ILB	Egyptair			03/APR/81	Leased
	OE-ILB	Air Sinai			01/AUG/82	Leased
	OE-ILB	Lauda Air			14/APR/83	
	EC-DSS	Aviaco			APR/83	
	OE-ILB	Lauda Air			APR/84	
	OE-ILB	WDL			OCT/84	
	OE-ILB	DLT			SEP/84	Leased
	D-AELB	WDL			JUL/85	
10563	PH-EXM	Fokker	600	04/OCT/77		
		Air Algerie				Not taken-up
	PH-FTH	Fokker				
	PH-FTH	Air Niger			07/MAR/78	Leased
	5U-BAH	Air Niger			07/JUN/78	Purchased
	5U-BAH	Aviolease			17/DEC/81	
	PH-FTH	Fokker			01/MAR/82	Leased
	PH-FTH	Aviolease			12/MAY/82	
	HB-AAT	Air Sinai			31/AUG/82	Leased
	HB-AAT	Aviona Leasing			17/MAR/83	
	EC-DSP	Aviaco			17/MAR/83	Leased
	HB-AAT	Aviona Leasing			MAR/84	
	7P-LAJ	Air Lesotho			SEP/85	
10564	PH-EXA	Fokker	400M	27/SEP/77		
	6V-STA	Senegal Air Force			27/NOV/77	
10565	PH-EXB	Fokker	400M	14/OCT/77		
	6V-STB	Senegal Air Force			06/JAN/78	
10566	PH-EXC	Fokker	600	31/OCT/77		
	PH-FTD	Fokker			20/NOV/77	
	5H-MPT	Air Tanzania			22/NOV/77	
10567	PH-EXF	Fokker	600	25/NOV/77		
	5-4041	Imperial Iranian Army			06/JAN/78	
	5-3031	Imperial Iranian Army			01/SEP/78	
	5-3031	Iranian Army Aviation			01/FEB/79	
10568	PH-EXG	Fokker	400M	05/DEC/77		
	5-4042	Imperial Iranian Army			09/JAN/78	
	5-3032	Imperial Iranian Army			01/SEP/78	
	5-3032	Iranian Army Aviation			01/FEB/79	
10569	PH-EXH	Fokker	600	09/DEC/77		
	PH-FTE	Fokker			27/DEC/77	
	5H-MPU	Air Tanzania			29/DEC/77	
10570	PH-EXA	Fokker	500	03/JAN/78		
	F-BYAH	Air Rouergue			02/FEB/78	W/O 28/JAN/79,Nr.Rodez,France
10571	PH-EXB	Fokker	600	16/FEB/78		
	PH-FTF	Fokker			08/MAY/78	
	SU-AZN	Egypt Air Charter			09/MAY/78	
	5X-UAO	Uganda Airlines			10/MAY/78	
	5X-UWX	Uganda Airlines			01/NOV/79	
10572	PH-EXC	Fokker	600	09/MAR/78		
	XY-ADY	Burma Airways Corp.			19/MAY/78	W/O 03/OCT/78,Mandalay Ap.
10573	PH-EXE	Fokker	600	05/APR/78		
	TU-TIF	Air Ivoire			16/FEB/79	
10574	PH-EXF	Fokker	600	20/APR/78		
	XY-ADZ	Burma Airways Corp.			20/OCT/78	
10575	PH-EXG	Fokker	400M	26/MAY/78		
	TC-79	Argentine Air Force			07/FEB/79	
10576	PH-EXH	Fokker	600	19/JUN/78		
	PH-FTI	Fokker			25/SEP/78	
	SU-AZZ	Egypt Air Charter				Not taken-up
	5X-UAP	Uganda Airlines			18/JAN/80	
10577	PH-EXK	Fokker	400M	13/JUL/78		
	TU-VAD	Ivory Coast Government			10/MAY/79	
	TU-TIP	Air Ivoire			12/MAY/79	
10578	PH-EXL	Fokker	400M	01/AUG/78		
	PH-FTN	Fokker			28/APR/79	
	TAM-90	TAM			01/MAY/79	
10579	PH-EXF	Fokker	600	11/JAN/79		
	TU-TIH	Air Ivoire			16/FEB/79	
10580	PH-EXM	Fokker	400M	14/NOV/78		
	PH-FTO	Fokker			23/JAN/79	
	TAM-91	TAM			29/MAY/79	
10581	PH-EXA	Fokker	200MPA	23/NOV/78		

FOKKER F-27 FRIENDSHIP

C/N	Registration	Owner/Operator	Series	First Flight	Delivery	Remarks
	PH-FTK	Fokker			10/DEC/78	
	PH-FTK	Spanish Air Rescue			12/DEC/78	Leased
	PH-FTK	Fokker			23/JAN/79	
	D2-01	Spanish Air Rescue			06/APR/79	Call-sign 'EC-ZYM'
10582	PH-EXB	Fokker	400M	21/SEP/78		
	6W-STC	Senegal Air Force			10/NOV/78	
10583	PH-EXC	Fokker	400M	10/NOV/78		
	6W-STD	Senegal Air Force			10/NOV/78	
10584	PH-EXH	Fokker	400M	19/FEB/79		
	PH-FTM	Fokker			10/APR/79	
	TAM-92	TAM			17/APR/79	
10585	PH-EXD	Fokker	200MPA	20/DEC/78		
	D2-02	Spanish Air Rescue			28/FEB/79	Call-sign 'EC-ZYN'
10586	PH-EXA	Fokker	600	06/MAR/79		
	5A-DDU	Libyan Arab Airlines			14/SEP/79	
10587	PH-EXB	Fokker	200MPA	27/MAR/79		
	PH-FTL	Fokker			26/JUN/79	
	D2-03	Spanish Air Rescue			10/JUL/79	Call-sign 'EC-ZYO'
10588	PH-EXC	Fokker	600	17/APR/79		
	5A-DDV	Libyan Arab Airlines			23/OCT/79	
10589	PH-EXD	Fokker	600	23/APR/79		
	PH-FTP	Fokker			15/MAY/79	
	5H-MRM	Air Tanzania			29/MAY/79	
10590	PH-EXE	Fokker	400M	22/MAY/79		
	6W-STE	Senegal Air Force			01/OCT/79	
10591	PH-EXF	Fokker	400M	22/JUL/79		
	PH-FTS	Fokker			23/SEP/79	
	6W-STF	Senegal Air Force			01/OCT/79	
10592	PH-EXG	Fokker	600	14/AUG/79		
	N421SA	Swift Aire			14/JAN/80	
	N421SA	Air North			25/APR/82	
	N421SA	Brockway Air			SEP/84	
10593	PH-EXH	Fokker	600	26/SEP/79		
	N422SA	Swift Aire			14/JAN/80	
	N422SA	Air North			25/APR/82	
	N422SA	Brockway Air			SEP/84	
10594	PH-EXK	Fokker	600	25/OCT/79		
	N423SA	Swift Aire			08/FEB/80	
	N423SA	Air North			25/APR/82	
	N423SA	Brockway Air			SEP/84	
10595	PH-EXL	Fokker	200MPA	13/MAR/80		
	PH-FTU	Fokker			08/AUG/80	
	TR-301	Angolan Air Force			26/SEP/80	
10596	PH-EXM	Fokker	500	01/FEB/80		
	N334MV	Mississippi Valley Airlines			31/OCT/80	
	N334MV	Air Wisconsin			MAY/85	
10597	PH-EXA	Fokker	500	12/FEB/80		
	ZK-NFD	Air New Zealand			13/MAR/80	
10598	PH-EXB	Fokker	500	21/MAR/80		
	ZK-NFE	Air New Zealand			16/APR/80	
10599	PH-EXC	Fokker	400M	21/APR/80		
	TAM-93	TAM			19/MAY/80	
10600	PH-EXD	Fokker	400M	21/MAY/80		
	PH-FTV	Fokker			14/AUG/80	Stored at Woensdrecht
	TAM-94	TAM			07/FEB/81	
10601	PH-EXE	Fokker	400M	20/JUN/80		
	PH-FTW	Fokker			14/AUG/80	Stored at Woensdrecht
	TAM-95	TAM			07/FEB/81	
10602	PH-EXF	Fokker	200MAR	05/SEP/80		
	10602	Philippine Air Force			09/FEB/81	
10603	PH-KFI	NLM	500	02/SEP/80	19/DEC/80	
10604	PH-EXG	Fokker	500	28/NOV/80		
	PH-FTZ	Fokker			18/MAY/81	
	N337MV	Mississippi Valley Airlines				Not taken-up
	PH-FTZ	Aviona Leasing			27/JUL/81	
	5A-DJE	United African Airlines			12/AUG/81	
	5A-DJE	Libyan Arab Airlines			82	
10605	PH-KFK	NLM	500	02/OCT/80	21/JAN/81	
10606	PH-KFL	NLM	500	21/OCT/80	21/JAN/81	
10607	PH-EXH	Fokker	500	23/DEC/80		
	ZK-NFF	Air New Zealand			05/MAR/81	
10608	PH-EXK	Fokker	500	26/JAN/81		
	N	Suburban Airlines			MAR/81	Not taken-up
	N424SA	Golden Gate Airlines			81	Not taken-up
	N424SA	Swift Aire			APR/81	Not taken-up
	PH-FSK	Fokker			11/MAR/82	
	D2-ESM	Diamang			DEC/82	Not taken-up
	D2-TFW	TAAG Angola			14/APR/83	
10609	PH-EXI	Fokker	500	06/FEB/81		
	ZK-NFG	Air New Zealand				Reg. not taken-up
	ZK-NFH	Air New Zealand			28/MAR/81	
10610	PH-EXJ	Fokker	500	13/MAR/81		
	PH-FTY	Fokker			31/MAR/81	
	D2-ESN	Sonangol			10/APR/81	
10611	PH-EXL	Fokker	500	27/MAR/81		
	N338MV	Mississippi Valley Airlines			APR/81	Not taken-up
	5A-DJF	United African Airlines			02/OCT/81	
	5A-DJF	Libyan Arab Airlines			82	
10612	PH-EXC	Fokker	200MAR	11/MAY/81		
	M-1	Royal Dutch Navy			30/SEP/81	Call-sign 'PE-MMA'
10613	PH-EXM	Fokker	500	20/MAY/81		
	9M-MCK	Malaysian Airline System			13/JUN/81	
10614	PH-EXB	Fokker	500	22/MAY/81		
	ZK-NFI	Air New Zealand			10/JUL/81	
10615	PH-EXD	Fokker	500	17/JUN/81		
	9M-MCL	Malaysian Airline System			06/AUG/81	
10616	PH-EXF	Fokker	200MAR	14/AUG/81		
	10616	Philippine Air Force			19/OCT/81	
10617	PH-EXE	Fokker	500	18/SEP/81		
	N339MV	Mississippi Valley Airlines				Not taken-up
	N425SA	Golden Gate Airlines			81	Not taken-up
	N425SA	Swift Aire			81	Not taken-up
	XY-AEJ	Burma Airways			19/DEC/81	
	XY-AEJ	Burmese Air Force			DEC/81	
10618	PH-EXG	Fokker	500	11/SEP/81		

C/N	Registration	Owner/Operator	Series	First Flight	Delivery	Remarks
	ZK-NFJ	Air New Zealand			01/OCT/81	
10619	PH-EXH	Fokker	400	29/SEP/81		
	TC-72	LADE			20/NOV/81	
10620	PH-EXI	Fokker	200MAR	27/OCT/81		
	10620	Philippine Air Force			15/FEB/82	Callsign 'RP-620'
10621	PH-EXM	Fokker	400	08/NOV/81		
	TC-75	LADE			18/DEC/81	
10622	PH-EXD	Fokker	200MAR	08/DEC/81		
	PH-FSI	Fokker			26/JAN/82	
	M-2	Royal Dutch Navy			26/FEB/82	
10623	PH-EXB	Fokker	500	14/DEC/81		
	PK-GRF	Merpati Nusantara			20/JAN/82	
	PK-MFG	Merpati Nusantara			JAN/82	
10624	PH-EXC	Fokker	500	22/DEC/81		
	PK-GRG	Merpati Nusantara			28/JAN/82	
	PK-MFI	Merpati Nusantara			JAN/82	
10625	PH-EXJ	Fokker	500	08/JAN/82		
	PK-GRH	Merpati Nusantara			10/FEB/82	
	PK-MFJ	Merpati Nusantara			FEB/82	
10626	PH-EXF	Fokker	500	27/JAN/82		
	PK-GRI	Merpati Nusantara			24/FEB/82	
	PK-MFK	Merpati Nusantara			FEB/82	
10627	PH-EXL	Fokker	500	17/FEB/82		
	9Q-	Air Zaire			82	Not taken-up
	VH-EWU	East West Airlines			28/SEP/83	
10628	PH-EXG	Fokker	500	26/FEB/82		
	PK-GRJ	Merpati Nusantara			24/MAR/82	
	PK-MFJ	Merpati Nusantara			MAR/82	
10629	PH-EXE	Fokker	500	05/MAR/82		
	PK-GRK	Merpati Nusantara			07/APR/82	
	PK-MFM	Merpati Nusantara			APR/82	
10630	PH-EXH	Fokker	500	31/MAR/82		
	A40-FB	Oman Aviation Services			28/MAY/82	
10631	PH-EXM	Fokker	500	13/APR/82		
	A40-FC	Oman Aviation Services			19/JUN/82	
10632	PH-FSJ	Fokker	500	21/APR/82		
	N426SA	Swift Aire			82	Not taken-up
	PT-LAJ	TAM			29/DEC/82	
10633	PH-EXC	Fokker	500	25/MAY/82		
	9Q-	Air Zaire			JUN/82	Not taken-up
	G-	Polar Airways				Not taken-up
	PH-FSO	Fokker			30/AUG/83	
	VH-EWV	East West Airlines			02/SEP/83	
10634	PH-EXJ	Fokker	500			
	N427SA	Swift Aire			82	Not taken-up
	PH-FSL	Fokker			JUL/82	
	PT-LAK	TAM			29/DEC/82	
10635	PH-EXD	Fokker	600	08/JUN/82		
	5A-DLK	Libyan Arab Airlines			29/JUL/82	
10636	PH-EXB	Fokker	600	21/JUN/82		
	5A-DLM	Libyan Arab Airlines			15/AUG/82	
10637	PH-EXE	Fokker	500			
	9Q-	Air Zaire			SEP/82	Cancelled order
	VH-EWW	East West Airlines			09/OCT/83	
10638	PH-EXF	Fokker	600	03/AUG/82		
	5A-DKD	Tebesti Air Transport			82	Not taken-up
	5A-DKD	Libyan Aeroclub			04/AUG/83	
10639	PH-EXG	Fokker	500	27/AUG/82		
	9Q-	Air Zaire			82	Not taken-up
	VH-EWX	East West Airlines			05/NOV/83	
10640	PH-EXH	Fokker	600			
	5A-DLN	Libyan Arab Airlines			01/NOV/82	
10641	PH-EXI	Fokker	500	01/OCT/82		
	A40-FE	Oman Aviation Services			07/APR/83	
10642	PH-EXJ	Fokker	500	12/OCT/82		
	A40-FG	Oman Aviation Services			26/NOV/82	
10643	PH-EXK	Fokker	500	08/MAR/83		
	PH-FSN	Fokker			25/MAY/83	Demonstrator
	N27SA	Suburban Airlines			17/MAY/84	
10644	PH-EXM	Fokker	600	08/NOV/82		
	5A-DLO	Libyan Arab Airlines			15/JAN/83	
10645	PH-EXB	Fokker	600	17/NOV/82		
	5A-DLP	Libyan Arab Airlines			17/MAR/83	W/O 15/APR/86, Tripoli
10646	PH-EXD	Fokker	600	08/NOV/82		
	5A-DLQ	Libyan Arab Airlines			19/MAY/83	
10647	PH-EXH	Fokker	600	05/JAN/83		
	5A-DLR	Libyan Arab Airlines			13/APR/83	
10648	PH-EXA	Fokker	600	17/JAN/83		
	5A-DLS	Libyan Arab Airlines			15/JUN/83	
10649	PH-EXJ	Fokker	400M	83		Stored Ypenburg
	9Q-CBH	Scibe Airlift			23/JUN/86	Stored Ypenburg
10650	PH-EXI	Fokker	400M	25/MAY/83		Stored Ypenburg
	10650	Royal Thai Navy			NOV/86	Sched.delivery
10651	PH-EXM	Fokker	400M	07/APR/83		Stored Ypenburg
	10651	Royal Thai Navy			FEB/87	Sched.delivery
10652	PH-EXB	Fokker	400M	20/APR/83		Stored Ypenburg
	85-1607	U.S. Army Parachute Team			28/NOV/85	
10653	PH-EXH	Fokker	200MAR	19/MAY/83		
	PH-FSM	Fokker			24/MAY/83	Demonstrator
	NAF-907	Nigerian Air Force			02/JUN/86	
10654	PH-EXJ	Fokker	500	18/MAY/83		
	SU-GAF	Air Sinai			24/FEB/84	
10655	PH-EXD	Fokker	400MAR	23/JUN/83		
	PH-FSR	Fokker			26/OCT/83	
	PH-FSR	Fokker	400M		86	Converted
	9Q-CBE	Scibe Airlift			23/JUN/86	
10656	PH-EXD	Fokker	200MAR			
	PH-FSP	Fokker			26/OCT/83	
	NAF-908	Nigerian Air Force			86	Sched.delivery
10657	PH-EXK	Fokker	500	16/AUG/83		
	7T-	Inter Air Service			84	Cancelled order
	N501AW	Air Wisconsin			02/DEC/85	
10658	PH-EXA	Fokker	500	15/SEP/83		
	N241MA	Midstate Airlines			28/FEB/85	
	N241MA	Chicago Air			JUL/86	Leased

FOKKER F-27 FRIENDSHIP

C/N	Registration	Owner/Operator	Series	First Flight	Delivery	Remarks
10659	PH-EXF	Fokker	500	15/NOV/83		
	SU-GAD	Air Sinai			03/DEC/83	W/O 10/JUN/86, nr. Cairo Ap.
10660	PH-EXC	Fokker	500	29/NOV/83		
	SU-GAE	Air Sinai			15/JAN/84	
10661	PH-EXE	Fokker	500	12/DEC/83		
	7T-	Inter Air Service			84	Cancelled order
	N502AW	Air Wisconsin			24/OCT/85	
10662	PH-EXL	Fokker	400			
	FF-3	Finnish Air Force			31/JAN/84	
10663	PH-EXH	Fokker	200MAR	18/FEB/84		
	PH-FSX	Fokker			84	
	10663	Royal Thai Navy			04/OCT/84	
10664	PH-EXG	Fokker	500F	30/JAN/84		
	7T-	Inter Air Service				Cancelled order
	N239MA	Midstate Airlines			29/JUL/84	
	N239MA	Chicago Air			MAY/86	Leased
10665	PH-EXL	Fokker	200MAR	07/MAR/84		
	PH-FSU	Fokker			02/APR/84	
	10665	Royal Thai Navy			20/APR/84	
10666	PH-EXC	Fokker	200MAR			
	10666	Royal Thai Navy			31/MAY/84	
10667	PH-EXI	Fokker	500			
	7T-	Inter Air Service				Cancelled order
	N240MA	Midstate Airlines			21/AUG/84	
	N240MA	Chicago Air			JUL/86	
10668	PH-EXJ	Fokker	400M			
	85-1608	U.S. Army Parachute Team			28/NOV/85	
10669	PH-EXL	Fokker	400			
	VH-EWY	East West Airlines			03/AUG/84	
10670	PH-ESU	Fokker	200MAR			
	PH-FSY	Fokker			23/AUG/84	
	PH-FSY	Fokker	200			Converted
	LN-AKA	Busy Bee			11/MAR/86	
10671	N503AW	Air Wisconsin	500		14/APR/86	
10672	PH-EXS	Fokker	500F			
	VH-EWZ	East West Airlines			28/AUG/84	
10673	PH-EXY	Fokker	200MAR			
	PH-EXY	Fokker	200			Converted
	LN-AKB	Busy Bee			03/APR/86	
10674	PH-EXU	Fokker	200			
	LN-AKC	Busy Bee			17/APR/86	
10675	PH-EXG	Fokker	200			
	LN-AKD	Busy Bee			29/APR/86	
10676	PH-EXT	Fokker	200MAR			
	10676	Royal Thai Navy			JUN/87	Sched.delivery
10677	PH-EXP	Fokker	500			
	N504AW	Air Wisconsin			10/OCT/85	
10678	PH-EXR	Fokker	500			
	N242MA	Midstate Airlines			11/JUN/85	
10679	PH-EXV	Fokker	500			
	N243MA	Midstate Airlines			17/DEC/85	
	N243MA	Chicago Air			MAY/86	Leased
10680	PH-EXW	Fokker	500			
	N244MA	Midstate Airlines			17/DEC/85	
10681	PH-EXN	Fokker	500			
	N505AW	Air Wisconsin			04/OCT/85	
10682	N506AW	Air Wisconsin	500		05/NOV/85	
10683	PH-EXX	Fokker	500			
	N508AW	Air Wisconsin			22/OCT/85	
10684	PH-EXM	Fokker	500			
	N509AW	Air Wisconsin			18/MAR/86	
10685	PH-OSO	Fokker	F-50	28/DEC/85		Prototype TA-1
10686	PH-EXF	Fokker	500			
	N510AW	Air Wisconsin			17/FEB/86	
10687	9Q-CBD	Scibe Airlift	500		23/JUN/86	
10688	PH-OSI	Fokker	F-50	30/APR/86		Prototype TA-2
10689	PH-	Fokker	600			
	XY-AEL	Burma Airways			19/DEC/85	
	PH-FUC	Fokker			24/DEC/85	
10690	PH-EXD	Fokker	500			
	N511AW	Air Wisconsin			13/MAY/86	
10691	N512AW	Air Wisconsin	500		28/MAY/86	
10692	PH-EXH	Fokker	500			
	N513AW	Air Wisconsin			25/JUN/86	

5A- Libya

10275	5A-DBE
10436	5A-DBN
10513	5A-DBO
10515	5A-DBP
10516	5A-DBQ
10517	5A-DBR
10519	5A-DBS
10521	5A-DBT
10586	5A-DDU
10588	5A-DDV
10469	5A-DFN
10604	5A-DJE
10611	5A-DJF
10430	5A-DJN
10638	5A-DKD
10635	5A-DLK
10636	5A-DLM
10640	5A-DLN
10644	5A-DLO
10645	5A-DLP
10646	5A-DLQ
10647	5A-DLR
10648	5A-DLS

5H- Tanzania

10212	5H-AAC
10213	5H-AAI
10241	5H-AAP
10566	5H-MPT
10569	5H-MPU
10212	5H-MRH
10589	5H-MRM
10241	5H-MRO

5N- Nigeria

10216	5N-AAV
10217	5N-AAW
10218	5N-AAX
10222	5N-AAY
10223	5N-AAZ
10399	5N-ABA
10400	5N-ABB
10473	5N-ANL
10476	5N-ANM
10493	5N-ANS
10487	5N-ANT
10354	5N-CLN

5U- Niger

10563	5U-BAH

5X- Uganda

10241	5X-AAP
10571	5X-UAO
10576	5X-UAP
10571	5X-UWX

5Y- Kenya

10211	5Y-AAB
10212	5Y-AAC
10213	5Y-BBS

60- Somalia

10557	6O-SAY
10559	6O-SAZ

6V- Senegal

10228	6V-AEG
10564	6V-STA
10565	6V-STB

7P- Lesotho

10563	7P-LAJ

7T- Algeria

10547	7T-VRJ
10553	7T-VRK
10495	7T-VRL
10496	7T-VRM
10527	7T-VRN
10526	7T-VRQ
10494	7T-VRU
10543	7T-VRV

8Q- Maldive Islands

10119	8Q-PNA

9M- Malaysia

10225	9M-AMI
10226	9M-AMJ
10231	9M-AML
10232	9M-AMM
10233	9M-AMN
10293	9M-AOJ
10359	9M-AOX
10364	9M-APP
10456	9M-APU
10461	9M-APV
10464	9M-APW
10468	9M-APX
10471	9M-ARE
10455	9M-ARI
10460	9M-ARJ
10467	9M-ARK
10470	9M-ARL
10472	9M-ASF
10455	9M-MCA
10456	9M-MCB
10460	9M-MCC
10461	9M-MCD
10464	9M-MCE
10467	9M-MCF
10468	9M-MCG
10470	9M-MCH
10471	9M-MCI
10472	9M-MCJ
10613	9M-MCK
10615	9M-MCL
10450	9M-MCY
10242	9M-MCZ

9N- Nepal

10290	9N-AAR
10302	9N-AAS
10308	9N-AAT
10302	9N-AAW

9Q- Zaire

10687	9Q-CBD
10655	9Q-CBE
10649	9Q-CBH
10459	9Q-CBI
10425	9Q-CBU
10208	9Q-CEB
10391	9Q-CLK
10392	9Q-CLL
10393	9Q-CLM
10394	9Q-CLN
10395	9Q-CLO
10402	9Q-CLP
10405	9Q-CLQ
10406	9Q-CLR
10358	9Q-CPC
10359	9Q-CPI

9V- Singapore

10225	9V-BAP
10231	9V-BAQ
10233	9V-BAR
10358	9V-BBF
10365	9V-BCN
10455	9V-BCS
10460	9V-BCT
10463	9V-BCU
10467	9V-BCV
10470	9V-BCW
10364	9V-BFK
10166	9V-BLP

A2- Botswana

10200	A2-ADG
10340	A2-AEC
10333	A2-ZEW

A40- Oman

10443	A40-FA
10630	A40-FB
10631	A40-FC
10323	A40-FD
10641	A40-FE
10642	A40-FG
10316	A40-FN
10325	A40-FU

AP- Pakistan

10163	AP-ALM
10164	AP-ALN
10165	AP-ALO
10187	AP-ALW
10188	AP-ALX
10250	AP-ATO
10279	AP-ATT
10278	AP-ATU
10281	AP-ATW
10307	AP-AUR
10314	AP-AUS
10330	AP-AUV
10331	AP-AUW
10335	AP-AUX
10368	AP-AUY
10453	AP-AWM
10438	AP-AWN
10288	AP-AXB
10354	AP-AXF
10243	AP-BAL
10230	AP-BAO
10207	AP-BBF
10262	AP-BBG

C- Canada

10473	C-GSFS

C9- Mozambique

10204	C9-AIA
10205	C9-AIB
10206	C9-AIC
10401	C9-AMD

CN- Morocco

10432	CN-CDA
10433	CN-CDB

CP- Bolivia

10138	CP-2013

CR- Mozambique

10204	CR-AIA
10205	CR-AIB
10206	CR-AIC
10401	CR-AMD

CR- Angola

10207	CR-LEO
10208	CR-LEP
10326	CR-LIJ
10439	CR-LLD
10457	CR-LMB
10358	CR-LMU
10359	CR-LMV

CX- Uruguay

10199	CX-BHV
10202	CX-BHW

D- West Germany

10562	D-AELB
10109	D-BAKA
10198	D-BAKA
10200	D-BAKE
10257	D-BAKE
10102	D-BAKI
10137	D-BAKU
10186	D-BAKU
10268	D-BARI
10270	D-BARO
10137	D-BATU
10176	D-BEKU
10106	D-BOBY
10257	D-BOBY

D2- Angola

10561	D2-EFA
10608	D2-ESM
10610	D2-ESN
10125	D2-FPH
10207	D2-LEO
10326	D2-LIJ
10423	D2-TAE
10424	D2-TAF
10207	D2-TEO
10125	D2-TFK
10424	D2-TFP
10423	D2-TFQ
10457	D2-TFR
10561	D2-TFS
10608	D2-TFW
10326	D2-TIJ
10457	D2-TMB

D6- Comores

10203	D6-CAI

EC- Spain

10107	EC-BFV
10332	EC-BMS
10343	EC-BMT
10347	EC-BMU
10106	EC-BNJ
10348	EC-BOA
10352	EC-BOB
10353	EC-BOC
10360	EC-BOD
10361	EC-BOE
10108	EC-BPJ
10116	EC-BPK
10109	EC-BRN
10396	EC-CAU
10421	EC-DBM
10429	EC-DBN
10450	EC-DSH
10563	EC-DSP
10562	EC-DSS

EI- Eire

10105	EI-AKA
10106	EI-AKB
10107	EI-AKC
10109	EI-AKD
10110	EI-AKE
10118	EI-AKF
10119	EI-AKG

EP- Iran

10554	EP-ANA
10498	EP-IAJ
10504	EP-IAK
10140	EP-IOK
10151	EP-IOS
10153	EP-IOT
10126	EP-MRP

F- France

10247	F-BIUK
10333	F-BOOC
10334	F-BOOD
10366	F-BPNA
10367	F-BPNB
10371	F-BPNC
10372	F-BPND
10375	F-BPNE
10376	F-BPNF
10380	F-BPNG
10381	F-BPNH
10383	F-BPNI
10384	F-BPNJ
10369	F-BPUA
10370	F-BPUB
10373	F-BPUC
10374	F-BPUD
10377	F-BPUE
10378	F-BPUF
10379	F-BPUG
10382	F-BPUH
10389	F-BPUI
10528	F-BPUI
10390	F-BPUJ
10397	F-BPUK
10398	F-BPUL
10137	F-BRHL
10268	F-BRQL
10229	F-BSIF
10247	F-BSIF
10447	F-BSUM
10506	F-BSUM
10506	F-BSUM
10448	F-BSUN
10449	F-BSUO
10242	F-BUFA
10243	F-BUFE
10259	F-BUFO
10228	F-BUFU
10227	F-BUTA
10230	F-BVTE
10247	F-BVTO
10258	F-BVTU
10340	F-BYAA
10342	F-BYAB
10431	F-BYAC
10425	F-BYAF
10570	F-BYAH
10459	F-BYAH
10443	F-BYAI
10127	F-BYAO
10113	F-BYAP
10430	F-BYAR
10121	F-GAOT
10469	F-GBDE
10196	F-GBDK
10413	F-GBGI
10203	F-GBRX
10244	F-GBRY
10361	F-GCJV
10228	F-GCMA
10324	F-GCMR
10258	F-GCPA
10443	F-GDFT
10227	F-OCSH
10230	F-OCSI
10229	F-OGIF
10247	F-OGJA
10258	F-OGJA
10320	F-SEBF
10409	F-SEBG
10443	F-WDFT

G- United Kingdom

10316	G-AVDN
10325	G-AWFU
10323	G-AZFD
10293	G-BAKL
10225	G-BAUR
10201	G-BCDN
10234	G-BCDO
10289	G-BDDH
10232	G-BDVS
10233	G-BDVT
10270	G-BFDS
10229	G-BHMW
10259	G-BHMX
10196	G-BHMY
10244	G-BHMZ
10120	G-BLFJ
10231	G-BLGW
10135	G-BLML
10318	G-BLMM
10256	G-BMAE
10302	G-BMAP
10134	G-BMAR
10227	G-BMAS
10241	G-BMAU
10212	G-BMAW
10106	G-IOMA
10324	G-JRSY
10228	G-NRSY
10120	G-OMAN
10120	G-SPUD
10131	G-STAN

HB- Switzerland

10141	HB-AAI
10125	HB-AAP
10563	HB-AAT
10200	HB-AAU
10276	HB-AAV
10323	HB-AAW
10351	HB-AAX
10268	HB-AAZ

HL South Korea

10239	HL5201
10240	HL5202
10414	HL5209
10417	HL5210
10427	HL5211
10428	HL5212
10316	HL5262

I- Italy

10450	I-ALML
10289	I-ATIB
10349	I-ATIC
10320	I-ATID
10321	I-ATIF
10288	I-ATIG
10324	I-ATIL
10249	I-ATIM
10350	I-ATIN
10251	I-ATIP
10301	I-ATIR
10256	I-ATIS
10363	I-ATIT
10419	I-ATIV
10420	I-ATIZ
10247	I-SARK
10258	I-SARO
10257	I-SARQ
10442	I-VANA

JA Japan

10177	JA8601
10178	JA8602
10179	JA8603
10195	JA8605
10196	JA8606
10197	JA8607
10203	JA8608
10201	JA8615
10227	JA8616
10228	JA8617
10229	JA8618
10230	JA8619
10234	JA8621
10242	JA8622
10243	JA8623
10244	JA8624
10252	JA8630
10253	JA8631
10254	JA8632
10255	JA8633
10259	JA8634
10260	JA8635
10261	JA8636
10262	JA8637
10263	JA8638

JY- Jordan

10106	JY-ADD
10354	JY-ADF

Fokker F-27 Friendship cross-reference index

LN- Norway

10670	LN-AKA
10673	LN-AKB
10674	LN-AKC
10675	LN-AKD
10289	LN-DAF
10258	LN-NPC
10319	LN-NPD
10186	LN-NPH
10266	LN-NPI
10287	LN-NPM
10321	LN-RNX
10419	LN-RNY
10386	LN-RNZ
10202	LN-SUA
10245	LN-SUE
10298	LN-SUF
10176	LN-SUG
10248	LN-SUL
10108	LN-SUN
10116	LN-SUO
10199	LN-SUW

LV- Argentina

10200	LV-PTO
10201	LV-PTP
10202	LV-PTQ
10203	LV-PTR

LX- Luxembourg

10224	LX-LGA
10269	LX-LGB
10338	LX-LGD
10280	LX-LGJ
10297	LX-LGK

N United States

10114	N1036P
10134	N1036S
10121	N1036U
10275	N10625
10114	N141PM
10122	N142PM
10109	N143PM
10107	N144PM
10116	N145PM
10176	N146PM
10108	N148PM
10368	N20XY
10664	N239MA
10667	N240MA
10658	N241MA
10678	N242MA
10679	N243MA
10679	N243MA
10680	N244MA
10324	N266MA
10228	N267MA
10284	N268MA
10434	N271FA
10341	N272FA
10643	N275A
10122	N300AS
10596	N334MV
10604	N337MV
10611	N338MV
10617	N339MV
10401	N379BS
10206	N379SF
10204	N379SL
10592	N421SA
10593	N422SA
10594	N423SA
10608	N424SA
10617	N425SA
10632	N426SA
10634	N427SA
10476	N4449C
10473	N4449D
10493	N4449E
10431	N4560Z
10124	N47SB
10125	N48SB
10657	N501AW
10661	N502AW
10671	N503AW
10677	N504AW
10681	N505AW
10682	N506AW
10683	N508AW
10684	N509AW
10686	N510AW
10690	N511AW
10691	N512AW
10692	N513AW
10514	N60AN
10508	N61AN
10525	N702A
10503	N703A
10294	N710A
10295	N714A
10530	N737A
10531	N739A
10550	N743A

OB- Peru

10508	OB-R-1042
10443	OB-R-1072
10514	OB-R-1082

OE- Austria

10257	OE-HLA
10562	OE-ILB

OH- Finland

10274	OH-KFA
10300	OH-KLC
10239	OH-LKA
10240	OH-LKB
10260	OH-LKC

OO- Belgium

10342	OO-HLN
10324	OO-PSF
10340	OO-SBP
10354	OO-SCA

OY- Denmark

10425	OY-APA
10426	OY-APB
10431	OY-APC
10437	OY-APD
10443	OY-APE
10459	OY-APF
10227	OY-BST
10443	OY-BST
10318	OY-CCK
10396	OY-DHW
10425	OY-DKR
10426	OY-DKS
10431	OY-DKT
10342	OY-DNF
10385	OY-KAC
10420	OY-KAD
10434	OY-STN
10341	OY-STO

PH- Netherlands

10268	PH-ARI
10270	PH-ARO
10670	PH-ESU
10442	PH-EXA
10451	PH-EXA
10466	PH-EXA
10472	PH-EXA
10489	PH-EXA
10491	PH-EXA
10493	PH-EXA
10499	PH-EXA
10508	PH-EXA
10519	PH-EXA
10536	PH-EXA
10551	PH-EXA
10564	PH-EXA
10570	PH-EXA
10581	PH-EXA
10586	PH-EXA
10597	PH-EXA
10648	PH-EXA
10658	PH-EXA
10439	PH-EXB
10440	PH-EXB
10441	PH-EXB
10454	PH-EXB
10458	PH-EXB
10477	PH-EXB
10494	PH-EXB
10509	PH-EXB
10521	PH-EXB
10537	PH-EXB
10544	PH-EXB
10552	PH-EXB
10565	PH-EXB
10571	PH-EXB
10582	PH-EXB
10587	PH-EXB
10598	PH-EXB
10614	PH-EXB
10623	PH-EXB
10636	PH-EXB
10645	PH-EXB
10652	PH-EXB
10334	PH-EXC
10490	PH-EXC
10510	PH-EXC
10522	PH-EXC
10538	PH-EXC
10545	PH-EXC
10557	PH-EXC
10566	PH-EXC
10572	PH-EXC
10583	PH-EXC
10588	PH-EXC
10599	PH-EXC
10612	PH-EXC
10624	PH-EXC
10633	PH-EXC
10660	PH-EXC
10666	PH-EXC
10429	PH-EXD
10443	PH-EXD
10453	PH-EXD
10459	PH-EXD
10465	PH-EXD
10511	PH-EXD
10524	PH-EXD
10540	PH-EXD
10548	PH-EXD
10233	PH-EXD
10585	PH-EXD
10589	PH-EXD
10600	PH-EXD
10615	PH-EXD
10622	PH-EXD
10635	PH-EXD
10646	PH-EXD
10655	PH-EXD
10656	PH-EXD
10690	PH-EXD
10421	PH-EXE
10424	PH-EXE
10444	PH-EXE
10500	PH-EXE
10512	PH-EXE
10523	PH-EXE
10541	PH-EXE
10549	PH-EXE
10573	PH-EXE
10590	PH-EXE
10601	PH-EXE
10617	PH-EXE
10629	PH-EXE
10637	PH-EXE
10661	PH-EXE
10488	PH-EXE
10445	PH-EXF
10471	PH-EXF
10472	PH-EXF
10492	PH-EXF
10501	PH-EXF
10514	PH-EXF
10525	PH-EXF
10542	PH-EXF
10550	PH-EXF
10567	PH-EXF
10574	PH-EXF
10579	PH-EXF
10591	PH-EXF
10602	PH-EXF
10616	PH-EXF
10626	PH-EXF
10638	PH-EXF
10659	PH-EXF
10686	PH-EXF
10513	PH-EXG
10547	PH-EXG
10559	PH-EXG
10568	PH-EXG
10575	PH-EXG
10592	PH-EXG
10604	PH-EXG
10639	PH-EXG
10664	PH-EXG
10675	PH-EXG
10546	PH-EXH
10558	PH-EXH
10569	PH-EXH
10576	PH-EXH
10584	PH-EXH
10593	PH-EXH
10607	PH-EXH
10619	PH-EXH
10630	PH-EXH
10640	PH-EXH
10647	PH-EXH
10653	PH-EXH
10663	PH-EXH
10692	PH-EXH
10502	PH-EXI
10561	PH-EXI
10609	PH-EXI
10620	PH-EXI
10641	PH-EXI
10650	PH-EXI
10667	PH-EXI
10610	PH-EXJ
10625	PH-EXJ
10642	PH-EXJ
10649	PH-EXJ
10654	PH-EXJ
10668	PH-EXJ
10503	PH-EXK
10515	PH-EXK
10530	PH-EXK
10554	PH-EXK
10562	PH-EXK
10577	PH-EXK
10594	PH-EXK
10608	PH-EXK
10643	PH-EXK
10657	PH-EXK
10504	PH-EXL
10560	PH-EXL
10578	PH-EXL
10595	PH-EXL
10611	PH-EXL
10627	PH-EXL
10662	PH-EXL
10665	PH-EXL
10669	PH-EXL
10341	PH-EXM
10505	PH-EXM
10531	PH-EXM
10563	PH-EXM
10580	PH-EXM
10596	PH-EXM
10613	PH-EXM
10621	PH-EXM
10631	PH-EXM
10644	PH-EXM
10651	PH-EXM
10684	PH-EXM
10681	PH-EXN
10532	PH-EXO
10553	PH-EXO
10677	PH-EXP
10507	PH-EXR
10526	PH-EXR
10678	PH-EXR
10527	PH-EXS
10533	PH-EXS
10543	PH-EXS
10556	PH-EXS
10572	PH-EXS
10421	PH-EXT
10423	PH-EXT
10529	PH-EXT
10555	PH-EXT
10676	PH-EXT
10516	PH-EXU
10674	PH-EXU
10517	PH-EXV
10679	PH-EXV
10497	PH-EXW
10518	PH-EXW
10534	PH-EXW
10680	PH-EXW
10498	PH-EXX
10520	PH-EXX
10535	PH-EXX
10683	PH-EXX
10539	PH-EXY
10673	PH-EXY
10105	PH-FAA
10106	PH-FAB
10107	PH-FAC
10108	PH-FAD
10109	PH-FAE
10110	PH-FAF
10111	PH-FAG
10112	PH-FAH
10113	PH-FAI
10114	PH-FAK
10116	PH-FAL
10115	PH-FAM
10118	PH-FAN
10119	PH-FAO
10120	PH-FAP
10121	PH-FAR
10122	PH-FAS
10123	PH-FAT
10124	PH-FAU
10125	PH-FAV
10126	PH-FAW
10127	PH-FAX
10131	PH-FAY
10132	PH-FAZ
10133	PH-FBA
10134	PH-FBB
10135	PH-FBC
10136	PH-FBD
10137	PH-FBE
10138	PH-FBF
10139	PH-FBG
10143	PH-FBH
10144	PH-FBI
10145	PH-FBK
10146	PH-FBL
10147	PH-FBM
10148	PH-FBN
10149	PH-FBO
10150	PH-FBP
10152	PH-FBR
10154	PH-FBS
10155	PH-FBT
10156	PH-FBU
10157	PH-FBV
10158	PH-FBW
10159	PH-FBX
10160	PH-FBY
10161	PH-FBZ
10162	PH-FCA
10163	PH-FCB
10164	PH-FCC
10165	PH-FCD
10166	PH-FCE
10167	PH-FCF
10168	PH-FCG
10169	PH-FCH
10170	PH-FCI
10171	PH-FCK
10172	PH-FCL
10173	PH-FCM
10174	PH-FCN
10175	PH-FCO
10176	PH-FCP
10177	PH-FCR
10178	PH-FCS
10179	PH-FCT
10180	PH-FCU
10181	PH-FCV
10182	PH-FCW
10183	PH-FCX
10184	PH-FCY
10185	PH-FCZ
10186	PH-FDA
10187	PH-FDB
10188	PH-FDC
10189	PH-FDD
10190	PH-FDE
10191	PH-FDF
10192	PH-FDG
10193	PH-FDH
10194	PH-FDI
10195	PH-FDK
10196	PH-FDL
10197	PH-FDM
10199	PH-FDN
10200	PH-FDO
10201	PH-FDP
10421	PH-FDR
10200	PH-FDR
10202	PH-FDR
10203	PH-FDS
10204	PH-FDT
10205	PH-FDU
10206	PH-FDV
10207	PH-FDW
10208	PH-FDX
10209	PH-FDY
10210	PH-FDZ
10211	PH-FEA
10212	PH-FEB
10213	PH-FEC
10214	PH-FED
10215	PH-FEE
10216	PH-FEF
10217	PH-FEG
10218	PH-FEH
10219	PH-FEI
10220	PH-FEK
10221	PH-FEL
10222	PH-FEM
10223	PH-FEN
10224	PH-FEO
10225	PH-FEP
10226	PH-FER
10227	PH-FES
10228	PH-FET
10229	PH-FEU
10230	PH-FEV
10231	PH-FEW
10232	PH-FEX
10233	PH-FEY
10234	PH-FEZ
10235	PH-FFA
10236	PH-FFB
10237	PH-FFC
10238	PH-FFD
10239	PH-FFE
10240	PH-FFF
10241	PH-FFG
10242	PH-FFH
10243	PH-FFI
10244	PH-FFK
10245	PH-FFL
10246	PH-FFM
10247	PH-FFN
10248	PH-FFO
10249	PH-FFP
10250	PH-FFR
10251	PH-FFS
10252	PH-FFT
10253	PH-FFU
10254	PH-FFV
10255	PH-FFW
10256	PH-FFX
10257	PH-FFY
10258	PH-FFZ
10259	PH-FGA
10260	PH-FGB
10261	PH-FGC
10262	PH-FGD
10263	PH-FGE
10264	PH-FGF
10265	PH-FGG
10266	PH-FGH

10267	PH-FGI	10372	PH-FMU	10547	PH-FRV
10268	PH-FGK	10373	PH-FMV	10553	PH-FRW
10269	PH-FGL	10374	PH-FMW	10555	PH-FRX
10270	PH-FGM	10375	PH-FMX	10556	PH-FRY
10271	PH-FGN	10376	PH-FMY	10554	PH-FRZ
10272	PH-FGO	10377	PH-FMZ	10118	PH-FSA
10273	PH-FGR	10378	PH-FNA	10119	PH-FSB
10274	PH-FGR	10379	PH-FNB	10158	PH-FSC
10275	PH-FGS	10380	PH-FNC	10137	PH-FSD
10276	PH-FGT	10381	PH-FND	10110	PH-FSE
10277	PH-FGU	10382	PH-FNE	10105	PH-FSF
10278	PH-FGV	10383	PH-FNF	10186	PH-FSG
10279	PH-FGW	10384	PH-FNG	10106	PH-FSH
10280	PH-FGX	10385	PH-FNH	10622	PH-FSI
10281	PH-FGY	10386	PH-FNI	10632	PH-FSJ
10282	PH-FGZ	10387	PH-FNK	10608	PH-FSK
10283	PH-FIA	10388	PH-FNL	10634	PH-FSL
10284	PH-FIB	10389	PH-FNM	10653	PH-FSM
10285	PH-FIC	10390	PH-FNN	10643	PH-FSN
10286	PH-FID	10391	PH-FNO	10633	PH-FSO
10287	PH-FIE	10392	PH-FNP	10656	PH-FSP
10288	PH-FIF	10393	PH-FNR	10655	PH-FSR
10289	PH-FIG	10394	PH-FNS	10665	PH-FSU
10290	PH-FIH	10395	PH-FNT	10663	PH-FSX
10291	PH-FII	10396	PH-FNU	10670	PH-FSY
10292	PH-FIK	10397	PH-FNV	10557	PH-FTA
10293	PH-FIL	10398	PH-FNW	10559	PH-FTB
10294	PH-FIN	10399	PH-FNX	10430	PH-FTC
10295	PH-FIO	10400	PH-FNY	10566	PH-FTD
10296	PH-FIP	10401	PH-FNZ	10569	PH-FTE
10297	PH-FIR	10402	PH-FOA	10571	PH-FTF
10298	PH-FIS	10403	PH-FOB	10424	PH-FTG
10299	PH-FIT	10404	PH-FOC	10563	PH-FTH
10300	PH-FIU	10405	PH-FOD	10576	PH-FTI
10301	PH-FIV	10406	PH-FOE	10581	PH-FTK
10302	PH-FIW	10407	PH-FOF	10587	PH-FTL
10303	PH-FIX	10408	PH-FOG	10584	PH-FTM
10304	PH-FIY	10409	PH-FOH	10578	PH-FTN
10305	PH-FIZ	10410	PH-FOI	10580	PH-FTO
10306	PH-FKA	10411	PH-FOK	10589	PH-FTP
10307	PH-FKB	10412	PH-FOL	10450	PH-FTR
10161	PH-FKB	10413	PH-FOM	10591	PH-FTS
10308	PH-FKC	10414	PH-FON	10561	PH-FTT
10309	PH-FKD	10415	PH-FOO	10595	PH-FTU
10310	PH-FKE	10416	PH-FOP	10600	PH-FTV
10311	PH-FKF	10417	PH-FOR	10601	PH-FTW
10312	PH-FKG	10418	PH-FOS	10610	PH-FTY
10313	PH-FKH	10419	PH-FOT	10604	PH-FTZ
10314	PH-FKI	10420	PH-FOU	10689	PH-FUC
10315	PH-FKK	10421	PH-FOV	10140	PH-IOK
10316	PH-FKL	10422	PH-FOW	10141	PH-IOP
10317	PH-FKM	10423	PH-FOX	10151	PH-IOS
10318	PH-FKN	10424	PH-FOY	10151	PH-IOS
10319	PH-FKO	10425	PH-FOZ	10153	PH-IOT
10320	PH-FKP	10426	PH-FPA	10539	PH-JBO
10321	PH-FKR	10427	PH-FPB	10159	PH-KFA
10322	PH-FKS	10428	PH-FPC	10200	PH-KFC
10323	PH-FKT	10429	PH-FPD	10276	PH-KFD
10324	PH-FKU	10430	PH-FPE	10351	PH-KFE
10325	PH-FKV	10431	PH-FPF	10249	PH-KFG
10326	PH-FKW	10432	PH-FPG	10256	PH-KFH
10327	PH-FKX	10433	PH-FPH	10603	PH-KFI
10328	PH-FKY	10434	PH-FPI	10605	PH-KFK
10329	PH-FKZ	10435	PH-FPK	10606	PH-KFL
10330	PH-FLA	10436	PH-FPL	10198	PH-LIP
10331	PH-FLB	10437	PH-FPM	10549	PH-MPA
10332	PH-FLC	10438	PH-FPN	10101	PH-NIV
10333	PH-FLD	10439	PH-FPN	10102	PH-NVF
10334	PH-FLE	10439	PH-FPO	10201	PH-OGA
10335	PH-FLF	10457	PH-FPP	10234	PH-OGB
10336	PH-FLG	10442	PH-FPR	10688	PH-OSI
10337	PH-FLH	10455	PH-FPR	10685	PH-OSO
10338	PH-FLI	10456	PH-FPS	10142	PH-PBF
10339	PH-FLK	10453	PH-FPU	10459	PH-RUA
10340	PH-FLL	10481	PH-FPV	10271	PH-SAB
10341	PH-FLM	10446	PH-FPW	10272	PH-SAD
10342	PH-FLN	10489	PH-FPW	10248	PH-SAF
10343	PH-FLO	10447	PH-FPX	10298	PH-SAN
10344	PH-FLP	10494	PH-FPX	10107	PH-SAP
10345	PH-FLR	10448	PH-FPY	10325	PH-SAR
10346	PH-FLS	10449	PH-FPZ	10294	PH-SFA
10347	PH-FLT	10495	PH-FPZ	10295	PH-SFB
10348	PH-FLU	10496	PH-FRA	10562	PH-YEM
10349	PH-FLV	10151	PH-FRA	10109	PH-YFF
10350	PH-FLW	10451	PH-FRB		
10351	PH-FLX	10477	PH-FRB		
10352	PH-FLY	10153	PH-FRB		
10353	PH-FLZ	10526	PH-FRC	**P2- Papua New Guinea**	
10354	PH-FMA	10473	PH-FRD		
10355	PH-FMB	10488	PH-FRD	10111	P2-ANA
10356	PH-FMC	10527	PH-FRD	10134	P2-ANB
10357	PH-FMD	10507	PH-FRE	10135	P2-ANC
10358	PH-FME	10505	PH-FRF	10138	P2-AND
10359	PH-FMF	10512	PH-FRG	10179	P2-ANE
10360	PH-FMG	10518	PH-FRH	10261	P2-ANF
10361	PH-FMH	10520	PH-FRI	10291	P2-ANI
10362	PH-FMI	10529	PH-FRK	10133	P2-ANJ
10363	PH-FMK	10536	PH-FRL	10170	P2-ANK
10364	PH-FML	10537	PH-FRM	10280	P2-ANL
10365	PH-FMM	10538	PH-FRN	10297	P2-ANM
10366	PH-FMN	10540	PH-FRO	10318	P2-ANS
10367	PH-FMO	10541	PH-FRP	10134	P2-ANZ
10368	PH-FMP	10542	PH-FRR	10261	P2-BNF
10369	PH-FMR	10544	PH-FRS	10179	P2-MNE
10370	PH-FMS	10546	PH-FRT	10111	P2-TFA
10371	PH-FMT	10543	PH-FRU	10134	P2-TFI
				10135	P2-TFJ

PI- Philippines

10147	PI-C501
10148	PI-C502
10191	PI-C503
10209	PI-C504
10210	PI-C506
10246	PI-C507
10247	PI-C508
10257	PI-C509
10258	PI-C512
10265	PI-C514
10267	PI-C516
10285	PI-C527
10296	PI-C528
10106	PI-C530
10310	PI-C531
10311	PI-C532
10327	PI-C534
10328	PI-C536

PJ- Netherlands Antilles

10364	PJ-FRE
10365	PJ-FRM

PK- Indonesia

10362	PK-CFD
10409	PK-GFE
10410	PK-GFF
10413	PK-GFG
10415	PK-GFH
10421	PK-GFI
10422	PK-GFJ
10423	PK-GFK
10424	PK-GFL
10429	PK-GFM
10430	PK-GFN
10432	PK-GFO
10462	PK-GFO
10462	PK-GFP
10465	PK-GFQ
10466	PK-GFR
10222	PK-GRA
10223	PK-GRC
10399	PK-GRD
10400	PK-GRE
10623	PK-GRF
10624	PK-GRG
10625	PK-GRH
10626	PK-GRI
10628	PK-GRJ
10629	PK-GRK
10410	PK-JFF
10413	PK-JFG
10396	PK-JFH
10362	PK-JFI
10226	PK-JFK
10270	PK-JFM
10242	PK-JFN
10231	PK-KFG
10142	PK-KFR
10222	PK-MFA
10223	PK-MFC
10399	PK-MFD
10400	PK-MFE
10623	PK-MFG
10415	PK-MFH
10624	PK-MFI
10625	PK-MFJ
10628	PK-MFJ
10626	PK-MFK
10629	PK-MFM
10435	PK-MFO
10136	PK-MFP
10143	PK-MFR
10166	PK-MFS
10299	PK-MFT
10166	PK-OBP
10299	PK-PFA
10306	PK-PFB
10339	PK-PFC
10195	PK-PFR
10365	PK-PFS
10197	PK-PFT
10203	PK-PFU
10244	PK-PFV
10177	PK-PFW
10178	PK-PFX
10430	PK-RFN
10430	PK-RFT
10538	PK-VTE

PT- Brasil

10177	PT-LAF
10197	PT-LAG
10178	PT-LAH
10326	PT-LAI
10632	PT-LAJ
10634	PT-LAK
10204	PT-LCF
10206	PT-LCG
10133	PT-LCX
10170	PT-LCY
10291	PT-LCZ
10253	PT-LDJ
10401	PT-LDT
10134	PT-LGH
10195	PT-ODM

S2- Bangladesh

10302	S2-ABF
10308	S2-ABG
10439	S2-ABH
10453	S2-ABJ
10232	S2-ABK
10233	S2-ABL
10477	S2-ABO
10442	S2-ABP

S9- Sao Tome

10487	S9-TAC

SE- Sweden

10329	SE-IRF
10387	SE-IRG
10349	SE-ITI
10350	SE-ITI

ST- Sudan

10192	ST-AAA
10193	ST-AAR
10194	ST-AAS
10238	ST-AAY
10282	ST-ADW
10273	ST-ADX
10277	ST-ADY

SU- Egypt

10571	SU-AZN
10576	SU-AZZ
10659	SU-GAD
10660	SU-GAE
10654	SU-GAF

TC- Turkey

10182	TC-TAY
10183	TC-TEK
10123	TC-TEZ
10124	TC-TON
10125	TC-TOY

TF- Iceland

10274	TF-FIJ
10300	TF-FIK
10356	TF-FIL
10263	TF-FIM
10255	TF-FIN
10176	TF-FIP
10274	TF-FLJ
10300	TF-FLK
10263	TF-FLM
10255	TF-FLN
10414	TF-FLO
10176	TF-FLP
10240	TF-FLP
10417	TF-FLR
10239	TF-FLS
10260	TF-FLS
10240	TF-FLT
10545	TF-SYN
10260	TF-SYR

TG- Guatemala

10270	TG-ACA
10179	TG-AEA
10493	TG-AFA
10111	TG-AIA
10261	TG-AOA

TN- Congo

10446	TN-ABZ
10137	TN-ACR

TS- Tunisia

10110	TS-LVA
10118	TS-LVB
10119	TS-LVC

TT- Chad

10430	TT-AAK

TU- Ivory Coast

10450	TU-TIA
10573	TU-TIF
10579	TU-TIH
10577	TU-TIP
10577	TU-VAD

Fokker F-27 Friendship cross-reference index

10450	TU-VAJ
10469	TU-VAK

TY- Benin

10409	TY-AAG
10413	TY-AAG
10409	TY-ATM
10413	TY-ATM
10409	TY-BBI
10413	TY-BBJ

TZ- Mali

10242	TZ-BAB

VH- Australia

10132	VH-CAT
10131	VH-CAV
10127	VH-EWA
10266	VH-EWG
10190	VH-EWH
10287	VH-EWJ
10319	VH-EWK
10344	VH-EWL
10434	VH-EWN
10341	VH-EWO
10534	VH-EWP
10539	VH-EWQ
10459	VH-EWR
10425	VH-EWS
10431	VH-EWT
10627	VH-EWU
10633	VH-EWV
10637	VH-EWW
10639	VH-EWX
10669	VH-EWY
10672	VH-EWZ
10522	VH-FCA
10524	VH-FCB
10532	VH-FCC
10533	VH-FCD
10558	VH-FCE
10560	VH-FCF
10133	VH-FNA
10136	VH-FNB
10143	VH-FNC
10144	VH-FND
10145	VH-FNE
10146	VH-FNF
10170	VH-FNG
10180	VH-FNH
10181	VH-FNI
10264	VH-FNJ
10280	VH-FNK
10291	VH-FNL
10292	VH-FNM
10297	VH-FNN
10304	VH-FNO
10305	VH-FNP
10315	VH-FNQ
10317	VH-FNR
10318	VH-FNS
10322	VH-FNT
10334	VH-FNU
10252	VH-FNV
10254	VH-FNW
10186	VH-MMB
10146	VH-MMO
10303	VH-MMR
10139	VH-MMS
10258	VH-MMU
10355	VH-MMV
10105	VH-NLS
10111	VH-TFA
10112	VH-TFB
10113	VH-TFC
10114	VH-TFD
10120	VH-TFE
10121	VH-TFF
10122	VH-TFG
10127	VH-TFH
10176	VH-TFH
10134	VH-TFI
10135	VH-TFJ
10138	VH-TFK
10139	VH-TFL
10284	VH-TFL
10329	VH-TFM
10253	VH-TFW
10385	VH-TQN
10386	VH-TQO
10387	VH-TQP
10388	VH-TQQ
10440	VH-TQR
10441	VH-TQS
10458	VH-TQT

VP- Kenya

10211	VP-KSA
10212	VP-KSB
10213	VP-KSC
10241	VP-KTK

VQ- Grenada

10358	VQ-GAC

VT- India

10171	VT-DMA
10172	VT-DMB
10173	VT-DMC
10174	VT-DMD
10175	VT-DME
10214	VT-DOJ
10215	VT-DOK
10219	VT-DOL
10220	VT-DOM
10221	VT-DON
10302	VT-DUT
10308	VT-DVF
10309	VT-DVG
10336	VT-DWT
10337	VT-DWU
10333	VT-EBJ

XY- Burma

10235	XY-ADK
10236	XY-ADL
10237	XY-ADM
10312	XY-ADN
10313	XY-ADO
10357	XY-ADP
10452	XY-ADQ
10501	XY-ADS
10523	XY-ADT
10572	XY-ADY
10574	XY-ADZ
10617	XY-AEJ
10325	XY-AEK
10689	XY-AEL

YN- Nicaragua

10118	YN-

ZK- New Zealand

10166	ZK-BXA
10167	ZK-BXB
10168	ZK-BXC
10169	ZK-BXD
10184	ZK-BXE
10185	ZK-BXF
10189	ZK-BXG
10190	ZK-BXH
10286	ZK-BXI
10444	ZK-DCA
10445	ZK-DCB
10262	ZK-DCG
10118	ZK-NAA
10119	ZK-NAB
10110	ZK-NAF
10105	ZK-NAH
10365	ZK-NAN
10364	ZK-NAO
10551	ZK-NFA
10552	ZK-NFB
10456	ZK-NFC
10597	ZK-NFD
10598	ZK-NFE
10607	ZK-NFF
10609	ZK-NFG
10609	ZK-NFH
10614	ZK-NFI
10618	ZK-NFJ

ZS- South Africa

10144	ZS-JVA
10181	ZS-KVI
10264	ZS-KVJ
10227	ZS-LMZ

Military operated

Algeria

10494	7T-WAI
10495	7T-WAK
10496	7T-WAL
10529	7T-WAM
10526	7T-WAO
10543	7T-WAQ
10547	7T-WAS
10553	7T-WAT
10555	7T-WAU
10556	7T-WAV

Angola

10561	T-101
10595	TR-301

Argentina

10345	T-41
10346	T-42
10368	T-45
10346	T-79
10345	T-80
10451	TC-43
10454	TC-44
10403	TC-71
10619	TC-72
10404	TC-72
10407	TC-73
10408	TC-74
10621	TC-75
10411	TC-75
10412	TC-76
10416	TC-77
10418	TC-78
10575	TC-79
10368	TC-79

Bolivia

10578	TAM-90
10580	TAM-91
10584	TAM-92
10599	TAM-93
10600	TAM-94
10601	TAM-95

Burma

10124	5001

Finland

10300	FF-1
10274	FF-2
10662	FF-3

Ghana

10505	G-520/A
10507	G-521/B
10518	G-522/C
10520	G-523/D
10535	G-524/E

Guatemala

10111	1094
10270	1467
10493	1770

India

10173	CG-710
10221	CG-711

Indonesia

10536	T-2701
10537	T-2702
10538	T-2703
10540	T-2704
10541	T-2705
10542	T-2706
10544	T-2707
10546	T-2708

Iran

10474	5-201
10475	5-202
10478	5-203
10479	5-204
10480	5-205
10481	5-206
10482	5-207
10483	5-208
10484	5-209
10495	5-209
10485	5-210
10486	5-210
10486	5-211
10489	5-211
10489	5-212
10491	5-212
10491	5-213
10492	5-213
10492	5-214
10497	5-214
10498	5-215
10499	5-216
10500	5-217
10502	5-218
10504	5-219
10509	5-2601
10512	5-2601
10510	5-2602
10511	5-2603
10509	5-2604
10512	5-2604
10567	5-3031
10568	5-3032
10567	5-4041
10568	5-4042
10474	5-8801
10475	5-8802
10478	5-8803
10479	5-8804
10480	5-8805
10481	5-8806
10482	5-8807
10483	5-8808
10495	5-8809
10486	5-8810
10491	5-8811
10492	5-8812
10497	5-8813
10498	5-8814
10499	5-8815
10500	5-8816
10502	5-8817
10504	5-8818

Netherlands

10152	C-1
10149	C-2
10150	C-3
10154	C-4
10155	C-5
10156	C-6
10157	C-7
10158	C-8
10159	C-9
10160	C-10
10161	C-11
10162	C-12
10612	M-1
10622	M-2

New Zealand

10167	NZ2781
10168	NZ2782
10169	NZ2783

Nigeria

10473	NAF-701
10476	NAF-702
10473	NAF-901
10476	NAF-902
10487	NAF-903
10488	NAF-904
10490	NAF-905
10493	NAF-906
10653	NAF-907
10656	NAF-908

Pakistan

10281	J-752
10262	PN-62

Peru

10548	AE-560
10549	AE-561

Philippines

10148	10148
10210	10210
10246	10246
10262	10262
10265	10265
10267	10267
10296	10296
10310	10310
10327	10327
10328	10328
10602	10602
10616	10616
10620	10620
10115	59-0259

Senegal

10582	6W-STC
10583	6W-STD
10590	6W-STE
10591	6W-STF

Spain

10581	D2-01
10585	D2-02
10587	D2-03

Sudan

10273	833
10277	844
10282	888
10283	899

Thailand

10650	10650
10651	10651
10663	10663
10665	10665
10666	10666
10676	10676

United States

10652	85-1607
10668	85-1608

Uruguay

10199	560
10202	561
10199	T-560
10202	T-561

FOKKER F.50

Medium-range, high-wing transport for up to 50 passengers. Developed from the F.27-500, the F-50 differs largely in having lighter and more fuel-efficient Pratt & Whitney of Canada PW124 turboprop engines. First flight occurred on December 28th 1985 with deliveries to customers due to commence this year. To date orders total 38 aircraft.

Dimensions :	Wing span: 95ft 1in (29.0m) Length: 82ft 8in (25.19m) Height: 28ft 5in (8.60m)
Powerplant :	Two PWAC PW124 turboprops
Performance :	Max cruising speed 278 knots (515km/h) Range: with max payload 1,129nm (2,091km)
Accommodation:	50 passengers in a four abreast layout
Manufacturer :	Fokker - PO Box 1065, 1000 BB Amsterdam, The Netherlands Telephone: (020) 544 9111 Telex: 11526 NL

C/N	Registration	Owner/Operator	Series	First Flight	Delivery	Remarks
10685	PH-OSO	Fokker	50	28/DEC/85		Test Aircraft TA1
10688	PH-OSI	Fokker	50	30/APR/86		Test Aircraft TA2
003	PH-	Fokker	50			
004	D-	DLT	50		FEB/87	Sched.delivery
005	D-	DLT	50		MAY/87	Sched.delivery
006	VH-	Ansett	50		JAN/87	Sched.delivery
007	VH-	Ansett	50		87	Sched.delivery
008	VH-	Ansett	50		87	Sched.delivery
009	VH-	Ansett	50		87	Sched.delivery
010	VH-	Ansett	50		87	Sched.delivery
011	VH-	Ansett	50		87	Sched.delivery
012	VH-	Ansett	50		87	Sched.delivery
013	VH-	Ansett	50		87	Sched.delivery
014	VH-	Ansett	50		87	Sched.delivery
015	VH-	Ansett	50		87	Sched.delivery
016	VH-	Ansett	50		87	Sched.delivery
017	VH-	Ansett	50		87	Sched.delivery
018	VH-	Ansett	50		87	Sched.delivery
019	VH-	Ansett	50		87	Sched.delivery
020	VH-	Ansett	50		87	Sched.delivery
021	D-	DLT			87	Sched.delivery
022	OE-	Austrian Airlines	50		87	Sched.delivery
023	OE-	Austrian Airlines	50		87	Sched.delivery
024	OY-	Maersk Air	50		87	Sched.delivery
025	OY-	Maersk Air	50		87	Sched.delivery
026	OY-	Maersk Air	50		87	Sched.delivery
027	OY-	Maersk Air	50		87	Sched.delivery
028	N	Corsair	50		87	Sched.delivery
029	N	Corsair	50		87	Sched.delivery
030	LN-	Busy Bee	50		88	Sched.delivery
031	LN-	Busy Bee	50		88	Sched.delivery
032	LN-	Busy Bee	50		88	Sched.delivery
033	LN-	Busy Bee	50		88	Sched.delivery
034	D-	DLT	50		88	Sched.delivery
035	D-	DLT	50		87	Sched.delivery
036	N	Corsair	50		88	Sched.delivery
037	N	Corsair	50		88	Sched.delivery
038	N	Corsair	50		88	Sched.delivery
039	N	Corsair	50		88	Sched.delivery
040	N	Corsair	50		88	Sched.delivery
041	D-	DLT	50		88	Sched.delivery

SAAB 340

34-seat short-range commuter aircraft powered by two wing-mounted General Electric CT7-5A turboprops. A collaborative venture between Saab-Scania of Sweden and Fairchild Industries of the USA, the SF-340 first flew on 25 January 1983 and entered service with Crossair of Switzerland on June 15th 1984. Production version known as the SF-340A. To date, more than 60 aircraft have been delivered and over 40 are on order with the production rate currently four aircraft per month.

Dimensions :   Wing span: 70ft 4in (21.44m) Length: 64ft 7in (19.72m) Height: 22ft 6in (6.87m)

Powerplant :   Two General Electric CT7A-5A1 turboprops

Performance :   Max cruising speed 270 knots (500km/h) Range: with max payload 643nm (1,191km)

Accommodation: 35 passengers in a three abreast layout

Manufacturer :   SAAB- S-581 88 Linkoping. Telephone: Sweden 13 11 54 00

SAAB

C/N	Registration	Owner/Operator	Series	First Flight	Delivery	Remarks
001	SE-ISF	SAAB-Fairchild	340A	25/JAN/83		Prototype.
002	SE-ISA	SAAB-Fairchild	340A	11/MAY/83		Prototype
003	SE-ISB	SAAB-Fairchild	340A	25/AUG/83		Pre-production aircraft.
	N9668N	Fairchild Industries				
004	SE-E04	SAAB-Fairchild	340A	05/MAR/84		
	N340CA	Comair			OCT/84	
005	SE-E05	SAAB-Fairchild	340A	11/APR/84		
	HB-AHA	Crossair			JUN/84	
006	SE-E06	SAAB-Fairchild	340A	10/MAY/84		
	N360CA	Comair			JUL/84	
007	SE-E07	SAAB-Fairchild	340A	16/JUN/84		
	HB-AHB	Crossair			AUG/84	
008	SE-E08	SAAB-Fairchild	340A	04/AUG/84		
	G-BSFI	Birmingham Executive			DEC/84	
	SE-ISC	SAAB			DEC/85	
	SE-ISC	Swedair			FEB/86	Leased
	SE-ISC	SAAB			MAR/86	
	SE-ISC	Bar Harbor Airlines			APR/86	Leased
	SE-ISC	SAAB			JUN/86	
	SE-ISC	Swedair			AUG/86	Leased
	SE-ISC	SAAB			SEP/86	
	SE-ISC	Manx Airlines			DEC/86	Sched.lease
009	SE-E09	SAAB-Fairchild	340A	28/AUG/84		
	HB-AHC	Crossair			OCT/84	
010	SE-E10	SAAB-Fairchild	340A	03/OCT/84		
	N370CA	Comair			DEC/84	
011	SE-E11	SAAB-Fairchild	340A	20/OCT/84		
	N342AM	Air Midwest			FEB/85	
012	SE-E12	SAAB-Fairchild	340A	26/FEB/85		
	N380CA	Comair			MAR/85	
013	SE-E13	SAAB-Fairchild	340A	25/NOV/84		
	SE-ISO	Swedair			DEC/84	
014	SE-E14	SAAB-Fairchild	340E	16/NOV/84		
	N340SF	Fairchild Aircraft			JAN/85	Corporate demonstrator
	N340SF	Mellon Bank			85	Leased
	N340SF	SAAB Aircraft of America			DEC/85	
	N340SF	Amcomp			JUL/86	
015	SE-E15	SAAB-Fairchild	340A	07/DEC/84		
	SE-ISP	Swedair			DEC/84	
016	SE-016	SAAB-Fairchild	340A	08/JAN/85		
	VH-KDK	Kendell Airlines			FEB/85	
017	SE-E17	SAAB-Fairchild	340A	10/DEC/84		
	SE-ISR	Swedair			JAN/85	
018	SE-E18	SAAB-Fairchild	340A	05/FEB/85		
	HB-AHD	Crossair			MAR/85	
019	SE-E19	SAAB-Fairchild	340A	20/DEC/84		
	N343AM	Air Midwest			MAR/85	
020	SE-E20	SAAB-Fairchild	340A	14/FEB/85		
	HB-AHE	Crossair			MAR/85	
021	SE-E21	SAAB-Fairchild	340A	12/MAR/85		
	N341CA	Comair			APR/85	
022	SE-E22	SAAB-Fairchild	340E	21/APR/85		
	N19M	Mellon Bank			NOV/85	
023	SE-E23	SAAB-Fairchild	340A	24/MAR/85		
	N342CA	Comair			APR/85	
024	SE-E24	SAAB-Fairchild	340A	09/APR/85		
	N343CA	Comair			MAY/85	
025	SE-E25	SAAB-Fairchild	340A	25/APR/85		
	N344CA	Comair			MAY/85	
026	SE-E26	SAAB-Fairchild	340A	08/MAY/85		
	HB-AHF	Crossair			JUN/85	
027	SE-E27	SAAB-Fairchild	340A	29/MAY/85		
	N320PX	Republic Express			JUL/85	
028	SE-E28	SAAB-Fairchild	340A	30/MAY/85		
	N347CA	Comair			JUL/85	
029	SE-E29	SAAB-Fairchild	340E	13/JUN/85		
	N100PM	Philip Morris			MAR/86	
030	SE-E30	SAAB-Fairchild	340A	20/JUN/85		

C/N	Registration	Owner/Operator	Series	First Flight	Delivery	Remarks
	N344AM	Air Midwest			AUG/85	
031	SE-E31	SAAB-Fairchild	340A	10/JUL/85		
	N321PX	Republic Express			SEP/85	
032	SE-E32	SAAB-Fairchild	340A	14/AUG/85		
	N346AM	Air Midwest			SEP/85	
033	SE-E33	SAAB-Fairchild	340A	23/AUG/85		
	SE-ISS	Swedair			SEP/85	
034	SE-E34	SAAB-Fairchild	340A	24/AUG/85		
	N356CA	Comair			SEP/85	
035	SE-E35	SAAB-Fairchild	340A	03/SEP/85		
	SE-IST	Swedair			OCT/85	
036	SE-E36	SAAB	340E	27/SEP/85		
	N200PM	Philip Morris			APR/86	
037	SE-037	SAAB	340A	16/SEP/85		
	LN-NVD	Norving			DEC/85	
	LN-NVD	Swedair			DEC/85	Leased
	LN-NVD	Norving			FEB/86	
038	SE-E38	SAAB	340A	04/OCT/85		
	HB-AHG	Crossair			NOV/85	
039	SE-E39	SAAB	340A	19/OCT/85		
	N347AM	Air Midwest			NOV/85	
040	SE-E40	SAAB	340A	05/NOV/85		
	HB-AHH	Crossair			DEC/85	
041	SE-E41	SAAB	340A	09/NOV/85		
	N322PX	Republic Express			DEC/85	
042	SE-E42	SAAB	340A	17/NOV/85		
	SE-ISU	Swedair			DEC/85	
043	SE-E43	SAAB	340A	22/NOV/85		
	HB-AHI	Crossair			JAN/86	
044	SE-E44	SAAB	340A	24/NOV/85		
	N357CA	Comair			DEC/85	
045	SE-E45	SAAB	340A	10/DEC/85		
	SE-ISV	Swedair			JAN/86	
046	SE-E46	SAAB	340A	11/JAN/86		
	N323PX	Republic Express			FEB/86	
047	SE-E47	SAAB	340A	28/NOV/85		
	N358CA	Comair			DEC/85	
048	SE-E48	SAAB	340A	31/JAN/86		
	N324PX	Republic Express			MAR/86	
049	SE-E49	SAAB	340A	07/FEB/86		
	HB-AHK	Crossair			MAR/86	
050	SE-E50	SAAB	340E	25/FEB/86		
	N340SA	SAAB Aircraft of America			APR/86	
	N340SA	Kelly Springfield			86	
051	SE-E51	SAAB	340A	08/MAR/86		
	N325PX	Republic Express			APR/86	
052	SE-E52	SAAB	340A	21/MAR/86		
	VH-KDI	Kendell Airlines			APR/86	
053	SE-E53	SAAB	340A	09/APR/86		
	N359CA	Comair			MAY/86	
054	SE-E54	SAAB	340A	04/APR/86		
	N326PX	Republic Express			MAY/86	
055	SE-E55	SAAB	340A	08/MAY/86		
	LN-NVE	Norving			JUN/86	
056	SE-E56	SAAB	340A	23/APR/86		
	N361CA	Comair			JUN/86	
057	SE-E57	SAAB	340A	12/MAY/86		
	N401BH	Bar Harbor Airlines			JUN/86	Op. for Eastern Express
058	SE-E58	SAAB	340A			
	N402BH	Bar Harbor Airlines			JUL/86	Op. for Eastern Express
059	SE-E59	SAAB	340A			
	N327PX	Republic Express			JUL/86	
060	SE-E60	SAAB	340A			
	N403BH	Bar Harbor Airlines			JUL/86	Op. for Eastern Express
061	SE-E61	SAAB	340A			
	N404BH	Bar Harbor Airlines			AUG/86	Op. for Eastern Express
062	SE-E62	SAAB	340A			
	N340BE	Business Express			OCT/86	Sched.delivery
063	SE-E63	SAAB	340A			
	N341BE	Business Express			OCT/86	Sched.delivery
064	SE-E64	SAAB	340A			
	N320CA	Comair			AUG/86	
065	SE-E65	SAAB	340A			
	OH-FAA	Finnaviation			SEP/86	Sched.delivery
066	SE-E66	SAAB	340A			
	OH-FAB	Finnaviation			SEP/86	Sched.delivery
067	SE-E67	SAAB	340A			
	SE-ISX	Swedair			SEP/86	Sched.delivery
068	SE-E68	SAAB	340A			
	VH-KDI	Kendell Airlines			86	Sched.delivery
069	SE-E69	SAAB	340A			
	N340CL	Chicago Airlines			OCT/86	Sched.delivery
070	SE-E70	SAAB	340A			
	OH-FAC	Finnaviation			86	Sched.delivery
071	SE-E71	SAAB	340A			
	D-CDIA	Delta Air			86	Sched.delivery
072	SE-E72	SAAB	340A			
	N341CL	Chicago Airlines			86	Sched.delivery
074	SE-E74	SAAB	340A			
	SE-ISY	Swedair			86	Sched.delivery
075	SE-E75	SAAB	340A			
	D-CDIB	Delta Air			NOV/86	Sched.delivery
076	SE-E76	SAAB	340A			
	N342CL	Chicago Airlines			86	Sched.delivery

ADDITIONAL ORDERS

C/N	Registration	Owner/Operator	Series	First Flight	Delivery	Remarks
	SE-ISZ	Swedair	340A			
	LN-NVF	Norving	340A			
	N342BE	Business Express	340A			
	N343BE	Business Express	340A		JAN/87	Sched.delivery
	N344BE	Business Express	340A			
	N345BE	Business Express	340A			
	N343CL	Chicago Air	340A			
	N344CL	Chicago Air	340A			

SAAB 340

C/N	Registration	Owner/Operator	Series	First Flight	Delivery	Remarks
	N345CL	Chicago Air	340A			
	N346CL	Chicago Air	340A			
	N347CL	Chicago Air	340A			
	N348CL	Chicago Air	340A			
	N349CL	Chicago Air	340A			
	N350CL	Chicago Air	340A			
	HS-	Bangkok Airways	340A		87	Sched.delivery
	HS-	Bangkok Airways	340A		87	Sched.delivery
	VH-	Kendell Airlines	340A			
	N	Tennessee Airways	340A			
	N	Tennessee Airways	340A			
	N	Tennessee Airways	340A			
	G-	Aerotime	340A			
	G-	Aerotime	340A			

SAAB 340
Cross reference index

D- West Germany
071	D-CDIA
075	D-CDIB

G- United Kingdom
008	G-BSFI

HB- Switzerland
005	HB-AHA
007	HB-AHB
009	HB-AHC
018	HB-AHD
020	HB-AHE
026	HB-AHF
038	HB-AHG
040	HB-AHH
043	HB-AHI
049	HB-AHK

LN- Norway
037	LN-NVD
055	LN-NVE

N United States
029	N100PM
022	N19M
036	N200PM
064	N320CA
027	N320PX
031	N321PX
046	N323PX
048	N324PX
051	N325PX
054	N326PX
059	N327PX
062	N340BE
004	N340CA
069	N340CL
050	N340SA
014	N340SF
063	N341BE
021	N341CA
072	N341CL
011	N342AM
023	N342CA
076	N342CL
019	N343AM
024	N343CA
030	N344AM
025	N344CA
032	N346AM
039	N347AM
028	N347CA
034	N356CA
044	N357CA
047	N358CA
053	N359CA
006	N360CA
056	N361CA
010	N370CA
012	N380CA
057	N401BH
058	N402BH
041	N322PX
060	N403BH
061	N404BH
003	N9668N

OH- Finland
065	OH-FAA
066	OH-FAB
070	OH-FAC

SE- Sweden
016	SE-016
037	SE-037
004	SE-E04
005	SE-E05
006	SE-E06
007	SE-E07
008	SE-E08
009	SE-E09
010	SE-E10
011	SE-E11
012	SE-E12
013	SE-E13
014	SE-E14
015	SE-E15
017	SE-E17
018	SE-E18
019	SE-E19
020	SE-E20
021	SE-E21
022	SE-E22
023	SE-E23
024	SE-E24
025	SE-E25
026	SE-E26
027	SE-E27
028	SE-E28
029	SE-E29
030	SE-E30
031	SE-E31
032	SE-E32
033	SE-E33
034	SE-E34
035	SE-E35
036	SE-E36
038	SE-E38
039	SE-E39
040	SE-E40
041	SE-E41
042	SE-E42
043	SE-E43
044	SE-E44
045	SE-E45
046	SE-E46
047	SE-E47
048	SE-E48
049	SE-E49
050	SE-E50
051	SE-E51
052	SE-E52
053	SE-E53
054	SE-E54
055	SE-E55
056	SE-E56
057	SE-E57
058	SE-E58
059	SE-E59
060	SE-E60
061	SE-E61
062	SE-E62
063	SE-E63
064	SE-E64
065	SE-E65
066	SE-E66
067	SE-E67
068	SE-E68
069	SE-E69
070	SE-E70
071	SE-E71
072	SE-E72
074	SE-E74
075	SE-E75
076	SE-E76
002	SE-ISA
003	SE-ISB
008	SE-ISC
001	SE-ISF
013	SE-ISO
015	SE-ISP
017	SE-ISR
033	SE-ISS
035	SE-IST
042	SE-ISU
045	SE-ISV
067	SE-ISX
074	SE-ISY

VH- Australia
052	VH-KDI
068	VH-KDI
016	VH-KDK

SHORTS 330

Short-haul twin-turboprop commuter airliner for up to 30 passengers. The prototype made its maiden flight on 22 August 1974, and the first revenue service was operated by the Canadian regional airline, Time Air, on 24 August 1976.
Initial production aircraft, designated 330-100, were powered by PWAC PT6A-45A and 45B engines, but these were replaced by the more powerful PT6A-45R in the 330-200 which is now the standard passenger version. Other variants are the 330-UTT, a military utility tactical transport, and the Sherpa, a freighter derivative of the series -200. To date, more than 120 aircraft have been delivered.

Dimensions :	Wing span: 74ft 8in (27.76m) Length: 58ft 1in (17.69m) Height: 16ft 3in (4.95m)
Powerplant :	Two PWAC PT6A-45A or PWAC PT6A-45B turboprops (100), two PWAC PT6A-45R turboprops (200)
Performance :	Max cruising speed 190 knots (352km/h) Range: with max payload 473nm (761km)
Accommodation :	30 passengers in a three abreast layout
Manufacturer :	Shorts - PO Box 241, Airport Road, Belfast, BT3 9DZ, Northern Ireland Telephone: (0232) 58444 Telex: 74688 G

SHORTS

C/N	Registration	Owner/Operator	Series	First Flight	Delivery	Remarks
3000	G-BSBH	Shorts	100	22/AUG/74		Stored at Belfast
3001	G-BDBS	Shorts	100	08/JUL/75		
	G-BDBS	Shorts		10/SEP/82	82	Converted to 'UTT' prototype
3002	G-BDMA	Shorts	100	15/DEC/75		
	N330US	Shorts				
	N330US	Goldenwest Airlines			JUL/78	Leased
	N330US	Shorts				
	N330US	Henson Aviation			79	Leased
	N330US	Shorts				
	N330US	Pennsylvania Commuter			80	Leased
	N330US	Shorts				
	N330US	Suburban Airlines				Leased
	N330US	Shorts				
	N789US	Henson Airlines			85	Leased
	N789US	Shorts			85	
	N789US	CC Air			85	Leased
	N789US	Shorts			86	
3003	G-14-3003	Shorts	100	15/APR/76		
	G-BDSU	Shorts				
	D-CBVK	DLT			02/JUN/77	
	N57DD	Command Airways			APR/81	
3004	G-14-3004	Shorts	100	14/MAY/76		
	N51DD	Command Airways			28/JUN/76	
3005	G-14-3005	Shorts	100	26/JUN/76		
	C-GTAS	Time Air			11/AUG/76	
	G-BKIE	Genair			OCT/82	
	G-METO	Metropolitan Airways				
3006	G-14-3006	Shorts	100	26/AUG/76		
	G-BEEO	Shorts				
	C-GTAM	Time Air			04/OCT/76	
	G-BEEO	Jersey European Airways			19/MAR/84	
	G-BEEO	Spcaegrand Aviation			85	Leased
	G-BEEO	Jersey European Airways			26/OCT/85	
	G-BEEO	Brown Air			MAY/86	
3007	C-GTAV	Time Air	100	24/OCT/76	08/NOV/76	
	G-NICE	Eastern Airways			MAR/82	
	G-NICE	Genair				
	G-BLTD	Metropolitan Airways			DEC/84	
	G-BMTD	Metropolitan Airways			12/SEP/85	
3008	G-14-3008	Shorts	100	10/JAN/77		
	G-BENB	Shorts			24/FEB/77	
	D-CDLT	DLT			APR/79	
	N330SB	Shorts				
	N330SB	Air North				Leased
	N330SB	Shorts				
	N330SB	Crown Airways				Leased
	N330SB	Shorts				
	N330SB	Golden West			NOV/80	Leased
	N330SB	Shorts			NOV/80	
	N330SB	Coral Air			DEC/80	Leased
	N330SB	Shorts			81	
	N58DD	Command Airways			MAR/83	
3009	G-14-3009	Shorts	100	07/APR/77		
	N52DD	Command Airways			02/MAY/77	
3010	G-14-3010	Shorts	100	22/MAY/77		
	G-BETN	Shorts				
	N330GW	Goldenwest Airlines			05/JUL/77	WFU 22/APR/83
	85-25342	United States Army			85	
3011	G-14-3011	Shorts	100	28/JUN/77		
	G-BEWT	Shorts				
	N331GW	Goldenwest Airlines			27/AUG/77	WFU 22/APR/83
	85-25343	United States Army			85	
3012	G-14-3012	Shorts	100	15/AUG/77		
	G-BEZX	Shorts				
	N696HA	Henson Airlines			06/OCT/77	
3013	G-14-3013	Shorts	100	21/SEP/77		
	G-BFDX	Shorts				
	D-CODO	DLT			21/DEC/77	

SHORTS 330

C/N	Registration	Owner/Operator	Series	First Flight	Delivery	Remarks
	N241CA	Pennsylvania Airlines			12/FEB/81	
	N330SB	Shorts Inc.			OCT/84	
	N330SB	Henson Airlines				
3014	G-BFDY	Shorts	100	07/FEB/78		
	N796HA	Henson Airlines			10/APR/78	
3015	G-14-3015	Shorts	100	03/MAR/78		
	G-BFHY	Shorts				
	D-CDLA	DLT			23/MAR/78	
	N331CA	Pennsylvania Airlines			10/DEC/80	
	N331SB	Shorts Inc.			APR/85	
	N331SB	Henson Airlines			85	Leased
3016	G-14-3016	Shorts	100	18/APR/78		
	G-BFMA	Shorts				
	D-CDLB	DLT			22/MAY/78	
	N412CA	Pennsylvania Airlines			16/JUN/83	
3017	G-14-3017	Shorts	100	19/JUN/78		
	G-BFMB	Shorts				
	PJ-DDA	ALM			31/JUL/78	
	N335MV	Mississippi Valley Airlines			19/MAR/80	
	N335MV	Shorts Inc.				
	N335MV	Sunbird Airlines				Leased
	N335MV	CC Air			85	Leased
	N335MV	Shorts Inc.			86	
3018	G-14-3018	Shorts	100	28/JUL/78		
	G-BFMD	Shorts				
	PJ-DDB	ALM			09/AUG/78	
	N336MV	Mississippi Valley Airlines			19/MAR/80	
	N336MV	Shorts Inc.				
	N336MV	Sunbird Airlines				Leased
	N336MV	CC Air			85	Leased
	N336MV	Shorts			86	
3019	G-BFSW	Shorts	100	25/JUL/78		
	N332GW	Goldenwest Airlines			10/SEP/78	WFU 22/APR/83
	85-25344	United States Army			85	
3020	G-BFSX	Shorts	100	21/SEP/78		
	N371HA	Hawaiian Airlines			22/NOV/78	
	N371HA	Air North			AUG/79	Leased
	N58AN	Air North				Purchased
	N58AN	Crown Airways				
	N58AN	Brockway Air				
3021	G-BFTP	Shorts	100	12/OCT/78		
	D-CDLC	DLT			30/OCT/78	
	N115CA	Pennsylvania Airlines			JUN/84	
3022	G-BFUH	Shorts	100	15/NOV/78		
	N372HA	Hawaiian Airlines			26/JAN/79	
	N372HA	West Air			APR/84	
	N372HA	Metro Airlines				
3023	G-BFZW	Shorts	100	23/NOV/78		
	D-CDLD	DLT			26/JAN/79	
	G-RNMO	Fairflight			16/DEC/85	
	G-RNMO	Air Ecosse			86	
3024	G-BFZX	Shorts	100	09/DEC/78		
	N724SA	Suburban Airlines			20/JAN/79	
3025	G-BFZY	Shorts	100	09/FEB/79		
	N373HA	Hawaiian Airlines			05/JUN/79	
	N373HA	Air North			09/JUN/79	Leased
	N55AN	Air North				Purchased
	N55AN	Brockway Air				
3026	G-BGEY	Shorts	100	23/FEB/79		
	N330L	Chautauqua Airlines			19/APR/79	
3027	G-BGEZ	Shorts	100	20/APR/79		
	N334GW	Goldenwest Airlines			08/MAY/79	WFU 22/APR/83
	85-25345	United States Army			85	
3028	G-BGMZ	Shorts	100	02/MAY/79		
	N896HA	Henson Airlines			29/MAY/79	
3029	G-BGNA	Shorts	100	31/MAY/79		
	G-BGNA	Loganair			28/JUN/79	
	G-BGNA	Shorts			APR/83	
	G-BGNA	Manx Airlines			12/APR/83	Leased
	G-BGNA	Air Ecosse			83	
	G-BGNA	Metropolitan Airways			26/MAR/84	
	G-BTJR	Shorts			DEC/85	
3030	G-BGNB	Shorts	100	09/JUL/79		
	N330MV	Mississippi Valley Airlines			10/AUG/79	
	N330MV	Air Wisconsin			86	
3031	G-BGNC	Shorts	100	29/JUN/79		
	N799SA	Suburban Airlines			02/AUG/79	
3032	G-BGNE	Shorts	100	04/JUL/79		
	N935MA	Metro Airlines			21/AUG/79	
3033	G-BGNF	Shorts	100	24/JUL/79		
	N996HA	Henson Airlines			28/AUG/79	
3034	G-BGNG	Shorts	100	24/AUG/79		
	N331MV	Mississippi Valley Airlines			31/AUG/79	
	N331MV	LAPA			85	Leased
	N330FL	Flight Levels Corp.			FEB/86	
3035	G-BGNH	Shorts	100	15/AUG/79		
	N331L	Chautauqua Airlines			09/OCT/79	
3036	G-BGNI	Shorts	100	10/OCT/79		
	N936MA	Metro Airlines			28/NOV/79	
	N936MA	Comair			JUL/83	Leased
	N936MA	Henson Airlines				
3037	G-BGNJ	Shorts	100	01/NOV/79		
	N50AN	Air North			08/JAN/80	
	N50AN	Mississippi Valley Airlines			82	Leased
	N50AN	Air North				
	N50AN	Shorts				
	N50AN	Crown Airways				Leased
	N50AN	Brockway Air				Leased
	N50AN	Shorts			JUL/86	
	N50AN	Henson Airlines			JUL/86	Leased
3038	G-BGZV	Shorts	100	29/NOV/79		
	N332L	Chautauqua Airlines				
	N690RA	Royal Airlines			22/JAN/80	
	N690RA	Metro Airlines				
	N690RA	Henson Airlines			85	Leased

C/N	Registration	Owner/Operator	Series	First Flight	Delivery	Remarks
3039	G-BGZU	Shorts	100	17/DEC/79		
	N51AN	Air North			31/JAN/80	
	N51AN	Command Airways			MAY/81	Leased
	N51AN	Air North			82	
	N51AN	Mississippi Valley Airlines				
	N51AN	Crown Airways				
3040	G-BGZT	Shorts	100	22/JAN/80		
	N937MA	Metro Airlines			03/MAR/80	
3041	G-BHCG	Shorts	100	08/FEB/80		
	N844SA	Suburban Airlines			15/FEB/80	W/O 03/JUN/80, Allentown, Pa.
3042	G-BHHU	Shorts	100	26/FEB/80		
	N332MV	Mississippi Valley Airlines			27/MAR/80	
	N332MV	Fokker			JUN/85	Traded-in
	N332MV	Air Puerto Rico			21/APR/86	
3043	G-BHJM	Shorts	100	14/MAR/80		
	SX-BGA	Olympic Airways			23/MAY/80	
3044	G-BHHV	Shorts	100	29/MAR/80		
	N53DD	Command Airways			07/MAY/80	
3045	G-BHHW	Shorts	100	18/APR/80		
	N846SA	Suburban Airlines			16/MAY/80	
3046	G-BHJJ	Shorts	100	13/MAY/80		
	N938MA	Metro Airlines			23/JUN/80	
	N938MA	Henson Airlines			85	
3047	G-BHSH	Shorts	100	27/MAY/80		
	N939MA	Metro Airlines			11/JUL/80	
	N939MA	Command Airways			85	
3048	G-BHVL	Shorts	100	06/JUN/80		
	SX-BGB	Olympic Airways			27/JUN/80	
3049	G-BHWT	Shorts	100	07/JUL/80		
	N333MV	Mississippi Valley Airlines			16/JUL/80	
	N333MV	Westair Commuter Airlines			85	Leased
3050	G-BHWU	Shorts	100	25/JUN/80		
	YV-373C	Aeronaves Del Centro			15/AUG/80	
3051	G-BHWV	Shorts	100	11/JUL/80		
	N140CN	Crown Airways			07/AUG/80	
3052	G-BHYJ	Shorts	100	09/AUG/80		
	N304CA	Pennsylvania Airlines			20/AUG/80	
3053	G-BHYK	Shorts	100	15/AUG/80		
	N847SA	Suburban Airlines			26/AUG/80	
3054	G-BHYL	Shorts	100	06/AUG/80		
	YV-374C	Aeronaves Del Centro			27/AUG/80	
3055	G-BHYM	Shorts	100	25/AUG/80		
	N141CN	Crown Airways			29/AUG/80	
3056	G-BIFG	Shorts	100	26/SEP/80		
	LV-OJG	LAPA			19/NOV/80	
3057	G-BIFH	Shorts	100	15/OCT/80		
	LV-OJH	LAPA			27/NOV/80	Used for spares at Aeroparque Jorge Newbury, Buenos Aires
3058	G-BIFI	Shorts	100	16/NOV/80		
	N848SA	Suburban Airlines			20/NOV/80	
3059	G-BIFJ	Shorts	100	21/NOV/80		
	N54DD	Command Airways			19/DEC/80	
3060	G-BIFK	Shorts	100		16/DEC/80	
	VH-KNN	Jet Charter Airlines				
	VH-KNN	Wings Airways			82	WFU APR/83, stored Sydney
3061	G-BIGA	Shorts	100	07/JAN/81		
	YV-375C	Aeronaves del Centro				Cancelled order
	VH-KNO	Jet Charter Airlines			JUL/81	
	VH-KNO	Wings Airways			82	
	VH-KNO	Sun State Airlines			01/JAN/83	
3062	G-BIOD	Shorts	100	20/JAN/81		
	SU-BCP	Arabia				Not taken-up
	N335GW	Golden West			28/JUL/81	WFU 22/APR/83
	N156DD	Command Airways			JAN/84	
3063	G-BIOE	Shorts	100	11/FEB/81		
	VH-KNP	Jet Charter Airlines				
	VH-KNP	Wings Airways			82	WFU APR/83, stored Sydney
3064	G-BIOF	Shorts	100	20/FEB/81		
	N4270A	Coral Air			12/MAR/81	
	N280VY	Coral Air			81	
	N280VY	Shorts	200		APR/82	Converted
	N280VY	Pennsylvania Airlines			82	Leased
	G-BIOF	Shorts			83	
	EI-BNM	Avair			83	Leased
	G-14-3064	Shorts			MAR/84	
	G-BIOF	Fairflight/Air Ecosse			84	
	G-DIOH	Fairflight/Air Ecosse			11/MAY/85	Registration not taken-up
	G-BIOF	Fairflight/Air Ecosse			11/MAY/85	
	5N-AOX	Okada Air			21/SEP/85	
3065	G-BIOG	Shorts	100	06/MAR/81		
	SX-BGC	Olympic Airways			07/APR/81	
3066	G-BITU	Shorts	100	16/MAR/81		
	SX-BGD	Olympic Airways			07/APR/81	
3067	G-BIRN	Loganair	100	24/MAR/81	06/APR/81	
	G-BIRN	Shorts			31/MAR/84	
	G-BIRN	Fairflight/Air Ecosse			84	
	G-BIRN	Brymon Airways			01/APR/85	Leased
	G-BIRN	Fairflight/Air Ecosse				
3068	G-BITV	Inter City Airlines	200	03/APR/81	16/APR/81	
	G-BITV	British Air Ferries			AUG/83	Leased
	G-BITV	Shorts			25/NOV/83	
	G-BITV	Fairflight/Air Ecosse			30/JAN/84	
	G-BITV	Brymon Airways			01/APR/85	Leased
	G-BITV	Fairflight/Air Ecosse			85	
	G-BITV	London European Airways			85	
	G-BITV	Fairflight/Air Ecosse				
3069	G-BITX	Inter City Airlines	200	08/MAY/81	15/MAY/81	
	G-BITX	Guernsey Airlines			15/MAY/81	Leased
	G-BITX	Inter City Airlines			01/AUG/83	Stored East Midlands Ap.
	G-BITX	Guernsey Airlines				
3070	G-BITW	Shorts	200	21/MAY/81		
	G-EASI	Eastern Airways			JUL/81	
	G-EASI	Genair			82	
	G-BITW	Shorts			NOV/84	
	G-BITW	Fairflight/Air Ecosse				

SHORTS 330

C/N	Registration	Owner/Operator	Series	First Flight	Delivery	Remarks
	G-BITW	Brymon Airways			01/APR/85	Leased
	G-BITW	Fairflight/Air Ecosse			85	
	G-BITW	Shorts			26/JUN/86	WFU 26/JUN/86, stored
3071	G-BIYA	Shorts	200	29/MAY/81		
	N330AE	Atlanta Express Airlines			81	
	N2679U	Atlanta Express Airlines			82	
	N2679U	Pennsylvania Airlines				
3072	G-BIYD	Shorts	200	17/JUN/81		
	N2678G	Comair			08/DEC/81	
3073	G-BIYE	Shorts	200	11/JUN/81		
	VH-KNQ	Jet Charter Australia			19/AUG/81	
	VH-KNQ	Wings Airways			82	
	VH-KNQ	Murray Valley Airlines			01/JAN/83	Leased
	VH-KNQ	Murray Valley Airlines			FEB/83	Purchased
3074	G-BIYF	Shorts	200	24/JUN/81		
	N26288	Atlanta Express Airlines			08/DEC/81	
	N26288	Pennsylvania Airlines				
3075	G-BIYG	Shorts	200	03/JUL/81		
	N337MV	Mississippi Valley Airlines	200		25/SEP/81	
	N337MV	Fokker			JUN/85	Traded-in
	N337MV	Air Puerto Rico			21/APR/86	
3076	G-BIYH	Shorts	200	16/JUL/81		
	N338MV	Mississippi Valley Airlines			09/DEC/81	
	N338MV	Fokker			JUN/85	Traded-in
	N338MV	Air Puerto Rico			21/APR/86	
3077	G-BJFK	Inter City Airlines	200	11/AUG/81	25/SEP/81	
	G-BJFK	British Midland Airways			25/SEP/81	Leased
	G-BJFK	British Midland Airways			02/AUG/83	Purchased
	G-BJFK	Shorts			01/APR/84	
	G-BJFK	Air UK			05/MAY/84	
	G-BJFK	Shorts				
	G-BJFK	Spacegrand			01/APR/85	
	G-BJFK	Jersey European Airways			26/OCT/85	
3078	EI-BLP	Avair	200		OCT/81	Leased
	EI-BLP	Shorts			MAR/84	
	N5369X	Shorts Inc.			84	
	G-BJLK	Fairflight/Air Ecosse			JAN/85	
	G-BJLK	Connectair			01/APR/86	
3079	G-BJLL	Shorts	200	16/OCT/81		
	N2629P	Mississippi Valley Airlines			12/DEC/81	
	N2629P	Comair			83	
3080	G-BJLM	Shorts	200	11/SEP/81		
	N2629Y	Mississippi Valley Airlines			16/DEC/81	
	N2629Y	Fischer Brothers Aviation				
3081	G-BJUJ	Shorts	200	19/OCT/81		
	N2630A	Comair			02/JUN/82	
3082	G-14-3082	Shorts	200	13/NOV/81		
	G-BJUK	Casair			14/MAY/82	
	G-OCAS	Casair			MAY/82	
	G-OCAS	Genair			82	
	G-BJUK	Shorts			DEC/84	
	G-BJUK	Spacegrand			MAR/85	
	G-BJUK	Jersey European Airways			26/OCT/85	
3083	G-BJUL	Shorts	200	07/JAN/82		
	SX-BGE	Olympic Airways			14/MAY/82	
3084	G-BJWA	Shorts	200	07/JAN/82		
	SX-BGF	Olympic Airways			14/MAY/82	
3085	G-BJXF	Shorts	200	01/FEB/82		
	HS-TSA	Thai Airways	200		14/MAY/82	
3086	G-BJXG	Shorts	200			
	HS-TSB	Thai Airways	200		14/MAY/82	
3087	G-BJXH	Shorts	200	15/MAR/82		
	HS-TSC	Thai Airways			04/JUN/82	
3088	G-BKDL	Shorts	200	19/APR/82		
	HS-TSD	Thai Airways			02/JUL/82	
3089	G-BKDM	Shorts	200	22/JUN/82		
	N330CA	Shorts Inc.			82	
	N330CA	Colgan Airways			82	Leased
3090	G-BKDN	Shorts	200	08/JUL/82		
	G-BKDN	Eastern Airways			82	Leased
	G-BKDN	Shorts			82	
	G-BKDN	Spacegrand Aviation			02/FEB/83	Leased
	G-BKDN	Shorts			03/FEB/83	
	G-BKDN	Air UK			29/MAR/83	Leased
	G-BKDN	Fairflight/Air Ecosse				
	G-BKDN	North African Airways			05/MAR/85	Leased
	G-BKDN	Fairflight/Air Ecosse			85	
	G-BKDN	London European Airways			85	Leased
	G-BKDN	Fairflight/Air Ecosse			85	
3091	G-BKDO	Shorts	200	29/JUL/82		
	G-BKDO	Eastern Airways			82	
	G-BKDO	Genair				
	G-BKDO	Fairflight/Air Ecosse				
3092	G-BKMU	Shorts	200	24/MAR/83		
	EI-BEG	Aer Lingus			30/MAR/83	
	EI-BEH	Aer Lingus			25/MAY/83	
	G-BKMU	Shorts			DEC/84	
	G-BKMU	Fairflight/Air Ecosse			85	
	G-BKMU	Manx Airlines			05/MAR/85	Leased
	G-BKMU	Fairflight/Air Ecosse				
	G-BKMU	Guernsey Airlines			85	Leased
3093	G-BKMV	Shorts	200	21/APR/83		
	N155DD	Command Airways			29/APR/83	
3094	G-BKMW	Shorts	Sherpa	23/DEC/82		Sherpa demonstrator
3095	G-BKSU	Shorts	200	10/JUN/83		
	G-BKSU	Air UK			15/JUN/83	Leased
	G-BKSU	Fairflight/Air Ecosse				
3096	G-BKSV	Shorts	200	31/AUG/83		
	G-BKSV	Fairflight/Air Ecosse			20/FEB/84	
	G-14-3096	Shorts			APR/85	Stored East Midlands
	N332SB	Sunbird Airlines			09/AUG/85	
	N332SB	CC Air			85	
3097	G-BLGG	Shorts	200	06/MAR/84		
	SE-INZ	Syd-Aero			31/MAR/84	
3098	G-14-3098	Shorts	UTT	16/MAY/84		

C/N	Registration	Owner/Operator	Series	First Flight	Delivery	Remarks
	G-BLJA	Shorts			MAY/84	
	3098	Royal Thai Army			10/JUN/84	
3099	G-BLJB	Shorts	UTT			
		Royal Thai Police			26/SEP/84	
3100	G-BLLJ	Shorts	C-23A	06/AUG/84		
	83-512	United States Air Force			02/NOV/84	
3101	G-BLLK	Shorts	C-23A	31/AUG/84		
	83-513	United States Air Force			06/NOV/84	
3102	G-BLLL	Shorts	UTT			
	3102	Royal Thai Army			22/FEB/85	
3103	G-14-3103	Shorts	C-23A	04/DEC/84		
	84-458	United States Air Force			15/DEC/84	
3104	G-14-3104	Shorts	C-23A	17/JAN/85		
	84-459	United States Air Force			30/JAN/85	
3105	G-BLRR	Shorts	UTT	13/MAR/85		
		Royal Thai Police			23/MAR/85	
3106	G-14-3106	Shorts	C-23A	22/FEB/85		
	84-460	United States Air Force			06/MAR/85	
3107	G-14-3107	Shorts	C-23A	19/MAR/85		
	84-461	United States Air Force			28/MAR/85	
3108		Shorts	UTT			
	3108	Royal Thai Army			85	
3109	G-14-3109	Shorts	C-23A	03/APR/85		
	84-462	United States Air Force			20/APR/85	
3110	G-14-3110	Shorts	C-23A	18/APR/85		
	84-463	United States Air Force			26/APR/85	
3111	G-14-3111	Shorts	C-23A	10/MAY/85		
	84-464	United States Air Force			21/MAY/85	
3112	G-14-3112	Shorts	C-23A	26/MAY/85		
	84-465	United States Air Force			01/JUN/85	
3113	G-14-3113	Shorts	C-23A	11/JUN/85		
	G-BLZG	Shorts			12/JUN/85	
	84-466	United States Air Force			21/JUN/85	
3114	G-14-3114	Shorts	C-23A	26/JUN/85		
	84-466	United States Air Force			09/JUL/85	
3115	G-14-3115	Shorts	C-23A	22/JUL/85		
	84-467	United States Air Force			01/AUG/85	
3116	G-14-3116	Shorts	C-23A	20/AUG/85		
	84-468	United States Air Force			05/SEP/85	
3117	G-14-3117	Shorts	C-23A	04/SEP/85		
	84-469	United States Air Force			20/SEP/85	
3118	G-14-3118	Shorts	C-23A	30/SEP/85		
	84-470	United States Air Force			10/OCT/85	
3119	G-14-3119	Shorts	C-23A			
	84-471	United States Air Force			85	
3120	G-14-3120	Shorts	C-23A			
	84-472	United States Air Force			85	
3121	G-BMGX	Shorts	UTT	23/MAR/86		
	AGAW.131	Emiri Guard			16/MAY/86	
3122	G-BMLF	Shorts	UTT			Stored at Belfast
3123	G-BMLG	Shorts	UTT	29/MAY/86		
	YV-	Industria Venezolana de Aluminio C.A.			AUG/86	

Shorts 330 cross-reference index

3027	N334GW	3012	N696HA	3097	SE-INZ	3050	YV-373C	3107	84-461
3062	N335GW	3024	N724SA			3054	YV-374C	3109	84-462
3017	N335MV	3002	N789US	**SU- Egypt**		3061	YV-375C	3110	84-463
3018	N336MV	3014	N796HA					3111	84-464
3075	N337MV	3031	N799SA	3062	SU-BCP	**Military operated**		3112	84-465
3076	N338MV	3041	N844SA					3113	84-466
3020	N371HA	3045	N846SA	**SX- Greece**		**Thailand**		3114	84-466
3022	N372HA	3053	N847SA					3115	84-467
3025	N373HA	3058	N848SA	3043	SX-BGA	3098	3098	3116	84-468
3016	N412CA	3028	N896HA	3048	SX-BGB	3102	3102	3117	84-469
3064	N4270A	3032	N935MA	3065	SX-BGC	3108	3108	3118	84-470
3037	N50AN	3036	N936MA	3066	SX-BGD			3119	84-471
3039	N51AN	3040	N937MA	3083	SX-BGE	**United Arab Emirates**		3120	84-472
3004	N51DD	3046	N938MA	3084	SX-BGF			3010	85-25342
3009	N52DD	3047	N939MA			3121	AGAW.131	3011	85-25343
3078	N5369X	3047	N939MA	**VH- Australia**				3019	85-25344
3044	N53DD	3033	N996HA			**United States**		3027	85-25345
3059	N54DD	**PJ- Netherlands**		3060	VH-KNN				
3025	N55AN			3061	VH-KNO	3100	83-512		
3003	N57DD	3017	PJ-DDA	3063	VH-KNP	3101	83-513		
3020	N58AN	3018	PJ-DDB	3073	VH-KNQ	3103	84-458		
3008	N58DD	**SE- Sweden**		**YV- Venezuela**		3104	84-459		
3038	N690RA					3106	84-460		

SHORTS 360

Stretched development of the Shorts 330 with accommodation for 36 passengers, and other improvements including a re-designed tail fin. The 360 made its first flight on 1 June 1981 and entered service with Surburban Airlines in the USA on 1 December 1982. Production models are powered by two of the more economical PT6A-65R turboprop engines. To date, more than 100 aircraft have been delivered.

Dimensions :	Wing span: 74ft 10in (22.81m) Length: 70ft 10in (21.59m) Height: 23ft 7in (7.21m)
Powerplant :	Two PWAC PT6A-65AR turboprops
Performance :	Max cruising speed 212 knots (393km/h) Range: with max payload 225nm (417km)
Accommodation:	36 passengers in a three abreast layout
Manufacturer :	Shorts - PO Box 241, Airport Road, Belfast, BT3 9DZ, Northern Ireland
	Telephone: (0232) 58444 Telex: 74688 G

SHORTS

C/N	Registration	Owner/Operator	Series	First Flight	Delivery	Remarks
3600	G-ROOM	Shorts	360	01/JUN/81		Prototype
3601	G-WIDE	Shorts	360	19/AUG/82		
	N360SA	Suburban Airlines			11/NOV/82	
3602	G-BKJC	Shorts	360	09/NOV/82		
	N360MQ	Simmons Airlines			01/DEC/82	
3603	G-BKKT	Shorts	360	10/DEC/82		
	G-BKKT	Genair			20/DEC/82	
	N368MQ	Simmons Airlines			13/NOV/84	
	G-OJSY	Jersey European Airways	360		MAY/86	
3604	G-BKKU	Shorts	360	30/DEC/82		
	G-RMSS	Air Ecosse			06/JAN/83	
	G-RMSS	Air UK			JAN/85	Leased
	G-RMSS	Shorts			85	
	G-RMSS	Air Ecosse			85	
	G-RMSS	Manx Airlines			85	Leased
3605	G-BKKV	Shorts	360	26/JAN/83		
	N342MV	Mississippi Valley			08/FEB/83	
	N342AW	Air Wisconsin				
3606	G-BKKW	Shorts	360	14/FEB/83		
	G-DASI	Air Ecosse			22/FEB/83	
	G-DASI	Manx Airlines			07/SEP/83	Leased
	G-DASI	Air Ecosse				
	G-DASI	Air UK			24/SEP/84	Leased
3607	G-BKKX	Shorts	360	22/MAR/83		
	N361MQ	Simmons Airlines			08/MAR/83	
3608	G-BKMX	Shorts	360	11/MAR/83		
	G-BKMX	Loganair			22/MAR/83	
3609	G-BKMY	Shorts	360	22/MAR/83		
	N343MV	Mississippi Valley			28/MAR/83	
	N343MV	Air Wisconsin				
3610	G-BKMZ	Shorts	360	28/MAR/83		
	N715NC	Newair			02/APR/83	
	N715NC	Shorts				
	N715NC	Suburban Airlines				Leased
	N715NC	Shorts				
	N715NC	Simmons Airlines				Leased
	N715NC	Shorts				
	N715NC	Republic Express				
3611	G-BKPO	Shorts	360	05/MAY/83		
	G-BMAJ	British Midland Airways			11/MAY/83	
	G-WACK	Manx Airlines			25/APR/86	
3612	G-BKPP	Shorts	360	20/MAY/83		
	N362MQ	Simmons Airlines			25/MAY/83	
3613	G-BKPR	Shorts	360	21/JUN/83		
	N601A	Imperial Airlines			83	
3614	G-BKSL	Shorts	360	24/MAY/83		
	N363MQ	Simmons Airlies			23/JUN/83	
3615	G-BKSM	Shorts	360	29/JUN/83		
	N344MV	Mississippi Valley			08/JUL/83	
	N344MV	Air Wisconsin				
3616	G-BKSN	Shorts	360	10/JUL/83		
	N345MV	Mississippi Valley			25/AUG/83	
	N345MV	Air Wisconsin				
3617	G-BKUF	Shorts	360	20/JUL/83		
	N617FB	Fischer Brothwers			28/JUL/83	
3618	G-BKUG	Shorts	360	03/AUG/83		
	N691A	Imperial Airlines			20/AUG/83	
	N691A	Shorts				
	N691A	Business Express			JUL/86	Leased
3619	G-BKUH	Shorts	360	13/AUG/83		
	N364MQ	Simmons Airlines			27/AUG/83	
3620	G-BKWJ	Shorts	360	24/AUG/83		
	VH-MVX	Murray Valley Airlines			• 02/SEP/83	
3621	G-BKWK	Shorts	360	19/SEP/83		
	N365MQ	Simmons Airlines			12/NOV/83	
3622	G-BKWL	Shorts	360	22/SEP/83		
	N622FB	Fischer Brothers			10/OCT/83	
3623	G-BKWM	Shorts	360	13/OCT/83		

SHORTS 360

C/N	Registration	Owner/Operator	Series	First Flight	Delivery	Remarks
	N601CA	Pennsylvania Airlines			21/OCT/83	
3624	G-BKWN	Shorts	360	27/OCT/83		
	N912SB	Sunbelt Airlines			18/NOV/83	WFU 84, stored Marana
	N912SB	Shorts Inc.			02/MAY/85	
	N912SB	'CAAC'			24/MAY/85	Painted for Paris Air Show
	N912SB	Shorts Inc.			85	
	N912SB	Simmons Airlines			85	Leased
3625	G-BKZN	Shorts	360	07/NOV/83		
	N4498Y	Pennsylvania Airlines			12/NOV/83	
3626	G-BKZO	Shorts	360	15/NOV/83		
	VH-MVW	Murray Valley Airlines			31/DEC/83	
	VH-MVW	State Air			22/APR/86	
3627	G-BKZP	Shorts	360	25/NOV/83		
	N701A	Imperial Airlines			02/DEC/83	
3628	G-BKZR	Shorts	360	02/DEC/83		
	G-BKZR	Genair			15/DEC/83	
	G-BKZR	Shorts				
	OY-MMC	Maersk/Air Business			OCT/84	Leased
	G-SALU	Shorts			05/OCT/85	Stored East Midlands
	G-SALU	Loganair			10/JAN/86	Leased
3629	G-BKZS	Shorts	360	08/DEC/83		
	N913SB	Sunbelt Airlines			16/DEC/83	WFU 84, stored Marana
	N913SB	Simmons Airlines				
3630	G-BLCN	Shorts	360	12/JAN/84		
	VH-SVU	Sunstate Airlines			84	Sched.delivery
3631	G-BLCO	Shorts	360	21/DEC/83		
	N914SB	Sunbelt Airlines			30/DEC/83	
	N131DA	Shorts Inc.			AUG/84	
	N131DA	Dash Air			AUG/84	Leased
	N131DA	Shorts Inc.			13/SEP/84	WFU
	N131DA	Atlantic Southeast			MAY/85	Leased
	N131DA	Shorts Inc.				
	N131DA	Westair Commuter			JUL/86	
	N131DA	Shorts Inc.				
	N131DA	Business Express			12/JUL/86	Leased
3632	G-BLCP	Shorts	360	06/JAN/84		
	OY-MMA	Maersk/Air Business			12/JAN/84	
3633	G-BLCR	Shorts	360	20/JAN/84		
	G-BMAR	British Midland Airways			23/MAR/84	
	G-POOL	Manx Airlines			MAY/86	Sched.delivery
3634	G-BLCS	Shorts	360	26/JAN/84		
	N132DA	Dash Air			23/MAR/84	
	N132DA	Shorts Inc.			13/SEP/84	WFU
	N132DA	Business Express			86	Sched.lease
3635	G-BLED	Shorts	360	07/FEB/84		
	EI-BEK	Aer Lingus			07/MAR/84	
3636	G-BLEE	Shorts	360	15/FEB/84		
	EI-BEL	Aer Lingus			07/MAR/84	
3637	G-BLEF	Shorts	360	23/FEB/84		
	G-LEGS	Manx Airlines			09/MAR/84	
3638	G-BLEG	Shorts	360	01/MAR/84		
	G-ISLE	Manx Airlines			28/MAR/84	
3639	G-BLEH	Shorts	360	13/MAR/84		
	N366MQ	Simmons Airlines			17/MAR/84	
3640	G-BLGA	Shorts	360	20/MAR/84		
	N367MQ	Simmons Airlines			31/MAR/84	
3641	G-BLGB	Shorts	360	27/MAR/84		
	G-BLGB	Loganair			30/MAR/84	
3642	G-BLGC	Shorts	360	05/APR/84		
	EI-BEM	Aer Lingus			21/JUN/84	W/O 31/JAN/86, East Midlands Ap.
3643	G-BLGD	Shorts	360	10/APR/84		
	N631KC	Wright Airlines			16/MAY/84	
	N631KC	Shorts			84	
	N631KC	Atlantic Southeast			84	Leased
3644	G-BLGE	Shorts	360	16/APR/84		
	N632KC	Wright Airlines			19/MAY/84	
	N632KC	Shorts			84	
	N632KC	Atlantic Southeast			84	Leased
3645	G-BLGF	Shorts	360	01/MAY/84		
	N633KC	Wright Airlines			04/JUN/84	
	N633KC	Shorts			84	
	N633KC	Atlantic Southeast			84	Leased
3646	G-BLIJ	Shorts	360	15/MAY/84		
	N634KC	Wright Airlnes			11/JUN/84	
	N634KC	Shorts			84	
	N634KC	Atlantic Southeast			84	Leased
3647	G-BLIK	Shorts	360	25/MAY/84		
	N635KC	Wright Airlines			04/JUL/84	
	N635KC	Shorts			84	
	N635KC	Atlantic Southeast			84	Leased
3648	G-BLIL	Shorts	360	01/JUN/84		
	OY-MMB	Maersk/Air Business			SEP/84	
3649	G-BLIM	Shorts	360	15/JUN/84		
	N346MV	Mississippi Valley			06/JUL/84	
	N346MV	Air Wisconsin				
3650	G-BLIN	Shorts	360	28/JUN/84		
	N347MV	Mississippi Valley			13/JUL/84	
	N347MV	Air Wisconsin				
3651	G-BLIR	Shorts	360			
	9M-KGN	Malaysia Air Charter			SEP/84	
3652	G-BLIS	Shorts	360			
	N124CA	Pennsylvania Airlines			SEP/84	
3653	N151CA	Pennsylvania Airlines	360		OCT/84	
3654	G-BLIU	Shorts	360			
	N369MQ	Simmons Airlines				
3655	G-BLIV	Shorts	360			
	N370MQ	Simmons Airlines				
3656	G-BLPU	Shorts	360			
	EI-BPD	Aer Lingus			01/NOV/84	
3657	G-BLPV	Shorts	360	06/NOV/84		
	G-BLPV	Air UK			NOV/84	
3658	G-BLPW	Shorts	360	13/NOV/84		
	N371MQ	Simmons Airlines			JAN/85	
3659	G-BLPX	Shorts	360	14/NOV/84		
	N372MQ	Simmons Airlines			JAN/85	

C/N	Registration	Owner/Operator	Series	First Flight	Delivery	Remarks
3660	G-BLPY	Shorts	360			
3661	G-BLRT	Shorts	360			
	G-BLRT	Fairflight			12/JAN/85	
	G-BLRT	Air Ecosse			12/JAN/85	Leased
	G-BLRT	Fairflight			09/APR/85	
	G-BLRT	Maersk/Air Business			09/APR/85	Leased
	G-BLRT	Fairflight			28/JUN/85	
	G-BLRT	Air Ecosse			28/JUN/85	Leased
3662	G-14-3662	Shorts	360	26/APR/85		
	G-BLWA	Shorts			APR/85	
	N362SA	Suburban Airlines			03/MAY/85	
3663	G-14-3663	Shorts	360	28/JAN/85		
	N360SE	Westair Commuter			02/FEB/85	
3664	G-BLTO	Shorts	360	14/FEB/85		
	G-BLTO	Fairflight			04/MAR/85	
	G-BLTO	Air UK			04/MAR/85	Leased
	G-BLTO	Fairflight			02/MAR/86	Leased
	EI-BSM	Aer Lingus			86	
	G-BLTO	Fairflight				
3665	G-BLUC	Shorts	360	22/FEB/85		
	N190SB	Atlantic Southeast			01/MAR/85	
3666	G-BLUD	Shorts	360	01/MAR/85		
	N191SB	Atlantic Southeast			05/MAR/85	
3667	G-BLRU	Shorts	360	09/MAY/85		
	B-3601	CAAC			01/JUN/85	
3668	G-BLUR	Shorts	360			
	N360SY	Atlantic Southeast			APR/85	
3669	G-BLUU	Shorts	360	06/JUN/85		
	B-3602	CAAC			21/JUN/85	
3670	G-BLWJ	Shorts	360	04/JUN/85		
	B-3603	CAAC			11/JUN/85	
3671	G-BLWK	Shorts	360	07/JUN/85		
	B-3604	CAAC			15/JUN/85	
3672	G-BLWN	Shorts	360	27/JUN/85		
	B-3605	CAAC			05/JUL/85	
3673	G-BLYF	Shorts	360	09/JUL/85		
	B-3606	CAAC			18/JUL/85	
3674	G-BLYG	Shorts	360	23/JUL/85		
	B-3607	CAAC			31/JUL/85	
3675	G-BLYH	Shorts	360	07/AUG/85		
	B-3608	CAAC			14/AUG/85	
3676	G-BLZT	Shorts	360	16/AUG/85		
	G-BLZT	Air UK			20/AUG/85	
3677	G-BLZU	Shorts	360	06/SEP/85		
	C-GTAU	Time Air			19/SEP/85	
3678	G-BLZV	Shorts	360			
	N342SB	Westair Commuter			26/NOV/85	
3679	G-BMEN	Shorts	360	04/OCT/85		
	C-GTAX	Time Air			18/OCT/85	
3680	G-BMEO	Shorts	360 ADV			
	HS-TSE	Thai Airways			22/OCT/85	
3681	G-BMEP	Shorts	360 ADV			
	HS-TSF	Thai Airways			15/NOV/85	
3682	G-BMER	Shorts	360 ADV			
	N373MQ	Simmons Airlines			06/DEC/85	
3683	G-BMES	Shorts	360 ADV			
	N374MQ	Simmons Airlines			11/DEC/85	
3684	G-BMHV	Shorts	360 ADV			
	N375MQ	Simmons Airlines			19/DEC/85	
3685	G-BMHW	Shorts	360 ADV			
	N376MQ	Simmons Airlines			20/DEC/85	
3686	G-BMHX	British Midland	360 ADV		27/MAR/86	
3687	G-BMHY	British Midland	360 ADV		27/MAR/86	
3688	G-BMLC	Loganair	360 ADV		27/MAR/86	
3689	G-BMLD	Shorts	360 ADV			
	EI-BSP	Aer Lingus			27/MAR/86	
3690	G-BMLE	Shorts	360 ADV			
	N690PC	CC Air/Piedmont Commuter			30/JUN/86	
3691	G-BMNG	Shorts	360 ADV			
	N360PC	CC Air/Piedmont Commuter			19/JUN/86	
3692	G-BMNH	Shorts	360 ADV			
	N693PC	CC Air/Piedmont Commuter			15/JUN/86	
3693	G-BMNI	Shorts	360 ADV			
	N695PC	CC Air/Piedmont Commuter			31/MAR/86	
3694	G-BMNJ	Shorts	360 ADV			
	N694PC	CC Air/Piedmont Commuter			31/MAR/86	
3695	G-BMNK	Shorts	360 ADV			
3696	G-BMUV	Shorts	360 ADV			
	N711PK	Stateswest Airlines			16/JUL/86	
3697	G-BMUW	Shorts	360 ADV			
	N711HJ	Stateswest Airlines			29/JUL/86	
3698	G-BMUX	Shorts	360 ADV			
	N711MP	Stateswest Airlines			13/AUG/86	
3699	G-BMUY	Shorts	360 ADV			
	N377MQ	Simmons Airlines			09/OCT/86	
3700	G-BMXP	Shorts	360 ADV			
	N378MQ	Simmons Airlines			09/OCT/86	
3701	G-	Shorts	360 ADV			
	N379MQ	Simmons Airlines			17/OCT/86	
3702	G-	Shorts	360 ADV			
	N380MQ	Simmons Airlines			17/OCT/86	

ADDITIONAL ORDERS

C/N	Registration	Owner/Operator	Series	First Flight	Delivery	Remarks
	N	Simmons Airlines	360 ADV			
	N	Simmons Airlines	360 ADV			
	N	Simmons Airlines	360 ADV			
	N	Simmons Airlines	360 ADV			
	N	Simmons Airlines	360 ADV			
	N	Simmons Airlines	360 ADV			
	N	Simmons Airlines	360 ADV			

Shorts 360 cross-reference index

9M- Malaysia

3651	9M-KGN

B- China

3667	B-3601
3669	B-3602
3670	B-3603
3671	B-3604
3672	B-3605
3673	B-3606
3674	B-3607
3675	B-3608

C- Canada

3677	C-GTAU
3679	C-GTAX

EI- Eire

3635	EI-BEK
3636	EI-BEL
3642	EI-BEM
3656	EI-BPD
3664	EI-BSM
3689	EI-BSP

G- United Kingdom

3662	G-14-3662
3663	G-14-3663
3602	G-BKJC
3603	G-BKKT
3604	G-BKKU
3605	G-BKKV
3606	G-BKKW
3607	G-BKKX
3608	G-BKMX
3609	G-BKMY
3610	G-BKMZ
3611	G-BKPO
3612	G-BKPP
3613	G-BKPR
3614	G-BKSL
3615	G-BKSM
3616	G-BKSN
3617	G-BKUF
3618	G-BKUG
3619	G-BKUH
3620	G-BKWJ
3621	G-BKWK
3622	G-BKWL
3623	G-BKWM
3624	G-BKWN
3625	G-BKZN
3626	G-BKZO
3627	G-BKZP
3628	G-BKZR
3629	G-BKZS
3630	G-BLCN
3631	G-BLCO
3632	G-BLCP
3633	G-BLCR
3634	G-BLCS
3635	G-BLED
3636	G-BLEE
3637	G-BLEF
3638	G-BLEG
3639	G-BLEH
3640	G-BLGA
3641	G-BLGB
3642	G-BLGC
3643	G-BLGD
3644	G-BLGE
3645	G-BLGF
3646	G-BLIJ
3647	G-BLIK
3648	G-BLIL
3649	G-BLIM
3650	G-BLIN
3651	G-BLJR
3652	G-BLJS
3654	G-BLJU
3655	G-BLJV
3656	G-BLPU
3657	G-BLPV
3658	G-BLPW
3659	G-BLPX
3660	G-BLPY
3661	G-BLRT
3667	G-BLRU
3664	G-BLTO
3665	G-BLUC
3666	G-BLUD
3668	G-BLUR
3669	G-BLUU
3662	G-BLWA
3670	G-BLWJ
3671	G-BLWK
3672	G-BLWN
3673	G-BLYF
3674	G-BLYG
3675	G-BLYH
3676	G-BLZT
3677	G-BLZU
3678	G-BLZV
3611	G-BMAJ
3633	G-BMAR
3679	G-BMEN
3680	G-BMEO
3681	G-BMEP
3682	G-BMER
3683	G-BMES
3684	G-BMHV
3685	G-BMHW
3686	G-BMHX
3687	G-BMHY
3688	G-BMLC
3689	G-BMLD
3690	G-BMLE
3691	G-BMNG
3692	G-BMNH
3693	G-BMNI
3694	G-BMNJ
3695	G-BMNK
3696	G-BMUV
3697	G-BMUW
3698	G-BMUX
3699	G-BMUY
3700	G-BMXP
3606	G-DASI
3638	G-ISLE
3637	G-LEGS
3603	G-OJSY
3633	G-POOL
3604	G-RMSS
3600	G-ROOM
3628	G-SALU
3611	G-WACK
3601	G-WIDE

HS- Thailand

3680	HS-TSE
3681	HS-TSF

N United States

3652	N124CA
3631	N131DA
3634	N132DA
3653	N151CA
3665	N190SB
3666	N191SB
3605	N342AW
3605	N342MV
3678	N342SB
3609	N343MV
3615	N344MV
3616	N345MV
3649	N346MV
3650	N347MV
3602	N360MQ
3691	N360PC
3601	N360SA
3663	N360SE
3668	N360SY
3607	N361MQ
3612	N362MQ
3662	N362SA
3614	N363MQ
3619	N364MQ
3621	N365MQ
3639	N366MQ
3640	N367MQ
3603	N368MQ
3654	N369MQ
3655	N370MQ
3658	N371MQ
3659	N372MQ
3682	N373MQ
3683	N374MQ
3684	N375MQ
3685	N376MQ
3625	N449BY
3613	N601A
3623	N601CA
3617	N617FB
3622	N622FB
3643	N631KC
3644	N632KC
3645	N633KC
3646	N634KC
3647	N635KC
3690	N690PC
3618	N691A
3692	N693PC
3694	N694PC
3693	N695PC
3627	N701A
3697	N711HJ
3698	N711MP
3696	N711PK
3610	N715NC
3624	N912SB
3629	N913SB
3631	N914SB

OY- Denmark

3632	OY-MMA
3648	OY-MMB
3628	OY-MMC

VH- Australia

3626	VH-MVW
3620	VH-MVX
3630	VH-SVU

AEROSPATIALE CARAVELLE (EXISTING AIRCRAFT ONLY)

Rear-engined, short/medium range jet airliner. The first French jet airliner, the prototype Caravelle flew for the first time on 27 May 1955. Initial production versions included the Caravelle I, IA, III, VIN, and VIR. All were powered by Rolls Royce Avon turbojets, and had accommodation for up to 99 passengers. The Super Caravelle followed in 1964 and included a stretch to 104 passengers and Pratt & Whitney JT8D-7 turbofans, as did the 10R. The Caravelle 11R was a mixed passenger/cargo version, and the final model, the Caravelle 12 had seating for up to 140. A total of 280 production aircraft were built and production ceased in February 1973.

Dimensions :	Wing span: 112ft 5in (34.29m) Length: 105ft 0in (32.00m) Height: 28ft 7in (8.72m) (III/, VIR/VIN/10R)
	Wing span: 112ft 5in (34.29m) Length: 108ft 4in (33.03m) Height: 29ft 7in (9.03m) (10B)
	Wing span: 112ft 5in (34.29m) Length: 107ft 4in (32.72m) Height: 28ft 7in (8.72m) (11R)
	Wing span: 112ft 5in (34.29m) Length: 118ft 11in (36.26m) Height: 29ft 7in (9.03m) (12)
Powerplant :	Two Rolls Royce Avon turbojets (Caravelle I/III/VI): Two Pratt & Whitney JT8D-7 (Caravelle 10/11/12)
Performance :	Max cruising speed 434 Knots(805km/h) (III) Range: with max payload 917nm (1,700km) (III)
	Max cruising speed 456 knots (845km/h) (VI) Range: with max payload 1,241nm (2,300km) (VIN)
	Max cruising speed 445 knots (825km/h) (12) Range: with max payload 1,889nm. (2,540km) (12)
Accommodation:	99 passengers (Caravelle I/III/VI), 104 passengers (10) and 140 passengers (12).
	The Caravelle 11R offers a mixed passenger-cargo configuration.
Manufacturer :	Aerospatiale - 37 Boulevard de Montmorency, F-75781, Paris Cedex 16, France
	Telephone: (33) 1 524 438 Telex: 620059 F AISPA

aerospatiale

C/N	Registration	Owner/Operator	Series	First Flight	Delivery	Remarks
01	F-WHHH	Sud Aviation	Proto.	27/MAY/55		
	F-BHHH	Sud Aviation				WFU, preserved Orly
02	F-WHHI	Sud Aviation	Proto.	06/MAY/56		
	F-BHHI	Sud Aviation				WFU, nose preserved Le Bourget
1	F-WHRA	Sud Aviation	1	18/MAY/58		
	F-BHRA	Air France	3		03/APR/59	WFU 19/DEC/75, Instructional airframe, Vilgenis
3	LN-KLH	SAS	3	23/MAR/59	10/APR/59	cvtd. srs.1 WFU 29/AUG/74, preserved Oslo
4	SE-DAA	SAS	3	15/APR/59	25/APR/59	cvtd. srs.1 WFU 28/JUL/74, used by fire department at Stockholm-Arlanda
5	F-BHRC	Air France	3	09/MAY/59	15/MAY/59	cvtd. srs.1
	6V-ACP	Senegal Govt.			28/DEC/71	Leased
	6V-AAR	Senegal Govt.			72	Leased
	6V-AAR	Senegal Govt.			27/DEC/77	Purchased
12	F-BHRF	Air France	3	08/OCT/59	17/OCT/59	cvtd. srs.1 WFU MAR/81. Preserved.
16	F-BHRH	Air France	3	02/DEC/59	11/DEC/59	cvtd. srs.1 WFU MAR/81, preserved
18	F-OBNG	Air Algerie	3	21/DEC/59	26/DEC/59	cvtd. srs.1
	7T-VAG	Air Algerie				WFU JUL/75
21	OH-LEA	Finnair	3	11/FEB/60	18/FEB/60	cvtd. srs.1
	D-ABAF	LTU			05/FEB/65	
	F-WLGA	Sud Aviation			08/AUG/68	
	PH-TRM	Transavia			11/FEB/69	Leased
	F-BSRR	Aerospatiale			OCT/70	
	F-BSRR	Air Inter			19/MAR/71	Leased
	F-BSRR	Aerospatiale			MAY/73	
	F-BSRR	Air Inter			06/JAN/74	Leased
	F-BSRR	Aerospatiale			DEC/74	
	F-BSRR	Air Inter			06/JUN/75	Leased
	I-GISA	Altair			06/JAN/81	WFU 83
	9Q-CPS	IAC-Zaire			JUL/84	
22	OH-LEB	Finnair	3	23/MAR/60	30/MAR/60	cvtd. srs.1
	F-BJTR	Air France			31/AUG/64	WFU 07/NOV/80, preserved Le Bourget (Musee de L'Air)
29	OY-KRC	SAS	3	23/MAR/60	02/APR/60	cvtd. srs.1A
	HS-TGH	Thai International			05/OCT/65	Leased
	OY-KRC	SAS			03/APR/70	WFU 27/SEP/74 Derelict Stockholm-Arlanda
35	I-DAXA	Alitalia	6N	21/APR/60	29/APR/60	cvtd. srs.3
	HC-BAD	Saeta			DEC/75	WFU JAN/82, stored Quito
36	I-DAXE	Alitalia	6N	13/MAY/60	19/MAY/60	cvtd. srs.3
	PH-TVW	Transavia			28/APR/73	
	PH-TVW	Schipol Airport Fire Service			18/APR/75	WFU 28/SEP/74 Used for Fire practice
37	F-BHRM	Air France	3	27/MAY/60	30/MAY/60	WFU APR/79
	F-BHRM	Aeroport de Lyon-Satolas			AUG/79	Static display
38	F-WJAL	Sud Aviation	3	17/JUN/60		
	F-WJAL	SAS				Not taken-up
	HB-ICX	Swissair			24/JUN/60	Leased
	HB-ICX	Swissair			30/MAR/65	Purchased
	F-BSRD	Catair			27/APR/71	
	B-1854	China Airlines			17/JAN/73	
	F-WJAL	Aerospatiale			AUG/77	
	F-WJAL	CEAT			09/JUL/77	WFU 09/JUL/77, used for structural tests.
41	F-BHRO	Air France	3	24/JUN/60	29/JUN/60	WFU MAY/78, preserved Angers
42	F-WJAO	Sud Aviation	3	15/JUL/60		
	F-BJAO	Sud Aviation			16/JUL/60	
	F-WJAM	Sud Aviation			18/JUL/60	
	N420GE	General Electric			18/JUL/60	
	N420GE	General Electric	7	29/DEC/60		Converted
	F-BJSO	Sud Aviation			14/DEC/61	
	F-WLKF	Sud Aviation	3	14/DEC/62		
	F-BLKF	Air France			31/JUL/63	WFU 81
	F-BLKF	Air Charter International			NOV/80	

AEROSPATIALE CARAVELLE (EXISTING AIRCRAFT ONLY)

C/N	Registration	Owner/Operator	Series	First Flight	Delivery	Remarks
	F-BLKF	Air France			82	
	F-BLKF	Central African Govt.			MAR/82	
	TL-KAB	Central African Govt.			82	
	TL-FCA	Central African Govt.				
46	F-BHRQ	Air France	3		28/AUG/60	
	F-BHRQ	Air Inter			31/MAR/72	WFU JAN/83
	F-BHRQ	Intercontinental Airlines			01/MAR/83	For spares
47	OY-KRD	SAS	3	26/JUL/60	30/JUL/60	WFU 21/AUG/74, stored Kastrup
50	F-BHRR	Air France	3	17/SEP/60	23/SEP/60	
	F-BHRR	Air Inter			31/MAR/73	
	5N-AWK	Kabo Air			AUG/83	
51	F-WBNJ	Sud Aviation	3	08/SEP/60		
	F-OBNJ	Air Algerie			12/SEP/60	
	F-BLCZ	Air France			NOV/61	Leased
	OD-ADZ	Air Liban			JAN/62	Sub-leased
	F-BLCZ	Air France			23/JUN/63	Leased
	F-BLCZ	Air Algerie			14/AUG/63	
	7T-VAE	Air Algerie			20/SEP/67	WFU JUN/76, derelict Algiers
53	F-BJTA	Air France	3	29/MAR/61	07/APR/61	
	XU-JTB	Air Cambodge			19/JAN/73	WFU 01/APR/75, used by Bangkok fire department
55	F-BHRT	Air France	3	04/OCT/60	14/OCT/60	WFU NOV/79, preserved Merville
57	CN-CCX	Royal Air Maroc	3	04/FEB/61	25/FEB/61	WFU 03/MAY/76, ground trainer
61	F-BHRY	Air France	3	29/NOV/60	15/DEC/60	WFU MAR/81, preserved
62	F-WJAP	Sud Aviation	6R	06/FEB/61		
	N2001U	United				Not taken-up
	F-BJAP	Sud Aviation				
	PP-CJC	Cruzeiro			30/JUL/63	
	N901MW	Midwest Air Charter			23/MAY/79	
	N901MW	Airborne Express			17/APR/80	WFU DEC/83, preserved
64	OO-SRA	Sabena	6N	14/JAN/61	20/JAN/61	WFU 03/AUG/74, preserved Brussels museum
67	OO-SRE	Sabena	6N	20/MAR/61	24/MAR/61	
	F-BYCD	Catair			30/MAY/76	
	F-BYCD	Europe Aero Services			MAR/78	
	F-BYCD	Corse Air International			APR/84	Leased
70	F-BJAU	Sud Aviation		03/JUL/61		
	OO-SRG	Sabena	6N		12/JUL/61	
	OO-SRG	Sud Aviation			19/SEP/73	
	VT-ECG	Indian Airlines			05/NOV/73	Leased WFU 25/OCT/76
	VT-ECG	Pushpaka Aviation			78	For spares
71	I-DABA	Alitalia	6N	11/MAR/61	21/MAR/61	WFU 21/DEC/76
	9Q-CRU	Afro Cargo			FEB/80	
	9Q-CRU	Coastal Airways				WFU APR/84, stored
72	I-DABE	Alitalia	6N	23/MAR/61	30/MAR/61	WFU OCT/75
	I-DABE	Saeta			11/DEC/76	WFU 11/DEC/76, for spares
74	I-DABI	Alitalia	6N	14/APR/61	22/APR/61	WFU APR/84, stored
	9Q-CMD	African Air Charter			83	
75	F-OBNL	Air Algerie	6N	17/JUN/61	20/JUN/61	
	7T-VAL	Air Algerie			09/NOV/64	WFU JUN/76, derelict Angiers
77	I-DABU	Alitalia	6N	09/MAY/61	17/MAY/61	WFU 26/OCT/76 Instructional
78	OO-SRH	Sabena	6N	08/AUG/61	11/AUG/61	
	F-WLGA	Aerospatiale			03/SEP/73	
	VT-ECH	Indian Airlines			12/OCT/73	
	VT-ECH	Aerospatiale			21/NOV/75	
	TU-TXR	Air Afrique			07/JAN/76	Instructional
79	I-DAXU	Alitalia	6N	02/JUN/61	09/JUN/61	WFU JUL/75 Used as a restaurant at Valcamonica, Breno
80	I-DAXT	Alitalia	6N	09/OCT/61	17/OCT/61	WFU 19/FEB/77
81	I-DABR	Alitalia	6N	10/JAN/62	19/JAN/62	WFU 19/OCT/77
	'I-ALBA'	Alidelta			83	Preserved, Tavazzano.
82	I-DABZ	Alitalia	6N	31/JAN/62	09/FEB/62	
	HC-BAI	Saeta			14/NOV/75	WFU DEC/76, for spares
85	I-DABT	Alitalia	6N	24/MAR/62	02/APR/62	
	I-DABT	SAM			01/JUN/68	
	I-DABT	Alitalia			74	
	I-DABT	SAM			FEB/75	Leased
	I-DABT	Alitalia			NOV/76	WFU NOV/76, stored Treviso-Castrette, fuselage only
86	N1001U	United Airlines	6R	19/MAY/61	10/JUN/61	
	N1001U	Litton Industries			27/JAN/71	
	PT-DUW	LASA			MAY/71	Leased
	N1001U	Litton Industries			MAY/73	
87	N1002U	United Airlines	6R	08/JUN/61	20/JUN/61	
	PH-TRY	Transavia			01/MAY/70	
	N777VV	Atlanta Skylarks			31/JUL/76	
	N777VV	Independent Air			02/AUG/76	
	N777VV	Ronald J.Clark			13/OCT/77	WFU 13/OCT/77
	N240RC	Go Group			80	WFU, stored Tucson
88	N1003U	United Airlines	6R	26/JUN/61	02/JUL/61	
	OY-SAH	Sterling			26/NOV/71	
	OY-SAH	Egyptair			01/MAY/71	Leased
	OY-SAH	Sterling			OCT/75	
	N902MW	Midwest Air Charter			20/DEC/78	
	N902MW	Airborne Express			17/APR/80	WFU DEC/82, Wilmington, Ohio. Preserved, Bradley Air Museum
91	N1006U	United Airlines	6R	05/AUG/61	11/AUG/61	
	OY-SBV	Sterling			03/MAR/72	
	PH-TVZ	Transavia			08/MAR/72	Leased
	OY-SBV	Sterling			02/DEC/72	
	5T-CJW	Mauretanian Govt.			07/MAY/74	
	5T-MAL	Mauretanian Govt.			76	
	5T-RIM	Mauretanian Govt.			25/APR/76	
94	N1009U	United Airlines	6R	29/SEP/61	07/OCT/61	
	OY-SBY	Sterling			22/MAR/72	
	F-BUZC	Minerve			18/OCT/75	Leased
	F-BUZC	Minerve			02/APR/76	Purchased, WFU DEC/83, stored
102	N1017U	United Airlines	6R	12/DEC/61	29/DEC/61	
	PH-TRU	Transavia			30/NOV/70	
	N555SL	Atlanta Skylarks			31/AUG/76	
	N98KT	Kearney and Trecker Co.			01/SEP/78	
	N98KT	E & H Associates			JAN/82	

C/N	Registration	Owner/Operator	Series	First Flight	Delivery	Remarks
105	F-BJTI	Air France	6R	09/MAY/62	23/MAY/62	
	F-BJTI	Kingdom of Libya Airlines			07/OCT/67	Leased
	F-BJTI	Air France			08/NOV/67	
	F-BJTI	Air Charter International			01/SEP/70	Leased
	F-BJTI	Air Charter International			01/APR/71	Purchased
	F-BJTI	Royal Air Maroc			FEB/73	Leased
	F-BJTI	Air Charter International			MAR/73	
	F-BJTI	SFACT			04/SEP/73	
106	I-DABS	Alitalia	6N	01/APR/62	06/APR/62	WFU 01/OCT/76
	EL-AIW	Coastal Aviation				WFU JUN/83, stored
109	EC-ARK	Iberia	6R	12/MAR/62	30/MAR/62	
	EC-ARK	Aviaco			04/JUN/73	
	HK-1812	Aerocesar			20/NOV/76	WFU APR/83, stored
111	F-BJTE	Air France	3	28/DEC/61	12/JAN/62	
	F-BJTE	Air Charter International			01/APR/71	Leased
	F-BJTE	Air France			01/APR/73	WFU 11/MAY/79
	F-BJTE	Air Charter International			NOV/80	
	F-BJTE	Kabo Air			MAR/82	For spares, derelict at Kano
112	SE-DAF	SAS	3	08/FEB/62	17/FEB/62	WFU 23/SEP/74
						Preserved Stockholm-Arlanda
115	F-BJTG	Air France	3	19/APR/62	04/MAY/62	
	F-BJTG	Air Charter International			01/SEP/70	WFU NOV/81 to MAY/84
	9Q-CLP	Fontshi Aviation Service			MAY/84	
116	OH-LED	Finnair	3	19/FEB/62	23/FEB/62	
	F-ZACE	CEV			01/DEC/62	
117	CS-TCA	TAP	6R	09/JUL/62	13/JUL/62	
	HC-BAJ	SAN			23/NOV/75	WFU MAY/83, stored
119	F-BJTJ	Air France	3	05/JUN/62	18/JUN/62	
	HB-ICR	Swissair			28/FEB/64	Leased
	F-BJTJ	Air France			01/MAR/66	
	F-BJTJ	Air Charter International			01/SEP/70	Leased
	F-BJTJ	Air Charter International			01/APR/71	Purchased
	F-BJTJ	Europe One			09/FEB/77	Leased
	F-BJTJ	Air Charter International			01/MAR/77	WFU NOV/81
	9Q-CGC	Fontshi Aviation Service			04/MAR/83	
123	HB-ICU	SAS	3	12/APR/62	19/APR/62	
	HB-ICU	Swissair			19/APR/62	Leased
	HB-ICU	Swissair			APR/65	Purchased
	HB-ICU	N.V.Huygen & Co.			20/OCT/70	WFU 10/NOV/70
	OO-SBQ	Sobelair			MAY/71	Leased
	F-BUFH	Aerotechnique Internationale			01/JUN/74	
	F-BUFH	Catair			01/JUN/74	Leased
	F-BUFH	Aerotour			MAR/76	Leased, WFU 23/NOV/80
	F-BUFH	Turkhol Hava Yollari			JAN/81	Not taken-up
	9Q-CZL	Inter-Fret			APR/81	WFU APR/84, stored
124	F-BJTH	Air France	3	26/APR/62	10/MAY/62	
	F-BJTH	Air Charter International			01/SEP/70	WFU APR/81, preserved at Nice
129	PP-CJA	Cruzeiro	6R	26/NOV/62	10/DEC/62	
	N907MW	Midwest Air Charter			08/AUG/79	
	N907MW	Airborne Express			17/APR/80	WFU SEP/82, stored
131	PP-PDZ	Panair do Brasil	6R	02/AUG/62	17/SEP/62	
	PP-PDZ	Gobierno do Brasil			16/FEB/65	
	PP-PDZ	Cruzeiro			25/MAR/66	
	HK-2212	Aerotal			NOV/78	WFU DEC/81, stored Bogota
135	F-WJAK	Sud Aviation		24/JUL/63		
	YU-AHB	JAT	6N		27/JUL/63	WFU MAY/76, stored Belgrade
136	F-BLKI	Sud Aviation	6R	20/JAN/64		Sud Lear Autoland
	OE-LCU	Austrian Airlines			13/MAY/66	
	F-BTDL	Euralair			15/JAN/72	
	F-OGJD	Air Martinique			10/MAR/80	WFU NOV/80
	HK-2597	Aerocesar			APR/81	WFU APR/83, stored
138	N210G	Garrett	6R	25/JUL/63	31/JUL/63	
	EC-AXU	Iberia			07/JAN/65	
	EC-AXU	Aviaco			04/JUN/73	
	HK-1811	Aerocesar			14/FEB/76	WFU APR/83, stored
139	F-WLGA	Sud Aviation	6N	05/JAN/63		
	YU-AHA	JAT			11/JAN/63	
	F-BYAI	Aerotour			10/FEB/78	WFU NOV/80, stored Orly
	F-BYAI	Corse Air International			JUN/81	Instructional
141	F-BJTK	Air France	3	01/FEB/63		Not taken-up
	141	GTLA			13/SEP/63	Callsign 'F-RAFG'
						WFU 28/MAR/80, preserved
						Le Bourget (Musee de L'Air)
142	F-BJTL	Air France	3	22/FEB/63	05/MAR/63	
	F-BJTL	Air Charter International			01/JAN/71	Leased
	F-BJTL	Air France			72	WFU JUL/81,
						preserved Zurich Airport.
143	F-WJSO	Sud Aviation	6N	20/DEC/62	DEC/62	
	F-BJSO	Sud Aviation				Smiths Autoland
	I-DABM	Alitalia			27/MAY/64	
	I-DABM	SAM			69	Leased
	I-DABM	Alitalia				
	I-DABM	SAM			APR/74	Leased
	I-DABM	Alitalia			76	WFU JAN/77
144	F-BJTM	Air France	3	13/MAR/63	09/APR/63	
	9U-BTA	Air Burundi			20/MAY/76	
146	I-DABV	Alitalia	6N	05/MAR/63	14/MAR/63	
	I-DABV	SAM			11/NOV/68	Leased
	HC-BDS	Saeta			25/JAN/77	WFU MAY/83, stored
152	F-BJTP	Air France	3	06/MAY/63	16/MAY/63	
					71	WFU MAY/80, displayed Bordeaux
						JUL/81 as 'F-CCIB'
154	CN-CCY	Royal Air Maroc	3	24/MAY/63	01/JUN/63	
	CN-CCY	MEA			23/JAN/69	Leased
	CN-CCY	Royal Air Maroc			JUL/69	WFU 17/DEC/77
	SU-BBU	Air Alexandrie			14/APR/80	WFU 80 to AUG/83
	EL-AAS	Atlantic Aviation Services			AUG/83	
158	F-WLHY	Sud Aviation	6R	27/SEP/63		
	F-BLHY	Sud Aviation				
	158	GLAM			AUG/64	Leased Callsign 'F-RAFA'
	5A-DAA	Kingdom of Libya Airlines			24/JUL/65	
	5A-DAA	Libyan Arab Airlines			01/SEP/69	WFU SEP/79, derelict Tripoli
160	CC-CCQ	Lan-Chile	6R	25/JUN/64	02/JUL/64	
	HK-1780	Aerotal			AUG/75	WFU DEC/81, stored Bogota
161	OE-LCA	Austrian Airlines	6R	06/FEB/63	18/FEB/63	

AEROSPATIALE CARAVELLE (EXISTING AIRCRAFT ONLY)

C/N	Registration	Owner/Operator	Series	First Flight	Delivery	Remarks
	F-BUFC	Catair			22/JAN/73	
	F-BUFC	Euralair			APR/78	
	HK-2402	Aerotal			27/NOV/79	WFU DEC/81, stored
164	CC-CCP	Lan-Chile	6R	18/APR/64	04/MAY/64	
	HK-1779	Aerotal			AUG/75	WFU JUN/79, stored
166	OE-LCI	Austrian Airlines	6R	20/MAR/64	28/MAR/64	
	LX-LGF	Luxair			04/MAR/72	Leased
	LX-LGF	Luxair			02/FEB/73	Purchased, WFU 01/MAY/78
	HC-BFN	SAN			17/JUN/78	WFU MAY/83, stored
167	OE-LCO	Austrian Airlines	6R	13/APR/65	22/APR/65	
	F-BSEL	Euralair			28/NOV/71	
	F-OGJE	Air Martinique			25/JUN/80	WFU NOV/80
	HK-2598	Aerocesar			APR/81	WFU DEC/83, stored
168	PP-CJD	Cruzeiro	6R	28/JUN/63	08/JUL/63	
	HK-2287	TAC-Colombia			19/APR/79	WFU APR/83, stored
169	F-WLKJ	Sud Aviation	10B3	03/MAR/64		
	F-BLKJ	Sud Aviation				
	OH-LSG	Finnair			31/MAY/66	
	I-GISU	Altair			MAY/84	
	I-GISU	Fiscambi Leasing			MAY/86	WFU MAY/86
172	SE-DAG	SAS	3	12/DEC/64	17/DEC/64	
	85172	Swedish Air Force			04/MAR/71	
175	OO-SRI	Sabena	6N	22/DEC/64	29/DEC/64	
	OO-SRI	Sobelair			01/OCT/73	
	F-BYCB	Catair			26/APR/76	
	F-BYCB	Europe Aero Services			MAR/78	Not taken-up
	OO-SRI	Sobelair			JUN/78	
	F-GATZ	Minerve			22/DEC/78	
176	F-WLKS	Sud Aviation	10B1R	18/JAN/65		
	F-BLKS	Sud Aviation				
	EC-BDC	Iberia			01/APR/66	
	EC-CAE	Aviaco			01/APR/72	
	D-ACVK	Aero Lloyd			81	
178	TS-TAR	Tunis Air	3	12/MAR/64	18/MAR/64	WFU 77, derelict Tunis-Carthage
180	LV-PPJ	Aerolineas Argentinas			19/SEP/64	
	LV-III	Aerolineas Argentinas	6N	03/SEP/64	SEP/64	
	TC-93	Fuerza Aerea Argentina			24/APR/73	
	T-93	Fuerza Aerea Argentina			73	
	N49SB	International Air			05/SEP/75	
	N49SB	Nevada Airtours			29/MAR/78	
	F-GBMK	Europe Aero Services			04/FEB/79	
	5N-AOY	Okada Air			JAN/84	
181	OH-LSA	Finnair	10B3	11/JUL/64	22/JUL/64	
	OH-LSA	Kar Air			MAR/70	Leased
	OH-LSA	Finnair			70	
	F-BMKS	Europe Aero Service			05/MAR/81	
	F-BMKS	Air Charter International			05/MAR/81	Leased
182	OH-LSB	Finnair	10B3	30/JUL/64	05/AUG/64	
	F-GDFY	Europe Aero Service			MAR/82	
	F-GDFY	Air Charter International			MAR/82	Leased
183	OY-STA	Sterling	10B3	30/DEC/64	30/MAR/65	
	YK-AFC	Syrian Arab Airlines			19/JUN/71	Damaged 05/JUN/82, Damascus
	F-GDJU	Europe Aero Service			OCT/82	
184	OY-STD	Sterling	10B3	12/OCT/65	20/OCT/65	
	YK-AFA	Syrian Arab Airlines			06/JUN/71	
	TZ-ADS	Air Mali			SEP/80	
	TZ-ADS	CTA			24/APR/81	Leased
	TZ-ADS	Air Mali			31/OCT/81	
	TZ-ADS	Corse Air International			14/JUL/83	Leased
	F-GEPC	Corse Air International			84	Purchased
	F-GEPC	Air Caledonie			26/NOV/84	Leased
	F-GEPC	Air Caledonie			FEB/86	Purchased
185	OH-LSC	Finnair	10B3	21/AUG/64	27/AUG/64	
	F-BJEN	Europe Aero Service			04/FEB/81	
	F-BJEN	Air Charter International			04/FEB/81	Leased
186	OY-STB	Sterling	10B3	05/APR/66	08/APR/66	
	YK-AFD	Syrian Arab Airlines			20/NOV/71	
187	OH-LSD	Finnair	10B3	05/SEP/64	10/SEP/64	
	OH-LSD	CTA			01/APR/80	Leased
	OH-LSD	Finnair			28/NOV/80	
	I-GISO	Altair			15/MAY/84	
	I-GISO	Fiscambi Leasing			MAY/86	WFU MAY/86, stored Milan
188	OH-LSF	Finnair	10B3	07/MAR/66	12/MAR/66	
	I-GISI	Altair			27/MAR/84	
	SE-DEH	Air Charter West			DEC/85	Op. by Transwede
189	OH-LSE	Finnair	10B3	14/SEP/64	20/SEP/64	
	F-BJTU	Europe Aero Service			08/JAN/81	
	F-BJTU	Air Charter International			08/JAN/81	Leased
190	YK-AFB	Syrian Arab Airlines	10B3	23/JUN/66	30/JUN/66	
191	OY-KRG	Sud Aviation	3	08/FEB/65		
	OY-KRG	SAS			16/FEB/65	Leased
	OY-KRG	Sud Aviation			69	
	PH-TRN	Transavia			04/APR/69	Leased
	PH-TRN	Sud Aviation			15/OCT/70	
	YU-AJG	JAT			MAY/72	Leased, WFU 21/NOV/72 Cabin Trainer, Belgrade
193	SE-DAH	Sud Aviation	3	03/MAR/65		
	SE-DAH	SAS			12/MAR/65	Leased
	SE-DAH	Sud Aviation			12/MAR/69	
	F-BRIM	Transunion			30/APR/69	Leased
	F-BRIM	Panair			13/MAY/69	Sub-leased
	F-BRIM	Transunion			JUL/69	Leased
	F-BRIM	Aerospatiale			05/JAN/72	
	F-ZACF	SOGERMA			MAY/72	
	F-ZACF	CEV			OCT/78	
194	YU-AHE	JAT	6N	05/JUL/65	09/JUL/65	WFU JUN/75, preserved Zagreb
195	CN-CCZ	Royal Air Maroc	3	16/JUN/65	25/JUN/65	WFU 07/NOV/76, Ground training Casablanca
199	JY-ACS	Alia	10B1R	22/JUL/65	28/JUL/65	
	TU-TCN	Air Afrique			13/DEC/73	
	EC-DCN	TransEuropa			JUL/78	
	EC-DCN	Hispania			DEC/82	
201	F-BNRA	UTA	10B1R	21/JAN/66	26/JAN/66	
	TU-TXQ	Air Afrique			19/SEP/75	Leased
	F-BNRA	UTA			APR/76	

C/N	Registration	Owner/Operator	Series	First Flight	Delivery	Remarks
	TU-TXQ	Air Afrique			07/OCT/76	Leased
	F-BNRA	UTA			18/JAN/77	
	201	French Air Force			DEC/77	Callsign 'F-RAFH'
203	VT-DUH	Indian Airlines	6N	08/NOV/65	28/DEC/65	
	VT-DUH	Pushpaka Airlines			18/JUN/79	
	VT-DUH	Indian Airlines				Leased
	VT-DUH	Pushpaka Airlines			07/JUL/80	Stored Bombay
206	F-BNKA	Air France	3	22/JUN/66	28/JUN/66	
	F-BNKA	Air Inter			AUG/66	Leased
	F-BNKA	Air Inter			23/JAN/75	Purchased
	5N-AWF	Kabo Air			APR/82	
207	TS-MAC	Tunis Air	3	10/MAR/66	17/MAR/66	WFU 78, derelict Tunis-Carthage
208	F-BNKB	Air France	3	08/APR/66	15/APR/66	
	F-BNKB	Air Inter			AUG/66	Leased
	F-BNKB	Air Inter			23/JAN/75	Purchased
	I-GISE	Altair			82	WFU 84 to MAY/86
	I-GISE	Fiscambi Leasing			MAY/86	WFU MAY/86
209	LN-KLN	Sud Aviation	3	06/DEC/65		
	LN-KLN	SAS			17/DEC/65	Leased
	LN-KLN	Sud Aviation			16/DEC/69	
	F-BRUJ	Transunion			15/MAR/70	
	F-BRUJ	Royal Air Maroc			MAY/70	Leased
	F-BRUJ	Transunion			JAN/71	
	F-BRUJ	Air Mali			JAN/71	Leased
	F-BRUJ	Transunion			MAR/71	
	F-BRUJ	Tunis Air			09/APR/71	Leased
	F-BRUJ	Transunion			JUL/71	
	F-BRUJ	Aerospatiale			28/DEC/71	WFU 28/DEC/71
	YU-AJE	Inex Adria			09/MAY/72	Leased
	YU-AJE	Aerospatiale			28/NOV/72	
	F-BUFM	Aerospatiale			21/MAR/73	
	F-BUFM	Tunis Air			01/APR/73	Leased
	F-BUFM	Aerospatiale			01/NOV/73	
	9XR-CH	Rwanda Govt.			28/MAR/74	
210	SE-DAI	SAS	3	01/FEB/66	10/FEB/66	
	85210	Swedish Air Force			27/SEP/71	
211	OH-LSH	Finnair	10B3	13/JAN/67	20/JAN/67	
	F-GDFY	Europe Aero Service			FEB/82	
	F-GDFZ	Air Charter International			FEB/82	Leased
212	F-BOEE	Sud Aviation	10B3	25/AUG/66	31/AUG/66	Leased
	F-BOEE	UTA			12/MAR/67	
	F-BOEE	Sud Aviation			30/MAR/67	
	OY-STC	Sterling			17/DEC/74	Leased
	OH-LSK	Finnair			12/MAR/76	
	OH-LSK	Sterling			13/MAR/76	Leased
	EC-CUM	TAE			18/DEC/81	
	OY-STC	Sterling				
213	VT-DVI	Indian Airlines	6N	19/OCT/66	23/OCT/66	WFU 31/OCT/79
	VT-DVI	Pushpaka Airlines			80	WFU, stored Bombay
215	TU-TCO	Air Afrique	11R	21/APR/67	17/JUL/67	
	5N-AWT	Kabo Air			JUL/83	
217	F-BNKC	Air Inter	3	15/FEB/67	15/MAR/67	
	I-GISI	Altair			JAN/83	
	5N-AWO	Kabo Air			JUL/83	
218	YU-AHF	JAT	6N	23/MAY/67	29/MAY/67	
	F-BVPZ	Aerotour			15/MAY/78	WFU 23/NOV/80
	F-BVPZ	Corse Air International			JUN/81	
219	F-WJAK	Sud Aviation	11R	01/JUN/67		
	F-BJAK	Sud Aviation				
	TU-TCY	Air Afrique			17/JUL/67	
	5N-AWQ	Kabo Air			JUL/83	
220	F-BNKD	Air Inter	3	18/FEB/67	25/FEB/67	
	5N-AVQ	Intercontinental Airlines			MAY/81	
221	5A-DAE	Kingdom of Libya Airlines	6R	22/APR/67	29/APR/67	
	5A-DAE	Libyan Arab Airlines			01/SEP/69	WFU 01/APR/75, derelict Tripoli Ap.
222	F-BNRB	UTA	10B1R	01/MAR/67	07/MAR/67	
	HB-ICQ	SATA			05/DEC/72	
	HB-ICQ	CTA			01/NOV/78	
	HB-ICQ	International Red Cross			07/JAN/81	Leased
	HB-ICQ	CTA			30/JUN/81	
223	F-WJAQ	Sud Aviation	10B1R	30/MAY/67	07/JUN/67	
	EC-BIB	Iberia			17/MAY/72	
	EC-BIB	Aviaco			MAR/79	WFU 82
	EC-BIB	TransEuropa			83	WFU 85, stored
	HK-2860	Aerosucre				
224	F-BNKE	Air Inter	3	25/MAR/67	31/MAR/67	WFU DEC/80 Preserved Marseille-Marignane
229	F-BNKG	Air Inter	3	30/NOV/67	02/JAN/68	
	F-BNKG	Altair			AUG/83	
	9Q-CCP	IAC-Zaire			JUN/85	
230	EC-BIE	Iberia	10B1R	12/JUL/67	20/JUL/67	
	EC-BIE	Aviaco			17/MAY/72	
	D-AAST	Aero Lloyd			MAY/80	
232	EC-BIF	Iberia	10B1R	21/SEP/67	29/SEP/67	
	EC-BIF	Aviaco			17/MAY/72	
	D-ABAK	Aero Lloyd			MAR/80	
	D-ABAK	CTA			SEP/82	Leased, Not taken-up
	D-ABAK	Aero Lloyd			SEP/82	
233	YU-AHG	JAT	6N	26/DEC/67	11/JAN/68	WFU 76
	F-BYCY	Aero Centre Limoges			FEB/78	
	F-BYCY	Aerotour			14/APR/78	WFU 23/NOV/80, stored Orly
	F-BYCY	Corse Air International				
234	F-WJAL	Aerospatiale	6R	13/JUN/68		
	LX-LGE	Luxair			07/MAR/70	Leased
	LX-LGE	Aerospatiale			07/MAR/72	
	HB-ICP	SATA			24/MAR/72	Leased
	HB-ICP	Aerospatiale			24/JUN/73	
	HB-ICP	SATA			08/AUG/73	Leased
	F-BRGX	Aerospatiale			24/JUN/75	
	F-BRGX	Catair			24/JUN/75	Leased
	F-BRGX	Aerospatiale			15/OCT/75	
	F-BRGX	Air Inter			20/DEC/75	Leased
	F-BRGX	Aerospatiale			FEB/76	
	F-BRGX	Air Inter			APR/76	Leased

AEROSPATIALE CARAVELLE (EXISTING AIRCRAFT ONLY)

C/N	Registration	Owner/Operator	Series	First Flight	Delivery	Remarks
	F-BRGX	Aerospatiale			SEP/76	
	F-BRGX	SOGERMA			21/JAN/77	
	F-ZACQ	CEV			DEC/79	
235	D-ABAP	LTU	10B1R	13/DEC/67	18/DEC/67	
	D-ABAP	Special Air Transport			APR/79	
	TC-ARI	Istanbul Hava Yollari			JAN/86	
236	JY-ADG	Alia	10B1R	17/JUN/68	21/JUN/68	
	EC-CPI	TransEuropa			30/APR/75	
	EC-CPI	Hispania			DEC/82	
237	F-WLGC	Sud Aviation	6N	25/MAY/69		
	YU-AHK	JAT			07/JUN/69	Leased
	F-WLGC	Aerospatiale			07/NOV/70	
	YU-AHK	JAT			20/MAR/72	Leased
	YU-AHK	Aerospatiale			NOV/73	
	VT-ECI	Indian Airlines			12/DEC/73	Leased
	F-BRGU	Aerospatiale			06/MAY/75	
	F-BRGU	Air Inter			28/AUG/75	Leased
	F-BRGU	Aerospatiale			02/DEC/75	
	F-BRGU	Minerve			30/JUN/76	
238	OY-STD	Sterling	10B3	24/JAN/68	23/FEB/68	
	EC-CMS	TAE			03/MAR/75	Leased
	OY-STD	Sterling			18/DEC/81	
239	D-ABAW	LTU	10R	12/JUL/68	19/JUL/68	
	D-ABAW	SAT Flug			JAN/79	
240	9Q-CLC	Air Congo	11R	19/OCT/67	27/OCT/67	
	9Q-CLC	Air Zaire			25/OCT/71	
	240	French Air Force			09/JUL/76	Callsign 'F-RBPR'
241	7601	Yugoslav Air Force	6N	21/JAN/69	08/FEB/69	
	74101	Yugoslav Air Force			NOV/70	
	F-BVSF	Aerotex			14/JUL/79	WFU 05/NOV/80, stored Orly
	F-BVSF	Europe Aero Service			FEB/81	Leased
	F-BVSF	Aerotex			AUG/81	
	F-BVSF	Corse Air International			FEB/82	
242	F-BOHA	Air France	3	18/MAR/68	27/MAR/68	WFU MAR/81, preserved
243	D-ABAV	LTU	10B1R	20/FEB/68	28/FEB/68	
	D-ABAV	Special Air Transport			MAY/79	
	F-GFBA	Europe Aero Service			JUN/86	
246	TS-ITU	Tunis Air	3	05/FEB/68	16/FEB/68	WFU 77, derelict Tunis-Carthage
247	D-ANYL	LTU	10B1R	29/DEC/69	31/DEC/69	
	EC-CIZ	TransEuropa			16/FEB/74	WFU 82
	EC-CIZ	Hispania			83	
	SE-DEB	Air Charter West			FEB/86	Op. by Trans Swede
249	OY-STE	Sterling	10B3	02/APR/68	09/APR/68	
	F-WJAK	Aerospatiale			28/JAN/75	
	TL-ABB	Central African Govt.			28/JAN/75	
	F-GCJT	Europe Aero Services			19/APR/80	
250	EC-BRJ	TransEuropa	10B1R	11/FEB/70	03/MAR/70	
	HB-ICI	CTA			12/DEC/80	
251	9Q-CLD	Air Congo	11R	09/OCT/68	18/OCT/68	Leased
	9Q-CLD	Air Zaire			26/OCT/71	Leased
	9Q-CLD	Air Zaire			18/OCT/73	Purchased
	251	French Air Force			09/AUG/76	Callsign 'F-RBPS'
253	HB-ICN	SATA	10B1R	02/MAR/70	06/MAR/70	
	HB-ICN	CTA			01/NOV/78	
254	CN-CCT	Royal Air Maroc	3	05/AUG/68	09/AUG/68	WFU DEC/77
	SU-BBV	Air Alexandrie			14/APR/80	WFU 80 to AUG/83
	EL-AAG	Lebanese International Lease			AUG/83	
	EL-OSZ	Sheikh Zahran			DEC/84	Op. by Atlantic Aviation
255	OY-SAY	Sterling	10B1R	05/DEC/69	12/DEC/69	
	HB-ICO	SATA			12/FEB/71	
	HB-ICO	CTA			01/NOV/78	
256	F-BNKK	Sud Aviation	3	21/NOV/69		
	F-BNKK	Air Inter			04/DEC/69	Leased
	5N-AVO	Intercontinental Airlines			07/APR/81	
257	OY-STF	Sterling	10B3	03/FEB/69	12/FEB/69	
	RP-C123	Sterling Philippines			04/OCT/75	
	OY-STF	Sterling			26/FEB/79	
	EC-DFP	TAE			MAR/79	Leased
	OY-STF	Sterling			21/JAN/81	
	EC-DFP	TAE			81	Leased
	OY-STF	Sterling			07/NOV/81	
259	OY-STG	Sterling	10B3	07/MAR/69	14/MAY/69	
	OH-LSI	Finnair			01/APR/74	Leased
	OY-STG	Sterling			06/JUL/76	
	F-GATP	Minerve			NOV/79	
	LN-BSE	Furdal Air Brokers			17/DEC/84	
	LN-BSE	Swedair			01/MAR/85	Leased, op. by Transwede
260	F-BNKL	Aerospatiale	3	19/JAN/70		
	F-BNKL	Air Inter			24/JAN/70	Leased
	5N-AVP	Intercontinental Airlines			APR/81	
261	EC-BRX	TransEuropa	11R	21/JUL/69	30/JUL/69	
	HK-2850	Aerosucre	Freight		13/AUG/82	
262	OY-STH	Sterling	10B3	28/MAR/69	04/APR/69	
263	F-WJAN	Sud Aviation	10B1R	12/JAN/70		
	OY-SAZ	Sterling			16/JAN/70	Leased
	F-WJAN	Sud Aviation			27/OCT/71	
	D-ABAF	LTU			13/JAN/72	Leased
	F-OCKH	Aerospatiale			19/JAN/76	
	F-WJAK	Aerospatiale			18/MAR/76	
	EC-CYI	TransEuropa			14/JAN/77	
	EC-CYI	Hispania			83	
	SE-DEC	Bergen Aviation			MAY/86	Op. by Trans Swede
264	EC-BRY	TransEuropa	11R	11/SEP/69	19/SEP/69	
	264	French Air Force			31/OCT/76	Callsign 'F-RBPT',
265	OY-STI	Sterling	10B3	06/MAY/70	14/MAY/69	
266	OY-STK	Sterling	10B3	18/APR/70	06/MAY/70	W/O 15/MAR/74, Tehran
267	OY-STL	Sterling	10B3	10/MAY/70	19/MAY/70	W/O 14/MAY/72, nr. Dubai
268	OY-STM	Sterling	10B3	12/JUN/70	16/JUN/70	
269	OY-SAC	Sterling	12	29/OCT/70	18/MAY/70	
	F-BNOH	Air Inter			17/DEC/80	
270	OY-SAA	Sterling	12	01/FEB/71	12/MAR/71	
	OY-SAA	Tunis Air			AUG/71	Leased
	OY-SAA	Sterling			SEP/71	
	F-BVTB	Transunion			JUL/74	Leased
	OY-SAA	Sterling			SEP/74	

C/N	Registration	Owner/Operator	Series	First Flight	Delivery	Remarks
271	F-GCVM	Air Inter			MAR/83	
	OY-SAB	Sterling	12	22/MAR/71	26/MAR/71	
	F-BVPY	Catair			14/JAN/75	Leased
	F-BVPY	Air Inter			07/APR/76	Sub-leased
	OY-SAB	Sterling			29/NOV/76	
	F-BTOF	Air Inter				Not taken-up
	F-BNOG	Air Inter			19/APR/80	
272	OY-SAD	Sterling	12	14/MAY/71	07/JUN/71	
	F-GCVI	Air Inter			MAR/81	
273	OY-SAE	Sterling	12	22/FEB/72	28/FEB/72	
	F-GCVL	Air Inter			DEC/82	
274	F-BTOA	Sefiprom	12	04/MAY/72	20/OCT/72	
	F-BTOA	Air Inter			20/OCT/72	Leased
275	OY-SAF	Sterling	12	15/MAY/72	19/MAY/72	
	F-GCVJ	Air Inter			DEC/81	
276	OY-SAG	Sterling	12	10/JUN/72	19/JUN/72	
	F-GCVK	Air Inter			MAR/82	
277	F-BTOB	Sefiprom	12	01/DEC/72	20/DEC/72	
	F-BTOB	Air Inter			20/DEC/72	Leased
278	F-BTOC	Sefiprom	12	10/JAN/73	17/APR/73	
	F-BTOC	Air Inter			17/APR/73	Leased
279	F-BTOD	Sefiprom	12	12/FEB/73	20/FEB/73	
	F-BTOD	Air Inter			20/FEB/73	Leased
280	F-BTOE	Sefiprom	12	08/MAR/73	16/MAR/73	
	F-BTOE	Air Inter			16/MAR/73	Leased

Aerospatiale/Sud Aviation Caravelle cross-reference index

5A- Libya
158	5A-DAA
221	5A-DAE

5N- Nigeria
180	5N-AOY
256	5N-AVO
260	5N-AVP
220	5N-AVQ
206	5N-AWF
50	5N-AWK
217	5N-AWO
219	5N-AWQ
215	5N-AWT

5T- Mauritania
91	5T-CJW
91	5T-MAL
91	5T-RIM

6V- Senegal
5	6V-AAR
5	6V-ACP

7T- Algeria
51	7T-VAE
18	7T-VAG
75	7T-VAL

9Q- Zaire
229	9Q-CCP
119	9Q-CGC
240	9Q-CLC
251	9Q-CLD
115	9Q-CLP
74	9Q-CMD
21	9Q-CPS
71	9Q-CRU
123	9Q-CZL

9U- Burundi
144	9U-BTA

9XR- Rwanda
209	9XR-CH

B- Taiwan
38	B-1854

CC- Chile
164	CC-CCP
160	CC-CCQ

CN- Morocco
254	CN-CCT
57	CN-CCX
154	CN-CCY
195	CN-CCZ

CS- Portugal
117	CS-TCA

D- West Germany
230	D-AAST
21	D-ABAF
263	D-ABAF
232	D-ABAK
235	D-ABAP
243	D-ABAV
239	D-ABAW
176	D-ACVK
247	D-ANYL

EC- Spain
109	EC-ARK
138	EC-AXU
176	EC-BDC
223	EC-BIB
230	EC-BIE
232	EC-BIF
250	EC-BRJ
261	EC-BRX
264	EC-BRY
176	EC-CAE
247	EC-CIZ
247	EC-CIZ
238	EC-CMS
236	EC-CPI
211	EC-CUM
263	EC-CYI
199	EC-DCN
257	EC-DFP

EL- Liberia
254	EL-AAG
154	EL-AAS
106	EL-AIW
254	EL-OSZ

F- France
01	F-BHHH
02	F-BHHI
1	F-BHRA
5	F-BHRC
12	F-BHRF
16	F-BHRH
37	F-BHRM
41	F-BHRO
46	F-BHRQ
50	F-BHRR
55	F-BHRT
61	F-BHRY
219	F-BJAK
42	F-BJAO
62	F-BJAP
70	F-BJAU
185	F-BJEN
42	F-BJSO
143	F-BJSO
53	F-BJTA
111	F-BJTE
115	F-BJTG
124	F-BJTH
105	F-BJTI
119	F-BJTJ
141	F-BJTK
142	F-BJTL
144	F-BJTM
152	F-BJTP
22	F-BJTR
189	F-BJTU
51	F-BLCZ
51	F-BLCZ
158	F-BLHY
42	F-BLKF
136	F-BLKI
169	F-BLKJ
176	F-BLKS
181	F-BMKS
206	F-BNKA
208	F-BNKB
217	F-BNKC
220	F-BNKD
224	F-BNKE
229	F-BNKG
256	F-BNKK
260	F-BNKL
271	F-BNOG
269	F-BNOH
201	F-BNRA
222	F-BNRB
212	F-BOEE
242	F-BOHA
237	F-BRGU
234	F-BRGX
193	F-BRIM
209	F-BRUJ
167	F-BSEL
38	F-BSRD
21	F-BSRR
136	F-BTDL
274	F-BTOA
277	F-BTOB
278	F-BTOC
279	F-BTOD
280	F-BTOE
271	F-BTOF
161	F-BUFC
123	F-BUFH
209	F-BUFM
94	F-BUZC
271	F-BVPY
218	F-BVPZ
241	F-BVSF
270	F-BVTB
139	F-BYAI
175	F-BYCB
67	F-BYCD
233	F-BYCY
259	F-GATP
175	F-GATZ
180	F-GBMK
249	F-GCJT
272	F-GCVI
275	F-GCVJ
276	F-GCVK
273	F-GCVL
270	F-GCVM
182	F-GDFY
211	F-GDFY
211	F-GDFZ
183	F-GDJU
184	F-GEPC
243	F-GFBA
18	F-OBNG
51	F-OBNJ
75	F-OBNL
263	F-OCKH
136	F-OGJD
167	F-OGJE
51	F-WBNJ
01	F-WHHH
02	F-WHHI
1	F-WHRA
135	F-WJAK
219	F-WJAK
249	F-WJAK
263	F-WJAK
38	F-WJAL
38	F-WJAL
234	F-WJAL
42	F-WJAM
263	F-WJAN
42	F-WJAO
62	F-WJAP
223	F-WJAQ
143	F-WJSO
21	F-WLGA
78	F-WLGA
139	F-WLGA
237	F-WLGC
158	F-WLHY
42	F-WLKF
169	F-WLKJ
176	F-WLKS
116	F-ZACE
193	F-ZACF
234	F-ZACQ

HB- Switzerland
250	HB-ICI
253	HB-ICN
255	HB-ICO
234	HB-ICP
222	HB-ICQ
119	HB-ICR
123	HB-ICU
38	HB-ICX

HC- Ecuador
35	HC-BAD
82	HC-BAI
117	HC-BAJ
146	HC-BDS
166	HC-BFN

HK- Colombia
164	HK-1779
160	HK-1780
138	HK-1811
109	HK-1812
131	HK-2212
168	HK-2287
161	HK-2402
136	HK-2597
167	HK-2598
261	HK-2850
223	HK-2860

HS- Thailand
29	HS-TGH

I- Italy
71	I-DABA
72	I-DABE
74	I-DABI
143	I-DABM
81	I-DABR
106	I-DABS
85	I-DABT
77	I-DABU
146	I-DABV
82	I-DABZ
35	I-DAXA
36	I-DAXE
80	I-DAXT
79	I-DAXU
21	I-GISA
208	I-GISE
188	I-GISI
217	I-GISI
187	I-GISO
169	I-GISU

JY- Jordan
199	JY-ACS
236	JY-ADG

LN- Norway
259	LN-BSE
3	LN-KLH
209	LN-KLN

LV- Argentina
180	LV-III
180	LV-PPJ

LX- Luxembourg
234	LX-LGE
166	LX-LGF

N United States
86	N1001U
87	N1002U
88	N1003U
91	N1006U
94	N1009U
102	N1017U
62	N2001U
138	N210G
87	N240RC
42	N420GE
180	N495B
102	N555SL
87	N777VV
62	N901MW
88	N902MW
129	N907MW
102	N98KT

OD- Lebanon
51	OD-ADZ

OE- Austria
161	OE-LCA
166	OE-LCI
167	OE-LCO
136	OE-LCU

OH- Finland
21	OH-LEA
22	OH-LEB
116	OH-LED
181	OH-LSA
182	OH-LSB
185	OH-LSC
187	OH-LSD

Aerospatiale Caravelle Cross-Reference Index

189	OH-LSE
188	OH-LSF
169	OH-LSG
211	OH-LSH
259	OH-LSI
211	OH-LSK

OO- Belgium

123	OO-SBQ
64	OO-SRA
67	OO-SRE
70	OO-SRG
78	OO-SRH
175	OO-SRI

OY- Denmark

29	OY-KRC
47	OY-KRD
191	OY-KRG
270	OY-SAA
271	OY-SAB
269	OY-SAC
272	OY-SAD
273	OY-SAE
275	OY-SAF
276	OY-SAG
88	OY-SAH
255	OY-SAY
263	OY-SAZ
91	OY-SBV
94	OY-SBY
183	OY-STA

186	OY-STB
211	OY-STC
184	OY-STD
238	OY-STD
249	OY-STE
257	OY-STF
259	OY-STG
262	OY-STH
265	OY-STI
266	OY-STK
267	OY-STL
268	OY-STM

PH- Netherlands

21	PH-TRM
191	PH-TRN
102	PH-TRU
87	PH-TRY
36	PH-TVW
91	PH-TVZ

PP/PT- Brasil

129	PP-CJA
62	PP-CJC
168	PP-CJD
131	PP-PDZ
86	PT-DUW

RP- Philippines

257	RP-C123

SE- Sweden

4	SE-DAA
112	SE-DAF
172	SE-DAG
193	SE-DAH
210	SE-DAI
247	SE-DEB
263	SE-DEC
188	SE-DEH

SU- Egypt

154	SU-BBU
254	SU-BBV

TC- Turkey

235	TC-ARI

TL- Central African Rep.

249	TL-ABB
42	TL-FCA
42	TL-KAB

TS- Tunisia

246	TS-ITU
207	TS-MAC
178	TS-TAR

TU- Ivory Coast

199	TU-TCN
215	TU-TCO
219	TU-TCY

201	TU-TXQ
78	TU-TXR

TZ- Mali

184	TZ-ADS

VT- India

203	VT-DUH
213	VT-DVI
70	VT-ECG
78	VT-ECH
237	VT-ECI

XU- Cambodia

53	XU-JTB

YK- Syria

184	YK-AFA
190	YK-AFB
183	YK-AFC
186	YK-AFD

YU- Yugoslavia

139	YU-AHA
135	YU-AHB
194	YU-AHF
218	YU-AHF
233	YU-AHG
237	YU-AHK
209	YU-AJE

191	YU-AJG

Military operated

Argentina

180	T-93
180	TC-93

France

141	141
158	158
201	201
240	240
251	251
264	264

Sweden

172	85172
210	85210

Yugoslavia

241	74101
241	7601

BOEING 707 (EXISTING AIRCRAFT ONLY)

Medium/long range commercial transport with four wing-mounted jet engines. The 707 goes back to 15 July 1954 when the 367-80 (or 'dash-80') prototype made its first flight as a military demonstrator, leading to an eventual 800 plus tanker/transports for the USAF under the C-135 and C-137 designation. The first civil development produced the 707-120, a domestic version with Pratt & Whitney JT3C turbojets, which entered service with Pan American on 26 October 1958, followed closely by the 707-220 and the longer range 707-320. The installation of JT3D-7 turbofans resulted in the 707-320B and the 320C cargo or convertible, with maximum accommodation for 219 passengers. The 707-420 model was a long-range alternative powered by Rolls-Royce Conway turbofans. A total of 813 production aircraft were built and production ceased in October 1979 although military Boeing E3A early warning aircraft are still being manufactured.

Dimensions :	Wing span: 130ft 10in (39.87m) Length: 144ft 6in (44.04m) Height: 42ft 0in (12.80m) (120/220)
	Wing span: 142ft 5in (43.4m) Length: 152ft 11in (45.6m) Height: 41ft 8in (12.7m) (320/420)
	Wing span: 145ft 8in (44.42m) Length: 152ft 11in (45.6m) Height: 42ft 5in (12.94m) (320B/C)
Powerplants :	Four Pratt & Whitney JT3C-6 turbojets (120), four Pratt & Whitney JT3D-1 or JT3D-3 turbojets (120B), four Pratt & Whitney JT4A-3 turbojets (220), four Pratt & Whitney JT4A-3, JT4A-5, JT4A-9 or JT4A-11 turbojets (320), four Rolls Royce Conway 508 turbojets (420), four Pratt & Whitney JT3D-3 or JT3D-7 turbofans (320B/C)
Performance :	Max cruising speed 496 knots (919km/h) (120) Range: with max payload 2,795nm (5,177km) (120)
	Max cruising speed 537 knots (995km/h) (120B) Range: with max payload 3,682nm (6,820km) (120B)
	Max cruising speed 521 knots (965km/h) (320/B/C) Range: with max payload 3,995nm (7,400km) (320)
	Max cruising speed 523 knots (970km/h) (420) Range: with max payload 4,092nm (7,580km) (420)
	Range: with max payload 5,421nm (10,040km) (320B)
	Range: with max payload 3,736nm (6,920km) (320C)
Accommodation:	181 passengers (120/220), 195 passengers (320B), 219 passengers (320C)
Manufacturer :	Boeing - PO Box 3707, Seattle, Washington 98124, USA
	Telephone: (206) 237-2121 Telex: 32 94 30

BOEING

C/N	Registration	Owner/Operator	Series	First Flight	Delivery	Remarks
17587	N707PA	Pan American	121	21/MAR/58	19/DEC/58	
	N707PA	Pan American	121B		18/DEC/64	Converted
	TC-JBA	Turk Hava Yollari			JAN/74	Leased
	TC-JBA	Pan American			21/FEB/75	
	TC-JBA	F.B.Ayer			21/FEB/75	
	TC-JBA	Turk Hava Yollari			21/FEB/75	Leased
	HP-780	F.B.Ayer			11/DEC/77	
	N707PA	F.B.Ayer			82	
	N707PA	Greyhound Leasing			NOV/83	WFU NOV/83, Preserved
	N707PA	International Air Leases			02/OCT/59	
17597	N719PA	Pan American	321	18/SEP/59	26/APR/70	
	G-AYBJ	British Midland Airways			AUG/72	Leased
	G-AYBJ	El Al				
	G-AYBJ	British Midland Airways			13/AUG/74	Leased
	G-AYBJ	Iraqi Airways			74	
	G-AYBJ	British Midland Airways			DEC/74	Leased
	G-AYBJ	Nigeria Airways			JAN/75	
	G-AYBJ	British Midland Airways			APR/75	Leased
	G-AYBJ	Syrian Arab Airlines			75	
	G-AYBJ	British Midland Airways			NOV/75	Leased
	G-AYBJ	PIA				
	G-AYBJ	British Midland Airways			APR/76	Leased
	G-AYBJ	East African Airways			76	
	G-AYBJ	British Midland Airways			MAY/76	Leased
	G-AYBJ	Tunis Air			76	
	G-AYBJ	British Midland Airways			SEP/76	Leased
	G-AYBJ	East African Airways			76	
	G-AYBJ	British Midland Airways			NOV/76	Leased
	G-AYBJ	Nigeria Airways			76	
	G-AYBJ	British Midland Airways			FEB/77	Leased
	G-AYBJ	Kenya Airways			02/FEB/78	
	G-AYBJ	Jet Power Inc			APR/78	Leased
	N431MA	MCA Leasing			26/APR/78	Sub-leased
	N431MA	AeroAmerica			78	Sub-leased
	N431MA	PIA			78	Sub-leased
	N431MA	AeroAmerica			22/AUG/79	
	N431MA	MCA Leasing			SEP/79	Leased
	N431MA	Southeast			JUN/80	
	N431MA	MCA Leasing			JUL/80	Leased
	N431MA	Intercontinental Airlines			SEP/80	WFU SEP/80, stored Sharjah
	N431MA	Jet Power Inc.				
17602	N724PA	Pan American	321	23/NOV/59	09/DEC/59	
	N724PA	JAT			05/OCT/61	Leased
	N724PA	Pan American				
	G-AZOI	Donaldson International	321F		JAN/72	Converted, reg. not taken-up
	N724PA	Alaska Airlines			02/MAR/72	Leased
	G-BAEL	Donaldson International			16/OCT/72	
	G-BAEL	Cont III Bank			08/AUG/74	
	G-BAEL	British Midland Airways			AUG/75	
	G-BAEL	Syrian Arab Airlines			OCT/75	Leased
	G-BAEL	British Midland Airways			75	
	G-BAEL	PIA			JAN/76	Leased
	G-BAEL	British Midland Airways			76	
	G-BAEL	Syrian Arab Airlines			09/FEB/76	Leased
	G-BAEL	British Midland Airways			76	
	G-BAEL	Tunis Air			01/APR/76	Leased
	G-BAEL	British Midland Airways			76	
	G-BAEL	Malaysian Airlines System			AUG/76	Leased
	G-BAEL	British Midland Airways			NOV/76	
	G-BAEL	Kenya Airways			77	Leased
	G-BAEL	British Midland Airways			77	
	G-BAEL	Bahamas World			28/NOV/77	Leased
	G-BAEL	British Midland Airways			77	
	G-BAEL	Kuwait Airways			77	
	N2276X	International Air Leases			11/JUN/78	
	N2276X	Seagreen Air Transport			SEP/78	Leased
	N2276X	International Air Leases			DEC/79	
	HK-2477	Tampa Airlines			DEC/79	Leased

C/N	Registration	Owner/Operator	Series	First Flight	Delivery	Remarks
	N2276X	International Air Leases		JAN/81		
	N2276X	Inter-Fret			10/JAN/83	
	9Q-CZK	Inter-Fret			83	WFU NOV/84
17606	N728PA	Pan American	321	22/FEB/60	05/MAR/60	
	N11RV	Robert Vesco/Intl. Controls			14/JUN/71	
	N99WT	Skyways Leasing			74	
	N728PA	Pan American			27/OCT/75	WFU 27/OCT/75
	RP-C911	Air Manila			24/APR/77	
	RP-C911	Philippine Government			24/APR/77	Leased
	RP-C911	Air Manila			OCT/82	WFU OCT/82 used as Restaurant
17608	N730PA	Pan American	321	15/APR/60	28/APR/60	
	G-AYXR	Donaldson International	321F		DEC/70	Converted
	G-AYXR	Cont III Bank			08/AUG/74	
	G-AYXR	British Midland Airways			03/SEP/75	
	G-AYXR	Syrian Arab Airlines			FEB/76	Leased
	G-AYXR	British Midland Airways			76	
	G-AYXR	Tunis Air			APR/76	Leased
	G-AYXR	British Midland Airways			76	
	G-AYXR	Kuwait Airways			AUG/76	Leased
	G-AYXR	British Midland Airways			OCT/76	
	G-AYXR	Kenya Airways			FEB/77	Leased
	G-AYXR	Cont III Bank			OCT/77	
	G-AYXR	International Air Leases			OCT/77	
	G-AYXR	British Midland Airways			FEB/79	
	G-AYXR	PIA			FEB/79	Leased
	G-AYXR	British Midland Airways			31/MAR/80	
	N37681	International Air Leases			11/APR/80	
	N37681	General Electric			25/FEB/83	Leased, CFM-56 restbed
17610	N70774	Continental Airlines	124	09/MAY/59	28/MAY/59	
	N70774	Trans World Airlines			22/DEC/67	
	N70774	Israel Aircraft Industries			14/NOV/71	
	4X-JYB	Israeli Air Force			74	
	N196CA	Charlotte Aircraft			JUL/78	
	N196CA	Sky Safari			MAY/80	
	HI-384HA	Hispaniola Airways			29/SEP/81	WFU DEC/81, derelict Miami
17612	N70785	Continental Airlines	124	29/JUL/59	10/AUG/59	
	N70785	Trans World Airlines			31/DEC/67	
	4X-BYD	Israel Aircraft Industries			16/NOV/71	
	4X-JYD	Israeli Air Force			26/NOV/71	WFU 84, stored
17615	N74615	Boeing	328	21/NOV/59		
	F-BHSC	Air France			22/DEC/59	
	F-BHSC	Charlotte Aircraft			28/FEB/78	
	4X-BYV	Israel Aircraft Industries			JUN/78	
	4X-JYV	Israeli Air Force			SEP/78	
17617	F-BHSE	Air France	328	29/FEB/60	18/MAR/60	
	F-BHSE	Charlotte Aircraft			28/FEB/78	
	4X-BYW	Israel Aircraft Industries			JUN/78	
	4X-JYW	Israeli Air Force			SEP/78	
17619	N5093K	Boeing	328	29/APR/60		
	F-BHSG	Air France			12/MAY/60	
	CN-RMD	Royal Air Maroc			29/SEP/70	
	CN-RMD	Charlotte Aircraft			OCT/78	
	4X-BYN	Israel Aircraft Industries			MAY/80	
	4X-JYN	Israeli Air Force			JUN/80	
17623	OO-SJA	Sabena	329	03/NOV/59	04/DEC/59	
	OO-SJA	Air Algerie			73	Leased
	OO-SJA	Sabena			MAY/74	
	OO-SJA	Mandala Airlines			JAN/76	Leased
	OO-SJA	Sabena			FEB/76	
	OO-SJA	Air Cameroon			NOV/77	Leased
	OO-SJA	Sobelair			JAN/78	WFU JUN/81, Preserved Brussels
17625	OO-SJC	Sabena	329	26/JAN/60	12/FEB/60	
	4X-BYT	Israel Aircraft Industries			OCT/77	
	4X-JYT	Israeli Air Force			NOV/77	
17626	OO-SJD	Sabena	329	25/MAR/60	09/APR/60	
	OO-SJD	Air Congo			65	Leased
	OO-SJD	Sabena			68	
	OO-SJD	Sobelair			74	
	OO-SJD	Cameroon Airlines			DEC/75	Leased
	OO-SJD	Sobelair			JAN/76	WFU AUG/80, derelict Brussels
17631	N7504A	American Airlines	123	03/JAN/59	28/JAN/59	
	N7504A	American Airlines	123B		03/MAR/61	Converted, WFU 09/AUG/75
	5B-DAL	Cyprus Airways			FEB/79	
17632	N7505A	American Airlines	123	12/JAN/59	31/JAN/59	
	N7505A	American Airlines	123B		19/AUG/61	Converted
	G-BFMI	Monarch Airlines			24/FEB/78	
	5B-DAK	Cyprus Airways			DEC/78	WFU 31/OCT/83, stored Larnaca
17634	N7507A	American Airlines	123	06/FEB/59	28/FEB/59	
	N7507A	American Airlines	123B		15/MAY/61	Converted
	N707AR	ARCO			11/MAY/77	
17635	N7508A	American Airlines	123	15/FEB/59	27/MAR/59	
	N7508A	American Airlines	123B		15/MAY/61	Converted
	5B-DAP	Cyprus Airways			07/FEB/80	
17636	N7509A	American Airlines	123	06/MAR/59	09/APR/59	
	N7509A	American Airlines	123B		23/SEP/61	Converted
	N7509A	Tigerair			DEC/78	
	N7509A	American Airlines			JUN/79	Leased
	N7509A	Tigerair			10/MAR/80	
	N7509A	Air Berlin			06/MAY/80	Leased
	N7509A	Tigerair			NOV/80	WFU NOV/80 to 02/MAY/83
	N7509A	Boeing			02/MAY/83	WFU 02/MAY/83 for KC-135E Parts
17637	N7510A	American Airlines	123	11/MAR/59	23/APR/59	
	N7510A	American Airlines	123B		26/MAY/61	Converted
	D-ALAM	Paninternational			07/JAN/71	
	N8418A	American Airlines			22/OCT/71	
	N7510A	American Airlines			01/AUG/72	
	HK-1818	Aerocondor	123F		22/MAR/76	Converted
						WFU OCT/80, derelict Bogota
17638	N7511A	American Airlines	123	03/APR/59	12/MAY/59	
	N7511A	American Airlines	123B		10/JUN/61	Converted
	D-ALAL	Paninternational			01/FEB/70	
	N8420A	American Airlines			30/APR/72	
	N7511A	American Airlines			01/AUG/72	
	HK-1802	Aerocondor			25/NOV/75	
						WFU OCT/80, derelict Bogota
17639	N7512A	American Airlines	123	14/APR/59	21/MAY/59	

C/N	Registration	Owner/Operator	Series	First Flight	Delivery	Remarks
	N7512A	American Airlines	123B		28/OCT/61	Converted
	N7512A	Ports of Call			03/JUL/80	
	N701PC	Ports of Call			JUL/80	
	N701PC	Skyworld Airlines			SEP/85	
17640	N7513A	American Airlines	123	20/APR/59	28/AMY/59	
	N7513A	American Airlines	123B		22/JUN/61	Converted
	N7513A	Tigerair			17/MAR/78	
	9G-ACN	Transasian			01/APR/78	Leased
	G-TJAB	Transasian				Leased
	G-TJAB	Air Transcontinental			22/AUG/79	Leased
	G-TJAB	Tigerair			JAN/80	
	G-BHOX	Monarch Airlines			MAR/80	Leased
	N62TA	Tigerair			08/DEC/80	WFU 08/DEC/80 to 02/MAY/83
	N62TA	Boeing			02/MAY/83	WFU 02/MAY/83 for KC-135E Parts
17643	N7516A	American Airlines	123	26/MAY/59	29/JUN/59	
	N7516A	American Airlines	123B		01/JUL/61	Converted
	HK-1942	Aerocondor			26/NOV/76	WFU OCT/80, stored Baranquilla
17644	N7517A	American Airlines	123	09/JUL/59	27/JUL/59	
	N7517A	American Airlines	123B		11/JAN/62	Converted, WFU NOV/77
	N7517A	Tigerair			28/MAR/78	
	HZ-DAT	Dallah AVCO			AUG/78	
17645	N7518A	American Airlines	123	12/JUL/59	31/JUL/59	
	N7518A	American Airlines	123B		31/JAN/62	Converted
	N7518A	Ports of Call			26/AUG/80	
	N702PC	Ports of Call				
	N702PC	Skyworld Airlines			SEP/85	
17646	N7519A	American Airlines	123	12/JUL/59	31/JUL/59	
	N7519A	American Airlines	123B		27/JUL/61	Converted
	PH-TVA	Transavia			17/MAR/72	
	PH-TVA	Saudia			10/JUL/76	Leased
	PH-TVA	Transavia			09/AUG/76	WFU 01/NOV/81 to 25/MAY/82
	N519GA	Guy-America Airways			25/MAY/82	
	N519GA	Boeing			08/APR/83	WFU 08/APR/83 for KC-135E Parts
17648	N7521A	American Airlines	123	28/AUG/59	15/SEP/59	
	N7521A	American Airlines	123B		31/AUG/61	Converted
	N7521A	Tigerair			31/MAY/78	
	N7521A	AeroAmerica			31/MAY/78	Leased
	N752TA	Tigerair			20/JUN/80	
	N752TA	Air Manila			81	Leased
	N752TA	Tigerair				W/O MAR/82
	N752TA	Avery & Finch			MAY/82	
	N752TA	Air Capital			JUN/83	
	N752TA	MRH Leasing			NOV/83	WFU NOV/83, stored Marana
17651	N7524A	American Airlines	123	06/OCT/59	28/OCT/59	
	N7524A	American Airlines	123B		02/AUG/61	Converted
	N7524A	Tigerair			30/JUN/78	
	ST-AHG	Transasian			01/JUL/78	Leased
	9G-ACO	Transasian				Leased
	G-TJAC	Transasian				Leased
	G-TJAC	Air Transcontinental			22/AUG/79	Leased
	G-TJAC	Tigerair			JAN/80	
	G-BHOY	Monarch Airlines			MAR/80	Leased
	N61TA	Tigerair			21/NOV/80	
	N61TA	Charter Airlines			MAY/82	
	N61TA	Boeing			05/OCT/83	WFU 05/OCT/83 for KC-135E Parts
17652	N7525A	American Airlines	123	26/OCT/59	20/NOV/59	
	N7525A	American Airlines	123B		07/OCT/61	Converted
	N5038	Dresser Industries			22/DEC/77	
	N5038	Boeing			15/AUG/83	WFU 15/AUG/83 for KC-135E Parts
17658	N731TW	Trans World Airlines	131	03/DEC/59	29/JAN/59	
	N731TW	Israel Aircraft Industries			19/DEC/71	
	N731TW	Israel Aircraft Industries	131F		75	Converted
	F-BUZJ	Air Fret			28/FEB/76	
	F-BUZJ	Romacor			28/FEB/82	
	F-BUZJ	Air Supply Corp.			FEB/83	
	9Q-CBD	Lukum Air Services			25/MAR/83	
	9Q-CKP	Lukum Air Services				
	9Q-CKP	Omega Air			DEC/84	WFU DEC/84, stored Shannon
17661	N734TW	Trans World Airlines	131	08/MAR/59	03/APR/59	
	PI-C7071	Air Manila				Not delivered. WFU 20/DEC/71
	4X-AGT	Israeli Aircraft Industries			29/JAN/75	
	4X-JYI	Israeli Air Force			JAN/75	
	N198CA	Charlotte Aircraft			NOV/78	
	N198CA	Rodman Aviation			OCT/81	WFU OCT/81, derelict Mojave
17663	N736TW	Trans World Airlines	131	19/MAR/59	29/APR/59	
	N736TW	Israel Aircraft Industries			08/DEC/71	
	HS-VGC	Air Siam			29/SEP/73	Leased
	HS-VGC	Israel Aircraft Industries			74	
	N194CA	Charlotte Aircraft			JUL/78	
	N194CA	Rodman Aviation			30/MAY/79	WFU 30/MAY/79, derelict Mojave
17667	N740TW	Trans World Airlines	131	30/APR/59	28/MAY/59	
	4X-BYD	Israeli Aircraft Industries			11/DEC/71	
	4X-JYD	Israeli Air Force			11/DEC/71	WFU JUN/83
17675	N762TW	Trans World Airlines	331	15/OCT/59	10/NOV/59	
	N762TW	Caledonian Airlines			21/MAR/80	
	N762TW	Air Tanzania			21/MAR/80	Leased
	N762TW	Caledonian Airlines			JUL/81	WFU JUL/81, stored Dar-es-Salaam
	YN-BWL	Aeronica			MAR/82	Not delivered
17692	N7072	Braniff	227	13/NOV/59	03/DEC/59	
	9Y-TDO	BWIA			01/FEB/71	WFU 74
	9Y-TDO	Pan American			17/MAY/76	WFU 17/MAY/76
	N64757	ATASCO			30/JUN/77	
	N811UT	United Trade Industries			MAR/78	
	N3842X	Corporate Ventures Inc.			MAR/79	
	N3842X	Monarch Aviation	227F		AUG/79	Converted
	N3842X	Golden Air Leasing			JUN/80	
	N3842X	Inair Panama			JUN/80	Leased
	N3842X	Golden Air Leasing			80	
	N3842X	International Air Leases			AUG/83	
	N3842X	Monarch Aviation			DEC/83	WFU MAR/84, stored Miami
17696	N31239	Boeing	138	20/MAR/59		
	VH-EBA	Qantas	138B		16/JUL/59	
	CF-PWV	Pacific Western			03/NOV/67	
	N138TA	Tigerair			19/OCT/78	
	N138TA	Airmark Corp.			16/OCT/83	

Airliner Production List 1987

BOEING 707 (EXISTING AIRCRAFT ONLY)

C/N	Registration	Owner/Operator	Series	First Flight	Delivery	Remarks
	N220AM	Airmark Corp.			JUN/84	
	N220AM	Comtran			DEC/85	
17697	VH-EBB	Qantas	138	20/MAY/59	26/JUN/59	
	VH-EBB	Qantas	138B		19/OCT/61	Converted
	N790SA	Standard Airways			06/JUN/67	
	N790SA	El Al			AUG/68	Leased
	N790SA	Standard Airways				
	D-ABAP	Air Commerz			31/JAN/71	
	N790SA	F.B.Ayer			31/OCT/75	
	TC-JBP	Turk Hava Yollari			JUN/76	Leased, registered in error
	TC-JBN	Turk Hava Yollari			JUN/76	Leased
	N790FA	FBA Corp.			18/DEC/77	
	N790FA	Israel Aircraft Industries			15/FEB/78	
	N790FA	Jet Aviation			OCT/78	
	N790FA	Lowa Ltd			JUN/84	WFU MAR/85, stored Basle
17700	VH-EBE	Qantas	138	13/AUG/59	24/AUG/59	
	VH-EBE	Qantas	138B		30/NOV/61	
	N793SA	International Aerodyne			15/MAY/68	
	N793SA	Standard Airways			15/MAY/68	Leased
	CF-PWW	Pacific Western			20/JUL/69	Sub-leased
	N793SA	Standard Airways				Leased
	N793SA	Alaska Airlines			01/MAY/71	Sub-leased
	N793SA	International Aerodyne			30/SEP/71	
	VP-BDE	Bahamas World Airlines			18/NOV/71	Leased
	N793NA	National Aircraft Leasing			08/AUG/74	
	N793NA	AeroAmerica			JUN/75	Leased
	N793NA	Egyptair			FEB/76	Sub-leased
	N793NA	AeroAmerica			APR/76	Leased
	N793NA	Egyptair			77	Sub-leased
	N793NA	AeroAmerica			OCT/77	Leased
	N793NA	Tigerair			JAN/79	
	N793NA	TAG Aviation			20/JAN/79	
	N793NA	Boeing			24/APR/83	WFU 24/APR/83 for KC-135E Parts
17701	VH-EBF	Qantas	138	21/AUG/59	04/SEP/59	
	VH-EBF	Qantas	138B		19/DEC/61	Converted
	N792SA	Standard Airways			15/MAR/68	
	D-ADAQ	Air Commerz			24/MAR/71	
	N792SA	FBA Corp.			31/OCT/75	
	TC-JBP	Turk Hava Yollari			31/JUL/76	Leased
	N792FA	FBA Corp.			07/JAN/78	
	N792FA	Israel Aircraft Industries			21/FEB/78	Leased
	N792FA	El Al			MAR/78	Sub-leased
	N792FA	Israel Aircraft Industries				Leased
	N792FA	FBA Corp.			78	
	N792FA	Bouraq			SEP/78	Leased
	N792FA	FBA Corp.			AUG/79	WFU, stored Marana
17702	VH-EBG	Qantas	138	08/SEP/59	18/SEP/59	
	VH-EBG	Qantas	138B		10/JAN/62	Converted
	G-AWDG	British Eagle			15/MAR/68	
	G-AWDG	Laker Airways			21/JAN/69	
	G-AWDG	Charlotte Aircraft			08/DEC/78	
	N600JJ	IASCO			08/DEC/78	
	N600JJ	Trafalgar Leasing Inc.			AUG/80	
	N600JJ	Sheikh A.M.Baroom			MAY/81	
17711	G-APFJ	BOAC	436	09/SEP/60	22/SEP/60	
	G-APFJ	Malaysian Airlines System			04/NOV/71	Leased
	G-APFJ	British Airways			APR/75	
	G-APFJ	British Airtours			23/FEB/77	WFU 31/MAY/81, Preserved Cosford
17717	G-APFP	BOAC	436	29/NOV/60	22/DEC/60	
	G-APFP	British Airways			01/APR/72	
	G-APFP	Boeing			27/MAY/75	WFU 27/MAY/75, Preserved Franklin Inst.
17720	D-ABOD	Lufthansa	430	05/APR/60	23/APR/60	
	'26000'	United States of America				Painted for film
	D-ABOD	Lufthansa				WFU DEC/75, Apprentice trainer, Hamburg
17903	Cubana					Not taken-up
	N74613	Boeing	139	20/MAR/60		
	N74613	Western Airlines			13/MAY/60	Leased
	N74613	Boeing			21/SEP/62	
	N778PA	Pan American			05/DEC/62	
	N778PA	Pan American	139B		01/OCT/64	Converted
	N778PA	F.B.Ayer			28/FEB/75	
	N778PA	Fiduciarsch Fin.			31/JAN/76	
	N778PA	Pan American			18/APR/76	
	S2-AAL	Bangladesh Biman			APR/76	Leased
	S2-AAL	FBA Corp.			76	
	9G-ACJ	FBA Corp.			30/JUN/76	
	9G-ACJ	Intl. Freight Airways			24/JUN/77	Leased
	9G-ACJ	FBA Corp.			77	
	9G-ACJ	Merpati Nusantara			OCT/77	Leased
	9G-ACJ	FBA Corp.			77	
	9G-ACJ	Bahamas World			DEC/77	Leased
	G-TJAA	Aktien Investments			77	
	G-TJAA	Transasian			APR/79	Leased
	G-TJAA	Egyptair			79	Sub-leased
	G-TJAA	Air Transcontinental			79	Leased
	G-TJAA	Aktien Investments			JAN/80	
	G-TJAA	Israel Aircraft Industries			MAY/80	
	N778PA	Grant E. Sita			AUG/80	
	N778PA	Conframin Ltd			AUG/80	
	N778PA	MAOF Airlines			24/SEP/82	Leased
	N778PA	Conframin Ltd			NOV/84	
	N778PA	Aerocar Aviation			OCT/85	
	N778PA	Boeing			20/MAR/86	WFU 20/MAR/86 for KC-135E Parts
17905	N5090K	Boeing	441	02/APR/60		
	PP-VJA	Varig			07/JUN/60	
	N59RD	RDC Marine Inc.			04/OCT/79	WFU JAN/80, stored Houston
17919	F-BHSL	Air France	328	03/AUG/60	19/AUG/60	WFU OCT/76 Apprentice trainer, Vilgenis
17921	F-BHSN	Air France	328	30/AUG/60	18/SEP/60	
	F-BHSN	Charlotte Aircraft			28/FEB/78	
	OO-SBR	Sobelair			18/NOV/78	Leased
	N90287	Charlotte Aircraft			NOV/78	

C/N	Registration	Owner/Operator	Series	First Flight	Delivery	Remarks
	N90287	Intercontinental Airlines			JUL/79	Leased
	N90287	Charlotte Aircraft			MAR/80	
	N90287	Israel Aircraft Industries			MAR/80	
	4X-JY	Israeli Air Force			SEP/80	
17922	F-BHSO	Air France	328	01/SEP/60	16/SEP/60	
	TU-TBY	Air Afrique			APR/63	Leased
	F-BHSO	Air France			MAY/63	
	F-BHSO	Charlotte Aircraft			28/FEB/77	
	4X-BYX	Israel Aircraft Industries			MAR/78	
	4X-JYX	Israeli Air Force			SEP/78	Leased
17925	58-6970	USAF	VC137A	04/APR/59	04/MAY/59	
	58-6970	USAF	VC137B		18/FEB/63	Converted
17926	58-6971	USAF	VC137A	12/MAY/59	31/MAY/59	
	58-6971	USAF	VC137B		10/APR/63	Converted
17927	58-6972	USAF	VC137A	13/JUN/59	30/JUN/59	
	58-6972	USAF	VC137B		31/MAY/63	Converted
17929	ZS-CKD	South African Airways	344	09/AUG/60	22/AUG/60	
	ZS-SAB	South African Airways			68	
	ZS-SAB	British Midland Airways			27/JUL/77	
	ZS-SAB	International Air Leases			10/NOV/77	
	EI-BFU	Guinness Peat			OCT/78	
	VN-A304	Hang Khong Vietnam			OCT/78	WFU MAR/80
17930	ZS-CKE	South African Airways	344	10/AUG/60	22/AUG/60	
	ZS-SAC	South African Airways			68	
	LX-LGW	Luxair/Trek Airways			30/MAY/69	
	LX-LGW	Guinness Peat			77	
	LX-LGW	Transavia			29/JUN/77	Leased
	LX-LGW	Guinness Peat			77	
	LX-LGW	Ghana Airways			AUG/77	Leased
	LX-LGW	Guinness Peat			OCT/77	
	LX-LGW	Luxair			25/NOV/77	
	OO-SBW	Sabena			MAR/78	Leased
	OO-CZF	Sobelair			MAR/79	Sub-leased
	9Q-CZF	Inter-Fret			24/FEB/81	
18012	N74612	Continental Airlines	124	03/AUG/59	17/MAR/60	
	N74612	Trans World Airlines			08/DEC/67	
	4X-BYA	Israel Aircraft Industries			11/NOV/71	
	4X-JYA	Israeli Air Force			NOV/71	
	4X-JYA	Israel Aircraft Industries			SEP/83	WFU SEP/83, Apprentice trainer
18054	N7526A	American Airlines	123B	22/JAN/61	25/MAY/61	
	N7526A	Tigerair			12/JUL/78	
	G-BGCT	Monarch Airlines			10/DEC/78	
	5B-DAO	Cyprus Airways			12/DEC/79	
18056	D-ABOG	Lufthansa	430	23/FEB/61	16/MAR/61	
	N9985F	Air Trine			OCT/76	
	N9985F	M.M.Landy			06/OCT/76	
	N9985F	M.M.Landy	430F		02/FEB/77	Converted
	N9985F	Nigeria Airways			DEC/77	Leased for Hadj flights
	N9985F	M.M.Landy			78	
	N9985F	Interconair				
	N9985F	Air Trans			AUG/78	Stored Manston 09/AUG/80
	N9985F	Anderson Aviation			AUG/80	
	3C-ABH	BATA International			DEC/80	
	3C-ABH	Air Sinai			MAR/82	Leased
	3C-ABH	BATA International			82	
	3C-ABH	Israel Aircraft Industries			APR/84	WFU APR/84, Apprentice trainer
18067	N93134	Boeing	138B	13/APR/61		
	VH-EBH	Qantas			29/JUL/61	
	9Y-TDC	BWIA			28/SEP/69	
	9Y-TDC	Omni International			28/AUG/77	
	VR-CAN	Euro Air Finance			MAR/78	
	VR-CAN	Jet Aviation			MAR/78	
18068	VH-EBI	Qantas	138B	07/AUG/61	16/AUG/61	
	N105BN	Braniff			28/JUN/69	
	N105BN	Boeing			01/NOV/75	
	N105BN	Atlas Aircraft Co.			18/AUG/76	
	OE-IRA	Flugzeug Leasing			SEP/76	
	OE-IRA	Montana			17/SEP/76	Leased
	OE-IRA	Central Airways			APR/81	Sub-leased
	OE-IRA	Montana			81	Leased
	OE-IRA	Flugzeug Leasing			JUL/81	
	OE-URA	Flugzeug Leasing			13/NOV/82	
	SU-FAB	Misr Overseas			DEC/82	
	SU-FAB	Egyptair			MAR/83	Leased
	SU-FAB	Misr Overseas			83	
	SU-FAB	West Coast Airlines			DEC/85	
18069	VH-EBJ	Qantas	138B	09/AUG/61	24/AUG/61	
	N106BN	Braniff			05/JUL/69	WFU 10/SEP/73
	N106BN	Boeing			02/APR/75	
	OE-INA	Flugzeug Leasing			17/JUL/77	
	OE-INA	Montana			26/JUL/77	Leased
	OE-INA	Flugzeug Leasing			JUL/81	
	OE-UNA	Flugzeug Leasing			14/NOV/82	
	SU-FAA	Misr Overseas			DEC/82	
	SU-FAA	Egyptair			MAR/83	Leased
	SU-FAA	Misr Overseas			83	
18070	4X-ATA	El Al	458	14/APR/61	24/APR/61	WFU MAR/84, ground trainer
18071	4X-ATB	El Al	458	03/JUN/61	10/JUN/61	
	4X-ATB	Arkia			01/APR/84	Leased
	4X-ATB	El Al			JUN/85	WFU JUL/86 for Museum
18084	N758PA	Pan American	321	18/MAY/61	23/MAY/61	
	G-AYRZ	Lloyd International			01/JAN/71	
	G-AYRZ	GATX Leasing			72	
	VP-BDG	Bahamas World Airways			11/FEB/72	Leased
	C6-BDG	Bahamas World Airways			75	WFU AUG/75
	N433MA	MCA Leasing			SEP/78	
	N433MA	Quantum Leasing Corp			AUG/79	
	N707HD	Quantum Leasing Corp.			24/MAR/80	
	N707HD	Age of Enlightenment			JUL/84	
18246	F-BHSS	Air France	328	05/FEB/62	16/FEB/62	
	F-BHSS	Charlotte Aircraft			28/FEB/78	
	F-BHSS	Intercontinental Airways				Not taken-up
	4X-BYK	Israel Aircraft Industries			MAR/78	
	4X-JYK	Israeli Air Force			SEP/78	
18334	VH-EBK	Qantas	138B	14/AUG/61	29/AUG/61	

C/N	Registration	Owner/Operator	Series	First Flight	Delivery	Remarks
	9Y-TDB	BWIA			19/SEP/69	
	9Y-TDB	Omni International			OCT/77	
	N58937	Jet Aviation			MAR/78	
	N58937	TAG Aviation			JUN/78	
	CN-ANS	Moroccan Royal Flight			18/MAY/83	
18336	N761PA	Pan Am	321B	26/FEB/62	13/JUN/62	
	RP-C7075	Air Manila			05/JAN/77	WFU 81 to JUL/85
	N944JW	International Air Leases			JUL/85	
	N944JW	Boeing			07/MAY/86	WFU 07/MAY/86 for KC-135E Parts
18338	N763PA	Pan American	321B	21/APR/62	01/JUN/62	
	N763PA	ATASCO			27/MAY/77	
	N763W	Wedge Corp.				
	N763W	Wistair International			13/JUL/78	
	N111MF	Wistair International			16/MAY/79	
	N98WS	Wistair International			JUL/83	
18339	N764PA	Pan American	321B	17/MAY/62	01/JUN/62	
	N764PA	ATASCO			24/AUG/77	
	N764SE	S. Eisenberg			16/SEP/77	
	OE-IEB	Flyglobe Handels			JAN/79	Leased
	N764SE	ATASCO			JUN/79	
18372	VR-BBW	Cunard Eagle	465	16/FEB/62	27/FEB/62	
	G-ARWD	BOAC Cunard			28/SEP/62	
	G-ARWD	British Airways			01/APR/72	
	G-ARWD	British Airtours			15/MAY/73	
	G-ARWD	Air Mauritius			APR/79	Leased
	G-ARWD	British Airways			APR/81	
	G-ARWD	Boeing			31/MAY/81	WFU 31/MAY/81, Mockup-Renton.
18374	OO-SJF	Sabena	329	03/APR/62	17/APR/62	
	OO-SJF	Air Congo			08/DEC/67	Leased
	OO-SJF	Sabena			68	
	OE-LBA	Austrian Airlines			02/APR/69	Leased
	OO-SJF	Sabena			71	
	OO-SJF	Air Algerie			DEC/74	Leased
	OO-SJF	Sabena			JAN/75	
	OO-SJF	Mandala Airlines			NOV/75	Leased
	OO-SJF	Sabena			JAN/76	
	OO-SJF	Mandala Airlines			NOV/76	Leased
	OO-SJF	Sabena			JAN/77	
	OO-SJF	Israeli Aircraft Industries			19/JAN/77	
	4X-JYL	Israeli Air Force			JUN/77	
18385	N746TW	Trans World Airlines	131B	12/MAR/62	29/MAR/62	WFU 10/JUL/81
	N746TW	Boeing			28/APR/82	WFU 28/APR/82 for KC-135E Parts
18386	N747TW	Trans World Airlines	131B	27/MAR/62	10/APR/62	
	N747TW	Boeing			13/AUG/82	WFU 13/AUG/82 for KC-135E Parts
18387	N748TW	Trans World Airlines	131B	14/APR/62	13/APR/62	
	N748TW	Boeing			07/JUL/82	WFU 07/JUL/82 for KC-135E Parts
18388	N749TW	Trans World Airlines	131B	07/MAY/62	18/MAY/62	
	N749TW	Boeing			01/FEB/83	WFU 01/FEB/83 for KC-135E Parts
18389	N750TW	Trans World Airlines	131B	15/MAY/62	23/MAY/62	
	N750TW	Boeing			22/APR/82	WFU 22/APR/82 for KC-135E Parts
18390	N751TW	Trans World Airlines	131B	22/MAY/62	31/MAY/62	
	N751TW	Boeing			08/FEB/83	WFU 08/FEB/83 for KC-135E Parts
18391	N752TW	Trans World Airlines	131B	08/JUN/62	16/JUN/62	
	N752TW	Boeing			28/APR/82	WFU 28/APR/83 for KC-135E Parts
18392	N754TW	Trans World Airlines	131B	19/JUN/62	28/JUN/62	
	N754TW	Boeing			22/APR/82	WFU 22/APR/82 for KC-135E Parts
18393	N755TW	Trans World Airlines	131B	16/JUL/62	23/JUL/62	
	N755TW	Boeing			22/DEC/82	WFU 22/DEC/82 for KC-135E Parts
18394	N756TW	Trans World Airlines	131B	20/JUL/62	02/AUG/62	
	N756TW	Boeing			21/APR/82	WFU 21/APR/82 for KC-135E Parts
18396	N758TW	Trans World Airlines	131B	15/AUG/62	21/AUG/62	
	N758TW	Boeing			21/APR/82	WFU 21/APR/82 for KC-135E Parts
18397	N759TW	Trans World Airlines	131B	18/AUG/62	29/AUG/62	
	N759TW	Boeing			06/JUL/82	WFU 06/JUL/82 for KC-135E Parts
18400	N781TW	Trans World Airlines	131B	21/AUG/62	31/AUG/62	
	N781TW	Boeing			12/AUG/82	WFU 12/AUG/82 for KC-135E Parts
18401	N782TW	Trans World Airlines	131B	06/SEP/62	21/SEP/62	
	N782TW	Boeing			13/AUG/82	WFU 13/AUG/82 for KC-135E Parts
18402	N783TW	Trans World Airlines	131B	14/SEP/62	26/SEP/62	
	N783TW	Boeing			06/JUL/82	WFU 06/JUL/82 for KC-135E Parts
18403	N784TW	Trans World Airlines	131B	18/SEP/62	12/OCT/62	
	N784TW	Boeing			23/APR/82	WFU 23/APR/82 for KC-135E Parts
18404	N785TW	Trans World Airlines	131B	01/OCT/62	12/OCT/62	
	N785TW	Boeing			22/DEC/82	WFU 22/DEC/82 for KC-135E Parts
18405	N773TW	Trans World Airlines	331B	20/JUL/62	11/MAR/63	
	N773TW	Boeing			OCT/83	WFU OCT/83 for KC-135E Parts
18406	N774TW	Trans World Airlines	331B	17/OCT/62	10/NOV/62	
	N774TW	Boeing			20/DEC/83	WFU 20/DEC/83 for KC-135E Parts
18407	N775TW	Trans World Airlines	331B	12/NOV/62	03/DEC/62	
	N775TW	Boeing			09/MAY/84	WFU 09/MAY/84 for KC-135E Parts
18408	N776TW	Trans World Airlines	331B	13/DEC/62	23/JAN/63	
	N8739	Trans World Airlines				
	N28714	Trans World Airlines				WFU 02/MAR/80 to 16/DEC/83
	N28714	Boeing			16/DEC/83	WFU 16/DEC/83 for KC-135E Parts
18409	N778TW	Trans World Airlines	331B	05/FEB/63	21/FEB/63	WFU SEP/83
	N778TW	Boeing			03/APR/84	WFU 03/APR/84 for KC-135E Parts
18413	G-ARRC	BOAC Cunard	436	04/MAR/63	15/MAR/63	
	G-ARRC	BOAC			OCT/66	
	G-ARRC	British Airways			01/APR/72	
	G-ARRC	British Airtours			15/DEC/76	
	G-ARRC	Europe Aero Services			02/MAR/81	
	N4465C	F. Acevedo			AUG/83	
	N4465C	Coastal Airways			AUG/83	
18456	F-BHSV	Air France	328B	03/DEC/62	15/DEC/62	
	F-BHSV	TRATCO Leasing			APR/83	
	4X-ATE	El Al			17/JUL/83	Leased
	4X-ATE	TRATCO Leasing			10/OCT/83	WFU 10/OCT/83
18460	OO-SJG	Sabena	329	09/JAN/63	19/JAN/63	
	OO-SJG	Air Congo			65	Leased
	OO-SJG	Sabena			67	
	OO-SJG	Nigeria Airways			MAR/67	Leased
	OO-SJG	Sabena			67	
	4X-BYM	Israel Aircraft Industries			25/FEB/77	
	4X-BYM	El Al			77	Leased
	4X-BYM	Israel Aircraft Industries			77	

C/N	Registration	Owner/Operator	Series	First Flight	Delivery	Remarks
	4X-JYM	Israeli Air Force			DEC/77	
18461	62-6000	USAF	VC137C	10/AUG/62	09/OCT/62	
18583	N374WA	World Airways	373C	09/AUG/63	20/AUG/63	
	HZ-ACF	Saudia			19/AUG/73	
	HZ-ACF	Air Transport Sales			15/JUL/78	
	D2-TAG	TAAG Angola			15/JUL/78	
	D2-TOG	TAAG Angola			NOV/80	
18586	N353US	Northwest Orient	351B	12/JUL/63	30/JUL/63	
	VR-HGO	Cathay Pacific			28/AUG/72	
	VR-CAO	Diversified Investments			01/OCT/78	
	VR-CAO	ARAMCO			OCT/79	Leased
	N651TF	Diversified Investments			JUL/81	
	N651TF	Jet Charter Service			NOV/81	Leased
	N651TF	Diversified Investments			OCT/85	
18591	N767PA	Pan American	321C	01/MAY/63	07/JUN/63	
	N767PA	Sally Leasing			25/JUN/76	
	G-BEAF	Dan Air			24/JUL/76	
	G-BEAF	IAS Cargo			24/JUL/76	Leased
	G-BEAF	Dan Air			77	
	LV-MSG	International Air Leases			12/JUL/78	
	LV-MSG	TAR			12/JUL/78	WFU NOV/84 Derelict Buenos Aires
18686	F-BLCB	Air France	328B	17/JAN/64	30/JAN/64	
	TU-TXI	Air Afrique			01/APR/66	Leased
	F-BLCB	Air France			15/APR/66	
	TU-TXM	Air Afrique			23/MAR/67	Leased
	F-BLCB	Air France			15/APR/67	
	F-BLCB	Air Madagascar			19/APR/67	Leased
	5R-MFK	Air Madagascar			APR/72	
	F-BLCB	Air France			02/MAR/79	
	F-BLCB	TRATCO Leasing			15/APR/83	
	5A-DLT	Libyan Arab Airlines			15/APR/83	
18689	N7555A	American Airlines	323C	01/NOV/63	19/NOV/63	
	N7555A	TMA			23/FEB/76	Leased
	N7555A	American Airlines			AUG/76	
	N7555A	Tradewinds			28/FEB/78	
	G-WIND	Tradewinds			25/JUL/78	
	J6-SLF	St. Lucia Airways			18/MAR/82	
18690	N7556A	American Airlines	323C	27/NOV/63	13/DEC/63	
	G-SAIL	Tradewinds			29/SEP/78	
	G-SAIL	Boeing			21/APR/86	WFU 21/APR/86 for KC-135E Parts
18691	N7557A	American Airlines	323C	06/DEC/63	20/DEC/63	
	5X-UWM	Simbair			06/MAY/75	
	G-BFEO	Greyfin Nassau			14/OCT/77	
	G-BFEO	Tradewinds			14/OCT/77	Leased
	G-BFEO	Boeing			14/APR/86	WFU 14/APR/86 for KC-135E Parts
18692	N7558A	American Airlines	323C	23/DEC/63	30/DEC/63	
	N309EL	Eli Lilly and Co.			09/APR/75	
	CP-1365	Lloyd Aero Boliviano			28/SEP/77	
18694	PP-VJJ	Varig	441	22/OCT/63	12/NOV/63	
	N58RD	RDC Marine Inc.			30/SEP/79	WFU JAN/85, stored Miami
18708	VT-DPM	Air India	373B	19/MAY/64	24/MAY/64	
18709	N789TW	Trans World Airlines	373C	31/OCT/63	18/NOV/63	WFU AUG/79
	HK-2606	Aeronautics Services			27/FEB/81	
	HK-2606	Aerotal			MAR/81	Leased
	HP-1027	Aeronautics Services			NOV/83	
	HC-BLY	SAETA			MAR/81	Leased
	HC-BLY	SAETA			02/JUL/85	Purchased
18711	N786TW	Trans World Airlines	331C	16/APR/64	25/APR/64	
	N786TW	FBA Corp.			10/JAN/80	
	N786TW	Guinness Peat			22/AUG/80	Leased
	N786TW	Faucett			SEP/80	Sub-leased
	N786TW	Trans World Airlines			FEB/81	
	N786TW	Florida West			FEB/82	
	N786TW	Air Haiti			MAR/82	Leased
	N700FW	Florida West			APR/83	
18713	N788TW	Trans World Airlines	331C	05/JUN/64	12/JUN/64	WFU JAN/81 to MAY/84
	N788TW	Boeing			MAY/84	
	N788B	Boeing			MAY/84	E-3A Trainer
	N131EA	Boeing			MAR/85	E-3A Trainer
18714	N790PA	Pan American	321C	10/FEB/64	27/FEB/64	
	N790PA	ATASCO			01/SEP/77	
	HK-1718	Avianca			01/SEP/79	Leased
	HK-1718	ATASCO			NOV/79	
	HK-1718	ITEL			NOV/79	
	HK-1718	Avianca			NOV/79	Leased
	HK-1718	ITEL			DEC/80	
	HK-1718	GATX Leasing			DEC/80	
	HK-1718	Avianca			DEC/80	Leased
	HK-1718	Avianca			NOV/84	Purchased
	TF-AEA	Airxport			NOV/84	
	TF-AEA	Crown Arcot			NOV/85	
	TF-AEA	Arctic Air			DEC/84	Leased
	TF-AEA	Trans European Airways			JAN/85	Sub-leased
	TF-AEA	Atlanta Icelandic			JAN/86	
18715	N791PA	Pan American	321C	11/MAR/64	19/MAR/64	
	N791PA	Maverick			30/MAR/78	Leased
	N791PA	Pan American			15/JAN/79	
	N791PA	Charlotte Aircraft			26/FEB/79	
	N791PA	Global International			80	Leased
	N791PA	Charlotte Aircraft			80	
	N791PA	Intercontinental Airlines			80	Leased
	N791PA	Charlotte Aircraft			JUL/81	
	N791PA	International Air Leases			JAN/81	
	TC-JCC	Turk Hava Yollari			JUL/81	Leased
18716	N792PA	Pan American	321C	19/MAR/64	27/MAR/64	
	JY-AED	Jordanian World Airways			06/JUN/75	
	JY-AED	Alia			APR/82	
	JY-AED	Arab Air Cargo			83	
	JY-CAB	Arab Air Cargo			01/MAR/84	
	4YB-CAB	Arab Air Cargo				
18717	N793PA	Pan American	321C	27/MAR/64	03/APR/64	
	N793PA	ATASCO			MAR/79	
	G-BGIS	Scimitar Airlines			13/MAR/79	
	G-BGIS	IAS Cargo			01/JUN/79	Leased
	G-BGIS	British Cargo Airlines				Leased

C/N	Registration	Owner/Operator	Series	First Flight	Delivery	Remarks
	G-BGIS	Scimitar Airlines			80	Stored Lasham DEC/81
	G-BGIS	Greyhound Leasing			DEC/81	
	G-TRAD	Tradewinds Airways			24/JAN/84	Leased
	G-TRAD	Greyhound Leasing			DEC/85	
	HK-3232	Tampa Colombia			APR/86	
18718	N794PA	Pan American	321C	03/APR/64	30/APR/64	
	N794PA	Aires Air Cargo			25/MAR/73	Leased
	N794PA	Pan American			21/JUN/73	
	N794RN	Ron Air			05/APR/75	
	N794EP	Iran Air			10/APR/75	Leased
	N794RN	Ron Air			75	
	N794RN	Zimex Aviation			MAY/77	Leased
	N794RN	Uganda Airlines			MAY/77	Sub-leased
	N794RN	Ron Air			JUL/78	
	G-BFZF	Greyhound Leasing			21/SEP/78	
	G-BFZF	Simitar Airlines			21/SEP/78	Leased
	G-BFZF	IAS Cargo			01/JUN/79	Sub-leased
	G-BFZF	British Cargo Airlines				Sub-leased
	G-BFZF	Scimitar Airlines			80	Leased
	G-BFZF	Air Intergulf			01/APR/81	Sub-leased
	G-BFZF	Scimitar Airlines			81	Leased
	G-BNGH	Greyhound Leasing			MAR/82	
	G-BNGH	Tradewinds			MAY/86	Leased
18739	VH-EBL	Qantas	138B	06/AUG/64	19/AUG/64	
	N107BN	Braniff			19/JUN/69	
	N107BN	Boeing			01/NOV/75	
	N107BN	Commercial Transport Sales			15/JUL/76	
	N107BN	Offset Inc.			15/JUL/76	
	N107BN	Merpati Nusantara			15/JUL/76	Leased
	PK-MBA	Merpati Nusantara				WFU DEC/79, stored Jakarta
18740	VH-EBM	Qantas	138B	01/SEP/64	10/SEP/64	
	N108BN	Braniff			24/JUN/69	
	N108BN	Boeing			75	
	N108BN	Tracinda Investment Corp.			01/NOV/75	
	N108BN	Sheikh Akram			26/SEP/77	
	N108BN	TAG Aviation			26/SEP/77	
18746	N356US	Northwest Orient	351C	31/MAR/64	10/APR/64	
	CF-PWJ	Pacific Western			02/MAR/73	
	OO-ABA	Abelag			15/MAY/79	
	OO-ABA	UTA			13/JUN/79	Leased
	OO-ABA	Abelag			OCT/79	
	C-GRYO	Ontario Worldair			20/DEC/79	Leased
	OO-ABA	Air Belgium			22/DEC/80	
	5A-DIZ	United African Airlines			17/JUL/81	
		Jamahiriyan Air Transport			DEC/82	
18747	N357US	Northwest Orient	351C	14/APR/64	18/APR/64	
	VR-HHB	Cathay Pacific			21/JAN/74	
	5X-UAC	Uganda Airlines			MAY/80	
18748	N358US	Northwest Orient	351C	12/JUN/64	18/JUN/64	
	VR-HHD	Cathay Pacific			29/MAR/74	
	VR-HHD	Omni Aircraft			04/SEP/79	
	VR-CAR	Omni Aircraft				
	3X-GAZ	Air Guinee			OCT/79	
18756	N791TW	Trans World Airlines	331C	22/JUL/64	06/AUG/64	
	N791TW	Global International			12/MAR/79	
	N791TW	Trans World Airlines			21/MAY/81	WFU 21/MAY/81 to 11/MAY/84
	N791TW	Boeing			11/MAY/84	WFU 11/MAY/84 for KC-135E Parts
18757	N792TW	Trans World Airlines	331C	24/AUG/64	29/AUG/64	
	N792TW	Global International			10/JUL/80	Leased
	N792TW	Trans World Airlines			11/SEP/80	
	N792TW	Guinness Peat			11/NOV/81	Leased
	N792TW	Faucett			NOV/81	Sub-leased
	N792TW	Trans World Airlines			12/FEB/82	
	N792TW	Air Wing International			JUN/82	
	N792TW	Boeing			22/OCT/82	Tanker demonstrator
		South African Air Force	KC-137		AUG/86	Tanker
18758	N795TW	Trans World Airlines	131B	09/OCT/64	29/OCT/64	
	N795TW	Boeing			09/FEB/83	WFU 09/FEB/83 for KC-135E parts
18759	N796TW	Trans World Airlines	131B	27/OCT/64	13/NOV/64	
	N796TW	Boeing			07/JUL/82	WFU 07/JUL/82 for KC-135E Parts
18761	N798TW	Trans World Airlines	131B	03/DEC/64	31/DEC/64	
	N798TW	Boeing			13/SEP/82	WFU 13/SEP/82 for KC-135E Parts
18762	N799TW	Trans World Airlines	131B	08/DEC/64	23/DEC/64	
	N799TW	Boeing			08/FEB/83	WFU 08/FEB/83 for KC-135E Parts
18764	N779TW	Trans World Airlines	331B	31/DEC/64	15/JAN/65	
	N779TW	Boeing			14/DEC/83	WFU 14/DEC/83 for KC-135E Parts
18765	N795PA	Pan American	321C	25/APR/64	30/APR/64	
	N795RN	ATASCO			29/DEC/76	
	N795RN	Ecuatoriana			MAR/77	Leased
	G-BEZT	Dan Air			21/OCT/77	
	SU-BAG	Zimex			07/JUL/78	
	SU-BAG	Uganda Airlines			11/JUL/78	Leased
	AS.10.10	Libyan Air Cargo			APR/81	
	5A-DHL	United African Airlines			APR/81	
	5A-DHL	Jamahiriya Air Transport			DEC/82	WFU JUN/84, stored Tripoli
18766	N796PA	Pan American	321C	30/APR/64	08/MAY/64	
	HK-1849	Avianca			26/APR/76	
	HK-1849	ATASCO			NOV/85	
	N865BX	Burlington Northern			NOV/85	Op. by Southern Air Transport
18808	VH-EBN	Qantas	338C	29/JAN/65	09/FEB/65	
	9V-BFW	Singapore Airlines			16/JUL/74	
	N707GB	International Air Leases			MAR/81	
	N707GB	Arrow Airways			JUL/81	Leased
	N707GB	International Air Leases			APR/83	
	N707GB	Tampa Colombia			APR/83	Leased
	N707GB	Tampa Colombia			FEB/86	Purchased
18809	VH-EBO	Qantas	338C	15/FEB/65	05/MAR/65	
	9V-BFN	Singapore Airlines			20/NOV/72	
	N4225J	International Air Leases			FEB/81	
	N4225J	Arrow Airways			MAY/81	Leased
	N4225J	International Air Leases			OCT/83	
	5N-ARQ	Gas Air			OCT/83	
18810	VH-EBP	Qantas	338C	30/JUL/65	11/AUG/65	
	N14791	Trans World Airlines			20/NOV/72	
	SU-BBA	Air Cargo Egypt			26/MAR/79	WFU MAR/82, derelict Cairo

C/N	Registration	Owner/Operator	Series	First Flight	Delivery	Remarks
18819	D-ABOX	Lufthansa	330B	23/DEC/64	01/JAN/65	
	VP-WKR	Air Zimbabwe			19/FEB/81	
	Z-WKR	Air Zimbabwe			83	
18825	N17321	Continental Airlines	321C	14/AUG/64	21/AUG/64	
	B-1832	China Airlines			20/MAY/73	WFU SEP/81
	N987AA	Allen Aircraft			27/JUN/85	
	5X-DAR	Gas Air			12/FEB/86	
	5X-DAR	Das Air Cargo			12/FEB/86	Leased
18832	N401PA	Pan American	321B	25/JAN/65	05/FEB/65	
	N401PA	American Eagle			80	Leased
	N401PA	Pan American			APR/81	
	EI-BKO	Guinness Peat Aviation			10/APR/81	
	VN-B1416	Hang Khong Vietnam			11/APR/81	
18833	N402PA	Pan American	321B	02/FEB/65	17/FEB/65	
	N402PA	Guinness Peat			24/MAY/79	
	N402PA	AeroAmerica			MAY/79	Leased
	N402PA	Guinness Peat			79	
	N402PA	Bangladesh Biman			SEP/79	Leased
	N402PA	Guinness Peat			79	
	N402PA	AeroAmerica			DEC/79	Leased
	N402PA	American Eagle Airlines			80	
	N402PA	Pan American			81	
	N402PA	Barclays ABC			MAY/81	
	N402PA	Navaero Aviation			DEC/84	WFU DEC/84 to 08/MAY/86
	N402PA	Boeing			08/MAY/86	WFU 08/MAY/86 for KC-135E Parts
18834	N403PA	Pan American	321B	10/FEB/65	23/FEB/65	
	N403PA	ATASCO			29/JUN/78	
	TC-JBS	Turk Hava Yollari			30/JUN/78	Leased
	N5519V	ATASCO			JAN/85	
	N5519V	Boeing			JAN/86	WFU JAN/86 for KC-135E Parts
18835	N404PA	Pan American	321B	18/FEB/65	05/MAR/65	
	N404PA	ITEL			SEP/79	
	N404PA	AeroAmerica			79	Leased
	N404PA	American Eagle Airlines			80	
	N404PA	Pan American			81	
	N404PA	Barclays ABC			MAY/81	
	N404PA	Navaero Aviation			DEC/84	WFU DEC/84, stored Marana
18836	N405PA	Pan American	321B	24/FEB/65	10/MAR/65	
	N405PA	ATASCO			23/JUN/78	
	TC-JBT	Turk Hava Yollari			23/JUN/78	Leased
	N5519U	ATASCO			FEB/85	
	N5519U	Boeing			DEC/85	WFU DEC/85 for KC-135E Parts
18837	N406PA	Pan American	321B	08/MAR/65	17/MAR/65	
	N406PA	ATASCO			28/JUN/78	
	F-OGIV	SATT			JUL/78	
	F-BSGT	Le Point			DEC/80	
	F-BSGT	Point Air			82	
	XT-ABX	T-Air			84	Leased
	F-BSGT	Point Air			JUL/84	
18839	N408PA	Pan American	321B	09/APR/65	16/APR/65	
	N408PA	American Eagle			06/AUG/80	Leased
	N408PA	Pan American			23/APR/81	
	N4408F	Ports Of Call			01/DEC/81	
	N454PC	Ports Of Call				
	N454PC	Skyworld Airlines			SEP/85	
18840	N409PA	Pan American	321B	14/APR/65	21/APR/65	WFU NOV/78
	N409PA	ATASCO			16/MAY/79	
	F-OGIW	SATT			79	WFU MAY/80
	F-OGIW	International Air Leases			APR/82	
	N707GE	Arrow Air			82	
	N707GE	Guy America			18/DEC/82	
	N707GE	International Air Leases			83	
	N707GE	Jet Charter Service			MAY/83	Leased
	N707GE	International Air Leases				
	N707GE	Boeing			24/APR/84	WFU 24/APR/84 for KC-135E Parts
18841	N410PA	Pan American	321B	20/APR/65	27/APR/65	
	N410PA	ATASCO			20/OCT/78	
	ZP-CCE	LAP			OCT/78	
18842	N412PA	Pan American	321B	30/APR/65	21/MAY/65	
	N412PA	ATASCO			MAR/78	
	TC-JBU	Turk Hava Yollari			09/JUN/78	Leased
	N5517Z	ATASCO			FEB/85	
	N5517Z	Boeing			JAN/86	WFU JAN/86 for KC-135E Parts
18873	N68655	Boeing	337B	19/JAN/65		
	VT-DSI	Air India			12/MAR/65	
18880	EI-ANO	Aer Lingus	348C	22/MAR/65	13/APR/65	
	N318F	Flying Tiger Line			26/SEP/66	Leased
	EI-ANO	Aer Lingus			26/APR/68	
	EI-ANO	TMA			FEB/70	Leased
	EI-ANO	Aer Lingus			70	
	EI-ANO	Nigeria Airways			01/APR/72	Leased
	EI-ANO	Aer Lingus			31/MAR/73	
	EI-ANO	Cargolux			18/MAY/81	
	5A-DIX	United African Airlines			MAY/81	
	5A-DIX	Jamahiriyan Air Transport			DEC/82	
18881	F-BLCC	Air France	328C	16/JUL/65	05/AUG/65	
	TF-VLR	TRATCO Leasing			14/JAN/83	
	TF-VLR	Eagle Air			14/JAN/83	Leased
	TF-VLR	Libyan Arab Airlines			17/JAN/83	Sub-leased
	TF-VLR	Eagle Air			APR/83	Leased
	TF-VLR	TRATCO Leasing			APR/83	
	5A-DIK	Libyan Arab Airlines			APR/83	
18882	N7550A	American Airlines	123B	26/APR/65	28/MAY/65	
	N7550A	Boeing			28/SEP/81	WFU 28/SEP/81 for KC-135E Parts
18883	N7551A	American Airlines	123B	06/MAY/65	26/MAY/65	
	N7551A	Boeing			14/APR/83	WFU 14/APR/83 for KC-135E Parts
18884	N7552A	American Airlines	123B	26/MAY/65	15/JUN/65	
	N7552A	Boeing			28/FEB/83	WFU 28/FEB/83 for KC-135E Parts
18885	N7553A	American Airlines	123B	28/JUN/65	23/JUL/65	
	N7553A	Boeing			22/SEP/81	WFU 22/SEP/81 for KC-135E Parts
18886	N17323	Continental Airlines	324C	11/JUN/65	17/JUN/65	
	G-AZJM	Lloyd International			20/DEC/71	
	G-AZJM	British Caledonian			06/MAR/73	
	G-AZJM	Bangladesh Biman			NOV/75	Leased
	G-AZJM	British Caledonian			DEC/75	

BOEING 707 (EXISTING AIRCRAFT ONLY)

C/N	Registration	Owner/Operator	Series	First Flight	Delivery	Remarks
	G-AZJM	International Air Leases			MAR/77	
	G-AZJM	British Midland Airways			25/MAY/77	Leased
	G-AZJM	Kuwait Airways			AUG/77	Sub-leased
	G-AZJM	British Midland Airways				Leased
	G-AZJM	Air Algerie			AUG/78	Sub-Leased
	G-AZJM	British Midland Airways			15/JAN/80	Leased
	G-AZJM	PIA			01/FEB/80	Sub-leased
	G-AZJM	British Midland Airways			31/MAR/80	Leased
	N17323	International Air Leases			20/MAY/80	
	HK-2600	Tampa Colombia			JAN/81	
18888	N359US	Northwest Orient	351C	14/MAY/65	22/MAY/65	
	VR-HHE	Cathay Pacific			02/AUG/74	
	VR-HHE	TRATCO Leasing			29/APR/83	
	5A-DJS	Jamahirya Air Transport			JUL/83	
18889	N360US	Northwest Orient	351C	03/JUN/65	12/JUN/65	
	VR-HHJ	Cathay Pacific			31/MAY/74	
	VR-HHJ	TRATCO Leasing			29/APR/83	
	5A-DJT	Jamahirya Air Transport			JUL/83	
18891	ZS-DYL	South African Airways	344B	13/AUG/65	27/AUG/65	
	ZS-SAD	South African Airways			OCT/68	
	VP-WKW	Air Zimbabwe			DEC/80	Leased
	ZS-SAD	South African Airways				
	LX-LGR	Luxair			80	
	3B-NAE	Air Mauritius			01/APR/81	Leased
	3B-NAE	Air Mauritius			08/APR/83	Purchased
18913	N760TW	Trans World Airlines	331B	12/JAN/65	29/JAN/65	
	N760TW	Boeing			20/DEC/83	WFU 20/DEC/83 for KC-135E Parts
18916	N8705T	Trans World Airlines	331B	03/NOV/65	10/DEC/65	
	N8705T	Boeing			15/DEC/83	WFU 15/DEC/83 for KC-135E Parts
18918	N8725T	Trans World Airlines	331B	29/DEC/65	12/JAN/66	
	N8725T	Boeing			21/DEC/83	WFU 21/DEC/83 for KC-135E Parts
18921	N361US	Northwest Orient	351C	09/AUG/65	14/AUG/65	
	VR-HGR	Cathay Pacific			15/AUG/72	
	VR-HGR	Euro Air Finance			01/JUN/80	
	S2-ACF	Bangladesh Biman			AUG/80	
18922	N362US	Northwest Oreint	351C	09/SEP/65	15/SEP/65	
	VR-HGP	Cathay Pacific			18/NOV/72	
	VR-HGP	Euro Air Financing			17/DEC/81	
	N82TF	Omni International			DEC/81	
	N82TF	Satellite Inc.			MAY/82	
	5N-ASY	Dantata			MAY/82	
	5N-ASY	United Air Services			AUG/83	
18923	D-ABUB	Lufthansa	330B	16/JUL/65	04/AUG/65	
	VP-WKS	Air Zimbabwe			08/MAY/81	
	Z-WKS	Air Zimbabwe			83	
18925	G-ASZG	BOAC	336C	05/NOV/65	19/DEC/65	
	G-ASZG	British Airways			01/APR/72	WFU 14/NOV/81
	G-ASZG	MoD			82	Leased
	G-ASZG	British Airways			82	WFU
	LX-FCV	Air Supply Corp.			05/MAY/83	
	XT-ABX	Naganagani			MAR/84	
18926	D-ABUC	Lufthansa	330B	12/SEP/65	05/OCT/65	
	CC-CEA	LAN Chile			05/APR/67	
	903	Chilean Air Force			20/JUN/85	
18927	D-ABUD	Lufthansa	330B	11/NOV/65	24/NOV/65	
	VP-WKV	Air Zimbabwe			23/JUN/82	
	Z-WKV	Air Zimbabwe			83	
18928	D-ABUF	Lufthansa	330B	07/DEC/65	01/JAN/66	
	D-ABUF	Condor			APR/78	Leased
	D-ABUF	Condor			APR/81	
	N5381X	Aerommer Ltd			03/JUL/84	
	N88ZL	Lowa Ltd			MAR/85	
18929	D-ABUG	Lufthansa	330B	29/DEC/65	07/JAN/66	
	D-ABUG	Condor			01/NOV/70	Leased
	VP-WKT	Air Zimbabwe			19/MAY/81	
	Z-WKT	Air Zimbabwe			83	
18930	D-ABUH	Lufthansa	330B	07/JAN/66	15/JAN/66	
	VP-WKU	Air Zimbabwe			15/APR/82	
	Z-WKU	Air Zimbabwe			83	
18931	D-ABUK	Lufthansa	330B	18/MAR/66	27/MAR/66	
	A6-UAE	United Arab Emirates Govt.			06/JAN/81	
18932	D-ABUE	Lufthansa	330C	26/FEB/66	11/MAR/66	
	D-ABUE	German Cargo			25/MAY/77	
	PT-TCO	Transbrasil			27/MAY/85	Op. by Aerobrasil
18937	D-ABUA	Lufthansa	330C	28/OCT/65	10/NOV/65	
	D-ABUA	German Cargo			04/APR/77	
	VR-HTC	Transcorp Australia			20/JUN/85	
18939	N7530A	American Airlines	323C	19/JUL/65	30/AUG/65	
	OD-AGD	TMA			27/AUG/73	WFU 85, stored Beirut
18940	N7561A	American Airlines	323C	11/AUG/65	27/AUG/65	
	PP-VLP	Varig			20/AUG/73	
18941	F-BLCD	Air France	328B	01/FEB/66	09/FEB/66	WFU APR/83, preserved Le Bourget
18948	SX-DBA	Olympic Airways	384C	05/MAY/66	11/MAY/66	
	JY-AEB	Alia			06/MAR/75	
	JY-AEB	Sierra Leone Airlines			MAY/83	Leased
	JY-AEB	Alia			OCT/83	
18949	SX-DBB	Olympic Airways	384C	19/MAY/66	23/MAY/66	
	JY-AEC	Alia			06/MAR/75	
	JY-AEC	Sierra Leone Airlines			NOV/82	Leased
	JY-AEC	Alia			MAY/83	
	JY-AEC	Sierra Leone Airlines			OCT/83	Leased
18950	SX-DBC	Olympic Airways	384C	14/JUN/66	18/JUN/66	
18953	VH-EBQ	Qantas	338C	27/AUG/65	14/SEP/65	
	9M-ASQ	Malaysian Airline System			23/FEB/74	
	9M-MCQ	Malaysian Airline System			JUL/75	
	60-SBM	Somali Airlines			29/FEB/80	
	N342A	Omega Air			21/MAY/85	
	N342A	Boeing			02/APR/86	WFU 02/APR/86 for KC-135E Parts
18954	VH-EBR	Qantas	338C	09/DEC/65	30/DEC/65	
	9M-ATR	Malaysian Airline System			29/JUN/74	
	9M-MCR	Malaysian Airline System			JUL/75	
	60-SBN	Somali Airlines			29/FEB/80	
	G-BMJE	Omega Air			15/MAR/85	
	N449J	Omega Air			NOV/85	
	N449J	Boeing			NOV/85	WFU NOV/85 for KC-135E Parts

C/N	Registration	Owner/Operator	Series	First Flight	Delivery	Remarks
18957	N415PA	Pan American	321B	07/FEB/66	15/FEB/66	
	N415PA	ATASCO			09/NOV/78	
	ZP-CCF	LAP			09/NOV/78	
18958	N416PA	Pan American	321B	18/FEB/66	25/FEB/66	
	EP-IRJ	Iran Air			09/APR/75	
18961	CS-TBA	TAP Air Portugal	382B	02/DEC/65	16/DEC/65	
	CS-TBA	Air Atlantis			MAY/85	
18962	CS-TBB	TAP Air Portugal	382B	01/JUN/66	13/JUN/66	
	TF-VLV	Eagle Air			OCT/84	Leased
	CS-TBB	Air Portugal			OCT/85	WFU NOV/85, stored Lisbon
18964	N363US	Northwest Orient	351C	05/NOV/65	15/NOV/65	
	VR-HGQ	Cathay Pacific			01/JUN/73	
	N88TF	Frespa AG			28/MAY/82	
	TF-VLP	Libyan Arab Airlines			SEP/82	
	TF-VLP	Eagle Air			SEP/82	Leased
	TF-VLP	Eagle Air			JAN/83	
	TF-VLP	Frespa			JAN/83	
	5A-DJU	Jamahirya Air Transport			MAY/83	
18975	N322F	Flying Tiger Line	349C	11/SEP/65	27/SEP/65	
	G-AWTK	British Caledonian			20/DEC/68	
	G-BDCN	British Caledonian			75	
	D2-TAC	TAAG Angola			OCT/77	
	D2-TOI	TAAG Angola			NOV/80	
18976	N323F	Flying Tiger Line	349C	01/OCT/65	13/OCT/65	
	EI-ASN	Aer Lingus			28/MAR/69	
	9J-ADY	Zambia Airways			24/MAR/75	
18979	N18702	Trans World Airlines	331B	25/JAN/66	03/FEB/66	
	N18702	Royal Air Maroc			18/APR/80	Leased
	N18702	Trans World Airlines			JAN/81	WFU OCT/83 to 16/FEB/84
	N18702	Boeing			16/FEB/84	WFU 16/FEB/84 for KC-135E Parts
18980	N18703	Trans World Airlines	331B	27/JAN/66	05/FEB/66	
	N18703	Boeing			OCT/83	WFU OCT/83 for KC-135E Parts
18981	N18704	Trans World Airlines	331B	22/FEB/66	05/MAR/66	
	N18704	Boeing			21/DEC/83	WFU 21/DEC/83 for KC-135E Parts
18982	N18706	Trans World Airlines	331B	22/MAR/66	04/APR/66	
	N18706	Boeing			OCT/83	WFU OCT/83 for KC-135E Parts
18983	N18707	Trans World Airlines	331B	31/MAR/66	15/APR/66	WFU JAN/83 to 14/FEB/84
	N18707	Boeing			14/FEB/84	WFU 14/FEB/84 for KC-135E Par
18984	N18708	Trans World Airlines	331B	11/APR/66	20/APR/66	
	N18708	Royal Air Maroc			23/FEB/80	Leased
	N18708	Trans World Airlines			18/APR/80	
	N18708	Boeing			14/DEC/83	WFU 14/DEC/83 for KC-135E Parts
18985	N18709	Trans World Airlines	331B	18/MAY/66	21/MAY/66	
	4X-ATD	El Al			23/APR/82	
	4X-ATD	Arkia			MAY/85	Leased
18986	N6720	Trans World Airlines	131B	08/MAR/66	25/MAR/66	
	N6720	Boeing			21/DEC/83	WFU 21/DEC/83 for KC-135E Parts
18987	N6721	Trans World Airlines	131B	05/APR/66	15/APR/66	
	N6721	Boeing			21/DEC/83	WFU 21/DEC/83 for KC-135E Parts
18988	N6722	Trans World Airlines	131B	19/APR/66	28/APR/66	
	N6722	Boeing			19/MAY/82	WFU 19/MAY/82 for KC-135E Parts
18989	N6723	Trans World Airlines	131B	28/APR/66	06/MAY/66	
	N6723	Boeing			12/AUG/82	WFU 12/AUG/82 for KC-135E Parts
18991	N376WA	World Airways	373C	15/OCT/65	22/OCT/65	
	AP-AWU	PIA			22/JUN/71	Leased
	AP-AWU	PIA			14/JUN/74	Purchased
19000	N68657	Boeing	385C	13/SEP/65		
	CC-CEB	LAN Chile			20/DEC/69	
19001	EI-ANV	Aer Lingus	348C	15/APR/66	21/APR/66	
	EI-ANV	Trek Airways				Leased
	EI-ANV	Aer Lingus				
	9G-ACR	Clipper International			11/DEC/80	Leased
	EI-ANV	Aer Lingus			30/MAY/81	
	5A-DIY	United African Airlines			JUN/81	
	5A-DIY	Air Rwanda			81	Leased
	5A-DIY	United African Airlines			81	
	5A-DIY	Jamahiriyan Air Transport			DEC/82	
19004	4X-ATR	El Al	358B	10/DEC/66	07/JAN/66	
	N317F	Flying Tiger Line			07/JAN/66	
	4X-ATR	El Al			03/OCT/66	
	4X-ATR	Sun d'Or			AUG/81	Leased
	4X-ATR	El Al			01/MAY/82	
19034	N364US	Northwest Orient	351C	04/JAN/66	08/JAN/66	
	VR-HGU	Cathay Pacific			13/NOV/73	
	RP-C1886	Aero Filipinas			12/NOV/82	
	RP-C1886	Nepal Government			DEC/83	Leased
	RP-C1886	Aero Filipinas			JAN/84	
	RP-C1886	Samoa Air			AUG/84	Leased
	RP-C1886	Aero Filipinas			OCT/85	
	RP-C1886	Jet Trans USA			OCT/85	
	RP-C1886	Boeing			DEC/85	WFU DEC/85 for KC-135E Parts
19104	N7095	Braniff	327C	14/MAY/66	26/MAY/66	
	N7095	TMA			14/APR/71	Leased
	N7095	TMA			29/MAR/73	Purchased
	OD-AGX	TMA			80	WFU 85, stored Sharjah
19105	N7096	Braniff	327C	20/MAY/66	28/MAY/66	
	N7096	TMA			04/MAR/71	Leased
	N7096	TMA			29/JUN/73	Purchased
	OD-AGY	TMA			80	WFU 85, stored Sharjah
19108	N7099	Braniff	327C	16/JUL/66	27/JUL/66	
	N7099	Qantas			01/JAN/71	Leased
	N7099	Braniff			16/OCT/71	
	OD-AFY	TMA			OCT/72	WFU 85, stored Sharjah
19133	ZS-EKV	South African Airways	344B	15/DEC/66	09/JAN/67	
	ZS-SAE	South African Airways			68	
	LX-LGU	Luxair			20/JUL/77	
	3B-NAF	Air Mauritius			27/APR/83	
19162	OO-SJJ	Sabena	329C	10/MAR/66	24/MAR/66	
	9Q-CVG	Katale Aero Transport			22/JUL/83	
19163	N365US	Northwest Orient	351C	07/MAY/66	17/MAY/66	
	SX-DBP	Olympic Airways			18/MAY/73	
19164	N366US	Northwest Orient	351C	18/JUN/66	24/JUN/66	
	SX-DBO	Olympic Airways			23/MAY/73	
19168	N367US	Northwest Orient	351C	01/JUL/66	12/JUL/66	
	S2-ABN	Bangladesh Biman			30/DEC/73	

BOEING 707 (EXISTING AIRCRAFT ONLY)

C/N	Registration	Owner/Operator	Series	First Flight	Delivery	Remarks
19177	N17325	Continental Airlines	324C	22/JUL/66	29/JUL/66	
	PP-VLN	Varig			07/APR/73	
19179	N372WA	World Airways	373C	25/MAY/66	27/MAY/66	
	CS-TBJ	TAP Air Portugal			10/APR/74	
	CS-TBJ	IAS Cargo			23/JAN/79	Leased
	CS-TBJ	TAP Air Portugal			MAR/79	
19185	N7554A	American Airlines	123B	20/APR/66	30/APR/66	
	N7554A	American Transair			20/MAR/81	
	N7554A	Boeing			31/DEC/84	WFU 31/DEC/84 for KC-135E Parts
19186	N7570A	American Airlines	123B	24/APR/66	04/MAY/66	
	N7570A	American Transair			01/MAY/81	
	N7570A	Boeing			31/DEC/84	WFU 31/DEC/84 for KC-135E Parts
19187	N7571A	American Airlines	123B	02/MAY/66	12/MAY/66	WFU NOV/80 to 28/SEP/81
	N7571A	Boeing			28/SEP/81	WFU 28/SEP/81 for KC-135
19188	N7572A	American Airlines	123B	23/JUN/66	30/JUN/66	WFU NOV/80 to 28/FEB/83
	N7572A	Boeing			28/FEB/83	WFU 28/FEB/83 for KC-135E Parts
19209	N368US	Northwest Orient	351C	12/JUL/66	20/JUL/66	
	9Y-TED	BWIA			16/FEB/74	
	N29796	Lonnie Edwards (FTC) Corp			27/FEB/82	
	N29796	World Air Transport			82	
	N29796	Jet Charter Service			03/MAY/82	Leased
	N29796	InterAm			AUG/82	
	N29796	Guy America			NOV/82	
	N29796	Aeronaves Del Puerto Rico			10/DEC/82	
	N29796	Buffalo Airways			APR/83	
	N144SP	South Pacific Airways			APR/83	
	N144SP	Bank of Hawaii			SEP/85	
	N144SP	Comtran			FEB/86	
19210	N369US	Northwest Orient	351C	05/AUG/66	12/AUG/66	
	YU-AGI	JAT			09/APR/74	WFU OCT/82
	YU-AGI	Midair			AUG/85	
19212	N5771T	Trans World Airlines	331C	29/MAY/67	18/JUN/67	
	EI-BER	Guinness Peat			12/MAY/78	
	EI-BER	Aer Lingus			16/MAY/78	Leased
	EI-BER	Guinness Peat			06/OCT/78	
	LX-FCV	Cargolux			06/OCT/78	Leased
	LX-FCV	Aero Uruguay			06/OCT/78	Sub-leased
	CX-BJV	Aero Uruguay			07/MAR/79	Sub-leased
	CX-BJV	Cargolux			31/MAR/81	Leased
	CX-BJV	Cargolux			31/MAR/81	Purchased
	LX-BJV	Greenline Aviation			31/MAR/81	
	5A-DKA	Libyan Equestrian Federation			DEC/81	Leased
	5A-DKA	Greenline Aviation			JUL/82	
	9G-ACY	West Coast Airlines			13/JUL/82	
	9G-MAN	Transcorp			DEC/85	Leased
19214	N5773T	Trans World Airlines	331C	16/SEP/67	27/SEP/67	
	N5773T	Golden Sun Air Cargo			15/DEC/71	Leased
	N5773T	Trans World Airlines			26/MAR/72	
	OD-AGS	TMA			01/MAR/78	WFU 85, stored Beirut
19215	N6724	Trans World Airlines	131B	06/NOV/66	23/NOV/66	
	N6724	Boeing			01/FEB/83	WFU 01/FEB/83 for KC-135E Parts
19216	N6726	Trans World Airlines	131B	17/FEB/67	08/MAR/67	
	N6726	Boeing			19/MAY/82	WFU 19/MAY/82 for KC-135E Parts
19217	N6727	Trans World Airlines	131B	15/MAR/67	02/APR/67	
	N6727	Boeing			13/SEP/82	WFU 13/SEP/82 for KC-135E Parts
19218	N6728	Trans World Airlines	131B	20/MAR/67	02/APR/67	
	N6728	Boeing			13/SEP/82	WFU 13/SEP/82 for KC-135E Parts
19219	N6729	Trans World Airlines	131B	01/APR/67	14/APR/67	WFU 02/APR/80 to 28/APR/82
	N6729	Boeing			28/APR/82	WFU 28/APR/82 for KC-135E Parts
19220	N6763T	Trans World Airlines	131B	14/APR/67	22/APR/67	
	N6763T	Boeing			23/APR/82	WFU 23/APR/82 for KC-135E Parts
19221	N6764T	Trans World Airlines	131B	25/APR/67	13/MAY/67	
	N6764T	Boeing			07/JUL/82	WFU 07/JUL/82 for KC-135E Parts
19222	N6771T	Trans World Airlines	131B	13/MAY/67	27/MAY/67	
	N6771T	Boeing			12/AUG/82	WFU 12/AUG/82 for KC-135E Parts
19223	N6789T	Trans World Airlines	131B	27/JUN/67	13/JUL/67	
	N6789T	Boeing			12/MAY/82	WFU 12/MAY/82 for KC-135E Parts
19224	N18710	Trans World Airlines	331B	07/MAR/67	15/MAR/67	WFU OCT/83 to 05/APR/84
	N18710	Boeing			05/APR/84	WFU 05/APR/84 for KC-135E Parts
19225	N18711	Trans World Airlines	331B	23/MAR/67	05/APR/67	WFU 20/OCT/81 to 05/JUN/84
	N18711	Boeing			05/JUN/84	WFU 05/JUN/84 for KC-135E Parts
19226	N18712	Trans World Airlines	331B	18/MAY/67	31/MAY/67	
	N18712	Air Trans			20/NOV/81	Leased
	N18712	Egyptair			81	Sub-leased
	N18712	Air Trans			JUN/82	Leased
	N18712	Air Sinai			JUN/82	Sub-leased
	N18712	Air Trans			29/DEC/82	Purchased
	N18712	Air Sinai			29/DEC/82	Leased
	N18712	Air Trans			10/JAN/83	
	N18712	Maof Airlines			15/JUN/83	Leased
	N18712	Air Trans			APR/84	
	N18712	Boeing			30/APR/84	WFU 30/APR/84 for KC-135E Parts
19227	N18713	Trans World Airlines	331B	23/JUL/67	05/AUG/67	WFU 08/OCT/81
	N18713	Boeing			06/APR/84	WFU 06/APR/84 for KC-135E Parts
19236	N7563A	American Airlines	323C	08/SEP/66	28/SEP/66	WFU 81 to 29/APR/82
	81-0897	USAF	C-18A		29/APR/82	WFU 29/APR/82 for spares
19237	N7564A	American Airlines	323C	19/SEP/66	30/SEP/66	WFU AUG/81 to 07/JUN/85
	N7564A	Boeing			07/JUN/85	WFU 07/JUN/85 for KC-135E Parts
19238	LV-ISA	Aerolineas Argentinas	387B	04/NOV/66	23/NOV/66	
	LV-ISA	Argentine Air Force			18/JAN/83	
	T-96	Argentine Air Force			01/MAR/84	
19239	LV-ISB	Aerolineas Argentinas	387B	05/DEC/66	16/DEC/66	
	CX-BNU	Pluna			FEB/81	Leased
19240	LV-ISC	Aerolineas Argentinas	387B	19/DEC/66	22/DEC/66	WFU 83 to NOV/85
	CX-BOH	Pluna			NOV/85	Leased
19241	LV-ISD	Aerolineas Argentinas	387B	08/FEB/67	24/FEB/67	
	LV-ISD	Argentine Air Force			18/JAN/83	
	T-95	Argentine Air Force			01/MAR/84	
19247	VT-DVA	Air India	337B	27/AUG/66	12/OCT/66	
19248	VT-DVB	Air India	337C	20/JAN/67	12/FEB/67	
19263	N370US	Northwest Orient	351C	11/AUG/66	19/AUG/66	
	VR-HHK	Cathay Pacific				Not taken-up
	9J-AEB	Zambia Airways			01/JUL/75	
	EI-ASM	Aer Lingus			05/JUL/75	Leased
	9J-AEB	Zambia Airways			24/FEB/76	

C/N	Registration	Owner/Operator	Series	First Flight	Delivery	Remarks
19264	N419PA	Pan American	321B	16/OCT/66	06/NOV/66	
	N419PA	ATASCO			28/DEC/79	
	ZP-CCG	LAP			JUL/80	
19265	N420PA	Pan American	321B	27/OCT/66	09/NOV/66	
	N420PA	Israel Aircraft Industries			30/SEP/76	
	HC-BCT	Ecuatoriana			20/OCT/76	
19266	N421PA	Pan American	321B	11/NOV/66	29/NOV/66	
	N421PA	ATASCO			DEC/77	
	HK-2070	Avianca			DEC/77	Leased
	HK-2070	ATASCO			NOV/79	
	HK-2070	ITEL			NOV/79	
	HK-2070	Avianca			NOV/79	Leased
	HK-2070	ITEL			DEC/80	
	HK-2070	GATX Leasing			DEC/80	
	HK-2070	Avianca			DEC/80	Leased
	HK-2070	Avianca			NOV/84	Purchased
	HK-2070	ATASCO			NOV/84	
	9Q-CBL	Scibe Airlift			OCT/85	
19267	N445PA	Pan American	321C	04/DEC/66	15/DEC/66	
	EP-IRK	Iran Air			13/MAR/75	
19269	N447PA	Pan American	321C	10/APR/67	30/APR/67	
	OD-AGO	TMA			28/JUN/77	WFU 85, stored Beirut
19270	N448PA	Pan American	321C	25/APR/67	08/MAY/67	
	N448PA	ATASCO			SEP/77	
	N448PA	Maverick			OCT/77	
	N448M	Maverick				
	N448M	Pan American			FEB/79	
	N448M	British Midland Airways			FEB/79	
	N448M	PIA			79	Leased
	N448M	British Midland Airways			79	
	N448M	Air North			79	Leased
	N448M	Zaire Aero Services			01/AUG/79	Sub-leased
	G-BGIR	British Midland Airways				Reg. not taken-up
	N448M	British Midland Airways			79	
	N448M	Gulf Air			01/APR/80	Leased
	N448M	British Midland Airways			31/DEC/80	
	TF-VLL	Eagle Air			06/JUL/81	Leased
	TF-VLL	Libyan Arab Airlines			06/JUL/81	Sub-leased
	G-BMAZ	British Midland Airways			21/MAY/82	
	G-BMAZ	Tradewinds			OCT/82	Leased
	G-BMAZ	British Midland Airways			31/DEC/82	WFU 03/NOV/84 to NOV/85
	N863BX	Burlington Northern			NOV/85	Op. by Southern Air Transport
19271	N449PA	Pan American	321C	04/MAY/67	15/MAY/67	
	N449WA	ATASCO			18/JUN/77	
	G-BEVN	Dan Air			06/JUL/77	Leased
	G-BEVN	ATASCO			78	
	G-BEVN	Pelican Cargo			SEP/78	Leased
	G-BEVN	ATASCO			SEP/78	
	G-BEVN	Pelican Cargo			JAN/79	
	N707HT	International Air Leases			11/SEP/81	
	N707HT	Jet Charter Service			08/OCT/81	
	N707HT	International Air Leases			FEB/82	
	N707HT	Arrow Air			18/FEB/82	
	N707HT	International Air Leases			MAY/82	
	N707HT	Turk Hava Yollari			MAY/82	Leased
19272	N450PA	Pan American	321C	13/MAY/67	23/MAY/67	
	YR-ABM	Tarom			18/SEP/75	
19273	N451PA	Pan American	321C	19/MAY/67	31/MAY/67	
	N451PA	ATASCO			29/DEC/76	
	N451PA	Iran Air			31/JUL/77	
	N451RN	Iran Air			77	
	N451RN	ATASCO			MAR/79	
	HC-BGP	Ecuatoriana			MAY/79	
19274	N452PA	Pan American	321C	14/JUN/67	22/JUN/67	
	OD-AGP	TMA			28/JUN/77	WFU 85, stored Sharjah
19276	N423PA	Pan American	321B	22/JUN/67	30/JUN/67	
	HK-2016	Avianca			25/FEB/77	
19277	N424PA	Pan American	321B	18/JUL/67	27/JUL/67	
	N424PA	Merpati Nusantara			NOV/75	Leased
	N424PA	Pan American			JAN/76	
	N424PA	ATASCO			28/MAR/78	
	HC-BFC	Ecuatoriana			28/MAR/78	
19285	AP-AUO	PIA	340C	30/SEP/67	22/OCT/66	
	AP-AUO	Middle East Airlines			01/APR/69	Leased
	AP-AUO	PIA			30/SEP/69	
	YU-AGG	JAT			08/DEC/72	
	YU-AGG	Air Mali				Leased
	YU-AGG	JAT			80	
	YU-AGG	Midair			15/APR/85	
	YU-AGG	Eagle Air			15/APR/85	Leased
19286	AP-AUP	PIA	340C	14/SEP/67	21/SEP/67	
	AP-AUP	Air Algerie			22/FEB/67	Leased
	AP-AUP	PIA			03/MAY/67	
	YU-AGF	JAT			20/JUN/72	Leased
	AP-AUP	PIA			DEC/72	
	AP-AXA	PIA				
19291	F-BLCE	Air France	328B	21/FEB/67	07/MAR/67	
	TU-TXL	Air Afrique			13/FEB/68	Leased
	TU-TXL	Air France			22/FEB/68	
	TU-TXN	Air Afrique			11/MAR/68	Leased
	F-BLCE	Air France			22/MAR/68	
	3X-GCC	Air Guinee			AUG/81	
	3X-GCC	Progress Aviation			SEP/82	
	OO-TYC	Trans European Airways			JUN/84	
19292	F-BLCF	Air France	328C	25/FEB/67	15/MAR/67	
	9XR-JA	Air Rwanda			20/JUL/79	Op. by Zimex Aviation
19293	VH-EBT	Qantas	338C	29/DEC/67	28/JAN/67	
	G-BFLE	ITEL			17/MAY/78	
	G-BFLE	British Midland Airways			17/MAY/78	
	G-BFLE	Kuwait Airways			MAY/78	Leased
	G-BFLE	British Midland Airways				
	G-BFLE	PIA			JUL/78	Leased
	G-BFLE	British Midland Airways			01/APR/79	
	G-BFLE	Air Algerie			79	Leased
	G-BFLE	British Midland Airways			79	

C/N	Registration	Owner/Operator	Series	First Flight	Delivery	Remarks
	G-BFLE	Gulf Air			NOV/79	Leased
	G-BFLE	British Midland Airways			MAR/80	
	G-BFLE	DETA			14/APR/80	Leased
	G-BFLE	LAM			MAY/80	Sub-leased
	G-BFLE	British Midland Airways			29/MAR/81	
	G-BFLE	Ariana			14/APR/81	Leased
	G-BFLE	British Midland Airways			26/MAY/81	
	G-BFLE	Somali Airlines			26/JUL/81	Leased
	G-BFLE	British Midland Airways			26/SEP/81	
	N861BX	Burlington Northern			NOV/85	Op. by Southern Air Transport
19294	VH-EBU	Qantas	338C	13/FEB/67	08/MAR/67	
	P2-ANH	Air Niugini			26/NOV/76	
	P2-ANH	ITEL			OCT/79	
	P2-ANH	Air Niugini			OCT/79	Leased
	P2-ANH	ITEL			MAR/81	
	P2-ANH	GATX Leasing			09/MAR/81	
	N707MB	International Air Leases			81	
	N707MB	AMCO			28/SEP/81	Leased
	9Q-CDA	Zaire Cargo			28/SEP/81	Sub-leased
	N707HW	International Air Leases			MAY/82	
	N707HW	Arrow Airways			MAY/82	
	N707HW	International Air Leases			83	
	OB-T-1264	TAISA 'Train Cargo'			JAN/83	Leased
	N707HW	International Air Leases			FEB/85	
	B-2426	Shanghai Airlines			15/JUL/85	
19295	VH-EBV	Qantas	338C	31/AUG/67	06/SEP/67	
	9J-AEL	Zambia Airways			20/MAY/77	
19296	VH-EBW	Qantas	338C	27/SEP/67	10/OCT/67	
	G-BDEA	British Caledonian			30/MAY/75	
	G-BDEA	Anglo Cargo			29/DEC/83	
19297	VH-EBX	Qantas	338C	12/OCT/67	23/OCT/67	
	G-BCAL	British Caledonian			13/MAY/75	
	G-BCAL	Skyways Air International			14/DEC/79	
	G-BCAL	International Air Leases			DEC/79	
	LV-MZE	TAR			DEC/79	
19315	D-ABUL	Lufthansa	330B	31/DEC/66	20/JAN/67	
	D-ABUL	Condor			MAY/84	
19316	D-ABUM	Lufthansa	330B	20/JAN/67	30/JAN/67	
	D-ABUM	Condor			MAY/84	
	60-SBT	Somali Airlines			10/MAY/85	
19317	D-ABUI	Lufthansa	330C	21/FEB/67	06/MAR/67	
	D-ABUI	German Cargo Services			AUG/79	
	PT-TCM	Transbrasil			FEB/85	
19321	PP-VJS	Varig	341C	14/NOV/66	28/DEC/66	
	PP-VJS	Transbrasil			20/SEP/82	Leased
	PP-VJS	Varig			15/NOV/84	
19323	N7573A	American Airlines	123B	23/OCT/66	11/NOV/66	WFU OCT/80 to APR/82
	N7573A	American Transair			06/APR/82	
	N7573A	Boeing			31/DEC/84	WFU 31/DEC/84 for KC-135E Parts
19324	N7574A	American Airlines	123B	01/DEC/66	16/DEC/66	WFU 28/AUG/81 to 30/MAR/83
	N7574A	Boeing			30/MAR/83	WFU 30/MAR/83 for KC-135E Parts
19325	N7575A	American Airlines	123B	17/DEC/66	05/JAN/67	WFU NOV/80 to 28/SEP/81
	N7575A	Boeing			28/SEP/81	WFU 28/SEP/81 for KC-135E Parts
19326	N7576A	American Airlines	123B	12/JAN/67	24/JAN/67	WFU OCT/80 to 22/SEP/81
	N7576A	Boeing			22/SEP/81	WFU 22/SEP/81 for KC-135E Parts
19327	N7577A	American Airlines	123B	09/MAR/67	04/APR/67	
	N7577A	Boeing			SEP/81	WFU SEP/81 for KC-135E Parts
19328	N7578A	American Airlines	123B	15/MAR/67	23/MAR/67	WFU NOV/80 to 23/SEP/81
	N7578A	Boeing			23/SEP/81	WFU 23/SEP/81 for KC-135E Parts
19329	N7579A	American Airlines	123B	05/APR/67	14/APR/67	WFU 81 to 29/SEP/82
	N7579A	Boeing			29/SEP/82	WFU 29/SEP/82 for KC-135E Parts
19330	N7580A	American Airlines	123B	21/APR/67	28/APR/67	
	N7580A	Boeing			SEP/81	WFU SEP/81 for KC-135E Parts
19331	N7581A	American Airlines	123B	01/MAY/67	08/MAY/67	
	N7581A	Boeing			24/SEP/81	WFU 24/SEP/81 for KC-135E Parts
19332	N7582A	American Airlines	123B	19/MAY/67	26/MAY/67	WFU OCT/80 to 24/SEP/82
	N7582A	Boeing			24/SEP/82	WFU 24/SEP/82 for KC-135E Parts
19333	N7583A	American Airlines	123B	27/MAY/67	06/JUN/67	
	N7583A	Guy-America			15/MAY/81	
	N7583A	Boeing			08/APR/83	WFU 08/APR/83 for KC-135E Parts
19334	N7584A	American Airlines	123B	03/JUN/67	16/JUN/67	
	N7584A	Boeing			28/SEP/82	WFU 28/SEP/82 for KC-135E Parts
19335	N7585A	American Airlines	123B	10/JUN/67	20/JUN/67	
	N7585A	Ports of Call			81	
	N703PC	Ports of Call			02/APR/81	
	N703PC	Skyworld Airlines			SEP/85	
19336	N7586A	American Airlines	123B	15/JUN/67	27/JUN/67	WFU 81
	N7586A	Guy America			13/JAN/83	
	N7586A	Boeing			29/APR/83	WFU 29/APR/83 for KC-135E Parts
19337	N7587A	American Airlines	123B	30/JUN/67	07/JUL/67	WFU NOV/80 to SEP/81
	N7587A	Boeing			SEP/81	WFU SEP/81 for KC-135E Parts
19338	N7588A	American Airlines	123B	06/JUL/67	14/JUL/67	WFU NOV/80
	N7588A	Guy America			13/JAN/83	
	N7588A	Boeing			29/APR/83	WFU 29/APR/83 for KC-135E Parts
19339	N7589A	American Airlines	123B	12/JUL/67	20/JUL/67	WFU NOV/80 to 10/DEC/81
	N7589A	American Trans Air			10/DEC/81	
	N7589A	Boeing			31/DEC/85	WFU 31/DEC/85 for KC-135E Parts
19340	N7590A	American Airlines	123B	31/AUG/67	15/SEP/67	
	N7590A	Boeing			28/SEP/81	WFU 28/SEP/81 for KC-135E Parts
19341	N7591A	American Airlines	123B	21/FEB/68	02/MAR/68	
	N7591A	Boeing			29/SEP/82	WFU 29/SEP/82 for KC-135E Parts
19342	N7592A	Chase Manhattan Bank	123B	12/FEB/69	02/MAR/69	
	N7592A	American Airlines			02/MAR/69	Leased
	N7592A	American Airlines			07/MAR/79	Purchased, WFU NOV/80
	N7592A	Boeing			25/SEP/81	WFU 25/SEP/81 for KC-135E Parts
19343	N7593A	Chase Manhattan Bank	123B	07/MAR/69	11/MAR/69	
	N7593A	American Airlines			11/MAR/69	Leased
	N7593A	American Airlines			27/MAR/79	Purchased, WFU 81
	N7593A	Boeing			28/SEP/82	WFU 28/SEP/82 for KC-135E Parts
19344	N7594A	Chase Manhattan Bank	123B	14/APR/69	22/APR/69	
	N7594A	American Airlines			22/APR/69	Leased
	N7594A	American Airlines			20/APR/79	Purchased, WFU OCT/80
	N7594A	Boeing			25/SEP/82	WFU 25/SEP/82 for KC-135E Parts
19350	N17327	Continental Airlines	324C	19/NOV/66	02/DEC/66	
	PP-VLO	Varig			07/APR/73	

C/N	Registration	Owner/Operator	Series	First Flight	Delivery	Remarks
19351	N17328	Continental Airlines	324C	26/JAN/67	01/FEB/67	
	9V-BEW	Malaysian Singapore Airlines			01/JUL/72	
	9V-BEW	Singapore Airlines			OCT/72	
	TF-VLJ	Eagle Air			31/JAN/81	
	TF-VLJ	Transafrica			JAN/81	Leased
	TF-VLJ	Eagle Air			81	
	TF-VLJ	Libyan Arab Airlines			MAR/81	Leased
	TF-VLJ	Eagle Air			81	
	TF-VLJ	Boeing			03/JUN/86	Joint Stars - 3
19352	N17329	Continental Airlines	324C	19/APR/67	21/APR/67	
	9V-BEX	Malaysian Singapore Airlines			04/AUG/72	
	9V-BEX	Singapore Airlines			OCT/72	WFU 81
	N707JJ	International Air Leases			29/APR/82	
	N707JJ	Arrow Air			27/APR/82	
	N707JJ	International Air Leases			SEP/84	
	B-2423	Shanghai Airlines			12/AUG/85	
19353	N47330	Continental Airlines	324C	21/MAY/67	27/MAY/67	
	9V-BEY	Singapore Airlines			05/OCT/72	WFU 81
	N707SH	International Air Leases			22/NOV/81	
	N707SH	Arrow Air			DEC/82	
	N707SH	International Air Leases			JUN/84	
	N707SH	Jet America			JUN/84	Leased
	N707SH	International Air Leases			DEC/84	
	B-2422	Shanghai Airlines			20/MAY/85	
19354	N324F	Flying Tiger Line	349C	09/JUN/66	21/JUN/66	
	N324F	El Al			01/APR/68	Leased
	N324F	Flying Tiger Line			68	
	EI-ASO	Aer Lingus			02/APR/69	
	VH-EBZ	Qantas			15/SEP/70	Leased
	EI-ASO	Aer Lingus			30/SEP/71	
	G-BAWP	British Caledonian			25/APR/73	Leased
	EI-ASO	Aer Lingus			15/MAY/75	
	9J-AEC	Zambia Airways			05/JUL/75	Leased
	EI-ASO	Aer Lingus			23/FEB/76	
	9J-AEC	Zambia Airways			18/OCT/76	Leased
	EI-ASO	Aer Lingus			23/JAN/77	
	S2-ACG	Bangladesh Biman			80	Leased
	EI-ASO	Aer Lingus			21/NOV/80	
	EI-ASO	Libyan Arab Airlines			01/MAR/81	Leased
	EI-ASO	Aer Lingus			31/MAR/81	
	EI-ASO	Libyan Arab Airlines			81	Leased
	EI-ASO	Aer Lingus			31/OCT/82	
	EI-ASO	Arkia			DEC/84	Leased
	EI-ASO	Aer Lingus			FEB/85	
19355	N325F	Flying Tiger Line	349C	02/FEB/67	06/FEB/67	
	N325F	El Al			AUG/68	Leased
	N325F	Flying Tiger Line			68	
	G-AWWD	Caledonian Airways			08/JAN/69	Leased
	N325F	Flying Tiger Line			DEC/69	
	G-AWWD	British Caledonian			29/APR/71	
	D2-TAD	TAAG Angola			02/DEC/77	
	D2-TOJ	TAAG Angola			NOV/80	
19361	N426PA	Pan American	321B	26/AUG/67	21/SEP/67	
	HK-2015	Avianca			FEB/77	
19366	N435PA	Pan American	321B	02/OCT/67	13/OCT/67	
	N435PA	Merpati Nusantara			OCT/75	Leased
	N435PA	Pan American			08/DEC/75	
	N435PA	ATASCO			17/APR/78	
	HL7435	Korean Airlines			24/JUN/78	
19367	N457PA	Pan American	321C	18/OCT/67	27/OCT/67	
	N457PA	ATASCO			28/JUN/78	
	G-BPAT	Pelican Cargo			29/JUN/78	
	9J-AEQ	Zambia Airways			JUN/79	
19369	N459PA	Pan American	321C	14/NOV/67	27/NOV/67	
	N459PA	ATASCO			03/AUG/77	
	HL7431	Korean Airlines			07/SEP/77	
19370	N460PA	Pan American	321C	17/NOV/67	30/NOV/67	
	N460PA	ATASCO			19/SEP/75	
	F-BYCN	Air France			19/SEP/75	
	N720GS	Pan Aviation			JUL/83	
19372	N462PA	Pan American	321C	02/DEC/67	12/DEC/67	
	N462PA	ATASCO			28/DEC/76	
	HL7427	Korean Airlines			11/FEB/77	
19373	N463PA	Pan American	321C	04/DEC/67	11/DEC/67	
	N463PA	ATASCO			16/OCT/75	
	F-BYCO	Air France			16/OCT/75	
	N722GS	Pan Aviation			13/AUG/83	
19374	N453PA	Pan American	321B	12/DEC/67	20/DEC/67	
	N453PA	Air Vietnam			70	Leased
	N453PA	Pan American			71	
	N453PA	ATASCO			08/MAY/79	
	CC-CEK	LAN Chile			08/MAY/79	
19375	N473PA	Pan American	321C	28/DEC/67	09/JAN/68	
	N473PA	Ron Air			23/OCT/78	
	N473PA	Iran Air			23/OCT/78	Leased
	N473RN	Ron Air			JUN/79	
	N473RN	Transcargo			18/FEB/80	Leased
	N473RN	Ronair			APR/80	
	N473RN	ATASCO			80	
	HK-2473	Avianca			MAY/80	Leased
	HK-2473	ATASCO			FEB/82	
	OB-R-1243	Faucett			26/FEB/82	Leased
	OB-R-1243	ATASCO			DEC/83	
	N864BX	Burlington Northern			NOV/85	Op. by Southern Air Transport
19377	N474PA	Pan American	321B	11/JAN/68	17/JAN/68	
	N474PA	ATASCO			18/NOV/75	
	F-BYCP	Air France			03/APR/76	
	EL-AIY	Liberia World Airways			OCT/81	Not delivered
	F-BYCP	Pan Aviation			11/DEC/81	
	EL-AJA	Liberia World Airways			DEC/81	Leased
	EL-AJA	Pan Aviation			DEC/82	
	EL-AJA	Intercontinental Airlines			OCT/83	Leased
	N721GS	Pan Aviation			APR/85	
19378	N455PA	Pan American	321B	26/JAN/68	06/FEB/68	
	N455PA	Air Afrique			MAR/78	Leased

BOEING 707 (EXISTING AIRCRAFT ONLY)

C/N	Registration	Owner/Operator	Series	First Flight	Delivery	Remarks
	N455PA	Pan American				
	N455PA	ATASCO			JAN/79	
	OO-PSI	Comp.Europeene de Recherches			19/JAN/79	
	OO-PSI	Sobelair			MAR/79	Leased
	OO-PSI	Comp.Europeene de Recherches			01/FEB/81	
	5A-DJM	United African Airlines			SEP/81	
	5A-DJM	Libyan Arab Airlines			MAY/82	Leased
	5A-DJM	Libyan Arab Airlines			JAN/83	Purchased
19379	N475PA	Pan American	321C	08/FEB/68	21/FEB/68	
	N475PA	ATASCO			23/DEC/76	
	YR-ABN	Tarom			24/DEC/76	
19380	N7565A	American Airlines	323C	04/OCT/67	12/OCT/67	WFU APR/81 to APR/82
	81-0898	USAF	C-18A		APR/82	
19381	N7566A	American Airlines	323C	31/JUL/67	10/AUG/68	WFU APR/81 to MAY/82
	81-0895	USAF	C-18A		MAY/82	
19382	N7567A	American Airlines	323C	19/SEP/67	02/OCT/67	WFU 81 to FEB/82
	81-0892	USAF	C-18A		FEB/82	
19383	N7568A	American Airlines	323C	24/OCT/67	02/NOV/67	
	N7568A	Boeing			06/JUN/84	WFU 06/JUN/84 for KC-135E Parts
19384	N7569A	American Airlines	323C	09/NOV/67	21/NOV/67	WFU 81 to APR/82
	81-0893	USAF	C-18A		APR/82	
19411	N371US	Northwest Orient	351C	23/NOV/66	06/DEC/66	
	YU-AGJ	JAT			17/APR/74	
	YU-AGJ	Air Mali			80	Leased
	YU-AGJ	JAT			80	
	YU-AGJ	Midair			AUG/85	
19412	N372US	Northwest Orient	351C	07/MAR/67	18/MAR/67	
	VR-HHL	Cathay Pacific				Not taken-up
	9Y-TEE	BWIA			21/JUL/74	
	8P-CAC	Caribbean Air Cargo			FEB/81	
19415	G-AVKA	Caledonian Airways	399C	01/JUL/67	13/JUL/67	
	N319F	Flying Tiger Line			13/JUL/67	Leased
	G-AVKA	Caledonian Airways			29/MAY/68	
	CS-TBH	TAP Air Portugal			07/MAY/73	
	N106BV	Buffalo Airways			30/NOV/83	Op. for Burlington Northern
19416	G-ATZC	British Eagle	365C			Not taken-up
	G-ATZC	Caledonian Airways		19/FEB/67	14/APR/67	
	N737AL	Airlift International			14/APR/67	Leased
	G-ATZC	Caledonian Airways			02/JUN/68	
	PH-TRW	Transavia			02/APR/70	Leased
	G-ATZC	Caledonian Airways			26/JUN/70	
	G-ATZC	Bangladesh Biman			NOV/75	Leased
	G-ATZC	British Caledonian			DEC/75	
	C-GFLG	Worldways Canada			30/NOV/81	
	C-GFLG	Boeing			04/FEB/86	
	PT-TCP	Transbrasil			04/FEB/86	Leased
19417	N525EJ	Executive Jet Aviation	355C	11/MAY/67	19/MAY/67	
	N525EJ	Airlift International			19/MAY/67	Leased
	N525EJ	Executive Jet Aviation			30/JUN/68	
	N525EJ	Air Bahama			20/JUL/68	Leased
	N525EJ	Executive Jet Aviation			OCT/69	
	G-AYEX	Caledonian Airways			01/JUN/70	Leased
	G-AYEX	Executive Jet Aviation			SEP/71	
	G-AYEX	Britannia Airways			01/OCT/71	Leased
	G-AYEX	Executive Jet Aviation			MAR/73	
	G-AYEX	British Caledonian			16/MAR/73	Leased
	N525EJ	Aviation Consultants			18/JAN/85	
	N525EJ	St. Lucia Airways			18/JAN/85	Leased
19433	N8400	American Flyers Airline	385C			Not taken-up
	N8400	American Airlines		20/NOV/66	06/DEC/66	
	N8400	World American Airlift			MAY/69	Leased
	N8400	American Airlines			OCT/70	
	PP-VLI	Varig			01/SEP/71	
19434	N373US	Northwest Orient	351C	16/MAR/67	20/MAR/67	
	C-GTAI	Transair			15/OCT/74	
	C-GTAI	Pacific Western			74	
	S2-ACA	Bangladesh Biman			FEB/77	
19435	N5774T	Trans World Airlines	331C	26/SEP/67	12/OCT/67	
	CC-CAF	Fast Air Carrier			15/NOV/78	
19436	N6790T	Trans World Airlines	131B	18/JUL/67	01/AUG/67	
	N6790T	Boeing			12/MAY/82	WFU 12/MAY/82 for KC-135E Parts
19442	N370WA	World Airways	373C	27/JUL/67	03/AUG/67	
	N370WA	Korean Airlines			15/APR/71	Leased
	N370WA	World Airways			AUG/77	
	N370WA	British Midland Airways			15/AUG/77	Leased
	N370WA	Kuwait Airways			15/AUG/77	Sub-leased
	N370WA	British Midland Airways				Leased
	N370WA	Air Algerie			JUL/78	Sub-leased
	N370WA	British Midland Airways				
	N370WA	World Airways			JAN/79	
	OO-SBU	Sobelair			JAN/79	
	OO-SBU	Ontario Worldair			JAN/80	Leased
	OO-SBU	Sobelair			80	
	OO-SBU	Air Tanzania			NOV/80	Leased
	OO-SBU	Sobelair			80	
19443	N374US	Northwest Orient	351C	02/AUG/67	12/AUG/67	
	CC-CCK	LAN Chile			20/NOV/74	
	902	Chilean Air Force			11/NOV/82	
19498	G-ATWV	BOAC	336C	08/NOV/67	30/NOV/67	
	G-ATWV	British Airways			01/APR/72	
	9G-ACX	Greyhound Guarantee Ltd			22/JAN/82	
	9G-ACX	Clipper International			22/JAN/82	Leased
	9G-ACX	West Africa Aircargo			82	
	9G-ACX	Clipper International			APR/86	
	9G-ACX	Aviation Consultants			APR/86	
	N14AZ	St. Lucia Airways			MAY/86	
19502	4X-ATS	El Al	358B	23/JAN/67	02/FEB/67	
19515	N7595A	American Airlines	323C	03/AUG/67	15/AUG/67	WFU 81 to 24/NOV/82
	OD-AHD	Middle East Airlines			24/NOV/82	
19516	N7596A	American Airlines	323C	11/AUG/67	23/AUG/67	WFU 81 to 07/DEC/82
	OD-AHE	Middle East Airlines			07/DEC/82	
19517	N7597A	American Airlines	323C	14/AUG/67	28/AUG/67	WFU 01/SEP/81
	N7597A	American Transair			24/SEP/82	
	N7597A	Boeing			DEC/84	
	PT-TCL	Transbrasil			13/FEB/85	Leased

C/N	Registration	Owner/Operator	Series	First Flight	Delivery	Remarks
19518	N7598A	American Airlines	323C	18/AUG/67	31/AUG/67	WFU 81
	81-0891	USAF	EC-18B		FEB/82	
19519	N7599A	American Airlines	323C	27/AUG/67	11/SEP/67	WFU 81
	N7599A	American Transair			24/MAR/83	
	N7599A	Boeing			DEC/84	
	PT-TCK	Transbrasil			MAR/85	Leased
19521	F-BLCG	Air France	328C	19/MAY/67	05/JUN/67	WFU NOV/81
	SU-DAB	ZAS Airline of Egypt			07/MAR/83	
	ST-AKR	Nile Safari Aviation			MAY/86	Leased
19522	F-BLCH	Air France	328C	20/JUN/67	29/JUN/67	
	F-BLCH	TRATCO Leasing			DEC/82	
19529	N7102	Braniff	327C	02/OCT/67	10/OCT/67	
	9M-AQB	Malaysian Singapore Airlines			01/MAR/71	
	9V-BFC	Singapore Airlines			21/JUL/72	
	N707AD	International Air Leases			AUG/81	
	N707AD	Arrow Air			NOV/81	
	N707AD	International Air Leases			MAY/84	
	N707AD	Jet America			JUN/84	
	N707AD	International Air Leases			04/DEC/84	
	PT-TCJ	TransBrasil			04/DEC/84	Leased
19530	N7103	Braniff	327C	09/OCT/67	18/OCT/67	
	9V-BDC	Malaysian Singapore Airlines			23/APR/71	
	9V-BDC	Singapore Airlines			01/OCT/72	
	N707ME	International Air Leases			MAY/81	
	N707ME	Arrow Air			AUG/81	
	N707ME	International Air Leases			APR/84	
	B-2424	Shanghai Airlines			17/JUN/85	
19531	N7104	Braniff	327C	08/NOV/67	20/NOV/67	
	N7104	TMA			01/AUG/73	
	OD-AGZ	TMA			80	
	ET-AIV	Ethiopian Airlines			MAY/85	
19566	N15710	Trans World Airlines	331C	24/MAY/68	26/JUN/68	Leased
	N15710	Guinness Peat Aviation			28/MAR/79	Sub-leased
	N15710	Cargolux			02/APR/79	Leased
	N15710	Guinness Peat Aviation			79	Sub-leased
	N15710	Aerotal			DEC/79	Leased
	N15710	Guinness Peat Aviation			NOV/80	Sub-leased
	N15710	Faucett			FEB/81	
	N15710	Trans World Airlines			JUN/82	
	N15710	Citicorp				
	N5710	Boeing			02/AUG/84	E-3A Trainer
	N132EA	Boeing			MAR/85	E-3A Trainer
19567	N15711	Trans World Airlines	331C	07/JUN/68	27/JUN/68	Leased
	N15711	Guinness Peat Aviation			14/MAY/79	Sub-Leased
	N15711	Cargolux			15/MAY/79	Sub-Leased
	N15711	PIA			JUL/79	Leased
	N15711	Guinness Peat Aviation			05/MAR/80	Sub-leased
	N15711	Air Haiti			APR/80	WFU 08/MAR/82 to 03/OCT/84
	N15711	Trans World Airlines			08/MAR/82	WFU 03/OCT/84 for KC-135E Parts
	N15711	Boeing			03/OCT/84	
19568	N16738	Trans World Airlines	131B	22/JAN/68	12/MAR/68	WFU 10/FEB/83 for KC-135E Parts
	N16738	Boeing			10/FEB/83	
19569	N16739	Trans World Airlines	131B	17/FEB/68	08/MAR/68	WFU 10/FEB/83 for KC-135E Parts
	N16739	Boeing			10/FEB/83	
19570	N28724	Trans World Airlines	331B	02/FEB/68	16/FEB/68	
	N28724	Citicorp			26/MAY/83	
	N28724	Global International			26/MAY/83	Leased
	N28724	Citicorp			NOV/83	
	N7232X	Atlanta Skylarks			JAN/84	
	N7232X	Citicorp			27/FEB/85	
	N7232X	Exec-Aire			SEP/85	
	N7232X	Jetran Inc.			OCT/85	WFU, stored Marana
19572	N28727	Trans World Airlines	331B	11/MAR/68	22/MAR/68	
	N28727	ARAMCO				Leased
	N28727	Trans World Airlines			30/JUN/80	
	N28727	Citicorp			06/JUL/83	
	N7231T	Atlanta Skylarks			16/SEP/83	
	N7231T	Alaska International Air			26/AUG/83	Leased
	N7231T	Markair			84	Sub-leased
	N7231T	Independent Air			MAY/86	
19574	N8411	American Airlines	323C	07/MAY/68	21/MAY/68	WFU JAN/81 to 30/SEP/83
	N8411	Av Tech Support			30/SEP/83	
	N780JS	Boeing			09/JUN/86	Joint Stars 2
19575	N8412	American Airlines	323C	17/MAY/68	04/JUN/68	WFU 31/AUG/81
	N8412	Aeronautics Services			02/JUN/82	
	HK-2842	Aerotal			JUN/82	Leased
	HP-1028	Aeronautics Services			NOV/83	
	HP-1028	Israel Aircraft Industries			MAR/85	
19576	N8413	American Airlines	323C	31/MAY/68	17/JUN/68	
	N8413	ONA			01/APR/81	Leased
	N8413	Saudia			01/APR/81	Sub-leased
	N8413	ONA			82	Leased
	N8413	Pakistan International			DEC/82	
	AP-BBK	Pakistan International			83	Re-registered
19577	N8414	American Airlines	323C	13/JUN/68	26/JUN/68	
	N8414	The Western Co.			OCT/80	
	N8414	Chase National Bank			82	
	N8414	Aeronautics Services			82	
	N8414	Aerotal			02/JUN/82	Leased
	N8414	The Western Co.			82	
	N8414	MME Farms Maintenance Corp.			04/AUG/82	
19581	N8401	American Airlines	323C	19/OCT/67	31/OCT/67	WFU 81 to 24/JUN/82
	81-0896	USAF	EC-18B		24/JUN/82	
19582	N8402	American Airlines	323C	20/OCT/67	27/OCT/67	WFU 81
	N8402	Nautilus Sports			16/FEB/84	
	N8402	Premiere Airlines			APR/84	Leased
	N8402	Nautilus Sports			DEC/84	WFU DEC/84
19583	N8403	American Airlines	323C	15/NOV/67	28/NOV/67	WFU 81 to MAY/82
	81-0894	USAF	EC-18B		MAY/82	
19584	N8404	American Airlines	323C	29/DEC/67	11/JAN/68	WFU JUL/81 to 13/AUG/83
	N8404	Nautilus Sports			13/AUG/83	
	N8404	Premiere Airlines			APR/84	Leased
	N8404	Nautilus Airlines			JUL/84	
	N8404	Exec-Aire			DEC/84	
	N8404	Burlington Northern			NOV/85	Op. by Buffalo Airways

BOEING 707 (EXISTING AIRCRAFT ONLY)

C/N	Registration	Owner/Operator	Series	First Flight	Delivery	Remarks
19585	N8405	American Airlines	323C	16/JAN/68	26/JAN/68	WFU AUG/81 to 29/DEC/83
	N8405	Nautilus Sports			29/DEC/83	
	N8405	Nautilus Airlines			MAR/84	
	N8405	Premiere Airlines			APR/84	Leased
	N8405	Nautilus Sports			DEC/84	
	N8405	Falcon Aircraft Conversions			JUL/85	
	N8405	Burlington Northern			DEC/85	Op. by Buffalo Airways
19586	N8406	American Airlines	323C	21/JAN/68	05/FEB/68	
	CP-1698	Lloyd Aero Boliviano			29/JUN/81	
19587	N8408	American Airlines	323C	04/MAR/68	15/MAR/68	WFU 81 to 07/OCT/82
	N8408	Ports of Call			07/OCT/82	
	N705PC	Ports of Call			82	
	N705PC	Skyworld Airlines			SEP/85	
19588	N8409	American Airlines	323C	19/MAR/68	04/APR/68	WFU 81 to 21/MAY/82
	OD-AHB	Middle East Airlines			21/MAY/82	
19589	N8410	American Airlines	323C	11/APR/68	26/APR/68	WFU 30/AUG/81
	OD-AHC	Middle East Airlines			25/MAY/82	
19590	G-ATZD	British Eagle	365C	29/NOV/67	21/DEC/67	
	VR-BCP	British Eagle			04/FEB/68	
	VR-BCP	Middle East Airlines			01/MAR/68	Leased
	VR-BCP	British Eagle			68	
	G-ATZD	BOAC			18/MAY/69	
	G-ATZD	British Airways			01/APR/72	WFU MAY/82 to 09/MAY/83
	G-ATZD	Air Supply Corp.			09/MAY/83	
	5A-DJV	Jamahiriyan Air Transport			AUG/83	
19621	VH-EAA	Qantas	338C	20/NOV/67	08/DEC/67	
	OO-YCK	ITEL			06/MAY/77	
	OO-YCK	Young Cargo			06/MAY/77	Leased
	OO-YCK	Air France				Sub-leased
	OO-YCK	Young Cargo			10/OCT/78	Leased
	OO-YCK	ITEL			JUN/79	
	P2-ANB	Air Niugini			AUG/79	Leased
	P2-ANB	ITEL			DEC/80	
	P2-ANB	GATX Leasing			DEC/80	
	P2-ANB	Air Niugini			DEC/80	Leased
	P2-ANB	Air Niugini			DEC/84	Purchased
	P2-ANB	Airxport			01/APR/85	
	TF-AEB	Air Supply Corp.			30/JUN/85	
	TF-AEB	Air Arctic			30/JUN/85	Leased
	TF-AEB	Air Supply Corp.			SEP/85	
	TF-AEB	ZAS Airline of Egypt			FEB/86	
	TF-AEB	Atlantic Icelandic			JAN/86	Leased
	TF-AEB	ZAS Airline of Egypt			APR/86	
	5Y-AXA	African Express Airlines			MAY/86	Leased
19622	VH-EAB	Qantas	338C	28/DEC/67	10/JAN/68	
	OO-YCL	ITEL			28/DEC/77	
	OO-YCL	Young Cargo			28/DEC/77	Leased
	OO-YCL	ITEL			MAY/79	
	P2-ANA	Air Niugini			23/MAY/79	Leased
	P2-ANA	ITEL			DEC/80	
	P2-ANA	GATX Leasing			DEC/80	
	P2-ANA	Air Nuigini			DEC/80	Leased
	P2-ANA	Air Nuigini			DEC/84	Purchased
	P2-ANA	Airxport			01/APR/85	
	TF-AEC	Air Supply Corp.			30/JUN/85	
	TF-AEC	Air Arctic			30/JUN/85	Leased
	TF-AEC	Air Supply Corp.			SEP/85	
	SU-DAE	ZAS Airline of Egypt			DEC/85	
19623	VH-EAC	Qantas	338C	25/JAN/68	05/FEB/68	
	G-BDKE	British Caledonian			06/OCT/75	Leased
	VH-EAC	Qantas			31/DEC/75	
	VH-EAC	ITEL			24/NOV/78	
	C-GRYN	Ontario Worldair			24/NOV/78	Leased
	C-GRYN	Nordair			79	Sub-leased
	C-GRYN	Ontario Worldair			79	
	C-GRYN	ITEL			DEC/80	
	C-GRYN	Worldways Airlines			JUN/81	
	A20-623	Royal Australian Air Force			17/JUN/83	
19624	VH-EAD	Qantas	338C	18/MAR/68	27/MAR/68	
	A20-624	Royal Australian Air Force			30/MAR/79	
19625	VH-EAE	Qantas	338C	25/MAR/68	04/APR/68	
	G-BFLD	ITEL			25/MAR/78	
	G-BFLD	British Midland Airways			25/MAR/78	Leased
	G-BFLD	Kuwait Airways			06/APR/78	Sub-leased
	G-BFLD	British Midland Airways			31/AUG/78	Leased
	G-BFLD	Air Algerie			15/SEP/78	Sub-leased
	G-BFLD	British Midland Airways			78	Leased
	G-BFLD	DETA			03/JAN/79	Sub-leased
	G-BFLD	British Midland Airways				Leased
	G-BFLD	DETA			16/MAY/80	Sub-leased
	G-BFLD	ITEL			DEC/80	
	G-BFLD	GATX Leasing			DEC/80	
	G-BFLD	British Midland Airways			DEC/80	Leased
	G-BFLD	LAM			DEC/80	Sub-leased
	G-BFLD	British Midland Airways			28/MAR/81	Leased
	G-BFLD	Bangladesh Biman			01/JUL/81	Sub-leased
	G-BFLD	British Midland Airways			31/JUL/81	Leased
	G-BFLD	Chemco Leasing			82	
	G-BFLD	British Midland Airways			DEC/82	WFU OCT/84 to AUG/85
	G-BFLD	ATASCO			AUG/85	
	N862BX	Burlington Northern			NOV/85	Op. by Southern Air Transport
19626	VH-EAF	Qantas	338C	19/APR/68	04/MAY/68	
	HL7432	ITEL			05/APR/78	
	HL7432	Korean Airlines			05/APR/78	Leased
	HL7432	ITEL			DEC/80	
	HL7432	GATX Leasing			DEC/80	
	HL7432	Korean Airlines			DEC/80	Leased
	HL7432	Korean Airlines			OCT/83	Purchased
	N770JS	Boeing			19/JAN/86	Joint Stars 1
19627	VH-EAG	Qantas	338C	30/APR/68	16/MAY/68	
	A20-627	Royal Australian Air Force			30/MAR/79	
19628	VH-EAH	Qantas	338C	24/MAY/68	12/JUN/68	
	VH-EAH	ITEL			13/JUL/78	
	HL7433	Korean Airlines			13/JUL/78	Leased
	HL7433	ITEL			DEC/80	

C/N	Registration	Owner/Operator	Series	First Flight	Delivery	Remarks
19996	OO-SJL	Sabena	329C	19/SEP/68	30/SEP/68	
	OO-SJL	Wallonair			82	Not taken-up
	N3238N	Jet Charter Service			02/NOV/82	
	N3238N	Sabena			MAR/85	WFU MAR/85, stored Brussels
19997	1001	West German Air Force	307C	19/SEP/68	30/SEP/68	
19998	1002	West German Air Force	307C	27/SEP/68	15/OCT/68	
19999	1003	West German Air Force	307C	24/OCT/68	31/OCT/68	
20000	1004	West German Air Force	307C	06/NOV/68	18/NOV/68	
20008	N707N	Boeing	320C	15/AUG/69		
	PP-VJH	Varig			14/JUL/69	
	2403	Brazilian Air Force			13/MAR/86	Tanker
20016	N870PA	Pan American	321C	03/OCT/68	12/DEC/68	
	N870PA	Boreas International			09/JUL/75	
	9K-ACS	Kuwait Airways			09/JUL/75	
	N146SP	South Pacific Island Airways			23/MAR/84	
	N146SP	Bank of Hawaii			SEP/85	
	N146SP	Comtran			FEB/86	
20017	N871PA	Pan American	321C	03/OCT/68	25/OCT/68	
	N871PA	Boreas International			28/OCT/75	
	JY-AES	Alia			19/DEC/75	
	N710FW	Florida West			MAY/86	
20018	N872PA	Pan American	321C	14/NOV/68	22/NOV/68	
	N872PA	Boreas International			09/SEP/75	
	9K-ACU	Kuwait Airways			09/SEP/75	
	S2-ACK	Bangladesh Biman			23/SEP/81	
	S2-ACK	Tempair			25/APR/86	
	PT-TCR	Boeing			04/MAY/86	
	PT-TCR	Transbrasil			04/MAY/86	Leased
20019	N880PA	Pan American	321B	05/DEC/68	10/DEC/68	
	N880PA	Guyana Airways			12/DEC/81	Leased
	N880PA	Pan American			DEC/82	
	N880PA	Boeing			27/FEB/84	WFU 27/FEB/84 for KC-135E Parts
20020	N881PA	Pan American	321B	08/DEC/68	13/DEC/68	
	N881PA	Arrow Airways			OCT/81	Leased
	N881PA	Pan American			FEB/82	
	N881PA	Global International			APR/82	Leased
	N881PA	Pan American			SEP/83	WFU SEP/83 to MAR/84
	N881PA	US Leasing Corp.			MAR/84	
	N881PA	Boeing			07/FEB/85	WFU 07/FEB/85 for KC-135E Parts
20021	N882PA	Pan American	321B	10/DEC/68	17/DEC/68	
	CC-CEI	LAN Chile			21/NOV/78	
20022	N883PA	Pan American	321B	16/DEC/68	19/DEC/68	WFU 01/JUL/80
	N883PA	Global International			02/MAY/83	
	N883PA	Pan American			SEP/83	WFU SEP/83 to JUN/84
	N730Q	Falcon Aircraft Conversions			JUN/84	
20023	N884PA	Pan American	321B	02/JAN/69	08/JAN/69	WFU DEC/80 to DEC/82
	N884PA	ATEL			DEC/82	WFU DEC/82
20024	N885PA	Pan American	321B	03/JAN/69	10/JAN/69	WFU NOV/80 to 13/APR/84
	N885PA	Boeing			13/APR/84	WFU 13/APR/84 for KC-135E Parts
20025	N886PA	Pan American	321B	17/JAN/69	24/JAN/69	WFU OCT/80
	N886PA	Global International			02/MAY/83	
	N886PA	Pan American			SEP/83	
	N886PA	Falcon Aircraft Conversions			JUN/84	
	N728Q	Skystar International			APR/85	Leased
20026	N887PA	Pan American	321B	22/JAN/69	31/JAN/69	WFU DEC/80 to JUN/82
	N887PA	Global International			JUN/82	Leased
	N887PA	Global International			14/DEC/82	Purchased
	N160GL	Global International				
	N160GL	Boeing			SEP/85	WFU SEP/85 for KC-135E Parts
20027	N890PA	Pan American	321B	24/JAN/69	06/FEB/69	
	N890PA	ATASCO			15/JAN/76	
	9Y-TEX	BWIA			15/JAN/76	Leased
	N2213Y	Aviation Technical Support			JAN/83	Husk Kit development aircraft
	N2213Y	Boeing			OCT/85	WFU OCT/85 for KC-135E Parts
20028	N891PA	Pan American	321B	24/JAN/69	06/FEB/69	
	9Y-TEZ	BWIA			03/AUG/76	
	N3127K	FTC Corp.			JUN/82	
	VR-CBN	Esal Commodities			JAN/83	WFU JUN/83
20029	N892PA	Pan American	321B	20/FEB/69	04/MAR/69	WFU MAR/80 to 24/MAR/83
	N892PA	Global International			24/MAR/83	
	N892PA	Pan American			SEP/83	WFU SEP/83 to 08/MAY/84
	N729Q	Falcon Aircraft Conversions			08/MAY/84	
20030	N893PA	Pan American	321B	26/FEB/69	11/MAR/69	WFU DEC/79
	N893PA	Air Trans			13/NOV/80	Leased
	N893PA	Egyptair			13/NOV/80	Sub-leased
	N893PA	Air Trans			NOV/80	Leased
	N893PA	Nefertiti Aviation			NOV/80	Sub-leased
	N893PA	Pan American			NOV/81	
	N893PA	Air Trans			81	Leased
	N893PA	Pan American			81	
	N893PA	CAAC			24/DEC/82	WFU 24/DEC/82, Ground trainer
20031	N894PA	Pan American	321B	28/FEB/69	14/MAR/69	WFU 29/OCT/79 to 02/MAY/83
	N894PA	Global International			02/MAY/83	
	N894PA	Pan American			SEP/83	WFU SEP/83 to 12/APR/84
	N731Q	Falcon Aircraft Conversions			12/APR/84	
	N731Q	Jetran Inc.			OCT/85	
	N731Q	Skystar International			FEB/86	Leased
20032	N895PA	Pan American	321B	06/MAR/69	14/MAR/69	WFU 01/DEC/79 to JUL/82
	N895PA	Skystar International			JUL/82	
	N895PA	Guy America Airways			JUL/82	Leased
	N895SY	Skystar International			27/JAN/83	
	N895SY	Queen of the World			83	Leased
	N895SY	Skystar International			83	
	N895SY	Jet 24 International			JAN/84	Leased
	N895SY	Skystar International			NOV/84	
20033	N896PA	Pan American	321B	18/MAR/69	26/MAR/69	WFU 11/JAN/80 to 18/FEB/81
	HC-BHY	Ecuatoriana			18/FEB/81	
20034	N897PA	Pan American	321B	25/MAR/69	31/MAR/69	WFU JAN/80 to 05/APR/83
	N897PA	Global International			05/APR/83	
	N897PA	Pan American			SEP/83	WFU SEP/83 to JUN/84
	N732Q	Falcon Aircraft Conversions			JUN/84	
	N732Q	Jetran Inc.			AUG/85	
	N732Q	Skystar International			AUG/85	Leased
20035	SX-DBE	Olympic Airways	384B	12/DEC/68	19/DEC/68	
20036	SX-DBF	Olympic Airways	384B	14/JAN/69	23/JAN/69	

BOEING 707 (EXISTING AIRCRAFT ONLY)

C/N	Registration	Owner/Operator	Series	First Flight	Delivery	Remarks
20043	CF-QBG	Quebecair	396C			Not taken-up
	N1786B	Boeing		04/MAR/69		
	CF-ZYP	Wardair			14/MAR/69	
	OE-IDA	Flugzeug Leasing			11/DEC/78	
	OE-IDA	Montana			18/DEC/78	Leased
	OE-IDA	Sudan Airways			APR/79	Sub-leased
	OE-IDA	Montana			DEC/80	Leased
	OE-IDA	Ariana			JAN/81	Sub-leased
	OE-IDA	Montana			81	Leased
	OE-IDA	U.S. Justice Dept.			MAY/81	Impounded MAY/81
	85-6973	USAF	C-137C		JUL/85	
20056	N86740	Trans World Airlines	131B	18/DEC/68	08/JAN/69	
	N86740	Boeing			19/MAY/82	WFU 19/MAY/82 for KC-135E Parts
20057	N86741	Trans World Airlines	131B	09/JAN/69	23/JAN/69	
	N86741	Boeing			12/MAY/82	WFU 12/MAY/82 for KC-135E Parts
20058	N8729	Trans World Airlines	331B	27/NOV/68	12/DEC/68	
	N8729	Air Berlin			04/NOV/80	Leased
	N8729	Trans World Airlines			NOV/81	WFU OCT/83 to 15/FEB/84
	N8729	Boeing			15/FEB/84	WFU 15/FEB/84 for KC-135E Parts
20059	N8730	Trans World Airlines	331B	20/DEC/68	15/JAN/69	
	N8730	Boeing			15/JAN/73	Leased
	N8730	Trans World Airlines			06/JUL/73	WFU SEP/81 to 15/FEB/84
	N8730	Boeing			15/FEB/84	WFU 15/FEB/84 for KC-135E Parts
20060	N8731	Trans World Airlines	331B	30/DEC/68	03/MAR/69	
	N8731	Executive Aircraft Ltd.			MAY/80	
	N8731	ARAMCO			MAY/81	
	N708A	ARAMCO			81	
	N275B	South African Air Force	KC-137		01/JUL/85	
					AUG/86	Tanker
20061	N8732	Trans World Airlines	331B	04/FEB/69	07/MAR/69	
	N8732	BWIA				Leased
	N8732	Trans World Airlines			28/FEB/80	
	N8732	Guinness Peat Aviation			29/AUG/80	Leased
	N8732	Faucett			SEP/80	Sub-leased
	N8732	Trans World Airlines			02/APR/82	
	N8732	Boeing			15/DEC/83	WFU 15/DEC/83 for KC-135E Parts
20062	N8733	Trans World Airlines	331B	05/FEB/69	02/APR/69	
	N8733	ARAMCO			03/JUL/80	Leased
	N8733	Trans World Airlines			81	WFU OCT/83 to 02/APR/84
	N8733	Carefree Vacations			02/APR/84	
	N8733	Worldwide Aviation			02/APR/84	
	N8733	Carefree Vacations			DEC/85	
	N8733	Boeing			23/MAY/86	WFU 23/MAY/86 for KC-135E Parts
20064	N8735	Trans World Airlines	331B	01/APR/69	01/MAY/69	WFU OCT/83 to 19/JUN/84
	N8735	Aviation Sales			19/JUN/84	
	N8735	Boeing			19/JUN/84	WFU 19/JUN/84 for KC-135E Parts
20065	N8736	Trans World Airlines	331B	11/APR/69	07/MAY/69	WFU OCT/83 to MAR/84
	N8736	Carefree Vacations			MAY/84	
	N8736	Worldwide Airlines			MAY/84	
	N8736	Boeing			NOV/85	WFU NOV/85 for KC-135E Parts
20066	N8737	Trans World Airlines	331B	26/MAY/69	12/JUN/69	WFU MAR/82 to JUN/84
	N8737	Carefree Vacations			JUN/84	
	N8737	Worldwide Airlines			JUN/84	
	N8737	Falcon Aircraft Conversions			DEC/84	
	N8737	Boeing			SEP/85	WFU SEP/85 for KC-135E Parts
20067	N8738	Trans World Airlines	331B	05/JUN/69	17/JUN/69	WFU FEB/81 to 06/JUL/84
	N8738	Aviation Sales			06/JUL/84	
	N8738	Boeing			06/JUL/84	WFU 06/JUL/84 for KC-135E Parts
20069	N15713	Trans World Airlines	331C	30/JUN/69	16/JUL/69	
	N15713	Global International			31/JUL/78	
	N15713	British Midland Airways			16/DEC/78	Leased
	N15713	Air Algerie			16/DEC/78	Sub-leased
	N15713	Global International			14/MAR/79	
	N15713	Farhad Azima			MAR/85	
	N15713	Race Aviation			MAR/85	Leased
20076	N738AL	Airlift International	372C	07/JUN/68	14/JUN/68	
	N738AL	Aerolineas Argentinas			17/MAY/71	Leased
	LV-LGO	Aerolineas Argentinas			DEC/79	Purchased
	TC-94	Argentine Air Force			17/DEC/82	
	TC-93	Argentine Air Force			DEC/82	
20077	N739AL	Airlift International	372C	05/JUL/68	11/JUL/68	
	N739AL	Caledonian Airways			70	Leased
	N739AL	Airlift International			70	
	N739AL	Aerolineas Argentinas			01/MAR/71	Leased
	LV-LGP	Aerolineas Argentinas			DEC/79	
	TC-92	Argentine Air Force			01/SEP/80	
20084	9K-ACJ	Kuwait Airways	369C	29/OCT/68	04/NOV/68	
	N525SJ	Southern Air Transport			NOV/85	
20085	9K-ACK	Kuwait Airways	369C	07/NOV/68	14/NOV/68	
	N147SP	South Pacific Island Airways			12/APR/84	
	N147SP	Bank of Hawaii			SEP/85	
	N147SP	Comtran			FEB/86	
	N147SP	Florida West Airlines			05/MAR/86	
20086	9K-ACL	Kuwait Airways	369C	19/NOV/68	25/NOV/68	
	ST-AIX	Sudan Airways			30/JAN/84	
20087	N8415	American Airlines	323C	20/JUN/68	05/JUL/68	
	N8415	Overseas National Airways			12/AUG/81	Leased
	N8415	Pakistan International			12/AUG/81	Sub-leased
	N8415	Overseas National Airways			16/NOV/81	Leased
	N8415	American Airlines			16/NOV/81	
	N8415	Global International			19/AUG/82	Leased
	N8415	Global International			JUL/83	Purchased
	SU-FAC	Misr Overseas			DEC/83	
20088	N8416	American Airlines	323C	02/JUL/68	17/JUL/68	
	N8416	American Transair			08/NOV/82	Leased
	N8416	Boeing			31/DEC/84	
	PT-TCN	Transbrasil			MAR/85	
20089	N8417	American Airlines	323C	22/AUG/68	30/AUG/68	
	G-AYZZ	British Caledonian			06/JUN/71	Leased
	N8417	American Airlines			27/SEP/71	
	G-AYZZ	British Caledonian			08/JUN/72	Leased
	N8417	American Airlines			31/DEC/73	
	N8417	American Airlines			10/APR/74	
	N8417	Global International			MAY/81	Leased
	N162GL	Global International			11/MAR/83	Purchased

C/N	Registration	Owner/Operator	Series	First Flight	Delivery	Remarks
	N162GL	Abu Dhabi Bank			DEC/84	Impounded
	N8417	Red Apple Services			SEP/85	
	N8417	Boeing			NOV/85	WFU NOV/85 for KC-135E Parts
20097	4X-ATT	El Al	358B	15/JAN/69	22/JAN/69	
20110	ZS-FKT	South African Airways	344C			Not taken-up
	ZS-SAG	South African Airways		02/APR/69	17/APR/69	
	VP-WGA	Air Zimbabwe			MAR/80	Leased
	ZS-SAG	South African Airways			31/MAR/81	WFU AUG/81
	4X-BYQ	Israel Aircraft Industries			15/OCT/82	
	4X-JYQ	Israeli Air Force			JAN/83	
20122	4X-ATU	El Al	358C	06/MAY/69		Not taken-up
	4X-ATX	El Al			15/MAY/69	
20123	D-ABUJ	Lufthansa	330C	17/FEB/69	27/FEB/69	
	D-ABUJ	Condor			23/MAR/77	Leased
	D-ABUJ	Lufthansa			NOV/78	
	D-ABUJ	Condor			15/FEB/79	Leased
	D-ABUJ	Lufthansa			OCT/79	
	A6-DPA	United Arab Emirates Govt.			05/MAY/81	
	A6-DPA	Sudan Government			MAY/86	Leased
20124	D-ABUO	Lufthansa	330C	01/MAY/69	08/MAY/69	
	D-ABUO	German Cargo			01/NOV/78	
	N707HE	Challenge Air Transport			30/SEP/84	
20136	CS-TBE	TAP Air Portugal	382B	22/APR/69	28/APR/69	
	D2-TOP	TAAG Angola			01/JUN/83	
20170	N8431	American Airlines	323B	19/MAR/69	09/APR/69	WFU SEP/80 to OCT/83
	N708PC	Ports of Call			OCT/83	
	N708PC	Skyword Airlines			SEP/85	
20172	N8433	American Airlines	323B	21/APR/69	30/APR/69	WFU AUG/81 to 30/DEC/82
	N8433	Global International			30/DEC/82	Leased
	N161GL	Global International			JUL/84	Purchased
	N711PC	Skyword Airlines			NOV/85	
20174	N8435	American Airlines	323B	13/MAY/69	23/MAY/69	
	N8435	South Pacific Island Airways			20/MAR/81	Leased
	N8435	South Pacific Island Airways			01/NOV/83	Purchased
	N145SP	South Pacific Island Airways			01/FEB/84	
	N145SP	Bank of Hawaii			SEP/85	
	N145SP	Comtran			11/FEB/86	
	N145SP	South Pacific Island Airways			11/FEB/86	Leased
20175	N8436	American Airlines	323B	29/MAY/69	13/JUN/69	WFU 81, stored Marana
	N8436	Ports of Call			12/DEC/83	
	N709PC	Ports of Call				
	N709PC	Skyword Airlines			SEP/85	
20176	N8437	American Airlines	323B	21/JUL/69	31/JUL/69	
	N8437	Global International			26/APR/81	Leased
	N8437	Air Florida			OCT/83	Sub-Leased
	N8437	Global International			84	Leased
	N8437	Global International			JUL/84	Purchased
	N712PC	Skyword Airlines			NOV/85	
20177	N8438	American Airlines	323B	28/JUL/69	19/AUG/69	WFU AUG/81
	N706PC	Ports of Call			11/AUG/83	
	N706PC	Skyword Airlines			SEP/85	
20178	N8439	American Airlines	323B	15/AUG/69	09/SEP/69	WFU AUG/81
	N457PC	Ports of Call			13/SEP/83	
	N457PC	Skyword Airlines			SEP/85	
20179	N8440	American Airlines	323B	29/AUG/69	22/SEP/69	WFU APR/81 to 16/SEP/82
	N8440	Global International			16/SEP/82	Leased
	N8440	Global International			JUL/84	Purchased
20198	OO-SJM	Sabena	329C	13/JUN/69	20/JUN/69	
	PH-TVK	Transavia			12/FEB/76	Leased
	OO-SJM	Sabena			02/MAY/77	
	OO-SJM	Air Zaire			JUL/79	Leased
	OO-SJM	Sabena			JAN/80	
	OO-SJM	Sobelair			FEB/81	
	OO-SJM	Sabena				Leased
	OO-SJM	Sobelair			JUN/85	
		NATO			JUN/86	
20199	OO-SJN	Sabena	329C	11/JUL/69	22/JUL/69	
	OO-SJN	Sobelair			23/MAR/82	Leased
	OO-SJN	Sabena			APR/82	
	N3238S	Jet Charter Service			02/NOV/82	
	N3238S	Sabena			MAR/85	WFU MAR/85, stored Brussels
20200	OO-SJO	Sabena	329C	11/NOV/69	03/DEC/69	
	OO-SJO	ZICAS			80	Leased
	OO-SJO	Sabena			80	
	9Q-CBS	Scibe Zaire			23/DEC/84	
20230	ZS-FKG	South African Airways	344C			Not taken-up
	ZS-SAH	South African Airways		07/AUG/69	28/AUG/69	WFU 1981
	4X-BYS	Israel Aircraft Industries			15/OCT/82	
	4X-JYS	Israeli Air Force			JAN/83	
20259	OD-AFD	Middle East Airlines	384C	09/SEP/69	01/OCT/69	
	OD-AFD	Nigerian Airways			NOV/75	Leased
	OD-AFD	Middle East Airlines			JAN/76	
	OD-AFD	Saudia			01/MAY/76	Leased
	OD-AFD	Middle East Airlines			25/MAY/77	
20260	OD-AFE	Middle East Airlines	384C	25/SEP/69	19/OCT/69	
	OD-AFE	Nigeria Airways			NOV/75	Leased
	OD-AFE	Middle East Airlines			JAN/76	
	OD-AFE	Saudia			01/JUN/76	Leased
	OD-AFE	Middle East Airlines			JUL/80	
	OD-AFE	Saudia			JUL/80	Leased
	OD-AFE	Middle East airlines			80	
20261	B-1824	China Airlines	309C	27/OCT/69	07/NOV/69	
	N707ZS	Jet Cargo			31/JAN/83	
20283	ZS-SAI	South African Airways	344C	08/DEC/69	22/DEC/69	
	LX-LGS	Luxair			05/AUG/78	
	JY-AFQ	Alia			12/APR/79	Leased
	LX-LGS	Luxair			JAN/82	
	LX-LGS	TRATCO Leasing			27/DEC/84	
	LX-LGS	Trinair Leasing			SEP/85	
	ZS-LSF	Safair			SEP/85	Leased
20287	EP-IRL	Iran Air	386C	15/DEC/69	31/DEC/69	
20288	EP-IRM	Iran Air	386C	04/MAR/70	17/MAR/70	
20297	CS-TBF	TAP Air Portugal	382B	03/FEB/70	13/FEB/70	
	N105BV	Buffalo Airways			17/NOV/83	
	85-6974	USAF	C-137C		OCT/85	

BOEING 707 (EXISTING AIRCRAFT ONLY)

C/N	Registration	Owner/Operator	Series	First Flight	Delivery	Remarks
20298	CS-TBG	TAP Air Portugal	382B	12/MAR/70	25/MAR/70	
20301	4X-ATY	El Al	358C	20/JAN/70	26/JAN/70	
	4X-ATY	Sun D'Or			01/MAY/82	Leased
20315	N1506W	Western Airlines	347C			Not taken-up
	13701	Canadian Armed Forces		18/FEB/70	28/FEB/70	
20316	N1507W	Western Airlines	347C			Not taken-up
	N1785B	Boeing				
	13702	Canadian Armed Forces		11/FEB/70	28/FEB/70	
20317	N1508W	Western Airlines	347C			Not taken-up
	13703	Canadian Armed Forces		24/FEB/70	04/MAR/70	
20318	N1509W	Western Airlines	347C			Not taken-up
	13704	Canadian Armed Forces		03/MAR/70	10/MAR/70	
20319	N1510W	Western Airlines	347C			Not taken-up
	13705	Canadian Armed Forces		04/MAY/70	11/MAY/70	
20340	HK-1410	Avianca	359B	15/APR/70	24/APR/70	
20341	SU-APD	United Arab Airlines	366C	08/JAN/70	16/JAN/70	
	SU-APD	Egyptair			10/OCT/71	
20374	G-AXGW	BOAC	336C	20/FEB/70	08/MAR/70	
	G-AXGW	British Airways			01/APR/72	
	7O-ACO	Alyemda			24/DEC/81	
20375	G-AXGX	BOAC	336C	18/MAR/70	26/MAR/70	
	G-AXGX	British Airways			01/APR/72	
	G-AXGX	Ruler of Qatar			MAY/81	Leased
	A7-AAC	Ruler of Qatar			16/JUL/84	Purchased
20428	N1793T	Trans World Airlines	331C	20/JUL/70	23/JUL/70	WFU 01/JAN/81 to 23/AUG/83
	4X-JYY	Israeli Air Force			23/AUG/83	
20429	N794TW	Trans World Airlines	331C	17/AUG/70	24/AUG/70	WFU 08/FEB/81
	4X-JY	Israeli Air Force			23/AUG/83	
20456	G-AXXY	BOAC	336B	10/FEB/71	18/FEB/71	
	G-AXXY	British Airways			01/APR/72	
	G-AXXY	British Airtours			19/APR/82	
	G-AXXY	Maof Airlines			01/JUN/84	
	4X-BMC	Maof Airlines			22/JUL/84	
	N343A	Omega Air			NOV/85	
	N343A	Boeing			03/FEB/86	
	PT-TCQ	Transbrasil			03/FEB/86	Leased
20474	5N-ABJ	Nigeria Airways	3F9C	20/APR/71	05/AUG/71	
20488	AP-AWA	Pakistan International	340C	11/DEC/70	23/DEC/70	
	G-AZRO	British Caledonian			08/APR/72	Leased
	AP-AXG	Pakistan International			01/NOV/73	
20495	JY-ADP	Alia	3D3C	04/MAR/71	12/MAR/71	
	JY-ADP	Hashemite Kingdom of Jordan			83	
20514	CS-DGI	Potuguese Govt.	3F3C	15/SEP/71		Not taken-up
	8801	Portuguese Air Force			23/SEP/71	
	CS-TBT	TAP Air Portugal			07/OCT/76	
20515	CS-DGJ	Portuguese Govt.	3F3C	02/DEC/71		Not taken-up
	8802	Portuguese Air Force			14/DEC/71	
	CS-TBU	TAP Air Portugal			07/OCT/76	
	CS-TBU	Air Malta			01/MAY/86	Leased
	CS-TBU	TAP Air Portugal			31/OCT/86	Sched.return
20517	G-AYLT	BOAC	379C	18/MAY/71	28/MAY/71	
	G-AYLT	British Airways			01/APR/72	
	G-AYLT	GKN Contractors			10/NOV/81	
	9Q-CLY	GKN Contractors			81	
	9Q-CLY	Airlines Air Spares			01/AUG/84	
	SU-DAD	ZAS Airline of Egypt			15/JAN/85	
20518	71-1407	Boeing	EC137	09/FEB/72		
	71-1407	Boeing	E3A		24/FEB/75	Converted
	71-1407	USAF			OCT/78	
20519	71-1408	Boeing	EC137	10/FEB/72		
	71-1408	Boeing	E3A		19/APR/77	Converted
	71-1408	USAF			15/DEC/77	
20522	HL7406	Korean Airlines	3B5C	21/JUN/71	06/AUG/71	
20546	9K-ACM	Kuwait Airways	369C	11/JAN/72	15/JAN/72	
	N523SJ	Southern Air Transport			14/JUN/85	
20547	9K-ACN	Kuwait Airways	369C	21/FEB/72	25/FEB/72	
	70-ACS	Alyemda			JUL/84	
20629	TJ-CAA	Cameroon Airlines	3H7C	07/NOV/72	20/NOV/72	
20630	N8459	Boeing	353B	31/JUL/72		
	72-7000	USAF	VC137C		15/NOV/72	
20669	5N-ABK	Nigeria Airways	3F9C	15/DEC/72	16/JAN/73	
20714	B-2402	CAAC	3J6B	16/JUL/73	23/AUG/73	
20715	B-2404	CAAC	3J6B	15/AUG/73	17/SEP/73	
20716	B-2406	CAAC	3J6B	15/MAR/74	15/APR/74	
20717	B-2408	CAAC	3J6B	17/APR/74	10/MAY/74	
20718	B-2410	CAAC	3J6B	05/OCT/73	12/NOV/73	
20719	B-2412	CAAC	3J6B	31/OCT/73	22/NOV/73	
20720	B-2414	CAAC	3J6B	21/NOV/73	13/DEC/73	
20721	B-2416	CAAC	3J6B	15/DEC/73	14/JAN/74	
20722	B-2418	CAAC	3J6B	25/JAN/74	26/FEB/74	
20723	B-2420	CAAC	3J6B	27/FEB/74	19/MAR/74	
20741	N1785B	Boeing	386C	18/APR/73		
	EP-IRN	Iran Air			01/MAY/73	
20760	SU-AVX	Egyptair	366C	16/MAY/73	30/MAY/73	
20761	N1785B	Boeing	366C	15/MAY/73		
	SU-AVY	Egyptair			29/MAY/73	
20762	SU-AVZ	Egyptair	366C	13/JUN/73	29/JUN/73	
20803	YR-ABA	Tarom	3K1C	12/FEB/74	21/FEB/74	
20804	YR-ABB	Romanian Government	3K1C	16/MAY/74	03/JUN/74	
20805	YR-ABC	Tarom	3K1C	18/MAY/74	03/JUN/74	
20830	N1790B	Boeing	3J9C	20/FEB/74		
	5-241	Imperial Iranian Air Force			29/MAY/74	
	5-8301	Imperial Iranian Air Force				
	5-8301	Iranian Air Force			FEB/78	
20831	5-242	Imperial Iranian Air Force	3J9C	29/APR/74	10/MAY/74	
	5-8302	Imperial Iranian Air Force				
	5-8302	Iranian Air Force			FEB/78	
20832	5-243	Imperial Iranian Air Force	3J9C	18/JUL/74	26/JUL/74	
	5-8303	Imperial Iranian Air Force				
	5-8303	Iranian Air Force			FEB/78	
20833	5-244	Imperial Iranian Air Force	3J9C	16/SEP/74	30/SEP/74	
	5-8304	Imperial Iranian Air Force				
	5-8304	Iranian Air Force			FEB/78	
20834	5-245	Imperial Iranian Air Force	3J9C	14/NOV/74	27/NOV/74	
	5-8305	Imperial Iranian Air Force				

C/N	Registration	Owner/Operator	Series	First Flight	Delivery	Remarks
	5-8305	Iranian Air Force			FEB/78	
20835	5-246	Imperial Iranian Air Force	3J9C	03/DEC/74	16/DEC/74	
	5-8306	Imperial Iranian Air Force				
	5-8306	Iranian Air Force			FEB/78	
20889	YI-AGE	Iraqi Airways	370C	14/AUG/74	27/AUG/74	
20890	YI-AGF	Iraqi Airways	370C	12/SEP/74	23/SEP/74	
	JY-CAC	Arab Air Cargo			05/MAY/83	
	4YB-CAC	Arab Air Cargo			01/MAR/84	
20891	YI-AGG	Iraqi Airways	370C	26/SEP/74	07/OCT/74	
20898	ST-AFB	Sudan Airways	358C	29/JUN/74	10/JUL/74	
20919	SU-AXJ	Egyptian Government	366C	19/JUL/74	21/AUG/74	
20920	SU-AXK	Egyptair	366C	10/OCT/74	15/NOV/74	
21046	73-01674	Boeing	E3A	21/JUL/75		
21047	75-0556	USAF	E3A	19/SEP/75	05/MAY/78	
21049	N62393	Aviation Services	326B	16/DEC/74		
	9M-TDM	Malaysian Government			01/JAN/77	
	N62393	Aviation Services			76	
	A6-HPZ	Sheikh Zayed			MAR/77	
21070	T-01	Argentine Government	387B	04/FEB/75	11/JUN/75	
	TC-91	Argentine Air Force	387C		JUN/77	Converted
21081	HZ-HM1	Saudi Royal Flight	368C	29/JUL/75	25/SEP/75	
	HZ-HM2	Saudi Royal Flight				
21092	PK-PJQ	Pelita	3M1C	14/APR/75	25/APR/75	
	PK-PJQ	Sempati Air Transport			76	Leased
	PK-PJQ	Pelita			76	
	A-7002	Indonesian Air Force			NOV/82	Leased
	PK-PJQ	Pelita Air Services			MAY/85	
21096	N48055	Aviation Services	3L6C	20/MAY/75		
	9M-TMS	Malaysian Government			09/JUN/75	
	G-CDHW	British Caledonian			05/NOV/77	Leased
	G-CDHW	Sabah Government			JAN/79	
	A6-HRM	Ruler of Dubai			FEB/79	
21103	HZ-ACG	Saudia	368C	09/SEP/75	14/OCT/75	WFU MAR/86
21104	HZ-ACH	Saudia	368C	04/NOV/75	18/DEC/75	
	HZ-HM5	Saudi Royal Flight			85	Not taken-up
	ST-DRS	Sudan Government			01/NOV/83	
21123	5-207	Imperial Iranian Air Force	3J9C	17/FEB/76	27/FEB/76	
	5-8307	Imperial Iranian Air Force				
	5-8307	Iranian Air Force			FEB/78	
21124	5-208	Imperial Iranian Air Force	3J9C	23/APR/76	14/JUN/76	
	5-8308	Imperial Iranian Air Force				
	5-8308	Iranian Air Force			FEB/78	
21125	5-209	Imperial Iranian Air Force	3J9C	09/SEP/76	18/JUN/76	
	5-8309	Imperial Iranian Air Force				
	5-8309	Iranian Air Force			FEB/78	
21126	5-8310	Imperial Iranian Air Force	3J9C	18/AUG/76	31/AUG/76	
	5-8310	Iranian Air Force			FEB/78	
21127	5-8311	Imperial Iranian Air Force	3J9C	15/SEP/76	27/SEP/76	
	5-8311	Iranian Air Force			FEB/78	
21128	5-8312	Imperial Iranian Air Force	3J9C	11/NOV/76	19/NOV/76	
	5-8312	Iranian Air Force			FEB/78	
21129	5-8313	Imperial Iranian Air Force	3J9C	06/DEC/76	14/DEC/76	
	5-8313	Iranian Air Force			FEB/78	
21185	73-01675	USAF	E3A	JAN/76	AUG/78	
21207	75-0557	USAF	E3A	13/MAY/76	23/MAR/77	
21208	75-0558	USAF	E3A	10/SEP/76	29/MAY/77	
21209	75-0559	USAF	E3A	03/DEC/76	21/OCT/77	
21228	5A-DAK	Libyan Government	3L5C	08/JUN/76	18/JUL/76	
21250	75-0560	USAF	E3A	23/FEB/77	22/NOV/77	
21261	HZ-ACI	Saudia	368C	15/DEC/76	10/JAN/77	WFU MAR/86
21334	A7-AAA	Ruler of Qatar	3P1C	20/JUN/77	28/JUL/77	
21367	HZ-ACJ	Saudia	368C	25/MAR/77	04/APR/77	WFU MAR/86
21368	HZ-ACK	Saudia	368C	20/JUN/77	27/JUN/77	
	HZ-HM3	Saudi Royal Flight			JUN/79	
21396	EP-HIM	Iranian Government	386C	16/APR/78	03/MAY/78	
	1001	Iranian Air Force				
21428	5N-ANO	Nigeria Airways	3F9C	10/DEC/77	30/JAN/78	
21434	76-1604	USAF	E3A	17/JUN/77	15/DEC/77	
21435	76-1605	USAF	E3A	08/AUG/77	25/MAY/79	
21436	76-1606	USAF	E3A	09/DEC/77	22/JUN/78	
21437	76-1607	USAF	E3A	22/FEB/78	29/SEP/78	
21475	5-8314	Iranian Air Force	3J9C	04/DEC/78	20/DEC/78	
21551	77-0351	USAF	E3A	31/MAR/78	29/SEP/78	
21552	77-0352	USAF	E3A	15/MAY/78	20/NOV/78	
21553	77-0353	USAF	E3A	30/JUN/78	19/DEC/78	
21554	77-0354	USAF	E3A	15/AUG/78	19/JAN/79	
21555	77-0355	USAF	E3A	29/SEP/78	16/MAR/79	
21556	77-0356	USAF	E3A	13/NOV/78	22/MAY/79	
21651	YR-ABD	Romanian Government	3K1C	19/MAR/79	30/MAR/79	
21752	78-0576	USAF	E3A		SEP/79	
21753	78-0577	USAF	E3A	04/JUL/79	20/DEC/79	
21754	78-0578	USAF	E3A	16/OCT/79	03/JUN/80	
21755	79-0001	USAF	E3A	26/FEB/80	18/SEP/80	
21756	79-0002	USAF	E3A	30/MAY/80	19/DEC/80	
21757	79-0003	USAF	E3A	16/SEP/80	19/MAR/81	
21956	N707QT	Boeing	700C	27/NOV/79		Prototype
	CN-ANR	Government of Morocco	3W6C		10/MAR/82	
22829	80-0137	USAF	E3C	31/MAR/81	04/DEC/81	
22830	80-0138	USAF	E3C	26/AUG/81	06/APR/82	
22831	80-0139	USAF	E3C	03/FEB/82	23/JUL/82	
22832	81-0004	USAF	E3C	14/MAY/82	19/OCT/82	
22833	81-0005	USAF	E3C	08/OCT/82	20/APR/83	
22834	82-0006	USAF	E3C	22/FEB/83	29/JUL/83	
22835	83-0007	USAF	E3C	29/APR/83	01/NOV/83	
22836	83-0008	USAF	E3A	08/JUL/83	18/APR/84	
22837	83-0009	USAF	E3A	03/NOV/83	19/JUN/84	
22838	79-0443	Boeing	E3A	26/JUN/81		
	79-0444	Boeing	E3A	30/NOV/81	19/MAY/82	
22839	LX-N90443	NATO				
	LX-N90444	NATO			19/AUG/82	
22840	79-0445	Boeing	E3A	07/APR/82		
	LX-N90445	NATO			12/NOV/82	
22841	79-0446	Boeing	E3A	25/JUN/82		
	LX-N90446	NATO			10/MAR/83	
22842	79-0447	Boeing	E3A	17/AUG/82		

BOEING 707 (EXISTING AIRCRAFT ONLY)

C/N	Registration	Owner/Operator	Series	First Flight	Delivery	Remarks
	LX-N90447	NATO			05/JUN/83	
22843	79-0448	Boeing	E3A	15/NOV/82		
	LX-N90448	NATO			27/JUN/83	
22844	79-0449	Boeing	E3A	04/JAN/83		
	LX-N90449	NATO			19/AUG/83	
22845	79-0450	Boeing	E3A	29/MAR/83		
	LX-N90450	NATO			21/OCT/83	
22846	79-0451	Boeing	E3A	02/JUN/83		
	LX-N90451	NATO			20/JAN/84	
22847	79-0452	Boeing	E3A	11/AUG/83		
	LX-N90452	NATO			27/APR/84	
22848	79-0453	Boeing	E3A	28/SEP/83		
	LX-N90453	NATO			18/MAY/84	
22849	79-0454	Boeing	E3A	07/DEC/83		
	LX-N90454	NATO			02/NOV/84	
22850	79-0455	Boeing	E3A	09/FEB/84		
	LX-N90455	NATO			11/FEB/85	
22851	79-0456	Boeing	E3A	06/APR/84		
	LX-N90456	NATO			07/NOV/84	
22852	79-0457	Boeing	E3A			
	LX-N90457	NATO			DEC/84	
22853	79-0458	Boeing	E3A			
	LX-N90458	NATO			MAR/85	
22854	79-0459	Boeing	E3A	21/SEP/84		
	LX-N90459	NATO			30/APR/85	
22855	79-0442	Boeing	E3A	18/DEC/80		
	LX-N90442	NATO			22/JAN/82	
23417	82-0066	USAF	E3A			
	1801	Royal Saudi Air Force				
23418	82-0067	USAF	E3A			
	1802	Royal Saudi Air Force				
23419	82-0068	USAF	E3A	09/DEC/85		
	1803	Royal Saudi Air Force			29/JUN/86	
23420	82-0069	USAF	E3A			
	1804	Royal Saudi Air Force				
23421	82-0070	USAF	E3A			
	1805	Royal Saudi Air Force				
23422	82-0071	USAF	E3A			
	1806	Royal Saudi Air Force				
23423	82-0072	USAF	E3A			
	1807	Royal Saudi Air Force				
23424	82-0073	USAF	E3A			
	1808	Royal Saudi Air Force				
23425	82-0074	USAF	E3A			
	1809	Royal Saudi Air Force				
23426	82-0075	USAF	E3A			
	1810	Royal Saudi Air Force				
23427	82-0076	USAF	E3A			
	1811	Royal Saudi Air Force				
23428	83-0510	USAF	E3A			
	1812	Royal Saudi Air Force				
23429	83-0511	USAF	E3A			
	1813	Royal Saudi Air Force				
23430	162782	U.S. Navy	E6A			

Boeing 707 cross-reference index

3B- Mauritius

18891	3B-NAE
19133	3B-NAF

3C- Ecuatorial Guinea

18056	3C-ABH

3D- Swaziland

19706	3D-ASC

3X- Guinea Republic

18748	3X-GAZ
19291	3X-GCC

4X- Israel

17661	4X-AGT
18070	4X-ATA
18071	4X-ATB
18985	4X-ATD
18456	4X-ATE
19004	4X-ATR
19004	4X-ATR
19502	4X-ATS
20097	4X-ATT
20122	4X-ATU
20122	4X-ATX
20301	4X-ATY
20456	4X-BMC
18012	4X-BYA
17612	4X-BYD
17667	4X-BYD
18246	4X-BYK
18460	4X-BYM
17619	4X-BYN
20110	4X-BYQ
20230	4X-BYS
17625	4X-BYT
17615	4X-BYV
17617	4X-BYW
17922	4X-BYX
18012	4X-JYA
17610	4X-JYB
17612	4X-JYD
17667	4X-JYD
17661	4X-JYI
18246	4X-JYK
18374	4X-JYL
18460	4X-JYM
17619	4X-JYN
20110	4X-JYQ
20230	4X-JYQ
17625	4X-JYT
17615	4X-JYV
17617	4X-JYW
17922	4X-JYX
20428	4X-JYY

4YB- Jordan/Iraq

18716	4YB-CAB
20890	4YB-CAC

5A- Libya

21228	5A-DAK
18765	5A-DHL
18881	5A-DIK
18880	5A-DIX
19001	5A-DIY
18746	5A-DIZ
19378	5A-DJM
18888	5A-DJS
18889	5A-DJT
18964	5A-DJU
19590	5A-DJV
19212	5A-DKA
18686	5A-DLT

5B- Cyprus

17632	5B-DAK
17631	5B-DAL
18054	5B-DAO
17635	5B-DAP

5N- Nigeria

20474	5N-ABJ
20669	5N-ABK
21428	5N-ANO
19664	5N-AOQ
18809	5N-ARQ
18922	5N-ASY

5R- Malagasy Republic

18686	5R-MFK

5V- Togo

19739	5V-TAG

5X- Uganda

18825	5X-DAR
18747	5X-UAC
19630	5X-UBC
18691	5X-UWM

5Y- Kenya

19621	5Y-AXA
19634	5Y-BBI
19633	5Y-BBJ
19872	5Y-BBK

60- Somalia

18953	60-SBM
18954	60-SBN
19316	60-SBT

70- South Yemen

20547	7O-ACS
20374	7O-ACO

8P- Barbados

19412	8P-CAC
19632	8P-CAD

9G- Ghana

17903	9G-ACJ
17903	9G-ACJ
17640	9G-ACN
17651	9G-ACO
19001	9G-ACR
19498	9G-ACX
19212	9G-ACY
19843	9G-ACZ
19212	9G-MAN

9J- Zambia

18976	9J-ADY
19263	9J-AEB
19354	9J-AEC
19295	9J-AEL
19367	9J-AEQ

9K- Kuwait

20084	9K-ACJ
20085	9K-ACK
20086	9K-ACL
20546	9K-ACM
20547	9K-ACN
20016	9K-ACS
20018	9K-ACU
19789	9K-ACX

9M- Malaysia

19529	9M-AQB
18953	9M-ASQ
18954	9M-ATR
18953	9M-MCQ
18954	9M-MCR
21049	9M-TDM
21096	9M-TMS

9Q- Zaire

17658	9Q-CBD
19266	9Q-CBL
20200	9Q-CBS
19294	9Q-CDA
19821	9Q-CKI
17658	9Q-CKP
20517	9Q-CVG
19162	9Q-CVG
17930	9Q-CZF
17602	9Q-CZK

9V- Singapore

19739	9V-BBB
19530	9V-BDC
19530	9V-BDC
19351	9V-BEW
19352	9V-BEX
19353	9V-BEY
19529	9V-BFC
18809	9V-BFN
18808	9V-BFW

9XR- Rwanda

19292	9XR-JA

9Y- Trinidad & Tobago

18334	9Y-TDB
18067	9Y-TDC
17692	9Y-TDO
19209	9Y-TED
19412	9Y-TEF
19631	9Y-TEJ
19632	9Y-TEK
20027	9Y-TEX
20028	9Y-TEZ

A6- United Arab Emirates

20123	A6-DPA
21049	A6-HPZ

21096	A6-HRM
18931	A6-UAE

A7- Qatar

21334	A7-AAA
20375	A7-AAC

AP- Pakistan

19285	AP-AUO
19286	AP-AUP
19866	AP-AVL
20488	AP-AWA
19716	AP-AWD
18991	AP-AWU
19866	AP-AWY
19286	AP-AXA
20488	AP-AXG
19636	AP-AZW
19635	AP-BAA
19576	AP-BBK

B- Taiwan

20261	B-1824
18825	B-1832

B- China

20714	B-2402
20715	B-2404
20716	B-2406
20717	B-2408
20718	B-2410
20719	B-2412
20720	B-2414
20721	B-2416
20722	B-2418
20723	B-2420
19353	B-2422
19352	B-2423
19530	B-2424
19964	B-2425
19294	B-2426

C- Canada

19416	C-GFLG
19629	C-GGAB
19623	C-GRYN
18746	C-GRYO
19434	C-GTAI

C6- Bahamas

18084	C6-BDG

CC- Chile

19435	CC-CAF
19443	CC-CCK
18926	CC-CEA
19000	CC-CEB
20021	CC-CEI
19693	CC-CEJ
19374	CC-CEK

CF- Canada

19789	CF-FAN
18746	CF-PWJ
17696	CF-PWV
17700	CF-PWW
20043	CF-QBG
20043	CF-ZYP

CN- Morocco

21956	CN-ANR
18334	CN-ANS
19773	CN-RMB
19774	CN-RMC
17619	CN-RMD

CP- Bolivia

18692	CP-1365
19586	CP-1698

CS- Portugal

20514	CS-DGI
20515	CS-DGJ
18961	CS-TBA
18962	CS-TBB
19740	CS-TBC
19969	CS-TBD
20136	CS-TBE
20297	CS-TBF
20298	CS-TBG
19415	CS-TBH
19767	CS-TBI
19179	CS-TBJ
20514	CS-TBT
20515	CS-TBU

CX- Uruguay

19212	CX-BJV
19239	CX-BNU
19240	CX-BOH

D- West Germany

17697	D-ABAP
17720	D-ABOD
18056	D-ABOG
18819	D-ABOX
18937	D-ABUA
18923	D-ABUB
18926	D-ABUC
18927	D-ABUD
18932	D-ABUE
18928	D-ABUF
18929	D-ABUG
18930	D-ABUH
19317	D-ABUI
20123	D-ABUJ
18931	D-ABUK
19315	D-ABUL
19316	D-ABUM
20124	D-ABUO
17701	D-ADAQ
17638	D-ALAL
17637	D-ALAM

D2- Angola

18975	D2-TAC
19355	D2-TAD
18583	D2-TAG
19965	D2-TAL
19963	D2-TAM
18583	D2-TOG
18975	D2-TOI
19355	D2-TOJ
19963	D2-TOL
19965	D2-TOM
20136	D2-TOP

EI- Ireland

18880	EI-ANO
19001	EI-ANV
19263	EI-ASM
18976	EI-ASN
19354	EI-ASO
19212	EI-BER
17929	EI-BFU
18832	EI-BKO
19964	EI-BLC

EL- Liberia

19377	EL-AIY
19986	EL-AIY
19377	EL-AJA

EP- Iran

21396	EP-HIM
18958	EP-IRJ
19267	EP-IRK
20287	EP-IRL
20288	EP-IRM
20741	EP-IRN

ET- Ethiopia

19820	ET-ACQ
19531	ET-AIV

F- France

17615	F-BHSC
17617	F-BHSE
17619	F-BHSG
17919	F-BHSL
17921	F-BHSN
17922	F-BHSO
17922	F-BHSO
18246	F-BHSS
18456	F-BHSV
19986	F-BJCM
18686	F-BLCB
18881	F-BLCC
18941	F-BLCD
19291	F-BLCE
19292	F-BLCF
19521	F-BLCG
19522	F-BLCH
19723	F-BLCI
19916	F-BLCK
19917	F-BLCL
18837	F-BSGT
17658	F-BUZJ
19370	F-BYCN
19373	F-BYCO
19377	F-BYCP
18837	F-OGIV
18840	F-OGIW

G- United Kingdom

17711	G-APFJ
17717	G-APFP
18413	G-ARRC
18372	G-ARWD
18925	G-ASZG
19498	G-ATWV
19416	G-ATZC
19590	G-ATZD
19590	G-ATZD
19415	G-AVKA
19843	G-AVPB
19767	G-AVTW
17702	G-AWDG
19821	G-AWHU
18975	G-AWTK
19355	G-AWWD
20374	G-AXGW
20375	G-AXGX
19664	G-AXRS
20456	G-AXXY
17597	G-AYBJ
19417	G-AYEX
20517	G-AYLT
18084	G-AYRZ
17608	G-AYXR
20089	G-AYZZ
18886	G-AZJM
17602	G-AZOI
20488	G-AZRO
17602	G-BAEL
19354	G-BAWP
19297	G-BCAL
18975	G-BDCN
19296	G-BDEA
19623	G-BDKE
19629	G-BDLM
19630	G-BDSJ
18591	G-BEAF
19271	G-BEVN
18765	G-BEZT
18691	G-BFEO
19625	G-BFLD
19293	G-BFLE
17632	G-BFMI
18718	G-BFZF
18054	G-BGCT
19270	G-BGIR
18717	G-BGIS
17640	G-BHOX
17651	G-BHOY
19270	G-BMAZ
18954	G-BMJE
18718	G-BNGH
19367	G-BPAT
21096	G-CDHW
18690	G-SAIL
17903	G-TJAA
17640	G-TJAB
17651	G-TJAC
18717	G-TRAD
18689	G-WIND

HC- Ecuador

19265	HC-BCT
19277	HC-BFC
19273	HC-BGP
20033	HC-BHY
18709	HC-BLY

HI- Dominican Republic

17610	HI-384HA
17767	HI-442

HK- Colombia

19741	HK-1402
20340	HK-1410
18714	HK-1718
17638	HK-1802
17637	HK-1818
18766	HK-1849
17643	HK-1942
19361	HK-2015
19276	HK-2016
19266	HK-2070
19375	HK-2473
17602	HK-2477
18886	HK-2600
18709	HK-2606
19575	HK-2842
18717	HK-3232

HL- South Korea

20522	HL7406
19716	HL7425
19372	HL7427
19369	HL7431
19626	HL7432
19268	HL7433
19366	HL7435

HP- Panama

18709	HP-1027
19575	HP-1028
17587	HP-780

HS- Thailand

17663	HS-VGC

HZ- Saudi Arabia

19809	HZ-ACC
19810	HZ-ACD
18583	HZ-ACF
21103	HZ-ACG
21104	HZ-ACH
21261	HZ-ACI
21367	HZ-ACJ
21368	HZ-ACK
17644	HZ-DAT
21081	HZ-HM1
21081	HZ-HM2
21368	HZ-HM3
21104	HZ-HM5

J6- St. Lucia

18689	J6-SLF

JY- Jordan

20495	JY-ADP
18948	JY-AEB
18949	JY-AEC
18716	JY-AED
20017	JY-AES
20283	JY-AFQ
19706	JY-AFR
18716	JY-CAB
20890	JY-CAC

LV- Argentina

19238	LV-ISA
19239	LV-ISB
19240	LV-ISC
19241	LV-ISD
19962	LV-JGP
20076	LV-LGO
20077	LV-LGP
18591	LV-MSG
19297	LV-MZE

LX- Luxembourg

19212	LX-BJV
18925	LX-FCV
19212	LX-FCV
18891	LX-LGR
20283	LX-LGS
19706	LX-LGT
19133	LX-LGU
17930	LX-LGW

N United States

18068	N105BN
20297	N105BV
18069	N106BN
19415	N106BV
18739	N107BN
18740	N108BN
18338	N111MF
19693	N1181Z
17606	N11RV
18713	N131EA
19566	N132EA
17696	N138TA
19209	N144SP
20174	N145SP
20016	N146SP
18810	N14791
20085	N147SP
19498	N14AZ
19963	N1501W
19964	N1502W
19965	N1503W
19966	N1504W
19967	N1505W
20315	N1506W
20316	N1507W
20317	N1508W
20318	N1509W
20319	N1510W
19566	N15710
19567	N15711
20069	N15713
20026	N160GL
20172	N161GL
20089	N162GL
19568	N16738
19569	N16739
18825	N17321
18886	N17323
18886	N17323
19177	N17325
19350	N17327
19351	N17328
19352	N17329
20316	N1785B
20741	N1785B
20761	N1785B
20043	N1786B
20830	N1790B
20428	N1793T
18979	N18702
18980	N18703
18981	N18704
18982	N18706
18983	N18707
18984	N18708
18985	N18709
19224	N18710
19225	N18711
19226	N18712
19227	N18713
17663	N194CA
17610	N196CA
17661	N198CA
17696	N220AM
20027	N2213Y
19631	N2215Y
17602	N2276X
20060	N275B
18408	N28714
19570	N28724
19572	N28727
19209	N29796
18692	N309EL
17696	N31239
20028	N3127K
19004	N317F
18880	N318F
19415	N319F
18975	N322F
19996	N3238N
20199	N3238S
18976	N323F
19354	N324F
19355	N325F
18953	N342A
20456	N343A
18586	N353US
18746	N356US
18747	N357US
18748	N358US
18888	N359US
18889	N360US
18921	N361US
18922	N362US
18964	N363US
19034	N364US
19163	N365US
19164	N366US
19168	N367US
19209	N368US
19716	N368WA
19210	N369US
19263	N370US
19442	N370WA
19411	N371US
19412	N372US
19179	N372WA
19434	N373US
19443	N374US
18583	N374WA
19631	N375US
17608	N37681
19632	N376US
18991	N376WA
19633	N377US
19634	N378US
19635	N379US
19636	N380US
19872	N381US
19773	N382US
19774	N383US
17692	N3842X
19775	N384US
19776	N385US
18832	N401PA
18833	N402PA
18834	N403PA
18835	N404PA
18836	N405PA
18837	N406PA
18839	N408PA
18840	N409PA
18841	N410PA
18842	N412PA
18957	N415PA
18958	N416PA
19264	N419PA
19265	N420PA
19266	N421PA
18809	N4225J
19276	N423PA
19277	N424PA
19361	N426PA
17597	N431MA
18084	N433MA
19366	N435PA
18839	N4408F
19267	N444PA
18413	N4465C
19269	N447PA

Boeing 707 cross-reference index

c/n	Registration		c/n	Registration		c/n	Registration		c/n	Registration
19270	N448M		19105	N7096		19342	N7592A		20062	N8733
19270	N448PA		19108	N7099		19343	N7593A		20064	N8735
18954	N449J		20175	N709PC		19344	N7594A		20065	N8736
19271	N449PA		19529	N7102		19515	N7595A		20066	N8737
19271	N449WA		19530	N7103		19516	N7596A		20067	N8738
19272	N450PA		19531	N7104		19517	N7597A		18408	N8739
19273	N451PA		20017	N710FW		19518	N7598A		20019	N880PA
19273	N451RN		20172	N711PC		19519	N7599A		20020	N881PA
19274	N452PA		20176	N712PC		18397	N759TW		20021	N882PA
19374	N453PA		17597	N719PA		18913	N760TW		20022	N883PA
18839	N454PC		19370	N720GS		18336	N761PA		20023	N884PA
19378	N455PA		19377	N721GS		19820	N761U		20024	N885PA
19367	N457PA		19373	N722GS		17675	N762TW		20025	N886PA
20178	N457PC		19572	N7231T		19821	N762U		20026	N887PA
19369	N459PA		19570	N7232X		18338	N763PA		18964	N88TF
19370	N460PA		19986	N723GS		19822	N763U		18928	N88ZL
19372	N462PA		17602	N724PA		18338	N763W		20027	N890PA
19373	N463PA		17606	N728PA		18339	N764PA		20028	N891PA
19353	N47330		20025	N728Q		18339	N764SE		20029	N892PA
19869	N47331		20029	N729Q		18339	N764SE		20030	N893PA
19870	N47332		17608	N730PA		18591	N767PA		20031	N894PA
19375	N473PA		20022	N730Q		19626	N770JS		20032	N895PA
19375	N473RN		20031	N731Q		18405	N773TW		20032	N895SY
19377	N474PA		17658	N731TW		18406	N774TW		20033	N896PA
19379	N475PA		19840	N7321S		18407	N775TW		20034	N897PA
21096	N48055		19842	N7323S		18408	N776TW		17921	N90287
19693	N491PA		20034	N732Q		17903	N778PA		18067	N93134
19695	N493PA		17661	N734TW		18409	N778TW		18336	N944JW
19697	N495PA		17663	N736TW		18764	N779TW		18825	N987AA
19698	N496PA		19416	N737AL		19574	N780JS		18338	N98WS
19699	N497PA		20076	N738AL		18400	N781TW		18056	N9985F
19695	N498GA		20077	N739AL		18401	N782TW		17606	N99WT
17652	N5038		17667	N740TW		18402	N783TW			
17905	N5090K		18012	N74612		18403	N784TW			
17619	N5093K		17903	N74613		18404	N785TW			
17646	N519GA		17615	N74615		18711	N786TW			
20546	N523SJ		18385	N746TW		18385	N788B			
19789	N524SJ		18386	N747TW		18713	N788TW			
19417	N525EJ		18387	N748TW		18709	N789TW			
19417	N525EJ		18388	N749TW		17697	N790FA			
20084	N525SJ		17631	N7504A		18714	N790PA			
19664	N526EJ		17632	N7505A		17697	N790SA			
19986	N527EJ		17634	N7507A		18715	N791PA			
18928	N5381X		17635	N7508A		17856	N791TW			
18842	N5517Z		17636	N7509A		17701	N792FA			
18836	N5519U		18389	N750TW		17716	N792PA			
18834	N5519V		17637	N7510A		17701	N792SA			
19566	N5710		17637	N7510A		18757	N792TW			
19212	N5771T		17638	N7511A		17700	N793NA			
19214	N5773T		17638	N7511A		17717	N793PA			
19435	N5774T		17639	N7512A		17700	N793SA			
18334	N58937		17640	N7513A		18718	N794EP			
18694	N58RD		17643	N7516A		18718	N794PA			
17905	N59RD		17644	N7517A		18718	N794RN			
19739	N600CS		17645	N7518A		20429	N794TW			
17702	N600JJ		17646	N7519A		18765	N795PA			
17651	N61TA		18390	N751TW		18765	N795RN			
21049	N62393		17648	N7521A		18758	N795TW			
21049	N62393		17651	N7524A		18766	N796PA			
17640	N62TA		17652	N7525A		18759	N796TW			
17692	N64757		18054	N7526A		18761	N798TW			
18586	N651TF		17648	N752TA		18762	N799TW			
18986	N6720		18391	N752TW		17692	N811UT			
18987	N6721		18939	N7530A		18922	N82TF			
18988	N6722		18392	N754TW		19433	N8400			
18989	N6723		18882	N7550A		19581	N8401			
19215	N6724		18883	N7551A		19582	N8402			
19216	N6726		18884	N7552A		19583	N8403			
19217	N6727		18885	N7553A		19584	N8404			
19218	N6728		19185	N7554A		19585	N8405			
19219	N6729		18689	N7555A		19586	N8406			
19871	N67333		18690	N7556A		19587	N8408			
19220	N6763T		18691	N7557A		19588	N8409			
19221	N6764T		18692	N7558A		19589	N8410			
19222	N6771T		18393	N755TW		19574	N8411			
19223	N6790T		18940	N7561A		19575	N8412			
19436	N6790T		19236	N7563A		19576	N8413			
18873	N68655		19237	N7564A		19577	N8414			
19000	N68657		19380	N7565A		20087	N8415			
18711	N700FW		19381	N7566A		20088	N8416			
17639	N701PC		19382	N7567A		20089	N8417			
17645	N702PC		19383	N7568A		17637	N8418A			
19395	N703PC		19384	N7569A		17638	N8420A			
19587	N705PC		18394	N756TW		20170	N8431			
20177	N706PC		19186	N7570A		20172	N8433			
17692	N7072		19187	N7571A		20174	N8435			
17610	N70774		19188	N7572A		20175	N8436			
17612	N707B5		19323	N7573A		20176	N8437			
19529	N707AD		19324	N7574A		20177	N8438			
17634	N707AR		19325	N7575A		20178	N8439			
18808	N707GB		19326	N7576A		20179	N8440			
18840	N707GE		19327	N7577A		20630	N8459			
18084	N707HD		19328	N7578A		19293	N861BX			
20124	N707HE		19329	N7579A		19625	N862BX			
19271	N707HT		19330	N7580A		19270	N863BX			
19294	N707HW		19331	N7581A		19375	N864BX			
19352	N707JJ		19332	N7582A		17766	N865BX			
19294	N707MB		19333	N7583A		20056	N86740			
19530	N707ME		19334	N7584A		20057	N86741			
20008	N707N		19335	N7585A		18916	N8705T			
17587	N707PA		19336	N7586A		20016	N870PA			
19294	N707PD		19337	N7587A		20017	N871PA			
21956	N707QT		19338	N7588A		18918	N8725T			
19353	N707SH		19339	N7589A		20058	N8729			
20261	N707ZS		18084	N758PA		20018	N872PA			
20060	N708A		18396	N758TW		20059	N8730			
20170	N708PC		19340	N7590A		20060	N8731			
19104	N7095		19341	N7591A		20061	N8732			

OB- Peru

c/n	Registration
19375	OB-R-1243
19294	OB-T-1264

OD- Lebanon

c/n	Registration
20259	OD-AFD
20260	OD-AFE
19108	OD-AFY
18939	OD-AGD
19269	OD-AGO
19274	OD-AGP
19214	OD-AGS
19966	OD-AGU
19967	OD-AGV
19104	OD-AGX
19105	OD-AGY
19531	OD-AGZ
19588	OD-AHB
19589	OD-AHC
19515	OD-AHD
19516	OD-AHE

OE- Austria

c/n	Registration
20043	OE-IDA
18339	OE-IEB
18069	OE-INA
18068	OE-IRA
18374	OE-LBA
18069	OE-UNA
18068	OE-URA

OO- Belgium

c/n	Registration
18746	OO-ABA
19378	OO-PSI
17921	OO-SBR
19442	OO-SBU
17930	OO-SBW
17623	OO-SJA
17625	OO-SJC
17626	OO-SJD
18374	OO-SJF
18460	OO-SJG
19162	OO-SJJ
19996	OO-SJL
20198	OO-SJM
20199	OO-SJN
20200	OO-SJO
19706	OO-SJR
19291	OO-TYC
19621	OO-YCK
19622	OO-YCL

P2- Papua New Guinea

c/n	Registration
19622	P2-ANA
19621	P2-ANB
19294	P2-ANH

PH- Netherlands

c/n	Registration
19664	PH-TRF
19416	PH-TRW
17646	PH-TVA
20198	PH-TVK

PI- Philippines

c/n	Registration
17661	PI-C7071

PK- Indonesia

c/n	Registration
18739	PK-MBA
21092	PK-PJQ

PP/PT- Brasil

c/n	Registration
17905	PP-VJA
20008	PP-VJH
18694	PP-VJJ
19822	PP-VJK
19321	PP-VJS
19842	PP-VJX
19840	PP-VJY
19433	PP-VLI
19870	PP-VLK
19871	PP-VLL
19869	PP-VLM
19177	PP-VLN
19350	PP-VLO
18940	PP-VLP
19529	PT-TCI
19519	PT-TCK
19517	PT-TCL
19317	PT-TCM
20088	PT-TCN
18932	PT-TCO
19416	PT-TCP
20456	PT-TCQ
20018	PT-TCR

RP- Philippines

c/n	Registration
19034	RP-C1886
18336	RP-C7075
17606	RP-C911

S2- Bangladesh

c/n	Registration
17903	S2-AAL
19168	S2-ABN
19434	S2-ACA
17776	S2-ACE
18921	S2-ACF
19354	S2-ACG
20018	S2-ACK

ST- Sudan

c/n	Registration
20898	ST-AFB
17651	ST-AHG
20086	ST-AIX
19521	ST-AKR
21104	ST-DRS

SU- Egypt

c/n	Registration
19844	SU-AOU
20341	SU-APD
20760	SU-AVX
20761	SU-AVY
20762	SU-AVZ
20919	SU-AXJ
20920	SU-AXK
18765	SU-BAG
19775	SU-BAO
18810	SU-BBA
19916	SU-DAA
19521	SU-DAB
19843	SU-DAC
20517	SU-DAD
19622	SU-DAE
19775	SU-EAA
18069	SU-FAA
18068	SU-FAB
20087	SU-FAC

SX- Greece

c/n	Registration
18948	SX-DBA
18949	SX-DBB
18950	SX-DBC
19760	SX-DBD
20035	SX-DBE
20036	SX-DBF
19164	SX-DBO
19163	SX-DBP

TC- Turkey

c/n	Registration
17587	TC-JBA
17697	TC-JBN
17697	TC-JBP
17701	TC-JBP
18834	TC-JBS
18836	TC-JBT
18842	TC-JBU
18715	TC-JCC

TF- Iceland

c/n	Registration
18714	TF-AEA
19621	TF-AEB
19622	TF-AEC
19964	TF-VLG
19351	TF-VLJ
19270	TF-VLL
18964	TF-VLP
18881	TF-VLR
18962	TF-VLV

TJ- Cameroon

20629	TJ-CAA

TU- Ivory Coast

17922	TU-TBY
18686	TU-TXI
19291	TU-TXL
18686	TU-TXM
19291	TU-TXN

VH- Australia

19621	VH-EAA
19622	VH-EAB
19623	VH-EAC
19623	VH-EAC
19624	VH-EAD
19625	VH-EAE
19626	VH-EAF
19627	VH-EAG
19628	VH-EAH
19629	VH-EAI
19630	VH-EAJ
17696	VH-EBA
17697	VH-EBB
17700	VH-EBE
17701	VH-EBF
17702	VH-EBG
18067	VH-EBH
18068	VH-EBI
18069	VH-EBJ
18334	VH-EBK
18739	VH-EBL
18740	VH-EBM
18808	VH-EBN
18809	VH-EBO
18810	VH-EBP
18953	VH-EBQ
18954	VH-EBR
19293	VH-EBT
19294	VH-EBU
19295	VH-EBV
19296	VH-EBW
19297	VH-EBX
19354	VH-EBZ

VN- Vietnam

17929	VN-A304
18832	VN-B1416

VP- Bahamas

17700	VP-BDE
18084	VP-BDG

VP- Zimbabwe

20110	VP-WGA
18819	VP-WKR
18923	VP-WKS
18929	VP-WKT
18930	VP-WKU
18927	VP-WKV
18891	VP-WKW

VR- Bermuda

18372	VR-BBW
19590	VR-BCP

VR- Cayman Islands

18067	VR-CAN
18586	VR-CAO
18748	VR-CAR
20028	VR-CBN

VR- Hong Kong

18586	VR-HGO
18922	VR-HGP
18964	VR-HGQ
18921	VR-HGR
19034	VR-HGU
18747	VR-HHB
18748	VR-HHD
18888	VR-HHE
18889	VR-HHJ
19263	VR-HHK
19412	VR-HHL
18937	VR-HTC

VT- India

18708	VT-DPM
18873	VT-DSI
19247	VT-DVA
19248	VT-DVB
19988	VT-DXT

XT- Bourkina Faso

18837	XT-ABX
18925	XT-ABX

YI- Iraq

20889	YI-AGE
20890	YI-AGF
20891	YI-AGG

YN- Nicaragua

17675	YN-BWL

YR- Romania

20803	YR-ABA
20804	YR-ABB
20805	YR-ABC
21651	YR-ABD
19272	YR-ABM
19379	YR-ABN

YU- Yugoslavia

19866	YU-AGD
19286	YU-AGF
19285	YU-AGG
19210	YU-AGI
19411	YU-AGJ

Z- Zimbabwe

18819	Z-WKR
18923	Z-WKS
18929	Z-WKT
18930	Z-WKU
18927	Z-WKV

ZP- Paraguay

18841	ZP-CCE
18957	ZP-CCF
19264	ZP-CCG

ZS- South Africa

17929	ZS-CKD
17930	ZS-CKE
18891	ZS-DYL
19133	ZS-EKV
19706	ZS-EUX
20230	ZS-FKG
20110	ZS-FKT
20283	ZS-LSF
19706	ZS-LSL

17929	ZS-SAB
17930	ZS-SAC
18891	ZS-SAD
19133	ZS-SAE
19706	ZS-SAF
20110	ZS-SAG
20230	ZS-SAH
20283	ZS-SAI

Military operators

Argentina

21070	T-01
19241	T-95
19238	T-96
21070	TC-91
20077	TC-92
19962	TC-93
20076	TC-93
20076	TC-94
19962	VR-21

Australia

19623	A20-623
19624	A20-624
19627	A20-627
19629	A20-629

Brasil

20008	2403

Canada

20315	13701
20316	13702
20317	13703
20318	13704
20319	13705

Chile

19443	902
18926	903

Colombia

19716	FAC-1201

Indonesia

21092	A-7002

Iran

21396	1001
21123	5-207
21124	5-208
21125	5-209
20830	5-241
20831	5-242
20832	5-243
20833	5-244
20834	5-245
20835	5-246
20830	5-8301
20831	5-8302
20832	5-8303
20833	5-8304
20834	5-8305
20835	5-8306
21123	5-8307
21124	5-8308
21125	5-8309
21125	5-8309
21126	5-8310
21127	5-8311

21128	5-8312
21129	5-8313
21475	5-8314

Libya

18765	AS.10.10

Portugal

20514	8801
20515	8802

Saudi Arabia

23417	1801
23418	1802
23419	1803
23420	1804
23421	1805
23422	1806
23423	1807
23424	1808
23425	1809
23426	1810
23427	1811
23428	1812
23429	1813

United States

23430	162782
17925	58-6970
17926	58-6971
17927	58-6972
18461	62-6000
20518	71-1407
20519	71-1408
20630	72-7000
21046	73-01674
21185	73-01675
21047	75-0556
21207	75-0557
21208	75-0558
21209	75-0559
21250	75-0560
21434	76-1604
21435	76-1605
21436	76-1606
21437	76-1607
21551	77-0351
21552	77-0352
21553	77-0353
21554	77-0354
21555	77-0355
21556	77-0356
21752	78-0576
21753	78-0577
21754	78-0578
21755	79-0001
21756	79-0002
21757	79-0003
22855	79-0442
22838	79-0443
22839	79-0444
22840	79-0445
22841	79-0446
22842	79-0447
22843	79-0448
22844	79-0449
22845	79-0450
22846	79-0451
22847	79-0452
22848	79-0453
22849	79-0454
22850	79-0455
22851	79-0456
22852	79-0457
22853	79-0458

22854	79-0459
22829	80-0137
22830	80-0138
22831	80-0139
22832	81-0004
22833	81-0005
19518	81-0891
19382	81-0892
19384	81-0893
19583	81-0894
19381	81-0895
19581	81-0896
19236	81-0897
19380	81-0898
22834	82-0006
23417	82-0066
23418	82-0067
23419	82-0068
23420	82-0069
23421	82-0070
23422	82-0071
23423	82-0072
23424	82-0073
23425	82-0074
23426	82-0075
23427	82-0076
22835	83-0007
22836	83-0008
22837	83-0009
23428	83-0510
23429	83-0511
20043	85-6973
20297	85-6974

West Germany

19997	1001
19998	1002
19999	1003
20000	1004

NATO

22855	LX-N90442
22838	LX-N90443
22839	LX-N90444
22840	LX-N90445
22841	LX-N90446
22842	LX-N90447
22843	LX-N90448
22844	LX-N90449
22845	LX-N90450
22846	LX-N90451
22847	LX-N90452
22848	LX-N90453
22849	LX-N90454
22850	LX-N90455
22851	LX-N90456
22852	LX-N90457
22853	LX-N90458
22854	LX-N90459

BOEING 720 (EXISTING AIRCRAFT ONLY)

Medium range commercial airliner with four wing-mounted Pratt & Whitney jet engines. Initially known as the 707-020, the 720 featured a number of aerodynamic refinements over the 707-120, a shorter fuselage for up to 165 passengers and reduced fuel load, and was intended for intermediate stage lengths. The basic 720, powered by JT3C-7 turbojets, made its first flight on 23 November 1959 and entered service with United Airlines on 5 July 1960. It was closely followed by the improved 720B with JT3D-3 turbofan engines. A total of 154 production aircraft were built and production ceased in August 1967.

Dimensions : Wing span: 130ft 9in (39.88m) Length: 136ft 9in (41.72m) Height: 41ft 9in(12.73m)

Powerplants : Four Pratt & Whitney JT3C-7 or JT3C-12 turbojets (720), four Pratt & Whitney JT3D-1 or JT3D-3 turbofans (720B)

Performance : Max cruising speed 510 knots (945km/h) (720) Range: with max payload 3,682nm (6,820km)

Accommodation: 124 passengers

Manufacturer : Boeing - PO Box 3707, Seattle, Washington 98124, USA
Telephone: (206) 237-2121 Telex: 32 94 30

C/N	Registration	Owner/Operator	Series	First Flight	Delivery	Remarks
18013	N7527A	American Airlines	023	13/APR/60	30/JUL/60	
	N7527A	American Airlines	023B		18/AUG/61	Converted
	G-BCBB	Invicta International			15/MAR/74	
	G-BCBB	Tempair International			12/SEP/74	Leased
	G-BCBB	Somali Airlines			12/SEP/74	Sub-leased
	6O-SAU	Somali Airlines			NOV/75	Sub-leased
	G-BCBB	Tempair International			76	Leased
	C9-ARG	DETA			11/MAY/76	Sub-leased
	G-BCBB	Invicta International			MAY/76	
	G-BCBB	Stanhope SS Co.			14/MAY/76	
	G-BCBB	Monarch Airlines			27/AUG/76	Leased
	G-BCBB	Cyprus Airways			SEP/76	Sub-leased
	G-BCBB	Monarch Airlines			76	Leased
	4R-ACS	Air Ceylon			01/MAR/77	Sub-leased
	G-BCBB	Monarch Airlines			04/DEC/77	Leased
	G-BCBB	Monarch Airlines			01/APR/78	Purchased
	4X-BMB	Maof Airlines			DEC/81	WFU NOV/84 to NOV/85
	4X-BMB	Israel Aircraft Industries			NOV/85	WFU NOV/85
18014	N7528A	American Airlines	023	24/JUN/60	24/JUL/60	
	N7528A	American Airlines	023B		28/SEP/61	Converted
	G-BCBA	Invicta International			12/JUL/74	
	G-BCBA	Stanhope SS Co.			01/DEC/75	
	G-BCBA	Tempair International			01/DEC/75	Leased
	P2-ANG	Air Niugini			06/FEB/76	Sub-leased
	G-BCBA	Stanhope SS Co.			02/FEB/77	
	G-BCBA	Monarch Airlines			01/SEP/77	
	G-BCBA	Cyprus Airways			JAN/78	Leased
	G-BCBA	Monarch Airlines			78	
	G-BCBA	Royal Air Maroc			79	Leased
	G-BCBA	Monarch Airlines			MAR/80	
	4X-BMA	Maof Airlines			OCT/81	WFU NOV/84 to NOV/85
	4X-BMA	Israel Aircraft Industries			NOV/85	
	N341A	Omega Air			JAN/86	
	N341A	Boeing			JAN/86	WFU JAN/86 for KC-135E Parts
18015	N7529A	American Airlines	023	19/JUL/60	13/AUG/60	
	N7529A	American Airlines	023B		13/SEP/61	Converted, WFU 04/OCT/70 to 07/MAY/76
	6O-SAW	Somali Airlines			07/MAY/76	WFU AUG/83, stored Mogadishu
18016	N7530A	American Airlines	023	25/JUL/60	22/SEP/60	
	N7530A	American Airlines	023B		25/JUL/61	Converted
	N7530A	Dubai Air Wing			02/OCT/75	
	A6-HHR	Dubai Air Wing			09/MAY/77	
	70-ACP	Alyemda			26/JUN/82	
	70-ACP	Midair			29/JUN/85	WFU 29/JUN/85
	N720AC	Boeing			OCT/85	WFU OCT/85 for KC-135E Parts
18021	N7535A	American Airlines	023	04/NOV/60	23/NOV/60	
	N7535A	American Airlines	023B		09/OCT/71	Converted
	OD-AGB	Middle East Airlines			03/MAY/73	
18022	N7536A	American Airlines	023	11/NOV/60	03/DEC/60	
	N7536A	American Airlines	023B		17/OCT/61	Converted
	N1R	Los Angeles Dodgers			26/JAN/71	
	N1R	Great American Airways			01/APR/83	
	N1R	Boeing			22/APR/83	WFU 22/APR/83 for KC-135E Parts
18024	N7538A	American Airlines	023B	14/JAN/61	03/FEB/61	
	OD-AFQ	Middle East Airlines			30/SEP/71	
	OD-AFQ	Aviatek			JUL/85	
	C-FETB	Pratt & Whitney			DEC/85	
18025	N7539A	American Airlines	023B	06/JAN/61	17/MAR/61	
	OD-AFZ	Middle East Airlines			19/OCT/72	
18027	N7541A	American Airlines	023B	10/FEB/61	27/FEB/61	
	OD-AFM	Middle East Airlines			11/DEC/70	
18028	N7542A	American Airlines	023B	08/MAR/61	29/MAR/61	
	N7542A	McCulloch International			13/JUN/72	Leased
	N7542A	American Airlines			72	
	HK-1974	Aerocondor			15/MAY/74	WFU OCT/80, stored Barranquilla
18030	N7544A	American Airlines	023B	15/MAR/61	10/APR/61	
	OD-AFN	Middle East Airlines			01/JAN/71	
	OD-AFN	Saudia			76	Leased

C/N	Registration	Owner/Operator	Series	First Flight	Delivery	Remarks
	OD-AFN	Middle East Airlines			77	
18031	N7545A	American Airlines	023B	29/MAR/61	17/APR/61	WFU SEP/71 to 23/MAY/76
	6O-SAX	Somali Airlines			23/MAY/76	WFU AUG/83, stored Mogadishu
18033	N7547A	American Airlines	023B	27/APR/61	23/MAY/61	
	N780PA	Pan American			13/FEB/63	
	N780EC	DORAL Trading			19/JUL/74	
	N780EC	Ecuatoriana			JUL/74	Leased
	N780PA	DORAL Trading			MAR/76	
	N780PA	Israel Aircraft Industries	023F		MAR/76	Converted
	HC-BDP	Ecuatoriana			APR/77	
	N720BG	International Air Leases			DEC/84	
	N720BG	Boeing			SEP/85	WFU SEP/85 for KC-135E Parts
18034	N7548A	American Airlines	023B	27/JUN/61	22/JUN/61	
	OD-AFL	Middle East Airlines			15/OCT/70	WFU DEC/85, stored Beirut
18036	N7550A	American Airlines	023B	13/JUN/61	01/JUL/61	
	N781PA	Pan American			11/MAR/63	
	HC-AZP	Ecuatoriana			04/SEP/74	WFU DEC/85, stored Marana
18037	N7551A	American Airlines	023B	28/JUN/61	21/JUL/61	
	N782PA	Pan American			30/APR/63	
	HC-AZQ	Ecuatoriana			11/SEP/74	
	N782PA	International Air Leases			MAR/84	
	N782PA	Boeing			OCT/84	WFU OCT/84 for KC-135E Parts
18043	EI-ALC	Aer Lingus	048	22/MAR/61	06/APR/61	
	EI-ALC	PIA			19/OCT/64	Leased
	EI-ALC	Aer Lingus			MAY/65	
	N7082	Braniff			01/NOV/65	Leased
	EI-ALC	Aer Lingus			24/MAY/66	
	9Y-TCS	BWIA			15/DEC/66	Leased
	EI-ALC	Aer Lingus			15/APR/67	
	N8790R	Trans Caribbean			22/OCT/67	Leased
	EI-ALC	Aer Lingus			15/APR/68	
	N8790R	Trans Polar			16/OCT/70	Leased
	LN-TUV	Trans Polar			18/MAY/71	
	EI-ALC	Aer Lingus			10/AUG/72	
	OO-TEB	TEA			JUN/75	
	OO-TEB	Tunis Air			DEC/75	Leased
	OO-TEB	TEA			MAR/77	
	OO-TEB	El Al			AUG/77	Leased
	OO-TEB	TEA			SEP/78	Leased
	OO-TEB	Tunis Air			78	Leased
	OO-TEB	TEA			30/SEP/78	
	OO-TEB	El Al			OCT/78	Leased
	OO-TEB	TEA			16/NOV/78	
	N8790R	Ambassadair			MAR/81	
	N8790R	American Transair			APR/82	
	N8790R	American Travel Air				WFU DEC/84
18049	N7217U	United Airlines	022	25/JAN/61	13/FEB/61	
	N304AS	Alaska Airlines			12/MAY/74	
	N304AS	Pan American			28/NOV/75	WFU 28/NOV/75
	N304AS	AeroAmerica			30/SEP/76	
	N421MA	MCA Leasing			18/MAR/77	
	N421MA	Aviateca			01/APR/77	Leased
	N421MA	MCA Leasing			77	
	N421MA	Air Panama			77	Leased
	N421MA	MCA Leasing			77	
	N421MA	Air Charter SA			26/OCT/78	Leased
	N421MA	MCA Leasing			79	
	N421MA	Southeast Airlines			JUL/79	Leased
	N421MA	MCA Leasing			DEC/79	
	N421MA	Tropic Air			03/AUG/80	Leased
	N421MA	MCA Leasing			81	
	N421MA	Jet Power			81	
	N421MA	Hispaniola Airways			30/DEC/81	Leased
	HI-401	Hispaniola Airways			NOV/82	
18059	D-ABOL	Lufthansa	030B	21/APR/61	03/MAY/61	WFU AUG/83, stored Puerto Plata
	N784PA	Pan American			26/MAR/64	
	HK-676	Avianca			13/APR/73	
	HK-676	SAM			08/MAR/77	
	HK-676	Avianca			20/MAY/80	
	N3831X	Aeron Aviation			09/JAN/83	
	N3831X	International Air Leases			JUN/83	
	N3831X	Boeing			18/AUG/83	WFU 18/AUG/83 for KC-135E Parts
18063	N93143	Western Airlines	047B	25/MAY/61	07/JUN/61	
	9H-AAK	Air Malta			03/MAR/78	
18072	N7219U	United Airlines	022	17/NOV/61	01/DEC/61	
	N7219U	TL Industries			15/JUL/73	
	N7219U	AeroAmerica			75	Leased
	N7219U	TL Industries			75	
	N7219U	McCulloch International			18/NOV/75	WFU JAN/77
	N7219U	Agro Air International			28/FEB/78	
	N7219U	Aeromar			MAR/83	Leased
	HI-415	Aeromar			MAR/83	Leased
	HI-415	Agro Air International			DEC/84	WFU DEC/84, stored Miami
18073	N7220U	United Airlines	022	22/NOV/61	14/DEC/61	
	OO-VGM	Delta Air Transport			18/MAY/74	
	TF-VVC	Air Viking				Not taken-up
	N64696	Atlas Aircraft			19/NOV/75	
	N64696	Air Ceylon			26/DEC/76	Leased
	N64696	Atlas Aircraft				
	N64696	InterAmerican Air Cargo			28/FEB/78	
	N64696	Inair Panama			MAR/78	Leased
	N64696	Rowan Drilling			DEC/79	
	N64696	Baker Aviation School			NOV/80	WFU NOV/80, Instructional Miami
18077	N7224U	United Airlines	022	16/JAN/62	10/APR/62	
	N7224U	Braniff			06/JUN/72	Leased
	N7224U	United Airlines			31/DEC/72	
	N7224U	Todd Equipment Leasing Co.			31/MAR/75	
	N7224U	Caesars Palace			JUN/75	Leased
	N7224U	Dallah Avco			MAY/78	
	N7224U	Sinclare Air Service			AUG/78	
	N7224U	"Air France"			JAN/81	Titles applied for film
	N7224U	Sinclare Air Service			JAN/81	
	N7224U	Air Cruise			JUL/81	Leased
	N7224U	Sinclare Air Service			DEC/82	
	N7224U	Westwind Airlines			DEC/82	
	N7224U	Sinclare Air Service			AUG/83	WFU AUG/83, stored Redding, Ca.

BOEING 720 (EXISTING AIRCRAFT ONLY)

C/N	Registration	Owner/Operator	Series	First Flight	Delivery	Remarks
18078	N7225U	United Airlines	022	31/JAN/62	24/APR/62	
	N7225U	Jet Set Travel Club			18/OCT/73	
	N7225U	FAMCO Transport			SEP/82	
	N7225U	Sierra Transair			JUN/83	
	N7225U	FAMCO Transport			AUG/84	WFU AUG/84, Seattle
18080	N7227U	United Airlines	022	09/APR/62	15/MAY/62	
	N7227U	Aero Specialties			27/AUG/73	
	HP-679	Inair Panama			24/OCT/73	
	N62215	United States Global			28/JUL/75	
	N62215	Universal Applicators Inc.			28/NOV/75	
	N62215	Fiesta Air Travel Club			FEB/78	Leased
	N62215	Universal Applicators Inc.			MAY/79	
	N62215	Caledonian Airlines			21/DEC/79	
	N62215	Air Tanzania			21/DEC/79	Leased
	N62215	Caledonian Airlines			JUL/81	WFU JUL/81, stored Entebbe
18081	N7228U	United Airlines	022	26/MAY/62	01/JUN/62	
	N7228U	Atlanta Skylarks Club			02/JUL/73	
	N7228U	Independent Air				Leased
	N7228U	Atlanta Skylarks Club				
	N7228U	People's Rep. of China			DEC/84	WFU DEC/84, ground trainer
18082	N7229U	United Airlines	022	01/JUN/62	12/JUN/62	
	TF-VVA	Air Viking			08/APR/74	
	TF-VVA	Eagle Air			28/JUN/76	
	N419MA	Jet Power	022F		18/DEC/76	Converted
	N419MA	MCA Leasing			FEB/77	Leased
	N419MA	Jet Power			DEC/79	
	N419MA	Indian Government			DEC/80	Leased WFU DEC/80, stored Bombay
18086	HK-724	Avianca	059B	19/OCT/61	08/NOV/61	
	N4451B	Jet Star Inc.			AUG/83	
	N4451B	Leaseway International			NOV/83	WFU NOV/83, Derelict Miami
18159	N8705E	Eastern Airlines	025	14/SEP/61	27/SEP/61	
	N8705E	Boeing			27/JAN/70	
	OY-DSL	Conair			17/JUL/71	
	N7229L	Atlanta Skylarks			AUG/81	WFU DEC/84 to MAY/86
	N7229L	Independent Air			MAY/86	
	N7229L	Eagle Ministries			MAY/86	
18160	N8706E	Eastern Airlines	025	22/SEP/61	27/SEP/61	
	N8706E	Boeing			21/AUG/69	
	HL7402	Korean Airlines			22/SEP/69	WFU OCT/77, Crew Trainer, Seoul
18162	N8708E	Eastern Airlines	025	04/OCT/61	08/NOV/61	
	N8708E	Boeing			22/SEP/69	
	D-ACIP	Calair			11/DEC/70	WFU MAR/72
	VP-YNL	Air Rhodesia			13/APR/73	
	VP-YNL	Air Zimbabwe			80	
	Z-YNL	Air Zimbabwe				WFU JUN/82, stored Harare
18167	N93144	Western Airlines	047B	03/JUL/61	11/JUL/61	
	9H-AAL	Air Malta			07/MAR/79	
18240	N8711E	Eastern Airlines	025	24/OCT/61	08/JAN/62	
	N8711E	Boeing			22/JUN/70	
	D-ACIR	Calair			30/DEC/70	WFU MAR/72
	N8711E	Club America			29/OCT/72	
	N8711E	International Air Leases			OCT/73	
	N8711E	Ambassadair			22/DEC/73	Leased
	N8711E	American Trans Air			MAR/81	Leased
	N8711E	Windwalkers Air			24/JAN/83	
	N8711E	Aerotours			OCT/84	Leased
						WFU FEB/85, Santo Domingo
18242	N8713E	Eastern Airlines	025	13/NOV/61	22/NOV/61	
	N8713E	Boeing			17/JUN/70	
	D-ACIS	Calair			30/JAN/71	
	VP-YNM	Air Rhodesia			12/APR/73	
	VP-YNM	Air Zimbabwe			80	WFU MAY/83, stored Harare
18244	N8715E	Eastern Airlines	025	07/DEC/61	16/DEC/61	
	N8715E	Boeing			15/JUN/70	
	D-ACIT	Calair			30/DEC/70	
	VP-YNN	Air Rhodesia			11/APR/73	
	VP-YNN	Air Zimbabwe			80	
	Z-YNN	Air Zimbabwe				WFU JUN/82, stored Harare
18248	D-ABON	Lufthansa	030B	20/DEC/61	05/JAN/62	
	N786PA	Pan American			17/DEC/65	
	HK-749	Avianca			29/NOV/72	
	HK-749	SAM			30/SEP/77	
	HK-749	Avianca				
	HK-749	SAM			MAY/80	WFU DEC/80, derelict Bogota
18251	D-ABOR	Lufthansa	030B	16/FEB/62	27/FEB/62	
	N788PA	Pan American			01/JAN/65	
	JY-ADT	Alia			30/NOV/72	
	JY-ADT	Sierra Leone Airlines			NOV/83	Leased
	9L-LAZ	Sierra Leone Airlines			04/AUG/84	Purchased
	N720BC	Boreas Corp.			JUN/85	
	N720BC	Boeing			OCT/85	WFU OCT/85 for KC-135E Parts
18351	N721US	Northwest Orient	051B	20/MAY/61	26/MAY/61	
	N721US	Templewood Aviation			24/SEP/71	
	18351	Taiwan Government			05/DEC/71	
18352	N722US	Northwest Orient	051B	09/JAN/61	22/JUN/61	
	SX-DBG	Olympic Airways			05/FEB/72	WFU JUN/81, stored Athens
18353	N723US	Northwest Orient	051B	19/JUN/61	12/JUL/61	
	SX-DBH	Olympic Airways			30/MAR/72	WFU JUN/81, stored Athens
18356	N726US	Northwest Orient	051B	21/SEP/61	05/OCT/61	
	SX-DBK	Olympic Airways			15/MAR/72	WFU JUN/81, stored Athens
18380	AP-AMJ	PIA	040B	15/NOV/62	29/NOV/62	
	AP-AMJ	Air Malta			29/MAR/74	Leased
	9H-AAN	Air Malta			MAR/79	Purchased,
	N5487N	International Air Leases			20/SEP/84	
	N5487N	Boeing			04/OCT/84	WFU 04/OCT/84 for KC-135E Parts
18381	N791TW	Boeing	051B	14/JUL/61		
	N791TW	Trans World Airlines			22/JUL/61	Leased
	N791TW	Boeing			31/OCT/62	
	N730US	Northwest Orient			31/OCT/62	Leased
	N730US	Northwest Orient			01/JUL/68	Purchased
	G-AZFB	Monarch Airlines			28/NOV/71	
	G-AZFB	Iraqi Airways			AUG/74	Leased
	G-AZFB	Monarch Airlines			NOV/74	
	G-AZFB	Garuda			NOV/75	Leased
	G-AZFB	Monarch Airlines			13/JAN/76	

C/N	Registration	Owner/Operator	Series	First Flight	Delivery	Remarks
	G-AZFB	Cyprus Airways			MAR/77	Leased
	G-AZFB	Monarch Airlines				WFU NOV/82 to MAR/83
	N2464C	Jet 24			MAR/83	
	N2464C	Boeing			OCT/83	WFU OCT/83 for KC-135E Parts
18382	N792TW	Boeing	051B	25/JUL/61		
	N792TW	Trans World Airlines			02/AUG/61	Leased
	N792TW	Boeing			21/SEP/62	
	N731US	Northwest Orient			21/SEP/62	Leased
	N731US	Northwest Orient			01/JUL/68	Purchased
	G-AZKM	Monarch Airlines			25/JAN/72	
	G-AZKM	UTA			DEC/77	Leased
	G-AZKM	Monarch Airlines			JAN/78	
	G-AZKM	Cyprus Airways			83	Leased
	G-AZKM	Monarch Airlines			83	
	G-AZKM	Maof Airlines			83	Leased
	G-AZKM	Monarch Airlines			83	
	N2464K	Jet 24			MAR/83	
	N2464K	Boeing			21/JUN/83	WFU 21/JUN/83 for KC-135E Parts
18383	N793TW	Boeing	051B	11/AUG/61		
	N793TW	Trans World Airlines			27/AUG/61	Leased
	N793TW	Boeing			29/SEP/62	
	N732US	Northwest Orient			31/OCT/62	Leased
	N732US	Northwest Orient			01/JUL/68	Purchased
	G-AZNX	Monarch Airlines			11/APR/72	
	G-AZNX	Garuda			NOV/75	Leased
	G-AZNX	Monarch Airlines			JAN/76	
	N24666	Jet 24			14/MAR/83	
	N24666	Boeing			21/JUN/83	WFU 21/JUN/83 for KC-135E Parts
18384	N795TW	Boeing	051B	15/SEP/61		
	N795TW	Trans World Airlines			30/SEP/61	Leased
	N795TW	Boeing			26/OCT/62	
	N733US	Northwest Orient			26/OCT/62	Leased
	N733US	Northwest Orient			01/JUL/68	Purchased
	OY-APZ	Maersk Air			01/NOV/72	
	OY-APZ	Conair			16/FEB/81	
18417	N57202	Continental Airlines	024B	18/MAY/62	27/MAY/62	
	ET-AFK	Ethiopian Airlines			03/NOV/74	
	ET-AFK	Saudia			10/MAR/75	Leased
	ET-AFK	Ethiopian Airlines			FEB/76	
18418	N57203	Continental Airlines	024B	13/JUN/62	20/JUN/62	
	ET-AFA	Ethiopian Airlines			28/SEP/73	
	N769BE	Boeing			NOV/85	WFU NOV/85 for KC-135E Parts
18419	N57204	Continental Airlines	024B	29/JUN/62	07/JUL/62	
	ET-AFB	Ethiopian Airlines			16/SEP/74	
	N770BE	Boeing			NOV/85	WFU NOV/85 for KC-135E Parts
18420	N727US	Northwest Orient	051B	13/OCT/61	25/OCT/61	
	SX-DBL	Olympic Airways			06/FEB/72	WFU MAR/81, stored Athens
18421	N728US	Northwest Orient	051B	04/OCT/61	15/NOV/61	
	OY-APY	Maersk Air			08/FEB/73	
	G-BHGE	Monarch Airlines			12/NOV/79	
	OY-APY	Conair			JUN/81	
18422	N729US	Northwest Orient	051B	05/DEC/61	12/DEC/61	
	OY-APW	Maersk Air			14/MAR/73	
	OY-APW	Conair			16/FEB/81	
18424	4X-ABA	El Al	058B	16/MAR/62	26/MAR/62	
	N8498S	Jet Power Inc.			28/AUG/80	
	N8498S	Boeing			27/AUG/84	
	N8498S	USAF			27/AUG/84	WFU 27/AUG/84 for Electric Tests
18425	4X-ABB	El Al	058B	23/APR/62	30/APR/62	
	N8498T	Jet Power Inc.			28/AUG/80	
	N8498T	Central Airlines			NOV/80	
	N4228G	Jet Power Inc.			80	
	N4228G	Boeing			20/JUL/83	WFU 20/JUL/83 for KC-135E Parts
18451	N93145	Western Airlines	047B	19/JUL/62	27/JUL/62	
	HZ-NAA	Prince Nawaf Bin Abdul Aziz			NOV/78	
	HZ-KA1	Sheikh Kamal Adham			AUG/80	
18452	N93146	Western Airlines	047B	31/JUL/62	08/AUG/62	
	N93146	Overseas Intl. Distributors			13/JUN/79	
	N93146	Summit Aviation			AUG/80	
18453	N93147	Western Airlines	047B	22/AUG/62	28/AUG/62	
	HZ-KA4	Sheikh Kamal Adham			JUL/78	
18455	ET-AAH	Ethiopian Airlines	060B	01/NOV/62	27/NOV/62	
	ET-AAH	Middle East Airlines			01/JAN/66	Leased
	ET-AAH	Ethiopian Airlines			31/MAR/68	
18588	N93148	Western Airlines	047B	21/MAR/63	03/APR/63	
	N93148	International Lease Finance			18/MAY/78	
	5Y-BBX	Kenya Airways			18/MAY/78	Leased
	5Y-BBX	Kenya Airways			05/MAY/79	Purchased
18687	N734US	Northwest Orient	051B	24/SEP/63	22/OCT/63	
	SX-DBM	Olympic Airways			30/JUL/72	WFU JUN/81, stored Athens
18688	N735US	Northwest Orient	051B	17/JAN/64	23/JAN/64	
	SX-DBN	Olympic Airways			18/JAN/73	
	SX-DBN	Air Tanzania			01/OCT/80	Leased
	SX-DBN	Olympic Airways			FEB/81	
	YN-BYI	Aeronica			26/FEB/81	
18792	N736US	Northwest Orient	051B	18/JUN/64	26/JUN/64	
	OY-APU	Maersk Air			20/FEB/74	
	G-BBZG	Monarch Airlines			20/FEB/74	Leased
	OY-APU	Maersk Air			21/DEC/75	
	OY-APU	Tunis Air			APR/80	Leased
	OY-APU	Maersk Air			80	
	OY-APU	Conair			APR/81	
18793	N737US	Northwest Orient	051B	21/JUL/64	24/JUL/64	
	OY-APV	Maersk Air			16/JAN/74	
	OY-APV	Nigeria Airways			DEC/77	Leased
	OY-APV	Maersk Air			78	
	OY-APV	Conair			15/SEP/81	
18818	N93152	Western Airlines	047B	23/SEP/64	26/SEP/64	
	AP-AXL	PIA			12/AUG/74	
	AP-AXL	ATASCO			APR/86	
	AP-AXL	PIA			APR/86	Leased
	AP-AXL	ATASCO			26/JUL/86	WFU JUN/86, fuselage for preservation
18829	N3156	Western Airlines	047B	26/MAY/65	02/JUN/65	
	N3156	International Air Leases			28/MAR/79	

BOEING 720 (EXISTING AIRCRAFT ONLY)

C/N	Registration	Owner/Operator	Series	First Flight	Delivery	Remarks
	9H-AAO	Air Malta			28/MAR/79	
18830	N3157	Western Airlines	047B	11/JUN/65	17/JUN/65	
	OD-AGF	Middle East Airlines			15/FEB/74	
18831	HK-726	Avianca	059B	24/MAR/65	08/APR/65	
	HK-726	Jet Star Inc.			AUG/83	
	N4450Z	Leaseway International			02/OCT/84	
	N4450Z	Boeing			02/OCT/84	WFU 02/OCT/84 for KC-135E Parts
18977	ET-ABP	Ethiopian Airlines	060B	01/SEP/65	20/SEP/65	
	ET-ABP	Middle East Airlines			01/JAN/66	Leased
	ET-ABP	Ethiopian Airlines			31/MAR/68	
19207	N3161	Western Airlines	047B	23/JUN/66	30/JUL/66	
	N3161	Wicklund Aviation			OCT/79	
	N3161	Boeing			17/MAR/83	WFU 17/MAR/83 for KC-135E Parts
19208	N3162	Western Airlines	047B	26/JUL/66	29/JUL/66	
	N3162	Wicklund Aviation			25/JAN/80	
	N3162	Grella Aviation			AUG/80	
	N3162	Boeing			17/MAR/83	WFU 17/MAR/83 for KC-135E Parts
19413	N3163	Western Airlines	047B	05/MAY/67	13/MAY/67	
	N3163	Wicklund Aviation			20/DEC/79	
	N3163	Phylflow Aviation			AUG/80	
	N3163	Boeing			17/MAR/83	WFU 17/MAR/83 for KC-135E Parts
19414	N3164	Western Airlines	047B	22/JUN/67	28/JUN/67	
	N3164	Wicklund Aviation			21/NOV/79	
	N3164	Cisco Aviation			AUG/80	
	N3164	Boeing			17/MAR/83	WFU 17/MAR/83 for KC-135E Parts
19438	N3165	Western Airlines	047B	11/AUG/67	18/AUG/67	
	N3165	Wicklund Aviation			OCT/79	
	N3165	Finkel Aviation			JUN/80	
	N3165	Boeing			17/MAR/83	WFU 17/MAR/83 for KC-135E Parts
19523	N3167	Western Airlines	047B	08/SEP/67	20/SEP/67	
	N3167	Wicklund Aviation			OCT/79	
	N3167	Rogers Aviation			AUG/80	
	5V-TAD	Republic of Togo			OCT/80	
	N3833L	Conimex			83	
	N3833L	Boeing			20/JUN/83	WFU 20/JUN/83 for KC-135E Parts

Boeing 720
Cross-reference index

4R- Sri Lanka

18013	4R-ACS

4X- Israel

18424	4X-ABA
18425	4X-ABB
18014	4X-BMA
18013	4X-BMB

5V- Togo

| 19523 | 5V-TAD |

5Y- Kenya

| 18588 | 5Y-BBX |

60- Somalia

18013	6O-SAU
18015	6O-SAW
18031	6O-SAX

70- South Yemen

| 18016 | 70-ACP |

9H- Malta

18063	9H-AAK
18167	9H-AAL
18380	9H-AAN
18829	9H-AAO

9L- Sierra Leone

| 18251 | 9L-LAZ |

9Y- Trinidad & Tobago

| 18043 | 9Y-TCS |

A6- United Arab Emirates

| 18016 | A6-HHR |

AP- Pakistan

| 18380 | AP-AMJ |
| 18818 | AP-AXL |

C- Canada

| 18024 | C-FETB |

C9- Mozambique

| 18013 | C9-ARG |

D- West Germany

18059	D-ABOL
18248	D-ABON
18251	D-ABOR
18162	D-ACIP
18240	D-ACIR
18242	D-ACIS
18244	D-ACIT

EI- Eire

| 18043 | EI-ALC |

ET- Ethiopia

18455	ET-AAH
18977	ET-ABP
18418	ET-AFA
18419	ET-AFB
18417	ET-AFK

G- United Kingdom

18381	G-AZFB
18382	G-AZKM
18383	G-AZNX
18792	G-BBZG
18014	G-BCBA
18013	G-BCBB
18421	G-BHGE

HC- Ecuador

18036	HC-AZP
18037	HC-AZQ
18033	HC-BDP

HI- Domincan Republic

| 18049 | HI-401 |
| 18072 | HI-415 |

HK- Colombia

18028	HK-1974
18059	HK-676
18086	HK-724
18831	HK-726
18248	HK-749

HL South Korea

| 18160 | HL7402 |

HP- Panama

| 18080 | HP-679 |

HZ- Saudi Arabia

18451	HZ-KA1
18453	HZ-KA4
18451	HZ-NAA

JY- Jordan

| 18251 | JY-ADT |

LN- Norway

| 18043 | LN-TUV |

N United States

18022	N1R
18381	N2464C
18382	N2464K
18049	N304AS
18829	N3156
18830	N3157
19207	N3161
19208	N3162
19413	N3163
19414	N3164
19438	N3165
19523	N3167
18014	N341A
18059	N3831X
19523	N3833L
18082	N419MA
18049	N421MA
18425	N4228G
18831	N4450Z
18086	N5487N
18417	N57202
18418	N57203
18419	N57204
18080	N62215
18073	N64696
18043	N7082
18016	N720AC
18251	N720BC
18033	N720BG
18049	N7217U
18072	N7219U
18351	N721US
18073	N7220U
18077	N7224U
18078	N7225U
18080	N7227U
18081	N7228U
18159	N7229L
18082	N7229U
18352	N722US
18353	N723US
18356	N726US
18420	N727US
18421	N728US
18422	N729US
18381	N730US
18382	N731US
18383	N732US
18384	N733US
18687	N734US
18688	N735US
18792	N736US
18793	N737US
18013	N7527A
18014	N7528A
18015	N7529A
18016	N7530A
18021	N7535A
18022	N7536A
18024	N7538A
18025	N7539A
18027	N7541A
18028	N7542A
18030	N7544A
18031	N7545A
18033	N7547A
18034	N7548A
18036	N7550A
18037	N7551A
18418	N769BE
18419	N770BE
18033	N780EC
18033	N780PA
18036	N781PA
18037	N782PA
18059	N784PA
18248	N786PA
18251	N788PA
18381	N791TW
18382	N792TW
18383	N793TW
18384	N795TW
18424	N8498S
18425	N8498T
18159	N8705E
18160	N8706E
18162	N8708E
18240	N8711E
18242	N8713E
18244	N8715E
18043	N8790N
18043	N8790R
18063	N93143
18167	N93144
18451	N93145
18452	N93146
18453	N93147
18588	N93148
18818	N93152

OD- Lebanon

18034	OD-AFL
18027	OD-AFM
18030	OD-AFN
18024	OD-AFQ
18025	OD-AFZ
18022	OD-AGB
18830	OD-AGF

OO- Belgium

| 18043 | OO-TEB |
| 18073 | OO-VGM |

OY- Denmark

18792	OY-APU
18793	OY-APV
18422	OY-APW
18421	OY-APY
18384	OY-APZ
18159	OY-DSL

P2- Papua New Guinea

| 18014 | P2-ANG |

SX- Greece

18352	SX-DBG
18353	SX-DBH
18356	SX-DBK
18420	SX-DBL
18687	SX-DBM
18688	SX-DBN

TF- Iceland

| 18082 | TF-VVA |
| 18073 | TF-VVC |

VP- Zimbabwe

18162	VP-YNL
18242	VP-YNM
18244	VP-YNN

YN- Nicaragua

| 18688 | YN-BYI |

Z- Zimbabwe

| 18162 | Z-YNL |
| 18244 | Z-YNN |

Military operated

Taiwan

| 18351 | 18351 |

HAWKER SIDDELEY TRIDENT (EXISTING AIRCRAFT ONLY)

Rear-engined, short/medium haul jet transport, powered by three Rolls-Royce Spey turbofans. The first aircraft, a Trident 1, made its maiden flight on 9 January 1962, and other versions followed including the 1E,2E and 3B super, covering a seating capacity from 103 to 180 passengers. A total of 117 production aircraft were built and production ceased in July 1975

Dimensions :	Wing span: 89ft 11in (27.41m) Length: 114ft 9in (34.98m) Height: 27ft 0in (8.23m) (Trident 1)
	Wing span: 95ft 0in (28.95m) Length: 114ft 9in (34.98m) Height: 27ft 0in (8.23m) (Trident 1E)
	Wing span: 98ft 0in (28.95m) Length: 114ft 9in (34.98m) Height 27ft 0in (8.23m) (Trident 2)
	Wing span: 98ft 1in (29.9m) Length: 131ft 2in (40.0m) Height: 28ft 3in (8.61m) (Trident 3)
Powerplant :	Three Rolls Royce Spey 505-5 turbofans (1), three Rolls Royce Spey 511-5 turbofans (1E), three Rolls Royce Spey 512-5W turbofans (2) three Rolls Royce Spey 512-5W turbofans plus one RB.162-86 turbojet (3)
Performance :	Max cruising speed 526 knots (975km/h) (1) Range: with max payload 1,772nm (3,283km) (1)
	Max cruising speed 502 knots (960km/h) (2) Range: with max payload 2,741nm (5,078km) (2)
	Max cruising speed 492 knots (913km/h) (3) Range: with max payload 1,792nm (3,320km) (3)
Accommodation:	103 passengers (Trident 1), 149 passengers (Trident 2), 180 passengers (Trident 3)
Manufacturer :	Hawker Siddeley

C/N	Registration	Owner/Operator	Series	First Flight	Delivery	Remarks
2108	G-ARPH	BEA	1C	08/MAR/64	25/MAR/64	
	G-ARPH	British Airways			01/APR/72	WFU 26/MAR/82, Preserved Cosford Musuem
2111	G-ARPK	BEA	1C	13/JUN/64	26/JUN/64	
	G-ARPK	British Airways			01/APR/72	WFU 27/MAR/82, stored Manchester
2112	G-ARPL	BEA	1C	27/JUL/64	06/AUG/64	
	G-ARPL	British Airways			01/APR/72	WFU 26/MAR/82, to Edinburgh Airport fire service.
2115	G-ARPN	BEA	1C	24/NOV/64	04/DEC/64	
	G-ARPN	British Airways			01/APR/72	WFU 27/MAR/82, stored Aberdeen
2116	G-ARPO	BEA	1C	13/JAN/65	31/JAN/65	
	G-ARPO	British Airways			01/APR/72	WFU 16/MAR/83 to Teesside Fire School
2117	G-ARPP	BEA	1C	12/FEB/65	25/FEB/65	
	G-ARPP	British Airways			01/APR/72	WFU 23/FEB/83, stored Glasgow
2119	G-ARPR	BEA	1C	01/APR/65	12/APR/65	
	G-ARPR	British Airways			01/APR/72	WFU 16/SEP/81, to Teesside Airport fire service.
2123	G-ARPW	BEA	1C	07/OCT/65	15/OCT/65	
	G-ARPW	British Airways			01/APR/72	WFU 31/MAR/82, to Teesside Airport fire service.
2124	G-ARPX	BEA	1C	13/MAY/66	25/MAY/66	
	G-ARPX	British Airways			01/APR/72	WFU 23/OCT/82
2125	YI-AEA	Iraqi Airways	1E	07/SEP/65	03/OCT/65	WFU JUN/77, stored Baghdad
2127	YI-AEB	Iraqi Airways	1E	17/FEB/66	05/MAR/66	WFU APR/77, stored Baghdad
2128	G-ARPZ	BEA	1C	22/JUN/66	01/JUL/66	
	G-ARPZ	British Airways			01/APR/72	WFU 03/APR/83
	G-ARPZ	RFD Ltd			07/APR/83	Instructional, Dunsfold Airport
2129	YI-AEC	Iraqi Airways	1E	27/APR/66	13/MAY/66	WFU JUN/77, stored Baghdad
2130	G-ATNA	Hawker Siddeley	1E	23/NOV/65		
	AP-ATK	PIA			01/MAR/66	
	B-245	CAAC			JUN/70	
	50056	Chinese Air Force			JAN/82	
2132	AP-ATM	PIA	1E	26/MAY/66	17/JUN/66	
		CAAC			JUN/70	
	50050	Chinese Air Force			JAN/82	
2133	AP-AUG	Pakistan Air Force	1E	24/AUG/66	25/JAN/67	
	AP-AUG	PIA			13/FEB/67	
		CAAC			JUN/70	
	50152	Chinese Air Force			JAN/82	
2135	G-AVYA	Hawker Siddeley	1E	28/MAY/69		
	4R-ACN	Air Ceylon			04/JUL/69	WFU, used as a cabin trainer at Colombo Airport.
2139	G-AVYE	Channel Airways	1E	23/APR/68	14/JUN/68	
	G-AVYE	BEA			20/JAN/71	
	G-AVYE	British Airways			01/APR/72	WFU 30/SEP/80, preserved Wroughton
2141	G-AVFB	BEA	2E	02/NOV/67	06/JUN/68	
	G-AVFB	Cyprus Airways			27/MAR/72	
	5B-DAC	Cyprus Airways			01/JUN/73	
	G-AVFB	British Airways			12/MAY/77	WFU 27/MAR/82, Preserved Duxford
2146	G-AVFG	BEA	2E	19/JUN/68	04/JUL/68	
	G-AVFG	British Airways			01/APR/72	WFU 30/APR/85 Heathrow, for apprentice training
2149	G-AVFJ	BEA	2E	02/OCT/68	21/DEC/68	
	G-AVFJ	British Airways			01/APR/72	WFU 26/MAR/82 to Teesside Airport fire service
2152	G-AVFM	BEA	2E	25/MAR/69	25/APR/69	
	G-AVFM	British Airways			01/APR/72	WFU 28/NOV/83, to Brunel Tech. College, Bristol,
2157	G-AZFT	Hawker Siddeley	2E	21/OCT/72		
	B-240	CAAC			19/NOV/72	
2158	G-AZFU	Hawker Siddeley	2E	20/DEC/72		
	B-242	CAAC			08/FEB/73	
2159	G-AZFV	Hawker Siddeley	2E	19/MAY/73		
	B-244	CAAC			17/JUN/73	
	B-2218	CAAC			85	

HAWKER SIDDELEY TRIDENT (EXISTING AIRCRAFT ONLY)

C/N	Registration	Owner/Operator	Series	First Flight	Delivery	Remarks
2160	G-AZFW	Hawker Siddeley	2E	04/JUL/73		
	B-246	CAAC			05/AUG/73	
	B-2219	CAAC			85	
2161	G-AZFX	Hawker Siddeley	2E	05/SEP/73		
	B-248	CAAC			11/OCT/73	WFU
2162	G-AZFY	Hawker Siddeley	2E	09/NOV/73		
	B-250	CAAC			19/DEC/73	
2163	G-BABP	Hawker Siddeley	2E	21/JUN/74		
	B-252	CAAC			20/AUG/74	
	B-2214	CAAC			85	
2164	G-BABR	Hawker Siddeley	2E	24/AUG/74		
	B-254	CAAC			29/SEP/74	
2165	G-BABS	Hawker Siddeley	2E	25/OCT/74		
	B-256	CAAC			05/DEC/74	
	B-261	CAAC				
2166	G-BABT	Hawker Siddeley	2E	31/DEC/74		
	B-258	CAAC			10/FEB/75	
	B-2215	CAAC			85	
2168	G-BABV	Hawker Siddeley	2E	31/MAR/75		
	B-262	CAAC			01/MAY/75	
2171	G-BAJH	Hawker Siddeley	2E	12/JAN/76		
	B-272	CAAC			17/FEB/76	
	50052	Chinese Air Force			JAN/82	
2173	G-BAJJ	Hawker Siddeley	2E	31/MAR/76		
	B-276	CAAC			06/MAY/76	
2174	G-BAJK	Hawker Siddeley	2E	13/MAY/76		
	B-278	CAAC			19/JUN/76	
	50158	Chinese Air Force			JAN/82	
2175	G-BBVS	Hawker Siddeley	2E	30/JUN/76		
	B-280	CAAC			11/AUG/76	
2176	G-BBVT	Hawker Siddeley	2E	24/AUG/76		
	B-282	CAAC			11/OCT/76	
2177	G-BBVU	Hawker Siddeley	2E	28/SEP/76		
	B-284	CAAC			06/DEC/76	
	B-2216	CAAC			85	
2178	G-BBVV	Hawker Siddeley	2E	03/NOV/76		
	B-286	CAAC			31/DEC/76	
2179	G-BBVW	Hawker Siddeley	2E	31/DEC/76		
	B-288	CAAC			17/MAR/77	
	B-2217	CAAC			85	
2180	G-BBVX	Hawker Siddeley	2E	04/FEB/77		
	B-290	CAAC			14/APR/77	
2181	G-BBVY	Hawker Siddeley	2E	23/MAR/77		
	B-292	CAAC			24/APR/77	
2182	G-BBVZ	Hawker Siddeley	2E	13/JUN/77		
	B-294	CAAC			29/JUL/77	
2183	G-BBWA	Hawker Siddeley	2E	13/JUL/77		
	B-296	CAAC			07/SEP/77	
2184	G-BBWB	Hawker Siddeley	2E	24/AUG/77		
	B-298	CAAC			14/OCT/77	
2185	G-BBWD	Hawker Siddeley	2E	07/OCT/77		
	B-263	CAAC			13/SEP/78	
	B-263	Chinese Air Force			JAN/82	
2186	G-BBWE	Hawker Siddeley	2E	07/NOV/77		
	B-265	CAAC			21/DEC/77	WFU
	55054	Chinese Air Force			JAN/82	
2187	G-BBWF	Hawker Siddeley	2E	13/JAN/78		
	B-267	CAAC			08/MAR/78	
	B-267	Chinese Air Force			JAN/82	
2188	G-BBWG	Hawker Siddeley	2E	16/FEB/78		
	B-269	CAAC			05/APR/78	
	B-269	Chinese Air Force			JAN/82	
2189	G-BBWH	Hawker Siddeley	2E	17/APR/78		
	B-271	CAAC			28/JUN/78	WFU
	55053	Chinese Air Force			JAN/82	
2304	G-AWZC	BEA	3B	24/DEC/70	18/FEB/71	
	G-AWZC	British Airways			01/APR/72	WFU 01/NOV/84.
	9Q-CTM	Air Charter Service	Freight		21/NOV/84	
2305	G-AWZD	BEA	3B	05/MAR/71	26/MAR/71	
	G-AWZD	British Airways			01/APR/72	WFU FEB/85
	9Q-CTI	Air Charter Service			24/JUL/85	
2307	G-AWZF	BEA	3B	30/APR/71	11/MAY/71	
	G-AWZF	British Airways			01/APR/72	WFU JAN/85
2308	G-AWZG	BEA	3B	03/JUN/71	12/JUN/71	
	G-AWZG	British Airways			01/APR/72	
	9Q-CTD	Air Charter Service			AUG/85	
2310	G-AWZI	BEA	3B	04/AUG/71	09/AUG/71	
	G-AWZI	British Airways			01/APR/72	WFU 01/MAY/85, stored Heathrow
2311	G-AWZJ	BEA	3B	09/SEP/71	16/SEP/71	
	G-AWZJ	British Airways			01/APR/72	WFU 24/FEB/86, stored Prestwick
2312	G-AWZK	BEA	3B	08/OCT/71	16/OCT/71	
	G-AWZK	British Airways			01/APR/72	WFU 01/NOV/85, stored Heathrow
2314	G-AWZM	BEA	3B	08/DEC/71	16/DEC/71	
	G-AWZM	British Airways			01/APR/72	WFU 13/DEC/85, preserved Wroughton
2315	G-AWZN	BEA	3B	12/JAN/72	20/JAN/72	
	G-AWZN	British Airways			01/APR/72	WFU 22/DEC/85, preserved Cranfield
2316	G-AWZO	BEA	3B	09/FEB/72	16/FEB/72	
	G-AWZO	British Airways			01/APR/72	WFU 01/JAN/86
	G-AWZO	British Aerospace			18/APR/86	WFU 18/APR/86, stored Hatfield
2318	G-AWZR	British Airways	3B	05/APR/72	13/APR/72	WFU 27/SEP/85, to Teesside fire section
2319	G-AWZS	British Airways	3B	29/APR/72	05/MAY/72	WFU 05/DEC/85, to Teesside fire section
2321	G-AWZU	British Airways	3B	28/JUN/72	10/JUL/72	WFU 01/JAN/86, stored Stansted
2322	G-AWZV	British Airways	3B	02/AUG/72	09/AUG/72	
	9Q-CTZ	Air Charter Service			MAY/86	
2324	G-AWZX	British Airways	3B	24/JAN/73	29/JAN/73	WFU 01/OCT/84, to Gatwick fire service.
2326	G-AWZZ	British Airways	3B	03/APR/73	19/APR/73	WFU 04/NOV/84, to Birmingham fire service.
2327	G-BAJL	Hawker Siddeley	3B-104	09/JUL/75		
	B-268	CAAC			22/AUG/75	
	50057	Chinese Air Force			JAN/82	

HAWKER SIDDELEY TRIDENT (EXISTING AIRCRAFT ONLY)

C/N	Registration	Owner/Operator	Series	First Flight	Delivery	Remarks
2328	G-BAJM	Hawker Siddeley	3B-104	26/AUG/75		
	B-270	CAAC			26/SEP/75	
	50058	Chinese Air Force			JAN/82	

Hawker Siddeley Trident
Cross-reference index

4R- Sri Lanka

2135 4R-ACN

5B- Cyprus

2141 5B-DAC

9Q- Zaire

2308 9Q-CTD
2305 9Q-CTI
2304 9Q-CTM
2322 9Q-CTZ

AP- Pakistan

2130 AP-ATK
2132 AP-ATM
2133 AP-AUG

B- China

2163 B-2214
2166 B-2215
2177 B-2216
2179 B-2217
2159 B-2218
2160 B-2219
2157 B-240
2158 B-242

2159 B-244
2130 B-245
2160 B-246
2161 B-248
2162 B-250
2163 B-252
2164 B-254
2165 B-256
2166 B-258
2165 B-261
2168 B-262
2185 B-263
2186 B-265
2187 B-267
2327 B-268
2188 B-269
2328 B-270
2189 B-271
2171 B-272
2173 B-276
2174 B-278
2175 B-280
2176 B-282
2177 B-284
2178 B-286
2179 B-288
2180 B-290
2181 B-292
2182 B-294
2183 B-296
2184 B-298

G- United Kingdom

2108 G-ARPH
2111 G-ARPK
2112 G-ARPL
2115 G-ARPN
2116 G-ARPO
2117 G-ARPP
2119 G-ARPR
2123 G-ARPW
2124 G-ARPX
2128 G-ARPZ
2130 G-ATNA
2141 G-AVFB
2146 G-AVFG
2149 G-AVFJ
2152 G-AVFM
2135 G-AVYA
2139 G-AVYE
2304 G-AWZC
2305 G-AWZD
2307 G-AWZF
2308 G-AWZG
2310 G-AWZI
2311 G-AWZJ
2312 G-AWZK
2314 G-AWZM
2315 G-AWZN
2316 G-AWZO
2318 G-AWZR
2321 G-AWZU

2322 G-AWZV
2324 G-AWZX
2326 G-AWZZ
2157 G-AZFT
2158 G-AZFU
2159 G-AZFV
2160 G-AZFW
2161 G-AZFX
2162 G-AZFY
2163 G-BABP
2164 G-BABR
2165 G-BABS
2166 G-BABT
2168 G-BABV
2171 G-BAJH
2173 G-BAJJ
2174 G-BAJK
2327 G-BAJL
2328 G-BAJM
2175 G-BBVS
2176 G-BBVT
2177 G-BBVU
2178 G-BBVV
2179 G-BBVW
2180 G-BBVX
2181 G-BBVY
2182 G-BBVZ
2183 G-BBWA
2184 G-BBWB
2185 G-BBWD
2186 G-BBWE

2187 G-BBWF
2188 G-BBWG
2189 G-BBWH

Iraq

2125 YI-AEA
2127 YI-AEB
2129 YI-AEC

Military operated

China

2132 50050
2171 50052
2130 50056
2327 50057
2328 50058
2133 50152
2174 50158
2189 55053
2186 55054

MCDONNELL DOUGLAS DC-8-/20/30/40/50/62/72 (EXISTING AIRCRAFT ONLY)

Long-range, four-engined jet transport. The prototype of the DC-8 first flew on 30 May 1958, and the first series 10, a domestic version with P & W JT3C engines entered service with Delta Airlines and United Airlines on 18 September 1959. Other early examples were the series 20, also for domestic use with JT4A turbojets, the intercontinental Series 30 and 40, the former with more powerful JT4As and the latter with Rolls-Royce Conway turbofans. Last of the basic series was the DC-8-50 with Pratt & Whitney turbofans and accommodation for 179 passengers. A new stretched version, based on the series 50, followed in 1965 named the Super 62 with a new wing and small fuselage increase and much longer range, a great number of which have now been upgraded with the installation of the CMFI CFM 56 advance technology turbofans, and are designated DC-8-72.

Dimensions :	Wing span: 142ft 5in (43.41m) Length: 150ft 6in (45.87m) Height: 42ft 4in (12.91m) (20/30/40/50) Wing span: 142ft 5in (43.41m) Length: 157ft 5in (47.98m) Height: 42ft 4in (12.91m) (62/72)
Powerplant :	Four Pratt & Whitney JT4A-3, JT4A-5, JT4A-9, JT4A-10, JT4A-11, JT4A-12 turbojets (20/30), four Rolls Royce Conway 509 turbojets (40), four Pratt & Whitney JT3D-1, JT3D-3 or JT3D-3B turbojets (50), four CFMI CFM56-2-C5 turbofans (72)
Performance :	Max cruising speed 503 knots (932km/h) (20) Range: with max payload 4,044nm (7,490km) (20) Max cruising speed 514 knots (952km/h) (30) Range: with max payload 4,692nm (8,690km) (30) Max cruising speed 509 knots (943km/h) (40/62) Range: with max payload 4,859nm (9,000km) (40) Max cruising speed 504 knots (933km/h) (50) Range: with max payload 5,373nm (9,950km) (50) Range: with max payload 5,205nm (9,640km) (62) Range: with max payload 5,820nm (10,778km) (72)
Accommodation:	179 passengers
Manufacturer :	McDonnell Douglas - 3855 Lakewood Boulevard, Long Beach, California 90846, USA Telephone: (213) 593-5511

C/N	Registration	Owner/Operator	Series	First Flight	Delivery	Remarks
45252	N8008D	Douglas	10	30/MAY/58		
	N8008D	Douglas	51	20/DEC/60		Converted
	N8008D	National Airlines			21/JUN/61	Leased
	N8008D	Douglas			26/MAY/62	
	N8008D	Trans International			20/JUN/62	
	N8008D	Lufthansa			MAY/66	Leased
	CF-CPN	Canadian Pacific			02/OCT/66	
	N8008D	Trans International			01/OCT/67	
	N8008D	Delta Airlines			01/OCT/67	
	N8008D	F.B. Ayer			23/MAR/79	
	XA-DOE	Aeromexico			23/MAR/79	Leased
	N8008D	F.B. Ayer			07/JAN/82	
					85	WFU DEC/84, preserved Smithsonian Institute
45255	N8068D	Douglas	32	25/MAR/59		
	N802PA	Pan American	33		15/FEB/61	
	N8027	Delta Airlines			25/AUG/69	
	N8027	Charlotte Aircraft Corp.			23/JAN/74	
	LV-LTP	Trafe			09/APR/76	WFU JAN/78, Stored Ezeiza Ap.
45257	N804PA	Pan American	32		17/MAR/60	
	N8240U	United Airlines			15/NOV/68	
	N8240U	United Aircraft Leasing Corp			23/DEC/75	
	N8240U	Aire Cardinal			12/MAY/76	Leased
	N8240U	United Aircraft Leasing Corp			03/SEP/76	
	N8240U	Jet Freight Cargo			30/JUN/77	Leased
	N8240U	Zantop			29/JUL/77	
	N8240U	Air Transport International			23/OCT/84	
45258	N805PA	Pan American	32		20/MAY/60	
	N8243U	United Airlines			20/SEP/68	
	N8243U	Overseas National Airways			12/DEC/75	
	N8243U	United Aircraft Leasing			15/JUL/77	
	N8243U	JFC Enterprises			04/NOV/77	
	N8243U	Rosenbalm Aviation			02/FEB/81	
45259	N806PA	Pan American	32		07/MAY/60	
	N8245U	United Airlines			27/SEP/68	
	N8245U	United Aircraft Leasing Corp			20/JAN/76	
	N8245U	Aire Cardinal			09/APR/76	Leased
	N8245U	United Aircraft Leasing Corp			03/SEP/76	
	N8245U	Evergreen International			29/MAR/77	
	N8245U	Rosenbalm Aviation			02/JUL/79	
	N8245U	Evergreen International			79	Leased
	N8245U	Rosenbalm Aviation			JUL/79	Op. for Emery Worldwide
	HP-1048	Wellman				
		Trans Panama			FEB/85	Leased
45262	N809PA	Pan American	32		22/JUN/60	
	N8246U	United Airlines			18/OCT/68	
	N8246U	Overseas National Airways			04/DEC/75	
	N8246U	United Aircraft Leasing Corp			19/OCT/77	
	N8246U	Plymouth Leasing			17/NOV/77	
	N8246U	Rosenbalm Aviation			04/JAN/78	Leased
45264	N811PA	Pan American	32		23/AUG/60	
	N8252U	United Airlines			11/OCT/68	
	N8252U	Overseas National Airways			02/DEC/75	
	N8252U	United Aircraft Leasing Corp			19/OCT/77	
	N8252U	Plymouth Leasing			17/NOV/77	
	N8252U	Rosenbalm Aviation			04/JAN/78	Op. for Emery Worldwide
45265	N812PA	Pan American	32		10/SEP/60	
	OO-TCP	Pomair			13/MAY/71	
	OO-TCP	Air France			73	Leased
	OO-TCP	Pomair			73	
	N900CL	Capitol International			10/MAY/75	
	EC-CUS	TAE			18/APR/76	Leased
	N900CL	Capitol International			03/FEB/77	
	N900CL	United Aircraft Leasing Corp			15/AUG/78	
	N900CL	United Air Carriers			25/AUG/78	
	N900CL	Overseas National Airways			01/MAR/79	
	N900CL	United Aircraft Leasing Corp			01/NOV/80	
	N900CL	Saudia			80	Leased
	N900CL	United Aircraft Leasing Corp			80	

C/N	Registration	Owner/Operator	Series	First Flight	Delivery	Remarks
	N900CL	Rosenbalm Aviation			07/JAN/82	WFU JUN/82, stored
45266	N813PA	Pan American	32		13/OCT/60	
	9Q-CLE	Air Congo			31/DEC/68	
	9Q-CLE	Air Zaire			25/OCT/71	WFU DEC/82, stored N'djili
45267	N814PA	Pan American	32		18/OCT/60	
	N8148A	Delta Airlines	33		31/DEC/68	
	N8148A	Charlotte Aircraft Corp.			23/JAN/74	
	N8148A	Ramair Intl.			21/OCT/77	
	N8148A	Intercontinental Airways	33FM		21/OCT/77	
	N8148A	Rich International			79	Leased
	N8148A	Intercontinental Airways				
	N8148A	Air Nigeria			07/OCT/81	
	N8148A	Charlotte Aircraft			01/JAN/84	WFU 84, derelict
45268	N815PA	Pan American	33		07/NOV/60	
	N815PA	Air Zaire			31/DEC/68	
	9Q-CLF	Air Zaire			25/OCT/71	WFU 15/SEP/74, derelict N'djili
45269	N816PA	Pan American	33		10/NOV/60	
	N8166A	Delta Airlines			30/DEC/68	
	N8166A	Charlotte Aircraft Corp.			25/JAN/74	
	N8166A	Intercontinental			21/OCT/77	
	N8166A	Michigan Peninsula Airways			78	Leased
	N8166A	Rich International			02/AUG/79	
	N8166A	Charlotte Aircraft Corp.			01/OCT/84	WFU DEC/84, stored Laurinburg
45271	N818PA	Pan American	33		22/DEC/60	
	PP-PEF	Panair do Brasil			13/NOV/63	
	N818PA	Pan American			OCT/65	
	N8184A	Delta Airlines			30/DEC/68	
	N8184A	Charlotte Aircraft Corp.			22/JAN/74	
	N8184A	Ranger Air Cargo			02/JUL/75	Leased
	N8184A	Charlotte Aircraft Corp.			01/OCT/77	
	N8184A	Intercontinental Airways			21/OCT/77	
	N8184A	Ghana Airways			77	Leased
	N8184A	Intercontinental Airways			77	
	N8184A	Ramair International			21/OCT/77	Leased
	N8184A	Arzee Petroleum			10/DEC/77	Leased
	N8184A	Intercontinental Airways				WFU 15/SEP/81
45272	N819PA	Pan American	33		22/MAR/61	Not taken-up
	PP-PDS	Panair do Brasil			15/JUL/65	
	PP-PDS	Varig			15/FEB/78	
	N59AJ	American Jet Industries			JAN/80	
	N59AJ	Gulfstream American Corp.			JAN/85	WFU 15/JAN/84 to JAN/85
	N59AJ	Charlotte Aircraft Corp.				
45274	N8274H	Panagra	31		06/APR/60	
	N1800	Braniff			01/FEB/67	
	N4901C	Capitol International			10/NOV/67	
	N4901C	National Airlines			08/DEC/69	Leased
	N905CL	Capitol International			01/DEC/72	
	N905CL	Overseas National Airways			24/APR/79	
	N905CL	Air Fleets			01/NOV/79	
	N905CL	International Air Leases			14/JUL/80	
	N905CL	Sunland Airlines			09/JUN/80	
	N905CL	Air Fleets			10/JUN/80	
	N905CL	Sunland Airlines			16/SEP/80	
	N905CL	Texas Air Carrier			10/OCT/82	
	N905CL	Vuelos Especiales Liberianos			01/MAR/83	
45276	N8276H	Panagra	31		29/JUN/60	
	N8276H	Braniff			01/FEB/67	
	N8276H	Capitol International			10/OCT/67	
	N8276H	Air Congo			28/NOV/67	Leased
	N8276H	Capitol International			31/DEC/68	
	N4902C	Capitol International			69	
	N906CL	Capitol International			75	
	N906CL	Overseas National Airways			30/APR/79	
	N906CL	United Aircraft Leasing			01/NOV/80	
	N906CL	Saudia			NOV/80	Leased
	N906CL	Overseas National Airways			11/JUL/80	
	N906CL	Rosenbalm Aviation			07/JAN/82	WFU 07/JAN/82, stored
45280	N8038D	Douglas	11	02/JAN/59		
	N8003U	United Airlines	12		16/JAN/60	
	N8003U	United Airlines	21		MAY/65	Converted
	N8003U	Project Orbis Inc.			12/MAR/80	
	N220RB	Project Orbis Inc.				
45285	N8008U	United Airlines	11		03/SEP/59	
	N8008U	United Airlines	12			Converted
	N8008U	United Airlines	51		OCT/63	Converted
						WFU JAN/80 to 26/JUN/84
	N8008U	International Air Leases			26/JUN/84	WFU, stored Marana
45292	N8023U	United Airlines	21		26/FEB/60	
	N8023U	Boeing			23/NOV/77	WFU 23/NOV/77, Stored Kingman
45296	N8027U	United Airlines	21		25/MAY/60	
	N8027U	Sunland Airlines			01/NOV/78	
	N8027U	K and C Corp.				
	N8027U	SAT				
	N8027U	United Aircraft Leasing			29/MAR/79	
	XA-LSA	Aero Leon			17/JUL/79	Leased
45298	N8029U	United Airlines	21		17/AUG/60	
	N8029U	Merpati Nusantara				Leased
	N8029U	United Airlines				
	N8029U	Notombi International			12/OCT/78	
	N8029U	Commercial Air Transport			06/NOV/78	
	N8029U	Andes Airlines			79	Leased
	N8029U	Commercial Air Transport			79	
	N8029U	Tropical Air Leasing			JUN/80	
	HP-826	Trans Panama			SEP/80	Leased
	HP-826	Tropical Air Leasing				WFU, derelict Miami
45299	N8031U	United Airlines	21		11/SEP/60	
	N8031U	Sunland Airlines			02/NOV/78	
	N8031U	Plymouth Leasing			14/SEP/79	WFU OCT/81, stored
45300	N8033U	United Airlines	21		13/OCT/60	
	N8033U	Boeing			21/OCT/77	
	N8033U	Commercial Air Transport			21/OCT/77	
	N8033U	World Air Leasing				
	N8033U	T. A. Centrafricain			07/OCT/78	Leased
	N8033U	World Air Leasing				
	N8033U	Kuzey Kibris Hava Yollari				Leased

MCDONNELL DOUGLAS DC-8-20/30/40/50/62/72 (EXISTING AIRCRAFT ONLY)

C/N	Registration	Owner/Operator	Series	First Flight	Delivery	Remarks
	N8033U	Club Alaska		79		
	TL-AHI	T.A. Centrafricain		79		
	5A-DGK	United African Airlines		15/JAN/79		WFU 82, derelict
45303	N8036U	United Airlines	52	08/JUN/61		
	ZK-NZF	Air New Zealand		02/NOV/70		Leased
	ZK-NZF	Air New Zealand		01/JUN/71		Purchased
	N99862	Douglas			20/MAR/76	
	5B-CAC	Cyprus Airways			30/MAR/76	Leased, Reg. Not taken-up
	N99862	Cyprus Airways			30/MAR/76	Leased
	N99862	Douglas			01/MAR/78	
	N99862	American Jet Industries			01/MAR/78	
	N804EV	Evergreen International			03/OCT/78	WFU 15/JAN/84, for spares
45304	N8037U	United Airlines	12		25/JAN/61	
	N8037U	United Airlines	21		MAR/68	Converted
	N8037U	Sunland Airlines			06/NOV/78	
	N8037U	Jetway Corporation	21C		31/OCT/79	
	N8037U	K and C Corp.			15/DEC/80	
	N8037U	Jet Way			15/OCT/81	WFU OCT/81
	N8037U	Connie Kalitta Services			01/DEC/83	
45379	PH-DCD	KLM	32		04/JUL/60	
	PH-DCD	Martinair			15/NOV/67	Leased
	PH-DCD	KLM			15/APR/70	
	PH-DCD	Martinair			15/FEB/72	Leased
	5Y-ASA	African Safari			01/NOV/73	Sub-leased
	PH-DCD	Martinair			04/OCT/76	
	G-BETJ	Trans Meridian Air Cargo			09/MAY/77	WFU 16/OCT/77, used by Stansted Airport fire service
45380	PH-DCE	KLM	32		19/AUG/60	
	PI-C829	Philippine Airlines			22/MAR/67	Leased
	RP-C829	Philippine Airlines			74	
	N833DA	F.B. Ayer			10/OCT/78	
	N833DA	IFL Inc.				
	N833DA	Response Air			JUN/84	WFU JUN/84, stored Marana, Ar.
45382	PH-DCG	KLM	32		26/OCT/60	
	OO-CMB	BIAS			07/MAR/72	
	OO-CMB	Delta International				
	OO-CMB	Pomair			16/MAY/73	
	OO-CMB	Martinair			09/DEC/74	
	OO-CMB	Pomair			02/APR/75	
	N903CL	Capitol International			17/MAY/75	
	N903CL	ALM				Leased
	N903CL	Capitol International				
	N903CL	Overseas National Airways			01/MAY/79	
	5A-DGN	United African Airlines			03/MAR/80	WFU 28/OCT/82
45384	OY-KTA	SAS	32		22/MAR/60	
	HS-TGT	Thai International			27/SEP/71	
	N718UA	United Aircraft Leasing			28/APR/78	
	N718UA	Airlift International			16/NOV/78	Leased
	N718UA	United Aircraft Leasing			07/JAN/80	
	N718UA	Michigan Peninsula Airways			01/AUG/80	
	N718UA	Control Data Co.			JUN/81	
	N718UA	Barron Thomas Aviation			14/JUL/82	
	N718UA	Bailey Company			SEP/84	WFU SEP/84, derelict Miami
45387	OY-KTB	SAS	32		13/JUL/60	
	N8258U	United Airlines			01/DEC/68	
	N8258U	United Aircraft Leasing			30/APR/75	
	N8258U	Rosenbalm Aviation	32F		01/SEP/75	Leased
	C-GSWQ	Swiftair Cargo			29/JUL/80	
	N8258U	Dunwoody Ltd.			11/MAY/82	
	N8258U	Aeromar			23/OCT/84	WFU MAY/84, stored
45388	LN-MOT	SAS	32		31/AUG/60	
	N8266U	United Airlines			03/NOV/68	
	N8266U	United Aircraft Leasing			19/JUL/76	
	N421AJ	American Jet Industries			13/SEP/76	
	N8266U	Evergreen International			16/SEP/76	Leased
	N8266U	Rosenbalm Aviation			03/JUL/79	
	C-GSWX	Swiftair Cargo			03/SEP/80	
45410	N803E	Delta Airlines	11		10/OCT/59	
	N803E	Delta Airlines	12			
	N803E	Delta Airlines	51		JUN/63	Converted
	N803E	F.B. Ayer			05/DEC/80	Converted, WFU 80
	N803E	Barclays ABC			01/JUN/82	
	N803E	Navaero Aviation			JUN/85	WFU JUN/85, stored Marana, Ar.
45411	N804E	Delta Airlines	11		27/OCT/59	
	N804E	Delta Airlines	12			Converted
	N804E	Delta Airlines	51		JUN/63	Converted
	N804E	F.B. Ayer			23/JUL/79	
	N804E	Mackey International			15/SEP/79	Leased
	N804E	Airlift International			15/FEB/81	Leased
	N804E	F.B. Ayer			15/SEP/81	
	N804E	Barclays ABC			15/JUN/82	WFU 15/JUN/82 to NOV/84
	N804E	FBA Corp.			NOV/84	WFU, stored Marana
45413	N806E	Delta Airlines	11		11/NOV/59	
	N806E	Delta Airlines	12			Converted
	N806E	Delta Airlines	51		OCT/73	Converted
	N806E	F.B. Ayer			05/DEC/80	
	N806E	Barclays ABC			JUN/82	
	N806E	Navaero Aviation			JUN/85	WFU JUN/85, stored Marana
45416	HB-IDA	Swissair	32		22/APR/60	
	HB-IDA	Sudflug			15/MAR/68	Leased
	HB-IDA	Condor			NOV/68	Leased
	HB-IDA	Swissair			DEC/68	
	D-ADIM	Atlantis			DEC/68	
	D-ADIM	Swissair			JAN/73	
	HS-TGW	Thai International			16/APR/73	
	N45908	United Aircraft Leasing			21/JUL/77	
	N45908	Air Ceylon			01/NOV/77	Leased
	N45908	United Aircraft Leasing				
	N45908	Egyptair				Leased
	N45908	United Aircraft Leasing				
	N712UA	United Air Carriers			24/JUN/78	
	N712UA	Overseas National Airways			01/MAR/79	
	N712UA	United Aircraft Leasing			04/AUG/81	
	N712UA	Systems Control Leasing			16/APR/82	
	N45908	Agro Air International			15/MAY/82	

C/N	Registration	Owner/Operator	Series	First Flight	Delivery	Remarks
	N45908	Aeromar			82	Leased
	HI-435	Aeromar				
	HI-435	LAC Colombia			OCT/85	Leased
45418	JA8001	Japan Airlines	32		16/JUL/60	WFU 15/JAN/75, used as a crew trainer
45419	JA8002	Japan Airlines	32		29/JUL/60	
	N420AJ	American Jet Industries			03/JUN/74	
	N420AJ	Air Charter International			OCT/77	Painted for film use
	N420AJ	Gulfstream American Corp.			OCT/79	WFU 15/JAN/84 to JAN/85
	N420AJ	Charlotte Aircraft Corp.			JAN/85	
45420	JA8003	Japan Airlines	32		13/SEP/60	
	JA8008	Japan Airlines			30/MAR/63	
	JA8008	Japan Asia Airways			75	Leased
	OB-R-1223	Aeronaves Del Peru			01/JUL/81	Leased
	OB-R-1223	Faucett			82	
45421	JA8005	Japan Airlines	32		22/NOV/60	
	N421AJ	American Jet Industries	33		29/MAY/74	
	N421AJ	United Aircraft Leasing			15/JAN/76	
	N421AJ	Evergreen International			13/SEP/76	Leased
	N421AJ	United Aircraft Leasing			29/MAR/77	
	N421AJ	Rosenbalm Aviation	33C		30/MAR/77	
	N421AJ	Zantop International			80	Leased
	N421AJ	Rosenbalm Aviation			JAN/82	
	5N-AYZ	International Air Tours			AUG/85	
45425	N8604	Eastern Airlines	21		01/FEB/60	
	N8604	Concare Aircraft Leasing			07/SEP/73	
	N8604	Air Haiti			15/OCT/73	WFU 15/OCT/73 to 04/JUL/77
	N8604	American Jet Industries			04/JUL/77	WFU 04/JUL/77, derelict Mojave
45429	N8608	Eastern Airlines	21		08/AUG/60	
	EC-CDB	Air Spain			11/APR/73	
	N8608	Eastern Airlines			13/JUN/76	
	N8608	J.H.Goodwin & Assoc.			24/NOV/76	
	A6-SHA	Hamerein Air			01/FEB/77	
	TC-AAC	Bursa Hava Yollari			OCT/79	Leased
	TC-JBV	Bursa Hava Yollari			27/JAN/80	Leased
	TC-JBV	Bursa Hava Yollari			JUL/80	Purchased WFU 31/MAR/81 to 17/SEP/84
	TC-JBV	Omega Air			17/SEP/84	WFU 17/SEP/84 for spares
45430	N8609	Eastern Airlines	21		09/OCT/60	
	N8609	Concare Aircraft Leasing			01/AUG/73	
	N8609	Air Caledonia			15/JAN/74	Leased
	N8609	Concare Aircraft Leasing			14/JAN/75	
	N8609	American Jet Industries			15/JAN/75	WFU 15/JAN/81, derelict Van Nuys Airport, Ca.
45433	N8612	Eastern Airlines	21		15/NOV/60	
	N8612	Concare Aircraft Leasing			07/SEP/73	
	N821F	Overseas National Airways			18/SEP/73	
	N821F	United Aircraft Leasing			20/JUL/77	
	N821F	PIA			23/JUL/77	Leased
	N821F	United Aircraft Leasing			30/APR/78	
	N821F	Rosenbalm Aviation			01/JUL/78	
	N821F	Onyx Aviation			25/FEB/82	WFU
45434	N8613	Eastern Airlines	21		28/JUL/61	
	N8613	Concare Aircraft Leasing			01/AUG/73	
	N8613	Overseas National Airways			04/OCT/73	WFU 15/JAN/81 Used as restaurant, New Market, Ohio
45435	N8614	Eastern Airlines	21		15/AUG/61	
	N8614	Concare Aircraft Leasing			06/JUN/73	
	N820F	Overseas National Airways			20/JUN/73	
	N1976P	Overseas National Airways			76	
	N1976P	Club USA International			30/DEC/77	
	N1976P	International Air Leases			02/SEP/80	
	N1976P	Texas Air Carrier			08/JUL/81	
	TI-VEL	Vuelos Especiales Liberianos			01/MAR/83	
45437	N8617	Eastern Airlines	21		23/OCT/61	
	N8617	Concare Aircraft Leasing			07/SEP/73	
	N819F	Overseas National Airways			26/SEP/73	
	N819F	Air Jamaica			75	Leased
	N819F	Overseas National Airways			75	
	N819F	United Aircraft Leasing			20/JUL/77	
	N819F	PIA			23/JUL/77	Leased
	N819F	United Aircraft Leasing			21/APR/78	
	N819F	Rosenbalm Aviation			30/JUN/78	
	N819F	Zantop International			80	Leased
	N819F	Rosenbalm Aviation			82	WFU 82
45568	F-BJLB	UAT	32		05/AUG/60	
	F-BJLB	UTA			01/OCT/63	
	F-BJLB	UTA	53		04/MAY/65	Converted
	EC-CMT	TAE			17/MAR/75	
	F-BJLB	UTA			01/NOV/75	
	F-BJLB	Air Ceylon			FEB/76	
	F-BJLB	UTA			MAR/76	
	TU-ACP	Air Afrique			15/FEB/79	WFU MAY/85, used for fire practice
45570	F-BIUZ	TAI	31		28/FEB/61	
	F-BIUZ	UTA			01/OCT/63	
	F-ZARK	French Air Force	51		31/DEC/73	
	F-RAFE	Frnech Air Force			76	
45589	N8015U	United Airlines	11		21/NOV/59	
	N8015U	United Airlines	12			Converted
	N8015U	United Airlines	21		FEB/66	Converted
	N8015U	Jarrell And Assoc.			06/JUN/77	
	N8015U	Casino Royale			06/JUN/77	
	N8015U	Sundance Travel Club			15/SEP/77	
	N8015U	Florida Air Lease			30/JUN/78	
	N8015U	Fiesta Travel Club			12/MAR/79	
	N8015U	Charles F.Willis III Co.Inc.			MAY/80	
	N8015U	Trans Anatolian			JUN/80	
	N8015U	CHK Partnership			12/MAY/81	
	N8015U	American Jet Industries			01/APR/82	WFU 04/OCT/82, Mojave, Ca., for spares
45593	N8020U	United Airlines	11		14/JAN/60	
	N8020U	United Airlines	12			Converted
	N8020U	United Airlines	21		MAR/66	Converted

C/N	Registration	Owner/Operator	Series	First Flight	Delivery	Remarks
	N8020U	Plymouth Leasing			07/MAR/78	
	N8020U	Rosenbalm Aviation			07/MAR/78	WFU 07/MAR/78, used for spares
45594	N8021U	United Airlines	21		21/JAN/60	
	N8021U	Boeing			15/NOV/78	
	N8021U	Commercial Air Transport			15/NOV/78	
	N8021U	Jet Freight Cargo Enterprise			01/FEB/79	
	N8021U	North American				Painted for the film "The Pilot"
	N580JC	Jet Freight Cargo Enterprise				
	N580JC	General Air Services			15/APR/81	
	N580JC	LACSA			AUG/81	Leased
	N580JC	General Air Services			81	
45600	I-DIWI	Alitalia	42		22/JUL/60	
	I-DIWI	Alitalia	43			Converted
	N64804	International Air Leases			27/AUG/77	
	N64804	Saudia			29/OCT/77	Leased
	N64804	International Air Leases			28/DEC/77	
	OB-R-1214	Aero Peru			NOV/78	Leased
	N8418	International Air Leases				
	N8418	Bahamas World			JUN/79	Leased
	N8418	International Air Leases			79	
	OB-R-1214	Aeronaves Del Peru			15/MAY/81	Leased
45601	I-DIWO	Alitalia	42		02/NOV/60	
	I-DIWO	Alitalia	43			Converted
	N453FA	F.B. Ayer			28/FEB/77	
	N453FA	Trans Anatolian Airlines			AUG/79	Leased
	N453FA	F.B. Ayer			DEC/84	WFU DEC/84, stored
45603	N802US	Northwest Orient	32		03/JUL/60	
	N7182C	National Airlines			14/OCT/63	
	N7182C	Pan Aero International			28/JUN/73	
	N7182C	Jet Power Inc.			28/APR/74	
	N7182C	Trans African Airlines				Not taken-up
	N7182C	America's Supply of Miami			20/AUG/76	
	N7182C	Jet Power Inc.			29/APR/77	
	N995WL	Worldwide Air Leases			24/NOV/77	
	N995WL	F.A. Conner			15/SEP/78	
	N995WL	Cargo Mex			11/FEB/79	Leased
	XA-LSA	Aeroleon				Sub-leased
	N995WL	Worldwide Air Leases			25/MAR/80	
	YV-392C	Interamericana			15/JUN/84	Leased
45606	N805US	Northwest Orient	32		04/JAN/60	
	N7184C	National Airlines			01/JUL/64	
	OH-SOA	Spear Air			25/SEP/72	
	N7184C	National Airlines			05/AUG/74	
	OH-SOA	Concare Aircraft Leasing			05/AUG/74	
	N831F	Overseas National Airways	33		02/SEP/74	
	N831F	United Aircraft Leasing			11/AUG/77	
	HC-BEI	Andes Airlines	33FM		11/OCT/77	
45607	N9607Z	Douglas	53			
	PH-DCR	KLM			08/AUG/62	Leased
	PI-C804	Philippine Airlines			19/DEC/67	
	PI-C804	KLM			01/MAY/72	Leased
	RP-C804	KLM			FEB/74	
	RP-C804	Philippine Airlines			75	WFU OCT/80 to JUL/83
	9Q-CQM	African Air Charter			JUL/83	
45608	N9608Z	Douglas	53			
	PH-DCP	KLM			27/APR/62	Leased
	PI-C801	Philippine Airlines			16/JUN/62	
	RP-C801	Philippine Airlines			FEB/74	WFU OCT/80, stored Manila
45610	CF-TJH	Trans Canada Airlines	42		12/JAN/61	
	CF-TJH	Air Canada			01/JUN/64	
	N10DC	Douglas			01/MAY/77	
	N4561B	Douglas	54F			Converted
	N4561B	Zantop International	54FM		15/DEC/78	WFU JUN/85, stored Macon
45612	CF-TJJ	Trans Canada Airlines	43		22/MAR/61	
	CF-TJJ	Air Canada			01/JUN/64	
	CU-T-1210	Cubana			13/APR/76	Leased
	C-FTJJ	Air Canada			08/MAY/78	
	6Y-JMF	Air Jamaica			08/MAY/78	Leased
	OB-R-1142	Aero Peru			JUN/78	Sub-leased
	6Y-JMF	Air Jamaica			09/AUG/78	Leased
	N8021V	International Air Leases			25/JUN/79	
	N8021V	Capitol International			15/JUN/81	WFU 15/JUN/81, derelict
45618	EC-ARB	Iberia	52		27/MAY/61	
	EC-ARB	Aviaco			01/MAY/73	
	EC-ARB	TAE			OCT/77	
	N13627	Douglas			02/OCT/77	
	N60AJ	American Jet Industries			21/FEB/78	
	C-GNDE	Nordair			23/AUG/78	
	C-GNDE	Libyan Arab Airlines			79	Leased
	C-GNDE	Nordair			26/NOV/79	
	C-GNDE	Overseas National Airways			18/SEP/80	Leased
	C-GNDE	Air Fleets International			80	Sub-Leased
	C-GNDE	Nordair			31/JAN/81	WFU 31/JAN/81 to 05/OCT/83
	N4489M	Onyx Aviation			05/OCT/83	WFU 05/OCT/83 stored Miami
45619	EC-ARC	Iberia	52		19/JUN/61	
	OB-R-931	Aero Peru			31/MAR/69	Leased
	EC-ARC	Iberia			17/JUN/71	
	EC-ARC	Aviaco			01/MAY/73	
	EC-ARC	Iberia			01/FEB/79	
	C-GNDF	Nordair			01/FEB/79	
	N3751X	Air Fleets International			31/MAR/80	Leased
	N893AF	Air Fleets International			80	Leased
	C-GNDF	Nordair			15/MAY/80	WFU 15/MAY/80 to 25/OCT/83
	N893AF	Eagle Aviation			25/OCT/83	
	N893AF	Onyx Aviation			15/JAN/84	
	N893AF	The Lords Airline			SEP/85	WFU SEP/85, stored Miami
45620	CF-CPF	CP Air	43		22/FEB/61	
	CF-CPF	CP Air	51		JUL/76	Converted
	CF-CPF	ARCA Colombia			23/NOV/81	WFU 23/NOV/81, stored Miami
45622	CF-CPI	CP Air	43		20/MAY/61	
	CF-CPI	F.B. Ayer			16/NOV/80	WFU 16/NOV/80, derelict Opa Locka Airport, Fl.
45624	I-DIWU	Alitalia	43		28/APR/61	
	N353FA	F.B. Ayer			28/JAN/77	
	N353FA	Trans Anatolian Airlines			AUG/79	Leased

C/N	Registration	Owner/Operator	Series	First Flight	Delivery	Remarks
	N353FA	F.B. Ayer			DEC/84	WFU DEC/84, stored
45626	JA8006	Japan Airlines	33		04/MAY/61	
	N124AJ	American Jet Industries			02/APR/75	
	N124AJ	American Jet Industries	33F		75	Converted
	N124AJ	United Aircraft Leasing			15/SEP/75	
	N124AJ	Aeroamerica			01/MAR/76	Leased
	N124AJ	United Aircraft Leasing			76	
	N124AJ	Egyptair			MAY/76	Leased
	N124AJ	United Aircraft Leasing			06/JUN/76	
	N124AJ	Airlift International			24/JUN/76	Leased
	N124AJ	MSP Associates			15/OCT/81	
	N124AJ	Central American Airlines			NOV/81	Leased
	N124AJ	Canus Investment Corp.				WFU DEC/84, stored
45627	F-BJUV	UAI	33		03/JAN/61	
	F-BJUV	UTA			01/OCT/63	
	TU-TCD	Air Afrique			31/OCT/67	WFU 28/OCT/79
45628	N806US	Northwest Orient	51			Not taken-up
	N8780R	Trans Caribbean			06/NOV/62	
	N8780R	Eastern Airlines			14/DEC/64	Leased
	N8780R	Eastern Airlines			01/JAN/68	Purchased
	SE-DCR	Interswede			24/DEC/71	Leased
	N8780R	Eastern Airlines			01/MAR/72	
	OH-KDM	Kar Air			06/NOV/72	
	OH-KDM	Cyprus Airways			23/AUG/79	Leased
	OH-KDM	Kar Air			30/SEP/79	
	OH-KDM	Aeral			11/JUN/80	Leased
	OH-KDM	Kar Air			22/JUN/80	WFU 01/JUN/84 to FEB/85
	OH-KDM	Airxport Belgium			FEB/85	WFU FEB/85, stored Brussels
45629	N807US	Northwest Orient	53			Not taken-up
	PH-DCN	KLM			17/JAN/62	
	PH-DCN	Nigerian Airways			AUG/70	Leased
	PH-DCN	KLM				
	PH-DCN	Garuda			20/APR/72	Leased
	PH-DCN	KLM			29/JUL/74	
	OB-R-962	Aero Peru			21/MAY/75	Leased
	PH-DCN	KLM			JUN/75	
	OB-R-1116	Aero Peru			26/SEP/75	Leased
	PH-DCN	KLM			19/JUL/76	
	5Y-QSR	African Safari Airways				Not taken-up
	5Y-BAS	African Safari Airways			05/OCT/76	
	5Y-BAS	KLM			MAR/82	
	S7-SIA	Seychelles Intl. Airways			OCT/82	
	9Q-CBF	Air Supply Corp.			AUG/84	
	9Q-CBF	Aero Caribbean			SEP/84	Leased
	9Q-CBF	Air Supply Corp.				WFU, stored Basle
45635		Eastern Airlines	51			Not taken-up
	N875C	National Airlines			06/APR/62	
	N875C	Air Jamaica			01/JUL/72	
	N875C	National Airlines			07/SEP/72	
	N812BN	Braniff			01/SEP/73	
	HK-2587	ARCA Colombia	51C		15/FEB/80	WFU DEC/85, stored Miami
45636	I-DIWP	Alitalia	43		03/NOV/61	
	HK-1854	ARCA Colombia			18/OCT/76	WFU 18/OCT/76, stored Bogota
45637	I-DIWR	Alitalia	43		01/FEB/62	
	I-DIWR	Zambia Airways			69	Leased
	I-DIWR	Alitalia			70	
	N53AF	F.B. Ayer			30/APR/76	
	N53AF	F.B. Ayer	54F		19/MAR/77	Converted
	N53AF	Douglas			01/JUN/78	
	N53AF	Airlift International	54FM		15/NOV/78	
	N54FA	F.B. Ayer			15/SEP/81	
	N54FA	Barclays ABC			15/JUN/82	
	N54FA	Airlift International			01/DEC/82	
	N54FA	F.B. Ayer			21/JUL/83	
	N54FA	Rosenbalm Aviation			03/SEP/83	
	N54FA	Agro Air			MAR/85	WFU, stored Miami
45640	CF-TJL	Trans Canada Airlines	54F		24/APR/63	
	CF-TJL	Air Canada			01/JUN/64	
	CF-TJL	Loch Ness Corp.			18/DEC/84	
	HC-BLM	Andes Airlines			JAN/86	
45641	N276C	National Airlines	51		25/MAY/62	
	N276C	International Lease Finance			12/OCT/73	
	XA-DOD	Aeromexico			12/OCT/73	
45643	N278C	National Airlines	51		23/OCT/62	
	N278C	Air Jamaica			15/DEC/73	
	6Y-JGF	Air Jamaica			05/FEB/74	
	OB-R-1125	Aero Peru			16/JUL/76	Leased
	6Y-JGF	Air Jamaica			05/FEB/81	WFU 05/FEB/81 to 01/JUL/83
	N921CL	Capitol International			01/JUL/83	WFU 01/JUL/83, for spares
45645	N807E	Delta Airlines	51		27/APR/62	
	N807E	F.B. Ayer			16/DEC/77	
	RP-C840	Philippine Airlines			12/APR/78	Leased
						WFU 20/APR/83, stored Manila
45646	N808E	Delta Airlines	51		15/MAY/62	
	N808E	F.B. Ayer			19/JAN/78	
	RP-C837	Philippine Airlines			12/MAY/78	Leased WFU OCT/80 to 15/MAY/83
	N808E	F.B. Ayer			15/MAY/83	
	N808E	Aeromexico			29/JUN/83	WFU 01/JUL/83
	N808E	FBA Corp.				WFU, stored Marana
45647	JA8007	Japan Airlines	53		27/MAR/62	
	JA8007	Japan Asia Airways			15/SEP/76	
	N903R	Overseas National Airways			04/JUN/81	
	N903R	Saudia			04/JUN/81	Leased
	N903R	Overseas National Airways			03/MAY/82	
	N903R	Air Afrique			03/MAY/82	Leased
	N903R	National Airlines			15/APR/84	
	N903R	Saudia			84	Leased
	N903R	National Airlines			85	
	N903R	Airborne Express			MAR/86	
45648	N8781R	Trans Caribbean	51		06/JUL/62	
	N8781R	Eastern Airlines			01/APR/64	Leased
	N8781R	Eastern Airlines			01/JAN/68	Purchased
	SE-DCT	Interswede			30/NOV/71	Leased
	N8781R	Eastern Airlines			28/FEB/72	
	6Y-JGE	Air Jamaica			08/MAY/72	

    Airliner Production List 1987

MCDONNELL DOUGLAS DC-8-20/30/40/50/62/72 (EXISTING AIRCRAFT ONLY)

C/N	Registration	Owner/Operator	Series	First Flight	Delivery	Remarks
	OB-R-1124	Aero Peru			02/JUL/76	Leased
	6Y-JGE	Air Jamaica			01/SEP/79	
	N918CL	Capitol International			15/JUL/83	WFU 01/JUL/84, stored Smyrna Airport, Tn.
45649	N809E	Delta Airlines	51		20/JUN/62	
	N809E	F.B. Ayer			30/MAR/81	
45651	JA8010	Japan Airlines	53		31/JAN/64	
	HK-2667	ARCA Colombia	53F		20/AUG/81	WFU DEC/85, stored Miami
45655	CF-TJO	Trans Canada Airlines	54F		27/FEB/63	
	CF-TJO	Air Canada			01/JUN/64	WFU 16/MAY/84, Montreal, used for ground instruction.
45657	EC-AUM	Iberia	52		28/AUG/63	
	EC-AUM	Aviaco			25/OCT/74	WFU JAN/84, for spares
45658	EC-ATP	Iberia	52		29/MAR/63	
	EC-ATP	Aviaco			01/MAY/73	
	T.15-2	Spanish Air Force			01/FEB/80	
45659	EC-ASN	Iberia	52		04/OCT/62	
	EC-ASN	Aero Peru			FEB/70	Leased
	EC-ASN	Iberia			MAR/70	
	EC-ASN	Aviaco			01/MAY/73	
	EC-ASN	Aviation Facilities			06/NOV/81	
	5A-DJP	United African Airlines				
	5A-DJP	Air Supply Corp.			11/JAN/82	
	LX-III	Air Supply Corp.			82	
	OB-R-1259	Faucett			16/SEP/82	
45660	I-DIWG	Alitalia	43		21/MAY/63	
	N253FA	F.B. Ayer			22/DEC/76	
	RP-C349	Sterling Philippines			14/MAY/79	Leased
	N253FA	F.B. Ayer			28/OCT/83	WFU 28/OCT/83, stored
45661	CF-CPJ	CP Air	43		03/MAY/63	
	CF-CPJ	ARCA Colombia			09/DEC/81	WFU 09/DEC/81, stored Miami
45662	JA8009	Japan Airlines	53		16/JUL/73	
	JA8009	Japan Asia Airways			29/OCT/76	
	JA8009	Japan Airlines			29/MAR/79	
	F-GDPM	Minerve			05/MAR/82	
45663	N108RD	Riddle Airlines	54F		20/SEP/63	
	N108RD	Airlift International			MAR/64	
	N108RD	Sudflug			68	Leased
	N108RD	Airlift International			68	
	N108RD	Alitalia			68	Leased
	N108RD	Airlift International			69	
	N108RD	National Airlines			01/JUL/69	Leased
	N108RD	Airlift International			18/JUL/73	
	N108RD	Greyhound Leasing Finance			30/JAN/78	
	N108RD	Airlift International				
	N108RD	McDonnell Douglas			81	
	N108RD	Arrow Airways			15/SEP/81	Leased
	N108RD	McDonnell Douglas				
	YV-445C	Interamericana			APR/86	
45664	JA8011	Japan Airlines	54		15/JUN/64	
	F-BYFM	Minerve			02/MAR/81	
45665	I-DIWS	Alitalia	43		12/DEC/63	
	HK-1855	ARCA Colombia			29/NOV/76	WFU 29/NOV/76, derelict Miami
45666	I-DIWT	Alitalia	43		14/APR/64	
	N53FA	F.B. Ayer			08/NOV/76	
	N53FA	ITL Inc.				Leased
	N53FA	F.B. Ayer				WFU DEC/84, stored
45667	N8782R	Trans Caribbean	54F		21/JUN/63	
	N8782R	American Airlines			01/MAR/71	
	D-ACCA	Cargo Charter Airways				Not taken-up
	N8782R	Seaboard World			01/JUN/72	Leased
	N8782R	American Airlines			09/JAN/75	
	N8782R	IAS Cargo			09/JAN/75	
	G-BDHA	IAS Cargo			76	
	G-BDHA	British Cargo Airlines			20/AUG/79	
	G-BDHA	Systems Control Leasing			17/NOV/83	
	HI-426	Aeromar			23/NOV/83	WFU 01/MAR/80 to 17/NOV/83
45668	N4904C	Capitol International	54F		13/SEP/63	
	N8740	Eastern Airlines			12/DEC/67	Leased
	N4904C	Capitol International			29/APR/68	
	EC-CQM	Aviaco			11/MAY/75	Leased
	HC-BLU	AECA Carga			JUN/85	
45669	N8008F	Trans International	54F		26/APR/63	
	N8008F	Saturn Airways			27/OCT/68	
	TU-TCG	Air Afrique			10/NOV/74	
	TU-TCG	Charlotte Aircraft			01/MAR/79	
	N1041W	Airlift International			03/AUG/79	Leased
	N1041W	F.B. Ayer			15/SEP/81	
	N1041W	Far North Air			16/JUL/82	Leased
	N1041W	F.B. Ayer			01/OCT/82	
	N1041W	Airlift International			01/DEC/82	
	N141RD	Airlift International				WFU DEC/85, stored Miami
45670	TU-TCA	Air Afrique	53		19/OCT/63	
	TU-TCA	Saudi Arabian Airlines			13/FEB/69	Leased
	TU-TCA	Air Afrique			APR/69	
45671	TU-TCB	Air Afrique	53		10/JAN/64	
	F-BJCB	UTA			29/NOV/65	Leased
	TU-TCB	Air Afrique			15/JUL/68	WFU AUG/83, stored Luxembourg
45672	N811E	Delta Airlines	51		14/NOV/63	
	N811E	FBA Corp.			24/NOV/80	
	N3128H	FBA Corp.				WFU, stored Marana
45674	N109RD	Airlift International	54F		17/JUN/64	
	N109RD	Japan Airlines			01/MAY/68	Leased
	N109RD	Airlift International			69	
	N109RD	National Airlines			15/NOV/69	Leased
	N109RD	Airlift International			16/APR/74	
	N109RD	McDonnell Douglas Finance			30/JAN/78	
	N109RD	Airlift International				
	N109RD	Douglas			81	
	N109RD	International Air Leases			15/SEP/81	
	N109RD	Arrow Airways			15/SEP/81	Leased
	N109RD	International Air Leases			16/APR/84	WFU 16/APR/84
45675	N8041U	United Airlines	54F		18/FEB/64	
	N8041U	PK Finans			JUL/85	WFU, stored Las Vegas
45676	N8042U	United Airlines	54F		30/JAN/64	

C/N	Registration	Owner/Operator	Series	First Flight	Delivery	Remarks
	N8042U	PK Finans			JUL/85	WFU, stored Las Vegas
45677	N8043U	United Airlines	54F		14/FEB/64	
	N8043U	PK Finans			JUL/85	WFU, stored Las Vegas
45678	JA8014	Japan Airlines	55F		05/MAR/65	
	HP-950	International Air			16/JUN/82	
	N55FB	FBA Corp.				
	N55FB	Agro Air			JUN/85	WFU, stored Santo Domingo
45679	CF-TJP	Trans Canada Airlines	54F		25/MAR/64	
	CF-TJP	Air Canada			01/JUN/64	WFU 21/JUN/82 to 06/MAR/84
	C-FTJP	United Air Leasing			06/MAR/84	
	C-FTJP	International Air Leases			31/MAY/84	
	N4768G	Omega Aviation			OCT/83	WFU, stored Tucson
45683	PH-DCS	KLM	55F		25/JUL/64	
	PH-DCS	Philippine Airlines			NOV/76	Leased
	RP-C843	Philippine Airlines			25/FEB/77	Purchased
						WFU 26/MAR/81 to 11/AUG/84
	9Q-CKI	Lukum Air Service			11/AUG/84	
	9Q-CKI	TAAG Angola			NOV/84	Leased
45684	N8783R	Trans Caribbean	54F		16/DEC/63	
	N8783R	American Airlines			01/MAR/71	
	D-ACCB	Cargo Charter Airways				Not taken-up
	N8783R	Seaboard World			19/MAY/72	Leased
	N8783R	American Airlines			15/MAY/75	
	G-BDDE	IAS Cargo			20/JUL/75	
	G-BDDE	British Cargo Airlines			20/AUG/79	WFU 01/MAR/80 to 25/NOV/83
	G-BDDE	Systems Control Leasing			25/NOV/83	
	HI-427	Aeromar			01/DEC/83	WFU DEC/85, stored Miami
45685	XA-PIK	Aeromexico	51		30/APR/64	
45686	CF-TJQ	Air Canada	54F		27/AUG/64	WFU 01/DEC/82 to 06/MAR/84
	C-FTJQ	United Air Leasing			06/MAR/84	
	C-FTJQ	International Air Leases			31/MAY/84	
	9Q-CDM	Zaire Cargo			OCT/84	
45687	N814E	Delta Airlines	51		28/OCT/64	
	N814E	F.B. Ayer			27/FEB/81	
	XA-AMP	Aeromexico			28/APR/81	Leased
	XA-AMP	FBA Corp.			01/SEP/81	WFU, stored Marana
45689	N815E	Delta Airlines	51		05/NOV/64	
	N815E	F.B. Ayer	51C		30/MAR/81	
	N815E	Lacsa			09/OCT/81	Leased
	N815E	F.B. Ayer			15/MAR/82	
	N815E	Airlift International			09/DEC/83	
	N815E	Lockheed Finance Co.			16/OCT/84	
	8Q-CA005	Maldives Airways			AUG/84	
45690	N816E	Delta Airlines	51		24/MAR/65	
	N816E	F.B. Ayer			07/DEC/77	
	RP-C831	Philippine Airlines			05/MAR/78	Leased
	RP-C831	F.B. Ayer			24/NOV/80	WFU 24/NOV/80
45692	N801SW	Seaboard World	55		21/JUN/64	
	N801SW	Transcarga			MAR/69	Leased
	N801SW	Seaboard World			MAY/69	
	F-BOLN	UTA			05/APR/69	
	45692	French Air Force			15/AUG/69	Callsign "F-RAFB"
	5V-TAF	Togo Government			28/FEB/83	
45693	N8060U	United Airlines	52		17/APR/65	
	TC-JBZ	Bursa Hava Yollari			10/JUN/80	Leased
	TC-JBZ	United Airlines			25/MAR/81	WFU 25/MAR/81 to 17/SEP/84
	TC-JBZ	Omega Air			17/SEP/84	For spares
45752	ZK-NZC	Air New Zealand	52		17/SEP/65	
	ZK-NZC	International Lease Finance			03/JUL/82	
	N42920	Golden International			JUL/82	WFU, stored Marana
45753	SE-DBD	SAS	55		27/APR/65	
	SE-DBD	Swissair			15/NOV/69	Leased
	SE-DBD	SAS			15/MAR/70	
	SE-DBD	Scanair			75	
	N721UA	United Aircraft Leasing			30/OCT/79	
	EC-DIH	TAE			15/NOV/79	Leased
	N916R	Overseas National Airways			16/SEP/80	
	N916R	Sunland			22/NOV/80	Leased
	N916R	Overseas National Airways			26/JUN/81	
	N916R	Icelandair			09/MAY/82	Leased
	N916R	National Airlines			85	
	TF-FLB	Icelandair			JUL/86	
45755	I-DIWM	Alitalia	43		15/APR/65	
	N153FA	F.B. Ayer			08/DEC/76	
	RP-C348	Sterling Philippines			04/SEP/79	Leased, WFU 81
	RP-C348	F.B. Ayer			28/OCT/83	Stored
45758	N8063U	United Airlines	52		02/JUL/65	WFU NOV/79, stored Las Vegas
45759	N8064U	United Airlines	52		10/JUL/65	WFU JAN/80, stored Las Vegas
	N8064U	International Air Leases			29/MAY/84	
	N8064U	Cayman Airways			29/MAY/84	Leased
	OB-R-1287	Faucett			FEB/85	
45760	N8779R	Douglas	51			
	N8779R	Eastern Airlines			30/DEC/64	Leased
	N8779R	Douglas			30/DEC/70	
	6Y-JGD	Air Jamaica			18/NOV/71	
	OB-R-1123	Aero Peru			25/MAR/76	Leased
	OB-R-1123	Air Jamaica			30/MAY/80	
	OB-R-1123	Charlotte Aircraft Corp.			29/OCT/82	WFU 01/JAN/84
45762	PI-C802	Philippine Airlines	55F		25/AUG/65	
	PH-DCW	KLM			19/DEC/67	
	PI-C802	Philippine Airlines			JUL/73	Leased
	PH-DCW	KLM			19/JUL/74	
	PH-DCW	Surinam Airways			79	Leased
	PH-DCW	KLM			79	
	PH-DCW	Viasa			79	Leased
	PH-DCW	KLM			29/NOV/79	
	PH-DCW	Surinam Airways			30/DEC/79	Leased
	PH-DCW	KLM			15/JAN/81	
	PH-DCW	Surinam Airways			01/AUG/81	Leased
	PH-DCW	KLM			10/NOV/83	
	PH-DCW	Boreas International			10/NOV/83	WFU 10/NOV/83 to 29/MAY/84
	N4809E	Arrow Airways			29/MAY/84	
	C-FCWW	ACS			JUN/86	
45763	JA8015	Japan Airlines	55		10/NOV/65	
	N100JJ	International Air Services			16/NOV/76	

MCDONNELL DOUGLAS DC-8-20/30/40/50/62/72 (EXISTING AIRCRAFT ONLY)

C/N	Registration	Owner/Operator	Series	First Flight	Delivery	Remarks
	N100JJ	International Air Services	55F		16/NOV/76	Converted
	N100JJ	Japan Airlines			21/JUL/77	Leased
	N100JJ	International Air Services			20/OCT/80	
	N100JJ	Aero Cargo			27/MAY/82	
	OB-R-1244	Aeronaves Del Peru			SEP/85	
45764	JA8016	Japan Airlines	55		14/FEB/66	
	N907R	United Aircraft Leasing			01/JUL/80	
	N907R	Overseas National Airways			01/JUL/80	
	N907R	United Aircraft Leasing			01/NOV/80	
	N907R	Air Transport International			JUN/81	
	N907R	Orbis			01/JUL/83	
	ST-AJD	Trans Arabian			SEP/83	
45765		Garuda	55			Not taken-up
	N2310B	Douglas				
	N2310B	Overseas National Airways			13/JUN/66	Leased
	N2310B	Douglas			66	
	PK-GJD	Garuda			19/JUL/66	
	PH-DCY	KLM			24/MAR/69	Leased
	PK-GJD	Garuda			23/MAY/73	
	PK-GEA	Garuda			74	WFU 15/JAN/84
	N225VV	Omega Air			30/MAY/86	
45766	PH-DCV	KLM	55		19/AUG/66	
	PK-GJC	Garuda			FEB/74	
	PK-GJN	Garuda			04/MAR/74	
	PK-GEB	Garuda			21/MAR/74	WFU 15/JAN/84
	N226VV	Omega Air			30/MAY/86	
45767	LN-MOH	SAS	55		08/FEB/66	
	LN-MOH	Swissair			01/JAN/70	Leased
	LN-MOH	SAS			15/MAR/70	
	LN-MOH	Swissair			02/JAN/71	Leased
	LN-MOH	SAS			15/MAR/71	
	LN-MOH	Scanair			75	
	N722UA	United Aircraft Leasing			02/JUN/80	
	N722UA	Overseas National Airways			02/JUN/80	
	N722UA	Saudia			02/JUN/80	Leased
	N902R	Overseas National Airways	55F		JUN/82	
	N902R	Rich International			01/AUG/83	Leased
	N902R	Air Transport International			01/AUG/83	
	N902R	National Airlines			15/OCT/84	
	N902R	Air Transport International			15/OCT/84	Leased
	N902R	National Airlines			84	
	N902R	Equator Leasing			MAR/86	
	N902R	Vulcanair			OCT/86	Leased
45768	YV-C-VID	Viasa	53		04/NOV/66	
	OB-R-1083	Aero Peru			15/JUL/74	
	N5768X	Douglas			07/JUL/76	
	N5768X	Douglas	54F		MAR/77	Converted
	G-BTAC	Transmeridian Air Cargo	54F		30/JUL/77	
	G-BTAC	British Cargo Airlines	54FM		20/AUG/79	
	HK-2632	LAC Colombia			30/APR/81	
45800	N8044U	United Airlines	54F		10/SEP/65	
	N8044U	PK Finans			JUL/85	WFU, stored Las Vegas
45801	N8045U	United Airlines	54F		28/SEP/65	
	N8045U	PK Finans			JUL/85	WFU, stored Las Vegas
45802	N8046U	United Airlines	54F		12/JAN/66	
	N8046U	PK Finans			JUL/85	WFU, stored Las Vegas
45803	N8785R	Trans Caribbean	55F		15/JUN/65	
	N8785R	Overseas National Airways			29/NOV/68	Leased
	N8785R	Trans Caribbean			30/JAN/70	
	N8785R	American Airlines			01/MAR/71	
	TL-AAK	Air Centrafrique			27/MAY/71	
	N6842	American Airlines			15/MAY/72	
	F-BOLK	UTA			16/JUN/72	
	N29549	Charlotte Aircraft			05/FEB/82	
	N29549	LACSA			15/APR/82	Leased
	N29549	Charlotte Aircraft			18/JUN/84	WFU, stored Laurinberg
45804	OY-KTC	SAS	55F		16/MAR/66	
	PH-DCZ	KLM			29/APR/70	
	HP-927	Inair Panama			11/SEP/81	
	N855BC	Aviation Leasing			DEC/85	
	N855BC	Canafrica			DEC/85	Leased
45805	N4905C	Capitol International	55F		30/NOV/65	
	N4905C	Eastern Airlines			15/DEC/65	Leased
	N4905C	Capitol International			15/APR/66	
	N4905C	Seaboard World			12/JAN/67	Leased
	N4905C	Capitol International			67	
	TR-LVK	Air Gabon			26/APR/75	
	TR-LVK	Affretair			01/APR/80	
45806	N819E	Delta Airlines	51		10/DEC/65	
	N819E	F.B. Ayer			26/JUL/76	
	HP-768	Air Panama			21/SEP/76	Leased
	N819E	F.B. Ayer				
	RP-C832	Philippine Airlines			05/MAR/78	
	RP-C832	F.B. Ayer			11/NOV/82	WFU 11/NOV/82, stored Marana
45807	N817E	Delta Airlines	51		28/OCT/65	
	N817E	F.B. Ayer			23/JUN/77	
	RP-C345	Sterling Philippines			23/AUG/77	Leased, WFU 81 to 28/OCT/83
	RP-C345	F.B. Ayer			28/OCT/83	WFU 28/OCT/83, stored
45808	N818E	Delta Airlines	51		23/NOV/65	
	N818E	F.B. Ayer			30/MAR/81	
	8Q-PNC	Maldives Airways			AUG/84	
45809	CF-CPM	CP Air	53		31/MAY/66	
	N789FT	Flying Tigers			26/SEP/77	Leased
	CF-CPM	CP Air			01/FEB/78	WFU 15/NOV/81 to 15/JUN/82
	HK-3125	ARCA Colombia			15/JUN/82	WFU DEC/85, stored Miami
45814	EC-BAV	Iberia	52		21/APR/66	
	N45814	Douglas			24/FEB/76	
	T.15-1	Spanish Air Force			17/APR/78	
45815	N820E	Delta Airlines	51		21/JAN/66	
	N820E	F.B. Ayer			05/JUL/77	
	N820E	Braniff			28/JUL/77	Leased
	N820E	F.B. Ayer			15/FEB/80	
	N820E	Mackey International			15/JUN/80	
	N820E	F.B. Ayer			15/NOV/80	
	N820E	Barclays ABC			15/JUN/82	

C/N	Registration	Owner/Operator	Series	First Flight	Delivery	Remarks
	N820E	Navaero Aviation			JUN/85	WFU JUN/85, stored Marana
45816	N804SW	Flying Tiger Line	55F		29/SEP/65	
	N804SW	Seaboard World			29/SEP/65	Leased
	N804SW	Flying Tiger Line			22/DEC/68	
	N804SW	Transcarga			01/JUL/69	
	YV-C-VIM	Transcarga			20/OCT/72	
	N804SW	Seaboard World			25/JUL/75	
	N804SW	EFS Bahamas			01/SEP/76	
	N804SW	Seaboard World			10/NOV/76	
	N804SW	IAS Cargo			10/NOV/76	
	G-BIAS	IAS Cargo			15/NOV/77	
	G-BIAS	British Cargo Airlines			20/AUG/79	
	G-BIAS	Seaboard World			15/AUG/80	
	G-BIAS	Flying Tiger Line			15/SEP/80	
	N804SW	Challenge Air Transport			15/AUG/81	
	N804SW	W. Crawford			JUN/84	WFU, stored Seattle
45817	N805SW	Flying Tiger Line	55F		12/JAN/66	
	N805SW	Seaboard World			12/JAN/66	Leased
	N805SW	Flying Tiger Line			05/MAR/69	
	N805U	Universal Airlines			05/APR/69	
	N805U	SAS			10/JUN/70	Leased
	N805U	Universal Airlines			09/DEC/70	
	HB-IDU	Balair			02/APR/71	
	N9110V	Overseas National Airways			04/OCT/79	
	N9110V	Aeral			28/NOV/79	Leased
	N9110V	Overseas National Airways			18/SEP/80	
	N911R	Elan Air			15/JUL/81	
	N911R	Overseas National Airways			05/MAR/82	
	N911R	Saudia			82	Leased
	N911R	Overseas National Airways			MAR/82	
	N911R	Rich International			01/JUL/83	Leased
	N911R	Air Transport International			23/AUG/83	
	N911R	National Airlines			15/OCT/84	
45819	F-BNLD	UTA	55F		05/NOV/65	
	TU-TXG	Air Afrique			MAR/66	Leased
	F-BNLD	UTA			APR/66	
	F-RAFC	French Air Force			07/SEP/66	Leased
	F-BNLD	UTA			24/FEB/67	
	TU-TXK	Air Afrique			24/FEB/67	Leased
	F-BNLD	UTA			05/APR/67	
	F-RAFC	French Air Force			29/JUN/72	
45820	F-BLKX	UTA	55		31/DEC/65	
	F-RAFA	French Air Force			01/JAN/66	
45821	N803SW	Flying Tiger Line	55F		17/MAR/66	
	N803SW	Seaboard World			17/MAR/66	Leased
	N803SW	Universal Airlines			21/NOV/69	
	N803SW	Seaboard World			21/MAR/70	
	N803SW	Japan Airlines			01/APR/70	Leased
	N803SW	Seaboard World			31/MAR/72	
	TR-LQR	Affretair			09/OCT/72	
	TR-LQR	Air Gabon			JAN/77	
	A40-PA	Cargoman			20/JAN/77	Leased
	A40-PA	Affretair			01/APR/80	
	VP-WMJ	Affretair			82	
	Z-WMJ	Affretair				
45824	N851F	Overseas National Airways	55		20/JUN/66	
	PH-MAS	Martinair			22/NOV/68	
	PH-MAS	UTA			OCT/71	Leased
	PH-MAS	Martinair				
	PH-MAS	Iranair			SEP/76	Leased
	PH-MAS	Martinair			OCT/76	
	N45824	Douglas			14/JAN/77	Leased
	PH-MAS	KLM			19/APR/77	
	PH-MAS	Douglas			28/SEP/77	
	EC-DBE	Aviaco			30/SEP/77	
	EC-DBE	Cargandal			83	Not taken-up
	EC-DBE	Aviaco			83	
	N5824A	ARCA Colombia			SEP/85	WFU SEP/85, stored Luxembourg
45850	N8066U	United Airlines	52		01/APR/66	WFU 19/MAR/84, preserved
45851	N8067U	United Airlines	52		05/MAY/66	WFU JAN/80, Las Vegas
	OB-R-1270	Faucett			08/APR/83	WFU 08/APR/83, used for spares, derelict Lima
45852	N8068U	United Airlines	52		18/MAY/66	WFU JAN/80 to 11/APR/83
	OB-R-1269	Faucett			11/APR/83	WFU APR/85, stored Lima
45853	N8069U	United Airlines	52		16/JUN/66	WFU JAN/80 to 18/APR/83
	OB-R-1268	Faucett			18/APR/83	
45854	JA8017	Japan Airlines	55		27/SEP/66	
	N910R	Overseas National Airways			02/JUN/80	
	N910R	Saudia			02/JUN/80	Leased
	N910R	Overseas National Airways			82	
	N910R	Saudia				Leased
	N910R	National Airlines			30/APR/85	WFU 30/APR/85 to MAR/86
	N910R	Boreas Corp.			MAR/86	
45855	XA-SIB	Aeromexico	51		21/OCT/66	
45856	N852F	Overseas National Airways	55F		07/JUL/66	
	PH-MAU	Martinair			01/OCT/69	
	PH-MAU	UTA			31/OCT/71	Leased
	PH-MAU	Martinair			72	
	PH-MAU	Douglas			17/NOV/78	
	EC-DEM	Aviaco			27/DEC/78	
	EC-DEM	Cargandal			83	Not taken-up
	EC-DEM	Aviaco				WFU 15/JAN/84 to APR/85
	EC-DEM	Progressive Air			APR/85	
45857	TU-TCC	Air Afrique	55F		02/AUG/66	WFU 06/SEP/83, stored
45858	N1509U	Douglas	55F			
	N1509U	Panagra			02/SEP/66	Leased
	N1509U	Douglas			66	
	N1509U	Braniff			01/JAN/67	
	N1509U	Seaboard World			MAY/67	Leased
	N1509U	Braniff			AUG/67	
	CF-CPT	CP Air			17/NOV/67	
	N789FT	Flying Tiger Lines			26/SEP/77	Leased
	CF-CPT	CP Air			01/FEB/78	
	G-BSKY	IAS Cargo			15/FEB/78	
	G-BSKY	Alitalia			06/AUG/78	Leased

MCDONNELL DOUGLAS DC-8-20/30/40/50/62/72 (EXISTING AIRCRAFT ONLY)

C/N	Registration	Owner/Operator	Series	First Flight	Delivery	Remarks
	G-BSKY	IAS Cargo			03/SEP/78	
	G-BSKY	British Cargo Airlines			20/AUG/79	
	HC-BJT	Andes Airlines			17/FEB/82	
45859	PH-DCU	KLM	55F		27/FEB/66	
	PH-DCU	Philippine Airlines			30/MAY/76	Leased
	PH-DCU	KLM			02/AUG/76	
	PH-DCU	Surinam Airways			05/OCT/80	Leased
	PH-DCU	KLM			81	
	PH-DCU	Rich International			29/SEP/81	
	N29954	Air Transport International			83	
	N29954	Orbis			15/SEP/83	
	N29954	Trans Arabian Air Transport			85	
	N29954	Trans African			JUL/85	
	5N-ARH	Arax Airlines			MAR/86	
45860	CF-TJR	Air Canada	54F		07/MAY/66	WFU SEP/81 to 06/MAR/84
	N4769G	United Air Leasing			06/MAR/84	
	N4769G	Arrow Air			05/JUN/84	
	N4769G	International Air Leases				
	C-GQBG	Quebecair			JUL/85	Leased
45861	CF-TJS	Air Canada	54F		07/MAY/66	WFU 31/MAY/82 to 06/MAR/84
	C-FTJS	United Air Leasing			06/MAR/84	
	YV-128C	Viasa			31/MAY/84	Leased
	YV-128C	International Air Leases			MAR/85	WFU, stored Miami
45862	N4906C	Capitol International	55F		22/APR/66	
	N4906C	Seaboard World			03/JAN/67	Leased
	N4906C	Capitol International			03/APR/67	
	F-BOLN	UTA				Not taken-up
	F-BUOR	UTA			01/JUN/74	
	F-BUOR	SFAIR			16/MAR/83	
45877	N821E	Delta Airlines	51		25/AUG/66	
	N821E	F.B. Ayer			05/JUL/77	
	N821E	Braniff			28/JUL/77	Leased
	N821E	F.B. Ayer			22/FEB/80	
	N821E	Mackey International			15/JUN/80	Leased
	N821E	Airlift International			28/JAN/81	Leased
	N821E	F.B. Ayer			15/SEP/81	
	N821E	Barclays ABC			15/JUN/82	
	N821E	FBA Corp.			NOV/84	WFU, stored Marana
45878	N8954U	Douglas	51			
	XA-SIA	Aeromexico			14/OCT/66	
45881	N8048U	United Airlines	54F		28/SEP/66	
	N8048U	Electrospace Systems			13/NOV/84	
45882	JA8018	Japan Airlines	55F		16/OCT/66	
	OB-R-1200	Aeronaves del Peru			15/OCT/80	
45883	N806SW	Seaboard World	55F		20/OCT/67	
	N806SW	Japan Airlines			01/FEB/70	Leased
	N806SW	Seaboard World			31/MAR/72	
	YU-AGB	Inex Adria				Not taken-up
	N806SW	Inex Adria			20/APR/72	Leased
	N806SW	Seaboard World			08/OCT/72	
	N806SW	Cargolux			06/MAY/74	Leased
	N806SW	Seaboard World			05/AUG/75	
	TU-TCH	Air Afrique			08/AUG/75	
45884	N8050U	United Airlines	54F		12/MAR/68	
	N8050U	PK Finans			JUL/85	WFU, stored Las Vegas
45885	N8051U	United Airlines	54F		19/MAR/68	
	EC-DYA	Air Cargo Spain			JUL/85	
45886	N8049U	United Airlines	54F		10/NOV/66	
	N8049U	PK Finans			JUL/85	WFU, stored Las Vegas
45895		Panagra	62			Not taken-up
	N1803	Braniff			22/AUG/67	
	N1803	Pan Am			JAN/70	Leased
	N1803	Braniff			01/APR/71	WFU 12/MAY/82 to 01/DEC/83
	N1803	Hawaiian Air			01/DEC/83	
	N1803	International Air Leases				
	N1803	Arrow Air			FEB/86	Leases
	N1803	International Air Leases			86	
45896		Panagra	62			Not taken-up
	N1804	Braniff			20/SEP/67	WFU 12/MAY/82 to 15/MAR/84
	N1804	International Air Leases			OCT/83	
	N1804	Arrow Air			15/MAR/84	Leased
	N1804	Transglobal International			06/JUL/84	Sub-leased
	N1804	Rich International			26/DEC/84	Sub-leased
45899		Panagra	62			Not taken-up
	N1805	Braniff			29/SEP/67	WFU 12/MAY/82 to 31/OCT/83
	N1805	Rich International			31/OCT/83	
	N1805	Air Florida			NOV/83	Leased
	N1805	Rich International			SEP/85	
45904		Panagra	62CF			Not taken-up
	N1807	Braniff			11/NOV/67	WFU 12/MAY/82 to 01/DEC/83
	N1807	Hawaiian Air			01/DEC/83	
	N1807	International Air Leases			FEB/86	
45905	SE-DBF	SAS	62		08/AUG/67	
	N810BN	Braniff			14/JAN/77	WFU 12/MAY/82 to 01/DEC/83
	N810BN	Rich International			01/DEC/83	
	N810BN	International Air Leases			DEC/85	
45906	OY-KTD	SAS	62		29/AUG/67	
	OY-KTD	Scanair			08/FEB/76	
	SE-DDU	Scanair			21/AUG/79	
	SE-DDU	SAS			80	
	SE-DDU	Scanair			80	Leased
	SE-DDU	SAS			82	
	SE-DDU	Arista International			01/JUN/82	Leased
	SE-DDU	SAS			23/JAN/83	
	N	United Air Leasing			26/NOV/86	Sched.delivery
45909	N1505U	Douglas	62H			
	I-DIWN	Alitalia			28/OCT/67	
	N802BN	Braniff			15/NOV/78	WFU 12/MAY/82 to 01/DEC/83
	N802BN	Hawaiian Air			01/DEC/83	
	N802BN	International Air Leases			DEC/84	WFU, stored Marana
45910	I-DIWV	Alitalia	62H		16/NOV/67	
	I-DIWV	DETA			25/NOV/77	Leased
	I-DIWV	Alitalia			30/JAN/79	WFU 23/APR/81 to 15/DEC/82
	N39307	Sea and Sun Airlines			15/DEC/82	
	N39307	Guy America			01/FEB/83	Leased

C/N	Registration	Owner/Operator	Series	First Flight	Delivery	Remarks
	N39307	Sea and Sun Airlines			01/AUG/83	
	N39307	CIS Corp.			FEB/86	WFU FEB/86, stored Marana
45911		Panagra	62			Not taken-up
	N1806	Braniff			19/DEC/67	
	N806BN	Braniff				
	N1806	Braniff			81	WFU 12/MAY/82 to 13/FEB/84
	N1806	Rich International			14/FEB/84	
	N1806	Arrow Air			19/APR/84	
	N1806	International Air Leases				
	N1806	Surinam Airways			APR/84	Leased
45916	JA8019	Japan Airlines	55		18/SEP/67	
	N915R	Overseas National Airways			23/JUN/80	
	N915R	Saudia			23/JUN/80	Leased
	N915R	Overseas National Airways			82	
	N915R	Saudia				Leased
	N915R	National Airlines			30/APR/85	WFU 30/APR/85 to APR/86
	N915R	Aviation Transactions			MAR/86	
45917	F-BNLE	UTA	62		23/FEB/68	
	F-BNLE	Air Supply Corporation			26/JAN/84	
	N4761G	Airborne Express			FEB/86	
45918	F-BOLF	UTA	62		27/APR/68	
	F-BOLF	LAM			01/APR/81	Leased
	F-BOLF	UTA			FEB/83	
	N728PL	Interstate Airlines			APR/86	
45920	HB-IDF	Swissair	62		02/JAN/68	
	HB-IDF	TRATCO Leasing			06/OCT/83	
	C-GMXR	Nationair			SEP/85	
45921	SE-DBG	SAS	62		11/JAN/68	
	SE-DBG	Scanair			19/OCT/77	
	SE-DBG	SAS				
	SE-DBG	Scanair			21/OCT/79	Leased
	N	United Air Leasing			06/OCT/86	Sched.delivery
45922	OY-KTE	SAS	62CF		29/FEB/68	
	OY-KTE	Scanair			29/OCT/79	
	OY-KTE	SAS			80	
	OY-KTE	Scanair			80	Leased
	OY-KTE	SAS			JAN/83	
	OY-KTE	Arista International			JAN/83	Leased
	OY-KTE	SAS			DEC/83	
	OY-KTE	Northeastern International			01/DEC/83	Leased
	OY-KTE	SAS			01/OCT/84	
	OY-KTE	Thai International			01/OCT/84	Leased
	HS-TGQ	Thai International			01/SEP/85	Purchased
	60112	Royal Thai Air Force			01/SEP/85	
45925	HB-IDG	Swissair	62		24/FEB/68	
	HB-IDG	TRATCO Leasing			15/SEP/83	
	C-GMXY	LCA Partners				
	C-GMXY	Nationair			JUL/85	Leased
45932	ZK-NZD	Air New Zealand	52		27/JAN/68	
	ZK-NZD	Air New Zealand	52F		JUL/81	Converted
45935	XA-SID	Aeromexico	51		07/FEB/68	
45953	JA8031	Japan Airlines	62		19/APR/66	
	JA8031	Japan Asia			AUG/83	
	JA8031	Japan Airlines			SEP/84	
45954	JA8032	Japan Airlines	62		27/MAY/68	
	TF-BBA	Loch-Ness			17/MAR/83	
	TF-BBA	Hamzair			83	Leased
	5N-AON	Okada Air			JUL/84	
45955	JA8033	Japan Airlines	62		10/JUN/68	
	N163CA	Conner Airlines			17/JAN/84	
	N163CA	International Air Leases			SEP/85	WFU, stored Miami
45956	JA8034	Japan Airlines	62		19/JUL/68	
	N162CA	Conner Airlines			23/AUG/83	
	N162CA	Northeastern International			31/DEC/83	
	N814ZA	Zantop International			JUL/85	
45960	I-DIWC	Alitalia	62CF		10/APR/68	
	I-DIWC	Zambia Airways			71	Leased
	I-DIWC	Alitalia			71	WFU 01/JUL/82 to 24/NOV/82
	F-GDJM	Minerve			24/NOV/82	
45961	N8964U	Douglas	62F		30/JUN/68	
	I-DIWQ	Alitalia			01/AUG/83	
	N3931A	Sea & Sun Airlines				
	N3931A	CIS Corp.			FEB/86	WFU FEB/86, stored Marana
45965	EC-BMV	Iberia	55F		31/MAR/68	
	EC-BMV	Aviaco			26/NOV/79	
	EC-BMV	LACSA			02/AUG/82	Leased
	N801FB	Tagra Miami Inc.			MAY/85	Quiet Nacelle Test aircraft
45984	HB-IDH	Swissair	62CF		11/JUL/68	
	HB-IDH	Balair			01/APR/76	
	HB-IDH	Swissair			23/APR/79	Leased
	HB-IDH	Balair			11/SEP/79	
	371	Peruvian Air Force			31/DEC/81	
45985	ZK-NZE	Air New Zealand	52		27/FEB/68	
	N4292P	Golden International			06/JUL/82	WFU, stored Marana
45986	I-DIWJ	Alitalia	62H		26/JUL/68	WFU 23/APR/81 to 01/NOV/82
	N3931G	Sea and Sun Airlines			10/NOV/82	
	N3931G	Guy America			01/FEB/83	Leased
	N3931G	Sea and Sun Airlines			83	
	N3931G	Pacific East Air			23/JUN/83	Leased
	N3931G	Sea and Sun Airlines			84	
	N3931G	CIS Corp.			FEB/86	WFU FEB/86, stored Miami
45987	F-BOLG	UTA	62		14/JUN/68	
	OH-LFZ	Finnair			15/DEC/75	
	OH-LFZ	Air Afrique			31/AUG/79	Leased
	OH-LFZ	Finnair			02/SEP/79	
	OH-LFZ	Zambia Airways			02/SEP/79	Leased
	OH-LFZ	Finnair			11/SEP/79	
	OH-LFZ	Zambia Airways			19/AUG/80	Leased
	OH-LFZ	Finnair			22/SEP/80	
	OH-LFZ	Kar Air			APR/84	Leased
46009	N8052U	United Airlines	54F		31/OCT/68	
	ST-AJR	Trans Arabian			JUL/85	
46011	N8054U	United Airlines	54F		11/NOV/68	
	EC-DYB	Air Cargo Spain			JUL/85	
46012	N8055U	United Airlines	54F			

MCDONNELL DOUGLAS DC-8-20/30/40/50/62/72 (EXISTING AIRCRAFT ONLY)

C/N	Registration	Owner/Operator	Series	First Flight	Delivery	Remarks
	N8055U	Wind C.I. Ltd			05/NOV/84	
	EL-AJK	Trans Sahel Airlines			FEB/85	Leased
46013	OH-LFR	Finnair	62CF		27/JAN/69	
	OH-LFT	Finnair			APR/69	
	OH-LFT	IAS Cargo			04/JAN/78	Leased
	OH-LFT	Finnair				
	OH-LFT	IAS Cargo			08/NOV/78	Leased
	OH-LFT	Finnair			22/MAY/79	
	OH-LFT	Tunis Air			31/MAY/79	Leased
	OH-LFT	Finnair			01/JUL/79	
	OH-LFT	Air Algerie			02/OCT/79	Leased
	OH-LFT	Finnair			01/DEC/79	
	F-RAFG	French Air Force	72CF		23/NOV/81	
46022	JA8036	Japan Airlines	62F		13/DEC/68	
	JA8036	Orient Lease			28/APR/82	
	JA8036	Japan Airlines			28/APR/82	Leased
	JA8036	Japan Asia			85	
46023	JA8035	Japan Airlines	62		11/NOV/68	
46024	JA8037	Japan Airlines	62		27/JAN/69	
	N815ZA	Zantop International			NOV/85	
46025		Garuda	55			Cancelled order
46027	I-DIWY	Alitalia	62H		25/FEB/69	WFU 12/APR/81
	OB-R-1248	Aero Peru			25/MAY/82	
46028	F-BOLH	UTA	62		24/MAY/69	
	F-BOLH	Loch Ness Co.			19/OCT/84	
	N812ZA	Zantop International			NOV/85	
46043	OH-LFS	Finnair	62CF		22/MAR/69	
	OH-LFV	Finnair			APR/69	
	OH-LFV	UTA			29/SEP/75	
	F-RAFD	French Air Force			20/OCT/75	
	F-RAFD	French Air Force	72CF		03/JAN/83	Converted
46067	N8966U	United Airlines	62H		22/JUN/69	WFU MAY/80, stored Denver
	N8966U	NASR Associated Inc.			21/SEP/83	
46068	N8967U	United Airlines	62H		15/JUN/69	WFU 15/JAN/84 to DEC/85
	N816ZA	Zantop International			DEC/85	
46069	N8968U	United Airlines	62H		08/JUL/69	WFU FEB/80, stored Denver
	N8968U	Arrow Air			24/JUN/82	
	N8968U	United Airlines			20/JAN/84	
	N8968U	Arrow Air			19/JUN/84	
	N8968U	International Air Leases			FEB/86	
46070	N8969U	United Airlines	62H		16/JUL/69	WFU, stored Denver
	N8969U	Arrow Air			30/JAN/82	Leased
	N8969U	CIS Corp.			86	
	N8969U	Hawaiian Air			APR/86	Leases
46071	N8970U	United Airlines	62H		28/JUL/69	
	N8970U	General Electric Credit Corp			15/AUG/84	
	N8970U	Arrow Air			21/SEP/84	
	N8970U	CIS Corp.			86	
	N8970U	Hawaiian Air			JAN/86	Leased
46077	HB-IDI	Swissair	62		06/JUL/69	
	HB-IDI	TRATCO			11/APR/84	
	N801AX	Airborne Express			JAN/86	
46078	HB-IDK	Swissair	62CF		06/AUG/69	
	370	Peruvian Air Force			26/DEC/81	
46081	N8971U	United Airlines	62H		11/AUG/69	
	N8971U	Overseas National Airways			02/JUL/73	Leased
	N8971U	United Airlines			06/AUG/73	
	N8971U	Camma Corp.			31/MAR/81	
	N8971U	ARAMCO	72		29/JAN/82	Converted
	N728A	ARAMCO			83	
46082	I-DIWK	Alitalia	62H		14/MAY/69	
	N801BN	Braniff			07/JAN/79	WFU 12/MAY/82 to APR/86
	N801BN	NASA	72		APR/86	
46084	N8972U	United Airlines	62H		19/AUG/69	
	6Y-JII	Air Jamaica			29/OCT/73	
	N2547R	Camma Corp.	72		15/JUN/82	Converted
	N2547R	Bright Star Enterprises			08/AUG/84	
	HZ-MS11	Bright Star Enterprises				
46085	N8973U	United Airlines	62H		04/SEP/69	WFU MAY/80, stored Denver
	N8973U	Rich International			30/SEP/82	
	N8973U	Northeastern International			15/JAN/84	
	N8973U	General Electric Credit Corp			20/AUG/84	
	N8973U	Arrow Air			21/SEP/84	
	N8973U	International Air Leases			FEB/86	
46098	I-DIWW	Alitalia	62H		10/FEB/70	WFU 12/APR/81 to 10/NOV/82
	N39305	Sea and Sun Airlines			10/NOV/82	
	N39305	Guy America			01/FEB/83	Leased
	N39305	Sea and Sun Airlines			06/JUN/83	
	N39305	Pacific East Air			06/JUN/83	Leased
	N39305	Sea and Sun Airlines			84	
	N39305	CIS Corp.			FEB/86	WFU FEB/86, stored Miami
46102	LN-MOG	SAS	62		30/JAN/70	
	LN-MOG	Swissair			25/OCT/71	Leased
	LN-MOG	SAS			01/MAY/72	
	LN-MOG	Swissair			30/AUG/80	Leased
	LN-MOG	SAS			23/SEP/80	
	LN-MOG	Swissair			18/OCT/80	Leased
	LN-MOG	SAS			08/NOV/80	
	OB-R-1260	Aero Peru			15/DEC/82	
46105	N1808E	Braniff	62		23/OCT/69	
	N1808E	Douglas			23/OCT/81	WFU 23/OCT/81 to 01/AUG/83
	N1808E	Rich International			02/AUG/83	
46107	N1809E	Braniff	62		17/NOV/69	
	N1809E	Douglas			17/NOV/81	WFU 18/NOV/81 to 21/DEC/83
	N1809E	International Air Leases			21/DEC/83	
	N1809E	Arrow Air			21/DEC/83	Leased
	N1809E	International Air Leases				
	N1809E	Surinam Airways			MAR/86	
46110	N8974U	United Airlines	62H		23/SEP/69	
	N8974U	Arrow Air			11/JAN/82	Leased
	N8974U	International Air Leases			FEB/86	
46111	N8975U	United Airlines	62H		14/OCT/69	
	VR-BHM	Andalair Corp.			12/MAR/82	
	VR-BHM	Sigair Ltd			07/APR/82	
46130	N8731U	Douglas	62CF			

C/N	Registration	Owner/Operator	Series	First Flight	Delivery	Remarks
	OH-LFY	Finnair			29/DEC/70	
	OH-LFY	Mandala Airlines			06/OCT/78	Leased
	OH-LFY	Finnair			04/NOV/78	
	OH-LFY	Mandala Airlines			15/NOV/78	Leased
	OH-LFY	Finnair			13/DEC/78	
	OH-LFY	IAS Cargo			08/JAN/79	Leased
	OH-LFY	Finnair			05/APR/79	
	OH-LFY	Tunis Air			02/JUL/79	Leased
	OH-LFY	Finnair			01/SEP/79	
	OH-LFY	Egyptair			09/OCT/79	Leased
	OH-LFY	Finnair			01/APR/80	
	OH-LFY	Sudan Airways			27/SEP/80	Leased
	OH-LFY	Finnair			11/NOV/80	
	F-RAFF	French Air Force			JAN/81	
	F-RAFF	French Air Force	72CF		30/APR/84	Converted
46131	LN-MOW	SAS	62		25/FEB/70	
	N	United Air Leasing			DEC/87	Sched.delivery
46132	I-DIWH	Alitalia	62H		24/JUL/70	WFU 12/APR/81 to 25/MAY/82
	OB-R-1249	Aero Peru			25/MAY/82	
46134	HB-IDL	Swissair	62		06/FEB/70	
	N924CL	Capitol International			15/JUN/84	
	N924CL	National Airlines			28/JUL/84	
	N924CL	Airborne Express			MAR/86	
46139	JA8044	Japan Airlines	62AF		14/SEP/70	
	NB13ZA	Zantop International			FEB/85	
46142	I-DIWX	Alitalia	62H		12/MAR/71	
	OB-R-1210	Aero Peru			18/FEB/81	
46150	LN-MOC	SAS	62AF		22/OCT/70	
	LN-MOC	Scanair			79	Leased
	HS-TGS	Thai International			31/MAR/79	
	60109	Royal Thai Air Force			02/DEC/82	
46153	JA8052	Japan Airlines	62		05/OCT/71	
	JA8052	Japan Asia			OCT/84	
46154	JA8055	Japan Airlines	62AF		17/FEB/72	
	N811ZA	Zantop International			15/SEP/84	
46161	JA8053	Japan Airlines	62H		18/NOV/71	
46162	JA8056	Japan Airlines	62H		21/MAR/72	
	TF-BBB	Loch Ness Corp.			03/OCT/83	
	TF-BBB	Hamzair			83	Leased
	TF-BBB	Air ABC			83	
	TF-BBB	Cargolux			01/DEC/83	Leased
	N810ZA	Zantop International			28/AUG/84	

McDonnell Douglas DC-8
Cross-reference index

5A- Libya
45300	5A-DGK
45382	5A-DGN
45659	5A-DJP

5B- Cyprus
45303	5B-CAC

5N- Nigeria
45954	5N-AON
45859	5N-ARH
45421	5N-AYZ

5V- Togo
45692	5V-TAF

5Y- Kenya
45379	5Y-ASA
45629	5Y-BAS
45629	5Y-QSR

6Y- Jamaica
45760	6Y-JGD
45648	6Y-JGE
45643	6Y-JGF
46084	6Y-JII
45612	6Y-JMF

8Q- Maldives
45689	8Q-CA005
45808	8Q-PNC

9Q- Zaire
45629	9Q-CBF
45686	9Q-CDM
45683	9Q-CKI
45266	9Q-CLE
45268	9Q-CLE
45607	9Q-CQM

A40- Oman
45821	A40-PA

A6- Dubai
45429	A6-SHA

C/CF- Canada
45762	C-FCWW
45920	C-GMXR
45925	C-GMXY
45618	C-GNDE
45619	C-GNDF
45860	C-GQBG
45387	C-GSWQ
45388	C-GSWX
45620	CF-CPF
45622	CF-CPI
45661	CF-CPJ
45809	CF-CPM
45809	CF-CPM
45252	CF-CPN
45858	CF-CPT
45610	CF-TJH
45612	CF-TJJ
45640	CF-TJL
45655	CF-TJO
45679	CF-TJP
45686	CF-TJQ
45860	CF-TJR
45861	CF-TJS

CU- Cuba
45612	CU-T-1210

D- West Germany
45667	D-ACCA
45684	D-ACCB
45416	D-ADIM

EC- Spain
45618	EC-ARB
45619	EC-ARC
'45659	EC-ASN
45658	EC-ATP
45557	EC-AUM
45814	EC-BAV
45965	EC-BMV
45429	EC-CDB
45568	EC-CMT
45668	EC-CQM
45265	EC-CUS
45824	EC-DBE
45856	EC-DEM
45753	EC-DIH
45885	EC-DYA
46011	EC-DYB

EL- Liberia
46012	EL-AJK

F- France
45570	F-BIUZ
45671	F-BJCB
45568	F-BJLB
45627	F-BJUV
45820	F-BLKX
45819	F-BNLD
45917	F-BNLE
45918	F-BOLF
45987	F-BOLG
46028	F-BOLH
45803	F-BOLK
45692	F-BOLN
45862	F-BOLN
45862	F-BUOR
45664	F-BYFM
45960	F-GDJM
45662	F-GDPM

G- United Kingdom
45684	G-BDDE
45667	G-BDHA
45816	G-BIAS
45858	G-BSKY
45768	G-BTAC

HB- Switzerland
45416	HB-IDA
45920	HB-IDF
45925	HB-IDG
45984	HB-IDH
46077	HB-IDI
46078	HB-IDK
46134	HB-IDL
45817	HB-IDU

HC- Ecuador
45606	HC-BEI
45858	HC-BJT
45640	HC-BLM
45668	HC-BLU

HI- Dominican Republic
45667	HI-426
45684	HI-427
45416	HI-435

HK- Colombia
45636	HK-1854
45665	HK-1855
45635	HK-2587
45768	HK-2632
45651	HK-2667
45809	HK-3125

HP- Panama
45259	HP-1048
45806	HP-768
45298	HP-826
45804	HP-927
45678	HP-950

HS- Thailand
45922	HS-TGQ
46150	HS-TGS
45384	HS-TGT
45416	HS-TGW

HZ- Saudi Arabia
46084	HZ-MS11

I- Italy
45960	I-DIWC
45660	I-DIWG
46132	I-DIWH
45600	I-DIWI
45986	I-DIWJ
46082	I-DIWK
45755	I-DIWN
45909	I-DIWN
45601	I-DIWO
45636	I-DIWP
45961	I-DIWQ
45637	I-DIWR
45665	I-DIWS
46666	I-DIWT
45624	I-DIWU
45910	I-DIWV
46098	I-DIWW
46142	I-DIWX
46027	I-DIWY

JA Japan
45418	JA8001
45419	JA8002
45420	JA8003
45421	JA8005
45626	JA8006
45647	JA8007
45420	JA8008
45662	JA8009
45651	JA8010
45664	JA8011
45678	JA8014
45763	JA8015
45764	JA8016
45854	JA8017
45882	JA8018
45916	JA8019
45953	JA8031
45954	JA8032
45955	JA8033
45956	JA8034
46023	JA8035
46022	JA8036
46024	JA8037
46139	JA8044
46153	JA8052
46161	JA8053
46154	JA8055
46162	JA8056

LN- Norway
46150	LN-MOC
46102	LN-MOG
45767	LN-MOH
45388	LN-MOT
46131	LN-MOW

LV- Argentina
45255	LV-LTP

LX- Luxembourg
45659	LX-III

N United States
45763	N100JJ
45669	N1041W
45663	N108RD
45674	N109RD
45610	N10DC
45626	N124AJ
45618	N13627
45669	N141RD
45909	N1505U
45858	N1505U
45755	N153FA

Airliner Production List 1987

McDonnell Douglas DC-8 cross-reference index

45956	N162CA	45304	N8037U	45429	N8608
45955	N163CA	45280	N8038D	45430	N8609
45274	N1800	45410	N803E	45433	N8612
45895	N1803	45820	N803SW	45434	N8613
45896	N1804	45675	N8041U	45435	N8614
45899	N1805	45676	N8042U	45437	N8617
45911	N1806	45677	N8043U	46130	N8731U
45904	N1807	45800	N8044U	45668	N8740
46105	N1808E	45801	N8045U	45635	N875C
46107	N1809E	45802	N8046U	45760	N8779R
45435	N1976P	45881	N8048U	45628	N8780R
45280	N220RB	45886	N8049U	45648	N8781R
45765	N225VV	45411	N804E	45667	N8782R
45766	N226VV	45303	N804EV	45684	N8783R
45765	N2310B	45257	N804PA	45803	N8785R
45660	N253FA	45816	N804SW	45619	N893AF
46084	N2547R	45816	N804SW	45878	N8954U
45641	N276C	45884	N8050U	45961	N8964U
45643	N278C	45885	N8051U	46067	N8966U
45803	N29549	46009	N8052U	46068	N8967U
45889	N29954	46011	N8054U	46069	N8968U
45672	N3128H	46012	N8055U	46070	N8969U
45624	N353FA	45258	N805PA	46071	N8970U
45619	N3751X	45817	N805SW	46081	N8971U
46098	N39305	45817	N805U	46084	N8972U
45910	N39307	45606	N805US	46085	N8973U
45961	N3931A	45693	N8060U	46110	N8974U
45986	N3931G	45758	N8063U	46111	N8975U
45419	N420AJ	45759	N8064U	45265	N900CL
45421	N421AJ	45850	N8066U	45767	N902R
45388	N421AJ	45851	N8067U	45382	N903CL
45752	N42920	45255	N8068D	45647	N903R
45985	N4292P	45852	N8068U	45274	N905CL
45618	N4489M	45853	N8069U	45276	N906CL
45601	N453FA	45911	N806BN	45764	N907R
45610	N4561B	45413	N806E	45854	N910R
45814	N45814	45259	N806PA	45817	N9110V
45824	N45824	45883	N806SW	45817	N911R
45416	N45908	45628	N806US	45916	N915R
45917	N4761G	45645	N807E	45753	N916R
45679	N4768G	45629	N807US	45648	N918CL
45860	N4769G	45646	N808E	45643	N921CL
45762	N4809E	45649	N809E	46134	N924CL
45274	N4901C	45262	N809PA	45607	N9607Z
45276	N4902C	45905	N810BN	45608	N9608Z
45668	N4904C	46162	N810ZA	45603	N995WL
45805	N4905C	45672	N811E	45303	N99862
45805	N4905C	45264	N811PA		
45862	N4906C	46154	N811ZA		
45637	N53AF	45635	N812BN		

OB- Peru

45768	OB-R-1083
45629	OB-R-1116
45760	OB-R-1123
45648	OB-R-1124
45643	OB-R-1125
45612	OB-R-1142
45882	OB-R-1200
46142	OB-R-1210
45600	OB-R-1214
45420	OB-R-1223
45763	OB-R-1244
46027	OB-R-1248
46132	OB-R-1249
45659	OB-R-1259
46102	OB-R-1260
45853	OB-R-1268
45852	OB-R-1269
45851	OB-R-1270
45759	OB-R-1287
45619	OB-R-931
45629	OB-R-962

(continued N-registrations)

45666	N53FA	45265	N812PA
45637	N54FA	46028	N812ZA
45678	N55FB	45266	N813PA
45768	N5768X	46139	N813ZA
45594	N580JC	45267	N814AA
45824	N5824A	45687	N814E
45272	N59AJ	45267	N814PA
45618	N60AJ	45956	N814ZA
45600	N64804	45689	N815E
45803	N6842	45268	N815PA
45416	N712UA	46024	N815ZA
45603	N7182C	45269	N816AA
45606	N7184C	45690	N816E
45384	N718UA	45269	N816PA
45753	N721UA	46068	N816ZA
45767	N722UA	45807	N817E
45081	N728A	45271	N8184A
45918	N728PL	45808	N818E
45809	N789FT	45271	N818PA
45858	N789FT	45806	N819E
45280	N8003U	45437	N819PA
45252	N8008D	45272	N819PA
45669	N8008F	45815	N820E
45285	N8008U	45435	N820F
45589	N8015U	45877	N821E
46077	N801AX	45433	N821F
46082	N801BN	45257	N8240U
45965	N801FB	45258	N8243U
45692	N801SW	45259	N8245U
45593	N8020U	45262	N8246U
45594	N8021U	45264	N8252U
45612	N8021V	45387	N8258U
45292	N8023U	45388	N8266U
45255	N8027	45274	N8274H
45296	N8027U	45276	N8276H
45298	N8029U	45606	N831F
45909	N802BN	45380	N833DA
45255	N802PA	45600	N8418
45603	N802US	45824	N851F
45299	N8031U	45856	N852F
45300	N8033U	45804	N855BC
45303	N8036U	45425	N8604

OH- Finland

45628	OH-KDM
46013	OH-LFR
46043	OH-LFS
46013	OH-LFT
46043	OH-LFV
46130	OH-LFY
45987	OH-LFZ
45606	OH-SOA

OO- Belgium

45382	OO-CMB
45265	OO-TCP

OY- Denmark

45384	OY-KTA
45387	OY-KTB
45804	OY-KTC
45906	OY-KTD
45922	OY-KTE

PH- Netherlands

45379	PH-DCD
45380	PH-DCE
45382	PH-DCG
45629	PH-DCN
45608	PH-DCP
45607	PH-DCR
45683	PH-DCS
45859	PH-DCU
45766	PH-DCV
45762	PH-DCW
45765	PH-DCY
45804	PH-DCZ
45824	PH-MAS
45856	PH-MAU

PI- Philippines

45608	PI-C801
45762	PI-C802
45607	PI-C804
45380	PI-C829

PK- Indonesia

45765	PK-GEA
45766	PK-GEB
45766	PK-GJC
45765	PK-GJD
45766	PK-GJN

PP- Brasil

45272	PP-PDS
45271	PP-PEF

RP- Philippines

45807	RP-C345
45755	RP-C348
45660	RP-C349
45608	RP-C801
45607	RP-C804
45380	RP-C829
45690	RP-C831
45806	RP-C832
45645	RP-C837
45645	RP-C840
45643	RP-C843

S7- Seychelles

45629	S7-SIA

SE- Sweden

45753	SE-DBD
45905	SE-DBF
45921	SE-DBG
45628	SE-DCR
45648	SE-DCT
45906	SE-DDU

ST- Sudan

45764	ST-AJD
46009	ST-AJR

TC- Turkey

45429	TC-AAC
45429	TC-JBV
45693	TC-JBZ

TF- Iceland

45954	TF-BBA
46162	TF-BBB
45753	TF-FLB

TI- Costa Rica

45435	TI-VEL

TL- Central Africa

45803	TL-AAK
45300	TL-AHI

TR- Gabon

45821	TR-LQR
45805	TR-LVK

TU- Ivory Coast

45568	TU-ACP
45670	TU-TCA
45671	TU-TCB
45857	TU-TCC
45627	TU-TCD
45669	TU-TCG
45883	TU-TCH
45819	TU-TXG
45819	TU-TXK

VP- Zimbabwe

45821	VP-WMJ

VR- Bermuda

46111	VR-BHM

XA- Mexico

45687	XA-AMP
45641	XA-DOD
45252	XA-DOE
45603	XA-LSA
45296	XA-LSA
45685	XA-PIK
45878	XA-SIA
45855	XA-SIB
45935	XA-SID

YU- Yugoslavia

45883	YU-AGB

YV- Venezuela

45861	YV-128C
45603	YV-392C
45663	YV-445C
45768	YV-C-VID
45816	YV-C-VIM

Z- Zimbabwe

45821	Z-WMJ

ZK- New Zealand

45752	ZK-NZC
45932	ZK-NZD
45985	ZK-NZE
45303	ZK-NZF

Military operated

France

45820	F-RAFA
45819	F-RAFC
46043	F-RAFD
46130	F-RAFF
46013	F-RAFG
45570	F-ZARK

Peru

46078	370
45984	371

Spain

45814	T.15-1
45658	T.15-2

Thailand

46150	60109
45922	60112

HANDLEY PAGE HERALD (EXISTING AIRCRAFT ONLY)

High-wing, medium range airliner, powered by two Rolls-Royce Dart 527 turboprops. The Herald first flew on 25 August 1955, and 50 aircraft were subsequently produced, made up of the 47-seat Series 100, 56 series 200 (the main version), and the series 400 for the Malaysian Air Force. Production ceased in July 1968.

Dimensions :	Wing span: 94ft 7in (28.88m) Length: 71ft 11in (21.92m) Height: 24ft 1in (7.34m) (100) Wing span: 94ft 7in (28.88m) Length: 75ft 5in (23.01m) Height: 24ft 1in (7.34m) (200)
Powerplant :	Two Rolls Dart 527 turboprops
Performance :	Max cruising speed 237 knots (439km/h) (100) Range: with max payload 615nm (1,140km) (100) Max cruising speed 238 knots (441km/h) (200) Range: with max payload 944nm (1,786km) (200)
Accommodation:	47 passengers (100), 56 passengers (200)
Manufacturer :	Handley Page

C/N	Registration	Owner/Operator	Series	First Flight	Delivery	Remarks
149	G-APWA	Handley Page	100	30/OCT/59		Demonstrator
	G-APWA	Jersey Airlines			17/MAY/61	Leased
	G-APWA	Handley Page				
	G-APWA	BEA			20/JAN/62	Leased
	G-APWA	Handley Page				
	G-APWA	British United Airlines			62	Leased
	G-APWA	Handley Page				
	G-APWA	Autair			APR/63	Leased
	G-APWA	Handley Page			AUG/63	
	G-APWA	Royal Malaysian Air Force			31/AUG/63	Leased
	PP-ASV	Sadia			20/FEB/64	Leased
	G-APWA	Handley Page			24/OCT/65	
	G-APWA	British Midland Airways			14/APR/66	Leased
	G-APWA	Handley Page			SEP/66	
	PP-SDM	Sadia			18/NOV/66	Leased
	PP-SDM	TransBrasil			72	
	PP-SDM	TABA			75	Leased
	G-APWA	British Air Ferries			11/AUG/76	
	G-APWA	Touraine Air Transport			03/APR/79	Leased
	G-APWA	British Air Ferries			30/APR/79	
	G-APWA	Touraine Air Transport			05/JUN/79	Leased
	G-APWA	British Air Ferries			29/JUL/79	
	G-APWA	Touraine Air Transport			03/SEP/79	Leased
	G-APWA	British Air Ferries			02/OCT/79	
	G-APWA	Touraine Air Transport			08/JAN/80	Leased
	G-APWA	British Air Ferries			09/FEB/80	
	G-APWA	Nile Valley Aviation			80	Leased
	G-APWA	British Air Ferries			09/DEC/80	
	G-APWA	Air Ecosse			81	Leased
	G-APWA	British Air Ferries			82	WFU 82, stored Southend
	G-APWA	Keegan Leasing			83	WFU Southend
	G-APWA	General Aviation Sales				Derelict Southend
158	G-APWJ	British United (CI) Airways	201	29/MAY/63	13/JUN/63	
	G-APWJ	British United Island Airway			01/NOV/68	
	G-APWJ	British Island Airways			20/JUL/70	
	G-APWJ	Air UK			16/JAN/80	
	G-APWJ	Duxford Aviation Society			07/JUL/85	Preserved
161	CF-MCK	Maritime Central	211	05/JUL/62		Not taken-up
	PI-C910	Cruz Airways				Not taken-up
	G-ASKK	Handley Page				
	G-ASKK	Autair			AUG/63	Leased
	G-ASKK	Handley Page			DEC/63	
	PP-ASU	Sadia			06/DEC/63	Leased
	G-ASKK	Handley Page			19/OCT/64	
	G-ASKK	British Midland Airways			01/FEB/65	
	G-ASKK	British United (CI) Airways			15/FEB/67	
	G-ASKK	British United Island Airway			01/NOV/68	
	G-ASKK	British Island Airways			20/JUL/70	
	G-ASKK	Air UK			16/JAN/80	WFU 29/MAR/85, preserved Norwich Aviation Museum.
162	CF-MCM	Maritime Central	211	08/AUG/62		Not taken-up
	CF-MCM	Maritime Central	210			Not taken-up
	HB-AAG	Globe Air			04/MAY/63	
	G-ATHB	Handley Page			22/JUL/65	
	B-2001	Far Eastern Air Transport			16/FEB/66	WFU
165	CF-EPA	Eastern Provincial Airways	207	12/DEC/62		Not taken-up
	109	Royal Jordanian Air Force			22/JAN/63	
	JY-ACR	Alia			DEC/63	
	G-ATHE	Handley Page			27/JUL/65	
	G-ATHE	British Midland Airways			17/AUG/65	Leased
	G-ATHE	Handley Page			15/SEP/65	
	D-BOBO	Bavaria			04/APR/66	
	G-ATHE	Handley Page			14/OCT/68	
	B-2011	Far Eastern Air Transport			19/FEB/69	WFU
166	CF-EPI	Eastern Provincial Airways	206	27/JAN/63	13/FEB/63	
	G-BCWE	British Air Ferries			28/JAN/75	
	G-BCWE	Air Anglia			01/APR/76	Leased
	G-BCWE	British Air Ferries			MAY/76	

HANDLEY PAGE HERALD (EXISTING AIRCRAFT ONLY)

C/N	Registration	Owner/Operator	Series	First Flight	Delivery	Remarks
	G-BCWE	British Island Airways			01/JAN/79	Leased
	G-BCWE	Air UK			16/JAN/80	Leased
	G-BCWE	British Air Ferries			31/DEC/81	
	G-BCWE	Trans Azur Aviation			20/APR/82	Leased
	G-BCWE	British Air Ferries			82	
	G-BCWE	Keegan Leasing			83	
	G-BCWE	Keegan Leasing			84	WFU Southend 1984
	G-BCWE	British Air Ferries			20/JUL/85	
167	CF-EPC	Eastern Provincial Airways	206	08/MAR/63	29/MAR/63	
	VP-BCG	Bahamas Airways			FEB/64	Leased
	CF-EPC	Eastern Provincial Airways			MAY/64	
	G-BDFE	British Air Ferries			16/SEP/75	
	G-BDFE	Touraine Air Transport			06/APR/79	Leased
	G-BDFE	British Air Ferries			27/APR/79	
	G-BDFE	Air Algerie			25/APR/80	Leased
	G-BDFE	British Air Ferries			27/JUL/80	
	G-BDFE	Air Algerie			02/JAN/81	Leased
	G-BDFE	British Air Ferries				
	G-BDFE	Keegan Leasing			83	
	G-BDFE	Janus Airways			MAY/83	Leased
	G-BDFE	Keegan Leasing			FEB/84	
	9Q-CAA	MMM Aero Service			27/FEB/84	
169	HB-AAH	Globe Air	210	25/JUL/63	07/AUG/63	
	HB-AAH	British United (CI) Airways			12/DEC/66	
	G-AVEZ	British United (CI) Airways			17/MAR/67	
	PP-ASW	Sadia			13/JAN/68	Leased
	G-AVEZ	British United (CI) Airways			09/APR/68	
	G-AVEZ	British United Island Airway			01/NOV/68	
	G-AVEZ	British Island Airways			20/JUL/70	
	G-AVEZ	Air UK			16/JAN/80	WFU 83, preserved Norwich Aviation Museum. Later to Norwich Airport for training
173	HB-AAI	Globe Air	210	18/FEB/64		Not taken-up
	G-ASPJ	Handley Page				
	G-ASPJ	Alia			FEB/64	Leased
	G-ASPJ	Handley Page			10/MAR/64	
	HB-AAK	Globe Air			13/MAR/64	
	F-OCLY	Europe Aero Service			18/JUL/68	
	F-BLOY	Europe Aero Service			MAY/69	
	F-BLOY	Air Inter			AUG/78	Leased
	F-BLOY	Europe Aero Service				WFU Perpignan
174	G-8-1	Handley Page	209	18/APR/64		
	4X-AHS	Arkia			18/MAY/64	
	G-BEZB	Field Aviation			28/JUL/77	
	G-BEZB	Intra Airways			01/AUG/77	
	G-BEZB	Express Air Freights			14/JAN/78	
	G-BEZB	Jersey European Airways				
	G-BEZB	Express Air Services			04/SEP/81	
	G-BEZB	Channel Express			JAN/83	
175	FM1022	Royal Malaysian Air Force	401	03/JAN/64	17/JAN/64	
	G-BEYF	British Air Ferries			15/AUG/77	
	G-BEYF	Gulf Air			OCT/77	Leased
	G-BEYF	British Air Ferries			09/JAN/78	
	G-BEYF	British Island Airways			01/MAY/78	Leased
	G-BEYF	Air UK			16/JAN/80	Leased
	G-BEYF	British Air Ferries			80	
	G-BEYF	Occidental Oil			26/MAR/81	Leased
	G-BEYF	British Air Ferries			81	
	G-BEYF	Libyan Arab Airlines			29/DEC/81	Leased
	G-BEYF	British Air Ferries			28/APR/82	
	G-BEYF	Libyan Arab Airlines			02/MAY/82	Leased
	G-BEYF	British Air Ferries			82	
	G-BEYF	Keegan Leasing			APR/83	
	G-BEYF	Tunisavia			83	Leased
	G-BEYF	Keegan Leasing			84	
	G-BEYF	Elan Air			15/APR/84	Op. by Air Bridge
	G-BEYF	TNT-Ipec			14/DEC/85	
	G-BEYF	Elan Air			14/APR/86	Op. by Air Bridge
176	D-BIBI	Bavaria	213	02/APR/64	01/MAY/64	
	G-AVPN	Handley Page			22/JUN/67	
	I-TIVB	Itavia			21/JUL/67	
	G-AVPN	British Island Airways			13/JUL/73	
	G-AVPN	Air UK			16/JAN/80	
	G-AVPN	British Air Ferries			JUL/85	
	G-AVPN	Nordic Oil			FEB/86	Leased
	G-AVPN	Business Air Centre			APR/86	
	G-AVPN	Euroair			APR/86	Leased
177	G-ATIG	Handley Page	214	09/SEP/65		
	PP-SDI	Sadia			18/SEP/65	
	G-ATIG	British Midland Airways			28/JUL/73	
	G-ATIG	British Island Airways			01/APR/75	Leased
	G-ATIG	British Midland Airways			31/OCT/75	
	G-ATIG	Brymon Airways			01/JAN/77	
	G-ATIG	Janus Airways			NOV/82	
	G-ATIG	Business Air Centre			APR/86	WFU 20/APR/86, stored Norwich
178	FM1023	Royal Malaysian Air Force	401	30/JAN/64	08/FEB/64	
	G-BEYG	British Air Ferries			12/SEP/77	
	G-BEYG	Touraine Air Transport			27/SEP/79	Leased
	G-BEYG	British Air Ferries			29/SEP/79	
	G-BEYG	Touraine Air Transport			08/FEB/80	Leased
	G-BEYG	British Air Ferries			26/MAR/80	
	G-BEYG	British Air Ferries	401C		80	Converted
	HK-2701	Aerosucre			11/NOV/81	
179	D-BEBE	Bavaria	213	19/MAR/65	29/MAR/65	
	D-BEBE	Arkia			24/NOV/67	
	G-AYMG	British Island Airways			13/OCT/70	
	G-AYMG	Air UK			16/JAN/80	
	G-AYMG	Skyguard			24/MAY/83	
180	FM1024	Royal Malaysian Air Force	401	30/JUL/64	28/SEP/64	
	G-BEYH	British Air Ferries			18/JAN/78	
	G-BEYH	British Island Airways			78	Leased
	G-BEYH	British Air Ferries				
	G-BEYH	Touraine Air Transport			01/APR/79	Leased
	G-BEYH	British Air Ferries			08/APR/79	
	G-BEYH	Touraine Air Transport			27/APR/79	Leased

C/N	Registration	Owner/Operator	Series	First Flight	Delivery	Remarks
	G-BEYH	British Air Ferries			30/JUN/79	
	G-BEYH	Nile Valley Aviation			79	Leased
	G-BEYH	British Air Ferries				
	G-BEYH	Air Algerie			02/MAY/80	Leased
	G-BEYH	British Air Ferries			80	
	G-BEYH	Oasis Oil			80	Leased
	G-BEYH	British Air Ferries			03/DEC/80	
	G-BEYH	Occidental Oil			14/DEC/80	Leased
	G-BEYH	British Air Ferries			81	
	HK-2702	Aerosucre			24/DEC/81	
182	FM1026	Royal Malaysian Air Force	401	18/NOV/64	08/DEC/64	
	G-BEYJ	British Air Ferries			22/DEC/77	
	G-BEYJ	Air Mauretanie			79	Leased
	G-BEYJ	British Air Ferries			JAN/80	
	G-BEYJ	Air Algerie			30/MAY/80	Leased
	G-BEYJ	British Air Ferries			11/JAN/81	
	G-BEYJ	AGOCO			18/JAN/81	Leased
	G-BEYJ	Mobil Oil			MAY/81	Leased
	G-BEYJ	British Air Ferries			DEC/81	
	G-BEYJ	Tunisavia			83	Leased
	G-BEYJ	Keegan Leasing			83	
	TG-ALE	Aerovias Guatemala			OCT/84	
183	G-8-2	Handley Page	209	26/MAR/64		
	4X-AHR	Arkia			17/APR/64	
	G-BAZJ	British Island Airways			JUN/73	
	G-BAZJ	Air UK			16/JAN/80	WFU 31/OCT/84, to Airport Fire School, Guernsey
185	G-8-3	Handley Page	214	02/JUL/64		
	G-ASVO	Handley Page			13/AUG/64	
	PP-SDG	Sadia			23/OCT/64	
	G-ASVO	British Midland Airways			23/MAR/73	
	G-ASVO	Air Anglia			31/OCT/75	Leased
	G-ASVO	British Midland Airways			31/MAR/76	
	G-ASVO	British Air Ferries			07/JAN/77	
	G-ASVO	Gulf Air			25/NOV/77	Leased
	G-ASVO	British Air Ferries				
	G-ASVO	Europe Aero Services			78	Leased
	G-ASVO	British Air Ferries				
	G-ASVO	British Island Airways			01/JAN/79	Leased
	G-ASVO	Air UK			16/JAN/80	Leased
	G-ASVO	British Air Ferries			80	
	G-ASVO	Nile Valley Aviation			30/OCT/80	Leased
	G-ASVO	British Air Ferries			31/MAR/81	
	G-ASVO	Libyan Arab Airlines			NOV/81	Leased
	G-ASVO	British Air Ferries			22/FEB/82	
	G-ASVO	Air Ecosse			21/MAR/82	Leased
	G-ASVO	British Air Ferries			17/APR/82	
	G-ASVO	AGIP Oil			24/MAY/82	Leased
	G-ASVO	British Air Ferries			82	
	HP-	Turbo Air			27/OCT/82	Not taken-up
	G-ASVO	British Air Ferries			27/OCT/82	
	G-ASVO	Guernsey Airlines			AUG/83	
	G-ASVO	British Air Ferries				
186	PP-SDH	Sadia	214	05/JAN/65	26/JAN/65	
	PP-SDH	TransBrasil			72	
	PP-SDH	TABA			76	Leased
	G-BEBB	British Air Ferries			15/JUL/76	
	G-BEBB	British Island Airways			01/JAN/79	Leased
	G-BEBB	Air UK			16/JAN/80	Leased
	G-BEBB	British Air Ferries			80	
	G-BEBB	AGOGO Oil			80	Leased
	G-BEBB	British Air Ferries			80	
	G-BEBB	Air Algerie			06/FEB/81	Leased
	G-BEBB	British Air Ferries			81	
	G-BEBB	Nile Valley Aviation			30/MAR/81	Leased
	G-BEBB	British Air Ferries			81	
	G-BEBB	Libyan Arab Airlines			29/DEC/81	Leased
	G-BEBB	British Air Ferries			82	
	G-BEBB	AGOCO			09/MAY/82	Leased
	G-BEBB	British Air Ferries			82	
	G-BEBB	Keegan Leasing			83	
	G-BEBB	Janus Airways			MAY/83	Leased
	G-BEBB	Keegan Leasing			OCT/83	Stored Bournemouth
	G-BEBB	Channel Express				
	G-CEAS	Channel Express			MAR/86	
187	FM1027	Royal Malaysian Air Force	401	18/DEC/64	11/JAN/65	
	G-BEYK	British Air Ferries			05/MAR/78	
	G-BEYK	British Island Airways			23/MAR/78	Leased
	G-BEYK	Air UK			16/JAN/80	
	G-BEYK	Nordic Oil			APR/86	Leased, not taken-up
	G-BEYK	Air UK			APR/86	
	G-BEYK	Business Air Centre			APR/86	
	G-BEYK	Euroair			APR/86	Leased
188	HB-AAL	Globe Air	210	11/MAY/65	18/MAY/65	
	F-OCLZ	Europe Aero Service			16/JUL/68	
	F-BOIZ	Europe Aero Service			MAY/69	WFU 1982, stored Perpignan
189	G-ATDS	Handley Page	209	12/MAY/65		
	4X-AHT	Arkia			28/JUL/65	
	G-ATDS	Field Aviation			28/JUL/77	
	G-ATDS	Intra Airways			01/AUG/77	
	G-ATDS	Express Air Freight			02/JAN/78	
	G-ATDS	Express Air Services			78	
	G-ATDS	Channel Express			JAN/83	
191	PP-SDL	Sadia	214	03/JAN/66	01/FEB/66	
	PP-SDL	TransBrasil			72	
	PP-SDL	TABA			76	Leased
	PP-SDL	TransBrasil			76	
	G-BDZV	British Air Ferries			30/JUN/76	
	G-BDZV	Dan Air			22/AUG/77	Leased
	G-BDZV	British Air Ferries				
	G-BDZV	Nile Valley			18/DEC/77	Leased
	G-BDZV	British Island Airways			01/JAN/79	Leased
	G-BDZV	Air UK			16/JAN/80	Leased
	G-BDZV	British Air Ferries			80	
	G-BDZV	Oasis Oil			05/NOV/80	Leased

HANDLEY PAGE HERALD (EXISTING AIRCRAFT ONLY)

C/N	Registration	Owner/Operator	Series	First Flight	Delivery	Remarks
	G-BDZV	British Air Ferries			81	
	G-BDZV	Tunis Air			02/APR/81	Leased
	G-BDZV	AGOCO			MAR/81	Leased
	G-BDZV	British Air Ferries			81	
	F-BVFP	Trans Azur Aviation			24/SEP/81	WFU Perpignan
192	PI-C866	Air Manila	215	05/MAR/66	18/MAR/66	
	RP-C866	Air Manila			74	WFU Manila
194	PP-SDN	Sadia	214	28/DEC/67	10/JAN/68	
	G-BAVX	British Midland Airways			28/APR/73	WFU 29/SEP/76
	G-BAVX	British Air Ferries			13/JAN/77	
	G-BAVX	Nile Valley Aviation			17/AUG/77	Leased
	G-BAVX	British Air Ferries				
	G-BAVX	Europe Aero Service			13/MAY/79	Leased
	G-BAVX	Touraine Air Transport			01/JUL/79	Leased
	G-BAVX	British Air Ferries			JUL/79	
	G-BAVX	Air Algerie			24/APR/80	Leased
	G-BAVX	British Air Ferries			01/JUN/80	
	G-BAVX	Air Algerie			80	Leased
	G-BAVX	British Air Ferries			07/NOV/80	
	G-BAVX	Air Algerie			NOV/80	Leased
	G-BAVX	British Air Ferries			10/DEC/80	
	G-BAVX	Air Algerie			04/JAN/81	Leased
	G-BAVX	British Air Ferries			16/MAY/81	
	G-BAVX	Libyan Arab Airlines			19/FEB/82	Leased
	G-BAVX	British Air Ferries			82	
	G-BAVX	Turbo Air			20/OCT/82	Not taken-up
	G-BAVX	British Air Ferries			20/OCT/82	
	G-BAVX	Dan Air			08/JAN/84	Leased
	G-BAVX	British Air Ferries			01/MAR/84	
	G-BAVX	Janus Airways			85	Leased
	G-BAVX .	Euroair			19/MAY/86	Leased
195	4X-AHO	Arkia	209	05/APR/68	10/APR/68	
	G-BFRJ	Express Air Freight			30/MAR/78	
	G-BFRJ	Express Air Services			78	
	G-BFRJ	Air Ecosse			11/JUN/78	Leased
	G-BFRJ	Express Air Services			08/SEP/78	WFU 82, stored East Midlands
	G-BFRJ	Basic Metals Co.			APR/83	Not taken-up
	I-ZERC	Columbia			10/MAR/84	
	I-ZERC	Aligiulia			MAR/86	
197	4X-AHN	Arkia	209	13/AUG/68	16/AUG/68	
	G-BFRK	Express Air Freight			06/APR/78	WFU 82, Stored East Midlands
	G-BFRK	Express Air Services			78	
	I-ZERD	Columbia			01/DEC/84	
	I-ZERD	Aligiulia			MAR/86	

Handley Page Herald cross-reference index

VICKERS VISCOUNT (EXISTING AIRCRAFT ONLY)

Short range turboprop airliner. The world's first turboprop transport to enter service, the Viscount made its first flight on August 28th 1950 and entered service with BEA on April 18th 1953. Powered by four Rolls Royce Dart turboprops, it was available as the series -700, the more powerful series 700D and the stretched series -800. A total of 459 production aircraft were built before production was completed in November 1962.

Dimensions :	Wing span: 93ft 8in (28.5m) Length: 81ft 9in (24.93m) Height: 26ft 9in (8.16m) (700)
	Wing span: 93ft 8in (28.5m) Length: 85ft 8in (26.11m) Height: 26ft 9in (8.16m) (800)
Powerplant :	Four Rolls Royce Dart 506 turboprops (700) four Rolls Royce Dart 510 turboprops (800), four Rolls Royce Dart 525 turboprops (810)
Performance :	Max cruising speed 273 knots (507km/h) (700) Range: with max payload 1,519nm (2,815km) (700)
	Max cruising speed 303 knots (563km/h) (800) Range: with max payload 1,498nm (2,775km) (800)
Accommodation:	63 passengers in a five abreast layout (700), 71 passengers in a five abreast layout (800)
Manufacturer :	Vickers

C/N	Registration	Owner/Operator	Series	First Flight	Delivery	Remarks
5	G-ALWF	BEA	701	03/DEC/52	12/FEB/53	
	G-ALWF	Channel Airways			MAR/64	
	G-ALWF	British Eagle			18/NOV/64	Leased
	G-ALWF	Channel Airways			MAY/65	
	G-ALWF	Cambrian Airways			15/DEC/65	WFU, preserved Liverpool, then Duxford.
7	G-AMOG	BEA	701	11/FEB/53	27/MAR/53	
	G-AMOG	Cambrian Airways			28/JAN/63	
	G-AMOG	BOAC			72	Leased
	G-AMOG	British Airways			01/APR/72	
						WFU 76, Preserved Cosford
11	G-AMOB	BEA	701	10/APR/53	24/APR/53	
	PP-SRI	VASP			26/FEB/63	WFU 08/APR/70. Preserved Jacarepagua, Brasil
12	F-BGNM	Air France	708	03/JUL/53	23/SEP/53	
	G-ARER	Maitland Drewery			19/SEP/60	
	G-ARER	BKS Air Transport			MAY/61	Leased
	G-ARER	Maitland Drewery			02/NOV/61	
	G-ARER	Silver City Airways			DEC/61	Leased
	G-ARER	British United Airways			APR/62	
	F-BOEA	Air Inter			27/JUN/66	W/O 28/DEC/71, Clermont-Ferrand Used as office by Duco Paints.
14	F-BGNN	Air France	708	26/AUG/53	29/OCT/53	
	G-ARGR	Maitland Drewery			20/DEC/60	
	G-ARGR	BKS Air Transport			20/JUN/61	Leased
	G-ARGR	Maitland Drewery			DEC/61	
	G-ARGR	Silver City Airways			06/DEC/61	Leased
	G-ARGR	British United Airways			APR/62	
	F-BOEB	Air Inter			27/SEP/66	
	G-ARGR	Alidair			JAN/75	
	G-ARGR	Inter City Airlines			01/MAR/81	
	G-ARGR	British Air Ferries			AUG/83	
	G-ARGR	Janus Airways			JAN/84	
	9Q-CAN	MMM Aero Services			15/DEC/84	
15	G-AMOD	BEA	701	17/JUN/53	26/JUN/53	
	PP-SRJ	VASP			26/FEB/63	WFU 28/FEB/69
16	F-BGNO	Air France	708	19/SEP/53	12/DEC/53	
	F-BGNO	Air Inter			31/MAY/62	WFU 75
17	G-AMOE	BEA	701	26/JUN/53	13/JUL/53	
	G-AMOE	Channel Airways			DEC/63	
	G-AMOE	Starways				
	G-AMOE	British Eagle			26/MAR/64	Leased
	G-AMOE	Channel Airways			DEC/64	
	G-AMOE	Cambrian Airways			20/JAN/65	
	G-AMOE	Northeast Airlines			06/JAN/72	For use as a cabin trainer. Preserved Lampton Lion Park, APR/77
18	F-BGNP	Air France	708	13/OCT/53	21/DEC/53	
	F-BGNP	Air Inter			09/MAY/62	WFU 75
22	G-AMOI	BEA	701	20/OCT/53	05/NOV/53	
	PP-SRL	VASP			30/AUG/62	WFU 31/JUL/69
33	F-BGNQ	Air France	708	14/APR/54	27/MAY/54	
	F-BGNQ	Air Inter			09/APR/62	WFU 75
35	F-BGNR	Air France	708	06/MAY/54	29/JUN/54	
	F-BGNR	Air Inter			20/FEB/62	
	F-BGNR	Air Service Training			08/OCT/73	Instructional, Scone airport, Perth
36	F-BGNS	Air France	708	30/MAY/54	30/JUN/54	
	G-ARIR	Starways			03/FEB/61	
	F-BLHI	Air Inter			19/NOV/63	
	G-ARIR	Alidair			FEB/75	
	G-ARIR	Dan Air			MAR/76	Leased
	G-ARIR	Alidair				
	G-ARIR	Guernsey Airlines			79	Leased
	G-ARIR	Alidair			80	
	G-ARIR	Inter City Airlines			01/MAR/81	
	G-ARIR	British Air Ferries			AUG/83	WFU 83
	G-ARIR	Janus Airways			JAN/84	

VICKERS VISCOUNT (EXISTING AIRCRAFT ONLY)

C/N	Registration	Owner/Operator	Series	First Flight	Delivery	Remarks
	9Q-CAH	MMM Aero Services			15/DEC/84	Stored Ostend.
38	F-BGNU	Air France	708		28/JUL/54	
	F-BGNU	Air Vietnam			06/JAN/61	Leased
	F-BGNU	Air Inter			22/JAN/63	WFU 74. Preserved Habsheim Airport.
40	CF-TGI	Trans Canada Airlines	724	13/OCT/54	08/DEC/54	
	CF-TGI	Transair			10/MAR/63	WFU JAN/71
	CF-TGI	E.Nold			21/SEP/73	
	N22SN	Jerry Christensen				
	N22SN	Walter L. Cole				
41	CF-THJ	Trans Canada Airlines	724	24/DEC/54	30/JAN/55	
	CF-THJ	Maverick Equipment Inc.			OCT/63	
	N117H	Mercer Trucking Inc.			JUN/64	
	N117H	Kenneth Copeland Evangelisti			DEC/76	
	N81RR					
	N240RC	Go Group				
51	CF-TGN	Trans Canada Airlines	724	31/MAR/55	08/APR/55	
	CF-TGN	Canadian Schenly			20/NOV/63	
	N744W	Schenly Distillery			JUL/64	
	N1898M	Kearney & Trecker Corp.			JUN/65	
	N1898S	Boston Leasing Corp.			MAY/69	
	N1898S	Eldee Inc.			MAY/69	
	N1898S	Fidelity Management Co.				
	N1898S	Eldee Inc.			OCT/76	
	N1898S	Richard Jacobs			JAN/77	
	N1898S	Purdue University			SEP/77	
	N1898S	LRW Aircraft Sales			DEC/77	
	N1898S	Ron Clark Enterprises				
	N1898S	Wofford Aircraft Sales				
	N180RC	Go Group				
52	CF-TGO	Trans Canada Airlines	724	20/APR/55	01/MAY/55	
	F-BMCG	Air Inter			02/APR/64	
	G-BDRC	Alidair			25/OCT/75	
	G-BDRC	Intra Airways			25/MAR/76	Leased
	G-BDRC	Alidair			31/OCT/77	
	G-BDRC	Dan Air			MAR/78	Leased
	G-BDRC	Alidair				
	G-BDRC	Guernsey Airlines			MAR/80	Leased
	G-BDRC	Inter City Airlines			01/MAR/81	
	G-BDRC	Guernsey Airlines				Leased
	G-BDRC	Inter City Airlines			01/AUG/83	Impounded Guernsey
	G-BDRC	Janus Airways			JAN/84	
54	CF-TGQ	Trans Canada Airlines	724	27/MAY/55	05/JUN/55	
	F-BMCF	Air Inter			02/APR/64	WFU 74, Preserved Merville Ap.
55	CF-TGR	Trans Canada Airlines	724	12/JUN/55	21/JUN/55	
	CF-TGR	Air Canada			01/JUN/64	
	N911H	W.L.Wold			04/JAN/65	
	F-BNAX	Air Inter			JUN/65	WFU 76.
61	G-ANHA	BEA	701	07/OCT/54	19/OCT/54	
	PP-SRP	VASP			24/MAY/63	WFU 28/FEB/69
62	G-ANHB	BEA	701	02/NOV/54	20/NOV/54	
	PP-SRN	VASP			24/APR/63	WFU 28/FEB/69
64	G-ANHD	BEA	701	24/APR/55	04/MAY/55	
	PP-SRO	VASP			24/APR/63	WFU 28/FEB/69. Preserved Bebedouro, Brasil
67	YI-ACK	Iraqi Airways	735	23/SEP/55	13/OCT/55	
	G-BFMW	Alidair			17/FEB/78	
	G-BFMW	Inter City Airlines			01/MAR/81	Fuselage donated to East Midlands Fire Service 26/OCT/83
70	CF-GXK	Canadian Dept. of Transport	737	15/MAR/55	28/MAR/55	
75	G-ANRS	Hunting Clan	732	07/JUN/55	15/JUN/55	
	OD-ACH	Middle East Airlines			SEP/55	Leased
	G-ANRS	Hunting Clan			30/SEP/57	
	SU-AKY	Misrair			31/AUG/59	
	SU-AKY	United Arab Airlines			AUG/60	
	G-ANRS	British Eagle			MAR/65	
	G-ANRS	Cambrian Airways			JUL/69	Used as a cabin trainer, minus wings, undercarriage etc.
	'G-WHIZ'	Wales Aircraft Museum			77	Preserved, fuselage only.
98	VP-YNA	Central African Airways	748	28/MAR/56	01/MAY/56	
	VP-YNA	Air Rhodesia			01/JAN/68	
	7Q-YDK	Air Malawi			JAN/68	
	VP-YNA	Air Zimbabwe			80	
	Z-YNA	Air Zimbabwe			83	
99	VP-YNB	Central African Airways	748	05/MAY/56	17/MAY/56	
	VP-YNB	Kuwait Airways			JUN/58	Leased
	VP-YNB	Central African Airways			AUG/58	
	VP-YNB	Air Rhodesia			01/JAN/68	
	Z-YNB	Air Zimbabwe			80	
100	VP-YNC	Central African Airways	748	24/MAY/56	08/JUN/56	
	VP-YNC	Air Rhodesia			01/JAN/68	
	VP-YNC	Air Zimbabwe			80	WFU
106	N7408	Capital Airlines	745	10/DEC/55	23/DEC/55	
	N7408	United Airlines			01/JUN/61	
	N7408	Viscount International Corp.			11/JAN/69	WFU
	N7408	Embry Riddle				
	N7408	Mogan Rourke			DEC/79	
	N7408	Air Capital Aircraft Sales				
107	N7409	Capital Airlines	745	20/DEC/55	31/DEC/55	
	N7409	United Airlines			01/JUN/61	
	N7409	Viscount International Corp.			11/JAN/69	WFU
	N7409	Embry Riddle				
	N7409	Morgan Rourke			DEC/79	
	N7409	Air Capital Aircraft Sales				
109	N7411	Capital Airlines	745	20/JAN/56	08/MAR/56	
	N7411	United Airlines			01/JUN/61	
	N7411	Viscount International Corp.			11/JAN/69	WFU
	N7411	Embry Riddle			DEC/77	
	N7411	Morgan Rourke Aircraft Sales			DEC/79	
114	N7416	Capital Airlines	745	16/MAR/56	20/MAR/56	
	I-LIRC	Alitalia			17/DEC/60	
	60S-AAN	Somali Airlines			15/DEC/70	
	60-SAN	Somali Airlines			DEC/70	WFU JUN/76, derelict Mogadishu
117	N7419	Capital Airlines	745	10/APR/56	20/APR/56	
	N7419	United Airlines			01/JUN/61	
	N7419	Cathedral of Tomorrow			29/JUL/68	

C/N	Registration	Owner/Operator	Series	First Flight	Delivery	Remarks
	N7419	Penn Landmark Corp.				
	N7419	R.J.Clark and S.Birdman			13/SEP/77	
	N460RC	Go Group				
118	N7420	Capital Airlines	745	17/APR/56	20/APR/56	
	G-ARHY	Vickers			22/JAN/61	
	PI-C773	Philippine Airlines			05/APR/61	
	N745HA	Hawaiian Airlines			07/JUL/63	Leased
	PI-C773	Philippine Airlines			DEC/63	
	I-LIRT	Alitalia			MAR/65	
	HK-I057	Aerolineas TAO			13/NOV/68	W/O 25/OCT/71, Bucaramanga. later re-built. stored Eldorado Ap., Bogota
121	N7423	Capital Airlines	745	08/MAY/56	14/MAY/56	
	N7423	United Airlines			01/JUN/61	
	N7423	Pittburg Institute of Aeron.			JAN/69	Static training
	N7423	David Gower			DEC/79	Static training
122	N7424	Capital Airlines	745	15/MAY/56	19/MAY/56	
	N7424	United Airlines			01/JUN/61	
	N7424	Southern Illinois University			JAN/69	Static training
130	N7432	Capital Airlines	745	16/JUL/56	20/JUL/56	
	I-LIFS	Alitalia			05/DEC/60	
	CX-BHA	Pluna			05/DEC/67	WFU
137	N7439	Capital Airlines	745	10/SEP/56	13/SEP/56	
	N7439	United Airlines			01/JUN/61	
	N7439	Viscount International Corp.			11/JAN/69	
	N7439	Embry Riddle				
	N7439	Bass Aviation Inc.			DEC/79	
	N7439	Go Group				
138	N7440	Capital Airlines	745	14/SEP/56	24/SEP/56	
	N7440	United Airlines			01/JUN/61	
	N7440	Viscount International Corp.			11/NOV/69	WFU.
	HK-1708	Aeropesca				
	HK-1708	Intercontinental Colombia			83	
139	N7441	Capital Airlines	745	17/SEP/56	23/SEP/56	
	N7441	United Airlines			01/JUN/61	
	N7441	Viscount International Corp.			11/JAN/69	
	N7441	Jack Conroy - Turbo three			20/SEP/73	
	N7441	Embry Riddle				
142	CF-TGX	Trans Canada Airlines	757	18/MAR/56	28/MAR/56	
	CF-TGX	Air Canada			01/JUN/64	WFU 24/APR/73
144	CF-TGZ	Trans Canada Airlines	757	14/APR/56	12/MAY/56	
	CF-TGZ	Air Canada			01/JUN/64	
	CF-TGZ	Beaver Enterprises			74	Stored Winnipeg
	N3832S	Grupo Madero S.A.				
148	VH-TVJ	Trans Australia Airlines	756	14/JUN/56	22/JUN/56	WFU 02/OCT/68, Toowoomba
151	G-AOJB	BEA	802	29/SEP/56	06/FEB/57	
	G-AOJB	British Airways			01/APR/72	Derelict Liverpool Airport
152	G-AOJC	BEA	802	07/NOV/56	19/JAN/57	
	G-AOJC	British Airways			01/APR/72	Preserved Cardiff Museum
161	G-AOHL	BEA	802	29/MAR/57	17/APR/57	
	G-AOHL	British Airways			01/APR/72	
	G-AOHL	British Air Ferries			06/FEB/81	WFU 06/FEB/81, cabin trainer
162	G-AOHM	BEA	802	30/MAY/57	27/JUN/57	
	G-AOHM	British Airways			01/APR/72	
	G-AOHM	British Air Ferries			23/FEB/81	
	G-AOHM	Air Algerie			02/MAR/81	Leased
	G-AOHM	British Air Ferries			02/DEC/81	
	G-AOHM	BAF/Skyrider			JAN/84	
	G-AOHM	Loganair			FEB/84	Leased
	G-AOHM	British Air Ferries			APR/84	
163	G-AOHN	BEA	802	13/APR/57	01/MAY/57	
	G-AOHN	British Airways			01/APR/72	
164	G-AOHO	BEA	802	26/APR/57	04/MAY/57	
	G-AOHO	British Airways			01/APR/72	WFU 76, derelict Jersey
167	G-AOHS	BEA	802	07/JUN/57	22/JUN/57	
	G-AOHS	British Airways			01/APR/72	Derelict Cardiff
168	G-AOHT	BEA	802	20/JUN/57	03/JUL/57	
	G-AOHT	British Airways			01/APR/72	WFU 80, stored Cardiff
	G-AOHT	British Air Ferries			AUG/81	
	ZK-SKY	Skybus			81	Leased
	G-AOHT	British Air Ferries			JAN/82	
	G-AOHT	Bouraq			JAN/82	Not taken-up
	G-AOHT	British Air Ferries			82	
	G-AOHT	Polar Airways			01/AUG/82	Leased
	G-AOHT	Keegan Leasing			01/APR/83	
	G-AOHT	British Air Ferries			MAY/83	Leased
	G-AOHT	Keegan Leasing			OCT/83	WFU OCT/83, stored Southend
	G-AOHT	Euroair			APR/84	Leased
	G-AOHT	Keegan Leasing			FEB/85	
	G-AOHT	Virgin Atlantic			MAR/85	Leased
	G-AOHT	Keegan Leasing				
170	G-AOHV	BEA	802	10/JUL/57	25/JUL/57	
	G-AOHV	British Airways			01/APR/72	WFU 80, stored Cardiff
	G-AOHV	British Air Ferries			16/JAN/81	
	G-AOHV	Oasis Oil			08/FEB/81	Leased
	G-AOHV	British Air Ferries				
	G-AOHV	Polar Airways			26/FEB/83	
	G-AOHV	Keegan Leasing			01/APR/83	WFU 21/APR/83, East Midlands
	G-AOHV	Euroair			SEP/83	Leased
	G-AOHV	Air Commuter			FEB/84	Sub-leased
	G-AOHV	Euroair			MAR/84	Leased
	G-AOHV	Keegan Leasing				
171	G-AORD	BEA	802	22/AUG/57	13/SEP/57	
	G-AORD	British Airways			01/APR/72	Used by Birmingham Airport fire service
180	PH-VII	KLM	803	22/NOV/57	23/DEC/57	
	EI-AOH	Aer Lingus			25/FEB/67	WFU NOV/70, preserved Dublin Ap.
182	G-AOFX	BEA	701	16/JUL/56	22/JUL/56	
	PP-SRS	VASP			30/AUG/62	WFU 28/FEB/69
184	N906	US Steel Corp.	764	26/OCT/56	29/NOV/56	
	N906	Percell Jones			NOV/69	
	N906	Combs Aircraft/Gates Avn.			DEC/69	
	N906RB	Roger Brothers Investments			JAN/70	
	N906RB	Vanpac Carriers				
	N906RB	Royal American Airways			80	WFU 80
	N906RB	Fred S. Brown				Stored

VICKERS VISCOUNT (EXISTING AIRCRAFT ONLY)

C/N	Registration	Owner/Operator	Series	First Flight	Delivery	Remarks
189	XY-ADG	Union of Burma Airways	761	27/AUG/57	26/SEP/57	
	XY-ADG	Burma Airways Corp.			DEC/72	
	ZS-JVY	Air Botswana				
	A2-ABY	Air Botswana			01/MAR/79	
	ZS-JVY	United Air Services			82	Stored
190	XY-ADH	Union of Burma Airways	761	26/SEP/57	22/OCT/57	
	G-APZN	Kuwait Airways			APR/60	Leased
	XY-ADH	Union of Burma Airways			06/JAN/63	
	XY-ADH	Middle East Airlines			01/APR/63	Leased
	XY-ADH	Union of Burma Airways			64	
	XY-ADH	Burma Airways Corp.			DEC/72	
	9Q-CRH	Pearl International			76	
	9Q-CRH	International Air Charter			17/MAY/77	
	G-APZN	Intra Airways			01/FEB/78	
	G-APZN	Southern International			14/JUL/79	Stored Exeter Airport
191	N306	Standard Oil Corp.	765	24/JAN/57	11/FEB/57	
	N306	Lawrence Weitzman				
	N306	Stephen Birdman			JAN/78	
	N306	Go Group			80	
	N306	Royal American Airways			81	
	N140RA	Royal American Airways			81	
	N140RA	Go Group				
196	VT-DII	Indian Airlines	768	06/NOV/57	21/NOV/57	
197	VH-TVL	Trans Australia Airlines	757	22/FEB/57	01/MAR/57	WFU 10/AUG/69, preserved " Toowoomba Museum OCT/71
201	N7445	Capital Airlines	745	07/OCT/56	13/OCT/56	
	N7445	United Airlines			01/JUN/61	
	N923RC	Ray Charles Enterprises			05/FEB/68	
	N923RA	Ray Charles Enterprises			FEB/77	
	N500TL	T.Loving Insurance Agency			MAR/77	
	N500TL	Ronald Clarke Enterprises			APR/77	
	N220RC	Ronald Clarke Enterprises			DEC/79	
	N220RC	Go Group				
	XA-MOS	Aerolines Republica				
	N220RC	Go Group				WFU, stored Tucson
	N220RC	Walter L. Cole				
204	N7448	Capital Airlines	745	28/OCT/56	03/NOV/56	
	N7448	United Airlines			01/JUN/61	
	N7448	Viscount International Corp.			11/JAN/69	
	HC-AYZ	Saeta				WFU 81, Stored Quito
206	N7450	Capital Airlines	745	09/NOV/56	16/NOV/56	
	N7450	United Airlines			01/JUN/61	
	N7450	Viscount International Corp.			11/JAN/69	
		Saeta			JAN/74	
	N7450	Embry Riddle				
	N7450	Trans Florida Airlines			SEP/77	
213	N7458	Capital Airlines	745	28/DEC/56	06/JAN/57	
	N7458	United Airlines			01/JUN/61	
	N7458	National Aircraft Sales			JAN/69	
	N7458	Grekenheimer Productions			APR/70	
	N7458	National Aero Sales			JAN/71	
	XA-COT	Aero Sierra de Durango			01/JAN/73	Leased
	XA-COT	National Aero Sales				Stored Brown Field, Tx.
	N7458	Go Group			82	
	N7458	Island Air			82	
	N7458	Go Group				
218	CF-THA	Trans Canada Airlines	757	14/JAN/57	05/FEB/57	
	CF-THA	Canadian Inspection & Test			63	
	CF-THA	Wabush Mines			NOV/68	WFU
219	CF-THB	Trans Canada Airlines	757	18/JAN/57	29/JAN/57	
	CF-THB	Air Canada			01/JUN/64	WFU APR/74
220	CF-THC	Trans Canada Airlines	757	11/FEB/57	20/FEB/57	
	CF-THC	Air Canada			01/JUN/64	WFU 17/JUN/73
223	CF-THF	Trans Canada Airlines	757	10/MAR/57	14/MAR/57	
	CF-THF	Air Canada			01/JUN/64	WFU APR/74
224	CF-THG	Trans Canada Airlines	757	20/MAR/57	28/MAR/57	
	CF-THG	Air Canada			01/JUN/64	WFU APR/74
	CF-THG	Beaver Enterprises				
	CF-THG	Pacific Vocation and Inst.			80	Preserved
228	N7466	Capital Airlines	745	23/APR/57		Not taken-up
	G-16-3	Vickers Ltd.				
	EI-AJV	Aer Lingus			27/MAR/58	Leased
	G-APNG	Vickers Ltd.			58	
	G-APNG	BEA			26/JUN/58	Leased
	G-APNG	Vickers Ltd.			06/AUG/58	
	G-APNG	Kuwait Airways			13/SEP/58	Leased
	G-APNG	Vickers Ltd.			30/NOV/58	
	CF-RBC	Royal Bank of Canada	793	07/APR/59	21/APR/59	
	CF-RBC	Canadian Breweries				
	N505W	W.J.Groves & Sons			APR/61	
	N24V	The Ingersoll Milling Corp.			FEB/70	
	N24V	Trico Corp.			01/NOV/73	
	N24V	Lawrence Weitzman				
	N24V	Stephen Birdman			FEB/78	
	N24V	Go Group				
	N24V	Royal American Airways			80	
	N24V	Go Group			82	
229	N7467	Capital Airlines	745	28/APR/57		Not taken-up
	G-APFR	Vickers Ltd.	797	21/MAR/58		
	CF-DTA	Canadian Dept. of Transport			28/OCT/58	
	N660RC	Go Group				
230	N7468	Capital Airlines	745	07/JUN/57		Not taken-up
	G-16-6	Vickers Ltd				
	G-APLX	Vickers Ltd.				
	N6595C	Northeast Airlines	798	24/SEP/58	02/OCT/58	
	N776M	Continental Oil Drilling			10/OCT/63	
	N776M	J.W.Mecom			AUG/68	WFU 30/MAR/72
	N776M	Onyx Aviation			FEB/79	
	N776M	Go Group				
	N776M	United Financial Operations			AUG/79	
232	N7470	Capital Airlines	745	28/JUN/57		Not delivered
	N6590C	Northeast Airlines	798	22/JUL/58	08/AUG/58	
	N7416	Aloha Airlines			04/OCT/63	
	HK-1319	Aeropesca			25/NOV/71	
	HK-1319	Lineas Aereas La Urraca			73	Leased
	HK-1319	Aeropesca			74	WFU 83, stored

C/N	Registration	Owner/Operator	Series	First Flight	Delivery	Remarks
233	N7471	Capital Airlines	745	23/JUN/57		Not taken-up
	N6591C	Northeast Airlines	798	24/JUL/58	08/AUG/58	
	N820BK	Blaw Knox Corp.			DEC/63	
	N98KT	Kearney & Trecker Corp			FEB/78	
	N555SL	Kearney & Trecker Corp.			OCT/78	
	N555SL	Monarch Aircraft Inc.				
240	OD-ACU	Middle East Airlines	754	29/AUG/57	07/SEP/57	
	OD-ACU	Jersey Airlines			61	Leased
	OD-ACU	Middle East Airlines			61	
	JY-ACI	Jordanian Airways			30/SEP/61	Leased
	OD-ACU	Middle East Airlines			JAN/64	
	VP-WAR	Air Rhodesia			19/SEP/68	
	VP-WAR	Aircraft Hire and Travel			JAN/76	
	ZS-JPU	Swazi Air			JAN/76	Leased
	3D-AAL	Swazi Air			76	
	ZS-JPU	Air Zimbabwe			80	
	VP-WAR	Air Zimbabwe			14/AUG/81	WFU
241	OD-ACV	Middle East Airlines	754	19/SEP/57	27/SEP/57	
	VP-YCT	Central African Airways			23/FEB/61	
	VP-YCT	Air Rhodesia			01/JAN/68	
	7Q-YDL	Air Malawi			JAN/68	Leased
	ZS-KJG	Air Zimbabwe				
	VP-WJI	Air Zimbabwe			80	WFU
243	G-APCD	Cyprus Airways	754	22/OCT/57		Not taken-up
	OD-ADD	Middle East Airlines			09/NOV/57	
	JY-ACK	Jordanian Airways			07/OCT/61	Leased
	OD-ADD	Middle East Airlines			JAN/64	
	VP-YTE	Air Rhodesia			JUL/70	
	ZS-JUJ	Aircraft Hire and Travel			21/MAR/76	
	ZS-JUJ	United Air Services			82	
	VP-YTE	Air Zimbabwe			82	
	ZS-JUJ	Swazi Air			MAR/76	Leased
	A2-ABD	Air Services Botswana				
	ZS-JUJ	Air Zimbabwe				
	Z-YTE	Air Zimbabwe				
246	OD-ACY	Middle East Airlines	754			Not taken-up
	TC-SEC	Turk Hava Yollari	794	09/JAN/58	21/JAN/58	
	246	Turkish Air Force			28/MAR/72	
248	G-AOXU	Transair	804	31/AUG/57	17/SEP/57	
	G-AOXU	British United Airways			01/JUL/60	
	SP-LVC	LOT			21/DEC/62	
	ZK-NAI	NZNAC			27/JAN/67	
	VQ-GAB	Pearl Air				
	G-CSZB	Southern International			May/78	
	G-CSZB	Dan Air			79	Leased
	G-CSZB	Southern International				
	N141RA	Royal American Airways				Not taken-up
	G-CSZB	British Air Ferries			83	WFU, stored Southend
	G-CSZB	Euroair			85	
	G-CSZB	British Air Ferries				
250	LN-FOH	Fred Olsen Air Transport	799	13/APR/57	25/APR/57	
	OE-LAB	Austrian Airlines			01/JAN/58	Leased
	LN-FOH	Fred Olsen Air Transport			MAR/60	
	G-APZP	BEA			28/MAR/60	Leased
	LN-FOH	Fred Olsen Air Transport			01/MAR/61	
	LN-FOH	SAS			61	Leased
	LN-FOH	Fred Olsen Air Transport			DEC/61	
	VT-DOE	Indian Airlines			21/JAN/62	
	VT-DOE	Huns Air				WFU 80, used for spares
251	LN-FOI	Fred Olsen Air Transport	779	07/MAY/57	28/MAY/57	
	OE-LAC	Austrian Airlines			01/JAN/58	Leased
	LN-FOI	Fred Olsen Air Transport			01/APR/60	
	LN-FOI	SAS			NOV/60	Leased
	LN-FOI	Fred Olsen Air Transport			JAN/61	
	VT-DOH	Indian Airlines			21/JAN/62	
	VT-DOH	Huns Air			09/DEC/78	
253	G-AOHW	BEA	802	18/JUL/57	01/AUG/57	
	G-AOHW	British Airways			01/APR/72	Derelict Newcastle Ap.
256	G-AOYG	BEA	806	04/OCT/57	29/MAR/58	
	G-AOYG	Cambrian Airways			08/SEP/70	
	G-AOYG	British Airways			01/APR/72	
	G-AOYG	British Air Ferries			14/FEB/84	
	G-AOYG	Guernsey Airlines			14/FEB/84	Op. with British Air Ferries
257	G-AOYI	BEA	806	14/NOV/57	02/JAN/58	
	G-AOYI	Cambrian Airways			15/JUL/70	
	G-AOYI	British Airways			01/APR/72	WFU 80
	G-AOYI	British Air Ferries			AUG/81	
	G-AOYI	Esso Oil			81	Leased
	G-AOYI	British Air Ferries			81	
	G-AOYI	Occidental Oil			DEC/81	Leased
	G-AOYI	British Air Ferries			82	
	G-AOYI	Guernsey Airlines			AUG/83	Op. with British Air Ferries
	G-LOND	London European Airways			85	Stored
259	G-AOYJ	BEA	806	09/DEC/57	08/JAN/58	
	G-AOYJ	Cyprus Airways			28/OCT/65	Leased
	G-AOYJ	BEA			MAY/70	
	G-AOYJ	Cambrian Airways			15/OCT/70	
	G-AOYJ	British Airways			01/APR/72	
	G-AOYJ	British Air Ferries			14/APR/81	
	G-AOYJ	Air Algerie			09/MAY/81	Leased
	G-AOYJ	British Air Ferries			31/JAN/82	
	G-AOYJ	Keegan Leasing			01/MAY/83	WFU
	G-BLOA	British Air Ferries			84	
	G-BLOA	Manx Airlines			84	Leased
	G-BLOA	British Air Ferries			21/FEB/85	
	G-BLOA	Manx Airlines			APR/85	Leased
	G-BLOA	British Air Ferries			85	
261	G-AOYL	BEA	806	23/JAN/58	14/FEB/58	
	G-AOYL	BKS Air Transport			28/MAY/68	
	G-AOYL	Northeast Airlines			01/NOV/70	
	G-AOYL	British Airways			01/APR/72	
	G-AOYL	British Air Ferries			30/MAR/84	
262	G-AOYM	BEA	806	26/FEB/58	19/MAR/58	
	G-AOYM	Cambrian Airways			08/NOV/71	
	G-AOYM	British Airways			01/APR/72	
	G-AOYM	British Air Ferries			FEB/84	

Airliner Production List 1987

VICKERS VISCOUNT (EXISTING AIRCRAFT ONLY)

C/N	Registration	Owner/Operator	Series	First Flight	Delivery	Remarks
	G-AOYM	Manx Airlines			21/FEB/85	Leased
	G-AOYM	British Air Ferries			85	
	EC-DYC	Lineas Aereas Canarias				
263	G-AOYN	BEA	806	07/MAR/58	26/MAR/58	
	G-AOYN	Cambrian Airways			30/DEC/71	
	G-AOYN	British Airways			01/APR/72	WFU 80, stored Cardiff
	G-AOYN	British Air Ferries			16/FEB/81	
	G-AOYN	Oasis Oil			81	Leased
	G-AOYN	British Air Ferries			81	
	G-AOYN	Occidental Oil			09/JAN/82	
	G-AOYN	British Air Ferries			82	
	G-AOYN	British Air Ferries			JUN/83	
264	G-AOYO	BEA	806	18/MAR/58	03/APR/58	
	G-AOYO	BKS Air Transport			30/MAY/68	
	G-AOYO	Northeast Airlines			01/NOV/70	
	G-AOYO	British Airways			01/APR/72	
	G-AOYO	British Air Ferries			28/JAN/84	
	EC-DXU	Lineas Aereas Canarias			OCT/85	Leased
265	G-AOYP	BEA	806	01/MAY/58	16/APR/58	
	G-AOYP	Cambrian Airways			07/JAN/71	
	G-AOYP	British Airways			01/APR/72	WFU 80
	G-AOYP	British Air Ferries			13/APR/81	
	G-AOYP	Air Algerie			12/MAY/81	Leased
	G-AOYP	British Air Ferries			MAR/82	
	G-AOYP	Jersey Air Ferries			MAY/83	Op. by British Air Ferries
	G-AOYP	GB Airways			DEC/83	Leased
	G-AOYP	Jersey Air Ferries			DEC/83	Op. by British Air Ferries
	G-AOYP	British Air Ferries				
	G-AOYP	Virgin Atlantic			86	Leased
266	G-AOYR	BEA	806	21/MAR/58	13/JUN/58	
	G-AOYR	BKS Air Transport			29/DEC/69	
	G-AOYR	Northeast Airlines			01/NOV/70	
	G-AOYR	British Airways			01/APR/72	
	G-AOYR	British Air Ferries		MAR/84		
	G-AOYR	BCAL Commuter			85	Leased
267	G-AOYS	BEA	806	23/MAY/58	13/JUN/58	
	G-AOYS	Cambrian Airways		14/OCT/71		
	G-AOYS	British Airways		01/APR/72		WFU 80
	G-AOYS	British Air Ferries	806		22/MAY/81	Converted, WFU
	G-AOYS	Air Algerie			81	Leased
	G-AOYS	British Air Ferries			81	
	G-AOYS	British Air Ferries	806C		NOV/82	Converted, WFU
	G-AOYS	Keegan Leasing			01/APR/83	WFU
268	G-AOYT	BEA	806	21/APR/58	02/MAY/58	
	B-3001	Winner Airways			03/MAY/69	
	B-2035	Far Eastern Air Transport				
	PK-RVT	Mandala Airlines				Leased
270	CF-THI	Trans Canada Airlines	757	19/MAY/57	26/MAY/57	
	CF-THI	Air Canada			01/JUN/64	Preserved Rockcliffe museum 18/NOV/69, Trans Canada livery
272	CF-THL	Trans Canada Airlines	757	29/NOV/57	16/DEC/57	
	CF-THL	Air Canada			01/JUN/64	WFU APR/74
273	CF-THM	Trans Canada Airlines	757	08/DEC/57	18/DEC/57	
	CF-THM	Air Canada			01/JUN/64	WFU MAY/71
274	CF-THN	Trans Canada Airlines	757	18/DEC/57	03/JAN/58	
	CF-THN	Air Canada			01/JUN/64	WFU 29/OCT/73
275	CF-THO	Trans Canada Airlines	757	18/JAN/58	24/JAN/58	
	CF-THO	Air Canada			01/JUN/64	WFU APR/74
276	CF-THP	Trans Canada Airlines	757	22/JAN/58	29/JAN/58	
	CF-THP	Air Canada			01/JUN/64	WFU 04/DEC/73, stored Winnipeg
277	CF-THQ	Trans Canada Airlines	757	02/FEB/58	14/FEB/58	
	CF-THQ	Air Canada			01/JUN/64	
	C-FTHQ	Beaver Enterprises			74	
	C-FTHQ	Wabush Lake Railway Co.				
278	CF-THR	Trans Canada Airlines	757	17/FEB/58	27/FEB/58	
	CF-THR	Air Canada			01/JUN/64	WFU 30/AUG/71
280	150	South African Air Force	781	18/MAY/58	16/JUN/58	
281	ZK-BRD	NZNAC	807	11/DEC/57	31/DEC/57	
	G-BBVH	Gibraltar Airways			JAN/74	
	G-BBVH	GB Airways			81	
283	ZK-BRF	NZNAC	807	24/FEB/59	12/MAR/59	Preserved Ferrymead
284	N7473	Capital Airlines	745	31/JUL/57		Not taken-up
	N6594C	Northeast Airlines	798	13/SEP/58	22/SEP/58	
	I-LIRG	Alitalia			08/MAY/64	
	I-LIRG	Francesco de Pinedo Tech. College			70	Derelict, Rome
291	EI-AJK	Aer Lingus	808	13/FEB/58	21/FEB/58	
	EI-AJK	Aer Lingus	808C		67	Converted
	HB-ILR	SATA			04/NOV/69	Leased
	HB-ILR	Aer Lingus			09/DEC/71	
	HB-ILR	Air Tourisme Alpine			06/JAN/72	Leased
	HB-ILR	SATA			APR/72	
	HB-ILR	Air Tourisme Alpine			JUN/72	
	HB-ILR	Land Sales Development Corp.			31/MAR/73	
	G-BBDK	Nor Air			14/AUG/73	Leased
	G-BBDK	Air Bridge Carriers			APR/74	
	G-BBDK	Dan Air			MAR/75	Leased
	G-BBDK	Air Bridge Carriers			75	Stored East Midlands
	G-BBDK	Southern International			09/MAR/80	
	G-BBDK	Field Aircraft Services			OCT/83	
	G-BBDK	British Air Ferries				
293	VT-DIZ	Indian Airlines	768	06/MAR/58	18/MAR/58	WFU 13/JAN/72
294	VT-DJA	Indian Airlines	768	08/APR/58	21/APR/58	
	XU-LAM	Royal Air Lao				
	RDPL-34016	Lao Aviation				Stored
295	VT-DJB	Indian Airlines	768	17/MAY/58	22/MAY/58	WFU 21/FEB/71
298	EP-AHB	Iranian Airlines	782	28/MAR/58	16/APR/58	
	VP-WAT	Central African Airways			OCT/66	
	VP-WAT	Air Rhodesia			01/JAN/68	
	Z-WAT	Air Zimbabwe			80	
300	PI-C770	Philippine Airlines	784	01/MAY/57	10/MAY/57	
	SE-CNL	Falconair Charter			MAY/67	
	SE-CNL	Malmo Aero			22/MAR/71	
	SE-CNL	Skyline			20/AUG/71	Derelict, Stockholm-Arlanda Ap.
303	CF-THU	Trans Canada Airlines	757	03/MAR/58	08/MAR/58	

C/N	Registration	Owner/Operator	Series	First Flight	Delivery	Remarks
	CF-THU	Air Canada			01/JUN/64	
	CF-THU	Beaver Enterprises			74	
	9Q-CPD	Zaire Aero Services				W/O 28/AUG/84, N'djili Airport
	9Q-CPD	Zairean Airlines				
304	CF-THV	Trans Canada Airlines	757	13/MAR/58	21/MAR/58	
	CF-THV	Air Canada			01/JUN/64	WFU APR/74
	9Q-CKB	Zaire Aero Services				WFU 81, stored N'Dolo
305	CF-THW	Trans Canada Airlines	757	25/MAR/58	03/APR/58	
	CF-THW	Air Canada			01/JUN/64	
	CF-THW	Beaver Enterprises			74	
306	CF-THX	Trans Canada Airlines	757	13/APR/58	18/APR/58	
	CF-THX	Air Canada			01/JUN/64	WFU APR/74
307	CF-THY	Trans Canada Airlines	757	23/APR/58	03/MAY/58	
	CF-THY	Air Canada			01/JUN/64	WFU APR/74
	9Q-CKS	Zaire Aero Services				
308	CF-THZ	Trans Canada Airlines	757	09/MAY/58	15/MAY/58	
	CF-THZ	Air Canada			01/JUN/64	
	CF-THZ	Beaver Enterprises			74	Stored
	CF-THZ	Air Caravane				
	CF-THZ	Air Cardinal			80	WFU 81
310	CF-TIB	Trans Canada Airlines	757	05/JUN/58	11/JUN/58	
	CF-TIB	Air Canada			01/JUN/64	
	CF-TIB	Beaver Enterprises			74	
	9Q-CPP	Zaire Aero Services				Not taken-up
	CF-TIB	Air Caravane			80	
	CF-TIB	Air Cardinal			80	WFU 81
	9Q-CKI	Air Charter Service			06/JAN/86	
311	G-AOYH	BEA	806	25/OCT/57	23/DEC/57	
	G-AOYH	BKS Air Transport			31/JUL/68	
	G-AOYH	Northeast Airlines			01/NOV/70	
	G-AOYH	British Airways			31/JUL/73	
	G-AOYH	British Air Ferries			19/MAR/82	
	C-GWPY	North Cariboo Flying Service			83	
	G-BNAA	British Air Ferries			85	Leased
	G-BNAA	Euroair			85	
	G-BNAA	British Air Ferries				
316	G-AOYV	Vickers	810	23/DEC/57		Series 810 prototype
	PP-SRH	VASP			06/OCT/60	
	CX-BIZ	Pluna			76	Stored Carasco
318	CU-T622	Cubana	818	19/NOV/58	11/APR/59	W'FU JUN/70, preserved at
	VH-TVR	Trans Australia Airlines			MAR/62	Nunawadine Amusement Park
319	CU-T623	Cubana	818	25/JUN/59	18/AUG/59	
	VH-RML	Ansett ANA			FEB/62	
	B-2019	Far Eastern Air Transport			21/MAY/70	
	PK-MVK	Mandala Airlines				Leased
	B-2019	Far Eastern Air Transport			FEB/83	Stored
321	CX-AQN	Pluna	769	20/JAN/58	16/JUN/58	
	N410RC	Go Group			82	
322	CX-AQO	Pluna	769	03/FEB/58	17/APR/59	
325	I-LIFE	LAI	785	12/MAR/57	27/MAR/57	
	I-LIFE	Alitalia			01/OCT/57	
	60S-AAK	Somali Airlines			04/JUN/69	
	60-SAK	Somali Airlines			JUN/69	WFU JUN/77
327	I-LILI	LAI	785	18/MAY/57	26/MAY/57	
	I-LILI	Alitalia			01/OCT/57	
	HK-1061	Aerolineas TAO			04/SEP/70	Stored, Eldorado Ap., Bogota
334	HK-947	Lloyd Aereo Colombiano	786	19/JAN/58		Not taken-up
	AN-AKQ	Lanica			27/FEB/58	
	N200Q	Mrs Merriweather Post			FEB/59	
	N200Q	E.Systems Inc.				
	HC-BDL	SAN			02/FEB/77	
338	D-ANUN	Lufthansa	814	22/SEP/58	05/OCT/58	
	D-ANUN	Condor			05/FEB/62	Leased
	D-ANUN	Lufthansa			27/AUG/69	
	D-ANUN	Nora Air Services			26/JUL/71	
	G-BAPF	British Midland Airways			15/FEB/73	
	SE-FOY	Skyline			16/OCT/75	
	G-BAPF	British Midland Airways			02/APR/78	
	G-BAPF	British Aerospace			JAN/86	Traded-in
	G-BAPF	British Midland Airways			JAN/86	Leased
341	D-ANIP	Lufthansa	814	31/JAN/59	15/FEB/59	
	D-ANIP	Condor			01/NOV/61	Leased
	D-ANIP	Lufthansa			01/NOV/67	
	D-ANIP	Nora Air Services			20/AUG/71	
	G-BAPE	British Midland Airways			15/FEB/73	
	G-BAPE	British Airways			APR/76	Leased
	G-BAPE	British Midland Airways			MAR/77	
	G-BAPE	Intra Airways			21/OCT/77	
	4X-AVI	Arkia			17/DEC/79	Leased
	G-BAPE	Jersey European Airways			12/MAR/80	
	G-BAPE	British Midland Airways			28/MAR/80	Leased
	G-BAPE	Jersey European Airways			30/SEP/80	
	N145RA	Royal American Airways			FEB/81	
	N145RA	Go Group			82	
	N145RA	Inland Empire			83	Leased
	N145RA	Fred S. Brown				
344	D-ANIZ	Lufthansa	814	20/MAR/59	06/APR/59	
	D-ANIZ	Nora Air Services			26/JUL/71	
	G-BAPG	British Midland Airways			73	
	G-BAPG	British Airways			APR/76	Leased
	G-BAPG	British Midland Airways			MAR/77	
	G-BAPG	Intra Airways			JAN/78	
	4X-AVH	Arkia			12/DEC/79	Leased
	G-BAPG	Jersey European Airways			29/MAR/80	Leased
	G-BAPG	British Midland Airways			11/JAN/81	
	G-BAPG	Jersey European Airways			83	Stored Exeter
345	FAB-2101	Forca Aerea Brasileira	789	01/DEC/57	06/OCT/58	
	C-92 2101	Forca Aerea Brasileira				WFU 70
346	ZS-CDT	South African Airways	813	17/SEP/58	26/OCT/58	
	G-AZLP	British Midland Airways			20/JAN/72	WFU, stored Teesside
347	ZS-CDU	South African Airways	813	14/OCT/58	26/OCT/58	
	G-AZLR	British Midland Airways			20/JAN/72	WFU, stored East Midlands Ap.
348	ZS-CDV	South African Airways	813	07/NOV/58	18/NOV/58	

C/N	Registration	Owner/Operator	Series	First Flight	Delivery	Remarks
349	G-AZLS	British Midland Airways			28/JAN/72	WFU, stored Teesside
	ZS-CDW	South African Airways	813	26/NOV/58	08/DEC/58	
	G-AZLT	British Midland Airways			28/JAN/72	W/O 07/OCT/80 Leeds/Bradford Ap.
	G-BMAT	British Midland Airways		28/APR/81	29/APR/81	Re-built using C/N 340
	G-BMAT	British Aerospace			JAN/86	Traded-in
	G-BMAT	British Midland Airways			JAN/86	Leased
350	ZS-CDX	South African Airways	813	07/DEC/58	20/DEC/58	
	G-AZNA	British Midland Airways			09/MAR/72	
	G-AZNA	Manx Airlines			01/NOV/82	
	G-AZNA	British Midland Airways				
	G-AZNA	British Aerospace			JAN/86	Traded-in
	G-AZNA	British Midland Airways			JAN/86	Leased
351	ZS-CDY	South African Airways	813	22/DEC/58	10/JAN/58	
	G-AZNB	British Midland Airways			09/MAR/72	WFU East Midlands 08/APR/83 then to Teeside for storage
352	ZS-CDZ	South African Airways	813	15/JAN/59	29/JAN/59	
	G-AZNC	British Midland Airways			25/MAR/72	WFU 82, stored Teesside Ap.
355	N241V	Continental Airlines	812	01/APR/58	10/MAY/58	
	VH-RMK	Ansett-ANA			SEP/60	
	B-2021	Far Eastern Air Transport			10/JUL/70	
	PK-MVO	Mandala Airlines				Leased
	B-2021	Far Eastern Air Transport			FEB/83	Stored
358	N245V	Continental Airlines	812	01/JUL/58	08/JUL/58	
	G-AVIW	Channel Airways			17/MAR/67	
	G-AVIW	Alidair			27/MAY/72	
	G-AVIW	British Air Ferries			08/APR/73	Leased
	G-AVIW	Alidair			12/OCT/73	
	B-2031	Far Eastern Air Transport			JAN/75	Stored
366	N254V	Continental Airlines	812	02/APR/59	10/APR/59	
	G-ATVE	Channel Airways			19/MAY/66	
	G-ATVE	Treffield International			03/JAN/67	Leased
	G-ATVE	Channel Airways			23/JUN/67	WFU 26/OCT/69, scrapped 19/JUN/72. Nose section to Southend museum.
368	D-ANAM	Lufthansa	814	08/APR/59	17/APR/59	WFU 12/FEB/70 Preserved Hermeskiel
369	D-ANAB	Lufthansa	814	16/APR/59	29/APR/59	WFU 04/DEC/69. Preserved Eschenstrausen.
370	D-ANAC	Lufthansa	814	18/JUL/61	30/JUL/61	
	G-AYOX	Universal Aviation Supply			06/JAN/71	
	4X-AVA	Arkia			08/APR/71	
	G-AYOX	British Midland Airways			29/MAR/78	WFU 31/JAN/84 Teesside For spares. Fuselage to Teesside Airport Fire Service
	G-AYOX	British Air Ferries				
371	9G-AAV	Ghana Airways	838	06/SEP/61	03/OCT/61	
	XT661	Ministry of Technology (RAE)			FEB/65	
374	VH-TVN	Trans Australia Airlines	756	02/JUL/58	08/JUL/58	
	A2-ZEL	Botswana National Airways			27/MAR/69	
	VP-YNI	Overseas Holiday Hire			JAN/72	
	VP-YNI	Air Rhodesia			13/FEB/72	
	VP-YNI	Air Zimbabwe			80	
	Z-YNI	Air Zimbabwe			83	WFU
375	AP-AJF	PIA	815	14/AUG/59	31/AUG/59	
	G-AVJB	Hawker Siddeley Aviation			15/JUL/66	
	G-AVJB	British Midland Airways			08/OCT/69	
	G-AVJB	Kestrel International			72	Leased
	G-AVJB	British Midland Airways				
	G-AVJB	British Airways			.APR/76	Leased
	G-AVJB	British Midland Airways			JUN/76	
	G-AVJB	Intra Airways			23/DEC/76	WFU NOV/80
	G-AVJB	British Air Ferries			82	Leased
	G-AVJB	Field Aviation			01/APR/83	WFU 83, stored East Midlands Ap.
	G-AVJB	British Air Ferries			01/APR/83	Leased
	G-AVJB	Field Aviation			OCT/83	WFU, OCT/83 East Midlands Ap.
	G-AVJB	British Air Ferries			15/MAY/86	
381	G-APEX	BEA	806	13/JUN/58	24/JUN/58	
	G-APEX	BKS Air Transport			29/DEC/69	
	G-APEX	Northeast Airlines			01/NOV/70	
	G-APEX	British Airways			01/APR/72	WFU 80
	G-APEX	British Air Ferries			27/MAR/81	WFU 29/MAR/84
382	G-APEY	BEA	806	07/JUL/58	18/JUL/58	
	G-APEY	BKS Air Transport			02/APR/68	
	G-APEY	Northeast Airlines			01/NOV/70	
	G-APEY	British Airways			01/APR/72	
	G-APEY	British Air Ferries			09/APR/81	
	G-APEY	Occidental Oil			81	Leased
	G-APEY	British Air Ferries			81	
	G-APEY	Air Algerie			SEP/81	Leased
	G-APEY	British Air Ferries			JAN/82	
	G-APEY	Sirte Oil			JAN/82	Leased
	G-APEY	British Air Ferries			82	
383	CF-TIC	Trans Canada Airlines	757	23/JUN/58	30/JUN/58	
	CF-TIC	Air Canada			01/JUN/64	
	CF-TIC	Beaver Enterprises			74	
	9Q-CGQ	Air Charter Service				
384	CF-TID	Trans Canada Airlines	757	25/FEB/59	08/MAR/59	
	CF-TID	Air Canada			01/JUN/64	
	CF-TID	United Aircraft of Canada			27/ OV/72	
	C-FTID	Pratt and Whitney Corp.				
385	CF-TIE	Trans Canada Airlines	757	10/MAR/59	20/MAY/59	
	CF-TIE	Air Canada			01/JUN/64	WFU 29/APR/73, stored St Andrews, Winnipeg
386	CF-TIF	Trans Canada Airlines	757	23/MAR/59	28/MAY/59	
	CF-TIF	Air Canada			01/JUN/64	
	CF-TIF	Beaver Enterprises			74	
	9Q-CPY	Zaire Aero Services				WFU 81, stored N'Dolo
	9Q-CPY	Zairean Airlines			81	
387	CF-TIG	Trans Canada Airlines	757	16/APR/59	02/MAY/59	
	CF-TIG	Air Canada			01/JUN/64	WFU 01/MAR/73
389	N247V	Continental Airlines	812	23/JUL/58	20/AUG/58	
	G-AVJL	Channel Airways			09/FEB/67	
	G-AVJL	Alidair			03/JUN/72	
	B-2033	Far Eastern Air Transport			MAY/75	
	PK-RVW	Mandala				
391	N6597C	Northeast Airlines	798	30/NOV/58	11/DEC/58	
	N8989V	Weitzman, Weitzman & Birdman				

C/N	Registration	Owner/Operator	Series	First Flight	Delivery	Remarks
	N8989V	Ron Clark Enterprises			APR/78	
	N8989V	Go Group				
	N150RC	Go Group			80	
392	N6598C	Northeast Airlines	798	21/DEC/58	08/JAN/59	
	N6598C	Potash Corp. of America			MAY/64	
	N6598C	Red Maurite				
	N6598C	Ideal Basic Industries			69	
	N6598C	Bendix Corp.			30/DEC/69	
	N6598C	US Leasing Inc.				
	N6598C	Ronald Clark			JUL/79	
	N200RC	Ronald Clark			APR/80	
	N200RC	Royal American Airways			81	
	N200RC	Go Group				
396	G-APKF	BEA	806	02/JUL/58	12/JUL/58	
	XW-TDN	Lao Airlines			20/SEP/69	
	XW-TDN	Royal Air Lao			DEC/73	Stored
397	PP-SRC	VASP	827	30/SEP/58	20/OCT/58	
	CX-BIY	Pluna			76	
	N480RC	Go Group			82	
400	PP-SRF	VASP	827	06/DEC/58	22/DEC/58	
	CX-BJA	Pluna			76	Stored Carrasco
	N490RC	Go Group				
402	G-APND	Airwork	831	04/FEB/59	23/DEC/59	
	G-APND	British United Airways			01/JUL/60	
	JY-ADB	Alia			22/NOV/66	Leased
	G-APND	British United Airways			22/FEB/67	
	G-APND	British Midland Airways			10/JAN/69	
	G-APND	Ghana Airways			69	Leased
	G-APND	British Midland Airways			69	
	4X-AVF	Arkia			21/DEC/73	
	4X-AVF	Go Group			82	
403	G-APNE	Airwork	831	09/MAR/59	17/MAR/59	
	G-APNE	British United Airways			01/JUL/60	
	JY-ADA	Alia			NOV/66	Leased
	G-APNE	British United Airways			MAR/67	
	G-APNE	British Midland Airways			01/APR/67	
	G-APNE	Ghana Airways			15/OCT/68	Leased
	G-APNE	British Midland Airways			20/NOV/68	
	4X-AVE	Arkia			21/SEP/72	
	4X-AVE	Go Group			18/MAY/82	WFU 18/MAY/82, stored Tucson
412	G-APIM	BEA	806	04/JUN/58	23/JUN/58	
	G-APIM	Cambrian Airways			03/NOV/71	
	G-APIM	British Airways			01/APR/72	
	G-APIM	British Air Ferries			10/FEB/84	
414	VH-RMG	Ansett-ANA	832	23/FEB/59	12/MAR/59	
	B-2015	Far Eastern Air Transport			08/APR/70	
	PK-RVP	Mandala Airlines				Leased
417	VH-RMJ	Ansett-ANA	832	06/MAY/59	15/MAY/59	
	N3939V	Victor Comptometer Corp.			OCT/63	
	N8989V	Super Value Stores Inc.			DEC/66	
	N8989V	Trico Corp.			24/AUG/72	
	N8989V	Air Rent Inc.			15/NOV/73	
	B-2017	Far Eastern Air Transport				
	PK-MVN	Mandala Airlines			FEB/83	Leased
	B-2017	Far Eastern Air Transport				
418	G-APOX	BEA	806	24/MAR/59	11/APR/59	
	PK-RVL	Mandala Airlines			21/JUN/70	
	PK-RVL	PN Seulawah Air Services			71	Leased, WFU 16/MAR/71
419	G-ASED	Airwork	831	30/MAY/59	05/JUN/59	
	ST-AAN	Sudan Airways			05/JUN/59	Leased
	G-ASED	British United Airways			23/DEC/62	
	EC-AZK	Aviaco			28/APR/65	Leased
	G-ASED	British United Airways			04/NOV/65	
	G-ASED	British Midland Airways			15/FEB/67	
	G-ASED	Alidair			19/MAY/72	
	4X-AVG	Arkia			07/MAR/74	
	4X-AVG	Go Group			18/MAY/82	WFU 18/MAY/82, stored Tucson Ap.
421	EI-AKJ	Aer Lingus	808	21/DEC/58	07/JAN/59	
	EI-AKO	Aer Lingus			18/FEB/59	
	EI-AKO	Aer Lingus	808C		67	Converted
	D-ADAN	Air Commerz			06/OCT/70	
	D-ADAN	Aer Lingus			72	
	505	Sultan of Oman's Airforce			17/JUL/73	
	9Q-CBT	Air Zaire			OCT/76	
	9Q-CBT	Scibe-Zaire				
	9Q-CBT	MBM			81	Leased
	9Q-CBT	Scibe-Zaire				
	9Q-CGM	Air Charter Service				
423	EI-AKL	Aer Lingus	808	01/MAR/59	20/MAR/59	
	EI-AKL	Aer Lingus	808C		67	Converted
	D-ADAM	Air Commerz			12/JUN/70	
	D-ADAM	Aer Lingus			72	
	504	Sultan of Oman's Airforce			13/MAR/73	
	9Q-CBS	Air Zaire			OCT/76	
	9Q-CBS	Scibe-Zaire				
	9Q-CAN	MMM Aero Service			81	
424	G-APTB	Hunting Clan	833	13/MAY/58	18/JUN/59	
	G-APTB	British United Airways			01/JUL/60	
	4X-AVB	Arkia			20/DEC/69	
	4X-AVB	Go Group			82	
428	ZK-BWO	NZNAC	807	10/MAY/61	19/MAY/61	
	ZK-BWO	Air Caribbean			76	
	ZK-BWO	Australian Aircraft Sales				Stored
430	TC-SEL	Turk Hava Yollari	794	01/SEP/58	19/SEP/58	
	430	Turkish Airforce			03/JUN/71	
431	TC-SES	Turk Hava Yollari	794	12/OCT/58	24/OCT/58	
	431	Turkish Airforce			12/FEB/71	
433	VH-TVP	Trans Australia Airlines	816	08/MAY/59	23/MAY/59	
	B-2025	Far Eastern Air Transport			02/APR/71	
	B-2025	Air Vietnam			29/MAR/73	Leased
	B-2025	Far Eastern Air Transport				
	PK-RVS	Mandala Airlines				
434	VH-TVQ	Trans Australia Airlines	816	08/JUN/59	17/JUN/59	
	B-2027	Far Eastern Air Transport			16/APR/71	
	PK-MVL	Mandala Airlines				Leased
	B-2027	Far Eastern Air Transport			FEB/83	

VICKERS VISCOUNT (EXISTING AIRCRAFT ONLY)

C/N	Registration	Owner/Operator	Series	First Flight	Delivery	Remarks
435	VH-TVR	Trans Australia Airlines	816	24/AUG/59		Not taken-up
	N40N	Union Carbide Corp.			17/MAY/60	
	A6-435	Royal Australian Airforce			AUG/64	
	N40DA	Alda Corp.			NOV/69	
	VH-EQP	Jet Air Australia			DEC/69	
	VH-EQP	Jesp Investments			70	
	VH-EQP	Gates Propellor Sales			SEP/70	
	VH-EQP	Brins Finance Corp.			25/SEP/70	
	501	Sultan of Oman's Airforce			30/SEP/71	
	3D-ACM	Royal Swazi Air			78	
	G-BFZL	British Midland Airways			MAR/79	
	G-BFZL	Manx Airlines			83	Leased
	G-BFZL	British Midland Airways			DEC/83	Stored East Midlands Ap.
	G-BFZL	Manx Airlines			17/OCT/85	Leased
	G-BFZL	British Aerospace			JAN/86	Traded-in
	G-BFZL	Manx Airlines			JAN/86	Leased
	G-BFZL	British Midland Airways			JAN/87	Sched.return, Leased
436	VH-TVS	Trans Australia Airlines	816	06/JAN/61		Not delivered
	EP-MRS	Iran Government			15/MAY/61	
	EP-MRS	Iranian Airlines			MAR/63	
	A6-436	Royal Australian Airforce			29/SEP/64	
	N40NB	Alda Corp.			DEC/69	
	VH-EQQ	Jet Air Australia			DEC/69	
	VH-EQQ	Jesp.Investments			70	
	VH-EQQ	Gates Propellor Sales			JUL/70	
	502	Sultan of Oman's Airforce			12/AUG/71	
	3D-ACN	Royal Swazi				
	G-BGLC	Air Bridge Carriers				
	G-BGLC	Dan Air				Leased
	G-BGLC	Dan Air			80	Purchased
	VP-WGB	Air Zimbabwe			05/NOV/80	
	Z-WGB	Air Zimbabwe				
438	OE-LAG	Austrian Airlines	837	17/FEB/60	29/FEB/60	
	XT575	Ministry of Technology (RAE)			31/OCT/64	
445	G-ARKZ	Vickers	828	24/AUG/61		
	JA8203	All Nippon Airways			02/SEP/61	
	PK-MVG	Merpati Nusantara			24/SEP/70	
446	9G-AAU	Ghana Airways	838	05/NOV/61	26/NOV/61	
	G-BCZR	Field Aircraft Services			APR/75	
	G-BCZR	British Midland Airways			APR/76	Leased
	G-BCZR	Field Aircraft Services			OCT/76	
	G-BCZR	British Midland Airways			APR/77	Leased
	G-BCZR	Field Aircraft Services			OCT/77	
	G-BCZR	Southern International			78	Leased
	G-BCZR	Field Aircraft Services			78	
	G-BCZR	Dan Air			FEB/79	Leased
	G-BCZR	Dan Air			80	Purchased
	VP-WGC	Air Zimbabwe			05/MAY/81	
	Z-WGC	Air Zimbabwe				
447	D-ANAF	Lufthansa	814	09/DEC/61	06/JAN/62	WFU 30/JAN/69, derelict Frankfurt Rheinmain.
451	G-ASDP	Vickers	843	14/MAR/63		
	B-402	CAAC			16/JUL/63	
	RP-C792	HAECO			JUL/83	
	PK-IVZ	Bouraq			83	Leased
452	G-ASDR	Vickers	843	20/MAR/63		
	B-404	CAAC			23/AUG/63	
	RP-C794	HAECO			JUL/83	
	PK-IVW	Bouraq			83	Leased
453	G-ASDS	Vickers	843	08/AUG/63		
	B-406	CAAC			19/SEP/63	
454	G-ASDT	Vickers	843	01/OCT/63		
	B-408	CAAC			26/DEC/63	
	RP-C793	HAECO			JUL/83	
	PK-IVX	Bouraq			83	Leased
455	G-ASDU	Vickers	843	12/NOV/63		
	B-410	CAAC			19/FEB/64	
	RP-C795	HAECO			JUL/83	
	PK-IVY	Bouraq			83	Leased
456	G-ASDV	Vickers	843	02/JAN/64		
	B-412	CAAC			16/APR/64	
457	G-ASBM	Vickers	828	18/SEP/62		
	JA8208	All Nippon Airways			05/OCT/62	
	HC-ASP	SAN			05/SEP/70	
	HK-2404	Aerocesar				
458	G-ASBO	Vickers	828	22/OCT/62		
	JA8209	All Nippon Airways			02/NOV/62	
	HC-ATV	SAN			05/SEP/70	Stored
459	G-ASBR	Vickers	828	19/DEC/62		
	JA8210	All Nippon Airways			03/FEB/63	
	PK-MVM	Merpati Nusantara			MAR/70	

3D- Swaziland

240	3D-AAL
435	3D-ACM
436	3D-ACN

4X- Israel

370	4X-AVA
424	4X-AVB
403	4X-AVE
402	4X-AVF
419	4X-AVG
344	4X-AVH
341	4X-AVI

6O/6OS- Somalia

325	6O-SAK
114	6O-SAN
325	6OS-AAK
114	6OS-AAN

7Q- Malawi

98	7Q-YDK
241	7Q-YDL

9G- Ghana

446	9G-AAU
371	9G-AAV

9Q- Zaire

36	9Q-CAH
14	9Q-CAN
423	9Q-CAN
423	9Q-CBS
421	9Q-CBT
421	9Q-CGM
383	9Q-CGQ
304	9Q-CKB
310	9Q-CKI
307	9Q-CKS
303	9Q-CPD
310	9Q-CPP
386	9Q-CPY
190	9Q-CRH

A2- Botswana

243	A2-ABD
189	A2-ABY
374	A2-ZEL

AN- Nicaragua

334	AN-AKQ

AP- Pakistan

375	AP-AJF

B- Taiwan

414	B-2015
417	B-2017
319	B-2019
355	B-2021
433	B-2025
434	B-2027
358	B-2031
389	B-2033
268	B-2035
268	B-3001

B- China

451	B-402
452	B-404
453	B-406
454	B-408
455	B-410
456	B-412

C/CF- Canada

277	C-FTHQ
384	C-FTID
311	C-GWPY
229	CF-DTA
70	CF-GXK
228	CF-RBC
40	CF-TGI
51	CF-TGN
52	CF-TGO
54	CF-TGQ
55	CF-TGR
142	CF-TGX
144	CF-TGZ
218	CF-THA
219	CF-THB
220	CF-THC
223	CF-THF
224	CF-THG
270	CF-THI
41	CF-THJ
272	CF-THL
273	CF-THM
274	CF-THN
275	CF-THO
276	CF-THP
277	CF-THQ
278	CF-THR
303	CF-THU
304	CF-THV
305	CF-THW
306	CF-THX
307	CF-THY
308	CF-THZ
310	CF-TIB
383	CF-TIC
384	CF-TID
385	CF-TIE
386	CF-TIF
387	CF-TIG

CU- Cuba

318	CU-T622
319	CU-T623

CX- Uraguay

321	CX-AQN
322	CX-AQO
130	CX-BHA
397	CX-BIY
316	CX-BIZ
400	CX-BJA

D- West Germany

423	D-ADAM
421	D-ADAN
369	D-ANAB
370	D-ANAF
447	D-ANAF
368	D-ANAM
341	D-ANIP
344	D-ANIZ
338	D-ANUN

EC- Spain

419	EC-AZK
264	EC-DXU
262	EC-DYC

EI- Eire

291	EI-AJK
228	EI-AJV
421	EI-AKJ
423	EI-AKL
421	EI-AKO
180	EI-AOH

EP- Iran

298	EP-AHB
436	EP-MRS

F- France

12	F-BGNM
14	F-BGNN
16	F-BGNO
18	F-BGNP
33	F-BGNQ
35	F-BGNR
36	F-BGNS
38	F-BGNU
36	F-BLHI
54	F-BMCF
52	F-BMCG
55	F-BNAX
12	F-BOEA
14	F-BOEB

G- United Kingdom

228	G-16-3
230	G-16-6
5	G-ALWF
11	G-AMOB
15	G-AMOD
17	G-AMOE
7	G-AMOG
22	G-AMOJ
61	G-ANHA
62	G-ANHB
64	G-ANHD
75	G-ANRS
75	G-ANRS
182	G-AOFX
161	G-AOHL
162	G-AOHM
163	G-AOHN
164	G-AOHO
167	G-AOHS
168	G-AOHT
170	G-AOHV
253	G-AOHW
151	G-AOJB
152	G-AOJC
171	G-AORD
248	G-AOXU
256	G-AOYG
311	G-AOYH
257	G-AOYI
259	G-AOYJ
261	G-AOYL
262	G-AOYM
263	G-AOYN
264	G-AOYO
265	G-AOYP
266	G-AOYR
267	G-AOYS
268	G-AOYT
316	G-AOYV
243	G-APCD
381	G-APEX
382	G-APEY
229	G-APFR
412	G-APIM
396	G-APKF
230	G-APLX
402	G-APND
403	G-APNE
228	G-APNG
418	G-APOX
424	G-APTB
190	G-APZN
250	G-APZP
12	G-ARER
14	G-ARGR
118	G-ARHY
36	G-ARIR
445	G-ARKZ
457	G-ASBM
458	G-ASBO
459	G-ASBR
451	G-ASDP
452	G-ASDR
453	G-ASDS
454	G-ASDT
455	G-ASDU
456	G-ASDV
419	G-ASED
366	G-ATVE
358	G-AVIW
375	G-AVJB
389	G-AVJL
370	G-AYOX
346	G-AZLP
347	G-AZLR
348	G-AZLS
349	G-AZLT
350	G-AZNA
351	G-AZNB
353	G-AZNC
341	G-BAPE
338	G-BAPF
344	G-BAPG
291	G-BBDK
281	G-BBVH
446	G-BCZR
52	G-BDRC
67	G-BFMW
435	G-BFZL
436	G-BGLC
259	G-BLOA
349	G-BMAT
311	G-BNAA
248	G-CSZB
257	G-LOND

HB- Switzerland

291	HB-ILR

HC- Ecuador

457	HC-ASP
458	HC-ATV
204	HC-AYZ
334	HC-BDL

HK- Colombia

327	HK-1061
232	HK-1319
138	HK-1708
457	HK-2404
334	HK-947
118	HK-l057

I- Italy

325	I-LIFE
130	I-LIFS
327	I-LILI
114	I-LIRC
284	I-LIRG
118	I-LIRT

JA Japan

445	JA8203
457	JA8208
458	JA8209
459	JA8210

JY- Jordan

240	JY-ACI
243	JY-ACK
403	JY-ADA
402	JY-ADB

LN- Norway

250	LN-FOH
251	LN-FOI

N United States

41	N117H
191	N140RA
248	N141RA
341	N145RA
391	N150RC
51	N180RC
51	N1898M
51	N1898S
334	N200Q
392	N200RC
201	N220RC
40	N22SN
41	N240RC
355	N241V
358	N245V
389	N247V
228	N24V
366	N254V
191	N306
144	N3832S
417	N3939V
435	N40DA
435	N40N
436	N40NB
321	N410RC
117	N460RC
397	N480RC
400	N500RC
201	N500TL
228	N505W
233	N555SL
232	N6590C
233	N6591C
284	N6594C
230	N6595C
391	N6597C
392	N6598C
229	N660RC
106	N7408
107	N7409
109	N7411
114	N7416
232	N7416
117	N7419
118	N7420
121	N7423
122	N7424
130	N7432
137	N7439
138	N7440
139	N7441
201	N7445
204	N7448
51	N744W
206	N7450
213	N7458
118	N745HA
228	N7466
229	N7467
230	N74o8
232	N7470
233	N7471
284	N7473
230	N776M
41	N81RR
233	N820BK
391	N8989V
417	N8989V
184	N906
184	N906RB
55	N911H
201	N923RA
201	N923RC
233	N98KT

OD- Lebanon

75	OD-ACH
240	OD-ACU
241	OD-ACV
246	OD-ACY
243	OD-ADD

OE- Austria

250	OE-LAB
251	OE-LAC
438	OE-LAG

PH- Netherlands

180	PH-VII

PI- Philippines

300	PI-C770
118	PI-C773

PK- Indonesia

452	PK-IVW
454	PK-IVX
455	PK-IVY
451	PK-IVZ
445	PK-MVG
319	PK-MVK
434	PK-MVL
459	PK-MVM
417	PK-MVN
355	PK-MVO
418	PK-RVL
414	PK-RVP
433	PK-RVS
268	PK-RVT
389	PK-RVW

PP- Brasil

397	PP-SRC
400	PP-SRF
316	PP-SRH
11	PP-SRI
15	PP-SRJ
22	PP-SRL
62	PP-SRN
64	PP-SRO
61	PP-SRP
182	PP-SRS

RDPL- Laos

294	RDPL-34016

RP- Philippines

451	RP-C792
454	RP-C793
452	RP-C794
455	RP-C795

SE- Sweden

300	SE-CNL
338	SE-FOY

SP- Poland

248	SP-LVC

ST- Sudan

419	ST-AAN

SU- Egypt

75	SU-AKY

TC- Turkey

246	TC-SEC
430	TC-SEL
431	TC-SES

VH- Australia

435	VH-EQP
436	VH-EQQ
414	VH-RMG
417	VH-RMJ
355	VH-RMK
319	VH-RML
148	VH-TVJ
197	VH-TVL
374	VH-TVN
433	VH-TVP
434	VH-TVQ
318	VH-TVR
435	VH-TVR
436	VH-TVS

VP- Zimbabwe

240	VP-WAR
298	VP-WAT
436	VP-WGB
446	VP-WGC
241	VP-WJI
241	VP-YCT
98	VP-YNA
99	VP-YNB
100	VP-YNC

Vickers Viscount
Cross-reference index